HCPCS
Level II Expert
2015

AAPC
Advancing the Business of Healthcare

PUBLISHER'S NOTICE

Coding, billing, and reimbursement decisions should not be made based solely upon information within this book. Application of the information in this book does not imply or guarantee claims payment. Make inquiries of your local carriers' bulletins, policy announcements, etc., to resolve local billing requirements. Finally, the law, applicable regulations, payers' instructions, interpretations, enforcement, etc., of codes may change at any time in any particular area. Information in this book is solely based on rules and regulations.

This is designed to be an accurate and authoritative source regarding coding, and every reasonable effort has been made to ensure accuracy and completeness of content. However, AAPC makes no guarantee, warrantee, or representation that this publication is complete, accurate, or without errors. It is understood that AAPC is not rendering any legal or professional services or advice in this code book and bears no liability for any results or consequences arising from use of this book.

AAPC'S COMMITMENT TO ACCURACY

AAPC is committed to providing our members accurate and reliable materials. However, codes and the guidelines by which they are applied change or are reinterpreted through the year. Check www.aapc.com periodically for updates. To report corrections and updates, please contact AAPC Customer Service via 1-800-626-2633 or via email to code.books@aapc.com.

Images/Illustrations by the following artists at shutterstock.com
miucci - 119473492 | ducu59us - 104022683 | Alila Medical Media - 147943910, 155445662, 147943874, 108567068, 106263593, 106263560 | BlueRingMedia - 141161560, 149006000, 145028440 | snapgalleria - 142194094 | okili77 - 156466463 | Designua - 186535475, 165084413 | stockshoppe - 180896810, 187162247, 187162193, 187162175, 187162163, 187162142, 187162118, 187162106, 187162070, 180896873, 180896855, 180896738, 180896720, 177791516, 177790997 | lotan - 186878060 | sciencepics - 199873508

ACKNOWLEDGEMENTS PAGE

Reviewers:

We wish to thank the following AAPC Members for helping guide the development of the 2015 HCPCS Level II Expert. Many thanks to them for sharing their expertise and experience.

Alysia Martinez, CPC-A

Angela Teasley

Anita Robinson, CPC, CPC-H, CPC-P, CPMA, CPC-I

Anja Aplan, CPC

Belinda Shaw, RHIT, CCS, CPC

Betty Hovey, CPC, CPC-H, CPB, CPMA, CPC-I, CPCD

Beverly Abernathy, CPC

Brenda Edwards, CPC, CPB, CPMA, CPC-I, CEMC

Brooke Bierman, CPC

Camille Y. Betters, CPC, CMC, CMOM

Cathy Jennings, BS, CPC, CEDC, CHONC

Chastity Radcliff, CPC, CPMA

Danielle Wombough CPC-P

Darlene Britton, CPC, CPC-I, CEDC, RHIT

Darrelyn Rodman, CPC-A

Deborah Frizzle CPC, CIMC

Deborah Santos, CPC, CPMA

Diana Vincent, CPC

Elaine Griffel, CPC

Ellen Ontko, CPC

Geanetta Johnson Agbona CPC, CPC-I, CBCS

Gerry Pape, BA, CPC

Hope Dendy, CPC, CPC-P

Ila Callagan, CPC

Irene Castillo Leon, CPC, CEMC

Irene Quast-Beck, CPC, CPCO, CPMA, CPPM, CEMC

Jackie Stack, CPC, CPB, CPC-I, CEMC, CFPC, CIMC, CPEDC

Jacqueline Baer, RN, MSN, CPC-H

Jennifer Bartunek, CPC, CPB

Joyce McCoy, CPC

Julie Lytle, CPC-A

Karen K. Tritz, CPC

Karen Leonard, CPC, CPMA

Katalin Kerekes, CPC, CMCO

Kathleen Galioto, CPC-A

Katrina R. Tweedy, CPC, CPMA

Kent Williston BA, MS, CPC

Kim Pasienza, CPC

Kim Pichon, CPC

Kimberly Kiper-Mills CPC

Lena Staniscia,CPC

Leonta Julien-Williams, CPC

Lillian J. Galindo-Bryson, CPC

Linda Bovis, RN, CPC

Linda Gilbreath, CPC, CPC-I, CPC-H, CEMC, AHFI, CHCA

Linda Vargas, CPC, CPC-I, CEMC

Lisa A. Oakes CPC

Loretta Gaither, CPC, COBGC

Lynn Rawlings, CPC, CPMA, CPC-I, CHAP, CEMC, CCVTC, CEMC

Marcie Barker, CPC, CPMA

Maria Puerto, CPC-H, CPMA

Marie Guido, CPC-A

Martha B (Martie) Gaskin, RN, CPC

Martha Sims-Green, BS, CPC

Mary E. Wilds, CPC, CEMC

Melody Whilden, CPC

Michael Ann Fowler, CPC, CPMA, CPC-I

Michelle Lane, CPC-A

N. Carol Mitchell, CPC

Patricia Henry, CPC, CCA

Paula M Wright, CPC, CIRCC, CPMA, CEMC, CPC-I

Pearl Evelyn Parker-Hartfield, CPC-A

Peggy Stilley, CPC, CPB, CPMA, CPC-I, COBGC

Rhonda Buckholtz, CPC, CPMA, CPC-I, CENTC, CGSC, COBGC, CPEDC

Ronda Seubert, BSBM, CPC

Rose Gibbs, CPC

Rose Mukkadan, CPC

Ruby Woodward, BSN, CPC, COSC,

Sandra Pedersen, CPC, CEMC, CPMA

Sarah Mros, RHIT, CPC, CPMA

Shelia G. Hickman, RHIT, CPC

Shelly Noll, CPC, CHONC

Shirley Holtz CCS-P, CPC-H, CPC, ACS-AN

Stacey L. Murphy, MPA, RHIA, CPC

Staci Foster, CPC

Susan O'Loughlin

Susie Kottkamp, CPC

Suzanne L. Haile, CPC

Suzette Long, CPC, CPC-H

Thomas Penta, CPC, CCS, CHDA, PMP

Valerie Jones, CPC

Valerie McClanahan, CPC

Vanessa Coles, RHIT, CPC, CPMA, CEMC

Table of Contents

Introduction

This Healthcare Common Procedure Coding System (HCPCS) Level II manual goes beyond the basics to help you to code accurately and efficiently. In addition to including the official Alphabetic Index and Tabular List for services, supplies, durable medical equipment, and drugs which the Centers for Medicare and Medicaid Services (CMS) developed, we also included the Alphabetic Index and Tabular List for Current Dental Terminology (CDT® codes) from the American Dental Association.

Features

We've crafted a select set of bonus features based on requests from coders in the field as well as the recommendations of our core group of veteran coding educators. Features that you'll benefit from page after page include:

- HCPCS Coding Procedures guide from CMS to help you to better understand HCPCS codes
- Comprehensive list of new/revised/deleted codes for 2015
- Deleted Codes Crosswalk
- Symbols showing which codes have restrictions based on age or sex of the patient
- Medicare and carrier coverage and reimbursement alerts
- APC status indicators
- HCPCS code modifiers
- Full illustrations of body systems at the front of the book so you don't have to search the manual for these large color images of body systems
- Highlighted coding instructional and informational notes help you recognize important code usage guidance for specific sections
- Intuitive color-coded symbols and alerts identify critical coding and reimbursement issues quickly
- A user-friendly page design, including dictionary-style headers, color bleed tabs, and legend keys

Additionally, our dedicated team drew on their years of experience using coding manuals to develop this manual's user friendly symbols, highlighting, color coding, and tabs, all designed to help you find the information you need quickly.

Let Us Know What You Think

Our goal for this manual is to support those involved in the business side of healthcare, helping them to do their jobs and do them well. We'd appreciate your feedback, including your suggestions for what you'll need in a HCPCS resource, so we can be sure our manuals serve your needs.

Symbols and Conventions

Citations to AHA's Coding Clinic® for HCPCS

AHA's *Coding Clinic®*, a quarterly newsletter, is the official publication for coding guidelines and advice as designated by the four Cooperating Parties (American Hospital Association, American Health Information Management Association, Centers for Medicare and Medicaid Services (CMS), and National Center for Health Statistics) and the Editorial Advisory Board.

We've marked codes with related *Coding Clinic®* articles with a citation that includes the year, quarter, and page number(s) of the issue.

Symbols & Conventions used in the manual include:

2015 HCPCS code updates:

●   New code

▲   Revised Code

~~Strikethrough~~ Deleted Code - For dental codes only

Symbols and Alerts Related to Medicare or Carrier Coverage and Reimbursement (non-dental codes)

When relevant, you'll see the following symbols and alerts to the left of a code or beside or under the code descriptor:

C   Carrier judgment

D   Special coverage instructions apply

I   Not payable by Medicare

M   Non-covered by Medicare

S   Non-covered by Medicare statute

A2 - Z3 = ASC Payment Indicator

A - Y =   APC Status Indicator

ASC =   ASC Approved Procedure

Service not separately priced by Part B

Other carrier priced

Reasonable charge

Price established using national RVU's

Price subject to national limitation amount

Statute

Modifier Alerts Showing Applicable Modifiers for a HCPCS Code (non-dental codes)

DME Modifier - Alert appears under the code descriptor

References to Pub 100 (non-dental codes) – Alert appears under the code descriptor

Symbols for Age and Sex Codes (non-dental codes)

When relevant, you'll see the following symbols to the right of a code descriptor. We based symbol use on Medicare's Outpatient Code Editor (OCE).

♀   Female code symbol

♂   Male code symbol

A   Age

Symbols and Alerts Related to Services, Supplies, or Equipment (non-dental codes)

When relevant, you'll see the following symbols to the right of code descriptors:

DME   Paid under the DME fee schedule

PQRS   Physician Quality Reporting System

Understand Code Structure to Choose the Most Specific Code

HCPCS codes are made up of five alphanumeric characters, starting with a letter that represents a category of similar codes, followed by four numbers.

The Tabular List arranges codes in alphanumeric order, starting with codes beginning with the letter A.

Code descriptors identify a category of like items or services and typically do not identify specific products or brand/trade names.

Code Services, Supplies, Equipment, and Drugs With Confidence Following This Approach

➤ The first step in choosing the proper HCPCS code is reading the medical documentation to identify the service, supply, equipment, or drug that the provider documents and confirms.

   • Be sure to check online or hard copy references, such as medical dictionaries and anatomy resources, to look up unfamiliar terms.

➤ Next, decide which main term you will search in the Index based on the patient's specific case. You can look under the name of the service (magnetic resonance angiography, EMG), supply (dialysis drain bag, filler), equipment (bathtub, cane), or drug (hydrocortisone, ipratropium bromide), the body site involved (hip, knee), or the type of service (laboratory tests, oncology).

➤ When searching the Table of Drugs and Biologicals, search for the name of the drug, then the unit and route to find the drug code to cross-reference to the Tabular List.

➤ When searching in the CDT® Index for dental procedures and services, look under the condition (abscess, fractures), type of service (adjunctive general services, biopsy), specialty (endodontics, prosthodontics), item (dentures, fluoride), or drug (drugs).

➤ Once you find the term in the Index, note the recommended code. Start with the main term and review any available subterms. Cross-reference all codes listed, whether it is one code, a series of codes separated by commas, or a code range separated by a hyphen. Pay attention to the "see" convention that directs you to look elsewhere to find the code or the "see also" convention that directs you to look in an additional place to find the code.

➤ Turn to that code in the Tabular List, and read the full code descriptor for correct code assignment.

➤ Before making your final code decision, review the surrounding codes to be sure there isn't a more appropriate code available. Pay attention to the "see" convention that directs you to look elsewhere to find the code or the "see also" convention that directs you to look in an additional place to find the code.

➤ Finally, take a moment to confirm that your code choice complies with the philosophy of ethical coding. Never report a HCPCS code simply because it will support reimbursement from a payer. Report only those codes the documentation supports.

HCPCS Coding Procedures

HEALTHCARE COMMON PROCEDURE CODING SYSTEM (HCPCS) LEVEL II CODING PROCEDURES

This information provides a description of the procedures CMS follows in making coding decisions.

FOR FURTHER INFORMATION CONTACT:

Jennifer Carver (410) 786-6610 or Cindy Hake (410) 786-3404 for HCPCS level II coding issues.

A. HCPCS BACKGROUND INFORMATION

Each year, in the United States, health care insurers process over 5 billion claims for payment. For Medicare and other health insurance programs to ensure that these claims are processed in an orderly and consistent manner, standardized coding systems are essential. The HCPCS Level II Code Set is one of the standard code sets used for this purpose. The HCPCS is divided into two principal subsystems, referred to as level I and level II of the HCPCS. Level I of the HCPCS is comprised of CPT® (Current Procedural Terminology), a numeric coding system maintained by the American Medical Association (AMA). The CPT® is a uniform coding system consisting of descriptive terms and identifying codes that are used primarily to identify medical services and procedures furnished by physicians and other health care professionals. These health care professionals use the CPT® to identify services and procedures for which they bill public or private health insurance programs. Decisions regarding the addition, deletion, or revision of CPT® codes are made by the AMA. The CPT® codes are republished and updated annually by the AMA. Level I of the HCPCS, the CPT® codes, does not include codes needed to separately report medical items or services that are regularly billed by suppliers other than physicians.

Level II of the HCPCS is a standardized coding system that is used primarily to identify products, supplies, and services not included in the CPT® codes, such as ambulance services and durable medical equipment, prosthetics, orthotics, and supplies (DMEPOS) when used outside a physician's office. Because Medicare and other insurers cover a variety of services, supplies, and equipment that are not identified by CPT® codes, the level II HCPCS codes were established for submitting claims for these items. The development and use of level II of the HCPCS began in the 1980's. Level II codes are also referred to as alpha-numeric codes because they consist of a single alphabetical letter followed by 4 numeric digits, while CPT® codes are identified using 5 numeric digits.

In October of 2003, the Secretary of HHS delegated authority under the HIPAA legislation to CMS to maintain and distribute HCPCS Level II Codes. As stated in 42 CFR Sec. 414.40 (a) CMS establishes uniform national definitions of services, codes to represent services, and payment modifiers to the codes. Within CMS there is a CMS HCPCS Workgroup which is an internal workgroup comprised of representatives of the major components of CMS, as well as other consultants from pertinent Federal agencies. Prior to December 31, 2003, Level III HCPCS were developed and used by Medicaid State agencies, Medicare contractors, and private insurers in their specific programs or local areas of jurisdiction. For purposes of Medicare, level III codes were also referred to as local codes. Local codes were established when an insurer preferred that suppliers use a local code to identify a service, for which there is no level I or level II code, rather than use a "miscellaneous or not otherwise classified code." The Health Insurance Portability and Accountability Act of 1996 (HIPAA) required CMS to adopt standards for coding systems that are used for reporting health care transactions. We published, in the Federal Register on August 17, 2000 (65 FR 50312), regulations to implement this part of the HIPAA legislation. These regulations provided for the elimination of level III local codes by October 2002, at which time, the level I and level II code sets could be used. The elimination of local codes was postponed, as a result of section 532(a) of BIPA, which continued the use of local codes through December 31, 2003.

B. HCPCS LEVEL II CODES

The regulation that CMS published on August 17, 2000 (45 CFR 162.10002) to implement the HIPAA requirement for standardized coding systems established the HCPCS level II codes as the standardized coding system for describing and identifying health care equipment and supplies in health care transactions that are not identified by the HCPCS level I, CPT® codes. The HCPCS level II coding system was selected as the standardized coding system because of its wide acceptance among both public and private insurers. Public and private insurers were required to be in compliance with the August 2000 regulation by October 1, 2002. The purpose of this section is to provide a general description of the current HCPCS level II coding system.

The HCPCS level II coding system is a comprehensive and standardized system that classifies similar products that are medical in nature into categories for the purpose of efficient claims processing. For each alphanumeric HCPCS code, there is descriptive terminology that identifies a category of like items. These codes are used primarily for billing purposes. For example, suppliers use HCPCS level II codes to identify items on claim forms that are being billed to a private or public health insurer.

HCPCS is a system for identifying items and services. It is not a methodology or system for making coverage or payment determinations, and the existence of a code does not, of itself, determine coverage or non-coverage for an item or service. While these codes are used for billing purposes, decisions regarding the addition, deletion, or revision of HCPCS codes are made independent of the process for making determinations regarding coverage and payment.

Currently, there are national HCPCS codes representing over 4,000 separate categories of like items or services that encompass millions of products from different manufacturers. When submitting claims, suppliers are required to use one of these codes to identify the items they are billing. The descriptor that is assigned to a code represents the definition of the items and services that can be billed using that code.

In summary, the HCPCS level II coding system has the following characteristics:

- This system ensures uniform reporting on claims forms of items or services that are medical in nature. Such a standardized coding system is needed by public and private insurance programs to ensure the uniform reporting of services on claims forms by suppliers and for meaningful data collection.
- The descriptors of the codes identify a category of like items or services and typically do not identify specific products or brand/trade names.

- The coding system is not a methodology for making coverage or payment determinations. Each payer makes determinations on coverage and payment outside this coding process.

C. TYPES OF HCPCS LEVEL II CODES

There are several types of HCPCS level II codes depending on the purpose for the codes and who is responsible for establishing and maintaining them.

Permanent National Codes

National permanent HCPCS level II codes are maintained by the CMS HCPCS Workgroup. The Workgroup is responsible for making decisions about additions, revisions, and deletions to the permanent national alpha-numeric codes. These codes are for the use of all private and public health insurers. Since HCPCS is a national coding system all payers will be represented in the Workgroup including representatives from private insurance agencies, the Pricing, Data Analysis, and Coding (PDAC), and Medicaid will participate in the workgroup meetings and provide input as to what is necessary to meet each party's program operating needs.

The permanent national codes serve the important function of providing a standardized coding system that is managed jointly by private and public insurers. This standardized approach to developing a set of uniform codes provides a stable environment for claims submission and processing.

Dental Codes

The dental codes are a separate category of national codes. The Current Dental Terminology (CDT) is a publication copyrighted by the American Dental Association (ADA) that lists codes for billing for dental procedures and supplies. While the CDT codes are considered HCPCS level II codes, decisions regarding the revision, deletion, or addition of CDT codes are made by the ADA and not the CMS HCPCS Workgroup, and CDT codes are published by the ADA and not by CMS.

Miscellaneous Codes

National codes also include "miscellaneous/not otherwise classified" codes. These codes are used when a supplier is submitting a bill for an item or service and there is no existing national code that adequately describes the item or service being billed. The importance of miscellaneous codes is that they allow suppliers to begin billing immediately for a service or item as soon as it is allowed to be marketed by the Food and Drug Administration (FDA) even though there is no distinct code that describes the service or item. A miscellaneous code can be used during the period of time a request for a new code is being considered under the HCPCS review process. The use of miscellaneous codes also helps us to avoid the inefficiency and administrative burden of assigning distinct codes for items or services that are rarely furnished or for which we expect to receive few claims.

Because of miscellaneous codes, the absence of a specific code for a distinct category of products does not affect a supplier's ability to submit claims to private or public insurers and does not affect patient access to products. Claims with miscellaneous codes are manually reviewed, the item or service being billed must be clearly described, and pricing information must be provided along with documentation to explain why the item or service is needed by the beneficiary.

Ordinarily, before using a miscellaneous code on a claim form, a supplier should check with the entity that will receive the payment claim to determine whether there is a specific code that should be used rather than a miscellaneous code. In the case of claims that are to be submitted to one of the four Durable Medical Equipment Medicare Administrative Contractors (DME MACs), suppliers that have coding questions should check with the pricing, data analysis, and coding (PDAC), contractor to CMS. The PDAC is responsible for providing suppliers and manufacturers with assistance in determining which HCPCS code should be used to describe DMEPOS items for the purpose of billing Medicare. The PDAC has a toll free helpline for this purpose, (877) 735-1326. In addition, the PDAC publishes a product classification list on its website that lists individual items to code categories. More information about the PDAC and the PDAC's product classification list can be found at http://www.dmepdac.com.

If no code exists that describes the product category to which the item belongs, and if the item fits a Medicare Benefit Category, the PDAC may instruct the supplier to submit claims using a "miscellaneous/not otherwise classified" code. If an item does not fit a Medicare Benefit Category, the PDAC might assign a code that indicates that the product is not covered by Medicare for example, code A9270, NON-COVERED ITEM OR SERVICE. If an item is included or bundled into another code and not separately reimbursed by Medicare, the PDAC may assign the code that includes the item or a code that indicates that the item is included as a component of another code. In those cases in which a supplier or manufacturer has been advised to use a miscellaneous code because there is no existing code that describes a given product, and the supplier or manufacturer believes that the code is needed, it should submit a request to modify the HCPCS in accordance with the established process. The process for requesting a revision to the HCPCS level II codes is explained below.

Temporary National Codes

Temporary codes are for the purpose of meeting, within a short time frame, the national program operational needs of a particular insurer that are not addressed by an already existing national code. The CMS HCPCS Workgroup has set aside certain sections of the HCPCS code set to allow the Workgroup to develop temporary codes. Decisions regarding the number and type of temporary codes and how they are used are also made by the CMS HCPCS Workgroup. These codes are used at the discretion of CMS. This means that if, before the next scheduled annual update for permanent codes, the CMS HCPCS Workgroup needs a code in order to meet specific operating needs that pertain to its particular programs, it may establish a national temporary code. In the case of Medicare, decisions regarding temporary codes are made by the CMS HCPCS workgroup. For example, Medicare may need additional codes before the next scheduled annual HCPCS update to implement newly issued coverage policies or legislative requirements. Although we establish temporary codes to meet our specific operational needs, the temporary codes we establish can be used by other insurers. Temporary codes allow insurers the flexibility to establish codes that are needed before the next January 1 annual update for permanent national codes or until consensus can be achieved on a permanent national code. Permanent national codes are only updated once a year on January 1.

The CMS HCPCS Workgroup may decide to replace temporary codes with permanent codes. However, temporary codes do not have established expiration dates. Whenever a permanent code is established by the CMS HCPCS Workgroup to replace a temporary code, the temporary code is deleted and cross-referenced to the new permanent code.

Types of temporary HCPCS codes:

The C codes were established to permit implementation of section 201 of the Balanced Budget Refinement Act of 1999. HCPCS C codes are utilized to report drugs, biologicals, magnetic resonance angiography (MRA), and devices that must be used by OPPS hospitals. HCPCS C codes are reported for device categories, new technology procedures, and drugs, biologicals and radiopharmaceuticals that do not have other HCPCS code assignments. Non-OPPS hospitals, Critical Access Hospitals (CAHs), Indian Health Service Hospitals (IHS), hospitals located in American Samoa, Guam, Saipan, or the Virgin Islands, and Maryland waiver hospitals may report these codes at their discretion. More information regarding HOPPS can be found at http://www.cms.gov/HospitalOutpatientPPS/.

- The G codes are used to identify professional health care procedures and services that would otherwise be coded in CPT®-4 but for which there are no CPT®-4 codes. The Q codes are used to identify services that would not be given a CPT®-4 code, such as drugs, biologicals, and other types of medical equipment or services, and which are not identified by national level II codes but for which codes are needed for claims processing purposes.

- The K codes were established for use by the DME MACs when the currently existing permanent national codes do not include the codes needed to implement a DME MAC medical review policy. For example, codes other than the permanent national codes may be needed by the DME MACs to identify certain product categories and supplies necessary for establishing appropriate regional medical review coverage policies.

- The S codes are used by private insurers to report drugs, services, and supplies for which there are no national codes but for which codes are needed by the private sector to implement policies, programs, or claims processing. They are for the purpose of meeting the particular needs of the private sector. These codes are also used by the Medicaid program, but they are not payable by Medicare.

- Certain H codes are used by those State Medicaid agencies that are mandated by State law to establish separate codes for identifying mental health services such as alcohol and drug treatment services.

- The T codes are designated for use by Medicaid State agencies to establish codes for items for which there are no permanent national codes and for which codes are necessary to meet a national Medicaid program operating need. T codes are not used by Medicare but can be used by private insurers.

Code Modifiers

In some instances, insurers instruct suppliers that a HCPCS code must be accompanied by code modifier to provide additional information regarding the service or item identified by the HCPCS code. Modifiers are used when the information provided by a HCPCS code descriptor needs to be supplemented to identify specific circumstances that may apply to an item or service. For example, a UE modifier is used when the item identified by a HCPCS code is "used equipment," a NU modifier is used for "new equipment." The level II HCPCS modifiers are either alpha-numeric or two letters.

C. REQUESTING A REVISION TO THE HCPCS LEVEL II CODES

Anyone can submit a request for modifying the HCPCS level II national code set. A document explaining the HCPCS revision process, as well as a detailed format for submitting a request, is available on the HCPCS website at http://www.cms.hhs.gov/medicare/hcpcs. Besides the information requested in this format, a requestor should also submit any additional descriptive material, including the manufacturer's product literature and information, that it thinks would be helpful in furthering our understanding of the medical features of the item for which a coding revision is being recommended. The HCPCS coding review process is an ongoing continuous process. Requests may be submitted at any time throughout the year. Requests that are received and complete by January 4 of the current year will be considered for inclusion in the next annual update (January 1st of the following year). Requests received on or after January 5, and requests received earlier that require additional evaluation, will be included in a later HCPCS update. There are three types of coding revisions to the HCPCS that can be requested:

1. That a permanent code be added
   When there is not a distinct code that describes a product, a code may be requested (1) if the FDA allows the product to be marketed in the United States and (2) if the product is not a drug, the product has been on the market for at least 3 months; if the product is a drug, there is no requirement to submit marketing data; and (3) the product represents 3 percent or more of the outpatient use for that type of product in the national market. If a request for a new code is approved, the addition of a new HCPCS codes does not mean that the item is necessarily covered by any insurer. Whether an item identified by a new code is covered is determined by the Medicare law, regulations, and medical review policies and not by the assignment of a code.

2. That the language used to describe an existing code be changed when there is an existing code, a recommendation to modify the code can be made when an interested party believes that the descriptor for the code needs to be modified to provide a better description of the category of products represented by the code.

3. That an existing code be deleted

When an existing code becomes obsolete or is duplicative of another code, a request can be made to delete the code.

When there is no currently existing code to describe a product, a miscellaneous code/not otherwise classified code may be appropriate. The use of a miscellaneous code permits a claims history to be established for an item that can be used to support the need for a national permanent code.

Requests for coding revisions should be sent to the following:
Alpha-Numeric HCPCS Coordinator,
Center for Medicare Management,
Centers for Medicare and Medicaid Services,
C5-08-27,
7500 Security Boulevard,
Baltimore, MD 21244-1850.

CMS HCPCS Workgroup

The CMS HCPCS Workgroup is an internal workgroup comprised of representatives of the major components of CMS, the Medicaid State agencies, and the PDAC. The PDAC represents Medicare program operating needs with input from the four DME MACs which have responsibility for processing Durable Medical Equipment, Prosthetics, Orthotics and Supplies (DMEPOS) claims for the Medicare program. Coding decisions are coordinated with both public and private insurers. The CMS HCPCS workgroup considers each coding request, and beginning with the 2006 cycle, will determine whether HCPCS coding requests warrant a change to the national permanent codes. Prior to the 2006 cycle, the National Panel was responsible for final decisions.

When a recommendation for a revision to the HCPCS is received, it is reviewed at a regularly scheduled meeting of the CMS HCPCS Workgroup. Ordinarily, the CMS HCPCS Workgroup meets monthly to discuss whether coding requests warrant a change to the national permanent codes.

Evaluating HCPCS Coding Requests

The CMS HCPCS workgroup applies the following criteria to determine whether there is a demonstrated need for a new or modified code or the need to remove a code:

1. When an existing code adequately describes the item in a coding request, then no new or modified code is established. An existing code adequately describes an item in a coding request when the existing code describes products with the following:

    - Functions similar to the item in the coding request.
    - No significant therapeutic distinctions from the item in the coding request.

2. When an existing code describes products that are almost the same in function with only minor distinctions from the item in the coding request, the item in the coding request may be grouped with that code and the code descriptor modified to reflect the distinctions.

3. A code is not established for an item that is used only in the inpatient setting or for an item that is not diagnostic or therapeutic in nature.

4. A new or modified code is not established for an item unless the FDA allows the item to be marketed. FDA approval documentation is required to be submitted with the coding request application for all non-drug items. For drugs, FDA approval documentation will be accepted up to March 31 following the application deadline as long as the application is otherwise complete and submitted by the deadline.

5. There must be sufficient claims activity or volume, as evidenced by 3 months of marketing activity for non-drug products, so that the adding of a new or modified code enhances the efficiency of the system and justifies the administrative burden of adding or modifying a code. Applications for products/services that are not yet available on the U.S. market will be considered incomplete and will not be processed.

6. The determination to remove a code is based on the consideration of whether a code is obsolete (for example, products no longer are used, other more specific codes have been added) or duplicative and no longer useful (for example, new codes are established that better describe items identified by existing codes). In developing its decisions, the HCPCS Workgroup uses the criteria mentioned above. In deciding upon a recommendation, the workgroup does not include cost as a factor.

Opportunity for Public Input/Public Meeting Process for HCPCS

On December 21, 2000, the Congress passed the Medicare, Medicaid, and SCHIP Benefits Improvement and Protection Act of 2000 (BIPA), Pub. L. 106-554. Section 531(b) of BIPA mandated that we establish procedures that permit public consultation for coding and payment determinations for new DME under Medicare Part B of title XVIII of the Social Security Act (the Act). As part of HCPCS reform, CMS expanded the public meeting forum to include all public requests as of the 2005-2006 coding cycle. Accordingly, CMS hosts annual public meetings that provide a forum for interested parties to make oral presentations and/or to submit written comments in response to preliminary coding and pricing recommendations for new durable medical equipment that have been submitted using the Healthcare Common Procedure Coding System coding revision process. Agenda items for the meetings will be published in advance of the public meeting on the HCPCS website at http://www.cms.gov/medhcpcsgeninfo. The agenda will include descriptions of the coding requests, the requestor, and the name of the product or service. This change will provide more opportunities for the public to become aware of coding changes under consideration, as well as opportunities for public input into decision-making.

The HCPCS coordinator schedules meetings with interested parties, at their request, as time permits, to discuss their recommendations regarding possible changes to the HCPCS level II codes. These meetings are held at the Central Office of CMS. In addition to representatives from the CMS HCPCS Workgroup, staff from Medicaid and Medicare coverage, payment and operations are invited to attend these meetings. These meetings are not related to the meetings mandated by section 531(b) of BIPA, they are also not decision making meetings or CMS HCPCS Workgroup meetings.

Final Decisions

The CMS HCPCS Workgroup is responsible for making the final decisions pertaining to additions, deletions, and revisions to the HCPCS codes. The CMS HCPCS Workgroup reviews all requests for coding changes and makes final decisions regarding the annual update to the national codes. The Workgroup sends letters to those who requested coding revisions to inform them of the Workgroup's decision regarding their coding requests. The decision letters include, but may not be limited to, the following types of responses:

1. A change to the national codes has been approved that reflects, completely or in part, your coding request.

2. Your request for a coding revision to this year's update has not been approved because the scope of your request necessitates that additional consideration be given to your request before the CMS HCPCS Workgroup reaches a final decision.

3. Your reported sales volume was insufficient to support your request for a revision to the national codes. To determine whether there is sufficient sales volume to warrant a permanent code, we ask requestors to submit 3 months of the most recent sales volume for

non-drug items. There is not a requirement to submit marketing data for drugs.

4. Your request for a new national code has not been approved because there already is an existing permanent or temporary code that describes your product.

5. Your request for a code has not been approved because your product is not used by health care providers for diagnostic or therapeutic purposes.

6. Your request for a code has not been approved because the code you requested is for capital equipment.

7. Your request for a code has not been approved because your product is an integral part of another service and payment for that service includes payment for your product; therefore, your product may not be billed separately to Medicare.

8. Your request for a revision to the language that describes the current code has not been approved because it does not improve the code descriptor.

9. Your request for a new code has not been approved because your product is not primarily medical in nature (for example, generally not useful in the absence of an illness or injury).

10. Your request for a code has not been approved because your product is used exclusively in the inpatient hospital setting.

11. Your request for a code has not been approved because it is inappropriate for inclusion in the HCPCS Level II code set and request should be submitted independently to another coding authority (e.g. AMA for CPT® coding, ADA for CDT coding, etc.)

Decision letters also inform the requestors that they may contact the entity in whose jurisdiction a claim is filed for assistance in answering any coding questions. For Medicare, contact the PDAC. Contractor to CMS, the PDAC is responsible for providing suppliers and manufacturers with assistance in determining which HCPCS code should be used to describe DMEPOS items for the purpose of billing Medicare. The PDAC has a toll free helpline for this purpose, (877) 735-1326, which is operational during the hours of 9 AM to 4 PM (EST). For Medicaid, contact the state Medicaid agency. For private insurance, contact the individual insurer. A requestor who is dissatisfied with the final decision may submit a new request asking the CMS HCPCS Workgroup to reconsider and re-evaluate the code request. At that time, the requestor should include new information or additional explanations to support the request.

Reconsideration Process

CMS management is considering pilot-testing, a process by which denied applicants would be allowed an opportunity to have their application reconsidered during the same coding cycle. The basis for denial will be clearly delineated in a notice to the applicant and provided in a timely fashion.

D. HCPCS Updates
Permanent National Codes

The national codes are updated annually, according to the following schedule:

1. Coding requests have to be received by January 3 of the current year to be considered for the next January 1 update of the subsequent year. This means that completed requests must be received by no later than January 3 of the current year to be considered for inclusion in the January update of the following year unless January 3 falls on a weekend; then the due date is extended to the following Monday.

2. Computer tapes and instructions, that include an updated list of codes and identify which codes have been changed or deleted, are updated and sent to our contractors and Medicaid State agencies at least 60 days in advance of the January 1 implementation date for the annual update. In addition, the CMS HCPCS Workgroup's final decisions on all public requests for changes to the HCPCS coding system will be published on the official HCPCS web site at www.cms.gov/medhcpcsgeninfo in November of each year.

Temporary Codes

Temporary codes can be added, changed, or deleted on a quarterly basis. Once established, temporary codes are usually implemented within 90 days, the time needed to prepare and issue implementation instructions and to enter the new code into CMS's and the contractors' computer systems and initiate user education. This time is needed to allow for instructions such as bulletins and newsletters to be sent out to suppliers to provide them with information and assistance regarding the implementation of temporary CMS codes.

HCPCS/Medicare Website

Our website, http://www.cms.gov/medhcpcsgeninfo lists all of the current HCPCS codes, an alphabetical index of HCPCS codes by type of service or product, and an alphabetical table of drugs for which there are level II codes. The HCPCS Public Meeting Agendas (separated by product category) published on this website list applications submitted in the current coding cycle. Interested parties can submit comments regarding the agenda items to the CMS HCPCS Workgroup by sending an e-mail to CMS through this website. These comments are included as part of the Workgroup's review as it considers the coding requests.

The newly established temporary codes and effective dates for their use are also posted on the HCPCS website at http://www.cms.gov/medhcpcsgeninfo. This website enables us to quickly disseminate information on coding requests and decisions.

Code Assignment Following Medicare National Coverage Determination

Pursuant to Sec. 1862 (I) (3) (C) (iv) of the Social Security Act (added by Section 731 (a) of the Medicare Modernization Act), the Centers for Medicare and Medicaid Services (CMS), has developed a process by which the CMS HCPCS Workgroup will identify an appropriate existing code category and/or establish a new code category to describe the item that is the subject of a National Coverage Determination (NCD). If the item is considered Durable Medical Equipment, Prosthetic, Orthotic or Supply (DMEPOS), the CMS will defer to the Pricing, Data Analysis and Coding (PDAC) to determine the appropriate code category. Contractor to the CMS, the (PDAC) assigns individual DMEPOS products to HCPCS code categories for the purpose of billing Medicare.

As a matter of meeting on-going Medicare program operating needs, processes have existed for some time by which items and services that are newly covered by Medicare are assigned to a new or existing code category. Effective July 1, 2004, the process outlined below has been used by CMS to comply with the requirements of Sec. 1862 (l).

1. Assignment of an Existing "Temporary" or "Permanent" Code: When the CMS determines that an item is already identified by an existing "temporary" or "permanent" (as described in A and B above) HCPCS code category, but was previously not covered, the CMS will assign the item to the existing code category, and ensure that the coverage indicator assigned to the code category accurately reflects Medicare policy regarding payment for the item. Sec. 731 of the MMA does not require that a new code category or a product specific code be created for an item simply because a new coverage determination was made, without regard to codes available in the existing code set.

2. Assignment of a New "Temporary" or "Permanent" Code: When the CMS determines that a new code category is appropriate, CMS will make every effort to establish, publish, and implement the new code at the time the final coverage determination is made.

3. Assignment of an Unclassified Code: Under certain circumstances, the assignment of an item to an unclassified code may be necessary. A number of unclassified codes already exist under various headings throughout the HCPCS Level II code set. When an item is newly covered, but usage is narrow and the item would be billed infrequently, it may be more of an administrative burden to revise the code set than to use an unclassified code along with other, existing processing methods. When a new "temporary" or "permanent" code is appropriate, but the change cannot be implemented and incorporated into billing and claims processing systems at the time the final NCD decision memorandum is released, an unclassified code may be assigned in the interim, until a new code can be implemented, in order to ensure that claims can be processed for the item. The timing of implementation of new "temporary" or "permanent" codes relative to the date of the coverage determination depends on a variety of factors, some of which are not within the direct control of the code set maintainers, for example:

   - coding alternatives may require extensive research;
   - the timing of the coverage determination may be such that the publication deadline for the next Quarterly Update is missed;
   - there is insufficient time between NCD and Quarterly Update to incorporate new codes into new policy and accompanying billing instructions, and into claims processing systems along with any edits needed to operationalize the new code.

NEW CODES

Code	Code Descriptor
A4459	Manual pump-operated enema system, includes balloon, catheter and all accessories, reusable, any type
A4602	Replacement battery for external infusion pump owned by patient, lithium, 1.5 volt, each
A7048	Vacuum drainage collection unit and tubing kit, including all supplies needed for collection unit change, for use with implanted catheter, each
A9606	Radium Ra-223 dichloride, therapeutic, per microcurie
C2624	Implantable wireless pulmonary artery pressure sensor with delivery catheter, including all system components
C2644	Brachytherapy source, cesium-131 chloride solution, per millicurie
C9025	Injection, ramucirumab, 5 mg
C9026	Injection, vedolizumab, 1 mg
C9027	Injection, pembrolizumab, 1 mg
C9136	Injection, factor VIII, Fc fusion protein, (recombinant), per I.U.
C9349	Fortaderm, and fortaderm antimicrobial, any type, per square centimeter
C9442	Injection, belinostat, 10 mg
C9443	Injection, dalbavancin, 10 mg
C9444	Injection, oritavancin, 10 mg
C9446	Injection, tedizolid phosphate, 1 mg
C9447	Injection, phenylephrine and ketorolac, 4 ml vial
C9739	Cystourethroscopy, with insertion of transprostatic implant; 1 to 3 implants
C9740	Cystourethroscopy, with insertion of transprostatic implant; 4 or more implants
C9742	Laryngoscopy, flexible fiberoptic, with injection into vocal cord(s), therapeutic, including diagnostic laryngoscopy, if performed
G0276	Blinded procedure for lumbar stenosis, percutaneous image-guided lumbar decompression (pild) or placebo-control, performed in an approved coverage with evidence development (ced) clinical trial
G0277	Hyperbaric oxygen under pressure, full body chamber, per 30 minute interval
G0279	Diagnostic digital breast tomosynthesis, unilateral or bilateral (list separately in addition to G0204 or G0206)
G0464	Colorectal cancer screening; stool-based DNA and fecal occult hemoglobin (e.g., KRAS, NDRG4 and BMP3
G0466	Federally qualified health center (FQHC) visit, new patient; a medically-necessary, face-to-face encounter (one-on-one) between a new patient and a FQHC practitioner during which time one or more FQHC services are rendered and includes a typical bundle of medicare-covered services that would be furnished per diem to a patient receiving a FQHC visit

Code	Code Descriptor
G0467	Federally qualified health center (FQHC) visit, established patient; a medically-necessary, face-to-face encounter (one-on-one) between an established patient and a FQHC practitioner during which time one or more FQHC services are rendered and includes a typical bundle of medicare-covered services that would be furnished per diem to a patient receiving a FQHC visit
G0468	Federally qualified health center (FQHC) visit, IPPE or AWV; a FQHC visit that includes an initial preventive physical examination (IPPE) or annual wellness visit (AWV) and includes a typical bundle of medicare-covered services that would be furnished per diem to a patient receiving an IPPE or AWV
G0469	Federally qualified health center (FQHC) visit, mental health, new patient; a medically-necessary, face-to-face mental health encounter (one-on-one) between a new patient and a FQHC practitioner during which time one or more FQHC services are rendered and includes a typical bundle of medicare-covered services that would be furnished per diem to a patient receiving a mental health visit
G0470	Federally qualified health center (FQHC) visit, mental health, established patient; a medically-necessary, face-to-face mental health encounter (one-on-one) between an established patient and a FQHC practitioner during which time one or more FQHC services are rendered and includes a typical bundle of medicare-covered services that would be furnished per diem to a patient receiving a mental health visit
G0471	Collection of venous blood by venipuncture or urine sample by catheterization from an individual in a skilled nursing facility (SNF) or by a laboratory on behalf of a home health agency (HHA)
G0472	Hepatitis C antibody screening, for individual at high risk and other covered indication(s)
G0473	Face-to-face behavioral counseling for obesity, group (2-10), 30 minutes
G6001	Ultrasonic guidance for placement of radiation therapy fields
G6002	Stereoscopic X-ray guidance for localization of target volume for the delivery of radiation therapy
G6003	Radiation treatment delivery, single treatment area, single port or parallel opposed ports, simple blocks or no blocks: up to 5 MeV
G6004	Radiation treatment delivery, single treatment area, single port or parallel opposed ports, simple blocks or no blocks: 6-10 MeV
G6005	Radiation treatment delivery, single treatment area, single port or parallel opposed ports, simple blocks or no blocks: 11-19 MeV
G6006	Radiation treatment delivery, single treatment area, single port or parallel opposed ports, simple blocks or no blocks: 20 MeV or greater
G6007	Radiation treatment delivery, 2 separate treatment areas, 3 or more ports on a single treatment area, use of multiple blocks: up to 5 MeV

Code	Code Descriptor
G6008	Radiation treatment delivery, 2 separate treatment areas, 3 or more ports on a single treatment area, use of multiple blocks: 6-10 MeV
G6009	Radiation treatment delivery, 2 separate treatment areas, 3 or more ports on a single treatment area, use of multiple blocks: 11-19 MeV
G6010	Radiation treatment delivery, 2 separate treatment areas, 3 or more ports on a single treatment area, use of multiple blocks: 20 MeV or greater
G6011	Radiation treatment delivery, 3 or more separate treatment areas, custom blocking, tangential ports, wedges, rotational beam, compensators, electron beam; up to 5 MeV
G6012	Radiation treatment delivery, 3 or more separate treatment areas, custom blocking, tangential ports, wedges, rotational beam, compensators, electron beam; 6-10 MeV
G6013	Radiation treatment delivery, 3 or more separate treatment areas, custom blocking, tangential ports, wedges, rotational beam, compensators, electron beam; 11-19 MeV
G6014	Radiation treatment delivery, 3 or more separate treatment areas, custom blocking, tangential ports, wedges, rotational beam, compensators, electron beam; 20 MeV or greater
G6015	Intensity modulated treatment delivery, single or multiple fields/arcs, via narrow spatially and temporally modulated beams, binary, dynamic MLC, per treatment session
G6016	Compensator-based beam modulation treatment delivery of inverse planned treatment using 3 or more high resolution (milled or cast) compensator, convergent beam modulated fields, per treatment session
G6017	Intra-fraction localization and tracking of target or patient motion during delivery of radiation therapy (e.g., 3D positional tracking, gating, 3D surface tracking), each fraction of treatment
G6018	Ileoscopy, through stoma; with transendoscopic stent placement (includes predilation)
G6019	Colonoscopy through stoma; with ablation of tumor(s), polyp(s), or other lesion(s) not amenable to removal by hot biopsy forceps, bipolar cautery or snare technique
G6020	Colonoscopy through stoma; with transendoscopic stent placement (includes predilation)
G6021	Unlisted procedure, intestine
G6022	Sigmoidoscopy, flexible; with ablation of tumor(s), polyp(s), or other lesions(s) not amenable to removal by hot biopsy forceps, bipolar cautery or snare technique
G6023	Sigmoidoscopy, flexible; with transendoscopic stent placement (includes predilation)
G6024	Colonoscopy, flexible; proximal to splenic flexure; with ablation of tumor(s), polyp(s), or other lesion(s) not amenable to removal by hot biopsy forceps, bipolar cautery or snare technique
G6025	Colonoscopy, flexible, proximal to splenic flexure; with transendoscopic stent placement (includes predilation)
G6027	Anoscopy, high resolution (HRA) (with magnification and chemical agent enhancement); diagnostic, including collection of specimen(s) by brushing or washing when performed
G6028	Anoscopy, high resolution (HRA) (with magnification and chemical agent enhancement); with biopsy(ies)
G6030	Amitriptyline

Code	Code Descriptor
G6031	Benzodiazepines
G6032	Desipramine
G6034	Doxepin
G6035	Gold
G6036	Assay of imipramine
G6037	Nortriptyline
G6038	Salicylate
G6039	Acetaminophen
G6040	Alcohol (ethanol); any specimen except breath
G6041	Alkaloids, urine, quantitative
G6042	Amphetamine or methamphetamine
G6043	Barbiturates, not elsewhere specified
G6044	Cocaine or metabolite
G6045	Dihydrocodeinone
G6046	Dihydromorphinone
G6047	Dihydrotestosterone
G6048	Dimethadione
G6049	Epiandrosterone
G6050	Ethchlorvynol
G6051	Flurazepam
G6052	Meprobamate
G6053	Methadone
G6054	Methsuximide
G6055	Nicotine
G6056	Opiate(s), drug and metabolites, each procedure
G6057	Phenothiazine
G6058	Drug confirmation, each procedure
G9362	Duration of monitored anesthesia care (MAC) or peripheral nerve block (PNB) without the use of general anesthesia during an applicable procedure 60 minutes or longer, as documented in the anesthesia record
G9363	Duration of monitored anesthesia care (MAC) or peripheral nerve block (PNB) without the use of general anesthesia during an applicable procedure or general or neuraxial anesthesia less than 60 minutes, as documented in the anesthesia record
G9364	Sinusitis caused by, or presumed to be caused by, bacterial infection
G9365	One high-risk medication ordered
G9366	One high-risk medication not ordered
G9367	At least two different high-risk medications ordered
G9368	At least two different high-risk medications not ordered
G9369	Individual filled at least two prescriptions for any antipsychotic medication and had a proportion of days covered (PDC) of 0.8 or greater
G9370	Individual who did not fill at least two prescriptions for any antipsychotic medication or did not have a Individual who did not fill at least two prescriptions for any antipsychotic medication or did not have a proportion of days covered (PDC) of 0.8 or greater of 0.8 or greater
G9376	Patient continued to have the retina attached at the 6 months follow up visit (+/- 1 month) following only one surgery

Code	Code Descriptor
G9377	Patient did not have the retina attached after 6 months following only one surgery
G9378	Patient continued to have the retina attached at the 6 months follow up visit (+/- 1 month)
G9379	Patient did not achieve flat retinas six months post surgery
G9380	Patient offered assistance with end of life issues during the measurement period
G9381	Documentation of medical reason(s) for not offering assistance with end of life issues (e.g., patient in hospice and in terminal phase) during the measurement period
G9382	Patient not offered assistance with end of life issues during the measurement period
G9383	Patient received screening for HCV infection within the 12 month reporting period
G9384	Documentation of medical reason(s) for not receiving screening for HCV infection within the 12 month reporting period (e.g., decompensated cirrhosis including advanced disease [ie, ascites, esophageal variceal bleeding, hepatic encephalopathy], hepatocellular carcinoma, or waitlist for organ transplant, limited life expectancy, other medical reasons)
G9385	Documentation of patient reason(s) for not receiving screening for HCV infection within the 12 month reporting period (e.g., patient declined, other patient reasons)
G9386	Screening for HCV infection not received within the 12 month reporting period, reason not given
G9389	Unplanned rupture of the posterior capsule requiring vitrectomy
G9390	No unplanned rupture of the posterior capsule requiring vitrectomy
G9391	Patient achieves refraction +-1 d for the eye that underwent cataract surgery, measured at the one month follow up visit
G9392	Patient does not achieve refraction +-1 D for the eye that underwent cataract surgery, measured at the one month follow up visit
G9393	Patient with an initial PHQ-9 score greater than nine who achieves remission at twelve months as demonstrated by a twelve month (+/- 30 days) PHQ-9 score of less than five
G9394	Patient who had a diagnosis of bipolar disorder or personality disorder, death, permanent nursing home resident or receiving hospice or palliative care any time during the measurement or assessment period
G9395	Patient with an initial PHQ-9 score greater than nine who did not achieve remission at twelve months as demonstrated by a twelve month (+/- 30 days) PHQ-9 score greater than or equal to five
G9396	Patient with an initial PHQ-9 score greater than nine who was not assessed for remission at twelve months (+/- 30 days)
G9399	Documentation in the patient record of a discussion between the physician/clinician and the patient that includes all of the following: treatment choices appropriate to genotype, risks and benefits, evidence of effectiveness, and patient preferences toward the outcome of the treatment
G9400	Documentation of medical or patient reason(s) for not discussing treatment options; medical reasons: patient is not a candidate for treatment due to advanced physical or mental health comorbidity (including active substance use); currently receiving antiviral treatment; successful antiviral treatment (with sustained virologic response) prior to reporting period; other documented medical reasons; patient reasons: patient unable or unwilling to participate in the discussion or other patient reasons
G9401	No documentation of a discussion in the patient record of a discussion between the physician or other qualified healthcare professional and the patient that includes all of the following: treatment choices appropriate to genotype, risks and benefits, evidence of effectiveness, and patient preferences toward treatment
G9402	Patient received follow-up on the date of discharge or within 30 days after discharge
G9403	Clinician documented reason patient was not able to complete 30 day follow-up from acute inpatient setting discharge (e.g., patient death prior to follow-up visit, patient non-compliant for visit follow-up)
G9404	Patient did not receive follow-up on the date of discharge or within 30 days after discharge
G9405	Patient received follow-up within 7 days from discharge
G9406	Clinician documented reason patient was not able to complete 7 day follow-up from acute inpatient setting discharge (i.e patient death prior to follow-up visit, patient non-compliance for visit follow-up)
G9407	Patient did not receive follow-up on or within 7 days after discharge
G9408	Patients with cardiac tamponade and/or pericardiocentesis occurring within 30 days
G9409	Patients without cardiac tamponade and/or pericardiocentesis occurring within 30 days
G9410	Patient admitted within 180 days, status post cied implantation, replacement, or revision with an infection requiring device removal or surgical revision
G9411	Patient not admitted within 180 days, status post cied implantation, replacement, or revision with an infection requiring device removal or surgical revision
G9412	Patient admitted within 180 days, status post cied implantation, replacement, or revision with an infection requiring device removal or surgical revision
G9413	Patient not admitted within 180 days, status post cied implantation, replacement, or revision with an infection requiring device removal or surgical revision
G9414	Patient had one dose of meningococcal vaccine on or between the patient's 11th and 13th birthdays
G9415	Patient did not have one dose of meningococcal vaccine on or between the patient's 11th and 13th birthdays
G9416	Patient had one tetanus, diphtheria toxoids and acellular pertussis vaccine (Tdap) or one tetanus, diphtheria toxoids vaccine (TD) on or between the patient's 10th and 13th birthdays or one tetanus and one diptheria vaccine on or between the patient's 10th and 13th birthdays

Code	Code Descriptor
G9417	Patient did not have one tetanus, diphtheria toxoids and acellular pertussis vaccine (Tdap) or one tetanus, diphtheria toxoids vaccine (TD) on or between the patient's 10th and 13th birthdays or one tetanus and one diptheria vaccine on or between the patient's 10th and 13th birthdays
G9418	Primary non-small cell lung cancer biopsy and cytology specimen report documents classification into specific histologic type or classified as NSCLC-NOS with an explanation
G9419	Documentation of medical reason(s) for not reporting the histological type or NSCLC-NOS classification with an explanation (e.g., biopsy taken for other purposes in a patient with a history of primary non-small cell lung cancer or other documented medical reasons)
G9420	Specimen site other than anatomic location of lung or is not classified as primary non-small cell lung cancer
G9421	Primary non-small cell lung cancer biopsy and cytology specimen report does not document classification into specific histologic type or classified as NSCLC-NOS with an explanation
G9422	Non-small cell lung cancer biopsy and cytology specimen report documents classification into specific histologic type or classified as NSCLC-NOS with an explanation
G9423	Documentation of medical reason(s) for not reporting the histological type or NSCLC-NOS classification with an explanation (e.g., a solitary fibrous tumor in a person with a history of non-small cell carcinoma or other documented medical reasons)
G9424	Specimen site other than anatomic location of lung, is not classified as non-small cell lung cancer or classified as NSCLC-NOS
G9425	Non small cell lung cancer biopsy and cytology specimen report does not document classification into specific histologic type or classified as NSCLC-NOS with an explanation
G9426	Improvement in median time from ED arrival to initial ED oral or parenteral pain medication administration performed for ED admitted patients
G9427	Improvement in median time from ED arrival to initial ED oral or parenteral pain medication administration not performed for ED admitted patients
G9428	Pathology report includes the Pt category and a statement on thickness and ulceration and for pT1, mitotic rate
G9429	Documentation of medical reason(s) for not reporting Pt category and a statement on thickness and ulceration and for pT1, mitotic rate (e.g., negative skin biopsies in a patient with a history of melanoma or other documented medical reasons)
G9430	Specimen site other than anatomic cutaneous location
G9431	Pathology report does not include the Pt category and a statement on thickness and ulceration and for pT1, mitotic rate
G9432	Asthma well-controlled based on the ACT, C-ACT, ACQ, or ATAQ score and results documented
G9433	Death, permanent nursing home resident or receiving hospice or palliative care any time during the measurement period
G9434	Asthma not well-controlled based on the ACT, C-ACT, ACQ, or ATAQ score, or specified asthma control tool not used, reason not given
G9435	Aspirin prescribed at discharge

Code	Code Descriptor
G9436	Aspirin not prescribed for documented reasons (e.g., allergy, medical intolerance, history of bleed)
G9437	Aspirin not prescribed at discharge
G9438	P2Y inhibitor prescribed at discharge
G9439	P2Y inhibitor not prescribed for documented reasons (e.g., allergy, medical intolerance, history of bleed)
G9440	P2Y inhibitor not prescribed at discharge
G9441	Statin prescribed at discharge
G9442	Statin not prescribed for documented reasons (e.g., allergy, medical intolerance)
G9443	Statin not prescribed at discharge
G9448	Patients who were born in the years 1945-1965
G9449	History of receiving blood transfusions prior to 1992
G9450	History of injection drug use
G9451	Patient received one-time screening for HCV infection
G9452	Documentation of medical reason(s) for not receiving one-time screening for HCV infection (e.g., decompensated cirrhosis indicating advanced disease [ie, ascites, esophageal variceal bleeding, hepatic encephalopathy], hepatocellular carcinoma, waitlist for organ transplant, limited life expectancy, other medical reasons)
G9453	Documentation of patient reason(s) for not receiving one-time screening for HCV infection (e.g., patient declined, other patient reasons)
G9454	One-time screening for HCV infection not received within 12 month reporting period and no documentation of prior screening for HCV infection, reason not given
G9455	Patient underwent abdominal imaging with ultrasound, contrast enhanced CT or contrast MRI for HCC
G9456	Documentation of medical or patient reason(s) for not ordering or performing screening for HCC. medical reason: comorbid medical conditions with expected survival < 5 years, hepatic decompensation and not a candidate for liver transplantation, or other medical reasons; patient reasons: patient declined or other patient reasons (e.g., cost of tests, time related to accessing testing equipment)
G9457	Patient did not undergo abdominal imaging and did not have a documented reason for not undergoing abdominal imaging in the reporting period
G9458	Patient documented as tobacco user and received tobacco cessation intervention (must include at least one of the following: advice given to quit smoking or tobacco use, counseling on the benefits of quitting smoking or tobacco use, assistance with or referral to external smoking or tobacco cessation support programs, or current enrollment in smoking or tobacco use cessation program) if identified as a tobacco user
G9459	Currently a tobacco non-user
G9460	Tobacco assessment or tobacco cessation intervention not performed, reason not otherwise specified
G9463	I intend to report the sinusitis measures group
G9464	All quality actions for the applicable measures in the sinusitis measures group have been performed for this patient
G9465	I intend to report the acute otitis externa (AOE) measures group

Code	Code Descriptor
G9466	All quality actions for the applicable measures in the AOE measures group have been performed for this patient
G9467	Patient who have received or are receiving corticosteroids greater than or equal to 10 mg/day of prednisone equivalents for 60 or greater consecutive days or a single prescription equating to 600 mg prednisone or greater for all fills
G9468	Patient not receiving corticosteroids greater than or equal to 10 mg/day of prednisone equivalents for 60 or greater consecutive days or a single prescription equating to 600mg prednisone or greater for all fills
G9469	Patients who have received or are receiving corticosteroids greater than or equal to 10 mg/day of prednisone equivalents for 60 or greater consecutive days or a single prescription equating to 600 mg prednisone or greater for all fills
G9470	Patients not receiving corticosteroids greater than or equal to 10 mg/day of prednisone equivalents for 60 or greater consecutive days or a single prescription equating to 600 mg prednisone or greater for all fills
G9471	Within the past 2 years, central dual-energy X-ray absorptiometry (DXA) not ordered or documented
G9472	Within the past 2 years, central dual-energy X-ray absorptiometry (DXA) not ordered and documented, no review of systems and no medication history or pharmacologic therapy (other than minerals/vitamins) for osteoporosis prescribed
J0153	Injection, adenosine, 1 mg (not to be used to report any adenosine phosphate compounds)
J0571	Buprenorphine, oral, 1 mg
J0572	Buprenorphine/naloxone, oral, less than or equal to 3 mg
J0573	Buprenorphine/naloxone, oral, greater than 3 mg, but less than or equal to 6 mg
J0574	Buprenorphine/naloxone, oral, greater than 6 mg, but less than or equal to 10 mg
J0575	Buprenorphine/naloxone, oral, greater than 10 mg
J0887	Injection, epoetin beta, 1 microgram, (for ESRD on dialysis)
J0888	Injection, epoetin beta, 1 microgram, (for non ESRD use)
J1071	Injection, testosterone cypionate, 1 mg
J1322	Injection, elosulfase alfa, 1 mg
J1439	Injection, ferric carboxymaltose, 1 mg
J2274	Injection, morphine sulfate, preservative-free for epidural or intrathecal use, 10 mg
J2704	Injection, propofol, 10 mg
J3121	Injection, testosterone enanthate, 1 mg
J3145	Injection, testosterone undecanoate, 1 mg
J7181	Injection, Factor XIII a-subunit, (recombinant), per IU
J7182	Injection, Factor VIII, (antihemophilic factor, recombinant), (Novoeight), per IU
J7200	Injection, Factor IX, (antihemophilic factor, recombinant), Rixubis, per iu
J7201	Injection, Factor IX, fc fusion protein (recombinant), per IU
J7327	Hyaluronan or derivative, monovisc, for intra-articular injection, per dose
J7336	Capsaicin 8% patch, per square centimeter
J9267	Injection, paclitaxel, 1 mg

Code	Code Descriptor
J9301	Injection, obinutuzumab, 10 mg
K0901	Knee orthosis (KO), single upright, thigh and calf, with adjustable flexion and extension joint (unicentric or polycentric), medial-lateral and rotation control, with or without varus/valgus adjustment, prefabricated, off-the-shelf
K0902	Knee orthosis (KO), double upright, thigh and calf, with adjustable flexion and extension joint (unicentric or polycentric), medial-lateral and rotation control, with or without varus/valgus adjustment, prefabricated, off-the-shelf
L3981	Upper extremity fracture orthosis, humeral, prefabricated, includes shoulder cap design, with or without joints, forearm section, may include soft interface, straps, includes fitting and adjustments
L6026	Transcarpal/metacarpal or partial hand disarticulation prosthesis, external power, self-suspended, inner socket with removable forearm section, electrodes and cables, two batteries, charger, myoelectric control of terminal device, excludes terminal device(s)
L7259	Electronic wrist rotator, any type
L8696	Antenna (external) for use with implantable diaphragmatic/phrenic nerve stimulation device, replacement, each
Q4150	Allowrap DS or Dry, per square centimeter
Q4151	AmnioBand or Guardian, per square centimeter
Q4152	DermaPure, per square centimeter
Q4153	Dermavest, per square centimeter
Q4154	Biovance, per square centimeter
Q4155	NeoxFlo or clarixFlo, 1 mg
Q4156	Neox 100, per square centimeter
Q4157	Revitalon, per square centimeter
Q4158	MariGen, per square centimeter
Q4159	Affinity, per square centimeter
Q4160	NuShield, per square centimeter
S1034	Artificial pancreas device system (e.g., low glucose suspend (LGS) feature) including continuous glucose monitor, blood glucose device, insulin pump and computer algorithm that communicates with all of the devices
S1035	Sensor; invasive (e.g., subcutaneous), disposable, for use with artificial pancreas device system
S1036	Transmitter; external, for use with artificial pancreas device system
S1037	Receiver (monitor); external, for use with artificial pancreas device system
S8032	Low-dose computed tomography for lung cancer screening
S9901	Services by a journal-listed christian science nurse, per hour

REVISED CODES

Code	Code Descriptor
A4601	Lithium ion battery, rechargeable, for non-prosthetic use, replacement
C9741	Right heart catheterization with implantation of wireless pressure sensor in the pulmonary artery, including any type of measurement, angiography, imaging supervision, interpretation, and report
E0856	Cervical traction device, with inflatable air bladder(s)
E0986	Manual wheelchair accessory, push-rim activated power assist system
G0204	Diagnostic mammography, producing direct 2-D digital image, bilateral, all views
G0206	Diagnostic mammography, producing direct 2-D digital image, unilateral, all views
G0416	Surgical pathology, gross and microscopic examinations, for prostate needle biopsy, any method
G8461	Patient receiving antiviral treatment for hepatitis C during the measurement period
G8474	Angiotensin converting enzyme (ACE) inhibitor or angiotensin receptor blocker (ARB) therapy not prescribed for reasons documented by the clinician (eg, allergy, intolerance, pregnancy, renal failure due to ACE inhibitor, diseases of the aortic or mitral valve, other medical reasons) or (eg, patient declined, other patient reasons) or (eg, lack of drug availability, other reasons attributable to the health care system)
G8476	Most recent blood pressure has a systolic measurement of < 140 mmHg and a diastolic measurement of < 90 mmHg
G8477	Most recent blood pressure has a systolic measurement of >=140 mmHg and/or a diastolic measurement of >=90 mmHg
G8483	Influenza immunization was not administered for reasons documented by clinician (e.g., patient allergy or other medical reasons, patient declined or other patient reasons, vaccine not available or other system reasons)
G8484	Influenza immunization was not administered, reason not given
G8571	Development of deep sternal wound infection/mediastinitis within 30 days postoperatively
G8572	No deep sternal wound infection/mediastinitis
G8720	Total Kt/V less than 1.7 per week (total clearance of urea [Kt] / volume [V])
G8840	Documentation of reason(s) for not documenting an assessment of sleep symptoms (e.g., patient didn't have initial daytime sleepiness, patient visited between initial testing and initiation of therapy)
G8843	Documentation of reason(s) for not measuring an apnea hypopnea index (AHI) or a respiratory disturbance index (RDI) at the time of initial diagnosis (e.g., psychiatric disease, dementia, patient declined, financial, insurance coverage, test ordered but not yet completed)
G8861	Within the past 2 years, central dual-energy x-ray absorptiometry (DXA) ordered and documented, review of systems and medication history or pharmacologic therapy (other than minerals/vitamins) for osteoporosis prescribed

Code	Code Descriptor
G8876	Documentation of reason(s) for not performing minimally invasive biopsy to diagnose breast cancer preoperatively (e.g., lesion too close to skin, implant, chest wall, etc., lesion could not be adequately visualized for needle biopsy, patient condition prevents needle biopsy [weight, breast thickness, etc.], duct excision without imaging abnormality, prophylactic mastectomy, reduction mammoplasty, excisional biopsy performed by another physician)
G8924	Spirometry test results demonstrate fev1/fvc < 60% and patient has COPD symptoms (e.g., dyspnea, cough/sputum, wheezing)
G8936	Clinician documented that patient was not an eligible candidate for angiotensin converting enzyme (ACE) inhibitor or angiotensin receptor blocker (ARB) therapy (eg, allergy, intolerance, pregnancy, renal failure due to ACE inhibitor, diseases of the aortic or mitral valve, other medical reasons) or (eg, patient declined, other patient reasons) or (eg, lack of drug availability, other reasons attributable to the health care system)
G8968	Documentation of medical reason(s) for not prescribing warfarin or another oral anticoagulant that is FDA approved for the prevention of thromboembolism [e.g., patients with mitral stenosis or prosthetic heart valves, patients with transient or reversible causes of af (e.g., pneumonia, hyperthyroidism, pregnancy, cardiac surgery), allergy, risk of bleeding, other medical reasons]
G9160	Spoken language comprehension functional limitation, projected goal status at therapy episode outset, at reporting intervals, and at discharge or to end reporting
G9163	Spoken language expression functional limitation, projected goal status at therapy episode outset, at reporting intervals, and at discharge or to end reporting
G9166	Attention functional limitation, projected goal status at therapy episode outset, at reporting intervals, and at discharge or to end reporting
G9169	Memory functional limitation, projected goal status at therapy episode outset, at reporting intervals, and at discharge or to end reporting
G9172	Voice functional limitation, projected goal status at therapy episode outset, at reporting intervals, and at discharge or to end reporting
G9175	Other speech language pathology functional limitation, projected goal status at therapy episode outset, at reporting intervals, and at discharge or to end reporting
G9186	Motor speech functional limitation, projected goal status at therapy episode outset, at reporting intervals, and at discharge or to end reporting
G9210	Hepatitis C quantitative RNA testing not performed between 4-12 weeks after the initiation of antiviral treatment for documented reason(s) (e.g., patients whose treatment was discontinued during the testing period prior to testing, other medical reasons, patient declined, other patient reasons)
G9242	Documentation of viral load equal to or greater than 200 copies/ml or viral load not performed

Code	Code Descriptor
G9277	Documentation that the patient is on daily aspirin or anti-platelet or has documentation of a valid contraindication to aspirin/anti-platelet. automatic contraindications include anti-coagulant use, allergy, and history of gastrointestinal bleed. additionally, any reason documented by the physician as a reason for not taking daily aspirin or anti-platelet is acceptable (examples include non-steroidal anti-inflammatory agents, risk for drug interaction, or uncontrolled hypertension defined as > 180 systolic or > 110 diastolic
G9278	Documentation that the patient is not on daily aspirin or anti-platelet regimen
G9296	Patients with documented shared decision-making including discussion of conservative (non-surgical) therapy (e.g., nsaids, analgesics, weight loss, exercise, injections) prior to the procedure
G9297	Shared decision-making including discussion of conservative (non-surgical) therapy (e.g., nsaids, analgesics, weight loss, exercise, injections) prior to the procedure, not documented, reason not given
G9298	Patients who are evaluated for venous thromboembolic and cardiovascular risk factors within 30 days prior to the procedure (e.g., history of DVT, PE, MI, arrhythmia and stroke)
G9299	Patients who are not evaluated for venous thromboembolic and cardiovascular risk factors within 30 days prior to the procedure including (e.g., history of DVT, PE, MI, arrhythmia and stroke, reason not given)
G9303	Operative report does not identify the prosthetic implant specifications including the prosthetic implant manufacturer, the brand name of the prosthetic implant and the size of each prosthetic implant, reason not given
G9304	Operative report identifies the prosthetic implant specifications including the prosthetic implant manufacturer, the brand name of the prosthetic implant and the size of each prosthetic implant
G9329	Dicom format image data available to non-affiliated external healthcare facilities or entities on a secure, media free, reciprocally searchable basis with patient authorization for at least a 12-month period after the study not documented in final report, reason not given
G9340	Final report documented that dicom format image data available to non-affiliated external healthcare facilities or entities on a secure, media free, reciprocally searchable basis with patient authorization for at least a 12-month period after the study
G9341	Search conducted for prior patient CT studies completed at non-affiliated external healthcare facilities or entities within the past 12-months and are available through a secure, authorized, media-free, shared archive prior to an imaging study being performed
G9342	Search not conducted prior to an imaging study being performed for prior patient CT studies completed at non-affiliated external healthcare facilities or entities within the past 12-months and are available through a secure, authorized, media-free, shared archive, reason not given

Code	Code Descriptor
G9343	Due to medical reasons, search not conducted for dicom format images for prior patient CT imaging studies completed at non-affiliated external healthcare facilities or entities within the past 12 months that are available through a secure, authorized, media-free, shared archive (e.g., CT studies performed for radiation treatment planning or image-guided radiation treatment delivery)
G9344	Due to system reasons search not conducted for dicom format images for prior patient CT imaging studies completed at non-affiliated external healthcare facilities or entities within the past 12 months that are available through a secure, authorized, media-free, shared archive (e.g., non-affiliated external healthcare facilities or entities does not have archival abilities through a shared archival system)
G9345	Follow-up recommendations documented according to recommended guidelines for incidentally detected pulmonary nodules (e.g., follow-up CT imaging studies needed or that no follow-up is needed) based at a minimum on nodule size and patient risk factors
G9346	Follow-up recommendations not documented according to recommended guidelines for incidentally detected pulmonary nodules due to medical reasons (e.g., patients with known malignant disease, patients with unexplained fever, CT studies performed for radiation treatment planning or image-guided radiation treatment delivery)
G9347	Follow-up recommendations not documented according to recommended guidelines for incidentally detected pulmonary nodules, reason not given
J7195	Injection, factor IX (antihemophilic factor, recombinant) per IU, not otherwise specified
J7301	Levonorgestrel-releasing intrauterine contraceptive system, 13.5 mg
L7367	Lithium ion battery, rechargeable, replacement
Q4119	MatriStem Wound Matrix, per square centimeter
Q4147	Architect, Architect PX, or Architect FX, extracellular matrix, per square centimeter
S0183	Prochlorperazine maleate, oral, 5 mg (for circumstances falling under the medicare statute, use Q0164)
V2799	Vision item or service, miscellaneous

DELETED CODES

A7042	G0456	G8492	G8594	G8705	G8772	G8888	G8943	G9224	J3130
A7043	G0457	G8493	G8595	G8706	G8773	G8889	G8949	G9248	J3140
C1300	G0461	G8501	G8597	G8707	G8774	G8890	G8957	G9249	J3150
C9021	G0462	G8502	G8629	G8736	G8775	G8891	G9193	G9252	J7335
C9022	G0908	G8547	G8630	G8737	G8776	G8892	G9194	G9253	J9265
C9023	G0909	G8552	G8631	G8738	G8777	G8893	G9195	G9271	L6025
C9133	G0910	G8579	G8632	G8739	G8778	G8894	G9199	G9272	L7260
C9134	G0919	G8580	G8682	G8740	G8779	G8895	G9200	J0150	L7261
C9135	G0920	G8581	G8683	G8751	G8780	G8896	G9201	J0151	M0064
C9441	G0921	G8582	G8685	G8763	G8781	G8897	G9202	J0900	Q9970
C9735	G0922	G8583	G8699	G8764	G8782	G8904	G9214	J1060	Q9972
G0173	G8126	G8584	G8700	G8767	G8859	G8905	G9215	J1070	Q9973
G0251	G8127	G8585	G8701	G8768	G8860	G8930	G9216	J1080	Q9974
G0417	G8128	G8586	G8702	G8769	G8862	G8931	G9218	J2271	S0144
G0418	G8406	G8587	G8703	G8770	G8886	G8932	G9220	J2275	S3855
G0419	G8464	G8593	G8704	G8771	G8887	G8933	G9221	J3120	

Deleted Codes Crosswalk

Deleted Code	Descriptor	Crosswalk Code	Descriptor
C9022	Injection, elosulfase alfa, 1 mg	J1322	Injection, elosulfase alfa, 1 mg
C9023	Injection, testosterone undecanoate, 1 mg	J3145	Injection, testosterone undecanoate, 1 mg
C9133	Factor IX (antihemophilic factor, recombinant), RIXUBIS, per i.u.	J7200	Injection, Factor IX, (antihemophilic factor, recombinant), RIXUBIS, per i.u.
C9134	Factor XIII (antihemophilic factor, recombinant), tretten, per 10 i.u.	J7181	Injection, Factor XIII a-subunit, (recombinant), per i.u.
C9135	Factor IX (antihemophilic factor, recombinant), ALPROLIX, per i.u.	J7201	Injection, Factor IX, Fc Fusion protein (recombinant), per i.u.
C9735	Anoscopy; with directed submucosal injection(s), any substance	0377T	Anoscopy with directed submucosal injection of bulking agent for fecal incontinence
L7260	Electronic wrist rotator, otto bock or equal	L7259	Electronic wrist rotator, any type
L7261	Electronic wrist rotator, for utah arm	L7259	Electronic wrist rotator, any type
Q9972	Injection, epoetin beta, 1 microgram, (for esrd on dialysis)	J0887	Injection, epoetin beta, 1 microgram, (for ESRD on dialysis)
Q9973	Injection, epoetin beta, 1 microgram, (non-ESRD use)	J0888	Injection, epoetin beta, 1 microgram, (for Non ESRD use)
Q9974	Injection, morphine sulfate, preservative-free for epidural or intrathecal use, 10 mg	J2274	Injection, morphine sulfate, preservative-free for epidural or intrathecal use, 10 mg
S0144	Injection, propofol, 10 mg	J2704	Injection, propofol, 10 mg

Anatomical Illustrations

BRAIN FUNCTION

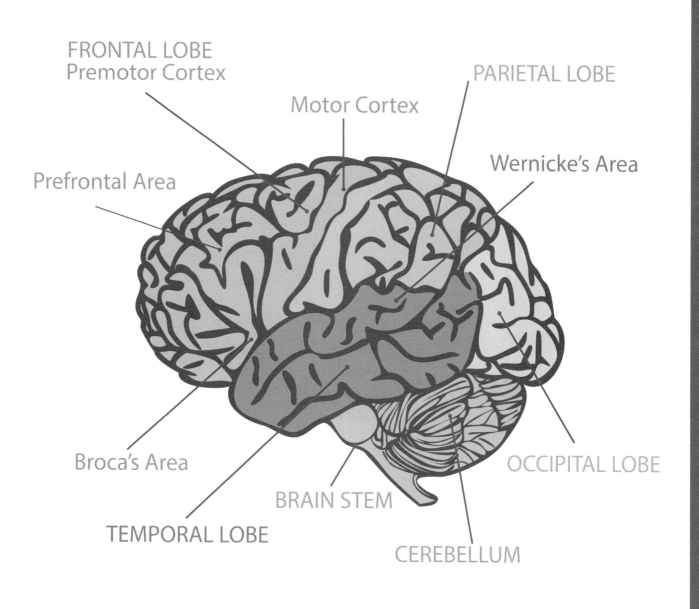

FRONTAL LOBE
Premotor Cortex

Motor Cortex

PARIETAL LOBE

Prefrontal Area

Wernicke's Area

Broca's Area

OCCIPITAL LOBE

BRAIN STEM

TEMPORAL LOBE

CEREBELLUM

BREAST ANATOMY

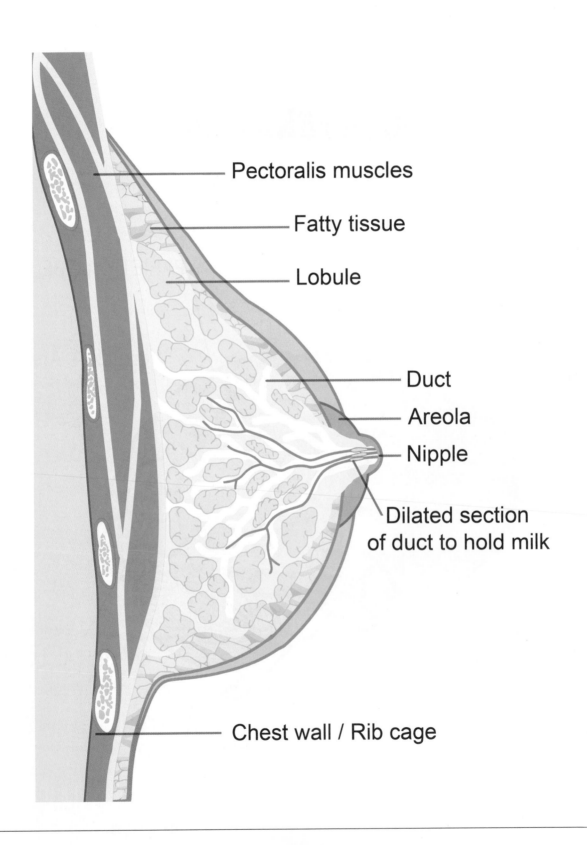

Pectoralis muscles

Fatty tissue

Lobule

Duct

Areola

Nipple

Dilated section
of duct to hold milk

Chest wall / Rib cage

CARDIAC CYCLE

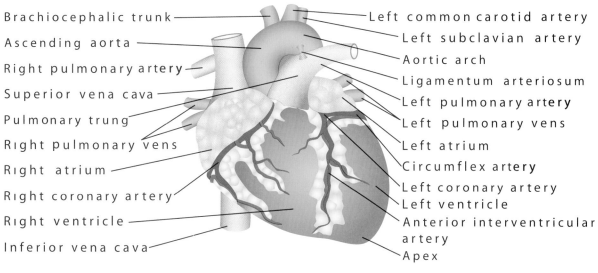

Brachiocephalic trunk
Ascending aorta
Right pulmonary artery
Superior vena cava
Pulmonary trung
Right pulmonary vens
Right atrium
Right coronary artery
Right ventricle
Inferior vena cava

Left common carotid artery
Left subclavian artery
Aortic arch
Ligamentum arteriosum
Left pulmonary artery
Left pulmonary vens
Left atrium
Circumflex artery
Left coronary artery
Left ventricle
Anterior interventricular artery
Apex

ANATOMY OF THE HEART

Right atrium

Left atrium
Mitral valve
Aortic valve
Tricuspid valve

Inferior vena cava   Right ventricle

Diastole Ventricular
Relaxation and Filling

Superior vena cava   Aorta   Pulmonary artery

Pulmonary valve   Left ventricle

Systole Ventricular
Contraction and Ejection

CIRCULATORY SYSTEM

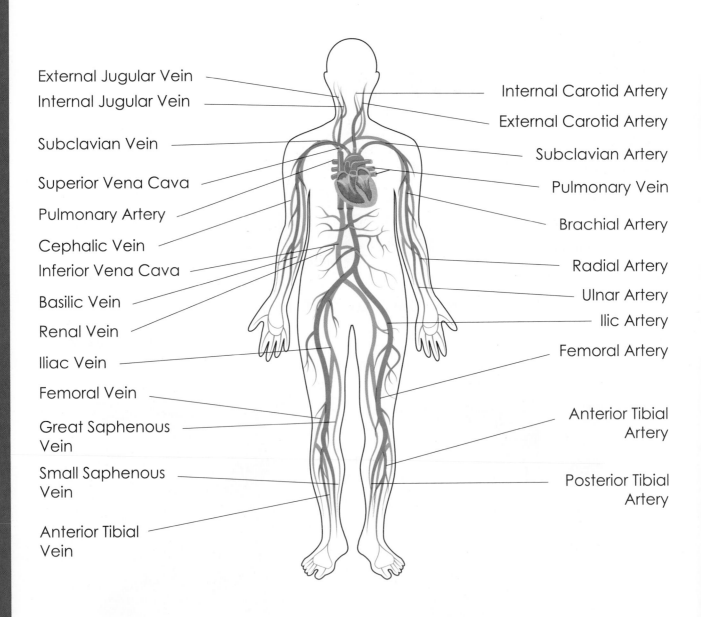

External Jugular Vein

Internal Jugular Vein

Subclavian Vein

Superior Vena Cava

Pulmonary Artery

Cephalic Vein

Inferior Vena Cava

Basilic Vein

Renal Vein

Iliac Vein

Femoral Vein

Great Saphenous Vein

Small Saphenous Vein

Anterior Tibial Vein

Internal Carotid Artery

External Carotid Artery

Subclavian Artery

Pulmonary Vein

Brachial Artery

Radial Artery

Ulnar Artery

Ilic Artery

Femoral Artery

Anterior Tibial Artery

Posterior Tibial Artery

DIGESTIVE SYSTEM

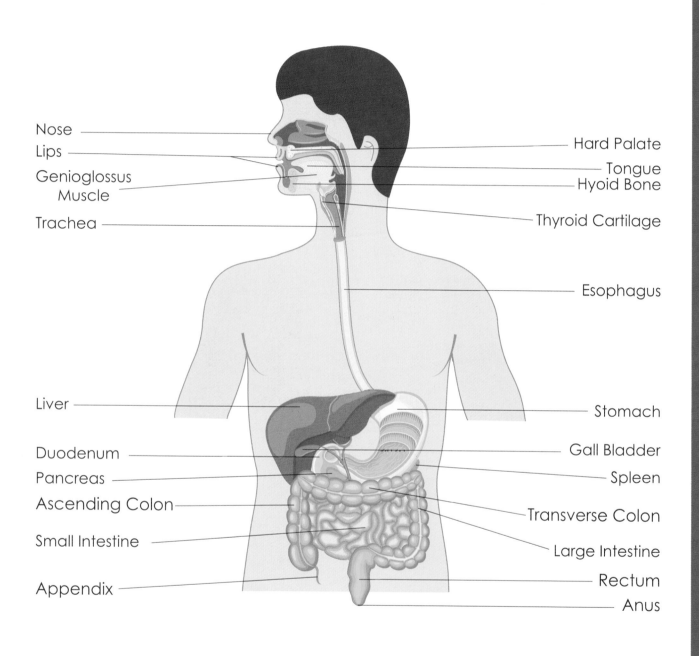

Nose

Lips

Genioglossus
Muscle

Trachea

Hard Palate

Tongue
Hyoid Bone

Thyroid Cartilage

Esophagus

Liver

Stomach

Duodenum

Gall Bladder

Pancreas

Spleen

Ascending Colon

Transverse Colon

Small Intestine

Large Intestine

Appendix

Rectum

Anus

EAR ANATOMY

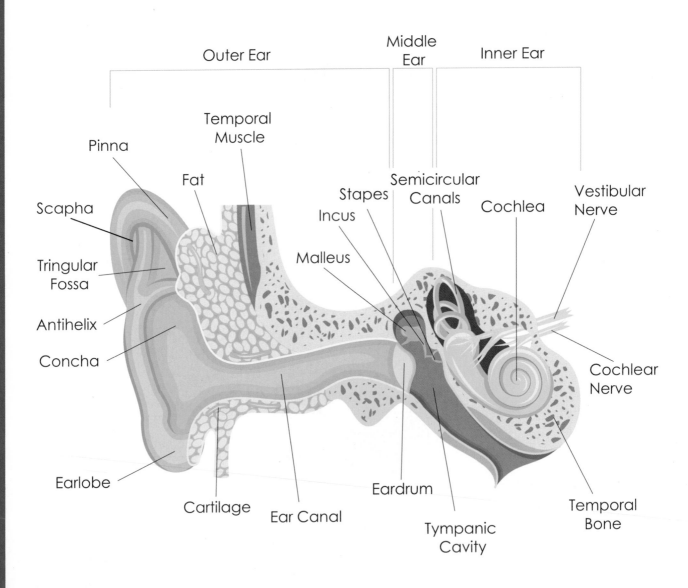

Outer Ear Middle Ear Inner Ear

Pinna

Temporal Muscle

Fat

Scapha

Tringular Fossa

Antihelix

Concha

Stapes

Incus

Malleus

Semicircular Canals

Cochlea

Vestibular Nerve

Cochlear Nerve

Earlobe

Cartilage

Ear Canal

Eardrum

Tympanic Cavity

Temporal Bone

ENDOCRINE SYSTEM

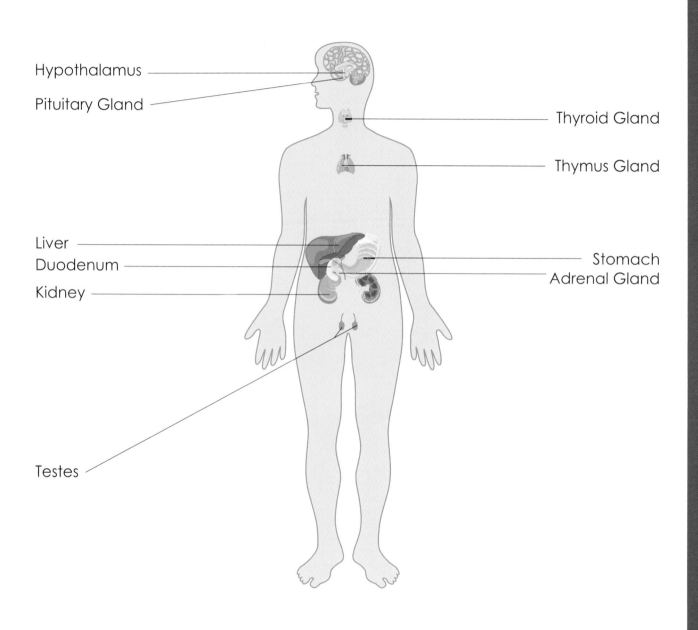

Hypothalamus

Pituitary Gland

Thyroid Gland

Thymus Gland

Liver

Duodenum

Kidney

Stomach

Adrenal Gland

Testes

EYE ANATOMY

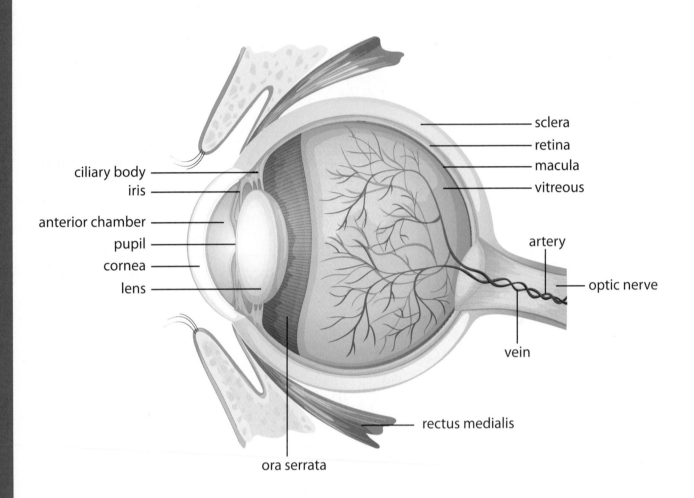

ciliary body

iris

anterior chamber

pupil

cornea

lens

sclera

retina

macula

vitreous

artery

optic nerve

vein

rectus medialis

ora serrata

FEMALE REPRODUCTIVE SYSTEM

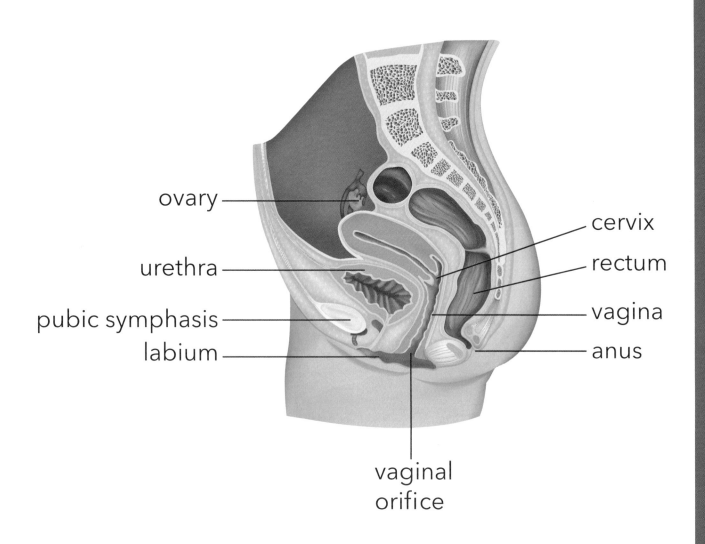

ovary

urethra

pubic symphasis

labium

cervix

rectum

vagina

anus

vaginal
orifice

FOOT BONES (right foot, lateral view)

Tibia

Fibula

Talus

Navicular

Intermediate cuneiform

Lateral cuneiform

Calcaneus

1
2
3
4
5

Phalanges

Cuboid

Metatarsal bones

FOREARM MUSCLES
(right arm, posterior compartment)

Superficial

Deep

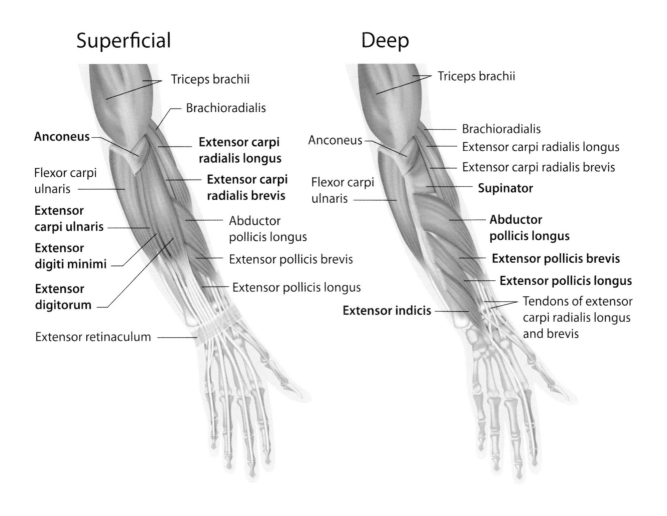

Triceps brachii

Brachioradialis

Anconeus

Extensor carpi radialis longus

Flexor carpi ulnaris

Extensor carpi radialis brevis

Extensor carpi ulnaris

Abductor pollicis longus

Extensor digiti minimi

Extensor pollicis brevis

Extensor digitorum

Extensor pollicis longus

Extensor retinaculum

Triceps brachii

Anconeus

Brachioradialis
Extensor carpi radialis longus
Extensor carpi radialis brevis

Flexor carpi ulnaris

Supinator

Abductor pollicis longus

Extensor pollicis brevis

Extensor pollicis longus

Extensor indicis

Tendons of extensor carpi radialis longus and brevis

HAND BONES

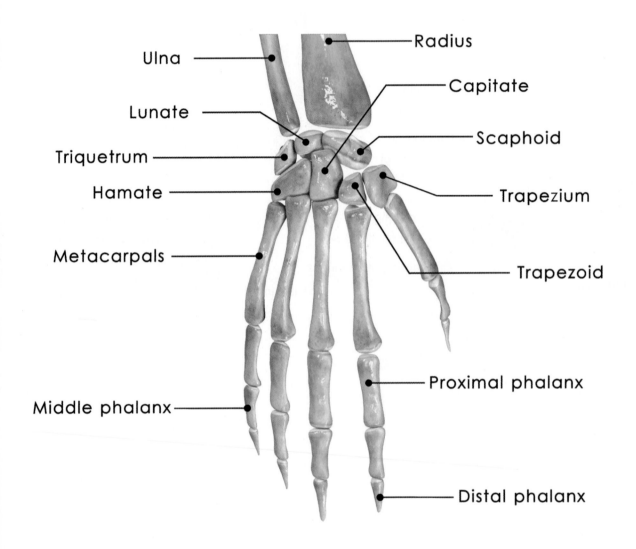

Ulna

Radius

Lunate

Capitate

Triquetrum

Scaphoid

Hamate

Trapezium

Metacarpals

Trapezoid

Proximal phalanx

Middle phalanx

Distal phalanx

KIDNEY ANATOMY

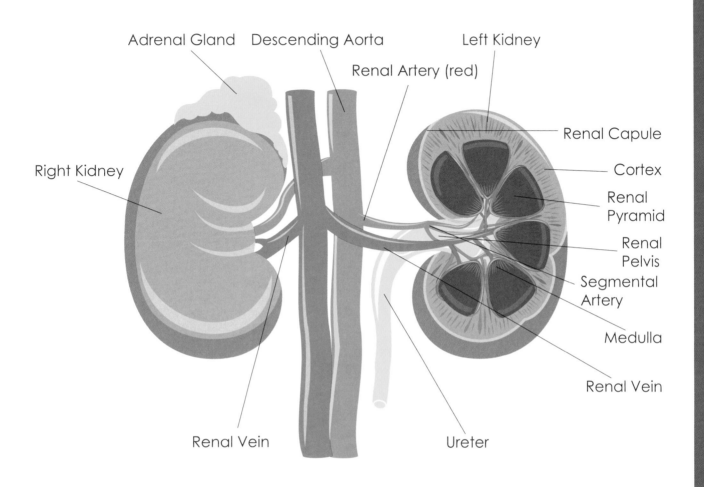

Adrenal Gland   Descending Aorta   Left Kidney

Renal Artery (red)

Right Kidney

Renal Capule

Cortex

Renal Pyramid

Renal Pelvis

Segmental Artery

Medulla

Renal Vein

Renal Vein   Ureter

LARGE INTESTINE ANATOMY

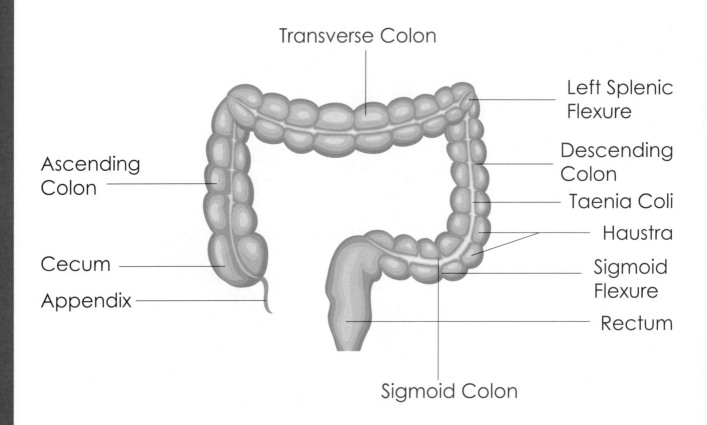

Transverse Colon

Left Splenic Flexure

Descending Colon

Ascending Colon

Taenia Coli

Haustra

Cecum

Sigmoid Flexure

Appendix

Rectum

Sigmoid Colon

LIVER ANATOMY

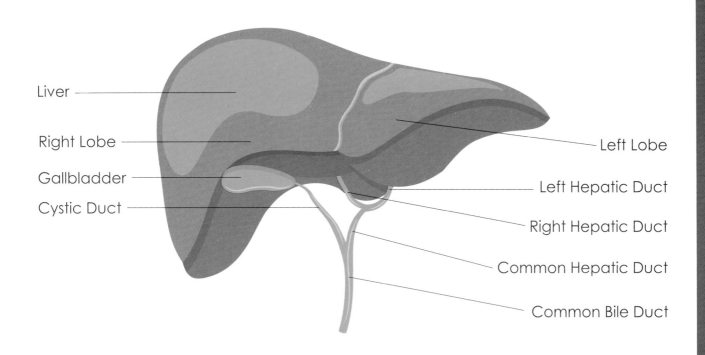

Liver

Right Lobe

Gallbladder

Cystic Duct

Left Lobe

Left Hepatic Duct

Right Hepatic Duct

Common Hepatic Duct

Common Bile Duct

LYMPHATIC SYSTEM

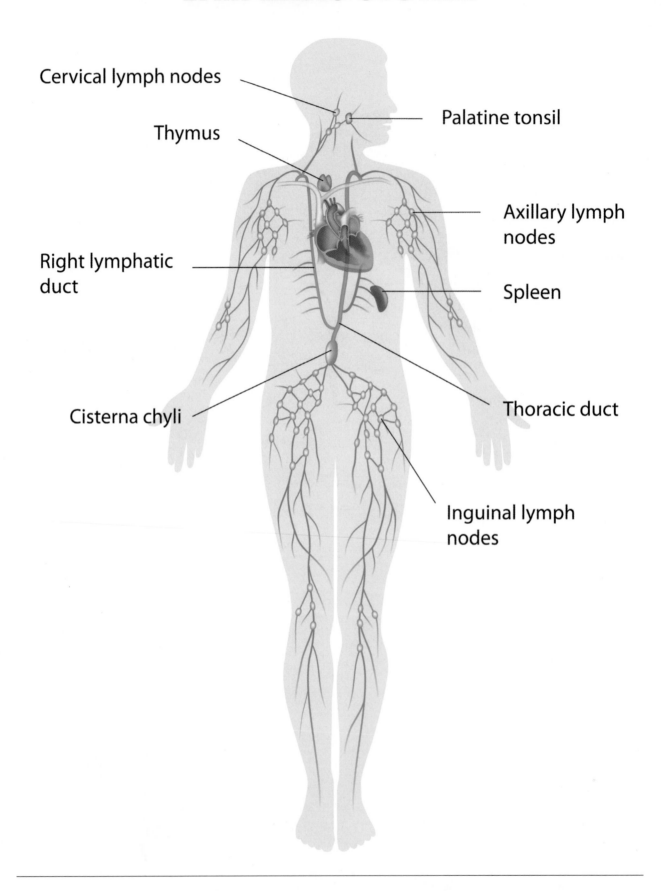

Cervical lymph nodes

Palatine tonsil

Thymus

Axillary lymph nodes

Right lymphatic duct

Spleen

Cisterna chyli

Thoracic duct

Inguinal lymph nodes

MALE REPRODUCTIVE SYSTEM

pubic bone

ductus deferens

penis

spongy urethra

seminal vesicle

bladder

prostate gland

epididymis

testis

scrotum

MOUTH ANATOMY

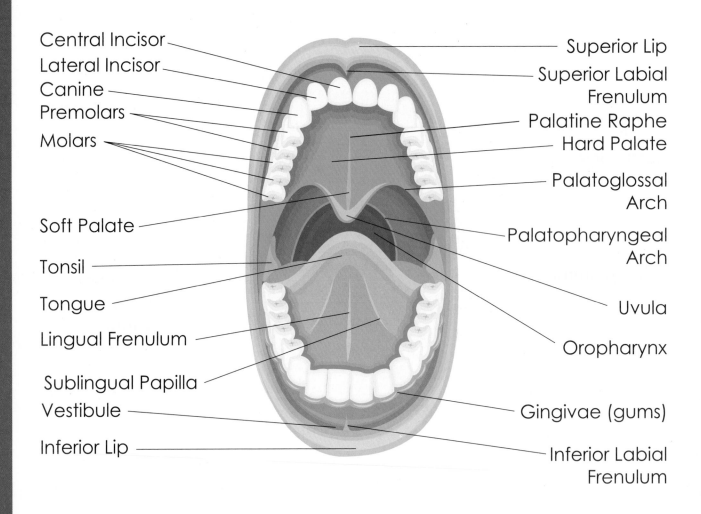

Central Incisor

Lateral Incisor

Canine

Premolars

Molars

Soft Palate

Tonsil

Tongue

Lingual Frenulum

Sublingual Papilla

Vestibule

Inferior Lip

Superior Lip

Superior Labial Frenulum

Palatine Raphe

Hard Palate

Palatoglossal Arch

Palatopharyngeal Arch

Uvula

Oropharynx

Gingivae (gums)

Inferior Labial Frenulum

MUSCULAR SYSTEM

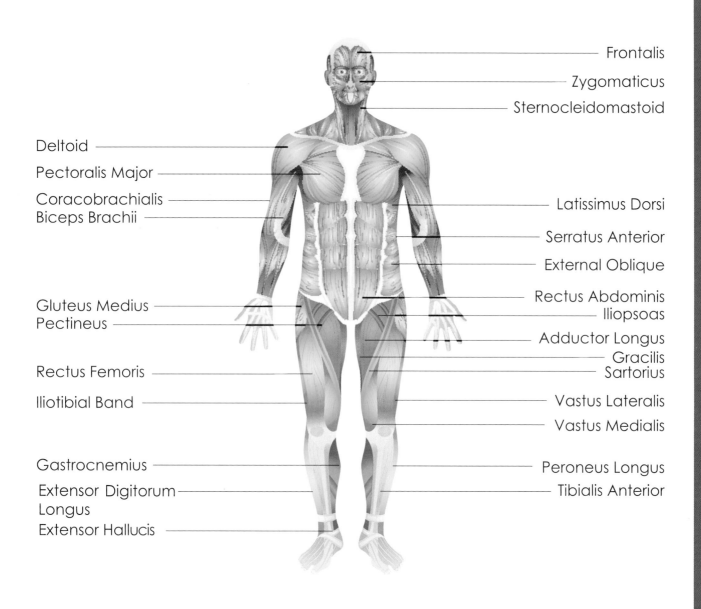

Frontalis

Zygomaticus

Sternocleidomastoid

Deltoid

Pectoralis Major

Coracobrachialis
Biceps Brachii

Latissimus Dorsi

Serratus Anterior

External Oblique

Gluteus Medius
Pectineus

Rectus Abdominis
Iliopsoas

Adductor Longus

Gracilis
Sartorius

Rectus Femoris

Iliotibial Band

Vastus Lateralis

Vastus Medialis

Gastrocnemius

Peroneus Longus

Extensor Digitorum
Longus

Tibialis Anterior

Extensor Hallucis

NERVOUS SYSTEM

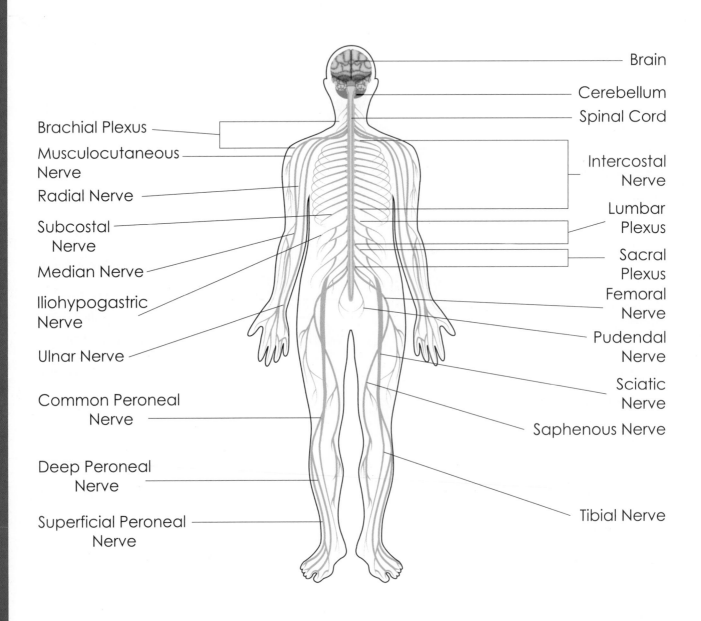

Brachial Plexus

Musculocutaneous Nerve

Radial Nerve

Subcostal Nerve

Median Nerve

Iliohypogastric Nerve

Ulnar Nerve

Common Peroneal Nerve

Deep Peroneal Nerve

Superficial Peroneal Nerve

Brain

Cerebellum

Spinal Cord

Intercostal Nerve

Lumbar Plexus

Sacral Plexus

Femoral Nerve

Pudendal Nerve

Sciatic Nerve

Saphenous Nerve

Tibial Nerve

NOSE ANATOMY

Frontal Sinus

Nasal Bone

Nasal Cavity

Nasal Vestibule

Hard Palate

Lips

Sphenoid Sinus

Superior Turbinate

Middle Turbinate

Inferior Turbinate

Adenoid Pad

Soft Palate

PANCREAS ANATOMY

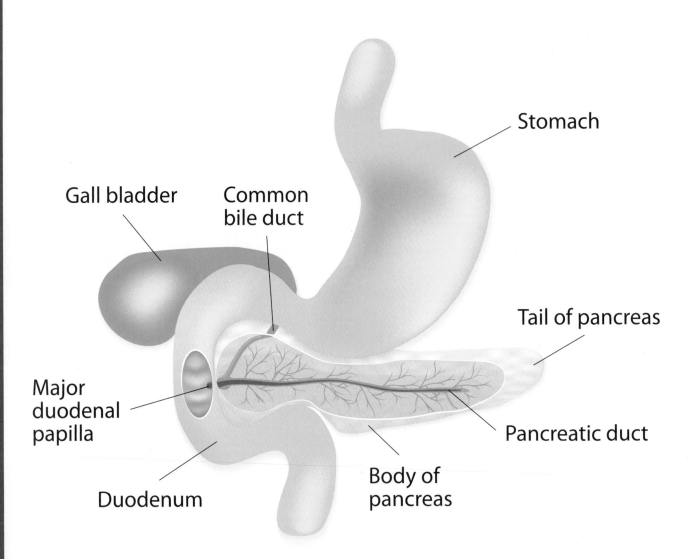

Stomach

Gall bladder

Common bile duct

Tail of pancreas

Major duodenal papilla

Pancreatic duct

Duodenum

Body of pancreas

PARASYMPATHETIC SYSTEM

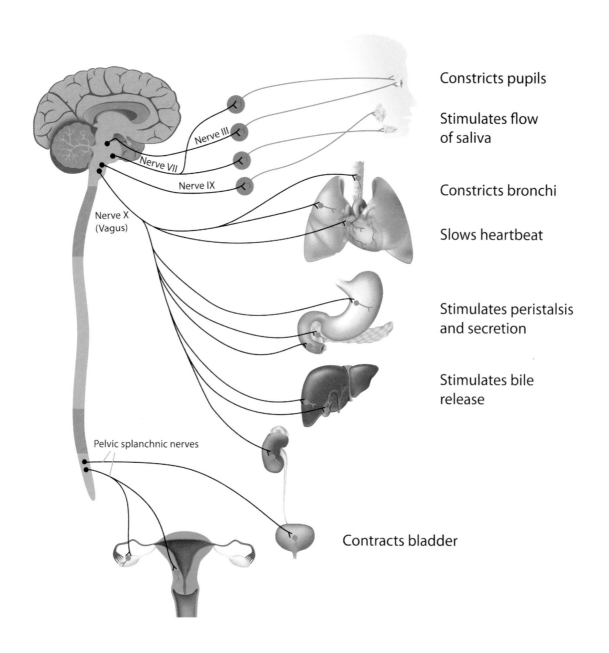

Constricts pupils

Stimulates flow of saliva

Nerve III

Nerve VII

Nerve IX

Nerve X (Vagus)

Constricts bronchi

Slows heartbeat

Stimulates peristalsis and secretion

Stimulates bile release

Pelvic splanchnic nerves

Contracts bladder

RESPIRATORY SYSTEM

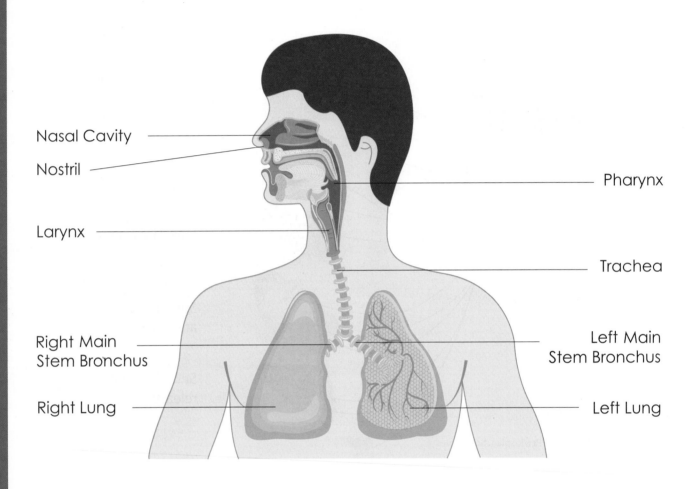

Nasal Cavity

Nostril

Larynx

Right Main
Stem Bronchus

Right Lung

Pharynx

Trachea

Left Main
Stem Bronchus

Left Lung

ROTATOR CUFF MUSCLES

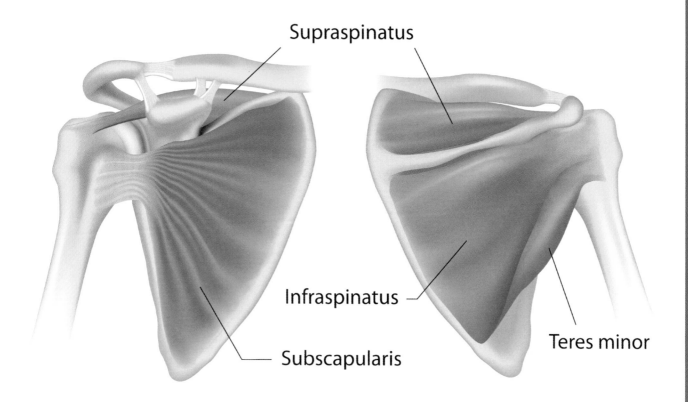

Supraspinatus

Infraspinatus

Subscapularis

Teres minor

Anterior view

Posterior view

SKELETAL SYSTEM

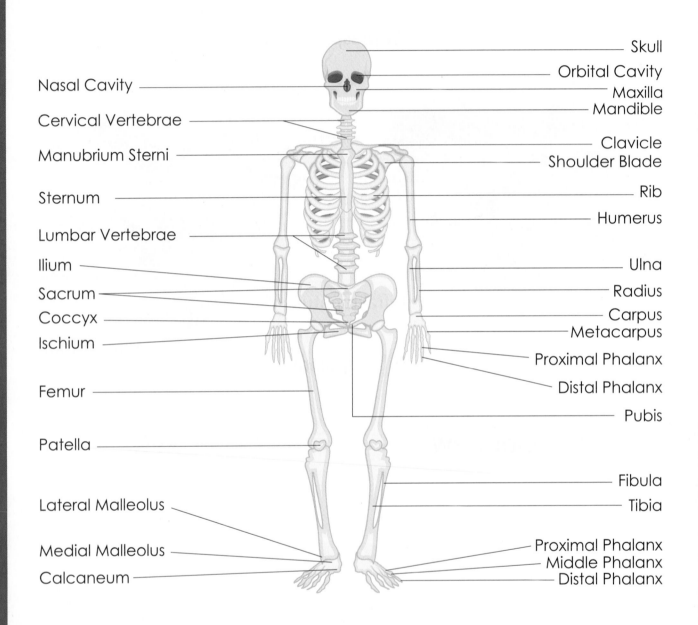

Skull

Orbital Cavity

Nasal Cavity

Maxilla

Mandible

Cervical Vertebrae

Manubrium Sterni

Clavicle

Shoulder Blade

Sternum

Rib

Lumbar Vertebrae

Humerus

Ilium

Ulna

Sacrum

Radius

Coccyx

Carpus

Ischium

Metacarpus

Proximal Phalanx

Distal Phalanx

Femur

Pubis

Patella

Fibula

Tibia

Lateral Malleolus

Medial Malleolus

Proximal Phalanx

Middle Phalanx

Calcaneum

Distal Phalanx

SKULL ANATOMY

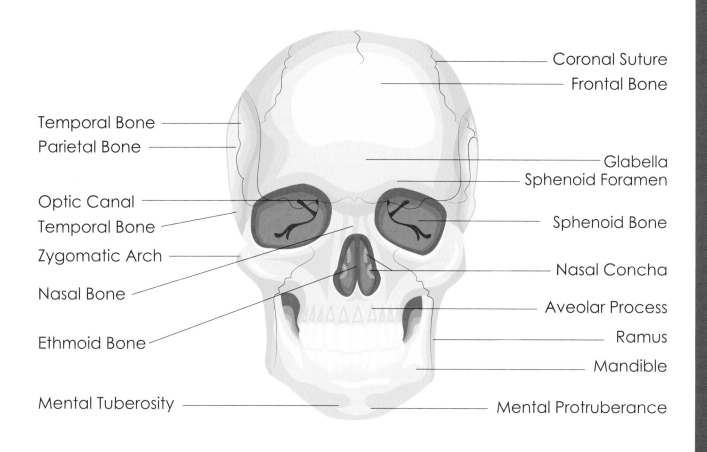

Coronal Suture

Frontal Bone

Temporal Bone

Parietal Bone

Glabella

Sphenoid Foramen

Optic Canal

Temporal Bone

Sphenoid Bone

Zygomatic Arch

Nasal Bone

Nasal Concha

Aveolar Process

Ethmoid Bone

Ramus

Mandible

Mental Tuberosity

Mental Protruberance

SMALL INTESTINE ANATOMY

Intestinal villi

Mucosa

Submucosa

Muscularis

Intestinal villi

STOMACH ANATOMY

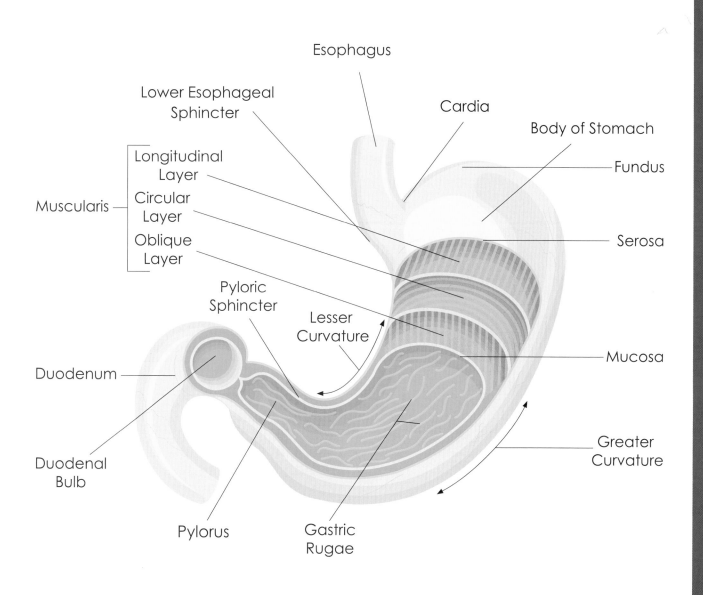

Esophagus

Lower Esophageal Sphincter

Cardia

Body of Stomach

Fundus

Longitudinal Layer

Circular Layer

Muscularis

Oblique Layer

Serosa

Pyloric Sphincter

Lesser Curvature

Mucosa

Duodenum

Greater Curvature

Duodenal Bulb

Pylorus

Gastric Rugae

SYMPATHETIC SYSTEM

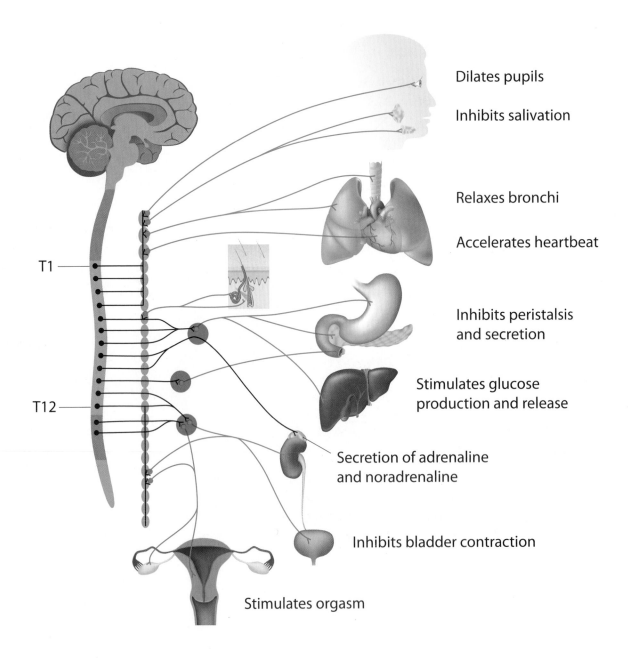

Dilates pupils

Inhibits salivation

Relaxes bronchi

Accelerates heartbeat

Inhibits peristalsis and secretion

Stimulates glucose production and release

Secretion of adrenaline and noradrenaline

Inhibits bladder contraction

Stimulates orgasm

T1

T12

THROAT ANATOMY

Middle Turbinate

Inferior Turbinate

Adenoid

Soft Palate

Tonsil

Tongue

Genioglosses
Muscle

Lingual Tonsil

Mandible

Epiglottis

Hyoid Bone

Vocal Cords

Thyroid Cartilage

Trachea

Esophagus

URINARY SYSTEM

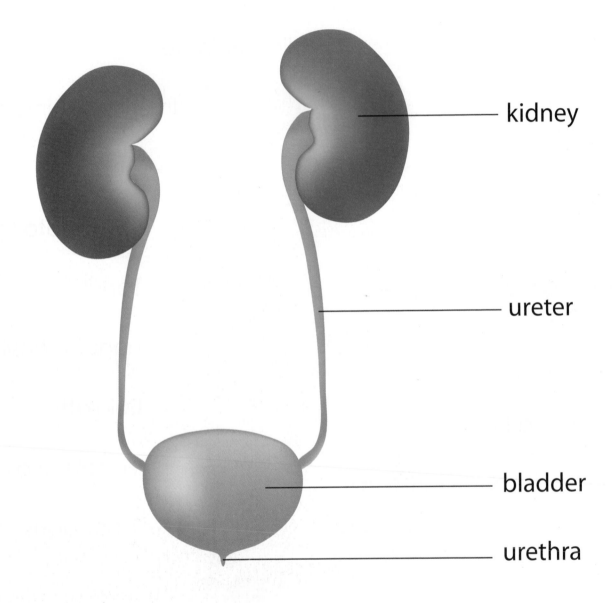

kidney

ureter

bladder

urethra

Index to Services, Supplies, Equipment, Drugs

A

Abatacept J0129
Abciximab J0130
Abdomen
    dressing holder/binder A4463
    pad, low profile L1270
Abduction control, each L2624
Abduction rotation bar, foot L3140-L3170
Abobotulinumtoxin type A J0586
Absorption dressing A6251-A6256
Access system A4301
Accessories
    ambulation devices E0153-E0159
    artificial kidney and machine (*see also*
        ESRD) E1510-E1699
    beds E0271-E0280, E0300-E0326
    wheelchairs E0950-E1030, E1050-E1298, E2300-E2399,
        K0001-K0109
Acetaminophen J0131
Acetazolamide sodium J1120
Acetylcysteine, inhalation solution J7604, J7608
Acetylcysteine, injection J0132
Acyclovir J0133
Adalimumab J0135
Adenosine J0150, J0151, J0153
Adhesive A4364
    bandage A6413
    disc or foam pad A5126
    remover A4455, A4456
    support, breast prosthesis A4280
Administration, vaccine
    hepatitis B G0010
    influenza G0008
    pneumococcal G0009
Administrative, Miscellaneous and
  Investigational A9000-A9999
Ado-trastuzumab J9354
Adrenalin J0171
Aerosol
    compressor E0571, E0572
    compressor filter K0178-K0179
    mask K0180
Aflibercept J0178
AFO E1815, E1830, L1900-L1990, L4392, L4396
Agalsidase beta J0180
Aggrastat J3245
A-hydroCort J1710
Air bubble detector, dialysis E1530
Air fluidized bed E0194
Air pressure pad/mattress E0186, E0197
Air travel and nonemergency transportation A0140
Alarm, pressure, dialysis E1540
Alatrofloxacin mesylate J0200
Albumin, human P9041, P9042
Albuterol, all formulations, inhalation solution,
  concentrated J7610, J7611
Albuterol, all formulations, inhalation solution, unit
  dose J7609, J7613
Albuterol, all formulations, inhalation solution J7620
Alcohol A4244
Alcohol wipes A4245
Aldesleukin (IL2) J9015
Alefacept J0215

Alemtuzumab J9010
Alert device A9280
Alginate dressing A6196-A6199
Alglucerase J0205
Alglucosidase J0220
Alglucosidase alfa J0221
Alphanate J7186
Alpha-1-proteinase inhibitor, human J0256, J0257
Alprostadil, injection J0270
Alprostadil, urethral suppository J0275
Alteplase recombinant J2997
Alternating pressure mattress/pad A4640, E0180, E0181,
  E0277
Ambulance A0021-A0999
    air A0430, A0431, A0435, A0436
    disposable supplies A0382-A0398
    non-emergency transport, fixed wing S9960
    non-emergency transport, rotary wing S9961
    oxygen A0422
Ambulation device E0100-E0159
Amikacin Sulfate J0278
Aminolevulinate J7309
Aminolevulinic acid HCl J7308
Aminophylline J0280
Amiodarone Hcl J0282
Amitriptyline HCl J1320
Ammonia N-13 A9526
Ammonia test paper A4774
Amniotic membrane V2790
Amobarbital J0300
Amphotericin B J0285
Amphotericin B Lipid Complex J0287-J0289
Ampicillin sodium J0290
Ampicillin sodium/sulbactam sodium J0295
Amputee
    adapter, wheelchair E0959
    prosthesis L5000-L7510, L7520, L7900, L8400-L8465
    stump sock L8470-L8485
    wheelchair E1170-E1190, E1200, K0100
Amygdalin J3570
Anadulafungin J0348
Anistreplase J0350
Ankle splint, recumbent K0126-K0130
Ankle-foot orthosis (AFO) L1900-L1990, L2106-L2116,
  L4361, L4392, L4396
Anterior-posterior-lateral orthosis L0700, L0710
Anti-emetic, oral Q0163-Q0181, J8498, J8597
Anti-hemophilic factor (Factor VIII) J7190-J7192
Anti-inhibitors, per I.U. J7198
Anti-neoplastic drug, NOC J9999
Antithrombin III J7197
Antithrombin recombinant J7196
Apomorphine J0364
Appliance
    cleaner A5131
    pneumatic E0655-E0673
Aprotinin J0365
Aqueous
    shunt L8612
    sterile J7051
Arbutamine HCl J0395
Arch support L3040-L3100
    Intralesional J3302
Arformoterol J7605

Aripiprazole J0400, J0401
Arm, wheelchair E0973
Arsenic trioxide, J9017
Artificial
  Cornea L8609
  kidney machines and accessories (*see also* Dialysis) E1510-E1699
  larynx L8500
  saliva A9155
Asparaginase J9019-J9020
Assembly K0050
  footrest, complete K0045
Assessment
  alcohol or drug H0001
  audiologic V5008-V5020
  cardiac output M0302
  nursing assessment/ evaluation T1001
  speech V5362-V5364
Assisted living T2030-T2031
Assistive Listening Devices and accessories V5281-V5290
Atropine, inhalation solution, concentrated J7635
Atropine, inhalation solution, unit dose J7636
Atropine sulfate J0461
Audiologic assessment V5008-V5020
Auditory osseointegrated device L8690-L8693
Aurothioglucose J2910
Azacitidine J9025
Azathioprine J7500, J7501
Azithromycin injection J0456

B

Back supports L0621-L0861, L0960
Baclofen J0475, J0476
Bacterial sensitivity study P7001
Bag
  drainage A4357
  irrigation supply A4398
  urinary A5112, A4358
Barrier
  adhesion C1765
Basiliximab J0480
Bathtub
  chair E0240
  stool or bench E0245, E0247-E0248
  transfer rail E0246
  wall rail E0241, E0242
Battery L7360, L7364-L7368
  charger E1066, L7362, L7366
  replacement for blood glucose monitor A4233-A4234
  replacement for cochlear implant device L8623-L8624
  replacement for TENS A4630
  ventilator A4611-A4613
BCG live, intravesical J9031
Beclomethasone inhalation solution J7622
Bed
  air fluidized E0194
  cradle, any type E0280
  drainage bag, bottle A4357, A5102
  hospital E0250-E0270, E0300-E0329
  pan E0275, E0276
  rail E0305, E0310
  safety enclosure frame/canopy E0316
Belatacept J0485
Belimumab J0490
Belt
  extremity E0945

  ostomy A4367
  pelvic E0944
  safety K0031
  wheelchair E0978, E0979
Bench, bathtub (*see also* Bathtub) E0245
Bendamustine HCl J9033
Benesch boot L3212-L3214
Benztropine J0515
Betadine A4246, A4247
Betameth J0704
Betamethasone inhalation solution J7624
Betamethasone acetate and betamethasone sodium phosphate J0702
Bethanechol chloride J0520
Bevacizumab J9035, Q2024
Bifocal, glass or plastic V2200-V2299
Bilirubin (phototherapy) light E0202
Binder A4465
Biofeedback device E0746
Bioimpedance, electrical, cardiac output M0302
Biperiden lactate J0190
Bitolterol mesylate, inhalation solution, concentrated J7628
Bitolterol mesylate, inhalation solution, unit dose J7629
Bivalirudin J0583
Bladder calculi irrigation solution Q2004
Bleomycin sulfate J9040
Blood
  fresh frozen plasma P9017
  glucose monitor E0607, E2100, E2101
  glucose test A4253
  granulocytes, pheresis P9050
  ketone test A4252
  leak detector, dialysis E1560
  leukocyte poor P9016
  mucoprotein P2038
  platelets P9019
  platelets, irradiated P9032
  platelets, leukocytes reduced P9031
  platelets, leukocytes reduced, irradiated P9033
  platelets, pheresis P9034
  platelets, pheresis, irradiated P9036
  platelets, pheresis, leukocytes reduced P9035
  platelets, pheresis, leukocytes reduced, irradiated P9037
  pressure monitor A4660, A4663, A4670
  pump, dialysis E1620
  red blood cells, deglycerolized P9039
  red blood cells, irradiated P9038
  red blood cells, leukocytes reduced P9016
  red blood cells, leukocytes reduced, irradiated P9040
  red blood cells, washed P9022
  strips A4253
  supply P9010-P9022
  testing supplies A4770
  tubing A4750, A4755
Blood collection devices accessory A4257, E0620
Body jacket
  scoliosis L1300, L1310
Body sock L0984
Body worn, hearing aid
  bilateral V5100
  monaural, air conduction V5030
  monaural, bone conduction V5040
Bond or cement, ostomy skin A4364
Boot
  pelvic E0944
  surgical, ambulatory L3260
Bortezomib J9041

Brachytherapy needle C1715
Brachytherapy radioelements Q3001
Breast prosthesis L8000-L8035, L8600
Breast prosthesis, adhesive skin support A4280
Breast pump
    accessories A4281-A4286
    electric, any type E0603
    heavy duty, hospital grade E0604
    manual, any type E0602
Breathing circuit A4618
Brentuximab Vedotin J9042
Brompheniramine maleate J0945
Budesonide inhalation solution J7626, J7627, J7633, J7634
Bulking agent L8604
Buprenorphine hydrochloride J0592
Buprenorphine/Naloxone J0571-J0575
Bus, nonemergency transportation A0110
Busulfan J0594, J8510
Butorphanol tartrate J0595

C-1 Esterase Inhibitor J0597-J0598
Cabazitaxel J9043
Cabergoline, oral J8515
Caffeine citrate J0706
Calcitriol J0636
Calcitonin-salmon J0630
Calcium disodium edetate J0600
Calcium gluconate J0610
Calcium glycerophosphate and calcium lactate J0620
Calcium lactate and calcium glycerophosphate J0620
Calcium leucovorin J0640
Calibrator solution A4256
Canakinumab J0638
Cane E0100, E0105
    accessory A4636, A4637
Canister, disposable, used with suction pump A7000
Canister, non-disposable, used with suction pump A7001
Cannula
    nasal A4615
    tracheostomy, inner A4623
Capecitabine, oral J8520, J8521
Capsaicin patch J7336
Carbon filter A4680
Carboplatin J9045
Cardia Event, recorder, implantable E0616
Cardiokymography Q0035
Cardiovascular services M0300-M0301
Carfilzomib J9047
Carmustine J9050
Case management T1016, T1017
Caspofungin acetate J0637
Cast
    hand restoration L6900-L6915
    materials, special A4590
    supplies A4580, A4590, Q4001-Q4051
    thermoplastic L2106, L2126
Caster, front, for power wheelchair K0099
Caster, wheelchair E0997, E0998
Catheter A4300-A4355
    anchoring device A5200, A4333, A4334
    cap, disposable (dialysis) A4860
    external collection device A4327-A4330, A4347, A7048
    indwelling A4338-A4346
    insertion tray A4354

    intermittent with insertion supplies A4353
    irrigation supplies A4355
    male external A4324, A4325, A4348
    oropharyngeal suction A4628
    starter set A4329
    trachea (suction) A4609, A4610, A4624
    transtracheal oxygen A4608
Catheterization, specimen collection P9612, P9615
Cefazolin sodium J0690
Cefepime HCl J0692
Cefotaxime sodium J0698
Ceftaroline fosamil J0712
Ceftazidime J0713
Ceftizoxime sodium J0715
Ceftriaxone sodium J0696
Cefuroxime sodium J0697
CellCept K0412
Cellular therapy M0075
Cement, ostomy A4364
Centrifuge A4650
Centruroides Immune F(ab) J0716
Cephalin Floculation, blood P2028
Cephalothin sodium J1890
Cephapirin sodium J0710
Certolizumab pegol J0717
Cervical
    halo L0810-L0830
    head harness/halter E0942
    orthosis L0100-L0200
    traction E0855, E0856
Cervical cap contraceptive A4261
Cervical-thoracic-lumbar-sacral orthosis (CTLSO) L0700, L0710
Cetuximab J9055
Chair
    adjustable, dialysis E1570
    lift E0627
    rollabout E1031
    sitz bath E0160-E0162
Chamber
    pacemaker, dual C1785
    pacemaker, single C1786
Chelation therapy M0300
Chemical endarterectomy M0300
Chemistry and toxicology tests P2028-P3001
Chemotherapy
    administration Q0083-Q0085 (hospital reporting only)
    drug, oral, not otherwise classified J8999
    drugs (*see also* drug by name) J9000-J9999
Chest shell (cuirass) E0457
Chest Wall Oscillation System E0483
    hose, replacement A7026
    vest, replacement A7025
Chest wrap E0459
Chin cup, cervical L0150
Chloramphenicol sodium succinate J0720
Chlordiazepoxide HCl J1990
Chloromycetin Sodium Succinate J0720
Chloroprocaine HCl J2400
Chloroquine HCl J0390
Chlorothiazide sodium J1205
Chlorpromazine HCl J3230
Chorionic gonadotropin J0725
Chromic phosphate P32 suspension A9564
Chromium CR-51 sodium chromate A9553
Cidofovir J0740
Cilastatin sodium, imipenem J0743
Ciprofloxacin, for intravenous infusion J0744

Cisplatin J9060

Cladribine J9065

Clamp
    dialysis A4910, A4918, A4920
    external urethral A4356

Cleanser, wound A6260

Cleansing agent, dialysis equipment A4790

Clofarabine J9027

Clonidine J0735

Clotting time tube A4771

Clubfoot wedge L3380

Cochlear prosthetic implant L8614
    accessories L8615-L8617
    batteries L8621-L8624
    replacement L8619, L8627-L8629

Codeine phosphate J0745

Colchicine J0760

Cold pad
    water circulating E0218

Colistimethate sodium J0770

Collagen
    skin test G0025
    urinary tract implant L8603
    wound dressing A6020-A6024

Collagenase, Clostridium Histolyticum J0775

Collar, cervical
    multiple post L0180-L0200
    nonadjust (foam) L0120

Coly-Mycin M J0770

Comfort items A9190

Commode E0160-E0175
    chair E0170-E0171
    lift E0625, E0172
    pail E0167
    seat, wheelchair E0968

Composite dressing A6200-A6205

Compressed gas system E0424-E0480

Compression bandage A4460

Compression burn garment A6501-A6512

Compression stockings A6530-A6549

Compressor E0565, E0570, E0571, E0572, E0650-E0652

Conduction
    glasses, air V5070
    hearing aid V5030

Conductivity meter, bath, dialysis E1550

Conformity, evaluation V5020

Congo red, blood P2029

Contact layer A6206-A6208

Contact lens V2500-V2599

Continent device A5081, A5082, A5083

Continuous glucose monitoring system
    receiver A9278
    sensor A9276
    transmitter A9277

Continuous passive motion exercise device E0936

Continuous positive airway pressure (CPAP) device E0601
    compressor K0269

Contraceptive
    cervical cap A4261
    condoms A4267, A4268
    diaphragm A4266
    intratubal occlusion device A4264
    intrauterine, copper J7300
    intrauterine, levonorgestrel releasing J7301, J7302
    levonorgestrel, implants and supplies A4260
    patch J7304
    spermicide A4269
    vaginal ring J7303

Contracts, maintenance, ESRD A4890

Contrast material
    injection during MRI A4643
    low osmolar A4644-A4646

Corneal tissue processing V2785

Corset, spinal orthosis L0970-L0976

Corticorelin ovine triflutate J0795

Corticotropin J0800

Corvert, *see* **Ibutilide fumarate**

Cosyntropin J0833, J0834

Cough stimulating device A7020, E0482

Counselling
    hospice, evaluation G0337

Cover, wound
    alginate dressing A6196-A6198
    foam dressing A6209-A6214
    hydrogel dressing A6242-A6248
    non-contact wound warming cover, and accessory A6000, E0231, E0232
    specialty absorptive dressing A6251-A6256

CPAP (continuous positive airway pressure) device E0601
    headgear K0185
    humidifier A7046
    intermittent assist E0452

Cradle, bed E0280

Crib E0300

Crisis intervention T2034

Cromolyn sodium, inhalation solution, unit dose J7631, J7632

Crotalidae polyvalent immune fab J0840

Crutches E0110-E0118
    accessories A4635-A4637, K0102

Cryoprecipitate, each unit P9012

CTLSO L1000-L1120, L0700, L0710

Cuirass E0457

Culture sensitivity study P7001

Cushion, wheelchair E0977

Cyanocobalamin Cobalt CO57 A9559

Cycler dialysis machine E1594

Cyclophosphamide J9070

Cyclophosphamide, oral J8530

Cyclosporine J7502, J7515, J7516

Cytarabine J9100

Cytarabine liposome J9098

Cytomegalovirus immune globulin (human) J0850

D

Dacarbazine J9130

Daclizumab J7513

Dactinomycin J9120

Dalalone J1100

Dalteparin sodium J1645

Daptomycin J0878

Darbepoetin Alfa J0881-J0882

Daunorubicin Citrate J9151

Daunorubicin HCl J9150

DaunoXome, *see* **Daunorubicin citrate**

Decitabine J0894

Decubitus care equipment E0180-E0199

Deferoxamine mesylate J0895

Defibrillator, external E0617, K0606
    battery K0607
    electrode K0609
    garment K0608

Degarelix J9155

Deionizer, water purification system E1615

Delivery/set-up/dispensing A9901
Denileukin diftitox J9160
Denosumab J0897
Depo-estradiol cypionate J1000
Desmopressin acetate J2597
Detector, blood leak, dialysis E1560
Device
    closure, vascular C1760
Dexamethasone acetate J1094
Dexamethasone, inhalation solution, concentrated J7637
Dexamethasone, inhalation solution, unit dose J7638
Dexamethasone, intravitreal implant J7312
Dexamethasone, oral J8540
Dexamethasone sodium phosphate J1100
Dextran J7100
Dextrose
    saline (normal) J7042
    water J7060, J7070
Dextrostick A4772
Diagnostic
    radiology services R0070-R0076
Dialysate concentrate additives A4765
Dialysate solution A4728
Dialysate testing solution A4760
Dialysis
    air bubble detector E1530
    bath conductivity, meter E1550
    chemicals/antiseptics solution A4674
    disposable cycler set A4671
    equipment E1510-E1702
    extension line A4672-A4673
    filter A4680
    fluid barrier E1575
    forceps A4910
    kit A4820
    pressure alarm E1540
    shunt A4740
    supplies A4650-A4927
    thermometer A4910
    tourniquet A4910
    unipuncture control system E1580
    venous pressure clamp A4918
Dialyzer A4690
Diaper T1500, T4521-T4540, T4543, T4544
Diaper, adult incontinence garment A4520
Diazepam J3360
Diazoxide J1730
Dicyclomine HCl J0500
Diethylstilbestrol diphosphate J9165
Digoxin J1160
Digoxin immune fab (ovine) J1162
Dihydroergotamine mesylate J1110
Dimenhydrinate J1240
Dimercaprol J0470
Dimethyl sulfoxide (DMSO) J1212
Diphenhydramine HCl J1200
Dipyridamole J1245
Directional
    transluminal, atherectomy C1714
Disarticulation
    lower extremities, prosthesis L5000-L5999
    upper extremities, prosthesis L6000-L6692
Dispensing fee
    cros V5200
    bicros V5240
    bilateral V5110
    binaural V5160
    monaural hearing aid, any type V5241

    unspecified hearing aid V5090
Disposable supplies, ambulance A0382, A0384, A0392-A0398
DMSO J1212
Dobutamine HCl J1250
Docetaxel J9171
Dolasetron mesylate J1260
Dome and mouthpiece (for nebulizer) A7016
Dopamine HCl J1265
Doripenem J1267
Dornase alpha, inhalation solution, unit dose form J7639
Doxercalciferol J1270
Doxil J9001
Doxorubicin HCl J9000, J9002
Drainage
    bag A4357, A4358
    board, postural E0606
    bottle A5102
Dressing (*see also* Bandage) A6020-A6406
    alginate A6196-A6199
    collagen A6020-A6024
    composite A6200-A6205
    contact layer A6206-A6208
    foam A6209-A6215
    gauze A6216-A6230, A6402-A6406
    holder/binder A4462
    hydrocolloid A6234-A6241
    hydrogel A6242-A6248
    specialty absorptive A6251-A6256
    transparent film A6257-A6259
    tubular A6457
Droperidol J1790
    and fentanyl citrate J1810
Dropper A4649
Drugs (*see also* Table of Drugs)
    administered through a metered dose inhaler J3535
    chemotherapy J8500-J9999
    disposable delivery system, 5 ml or less per hour A4306
    disposable delivery system, 50 ml or greater per hour A4305
    immunosuppressive J7500-J7599
    infusion supplies A4230-A4232, A4221, A4222
    inhalation solutions J7608-J7699
    not otherwise classified J3490, J7599, J7699, J7799, J8499, J8999, J9999
    prescription, oral J8499, J8999
Dry pressure pad/mattress E0179, E0184, E0199
Durable medical equipment (DME) E0100-E1830, K Codes
Duraclon, *see* Clonidine
Dyphylline J1180

E

Ear mold V5264
Ecallantide J1290
Echocardiography injectable contrast material A9700
Eculizumab J1300
Edetate calcium disodium J0600
Edetate disodium J3520
Eggcrate dry pressure pad/mattress E0184, E0199
Elastic garments A4466
Elbow
    disarticulation, endoskeletal L6450
    orthosis (EO) E1800, L3700-L3740, L3760
    protector E0191
Electrical work, dialysis equipment A4870

G

Gadobutrol A9585
Gadofosveset trisodium A9583
Gadoxetate disodium A9581
Gait trainer E8000-E8002
Gallium Ga67 A9556
Gallium nitrate J1457
Galsulfase J1458
Gammagard liquid J1569
Gamma globulin J1460, J1560
Gammaplex J1557
Gamunex J1561
Ganciclovir, implant J7310
Ganciclovir sodium J1570
Garamycin J1580
Gas system
    compressed E0424, E0425
    gaseous E0430, E0431, E0441, E0443
    liquid E0434-E0440, E0442, E0444
Gatifloxacin J1590
Gauze (see also Bandage)
    impregnated A6222-A6233, A6266
    non-impregnated A6402-A6404
Gefitinib J8565
Gel
    conductive A4558
    pressure pad E0185, E0196
Gemcitabine HCl J9201
Gemtuzumab ozogamicin J9300
Generator
    ultrasonic with nebulizer E0574
Gentamicin (Sulfate) J1580
Glasses
    air conduction V5070
    binaural V5120-V5150
    bone conduction V5080
    frames V2020, V2025
    hearing aid V5230
Gloves A4927
Glucagon HCl J1610
Glucose monitor with integrated lancing/blood sample
   collection E2101
Glucose monitor with integrated voice synthesizer E2100
Glucose test strips A4253, A4772
Gluteal pad L2650
Glycopyrrolate, inhalation solution, concentrated J7642
Glycopyrrolate, inhalation solution, unit dose J7643
Gold sodium thiomalate J1600
Golimumab J1602
Gomco drain bottle A4912
Gonadorelin HCl J1620
Goserelin acetate implant (see also Implant) J9202
Grab bar, trapeze E0910, E0940
Grade-aid, wheelchair E0974
Graft, vascular catheter C1768
Granisetron HCl J1626
Gravity traction device E0941
Gravlee jet washer A4470

H

Habilitation
    day T2020-T2021
    educational T2012-T2013
    prevocational T2014-T2015
    residential T2016-T2017
    supported employment T2018-T2019
Hair analysis (excluding arsenic) P2031
Hallus-Valgus dynamic splint L3100
Hallux prosthetic implant L8642
Haloperidol J1630
    decanoate J1631
Halo procedures L0810-L0860
Halter, cervical head E0942
Hand finger orthosis, prefabricated L3923
Hand restoration L6900-L6915
    partial prosthesis L6000-L6020
    orthosis (WHFO) E1805, E1825, L3800-L3805,
      L3900-L3954
    rims, wheelchair E0967
Handgrip (cane, crutch, walker) A4636
Harness E0942, E0944, E0945
Headgear (for positive airway pressure device) K0185
Hearing aid
    cros, glasses V5190
    cros, in the ear V5170
    bicros, glasses V5230
    bicros, in the ear V5210
Hearing devices V5000-V5299, L8614
Heat
    application E0200-E0239
    lamp E0200, E0205
    infrared heating pad system A4639, E0221
    pad A9273, E0210, E0215, E0237, E0249
Heater (nebulizer) E1372
Heel
    elevator, air E0370
    protector E0191
    shoe L3430-L3485
    stabilizer L3170
Height
    walker, folding E0135
    walker, rigid E0130
Helicopter, ambulance (see also Ambulance)
Helmet, cervical L0100, L0110
Helmet, head A8000-A8004
Hemin J1640
Hemi-wheelchair E1083-E1086
Hemipelvectomy prosthesis L5280
Hemodialysis
    machine E1590
Hemodialyzer, portable E1635
Hemofil M J7190
Hemophilia clotting factor J7190-J7198
Hemophilia clotting factor, NOC J7199
Hemostats A4850
Hemostix A4773
Hepagam B IM J1571
Hepagam B IV J1573
Heparin infusion pump, dialysis E1520
Heparin lock flush J1642
Heparin sodium J1644
Hep-Lock (U/P) J1642
Hexalite A4590
High osmolar contrast material Q9958-Q9964
Hip
    disarticulation prosthesis L5250, L5270
    orthosis (HO) L1600-L1690
Hip-knee-ankle-foot orthosis (HKAFO) L2040-L2090
Histrelin acetate J1675
Histrelin implant J9225
HKAFO L2040-L2090
Home Health Agency Services T0221
Hot water bottle A9273

Hotline service
  behavioral health H0030
Human fibrinogen concentrate J7178
Humidifier A7046, E0550-E0563
Hyalgan J7321
Hyaluronan J7326, J7327
Hyaluronate, sodium J7317
Hyaluronidase J3470
Hyaluronidase, ovine J3471-J3473
Hydralazine HCI J0360
Hydraulic patient lift E0630
Hydrocollator E0225, E0239
Hydrocolloid dressing A6234-A6241
Hydrocortisone
  acetate J1700
  sodium phosphate J1710
  sodium succinate J1720
Hydrogel dressing A6242-A6248, A6231-A6233
Hydromorphone J1170
Hydroxyprogesterone caproate J1725
Hydroxyzine HCI J3410
Hylan G-F 20 J7322
Hyoscyamine Sulfate J1980
Hyperbaric oxygen chamber, topical A4575
Hypertonic saline solution J7130

I

Ibandronate sodium J1740
Ibuprofen J1741
Ibutilide Fumarate J1742
Icatibant J1744
Ice
  cap E0230
  collar E0230
Idarubicin HCI J9211
Idursulfase J1743
Ifosfamide J9208
Iloprost Q4074
Imiglucerase J1786
Immune globulin
  Bivigam J1556
  Flebogamma J1572
  Gammagard liquid J1569
  Gammaplex J1557
  Gamunex J1561
  HepaGam B J1571
  Hizentra J1559
  Intravenous services, supplies and accessories Q2052
  NOS J1566
  Octagam J1568
  Privigen J1459
  Rho(D) J2788, J2790
  Rhophylac J2791
  Subcutaneous J1562
Immunosuppressive drug, not otherwise classified J7599
Implant
  access system A4301
  aqueous shunt L8612
  breast L8600
  cochlear L8614, L8619
  collagen, urinary tract L8603
  dextranomer/hyaluronic acid copolymer L8604
  ganciclovir J7310
  hallux L8642
  urinary tract L8603, L8606
  infusion pump, programmable E0783, E0786

  joint L8630, L8641, L8658
  lacrimal duct A4262, A4263
  metacarpophalangeal joint L8630
  metatarsal joint L8641
  neurostimulator pulse generator L8679, L8681-L8688
  not otherwise specified L8699
  ocular L8610
  ossicular L8613
  osteogenesis stimulator E0749
  percutaneous access system A4301
  replacement implantable intraspinal catheter E0785
  synthetic, urinary L8606
  vascular graft L8670
Implantable radiation dosimeter A4650
Impregnated gauze dressing A6222-A6230
Incobotulinumtoxin A J0588
Incontinence
  appliances and supplies A4310, A4360, A5071-A5075, A5102-A5114, K0280, K0281
  treatment system E0740
Indium IN-111 carpromab pendetide A9507
Indium IN-111 ibritumomab tiuxetan A9542
Indium IN-111 labeled autologous white blood cells A9570
Indium IN-111 labeled autologous platelets A9571
Indium IN-111 oxyquinoline A9547
Indium IN-111 pentetate A9548
Indium IN-111 pentetreotide A9572
Indium IN-111 satumomab A4642
Infliximab injection J1745
Infusion
  pump, ambulatory, with administrative equipment E0781
  pump, heparin, dialysis E1520
  pump, implantable E0782, E0783
  pump, implantable, refill kit A4220
  pump, insulin E0784
  pump, mechanical, reusable E0779, E0780
  pump, uninterrupted infusion of Epiprostenol K0455
  replacement battery A4602
  supplies A4219, A4221, A4222, A4230-A4232
  therapy, other than chemotherapeutic drugs Q0081
Inhalation solution (*see also* drug name) J7608-J7699, Q4074
Injections (*see also* drug name) J0120-J7320
  supplies for self-administered A4211
Insertion tray A4310-A4316
Insulin J1815, J1817
Interferon
  Alpha J9212-J9215
  Beta-1 a J1826, Q3027, Q3028
  Beta- 1 b J1830
  Gamma J9216
Intermittent
  assist device with continuous positive airway pressure device E0470-E0472
  limb compression device E0676
  peritoneal dialysis system E1592
  positive pressure breathing (IPPB) machine E0500
Interphalangeal joint, prosthetic implant L8658, L8659
Interscapular thoracic prosthesis
  endoskeletal L6570
  upper limb L6350-L6370
Intraconazole J1835
Intraocular lenses V2630-V2632
Intrapulmonary percussive ventilation system E0481
Intraspinal catheter C1755
Intrauterine copper contraceptive J7300
Iodine lobenguane sulfate I-131 A9508
Iodine I-123 iobenguane A9582

Lumbar flexion L0540
Lumbar-sacral orthosis (LSO) L0621-L0640
Lymphocyte immune globulin J7504, J7511

M

Magnesium sulphate J3475
Maintenance contract, ESRD A4890
Mannitol J2150, J7665
Mask
   aerosol K0180
   oxygen A4620
Mastectomy
   bra L8000
   form L8020
   prosthesis L8030, L8600
   sleeve L8010
Material
   cane E0100, E0105
Mattress
   air pressure E0186
   alternating pressure E0277
   dry pressure E0184
   gel pressure E0196
   hospital bed E0271, E0272
   non-powered, pressure reducing E0373
   overlay E0371-E0372
   powered, pressure reducing E0277
   water pressure E0187
Mecasermin J2170
Mechlorethamine HCl J9230
Medical and surgical supplies A4206-A8999
Medroxyprogesterone acetate J1050
Melphalan HCl J9245
Melphalan, oral J8600
Methylnaltrexone J2212
Meperidine J2175
Meperidine and promethazine J2180
Mepivacaine HCl J0670
Meropenem J2185
Mesna J9209
Metacarpophalangeal joint, prosthetic implant L8630, L8631
Metaproterenol sulfate, inhalation solution, concentrated J7667, J7668
Metaproterenol sulfate, inhalation solution, unit dose J7669, J7670
Metaraminol bitartrate J0380
Metatarsal joint, prosthetic implant L8641
Meter, bath conductivity, dialysis E1550
Methacholine chloride J7674
Methadone HCl J1230
Methocarbamol J2800
Methotrexate, oral J8610
Methotrexate sodium J9250, J9260
Methyldopate HCl J0210
Methylene blue Q9968
Methylprednisolone
   acetate J1020-J1040
   oral J7509
   sodium succinate J2920, J2930
Metoclopramide HCl J2765
Micafungin sodium J2248
Microbiology test P7001
Midazolam HCl J2250
Mileage, ambulance A0380, A0390
Milrinone lactate J2260

Mini-bus, nonemergency transportation A0120
Minocycline hydrochloride J2265
Mitomycin J7315, J9280
Mitoxantrone HCl J9293
Modalities, with office visit M0005-M0008
Moisture exchanger for use with invasive mechanical ventilation A4483
Moisturizer, skin A6250
Monitor
   blood glucose E0607
   blood pressure A4670
   pacemaker E0610, E0615
Monitoring feature/device A9279
Monoclonal antibodies J7505
Morphine sulfate J2270
   epidural or intrathecal use J2274
Mouthpiece (for respiratory equipment) A4617
Moxifloxacin J2280
Mucoprotein, blood P2038
Multiaxial ankle L5986
Multidisciplinary services H2000-H2001, T1023-T1028
Multiple post collar, cervical L0180-L0200
Multi-Podus type AFO L4396
Muromonab-CD3 J7505
Mycophenolate mofetil J7517
Mycophenolic acid J7518

N

Nabilone J8650
Nalbuphine HCl J2300
Naloxone HCl J2310
Naltrexone J2315
Nandrolone
   decanoate J2320
   Narrowing device, wheelchair E0969
Nasal application device K0183
Nasal pillows/seals (for nasal application device) K0184
Nasal vaccine inhalation J3530
Nasogastric tubing B4081, B4082
Natalizumab J2323
Nebulizer E0570-E0585
   aerosol compressor E0571
   aerosol mask A7015
   corrugated tubing, disposable A7010
   corrugated tubing, non-disposable A7011
   filter, disposable A7013
   filter, non-disposable A7014
   heater E1372
   large volume, disposable, prefilled A7008
   large volume, disposable, unfilled A7007
   not used with oxygen, durable, glass A7017
   pneumatic, administration set A7003, A7005, A7006
   pneumatic, nonfiltered A7004
   portable E0570
   small volume A7003-A7005
   ultrasonic E0575
   ultrasonic, dome and mouthpiece A7016
   ultrasonic, reservoir bottle, non-disposable A7009
   water collection device, large volume nebulizer, A7012
Needle A4215
   non-coring A4212
   with syringe A4206-A4209
Negative pressure wound therapy pump E2402
   accessories A6550
Nelarabine J9261
Neonatal transport, ambulance, base rate A0225

Neostigmine methylsulfate J2710
Nerve stimulator with batteries E0765
Nesiritide injection J2324
Neuromuscular stimulator E0745
Neurostimulator
    battery recharging system L8695
    pulse generator L8681-L8688
Nitrogen N-13 ammonia A9526
Nonchemotherapy drug, oral, NOS J8499
Noncovered services A9270
Nonemergency transportation A0080-A0210
Nonimpregnated gauze dressing A6216-A6221,
    A6402-A6404
Nonprescription drug A9150
Not otherwise classified drug J3490, J7599, J7699, J7799,
    J8499, J8999, J9999, Q0181
NPH J1820
NTIOL category 3 Q1003
NTIOL category 4 Q1004
NTIOL category 5 Q1005
Nursing care T1030-T1031
Nutrition
    enteral infusion pump B9000, B9002
    parenteral infusion pump B9004, B9006
    parenteral solution B4164-B5200

O

Occipital/mandibular support, cervical L0160
Ocriplasmin J7316
Octafluoropropane Q9956
Octagam J1568
Octreotide acetate J2353, J2354
Ocular prosthetic implant L8610
Ofatumumab J9302
Olanzapine J2358
Omacetaxine Mepesuccinate J9262
Omalizumab J2357
OnabotulinumtoxinA J0585
Ondansetron HCl J2405
Ondansetron oral Q0162
One arm, drive attachment K0101
Oprelvekin J2355
O & P supply/accessory/service L9900
Oral device/appliance E0485-E0486
Oral interface A7047
Oral/nasal mask A7027
    nasal pillows A7029
    oral cushion A7028
Oropharyngeal suction catheter A4628
Orphenadrine J2360
Orthopedic shoes
    arch support L3040-L3100
    footwear L3201-L3265
    insert L3000-L3030
    lift L3300-L3334
    miscellaneous additions L3500-L3595
    positioning device L3140-L3170
    transfer L3600-L3649
    wedge L3340-L3420
Orthotic additions
    carbon graphite lamination L2755
    fracture L2180-L2192, L3995
    halo L0860
    lower extremity L2200-L2999, L4320
    ratchet lock L2430
    scoliosis L1010-L1120, L1210-L1290

    shoe L3300-L3595, L3649
    spinal L0970-L0984
    upper limb L3810-L3890, L3970-L3974, L3995
Orthotic devices
    ankle-foot (AFO; see also Orthopedic shoes) E1815,
        E1816, E1830, L1900-L1990, L2102-L2116, L3160,
        L4361
    anterior-posterior-lateral L0700, L0710
    cervical L0100-L0200
    cervical-thoracic-lumbar-sacral (CTLSO) L0700, L0710
    elbow (EO) E1800, E1801, L3700-L3740
    fracture L2102-L2136, L3980-L3986
    halo L0810-L0830
    hand, finger, prefabricated L3923
    hand, (WHFO) E1805, E1825, L3807, L3900-L3954
    hip (HO) L1600-L1690
    hip-knee-ankle-foot (HKAFO) L2040-L2090
    interface material E1820
    knee (KO) E1810, E1811, L1800-L1885
    knee-ankle-foot (KAFO; see also Orthopedic
        shoes) L2000-L2038, L2126-L2136
    Legg Perthes L1700-L1755
    multiple post collar L0180-L0200
    not otherwise specified L0999, L1499, L2999, L3999,
        L5999, L7499, L8039, L8239
    pneumatic splint L4350-L4380
    pronation/supination E1818
    repair or replacement L4000-L4210
    replace soft interface material L4390-L4394
    sacroiliac L0600-L0620
    scoliosis L1000 - L1499
    shoe, see Orthopedic shoes
    shoulder (SO) L1840, L3650, L3674
    shoulder-elbow-wrist-hand (SEWHO) L3960-L3978
    side bar disconnect L2768
    spinal, cervical L0100-L0200
    spinal, DME K0112-K0116
    thoracic L0210
    thoracic-hip-knee-ankle (THKO) L1500-L1520
    toe E1830
    wrist-hand-finger (WHFO) E1805, E1806, E1825,
        L3900-L3954
Orthovisc J7324
Ossicula prosthetic implant L8613
Osteogenesis stimulator E0747-E0749, E0760
Ostomy
    accessories A5093
    belt A4396
    pouches A4416-A4435
    skin barrier A4401-A4449
    supplies A4361-A4421, A5051-A5149
Oxacillin sodium J2700
Oxaliplatin J9263
Oxygen
    ambulance A0422
    battery charger E1357
    battery pack/cartridge E1356
    catheter, transtracheal A7018
    chamber, hyperbaric, topical A4575
    concentrator E1390-E1391
    DC power adapter E1358
    Liquid oxygen system E0433
    mask A4620
    medication supplies A4611-A4627
    rack/stand E1355
    regulator E1352, E1353
    respiratory equipment/supplies A4611-A4627,
        E0424-E0480

Oxymorphone HCl - Prednisolone

supplies and equipment E0425-E0444, E0455
tent E0455
tubing A4616
water vapor enriching system E1405, E1406
wheeled cart E1354
Oxymorphone HCl J2410
Oxytetracycline HCl J2460
Oxytocin J2590

P

Pacemaker monitor E0610, E0615
Paclitaxel J9267
Paclitaxel protein-bound particles J9264
Pad
gel pressure E0185, E0196
heat E0210, E0215, E0217, E0238, E0249
orthotic device interface E1820
sheepskin E0188, E0189
water circulating cold with pump E0218
water circulating heat with pump E0217
water circulating heat unit E0249
Pail, for use with commode chair E0167
Palate, prosthetic implant L8618
Palifermin J2425
Paliperidone palmitate J2426
Palonosetron HCl J2469
Pamidronate disodium J2430
Pan, for use with commode chair E0167
Panitumumab J9303
Papanicolaou (Pap) screening smear P3000, P3001, Q0091
Papaverine HCl J2440
Paraffin A4265
Paraffin bath unit E0235
Paramedic intercept
rural area A0432
Parenteral nutrition
administration kit B4224
pump B9004, B9006
solution B4164-B5200
supply kit B4220, B4222
Paricalcitol J2501
Parking fee, nonemergency transport A0170
Paste, conductive A4558
Pathology and laboratory tests,
miscellaneous P9010-P9615
Patient support system E0636
Patient transfer system E1035-E1036
PEFR, peak expiratory flow rate meter A4614
Pegademase bovine J2504
Pegaptanib J2503
Pegaspargase J9266
Pegfilgrastim J2505
Peginesatide J0890
Pegloticase J2507
Pelvic belt/harness/boot E0944
Pemetrexed J9305
Penicillin
G benzathine/G benzathine and penicillin G
procaine J0558, J0561
G potassium J2540
G procaine, aqueous J2510
Pentamidine isethionate J2545, J7676
Pentastarch, 10% solution J2513
Pentazocine HCl J3070
Pentobarbital sodium J2515
Pentostatin J9268

Percussor E0480
Percutaneous access system A4301
Perflexane lipid microspheres Q9955
Perflutren lipid microspheres Q9957
Peroneal strap L0980
Peroxide A4244
Perphenazine J3310
Personal care services T1019-T1021
Pertuzumab J9306
Pessary A4561, A4562
Phenobarbital sodium J2560
Phentolamine mesylate J2760
Phenylephrine HCl J2370
Phenytoin sodium J1165
Phisohex solution A4246
Photofrin, *see* Porfimer sodium
Phototherapy light E0202
Phytonadione J3430
Pillow, cervical E0943
Pinworm examination Q0113
Plasma
single donor, fresh frozen P9017
multiple donor, pooled, frozen P9023
Plastazote L3002, L3252, L3253, L3265, L5654-L5658
Platelet
concentrate, each unit P9019
rich plasma, each unit P9020
Platform attachment
forearm crutch E0153
walker E0154
Plerixafor J2562
Plicamycin J9270
Plumbing, for home ESRD equipment A4870
Pneumatic
appliance E0655-E0673, L4350-L4380
compressor E0650-E0652
splint L4350-L4380
ventricular assist device Q0480-Q0505
Pneumatic nebulizer
administration set, small volume, filtered A7006
administration set, small volume, nonfiltered A7003
administration set, small volume, nonfiltered, non-
disposable A7005
small volume, disposable A7004
Porfimer J9600
Port
indwelling C1788
Portable
equipment transfer R0070-R0076
gaseous oxygen K0741, K0742
hemodialyzer system E1635
liquid oxygen system E0433
x-ray equipment Q0092
Positioning seat T5001
Positive airway pressure device,
accessories A7030-A7039, E0561-E0562
Positive expiratory pressure device E0484
Post-coital examination Q0115
Postural drainage board E0606
Potassium chloride J3480
Potassium hydroxide (KOH) preparation Q0112
Pouch
fecal collection A4330
ostomy A4375-A4378, A5051-A5054, A5061-A5065
urinary A4379-A4383, A5071-A5075
Pralatrexate J9307
Pralidoxime chloride J2730
Prednisolone

acetate J2650
oral J7506, J7510
Prednisone J7506
Prefabricated splint
elbow S8452
digit (specify digit by use of modifier) S8450
wrist or ankle S8451
Preparation kits, dialysis A4914
Preparatory prosthesis L5510-L5595
chemotherapy J8999
nonchemotherapy J8499
Pressure
alarm, dialysis E1540
pad A4640, E0180-E0199
Privigen J1459
Procainamide HCl J2690
Prochlorperazine J0780
Prolotherapy M0076
Promazine HCl J2950
Promethazine HCl J2550
Promethazine and meperdine J2180
Propranolol HCl J1800
Prosthesis
artificial larynx battery/accessory L8505
breast L8000-L8035, L8600
eye L8610, L8611, V2623-V2629
fitting L5400-L5460, L6380-L6388
foot/ankle one piece system L5979
hand L6000-L6020, L6025
implants L8600-L8690
larynx L8500
lower extremity L5700-L5999, L8640-L8642
mandible L8617
maxilla L8616
maxillofacial, provided by a non-physician L8040-L8048
miscellaneous service L8499
ocular V2623-V2629
repair of L7520, L8049
socks (shrinker, sheath, stump sock) L8400-L8485
taxes, orthotic/prosthetic/other L9999
tracheo-esophageal L8507-L8509
upper extremity L6000-L6999
vacuum erection system L7900
Prosthetic additions
lower extremity L5610-L5999
upper extremity L6600-L7405
Protamine sulfate J2720
Protectant, skin A6250
Protector, heel or elbow E0191
Protein C Concentrate J2724
Protirelin J2725
Pulse generator E2120
Pump
alternating pressure pad E0182
ambulatory infusion E0781
ambulatory insulin E0784
blood, dialysis E1620
breast E0602-E0604
enteral infusion B9000, B9002
external infusion E0779
heparin infusion E1520
implantable infusion E0782, E0783
implantable infusion, refill kit A4220
infusion, supplies A4230, A4232
negative pressure wound therapy E2402
parenteral infusion B9004, B9006
suction, portable E0600
water circulating pad E0236

Purification system E1610, E1615
Pyridoxine HCl J3415

Q

Quad cane E0105
Quinupristin/dalfopristin J2770

R

Rack/stand, oxygen E1355
Radiesse Q2026
Radioelements for brachytherapy Q3001
Radiology service R0070-R0076
Radiopharmaceutical diagnostic and therapeutic imaging agent A4641, A4642, A9500-A9699
Rail
bathtub E0241, E0242, E0246
bed E0305, E0310
toilet E0243**Rails**
bed side, full length E0310
bed side, half length E0305
Ranibizumab J2778
Rasburicase J2783
Reaching/grabbing device A9281
Reagent strip A4252
Reciprocating peritoneal dialysis system E1630
Reclast J3488
Recorder
event, cardiac C1764
Red blood cells P9021, P9022
Red congo
blood P2029
Regadenoson J2785
Regular insulin J1820
Regulator, oxygen E1353
Rehabilitation
program H2001
psychosocial rehabilitation services H2017-H2018
Repair
contract, ESRD A4890
durable medical equipment E1340
maxillofacial prosthesis L8049
orthosis L4000-L4130
prosthetic L7500, L7510
Replacement
battery A4630
pad (alternating pressure) A4640
tanks, dialysis A4880
tip for cane, crutches, walker A4637
underarm pad for crutches A4635
RespiGam, *see* **Respiratory syncytial virus immune globulin**
Restraint, any type E0710
Reteplase J2993
Rho(D) immune globulin, human J2788, J2790, J2791, J2792
Rib belt, thoracic A4572, L0220
Rilonacept J2793
RimabotulinumtoxinB J0587
Ringers lactate infusion J7120
Ring, ostomy A4404
Risperidone J2794
Rituximab J9310
Robin-Aids L6000, L6010, L6020, L6855, L6860
Rocking bed E0462
Rollabout chair E1031

Romidepsin - Succinylcholine chloride

Romidepsin J9315
Romiplostim J2796
Ropivacaine HCl J2795
Rubidium Rb-82 A9555

S

Sacral nerve stimulation test lead A4290
Safety equipment E0700
   vest, wheelchair E0980
Saline
   hypertonic J7130
   solution J7030-J7050, A4216-A4218
Saliva
   artificial, 30ml A9155
Samarium SM 153 Lexidronamm A9605
Sargramostim (GM-CSF) J2820
Scoliosis L1000 - L1499
   additions L1010-L1120, L1210-L1290
Screening, cancer
   colorectal G0104 - G0106, G0120 - G0122, G0328
Sculptra Q2028
Sealant
   skin A6250
Seat
   attachment, walker E0156
   insert, wheelchair E0992
   lift (patient) E0621, E0627-E0629
   upholstery, wheelchair E0975
Secretin J2850
Semen analysis G0027
Sensitivity study P7001
Sermorelin acetate Q0515
Serum clotting time tube A4771
Service
   ambulance, unlisted A0999
SEWHO L3960-L3974
Sheepskin pad E0188, E0189
Shoes
   arch support L3040-L3100
   for diabetics A5500-A5508
   insert L3000-L3030
   lift L3300-L3334
   miscellaneous additions L3500-L3595
   orthopedic L3201-L3265
   positioning device L3140-L3170
   transfer L3600-L3649
   wedge L3340-L3485
Shoulder
   disarticulation, prosthetic L6300-L6320, L6550
   orthosis (SO) L3650 - L3674
   spinal, cervical L0100-L0200
Shoulder-elbow-wrist-hand orthosis (SEWHO) L3960-L3969
Shoulder sling A4566
Shunt accessory for dialysis A4740
   aqueous L8612
Sigmoidoscopy, cancer screening G0104, G0106
Sign language, oral interpretive services T1013
Sincalide J2805
Sipuleucel-T Q2043
Sirolimus J7520
Sitz bath E0160-E0162
Skills training and development H2014
Skin
   barrier, ostomy A4362, A4363, A4369-A4373, A4385, A5120

   bond or cement, ostomy A4364
   sealant, protectant, moisturizer A6250
   substitute Q4100-Q4160
Sling A4565
   patient lift E0621, E0630, E0635
Social worker, nonemergency transport A0160
Sock
   body sock L0984
   prosthetic sock L8420-L8435, L8470, L8480, L8485
   stump sock L8470-L8485
Sodium
   chloride injection J2912
   ferric gluconate complex in sucrose J2916
   fluoride F-18 A9580
   hyaluronate
      Euflexxa J7323
     Hyalgan J7321
     Orthovisc J7324
     Supartz J7321
     Synvisc and Synvisc-One J7325
   phosphate P32 A9563
   succinate J1720
Solution,
   calibrator A4256
   dialysate A4760
   elliotts b J9175
   enteral formulae B4149-B4156
   parenteral nutrition B4164-B5200
Somatrem J2940
Somatropin J2941
Sorbent cartridge, ESRD E1636
Specialty absorptive dressing A6251-A6256
Spectinomycin HCl J3320
Speech assessment V5362-V5364
Speech generating device E2500-E2599
Spinal orthosis,
   cervical L0100-L0200
   cervical-thoracic-lumbar-sacral (CTLSO) L0700, L0710
   DME K0112-K0116
   halo L0810-L0830
   multiple post collar L0180-L0200
   scoliosis L1000-L1499
   torso supports L0960
Splint A4570, L3100, L4350-L4380
   ankle L4390-L4398
   dynamic E1800, E1805, E1810, E1815, E1825, E1830, E1840
   footdrop L4398
Static progressive stretch E1801, E1806, E1811, E1816, E1818, E1821
Sterile cefuroxime sodium J0697
Sterile water A4216-A4217
Stimulators
   neuromuscular E0744, E0745
   osteogenesis, electrical E0747-E0749
   ultrasound E0760
   salivary reflex E0755
   stoma absorptive cover A5083
Stomach tube B4083
Streptokinase J2995
Streptomycin J3000
Streptozocin J9320
Strip, blood glucose test A4253, A4772
   urine reagent A4250
Strontium-89 chloride, supply of A9600
Stump sock L8470-L8485
Stylet A4212
Succinylcholine chloride J0330

Suction pump
   gastric, home model E2000
   portable E0600
   respiratory, home model E0600
Sumatriptan succinate J3030
Supartz J7321
Supply/accessory/service A9900
Support
   arch L3040-L3090
   cervical L0100-L0200
   spinal L0960
   stockings L8100-L8239
Surgical
   boot L3208-L3211
   brush, dialysis A4910
   dressing A6196-A6406
   stocking A4490-A4510
   supplies A4649
   tray A4550
Swabs, betadine or iodine A4247
Syringe A4213
   with needle A4206-A4209
Synvisc and Synvisc-One J7325

T

Tables, bed E0274, E0315
Tacrolimus, oral J7507, J7508
Tacrolimus, parenteral J7525
Taliglucerace J3060
Targeted, case management
   each 15 minutes T1017
   per month T2023
Taxi, non emergency transportation A0100
Technetium TC 99M Arcitumomab A9568
Technetium TC 99M Bicisate A9557
Technetium TC 99M Depreotide A9536
Technetium TC 99M Disofenin A9510
Technetium TC 99M Exametazime A9521
Technetium TC 99M Exametazime labeled autologous white blood cells A9569
Technetium TC 99M Fanolesomab A9566
Technetium TC 99M Gluceptate A9550
Technetium TC 99M - Labeled red blood cells A9560
Technetium TC 99M Macroaggregated albumin A9540
Technetium TC 99M Mebrofenin A9537
Technetium TC 99M Mertiatide A9562
Technetium TC 99M Oxidronate A9561
Technetium TC 99M Pentetate A9539, A9567
Technetium TC 99M Pertechnetate A9512
Technetium TC 99M Pyrophosphate A9538
Technetium TC 99M Sestamibi A9500
Technetium TC 99M Succimer A9551
Technetium TC 99M Sulfur colloid A9541
Technetium TC 99M Teboroxime A9501
Technetium TC 99M Tetrofosmin A9502
Technetium TC 99M Tilmanocept A9520
TEEV J0900
Telavancin J3095
Telehealth Q3014
Telehealth transmission T1014
Temozolomide, injection J9328
Temozolomide, oral J8700
Temsirolimus J9330
Tenecteplase J3101
Teniposide Q2017
TENS A4595, E0720-E0749

Tent, oxygen E0455
Terbutaline sulfate J3105
Terbutaline sulfate, inhalation solution, concentrated J7680
Terbutaline sulfate, inhalation solution, unit dose J7681
Teriparatide J3110
Terminal devices L6700-L6895
Testosterone
   cypionate and estradiol cypionate J1071
   enanthate J3121
   undecanoate J3145
Tetanus immune globulin, human J1670
Tetracycline J0120
Thallous Chloride TL 201 A9505
Theophylline J2810
Therapeutic lightbox A4634, E0203
Therapy
   occupational H5300
Thermometer A4931-A4932
Thermometer, dialysis A4910
Thiamine HCl J3411
Thiethylperazine maleate J3280
Thiotepa J9340
Thoracic-hip-knee-ankle (THKAO) L1500-L1520
Thoracic-lumbar-sacral orthosis (TLSO)
   scoliosis L1200-L1290
   spinal L0430-L0492
Thoracic orthosis L0210
Thymol turbidity, blood P2033
Thyrotropin Alfa J3240
Tigecycline J3243
Tinzaparin sodium J1655
Tip (cane, crutch, walker) replacement A4637
Tire, wheelchair E0999
Tirofiban J3246
Tissue
   connective, human C1762
   connective, non-human C1763
Tissue marker A4648
TLSO L0430-L0492, L1200-L1290
Tobramycin, inhalation solution, unit dose J7682, J7685
Tobramycin sulfate J3260
Tocilizumab J3262
Toilet accessories E0167-E0179, E0243, E0244, E0625
Tolazoline HCl J2670
Toll, non emergency transport A0170
Topical hyperbaric oxygen chamber A4575
Topotecan J8705, J9351
Torsemide J3265
Tracheostoma heat moisture exchange system A7501-A7509
Tracheostomy
   care kit A4629
   filter A4481
   speaking valve L8501
   supplies A4623, A4629, A7523-A7524
   tube A7520-A7522
Tracheotomy mask or collar A7525-A7526
Traction device, ambulatory E0830
Traction equipment E0840-E0948
Training
   alcohol and/ or drug training service H0021
   medication training and support H0034
   skills training and development H2014
Transcutaneous electrical nerve stimulator (TENS) E0720-E0770
Transducer protector, dialysis E1575
Transfer (shoe orthosis) L3600-L3640

Transfer system with seat E1035
Transluminal, atherectomy (catheter) C1714, C1724
Transparent film (for dressing) A6257-A6259
Transplant
    laparoscopy, islet cell G0342
    laparotomy, islet cell G0343
Transportation
    ambulance A0021-A0999, Q3019, Q3020
    corneal tissue V2785
    EKG (portable) R0076
    handicapped A0130
    non emergency A0080-A0210, T2001-T2005
    service, including ambulance A0021-A0999, T2006
    taxi, non emergency A0100
    toll, non emergency A0170
    volunteer, non emergency A0080, A0090
    x-ray (portable) R0070, R0075
Transtracheal oxygen catheter A7018
Trapeze bar E0910-E0912, E0940
Tray
    insertion A4310-A4316
    irrigation A4320
    surgical (*see also* kits) A4550
    wheelchair E0950
Treprostinil J3285
Triamcinolone J3301-J3303
    acetonide J3300, J3301
    diacetate J3302
    hexacetonide J3303
    inhalation solution, concentrated J7683
    inhalation solution, unit dose J7684
Triflupromazine HCl J3400
Trifocal, glass or plastic V2300-V2399
Trimethobenzamide HCl J3250
Trimetrexate glucuoronate J3305
Triptorelin pamoate J3315
Truss L8300-L8330
Tube/Tubing
    anchoring device A5200
    blood A4750, A4755
    drainage extension A4331
    gastrostomy B4087, B4088
    irrigation A4355
    larynectomy A4622
    nasogastric B4081, B4082
    oxygen A4616
    serum clotting time A4771
    stomach B4083
    suction pump, each A7002
    tire K0091, K0093, K0095, K0097
    tracheostomy A4622
    urinary drainage K0280

U

Ultrasonic nebulizer E0575
Ultrasound
    intravascular C1753
Ultraviolet light therapy system A4633, E0691-E0694
Unclassified drug J3490
Unipuncture control system, dialysis E1580
Upper extremity addition, locking elbow L6693
Upper extremity fracture orthosis L3980-L3999
Upper limb prosthesis L6000-L7499
Urea J3350
Ureteral
    catheter, ureteral C1758

Ureterostomy supplies A4454-A4590
Urethral suppository, Alprostadil J0275
Urinal
    jug-type, female E0326
    jug-type, male E0325
Urinary
    catheter A4338-A4346, A4351-A4353
    collection and retention (supplies) A4310-A4360
    tract implant, collagen L8603
    tract implant, snythetic L8606
Urine
    sensitivity study P7001
    tests A4250
Urofollitropin J3355
Urokinase J3364, J3365
Ustekinumab J3357
U-V lens V2755

V

Vabra aspirator A4480
Vaccination, administration
    flublok Q2033
    hepatitis B G0010
    influenza virus G0008
    pneumococcal G0009
Vancomycin HCl J3370
Vaporizer E0605
Vascular
    catheter (appliances and supplies) A4300-A4306
    graft material, synthetic L8670
Vasoxyl J3390
Velaglucerase alfa J3385
Venous pressure clamp, dialysis A4918
Ventilator
    battery A4611-A4613
    moisture exchanger, disposable A4483
    negative pressure E0460
    volume, stationary or portable E0450, E0461-E0464
Ventricular assist device Q0478-Q0504, Q0506-Q0509
Verteporfin J3396
Vest, safety, wheelchair E0980
Vinblastine sulfate J9360
Vincristine sulfate J9370, J9371
Vinorelbine tartrate J9390
Vision service V2020-V2799
Vitamin B-12 cyanocobalamin J3420
Vitamin K J3430
Voice amplifier L8510
Voice prosthesis L8511-L8514
Von Willebrand Factor Complex, human J7183, J7187
Voriconazole J3465

W

Waiver T2012-T2050
Walker E0130-E0149
    accessories A4636, A4637
    attachments E0153-E0159
Walking splint L4386
Water
    distilled (for nebulizer) A7018
    pressure pad/mattress E0187, E0198
    purification system (ESRD) E1610, E1615
    softening system (ESRD) E1625
    sterile A4714
Wedges, shoe L3340-L3420

Wet mount Q0111
Wheel attachment, rigid pickup walker E0155
Wheelchair E0950-E1298, K0001-K0108
    accessories E0192, E0950-E1030, E1065-E1069,
       E2211-E2230, E2300-E2399
    amputee E1170-E1200
    back, fully reclining, manual E1226
    component or accessory, not otherwise specified K0108
    cushions E2601-E2625
    narrowing device E0969
    power add-on E0983-E0984
    shock absorber E1015-E1018
    specially sized E1220, E1230
    stump support system K0551
    tire E0999
    transfer board or device E0705
    tray K0107
    van, non-emergency A0130
    youth E1091
WHFO with inflatable air chamber L3807
WHO, wrist extension L3914
Whirlpool equipment E1300-E1310
Wig A9282
Wipes A4245, A4247
Wound cleanser A6260
Wound cover
    alginate dressing A6196-A6198
    collagen dressing A6020-A6024
    foam dressing A6209-A6214
    hydrocolloid dressing A6234-A6239
    hydrogel dressing A6242-A6247
    non-contact wound warming cover, and accessory E0231,
       E0232
    specialty absorptive dressing A6251-A6256
Wound filler
    alginate dressing A6199
    collagen based A6010
    foam dressing A6215
    hydrocolloid dressing A6240, A6241
    hydrogel dressing A6248
    not elsewhere classified A6261, A6262
Wound pouch A6154
Wrap
    chest E0459
Wrist
    disarticulation prosthesis L6050, L6055
    electronic wrist rotator L7259
    hand/finger orthosis (WHFO) E1805, E1825, L3800-L3954

X

Xenon Xe 133 A9558
Xylocaine HCl J2000
X-ray equipment, portable Q0092, R0070, R0075

Y

Yttrium Y-90 ibritumomab A9543

Z

Ziconotide J2278
Zidovudine J3485
Ziprasidone mesylate J3486
Zoledronic acid J3489

TRANSPORTATION SERVICES INCLUDING AMBULANCE (A0021- A0999)

▯ A0021 Ambulance service, outside state per mile, transport (Medicaid only)　　　　E
Service not separately priced by Part B

▯ A0080 Non-emergency transportation, per mile - vehicle provided by volunteer (individual or organization), with no vested interest　　E
Service not separately priced by Part B

▯ A0090 Non-emergency transportation, per mile - vehicle provided by individual (family member, self, neighbor) with vested interest　　E
Service not separately priced by Part B

▯ A0100 Non-emergency transportation; taxi　E
Service not separately priced by Part B

▯ A0110 Non-emergency transportation and bus, intra or inter state carrier　　　　E
Service not separately priced by Part B

▯ A0120 Non-emergency transportation: mini-bus, mountain area transports, or other transportation systems　　　　E
Service not separately priced by Part B

▯ A0130 Non-emergency transportation: wheel-chair van　　　　E
Service not separately priced by Part B

▯ A0140 Non-emergency transportation and air travel (private or commercial) intra or inter state　E
Service not separately priced by Part B

▯ A0160 Non-emergency transportation: per mile - case worker or social worker　　E
Service not separately priced by Part B

▯ A0170 Transportation ancillary: parking fees, tolls, other　　　　E
Service not separately priced by Part B

▯ A0180 Non-emergency transportation: ancillary: lodging-recipient　　　　E
Service not separately priced by Part B

▯ A0190 Non-emergency transportation: ancillary: meals-recipient　　　　E
Service not separately priced by Part B

▯ A0200 Non-emergency transportation: ancillary: lodging escort　　　　E
Service not separately priced by Part B

▯ A0210 Non-emergency transportation: ancillary: meals-escort　　　　E
Service not separately priced by Part B

▯ A0225 Ambulance service, neonatal transport, base rate, emergency transport, one way　E
Service not separately priced by Part B
Pub: 100-4, Chap. 1, 10.1.4.1

▯ A0380 BLS mileage (per mile)　　　　E
Service not separately priced by Part B
Pub: 100-4, Chap. 1, 10.1.4.1; 100-4, Chap. 15, 20.2; 100-4, Chap. 15, 30.2

▯ A0382 BLS routine disposable supplies　　A
Service not separately priced by Part B
Pub: 100-2, Chap. 10, 30.1.1

▯ A0384 BLS specialized service disposable supplies; defibrillation (used by ALS ambulances and BLS ambulances in jurisdictions where defibrillation is permitted in BLS ambulances)　　A
Service not separately priced by Part B

▯ A0390 ALS mileage (per mile)　　　　E
Service not separately priced by Part B
Pub: 100-4, Chap. 15, 20.2; 100-4, Chap. 15, 30.2

▯ A0392 ALS specialized service disposable supplies; defibrillation (to be used only in jurisdictions where defibrillation cannot be performed in BLS ambulances)　　A
Service not separately priced by Part B
Pub: 100-2, Chap. 10, 30.1.1

▯ A0394 ALS specialized service disposable supplies; IV drug therapy　　A
Service not separately priced by Part B

▯ A0396 ALS specialized service disposable supplies; esophageal intubation　　A
Service not separately priced by Part B

▯ A0398 ALS routine disposable supplies　　A
Service not separately priced by Part B

▯ A0420 Ambulance waiting time (ALS or BLS), one half (1/2) hour increments　　A
Service not separately priced by Part B

▯ A0422 Ambulance (ALS or BLS) oxygen and oxygen supplies, life sustaining situation　A
Service not separately priced by Part B

▯ A0424 Extra ambulance attendant, ground (ALS or BLS) or air (fixed or rotary winged); (requires medical review)　　A
Service not separately priced by Part B
Pub: 100-4, Chap. 15, 30.2.1

C A0425 Ground mileage, per statute mile　　A
Reasonable charge

C A0426 Ambulance service, advanced life support, non-emergency transport, level 1 (ALS 1)　A
Reasonable charge
Pub: 100-2, Chap. 10, 20; 100-4, Chap. 1, 10.1.4.1; 100-4, Chap. 15, 30.2; 100-4, Chap. 15, 30.2.1

C A0427 Ambulance service, advanced life support, emergency transport, level 1 (ALS 1-emergency)　　A
Reasonable charge
Pub: 100-2, Chap. 10, 20; 100-4, Chap. 1, 10.1.4.1; 100-4, Chap. 15, 30.2.1

♂ Male only　　♀ Female only　　Ⓐ Age　　A2 - Z3 = ASC Payment Indicator　　A - Y = APC Status Indicator
ASC = ASC Approved Procedure　　**DME** Paid under the DME fee schedule　　**PQRS** Physician Quality Reporting System

19

C **A0428** Ambulance service, basic life support, non-emergency transport, (BLS)   A

Reasonable charge

Pub: 100-2, Chap. 10, 20; 100-4, Chap. 1, 10.1.4.1; 100-4, Chap. 15, 20.6; 100-4, Chap. 15, 30.2.1

C **A0429** Ambulance service, basic life support, emergency transport (BLS-emergency)   A

Reasonable charge

Pub: 100-2, Chap. 10, 20; 100-4, Chap. 1, 10.1.4.1; 100-4, Chap. 15, 30.2.1

C **A0430** Ambulance service, conventional air services, transport, one way (fixed wing)   A

Reasonable charge

Pub: 100-2, Chap. 10, 20; 100-4, Chap. 1, 10.1.4.1; 100-4, Chap. 15, 20.3; 100-4, Chap. 15, 30.2.1

C **A0431** Ambulance service, conventional air services, transport, one way (rotary wing)   A

Reasonable charge

Pub: 100-2, Chap. 10, 20; 100-4, Chap. 1, 10.1.4.1; 100-4, Chap. 15, 30.2.1

C **A0432** Paramedic intercept (PI), rural area, transport furnished by a volunteer ambulance company which is prohibited by state law from billing third party payers   A

Reasonable charge

Pub: 100-2, Chap. 10, 20; 100-2, Chap. 10, 30.1.1; 100-4, Chap. 15, 30.2.1

C **A0433** Advanced life support, level 2 (ALS 2)   A

Reasonable charge

Pub: 100-2, Chap. 10, 20; 100-4, Chap. 15, 30.2.1

C **A0434** Specialty care transport (SCT)   A

Reasonable charge

Pub: 100-2, Chap. 10, 20; 100-4, Chap. 15, 30.2.1

C **A0435** Fixed wing air mileage, per statute mile   A

Reasonable charge

Pub: 100-2, Chap. 10, 20; 100-4, Chap. 15, 20.2; 100-4, Chap. 15, 20.3; 100-4, Chap. 15, 30.2; 100-4, Chap. 15, 30.2.1

C **A0436** Rotary wing air mileage, per statute mile   A

Reasonable charge

Pub: 100-2, Chap. 10, 20; 100-4, Chap. 15, 20.2; 100-4, Chap. 15, 30.2.1

M **A0888** Noncovered ambulance mileage, per mile (e.g., for miles traveled beyond closest appropriate facility)   E

Service not separately priced by Part B

Pub: 100-2, Chap. 10, 20; 100-4, Chap. 15, 20.2; 100-4, Chap. 15, 30.1.2; 100-4, Chap. 15, 30.2.4

I **A0998** Ambulance response and treatment, no transport   E

Service not separately priced by Part B

D **A0999** Unlisted ambulance service   A

Other carrier priced

Pub: 100-2, Chap. 10, 20

MEDICAL AND SURGICAL SUPPLIES
(A4206-A8004)

C **A4206** Syringe with needle, sterile, 1 cc or less, each   E
Service not separately priced by Part B

C **A4207** Syringe with needle, sterile 2 cc, each   E
Service not separately priced by Part B

C **A4208** Syringe with needle, sterile 3 cc, each   E
Service not separately priced by Part B

C **A4209** Syringe with needle, sterile 5 cc or greater, each   E
Service not separately priced by Part B

M **A4210** Needle-free injection device, each   E
Service not separately priced by Part B

D **A4211** Supplies for self-administered injections   E
Service not separately priced by Part B

C **A4212** Non-coring needle or stylet with or without catheter   B
Other carrier priced

C **A4213** Syringe, sterile, 20 cc or greater, each   E
Service not separately priced by Part B

C **A4215** Needle, sterile, any size, each   E
Service not separately priced by Part B

D **A4216** Sterile water, saline and/or dextrose, diluent/flush, 10 ml   **DME** A

D **A4217** Sterile water/saline, 500 ml   **DME** A
DME Modifier: AU

D **A4218** Sterile saline or water, metered dose dispenser, 10 ml   N1 N

D **A4220** Refill kit for implantable infusion pump   N1 N
Other carrier priced

C **A4221** Supplies for maintenance of drug infusion catheter, per week (list drug separately)   **DME** Y

C **A4222** Infusion supplies for external drug infusion pump, per cassette or bag (list drugs separately)   **DME** Y

C **A4223** Infusion supplies not used with external infusion pump, per cassette or bag (list drugs separately)   E
Service not separately priced by Part B

D **A4230** Infusion set for external insulin pump, non needle cannula type   N

Insulin Pump

D **A4231** Infusion set for external insulin pump, needle type   N

I **A4232** Syringe with needle for external insulin pump, sterile, 3 cc   E
Service not separately priced by Part B

C **A4233** Replacement battery, alkaline (other than J cell), for use with medically necessary home blood glucose monitor owned by patient, each   **DME** Y
DME Modifier: NU, KL
Pub: 100-4, Chap. 23, 60.3

C **A4234** Replacement battery, alkaline, J cell, for use with medically necessary home blood glucose monitor owned by patient, each   **DME** Y
DME Modifier: NU, KL

C **A4235** Replacement battery, lithium, for use with medically necessary home blood glucose monitor owned by patient, each   **DME** Y
DME Modifier: NU, KL

C **A4236** Replacement battery, silver oxide, for use with medically necessary home blood glucose monitor owned by patient, each   **DME** Y
DME Modifier: NU, KL

C **A4244** Alcohol or peroxide, per pint   E
Service not separately priced by Part B

C **A4245** Alcohol wipes, per box   E
Service not separately priced by Part B

C **A4246** Betadine or pHisoHex solution, per pint   E
Service not separately priced by Part B

C **A4247** Betadine or iodine swabs/wipes, per box   E
Service not separately priced by Part B

C **A4248** Chlorhexidine containing antiseptic, 1 ml   N1 N
Reasonable charge

M **A4250** Urine test or reagent strips or tablets (100 tablets or strips)   E
Service not separately priced by Part B
Pub: 100-2, Chap. 15, 110

♂ Male only   ♀ Female only   **A** Age   A2 - Z3 = ASC Payment Indicator   A - Y = APC Status Indicator
ASC = ASC Approved Procedure   **DME** Paid under the DME fee schedule   **PQRS** Physician Quality Reporting System

MEDICAL AND SURGICAL SUPPLIES (A4206-A8004)

21

S **A4252** Blood ketone test or reagent strip, each   E
Service not separately priced by Part B
Statute: 1861 (n)

D **A4253** Blood glucose test or reagent strips for home blood glucose monitor, per 50 strips   DME Y
DME Modifier: NU, KL
Pub: 100-4, Chap. 23, 60.3

D **A4255** Platforms for home blood glucose monitor, 50 per box   DME Y

D **A4256** Normal, low and high calibrator solution / chips   DME Y
DME Modifier: KL
Pub: 100-4, Chap. 23, 60.3

C **A4257** Replacement lens shield cartridge for use with laser skin piercing device, each   DME Y

D **A4258** Spring-powered device for lancet, each   DME Y
DME Modifier: KL
Pub: 100-4, Chap. 23, 60.3

D **A4259** Lancets, per box of 100   DME Y
DME Modifier: KL

S **A4261** Cervical cap for contraceptive use   ♀ E
Service not separately priced by Part B
Statute: 1862a1

D **A4262** Temporary, absorbable lacrimal duct implant, each   N1 N
Service not separately priced by Part B

D **A4263** Permanent, long term, non-dissolvable lacrimal duct implant, each   N1 N
Price established using national RVU's

I **A4264** Permanent implantable contraceptive intratubal occlusion device(s) and delivery system   ♀ E
Service not separately priced by Part B

D **A4265** Paraffin, per pound   DME Y

I **A4266** Diaphragm for contraceptive use   ♀ E
Service not separately priced by Part B

I **A4267** Contraceptive supply, condom, male, each   ♂ E
Service not separately priced by Part B

I **A4268** Contraceptive supply, condom, female, each   ♀ E
Service not separately priced by Part B

I **A4269** Contraceptive supply, spermicide (e.g., foam, gel), each   ♀ E
Service not separately priced by Part B

C **A4270** Disposable endoscope sheath, each   N1 N
Service not separately priced by Part B

C **A4280** Adhesive skin support attachment for use with external breast prosthesis, each   ♀ DME A

C **A4281** Tubing for breast pump, replacement   ♀ E
Service not separately priced by Part B

C **A4282** Adapter for breast pump, replacement   ♀ E
Service not separately priced by Part B

C **A4283** Cap for breast pump bottle, replacement   ♀ E
Service not separately priced by Part B

C **A4284** Breast shield and splash protector for use with breast pump, replacement   ♀ E
Service not separately priced by Part B

C **A4285** Polycarbonate bottle for use with breast pump, replacement   ♀ E
Service not separately priced by Part B

C **A4286** Locking ring for breast pump, replacement   . ♀ E
Service not separately priced by Part B

C **A4290** Sacral nerve stimulation test lead, each   B
Service not separately priced by Part B
Pub: 100-4, Chap. 32, 40.1

D **A4300** Implantable access catheter, (e, g., venous, arterial, epidural subarachnoid, or peritoneal, etc.) external access   N1 N
Price established using national RVU's

C **A4301** Implantable access total catheter, port/reservoir (e.g., venous, arterial, epidural, subarachnoid, peritoneal, etc.)   N1 N
Service not separately priced by Part B

C **A4305** Disposable drug delivery system, flow rate of 50 ml or greater per hour   N1 N
Service not separately priced by Part B

C **A4306** Disposable drug delivery system, flow rate of less than 50 ml per hour   N1 N
Service not separately priced by Part B

D **A4310** Insertion tray without drainage bag and without catheter (accessories only)   DME A

D **A4311** Insertion tray without drainage bag with indwelling catheter, Foley type, 2-way latex with coating (Teflon, silicone, silicone elastomer or hydrophilic, etc.)   DME A

D **A4312** Insertion tray without drainage bag with indwelling catheter, Foley type, 2-way, all silicone   DME A

D **A4313** Insertion tray without drainage bag with indwelling catheter, Foley type, 3-way, for continuous irrigation   DME A

D **A4314** Insertion tray with drainage bag with indwelling catheter, Foley type, 2-way latex with coating (Teflon, silicone, silicone elastomer or hydrophilic, etc.)   DME A

D **A4315** Insertion tray with drainage bag with indwelling catheter, Foley type, 2-way, all silicone   DME A

D **A4316** Insertion tray with drainage bag with indwelling catheter, Foley type, 3-way, for continuous irrigation   DME A

D **A4320** Irrigation tray with bulb or piston syringe, any purpose   DME A

D **A4321** Therapeutic agent for urinary catheter irrigation   DME A

D **A4322** Irrigation syringe, bulb or piston, each   DME A

D **A4326** Male external catheter with integral collection chamber, any type, each   ♂ DME A

▲ Revised Code   ● New code   **C** Carrier judgment   **D** Special coverage instructions apply
I Not payable by Medicare   **M** Non-covered by Medicare   **S** Non-covered by Medicare statute   AHA Coding Clinic®

D **A4327** Female external urinary collection device; meatal cup, each ♀ DME A

D **A4328** Female external urinary collection device; pouch, each ♀ DME A

D **A4330** Perianal fecal collection pouch with adhesive, each DME A

D **A4331** Extension drainage tubing, any type, any length, with connector/adaptor, for use with urinary leg bag or urostomy pouch, each DME A

D **A4332** Lubricant, individual sterile packet, each DME A

D **A4333** Urinary catheter anchoring device, adhesive skin attachment, each DME A

D **A4334** Urinary catheter anchoring device, leg strap, each DME A

D **A4335** Incontinence supply; miscellaneous A

D **A4336** Incontinence supply, urethral insert, any type, each DME A

D **A4338** Indwelling catheter; Foley type, 2-way latex with coating (Teflon, silicone, silicone elastomer, or hydrophilic, etc.), each DME A

D **A4340** Indwelling catheter; specialty type, e.g., Coude, mushroom, wing, etc.), each DME A

D **A4344** Indwelling catheter, Foley type, 2-way, all silicone, each DME A

D **A4346** Indwelling catheter; Foley type, three way for continuous irrigation, each DME A

Foley Catheter

D **A4349** Male external catheter, with or without adhesive, disposable, each ♂ DME A

D **A4351** Intermittent urinary catheter; straight tip, with or without coating (Teflon, silicone, silicone elastomer, or hydrophilic, etc.), each DME A

D **A4352** Intermittent urinary catheter; Coude (curved) tip, with or without coating (Teflon, silicone, silicone elastomeric, or hydrophilic, etc.), each DME A

D **A4353** Intermittent urinary catheter, with insertion supplies DME A

D **A4354** Insertion tray with drainage bag but without catheter DME A

D **A4355** Irrigation tubing set for continuous bladder irrigation through a 3-way indwelling Foley catheter, each DME A

D **A4356** External urethral clamp or compression device (not to be used for catheter clamp), each DME A

D **A4357** Bedside drainage bag, day or night, with or without anti-reflux device, with or without tube, each DME A

D **A4358** Urinary drainage bag, leg or abdomen, vinyl, with or without tube, with straps, each DME A

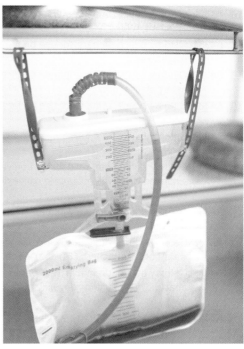

Urinary Drainage Bag

D **A4360** Disposable external urethral clamp or compression device, with pad and/or pouch, each DME A

D **A4361** Ostomy faceplate, each DME A

D **A4362** Skin barrier; solid, 4 x 4 or equivalent; each DME A

D **A4363** Ostomy clamp, any type, replacement only, each DME A

D **A4364** Adhesive, liquid or equal, any type, per oz DME A

C **A4366** Ostomy vent, any type, each DME A

D **A4367** Ostomy belt, each DME A

C **A4368** Ostomy filter, any type, each DME A

D **A4369** Ostomy skin barrier, liquid (spray, brush, etc), per oz DME A

D **A4371** Ostomy skin barrier, powder, per oz DME A

D **A4372** Ostomy skin barrier, solid 4x4 or equivalent, standard wear, with built-in convexity, each DME A

D **A4373** Ostomy skin barrier, with flange (solid, flexible or accordian), with built-in convexity, any size, each DME A

D **A4375** Ostomy pouch, drainable, with faceplate attached, plastic, each DME A

♂ Male only   ♀ Female only   🅐 Age   A2 - Z3 = ASC Payment Indicator   A - Y = APC Status Indicator

ASC = ASC Approved Procedure   DME Paid under the DME fee schedule   PQRS Physician Quality Reporting System

D **A4376** Ostomy pouch, drainable, with faceplate attached, rubber, each **DME** A

D **A4377** Ostomy pouch, drainable, for use on faceplate, plastic, each **DME** A

D **A4378** Ostomy pouch, drainable, for use on faceplate, rubber, each **DME** A

D **A4379** Ostomy pouch, urinary, with faceplate attached, plastic, each **DME** A

D **A4380** Ostomy pouch, urinary, with faceplate attached, rubber, each **DME** A

D **A4381** Ostomy pouch, urinary, for use on faceplate, plastic, each **DME** A

D **A4382** Ostomy pouch, urinary, for use on faceplate, heavy plastic, each **DME** A

D **A4383** Ostomy pouch, urinary, for use on faceplate, rubber, each **DME** A

D **A4384** Ostomy faceplate equivalent, silicone ring, each **DME** A

D **A4385** Ostomy skin barrier, solid 4x4 or equivalent, extended wear, without built-in convexity, each **DME** A

D **A4387** Ostomy pouch, closed, with barrier attached, with built-in convexity (1-piece), each **DME** A

D **A4388** Ostomy pouch, drainable, with extended wear barrier attached, (1-piece), each **DME** A

D **A4389** Ostomy pouch, drainable, with barrier attached, with built-in convexity (1-piece), each **DME** A

D **A4390** Ostomy pouch, drainable, with extended wear barrier attached, with built-in convexity (1-piece), each **DME** A

D **A4391** Ostomy pouch, urinary, with extended wear barrier attached (1-piece), each **DME** A

D **A4392** Ostomy pouch, urinary, with standard wear barrier attached, with built-in convexity (1-piece), each **DME** A

D **A4393** Ostomy pouch, urinary, with extended wear barrier attached, with built-in convexity (1-piece), each **DME** A

Ostomy Pouch

D **A4394** Ostomy deodorant, with or without lubricant, for use in ostomy pouch, per fluid ounce **DME** A

D **A4395** Ostomy deodorant for use in ostomy pouch, solid, per tablet **DME** A

D **A4396** Ostomy belt with peristomal hernia support **DME** A

D **A4397** Irrigation supply; sleeve, each **DME** A

D **A4398** Ostomy irrigation supply; bag, each **DME** A

D **A4399** Ostomy irrigation supply; cone/catheter, with or without brush **DME** A

D **A4400** Ostomy irrigation set **DME** A

D **A4402** Lubricant, per ounce **DME** A

D **A4404** Ostomy ring, each **DME** A

D **A4405** Ostomy skin barrier, non-pectin based, paste, per ounce **DME** A

D **A4406** Ostomy skin barrier, pectin-based, paste, per ounce **DME** A

D **A4407** Ostomy skin barrier, with flange (solid, flexible, or accordion), extended wear, with built-in convexity, 4 x 4 inches or smaller, each **DME** A

D **A4408** Ostomy skin barrier, with flange (solid, flexible or accordion), extended wear, with built-in convexity, larger than 4 x 4 inches, each **DME** A

D **A4409** Ostomy skin barrier, with flange (solid, flexible or accordion), extended wear, without built-in convexity, 4 x 4 inches or smaller, each **DME** A

D **A4410** Ostomy skin barrier, with flange (solid, flexible or accordion), extended wear, without built-in convexity, larger than 4 x 4 inches, each **DME** A

D **A4411** Ostomy skin barrier, solid 4x4 or equivalent, extended wear, with built-in convexity, each **DME** A

D **A4412** Ostomy pouch, drainable, high output, for use on a barrier with flange (2-piece system), without filter, each **DME** A

D **A4413** Ostomy pouch, drainable, high output, for use on a barrier with flange (2-piece system), with filter, each **DME** A

D **A4414** Ostomy skin barrier, with flange (solid, flexible or accordion), without built-in convexity, 4 x 4 inches or smaller, each **DME** A

D **A4415** Ostomy skin barrier, with flange (solid, flexible or accordion), without built-in convexity, larger than 4x4 inches, each **DME** A

C **A4416** Ostomy pouch, closed, with barrier attached, with filter (1-piece), each **DME** A

C **A4417** Ostomy pouch, closed, with barrier attached, with built-in convexity, with filter (1-piece), each **DME** A

C **A4418** Ostomy pouch, closed; without barrier attached, with filter (1-piece), each **DME** A

C **A4419** Ostomy pouch, closed; for use on barrier with non-locking flange, with filter (2-piece), each **DME** A

C **A4420** Ostomy pouch, closed; for use on barrier with locking flange (2-piece), each **DME** A

C **A4421** Ostomy supply; miscellaneous E
    Service not separately priced by Part B

▲ Revised Code   ● New code   C Carrier judgment   D Special coverage instructions apply
I Not payable by Medicare   M Non-covered by Medicare   S Non-covered by Medicare statute   AHA Coding Clinic®

D **A4422** Ostomy absorbent material (sheet/pad/ crystal packet) for use in ostomy pouch to thicken liquid stomal output, each `DME` A

C **A4423** Ostomy pouch, closed; for use on barrier with locking flange, with filter (2-piece), each `DME` A

C **A4424** Ostomy pouch, drainable, with barrier attached, with filter (1-piece), each `DME` A

C **A4425** Ostomy pouch, drainable; for use on barrier with non-locking flange, with filter (2-piece system), each `DME` A

C **A4426** Ostomy pouch, drainable; for use on barrier with locking flange (2-piece system), each `DME` A

C **A4427** Ostomy pouch, drainable; for use on barrier with locking flange, with filter (2-piece system), each `DME` A

C **A4428** Ostomy pouch, urinary, with extended wear barrier attached, with faucet-type tap with valve (1-piece), each `DME` A

C **A4429** Ostomy pouch, urinary, with barrier attached, with built-in convexity, with faucet-type tap with valve (1-piece), each `DME` A

C **A4430** Ostomy pouch, urinary, with extended wear barrier attached, with built-in convexity, with faucet-type tap with valve (1-piece), each `DME` A

C **A4431** Ostomy pouch, urinary; with barrier attached, with faucet-type tap with valve (1-piece), each `DME` A

C **A4432** Ostomy pouch, urinary; for use on barrier with non-locking flange, with faucet-type tap with valve (2-piece), each `DME` A

C **A4433** Ostomy pouch, urinary; for use on barrier with locking flange (2-piece), each `DME` A

C **A4434** Ostomy pouch, urinary; for use on barrier with locking flange, with faucet-type tap with valve (2-piece), each `DME` A

C **A4435** Ostomy pouch, drainable, high output, with extended wear barrier (1-piece system), with or without filter, each `DME` A

D **A4450** Tape, non-waterproof, per 18 square inches `DME` A
DME Modifier: AU, AV, AW

D **A4452** Tape, waterproof, per 18 square inches `DME` A
DME Modifier: AU, AV, AW

D **A4455** Adhesive remover or solvent (for tape, cement or other adhesive), per ounce `DME` A

D **A4456** Adhesive remover, wipes, any type, each `DME` A

C **A4458** Enema bag with tubing, reusable E
Service not separately priced by Part B

● C **A4459** Manual pump-operated enema system, includes balloon, catheter and all accessories, reusable, any type

C **A4461** Surgical dressing holder, non-reusable, each `DME` A

C **A4463** Surgical dressing holder, reusable, each `DME` A

C **A4465** Non-elastic binder for extremity N
Service not separately priced by Part B

M **A4466** Garment, belt, sleeve or other covering, elastic or similar stretchable material, any type, each E
Service not separately priced by Part B

D **A4470** Gravlee jet washer N
Service not separately priced by Part B

D **A4480** Vabra aspirator N
Service not separately priced by Part B

D **A4481** Tracheostoma filter, any type, any size, each `DME` A

D **A4483** Moisture exchanger, disposable, for use with invasive mechanical ventilation `DME` A

M **A4490** Surgical stockings above knee length, each E
Service not separately priced by Part B
Pub: 100-2, Chap. 15, 110

M **A4495** Surgical stockings thigh length, each E
Service not separately priced by Part B
Pub: 100-2, Chap. 15, 110

M **A4500** Surgical stockings below knee length, each E
Service not separately priced by Part B
Pub: 100-2, Chap. 15, 110

M **A4510** Surgical stockings full length, each E
Service not separately priced by Part B
Pub: 100-2, Chap. 15, 110

M **A4520** Incontinence garment, any type, (e.g., brief, diaper), each E
Service not separately priced by Part B

D **A4550** Surgical trays B
Price established using national RVU's

M **A4554** Disposable underpads, all sizes E
Service not separately priced by Part B

● I **A4555** Electrode/transducer for use with electrical stimulation device used for cancer treatment, replacement only
Service not separately priced by Part B

C **A4556** Electrodes, (e.g., apnea monitor), per pair `DME` Y

C **A4557** Lead wires, (e.g., apnea monitor), per pair `DME` Y

C **A4558** Conductive gel or paste, for use with electrical device (e.g., TENS, NMES), per oz `DME` Y

C **A4559** Coupling gel or paste, for use with ultrasound device, per oz `DME` Y

C **A4561** Pessary, rubber, any type ♀ `DME` N

Pessary

C **A4562** Pessary, non rubber, any type ♀ DME N

C **A4565** Slings N
Reasonable charge

I **A4566** Shoulder sling or vest design, abduction restrainer, with or without swathe control, prefabricated, includes fitting and adjustment E
Service not separately priced by Part B

I **A4570** Splint E
Reasonable charge

M **A4575** Topical hyperbaric oxygen chamber, disposable E
Service not separately priced by Part B

I **A4580** Cast supplies (e.g., plaster) E
Service not separately priced by Part B

I **A4590** Special casting material (e.g., fiberglass) E
Service not separately priced by Part B

D **A4595** Electrical stimulator supplies, 2 lead, per month, (e.g., TENS, NMES) DME Y

C **A4600** Sleeve for intermittent limb compression device, replacement only, each Y

▲ **C** **A4601** Lithium ion battery, rechargeable, for non-prosthetic use, replacement Y

● **C** **A4602** Replacement battery for external infusion pump owned by patient, lithium, 1.5 volt, each

C **A4604** Tubing with integrated heating element for use with positive airway pressure device DME Y
DME Modifier: NU
Pub: 100-4, Chap. 23, 60.3; 100-4, Chap. 36, 50.14

C **A4605** Tracheal suction catheter, closed system, each DME Y
DME Modifier: NU

C **A4606** Oxygen probe for use with oximeter device, replacement A
Service not separately priced by Part B

C **A4608** Transtracheal oxygen catheter, each DME Y
Service not separately priced by Part B
Pub: 100-4, Chap. 23, 60.3

S **A4611** Battery, heavy duty; replacement for patient owned ventilator Y
Service not separately priced by Part B
Statute: 1834a3A

S **A4612** Battery cables; replacement for patient-owned ventilator Y
Service not separately priced by Part B
Statute: 1834a3A

S **A4613** Battery charger; replacement for patient-owned ventilator Y
Service not separately priced by Part B
Statute: 1834a3A

C **A4614** Peak expiratory flow rate meter, hand held DME Y

D **A4615** Cannula, nasal DME Y
Service not separately priced by Part B
Pub: 100-4, Chap. 20, 100.2.2; 100-4, Chap. 23, 60.3

Nasal Cannula

D **A4616** Tubing (oxygen), per foot DME Y
Service not separately priced by Part B
Pub: 100-4, Chap. 20, 100.2.2

D **A4617** Mouth piece DME Y
Service not separately priced by Part B
Pub: 100-4, Chap. 20, 100.2.2

D **A4618** Breathing circuits DME Y
DME Modifier: NU, RR, UE
Pub: 100-4, Chap. 20, 100.2.2

D **A4619** Face tent DME Y
DME Modifier: NU
Pub: 100-4, Chap. 20, 100.2.2

D **A4620** Variable concentration mask DME Y
Service not separately priced by Part B
Pub: 100-4, Chap. 20, 100.2.2; 100-4, Chap. 23, 60.3

D **A4623** Tracheostomy, inner cannula DME A

C **A4624** Tracheal suction catheter, any type other than closed system, each DME Y
DME Modifier: NU

D **A4625** Tracheostomy care kit for new tracheostomy DME A

D **A4626** Tracheostomy cleaning brush, each DME A

M **A4627** Spacer, bag or reservoir, with or without mask, for use with metered dose inhaler E
Service not separately priced by Part B
Pub: 100-2, Chap. 15, 110

C **A4628** Oropharyngeal suction catheter, each DME Y
DME Modifier: NU

D **A4629** Tracheostomy care kit for established tracheostomy DME A

D **A4630** Replacement batteries, medically necessary, transcutaneous electrical stimulator, owned by patient DME Y
DME Modifier: NU

C **A4633** Replacement bulb/lamp for ultraviolet light therapy system, each DME Y
DME Modifier: NU

▲ Revised Code   ● New code   **C** Carrier judgment   **D** Special coverage instructions apply
I Not payable by Medicare   **M** Non-covered by Medicare   **S** Non-covered by Medicare statute   AHA Coding Clinic®

C **A4634** Replacement bulb for therapeutic light box, tabletop model A

Service not separately priced by Part B

D **A4635** Underarm pad, crutch, replacement, each **DME** Y

DME Modifier: NU, RR, UE

D **A4636** Replacement, handgrip, cane, crutch, or walker, each **DME** Y

DME Modifier: NU, KE, RR, UE

Pub: 100-4, Chap. 23, 60.3; 100-4, Chap. 36, 50.15

D **A4637** Replacement, tip, cane, crutch, walker, each. **DME** Y

DME Modifier: NU, KE, RR, UE

C **A4638** Replacement battery for patient-owned ear pulse generator, each **DME** Y

DME Modifier: NU, RR, UE

C **A4639** Replacement pad for infrared heating pad system, each **DME** Y

DME Modifier: NU

D **A4640** Replacement pad for use with medically necessary alternating pressure pad owned by patient **DME** Y

DME Modifier: NU, RR, UE

C **A4641** Radiopharmaceutical, diagnostic, not otherwise classified N1 N

Pub: 100-4, Chap. 13, 60.3; 100-4, Chap. 13, 60.3.1; 100-4, Chap. 13, 60.3.2

C **A4642** Indium In-111 satumomab pendetide, diagnostic, per study dose, up to 6 millicuries N1 N

C **A4648** Tissue marker, implantable, any type, each N1 N

Other carrier priced

C **A4649** Surgical supply; miscellaneous N

C **A4650** Implantable radiation dosimeter, each N1 N

Other carrier priced

D **A4651** Calibrated microcapillary tube, each A

Reasonable charge

D **A4652** Microcapillary tube sealant A

Reasonable charge

C **A4653** Peritoneal dialysis catheter anchoring device, belt, each A

Reasonable charge

D **A4657** Syringe, with or without needle, each N

Reasonable charge

Pub: 100-4, Chap. 8, 60.4.6.3; 100-4, Chap. 8, 60.7; 100-4, Chap. 13, 60.7.1

D **A4660** Sphygmomanometer/blood pressure apparatus with cuff and stethoscope N

Reasonable charge

D **A4663** Blood pressure cuff only N

Reasonable charge

M **A4670** Automatic blood pressure monitor E

Service not separately priced by Part B

D **A4671** Disposable cycler set used with cycler dialysis machine, each B

Reasonable charge

D **A4672** Drainage extension line, sterile, for dialysis, each B

Reasonable charge

D **A4673** Extension line with easy lock connectors, used with dialysis B

Reasonable charge

D **A4674** Chemicals/antiseptics solution used to clean/ sterilize dialysis equipment, per 8 oz B

Reasonable charge

D **A4680** Activated carbon filter for hemodialysis, each N

Reasonable charge

D **A4690** Dialyzer (artificial kidneys), all types, all sizes, for hemodialysis, each N

Reasonable charge

D **A4706** Bicarbonate concentrate, solution, for hemodialysis, per gallon N

Reasonable charge

D **A4707** Bicarbonate concentrate, powder, for hemodialysis, per packet N

Reasonable charge

D **A4708** Acetate concentrate solution, for hemodialysis, per gallon N

Reasonable charge

D **A4709** Acid concentrate, solution, for hemodialysis, per gallon N

Reasonable charge

D **A4714** Treated water (deionized, distilled, or reverse osmosis) for peritoneal dialysis, per gallon N

Reasonable charge

D **A4719** "Y set" tubing for peritoneal dialysis N

Reasonable charge

D **A4720** Dialysate solution, any concentration of dextrose, fluid volume greater than 249 cc, but less than or equal to 999 cc, for peritoneal dialysis N

Reasonable charge

D **A4721** Dialysate solution, any concentration of dextrose, fluid volume greater than 999 cc but less than or equal to 1999 cc, for peritoneal dialysis N

Reasonable charge

D **A4722** Dialysate solution, any concentration of dextrose, fluid volume greater than 1999 cc but less than or equal to 2999 cc, for peritoneal dialysis N

Reasonable charge

D **A4723** Dialysate solution, any concentration of dextrose, fluid volume greater than 2999 cc but less than or equal to 3999 cc, for peritoneal dialysis N

Reasonable charge

D **A4724** Dialysate solution, any concentration of dextrose, fluid volume greater than 3999 cc but less than or equal to 4999 cc, for peritoneal dialysis   N
Reasonable charge

D **A4725** Dialysate solution, any concentration of dextrose, fluid volume greater than 4999 cc but less than or equal to 5999 cc, for peritoneal dialysis   N
Reasonable charge

D **A4726** Dialysate solution, any concentration of dextrose, fluid volume greater than 5999 cc, for peritoneal dialysis   N
Reasonable charge

C **A4728** Dialysate solution, non-dextrose containing, 500 ml   B
Reasonable charge

D **A4730** Fistula cannulation set for hemodialysis, each   N
Reasonable charge

D **A4736** Topical anesthetic, for dialysis, per gram   N
Reasonable charge

D **A4737** Injectable anesthetic, for dialysis, per 10 ml   N
Reasonable charge

D **A4740** Shunt accessory, for hemodialysis, any type, each   N
Reasonable charge

D **A4750** Blood tubing, arterial or venous, for hemodialysis, each   N
Reasonable charge

D **A4755** Blood tubing, arterial and venous combined, for hemodialysis, each   N
Reasonable charge

D **A4760** Dialysate solution test kit, for peritoneal dialysis, any type, each   N
Reasonable charge

D **A4765** Dialysate concentrate, powder, additive for peritoneal dialysis, per packet   N
Reasonable charge

D **A4766** Dialysate concentrate, solution, additive for peritoneal dialysis, per 10 ml   N
Reasonable charge

D **A4770** Blood collection tube, vacuum, for dialysis, per 50   N
Reasonable charge

D **A4771** Serum clotting time tube, for dialysis, per 50   N
Reasonable charge

D **A4772** Blood glucose test strips, for dialysis, per 50   N
Reasonable charge

D **A4773** Occult blood test strips, for dialysis, per 50   N
Reasonable charge

D **A4774** Ammonia test strips, for dialysis, per 50   N
Reasonable charge

D **A4802** Protamine sulfate, for hemodialysis, per 50 mg   N
Reasonable charge

D **A4860** Disposable catheter tips for peritoneal dialysis, per 10   N
Reasonable charge

D **A4870** Plumbing and/or electrical work for home hemodialysis equipment   N
Reasonable charge

D **A4890** Contracts, repair and maintenance, for hemodialysis equipment   N
Reasonable charge

D **A4911** Drain bag/bottle, for dialysis, each   N
Reasonable charge

D **A4913** Miscellaneous dialysis supplies, not otherwise specified   N
Reasonable charge

D **A4918** Venous pressure clamp, for hemodialysis, each   N
Reasonable charge

D **A4927** Gloves, non-sterile, per 100   N
Reasonable charge

D **A4928** Surgical mask, per 20   N
Reasonable charge

D **A4929** Tourniquet for dialysis, each   N
Reasonable charge

D **A4930** Gloves, sterile, per pair   N
Reasonable charge

C **A4931** Oral thermometer, reusable, any type, each   N
Reasonable charge

C **A4932** Rectal thermometer, reusable, any type, each   E
Service not separately priced by Part B

D **A5051** Ostomy pouch, closed; with barrier attached (1-piece), each   **DME** A

D **A5052** Ostomy pouch, closed; without barrier attached (1-piece), each   **DME** A

D **A5053** Ostomy pouch, closed; for use on faceplate, each   **DME** A

D **A5054** Ostomy pouch, closed; for use on barrier with flange (2-piece), each   **DME** A

D **A5055** Stoma cap   **DME** A

D **A5056** Ostomy pouch, drainable, with extended wear barrier attached, with filter, (1-piece), each   **DME** A

D **A5057** Ostomy pouch, drainable, with extended wear barrier attached, with built in convexity, with filter, (1-piece), each   **DME** A

C **A5061** Ostomy pouch, drainable; with barrier attached, (1-piece), each   **DME** A

D **A5062** Ostomy pouch, drainable; without barrier attached (1-piece), each   **DME** A

D **A5063** Ostomy pouch, drainable; for use on barrier with flange (2-piece system), each   **DME** A

▲ Revised Code   ● New code   **C** Carrier judgment   **D** Special coverage instructions apply
I Not payable by Medicare   **M** Non-covered by Medicare   **S** Non-covered by Medicare statute   AHA Coding Clinic®

D **A5071** Ostomy pouch, urinary; with barrier attached (1-piece), each **DME** A

D **A5072** Ostomy pouch, urinary; without barrier attached (1-piece), each **DME** A

D **A5073** Ostomy pouch, urinary; for use on barrier with flange (2-piece), each **DME** A

D **A5081** Stoma plug or seal, any type **DME** A

D **A5082** Continent device; catheter for continent stoma **DME** A

C **A5083** Continent device, stoma absorptive cover for continent stoma **DME** A

D **A5093** Ostomy accessory; convex insert **DME** A

D **A5102** Bedside drainage bottle with or without tubing, rigid or expandable, each **DME** A

D **A5105** Urinary suspensory with leg bag, with or without tube, each **DME** A

D **A5112** Urinary drainage bag, leg or abdomen, latex, with or without tube, with straps, each **DME** A

D **A5113** Leg strap; latex, replacement only, per set **DME** A

D **A5114** Leg strap; foam or fabric, replacement only, per set **DME** A

D **A5120** Skin barrier, wipes or swabs, each **DME** A
  DME Modifier: AU, AV

D **A5121** Skin barrier; solid, 6 x 6 or equivalent, each **DME** A

D **A5122** Skin barrier; solid, 8 x 8 or equivalent, each **DME** A

D **A5126** Adhesive or non-adhesive; disk or foam pad **DME** A

D **A5131** Appliance cleaner, incontinence and ostomy appliances, per 16 oz. **DME** A

D **A5200** Percutaneous catheter/tube anchoring device, adhesive skin attachment **DME** A

D **A5500** For diabetics only, fitting (including follow-up), custom preparation and supply of off-the-shelf depth-inlay shoe manufactured to accommodate multi- density insert(s), per shoe **DME** Y
  Pub: 100-2, Chap. 15, 140

D **A5501** For diabetics only, fitting (including follow-up), custom preparation and supply of shoe molded from cast(s) of patient's foot (custom molded shoe), per shoe **DME** Y
  Pub: 100-2, Chap. 15, 140

D **A5503** For diabetics only, modification (including fitting) of off-the-shelf depth-inlay shoe or custom-molded shoe with roller or rigid rocker bottom, per shoe **DME** Y
  Pub: 100-2, Chap. 15, 140

D **A5504** For diabetics only, modification (including fitting) of off-the-shelf depth-inlay shoe or custom-molded shoe with wedge(s), per shoe **DME** Y
  Pub: 100-2, Chap. 15, 140

D **A5505** For diabetics only, modification (including fitting) of off-the-shelf depth-inlay shoe or custom-molded shoe with metatarsal bar, per shoe **DME** Y
  Pub: 100-2, Chap. 15, 140

D **A5506** For diabetics only, modification (including fitting) of off-the-shelf depth-inlay shoe or custom-molded shoe with off-set heel(s), per shoe **DME** Y
  Pub: 100-2, Chap. 15, 140

D **A5507** For diabetics only, not otherwise specified modification (including fitting) of off-the-shelf depth-inlay shoe or custom-molded shoe, per shoe **DME** Y
  Pub: 100-2, Chap. 15, 140

D **A5508** For diabetics only, deluxe feature of off-the-shelf depth-inlay shoe or custom-molded shoe, per shoe Y
  Pub: 100-2, Chap. 15, 140

D **A5510** For diabetics only, direct formed, compression molded to patient's foot without external heat source, multiple-density insert(s) prefabricated, per shoe E
  Pub: 100-2, Chap. 15, 140

C **A5512** For diabetics only, multiple density insert, direct formed, molded to foot after external heat source of 230 degrees Fahrenheit or higher, total contact with patient's foot, including arch, base layer minimum of 1/4 inch material of shore a 35 durometer or 3/16 inch material of shore a 40 durometer (or higher), prefabricated, each **DME** Y

C **A5513** For diabetics only, multiple density insert, custom molded from model of patient's foot, total contact with patient's foot, including arch, base layer minimum of 3/16 inch material of shore a 35 durometer (or higher), includes arch filler and other shaping material, custom fabricated, each **DME** Y

M **A6000** Non-contact wound warming wound cover for use with the non-contact wound warming device and warming card E
  Service not separately priced by Part B

D **A6010** Collagen based wound filler, dry form, sterile, per gram of collagen **DME** A

D **A6011** Collagen based wound filler, gel/paste, per gram of collagen **DME** A

D **A6021** Collagen dressing, sterile, size 16 sq. in. or less, each **DME** A

D **A6022** Collagen dressing, sterile, size more than 16 sq. in. but less than or equal to 48 sq. in., each **DME** A

D **A6023** Collagen dressing, sterile, size more than 48 sq. in., each **DME** A

D **A6024** Collagen dressing wound filler, sterile, per 6 inches **DME** A

C **A6025** Gel sheet for dermal or epidermal application, (e.g., silicone, hydrogel, other), each E
  Service not separately priced by Part B

♂ Male only   ♀ Female only   Ⓐ Age   A2 - Z3 = ASC Payment Indicator   A - Y = APC Status Indicator
ASC = ASC Approved Procedure   **DME** Paid under the DME fee schedule   **PQRS** Physician Quality Reporting System

29

D **A6154** Wound pouch, each **DME** A

D **A6196** Alginate or other fiber gelling dressing, wound cover, sterile, pad size 16 sq. in. or less, each dressing **DME** A

D **A6197** Alginate or other fiber gelling dressing, wound cover, sterile, pad size more than 16 sq. in. but less than or equal to 48 sq. in., each dressing **DME** A

D **A6198** Alginate or other fiber gelling dressing, wound cover, sterile, pad size more than 48 sq. in., each dressing A

D **A6199** Alginate or other fiber gelling dressing, wound filler, sterile, per 6 inches **DME** A

D **A6203** Composite dressing, sterile, pad size 16 sq. in. or less, with any size adhesive border, each dressing **DME** A

D **A6204** Composite dressing, sterile, pad size more than 16 sq. in. but less than or equal to 48 sq. in., with any size adhesive border, each dressing **DME** A

D **A6205** Composite dressing, sterile, pad size more than 48 sq. in., with any size adhesive border, each dressing A

D **A6206** Contact layer, sterile, 16 sq. in. or less, each dressing A

D **A6207** Contact layer, sterile, more than 16 sq. in. but less than or equal to 48 sq. in., each dressing **DME** A

D **A6208** Contact layer, sterile, more than 48 sq. in., each dressing A

D **A6209** Foam dressing, wound cover, sterile, pad size 16 sq. in. or less, without adhesive border, each dressing **DME** A

D **A6210** Foam dressing, wound cover, sterile, pad size more than 16 sq. in. but less than or equal to 48 sq. in., without adhesive border, each dressing **DME** A

D **A6211** Foam dressing, wound cover, sterile, pad size more than 48 sq. in., without adhesive border, each dressing **DME** A

D **A6212** Foam dressing, wound cover, sterile, pad size 16 sq. in. or less, with any size adhesive border, each dressing **DME** A

D **A6213** Foam dressing, wound cover, sterile, pad size more than 16 sq. in. but less than or equal to 48 sq. in., with any size adhesive border, each dressing A

D **A6214** Foam dressing, wound cover, sterile, pad size more than 48 sq. in., with any size adhesive border, each dressing **DME** A

D **A6215** Foam dressing, wound filler, sterile, per gram A

D **A6216** Gauze, non-impregnated, non-sterile, pad size 16 sq. in. or less, without adhesive border, each dressing **DME** A

D **A6217** Gauze, non-impregnated, non-sterile, pad size more than 16 sq. in. but less than or equal to 48 sq. in., without adhesive border, each dressing **DME** A

D **A6218** Gauze, non-impregnated, non-sterile, pad size more than 48 sq. in., without adhesive border, each dressing A

D **A6219** Gauze, non-impregnated, sterile, pad size 16 sq. in. or less, with any size adhesive border, each dressing **DME** A

D **A6220** Gauze, non-impregnated, sterile, pad size more than 16 sq. in. but less than or equal to 48 sq. in., with any size adhesive border, each dressing **DME** A

D **A6221** Gauze, non-impregnated, sterile, pad size more than 48 sq. in., with any size adhesive border, each dressing A

D **A6222** Gauze, impregnated with other than water, normal saline, or hydrogel, sterile, pad size 16 sq. in. or less, without adhesive border, each dressing **DME** A

D **A6223** Gauze, impregnated with other than water, normal saline, or hydrogel, sterile, pad size more than 16 sq. in., but less than or equal to 48 sq. in., without adhesive border, each dressing **DME** A

D **A6224** Gauze, impregnated with other than water, normal saline, or hydrogel, sterile, pad size more than 48 sq. in., without adhesive border, each dressing **DME** A

D **A6228** Gauze, impregnated, water or normal saline, sterile, pad size 16 sq. in. or less, without adhesive border, each dressing A

D **A6229** Gauze, impregnated, water or normal saline, sterile, pad size more than 16 sq. in. but less than or equal to 48 sq. in., without adhesive border, each dressing **DME** A

D **A6230** Gauze, impregnated, water or normal saline, sterile, pad size more than 48 sq. in., without adhesive border, each dressing A

D **A6231** Gauze, impregnated, hydrogel, for direct wound contact, sterile, pad size 16 sq. in. or less, each dressing **DME** A

D **A6232** Gauze, impregnated, hydrogel, for direct wound contact, sterile, pad size greater than 16 sq. in., but less than or equal to 48 sq. in., each dressing **DME** A

D **A6233** Gauze, impregnated, hydrogel, for direct wound contact, sterile, pad size more than 48 sq. in., each dressing **DME** A

D **A6234** Hydrocolloid dressing, wound cover, sterile, pad size 16 sq. in. or less, without adhesive border, each dressing **DME** A

D **A6235** Hydrocolloid dressing, wound cover, sterile, pad size more than 16 sq. in. but less than or equal to 48 sq. in., without adhesive border, each dressing **DME** A

D **A6236** Hydrocolloid dressing, wound cover, sterile, pad size more than 48 sq. in., without adhesive border, each dressing **DME** A

▲ Revised Code   ● New code   **C** Carrier judgment   **D** Special coverage instructions apply
I Not payable by Medicare   **M** Non-covered by Medicare   **S** Non-covered by Medicare statute   AHA Coding Clinic®

D **A6237** Hydrocolloid dressing, wound cover, sterile, pad size 16 sq. in. or less, with any size adhesive border, each dressing `DME` A

D **A6238** Hydrocolloid dressing, wound cover, sterile, pad size more than 16 sq. in. but less than or equal to 48 sq. in., with any size adhesive border, each dressing `DME` A

D **A6239** Hydrocolloid dressing, wound cover, sterile, pad size more than 48 sq. in., with any size adhesive border, each dressing A

D **A6240** Hydrocolloid dressing, wound filler, paste, sterile, per ounce `DME` A

D **A6241** Hydrocolloid dressing, wound filler, dry form, sterile, per gram `DME` A

D **A6242** Hydrogel dressing, wound cover, sterile, pad size 16 sq. in. or less, without adhesive border, each dressing `DME` A

D **A6243** Hydrogel dressing, wound cover, sterile, pad size more than 16 sq. in. but less than or equal to 48 sq. in., without adhesive border, each dressing `DME` A

D **A6244** Hydrogel dressing, wound cover, sterile, pad size more than 48 sq. in., without adhesive border, each dressing `DME` A

D **A6245** Hydrogel dressing, wound cover, sterile, pad size 16 sq. in. or less, with any size adhesive border, each dressing `DME` A

D **A6246** Hydrogel dressing, wound cover, sterile, pad size more than 16 sq. in. but less than or equal to 48 sq. in., with any size adhesive border, each dressing `DME` A

D **A6247** Hydrogel dressing, wound cover, sterile, pad size more than 48 sq. in., with any size adhesive border, each dressing `DME` A

D **A6248** Hydrogel dressing, wound filler, gel, per fluid ounce `DME` A

D **A6250** Skin sealants, protectants, moisturizers, ointments, any type, any size A
Service not separately priced by Part B

D **A6251** Specialty absorptive dressing, wound cover, sterile, pad size 16 sq. in. or less, without adhesive border, each dressing `DME` A

D **A6252** Specialty absorptive dressing, wound cover, sterile, pad size more than 16 sq. in. but less than or equal to 48 sq. in., without adhesive border, each dressing `DME` A

D **A6253** Specialty absorptive dressing, wound cover, sterile, pad size more than 48 sq. in., without adhesive border, each dressing `DME` A

D **A6254** Specialty absorptive dressing, wound cover, sterile, pad size 16 sq. in. or less, with any size adhesive border, each dressing `DME` A

D **A6255** Specialty absorptive dressing, wound cover, sterile, pad size more than 16 sq. in. but less than or equal to 48 sq. in., with any size adhesive border, each dressing `DME` A

D **A6256** Specialty absorptive dressing, wound cover, sterile, pad size more than 48 sq. in., with any size adhesive border, each dressing A

D **A6257** Transparent film, sterile, 16 sq. in. or less, each dressing `DME` A

D **A6258** Transparent film, sterile, more than 16 sq. in. but less than or equal to 48 sq. in., each dressing `DME` A

D **A6259** Transparent film, sterile, more than 48 sq. in., each dressing `DME` A

D **A6260** Wound cleansers, any type, any size A
Service not separately priced by Part B

D **A6261** Wound filler, gel/paste, per fluid ounce, not otherwise specified A

D **A6262** Wound filler, dry form, per gram, not otherwise specified A

D **A6266** Gauze, impregnated, other than water, normal saline, or zinc paste, sterile, any width, per linear yard `DME` A

D **A6402** Gauze, non-impregnated, sterile, pad size 16 sq. in. or less, without adhesive border, each dressing `DME` A

D **A6403** Gauze, non-impregnated, sterile, pad size more than 16 sq. in. less than or equal to 48 sq. in., without adhesive border, each dressing `DME` A

D **A6404** Gauze, non-impregnated, sterile, pad size more than 48 sq. in., without adhesive border, each dressing A

C **A6407** Packing strips, non-impregnated, sterile, up to 2 inches in width, per linear yard `DME` A

D **A6410** Eye pad, sterile, each `DME` A

D **A6411** Eye pad, non-sterile, each `DME` A

C **A6412** Eye patch, occlusive, each A
Service not separately priced by Part B

S **A6413** Adhesive bandage, first-aid type, any size, each E
Service not separately priced by Part B
Statute: 1861(s)(5)

C **A6441** Padding bandage, non-elastic, non-woven/non-knitted, width greater than or equal to 3 inches and less than 5 inches, per yard `DME` A

C **A6442** Conforming bandage, non-elastic, knitted/woven, non-sterile, width less than 3 inches, per yard `DME` A

C **A6443** Conforming bandage, non-elastic, knitted/woven, non-sterile, width greater than or equal to 3 inches and less than 5 inches, per yard `DME` A

C **A6444** Conforming bandage, non-elastic, knitted/woven, non-sterile, width greater than or equal to 5 inches, per yard `DME` A

C **A6445** Conforming bandage, non-elastic, knitted/woven, sterile, width less than 3 inches, per yard `DME` A

C **A6446** Conforming bandage, non-elastic, knitted/woven, sterile, width greater than or equal to 3 inches and less than 5 inches, per yard `DME` A

♂ Male only   ♀ Female only   **A** Age   A2 - Z3 = ASC Payment Indicator   A - Y = APC Status Indicator
ASC = ASC Approved Procedure   `DME` Paid under the DME fee schedule   `PQRS` Physician Quality Reporting System

A6237 - A6446

MEDICAL AND SURGICAL SUPPLIES (A4206-A8004)

A6447 - A6541

MEDICAL AND SURGICAL SUPPLIES (A4206-A8004)

C **A6447** Conforming bandage, non-elastic, knitted/ woven, sterile, width greater than or equal to 5 inches, per yard   DME A

C **A6448** Light compression bandage, elastic, knitted/woven, width less than 3 inches, per yard   DME A

C **A6449** Light compression bandage, elastic, knitted/ woven, width greater than or equal to 3 inches and less than 5 inches, per yard   DME A

C **A6450** Light compression bandage, elastic, knitted/ woven, width greater than or equal to 5 inches, per yard   DME A

C **A6451** Moderate compression bandage, elastic, knitted/woven, load resistance of 1.25 to 1.34 foot pounds at 50% maximum stretch, width greater than or equal to 3 inches and less than 5 inches, per yard   DME A

Elastic ACE Compression Bandage

C **A6452** High compression bandage, elastic, knitted/ woven, load resistance greater than or equal to 1.35 foot pounds at 50% maximum stretch, width greater than or equal to 3 inches and less than 5 inches, per yard   DME A

C **A6453** Self-adherent bandage, elastic, non-knitted/ non-woven, width less than 3 inches, per yard   DME A

C **A6454** Self-adherent bandage, elastic, non-knitted/ non-woven, width greater than or equal to 3 inches and less than 5 inches, per yard DME A

C **A6455** Self-adherent bandage, elastic, non-knitted/ non-woven, width greater than or equal to 5 inches, per yard   DME A

C **A6456** Zinc paste impregnated bandage, non-elastic, knitted/woven, width greater than or equal to 3 inches and less than 5 inches, per yard   DME A

C **A6457** Tubular dressing with or without elastic, any width, per linear yard   DME A

D **A6501** Compression burn garment, bodysuit (head to foot), custom fabricated   DME A

D **A6502** Compression burn garment, chin strap, custom fabricated   DME A

D **A6503** Compression burn garment, facial hood, custom fabricated   DME A

D **A6504** Compression burn garment, glove to wrist, custom fabricated   DME A

D **A6505** Compression burn garment, glove to elbow, custom fabricated   DME A

D **A6506** Compression burn garment, glove to axilla, custom fabricated   DME A

D **A6507** Compression burn garment, foot to knee length, custom fabricated   DME A

D **A6508** Compression burn garment, foot to thigh length, custom fabricated   DME A

D **A6509** Compression burn garment, upper trunk to waist including arm openings (vest), custom fabricated   DME A

D **A6510** Compression burn garment, trunk, including arms down to leg openings (leotard), custom fabricated   DME A

D **A6511** Compression burn garment, lower trunk including leg openings (panty), custom fabricated   DME A

D **A6512** Compression burn garment, not otherwise classified   A

C **A6513** Compression burn mask, face and/or neck, plastic or equal, custom fabricated   DME B
Service not separately priced by Part B

M **A6530** Gradient compression stocking, below knee, 18-30 mmHg, each   E
Service not separately priced by Part B

D **A6531** Gradient compression stocking, below knee, 30-40 mmHg, each   DME A
DME Modifier: AW

D **A6532** Gradient compression stocking, below knee, 40-50 mmHg, each   DME A
DME Modifier: AW

M **A6533** Gradient compression stocking, thigh length, 18-30 mmHg, each   E
Service not separately priced by Part B

M **A6534** Gradient compression stocking, thigh length, 30-40 mmHg, each   E
Service not separately priced by Part B

M **A6535** Gradient compression stocking, thigh length, 40-50 mmHg, each   E
Service not separately priced by Part B

M **A6536** Gradient compression stocking, full length/ chap style, 18-30 mmHg, each   E
Service not separately priced by Part B

M **A6537** Gradient compression stocking, full length/ chap style, 30-40 mmHg, each   E
Service not separately priced by Part B

M **A6538** Gradient compression stocking, full length/ chap style, 40-50 mmHg, each   E
Service not separately priced by Part B

M **A6539** Gradient compression stocking, waist length, 18-30 mmHg, each   E
Service not separately priced by Part B

M **A6540** Gradient compression stocking, waist length, 30-40 mmHg, each   E
Service not separately priced by Part B

M **A6541** Gradient compression stocking, waist length, 40-50 mmHg, each   E
Service not separately priced by Part B

▲ Revised Code   ● New code   **C** Carrier judgment   **D** Special coverage instructions apply
I Not payable by Medicare   **M** Non-covered by Medicare   **S** Non-covered by Medicare statute   AHA Coding Clinic®

M **A6544** Gradient compression stocking, garter belt E
Service not separately priced by Part B

D **A6545** Gradient compression wrap, non-elastic, below knee, 30-50 mmHg, each **DME** A
DME Modifier: AW

M **A6549** Gradient compression stocking/sleeve, not otherwise specified E
Service not separately priced by Part B

C **A6550** Wound care set, for negative pressure wound therapy electrical pump, includes all supplies and accessories **DME** Y
Pub: 100-4, Chap. 23, 60.3

C **A7000** Canister, disposable, used with suction pump, each **DME** Y
DME Modifier: NU, KE
Pub: 100-4, Chap. 23, 60.3

C **A7001** Canister, non-disposable, used with suction pump, each **DME** Y
DME Modifier: NU

C **A7002** Tubing, used with suction pump, each **DME** Y
DME Modifier: NU

C **A7003** Administration set, with small volume nonfiltered pneumatic nebulizer, disposable **DME** Y
DME Modifier: NU

C **A7004** Small volume nonfiltered pneumatic nebulizer, disposable **DME** Y
DME Modifier: NU

C **A7005** Administration set, with small volume nonfiltered pneumatic nebulizer, non-disposable **DME** Y
DME Modifier: NU

C **A7006** Administration set, with small volume filtered pneumatic nebulizer **DME** Y
DME Modifier: NU

C **A7007** Large volume nebulizer, disposable, unfilled, used with aerosol compressor **DME** Y
DME Modifier: NU

C **A7008** Large volume nebulizer, disposable, prefilled, used with aerosol compressor **DME** Y
DME Modifier: NU

C **A7009** Reservoir bottle, non-disposable, used with large volume ultrasonic nebulizer **DME** Y
DME Modifier: NU

C **A7010** Corrugated tubing, disposable, used with large volume nebulizer, 100 feet **DME** Y
DME Modifier: NU

C **A7011** Corrugated tubing, non-disposable, used with large volume nebulizer, 10 feet Y

C **A7012** Water collection device, used with large volume nebulizer **DME** Y
DME Modifier: NU

C **A7013** Filter, disposable, used with aerosol compressor or ultrasonic generator **DME** Y
DME Modifier: NU

C **A7014** Filter, nondisposable, used with aerosol compressor or ultrasonic generator **DME** Y
DME Modifier: NU

C **A7015** Aerosol mask, used with DME nebulizer **DME** Y
DME Modifier: NU

C **A7016** Dome and mouthpiece, used with small volume ultrasonic nebulizer **DME** Y
DME Modifier: NU

D **A7017** Nebulizer, durable, glass or autoclavable plastic, bottle type, not used with oxygen **DME** Y
DME Modifier: NU, RR, UE

C **A7018** Water, distilled, used with large volume nebulizer, 1000 ml **DME** Y

C **A7020** Interface for cough stimulating device, includes all components, replacement only **DME** Y
DME Modifier: NU

C **A7025** High frequency chest wall oscillation system vest, replacement for use with patient owned equipment, each **DME** Y
DME Modifier: NU

C **A7026** High frequency chest wall oscillation system hose, replacement for use with patient owned equipment, each **DME** Y
DME Modifier: NU

C **A7027** Combination oral/nasal mask, used with continuous positive airway pressure device, each **DME** Y
DME Modifier: NU

C **A7028** Oral cushion for combination oral/nasal mask, replacement only, each **DME** Y
DME Modifier: NU

C **A7029** Nasal pillows for combination oral/nasal mask, replacement only, pair **DME** Y
DME Modifier: NU

C **A7030** Full face mask used with positive airway pressure device, each **DME** Y
DME Modifier: NU
Pub: 100-4, Chap. 23, 60.3; 100-4, Chap. 36, 50.14

C **A7031** Face mask interface, replacement for full face mask, each **DME** Y
DME Modifier: NU

C **A7032** Cushion for use on nasal mask interface, replacement only, each **DME** Y
DME Modifier: NU

C **A7033** Pillow for use on nasal cannula type interface, replacement only, pair **DME** Y
DME Modifier: NU

C **A7034** Nasal interface (mask or cannula type) used with positive airway pressure device, with or without head strap **DME** Y
DME Modifier: NU

♂ Male only   ♀ Female only   **A** Age   A2 - Z3 = ASC Payment Indicator   A - Y = APC Status Indicator
ASC = ASC Approved Procedure   **DME** Paid under the DME fee schedule   **PQRS** Physician Quality Reporting System

A7035 - A8004

MEDICAL AND SURGICAL SUPPLIES (A4206-A8004)

C **A7035** Headgear used with positive airway pressure device   DME Y
DME Modifier: NU

C **A7036** Chinstrap used with positive airway pressure device   DME Y
DME Modifier: NU

C **A7037** Tubing used with positive airway pressure device   DME Y
DME Modifier: NU

C **A7038** Filter, disposable, used with positive airway pressure device   DME Y
DME Modifier: NU

C **A7039** Filter, non disposable, used with positive airway pressure device   DME Y
DME Modifier: NU

C **A7040** One way chest drain valve   DME A

C **A7041** Water seal drainage container and tubing for use with implanted chest tube   DME A

C **A7044** Oral interface used with positive airway pressure device, each   DME Y
DME Modifier: NU

D **A7045** Exhalation port with or without swivel used with accessories for positive airway devices, replacement only   DME Y
DME Modifier: NU, RR, UE

D **A7046** Water chamber for humidifier, used with positive airway pressure device, replacement, each   DME Y
DME Modifier: NU

C **A7047** Oral interface used with respiratory suction pump, each   DME
DME Modifier: NU

● C **A7048** Vacuum drainage collection unit and tubing kit, including all supplies needed for collection unit change, for use with implanted catheter, each

D **A7501** Tracheostoma valve, including diaphragm, each   DME A

D **A7502** Replacement diaphragm/faceplate for tracheostoma valve, each   DME A

D **A7503** Filter holder or filter cap, reusable, for use in a tracheostoma heat and moisture exchange system, each   DME A

D **A7504** Filter for use in a tracheostoma heat and moisture exchange system, each   DME A

D **A7505** Housing, reusable without adhesive, for use in a heat and moisture exchange system and/or with a tracheostoma valve, each   DME A

D **A7506** Adhesive disc for use in a heat and moisture exchange system and/or with tracheostoma valve, any type each   DME A

D **A7507** Filter holder and integrated filter without adhesive, for use in a tracheostoma heat and moisture exchange system, each   DME A

D **A7508** Housing and integrated adhesive, for use in a tracheostoma heat and moisture exchange system and/or with a tracheostoma valve, each   DME A

D **A7509** Filter holder and integrated filter housing, and adhesive, for use as a tracheostoma heat and moisture exchange system, each   DME A

C **A7520** Tracheostomy/laryngectomy tube, non-cuffed, polyvinylchloride (PVC), silicone or equal, each   DME A
Pub: 100-2, Chap. 1, 40

C **A7521** Tracheostomy/laryngectomy tube, cuffed, polyvinylchloride (PVC), silicone or equal, each   DME A
Pub: 100-2, Chap. 1, 40

C **A7522** Tracheostomy/laryngectomy tube, stainless steel or equal (sterilizable and reusable), each   DME A
Pub: 100-2, Chap. 1, 40

C **A7523** Tracheostomy shower protector, each   A

C **A7524** Tracheostoma stent/stud/button, each   DME A

C **A7525** Tracheostomy mask, each   DME A

C **A7526** Tracheostomy tube collar/holder, each   DME A

C **A7527** Tracheostomy/laryngectomy tube plug/stop, each   DME A

C **A8000** Helmet, protective, soft, prefabricated, includes all components and accessories   DME Y
DME Modifier: NU, RR, UE

C **A8001** Helmet, protective, hard, prefabricated, includes all components and accessories   DME Y
DME Modifier: NU, RR, UE

C **A8002** Helmet, protective, soft, custom fabricated, includes all components and accessories   DME Y
DME Modifier: NU, RR, UE

C **A8003** Helmet, protective, hard, custom fabricated, includes all components and accessories   DME Y
DME Modifier: NU, RR, UE

C **A8004** Soft interface for helmet, replacement only   DME Y
DME Modifier: NU, RR, UE

ADMINISTRATIVE, MISCELLANEOUS AND INVESTIGATIONAL (A9150-A9999)

D **A9150** Non-prescription drugs   B
Other carrier priced

I **A9152** Single vitamin/mineral/trace element, oral, per dose, not otherwise specified   E
Service not separately priced by Part B

I **A9153** Multiple vitamins, with or without minerals and trace elements, oral, per dose, not otherwise specified   E
Service not separately priced by Part B

C **A9155** Artificial saliva, 30 ml   B
Other carrier priced

I **A9180** Pediculosis (lice infestation) treatment, topical, for administration by patient/caretaker   E
Service not separately priced by Part B

M **A9270** Non-covered item or service   E
Service not separately priced by Part B
Pub: 100-4, Chap. 11, 100.1

S **A9272** Wound suction, disposable, includes dressing, all accessories and components, any type, each   E
Service not separately priced by Part B

M **A9273** Hot water bottle, ice cap or collar, heat and/or cold wrap, any type   Y
Service not separately priced by Part B

S **A9274** External ambulatory insulin delivery system, disposable, each, includes all supplies and accessories   E
Service not separately priced by Part B

M **A9275** Home glucose disposable monitor, includes test strips   E
Service not separately priced by Part B

S **A9276** Sensor; invasive (e.g., subcutaneous), disposable, for use with interstitial continuous glucose monitoring system, one unit = 1 day supply   E
Service not separately priced by Part B
Statute: 1861(n)

S **A9277** Transmitter; external, for use with interstitial continuous glucose monitoring system   E
Service not separately priced by Part B
Statute: 1861(n)

S **A9278** Receiver (monitor); external, for use with interstitial continuous glucose monitoring system   E
Service not separately priced by Part B
Statute: 1861(n)

S **A9279** Monitoring feature/device, stand-alone or integrated, any type, includes all accessories, components and electronics, not otherwise classified   E
Service not separately priced by Part B

S **A9280** Alert or alarm device, not otherwise classified   E
Service not separately priced by Part B
Statute: 1861

S **A9281** Reaching/grabbing device, any type, any length, each   E
Service not separately priced by Part B
Statute: 1862 SSA

S **A9282** Wig, any type, each   E
Service not separately priced by Part B
Statute: 1861SSA

S **A9283** Foot pressure off loading/supportive device, any type, each   E
Service not separately priced by Part B
Statute: 1862a(i)13

D **A9284** Spirometer, non-electronic, includes all accessories   N
Service not separately priced by Part B

M **A9300** Exercise equipment   E
Service not separately priced by Part B

C **A9500** Technetium Tc-99m sestamibi, diagnostic, per study dose   N1   N
Other carrier priced
Coding Clinic 2006, Q2, P5

C **A9501** Technetium Tc-99m teboroxime, diagnostic, per study dose   N1   N
Other carrier priced

C **A9502** Technetium Tc-99m tetrofosmin, diagnostic, per study dose   N1   N
Other carrier priced
Coding Clinic 2006, Q2, P5

C **A9503** Technetium Tc-99m medronate, diagnostic, per study dose, up to 30 millicuries   N1   N
Other carrier priced

C **A9504** Technetium Tc-99m apcitide, diagnostic, per study dose, up to 20 millicuries   N1   N
Other carrier priced

C **A9505** Thallium Tl-201 thallous chloride, diagnostic, per millicurie   N1   N
Other carrier priced

C **A9507** Indium In-111 capromab pendetide, diagnostic, per study dose, up to 10 millicuries   N1   N
Other carrier priced

C **A9508** Iodine I-131 iobenguane sulfate, diagnostic, per 0.5 millicurie   N1   N

C **A9509** Iodine I-123 sodium iodide, diagnostic, per millicurie   N1   N
Other carrier priced

C **A9510** Technetium Tc-99m disofenin, diagnostic, per study dose, up to 15 millicuries   N1   N

C **A9512** Technetium Tc-99m pertechnetate, diagnostic, per millicurie   N1   N
Other carrier priced

C **A9516** Iodine I-123 sodium iodide, diagnostic, per 100 microcuries, up to 999 microcuries   N1   N
Other carrier priced

♂ Male only   ♀ Female only   **A** Age   A2 - Z3 = ASC Payment Indicator   A - Y = APC Status Indicator
ASC = ASC Approved Procedure   **DME** Paid under the DME fee schedule   **PQRS** Physician Quality Reporting System

C **A9517** Iodine I-131 sodium iodide capsule(s), therapeutic, per millicurie   K

Other carrier priced   Drugs: SODIUM IODIDE I 131 CAPSULE

C **A9520** Technetium Tc-99m, tilmanocept, diagnostic, up to 0.5 millicuries   K2 ASC

Other carrier priced   Drugs: LYMPHOSEEK KIT

C **A9521** Technetium Tc-99m exametazime, diagnostic, per study dose, up to 25 millicuries   N1 N

Other carrier priced

C **A9524** Iodine I-131 iodinated serum albumin, diagnostic, per 5 microcuries   N1 N

Other carrier priced

C **A9526** Nitrogen N-13 ammonia, diagnostic, per study dose, up to 40 millicuries   N1 N

Pub: 100-4, Chap. 13, 60.3; 100-4, Chap. 13, 60.3.1; 100-4, Chap. 13, 60.3.2

C **A9527** Iodine I-125, sodium iodide solution, therapeutic, per millicurie   H2 ASC U

Other carrier priced

C **A9528** Iodine I-131 sodium iodide capsule(s), diagnostic, per millicurie   N1 N

Other carrier priced

C **A9529** Iodine I-131 sodium iodide solution, diagnostic, per millicurie   N1 N

Other carrier priced

C **A9530** Iodine I-131 sodium iodide solution, therapeutic, per millicurie   K

Other carrier priced

C **A9531** Iodine I-131 sodium iodide, diagnostic, per microcurie (up to 100 microcuries)   N1 N

Other carrier priced

C **A9532** Iodine I-125 serum albumin, diagnostic, per 5 microcuries   N1 N

Other carrier priced

C **A9536** Technetium Tc-99m depreotide, diagnostic, per study dose, up to 35 millicuries   N1 N

Other carrier priced

C **A9537** Technetium Tc-99m mebrofenin, diagnostic, per study dose, up to 15 millicuries   N1 N

Other carrier priced

C **A9538** Technetium Tc-99m pyrophosphate, diagnostic, per study dose, up to 25 millicuries   N1 N

Other carrier priced

C **A9539** Technetium Tc-99m pentetate, diagnostic, per study dose, up to 25 millicuries   N1 N

Other carrier priced

C **A9540** Technetium Tc-99m macroaggregated albumin, diagnostic, per study dose, up to 10 millicuries   N1 N

Other carrier priced

C **A9541** Technetium Tc-99m sulfur colloid, diagnostic, per study dose, up to 20 millicuries   N1 N

Other carrier priced

C **A9542** Indium In-111 ibritumomab tiuxetan, diagnostic, per study dose, up to 5 millicuries   N1 N

C **A9543** Yttrium Y-90 ibritumomab tiuxetan, therapeutic, per treatment dose, up to 40 millicuries   K

Drugs: ZEVALIN Y-90

C **A9544** Iodine I-131 tositumomab, diagnostic, per study dose   N1 N

Other carrier priced

C **A9545** Iodine I-131 tositumomab, therapeutic, per treatment dose   K

Other carrier priced   Drugs: BEXXAR

C **A9546** Cobalt Co-57/58, cyanocobalamin, diagnostic, per study dose, up to 1 microcurie   N1 N

C **A9547** Indium In-111 oxyquinoline, diagnostic, per 0.5 millicurie   N1 N

C **A9548** Indium In-111 pentetate, diagnostic, per 0.5 millicurie   N1 N

C **A9550** Technetium Tc-99m sodium gluceptate, diagnostic, per study dose, up to 25 millicurie   N1 N

C **A9551** Technetium Tc-99m succimer, diagnostic, per study dose, up to 10 millicuries   N1 N

C **A9552** Fluorodeoxyglucose F-18 FDG, diagnostic, per study dose, up to 45 millicuries   N1 N

Coding Clinic 2008, Q3, P7

Pub: 100-3, Chap. 1, Part-4, 220.6.17; 100-4, Chap. 13, 60.3.2

C **A9553** Chromium Cr-51 sodium chromate, diagnostic, per study dose, up to 250 microcuries   N1 N

C **A9554** Iodine I-125 sodium iothalamate, diagnostic, per study dose, up to 10 microcuries   N1 N

C **A9555** Rubidium Rb-82, diagnostic, per study dose, up to 60 millicuries   N1 N

Value not established

Pub: 100-3, Chap. 1, Part-4, 220.6.1; 100-4, Chap. 13, 60.3.2

C **A9556** Gallium Ga-67 citrate, diagnostic, per millicurie   N1 N

Other carrier priced

C **A9557** Technetium Tc-99m bicisate, diagnostic, per study dose, up to 25 millicuries   N1 N

Other carrier priced

C **A9558** Xenon Xe-133 gas, diagnostic, per 10 millicuries   N1 N

Other carrier priced

C **A9559** Cobalt Co-57 cyanocobalamin, oral, diagnostic, per study dose, up to 1 microcurie   N1 N

Other carrier priced

C **A9560** Technetium Tc-99m labeled red blood cells, diagnostic, per study dose, up to 30 millicuries   N1 N

Other carrier priced

Coding Clinic 2008, Q3, P7

▲ Revised Code   ● New code   C Carrier judgment   D Special coverage instructions apply

I Not payable by Medicare   M Non-covered by Medicare   S Non-covered by Medicare statute   AHA Coding Clinic®

C **A9561** Technetium Tc-99m oxidronate, diagnostic, per study dose, up to 30 millicuries   N1 N
Other carrier priced

C **A9562** Technetium Tc-99m mertiatide, diagnostic, per study dose, up to 15 millicuries   N1 N
Other carrier priced

C **A9563** Sodium phosphate P-32, therapeutic, per millicurie   K
Other carrier priced

C **A9564** Chromic phosphate P-32 suspension, therapeutic, per millicurie   K
Other carrier priced

C **A9566** Technetium Tc-99m fanolesomab, diagnostic, per study dose, up to 25 millicuries   N1 N
Other carrier priced

C **A9567** Technetium Tc-99m pentetate, diagnostic, aerosol, per study dose, up to 75 millicuries   N1 N
Other carrier priced

C **A9568** Technetium Tc-99m arcitumomab, diagnostic, per study dose, up to 45 millicuries   N1 N

C **A9569** Technetium Tc-99m exametazime labeled autologous white blood cells, diagnostic, per study dose   N1 N
Other carrier priced

C **A9570** Indium In-111 labeled autologous white blood cells, diagnostic, per study dose   N1 N
Other carrier priced

C **A9571** Indium In-111 labeled autologous platelets, diagnostic, per study dose   N1 N
Other carrier priced

C **A9572** Indium In-111 pentetreotide, diagnostic, per study dose, up to 6 millicuries   N1 N
Other carrier priced

C **A9575** Injection, gadoterate meglumine, 0.1 ml   N1
Other carrier priced

C **A9576** Injection, gadoteridol, (ProHance multipack), per ml   N1 N
Drugs: PROHANCE MULTIPACK

C **A9577** Injection, gadobenate dimeglumine (MultiHance), per ml   N1 N
Drugs: MULTIHANCE, MULTIHANCE 5X15 ML SYRINGE

C **A9578** Injection, gadobenate dimeglumine (MultiHance multipack), per ml   N1 N
Drugs: MULTIHANCE MULTIPACK

C **A9579** Injection, gadolinium-based magnetic resonance contrast agent, not otherwise specified (NOS), per ml   N1 N
Drugs: OPTIMARK, PROHANCE, PROHANCE PREFILLED SYRINGES, OMNISCAN, NOVAPLUS® OMNISCAN, MAGNEVIST 46.9%, MAGNEVIST 15ML RFID, MAGNEVIST 20MLRFID

C **A9580** Sodium fluoride F-18, diagnostic, per study dose, up to 30 millicuries   N1 N
Other carrier priced

Pub: 100-3, Chap. 1, Part-4, 220.6.19; 100-4, Chap. 13, 60.3.2

C **A9581** Injection, gadoxetate disodium, 1 ml   N1 N
Drugs: GADOXETATE DISODIUM, EOVIST

C **A9582** Iodine I-123 iobenguane, diagnostic, per study dose, up to 15 millicuries   N1 N

C **A9583** Injection, gadofosveset trisodium, 1 ml   N1 N
Drugs: ABLAVAR

C **A9584** Iodine 1-123 ioflupane, diagnostic, per study dose, up to 5 millicuries   N1 G
Other carrier priced

C **A9585** Injection, gadobutrol, 0.1 ml   N1 N
Other carrier priced Drugs: GADAVIST

D **A9586** Florbetapir F18, diagnostic, per study dose, up to 10 millicuries   N1 E
Service not separately priced by Part B

D **A9599** Radiopharmaceutical, diagnostic, for beta-amyloid positron emission tomography (PET) imaging, per study dose   N1
Other carrier priced

C **A9600** Strontium Sr-89 chloride, therapeutic, per millicurie   K
Other carrier priced Drugs: METASTRON

C **A9604** Samarium Sm-153 lexidronam, therapeutic, per treatment dose, up to 150 millicuries   K
Other carrier priced Drugs: QUADRAMET

● C **A9606** Radium Ra-223 dichloride, therapeutic, per microcurie

D **A9698** Non-radioactive contrast imaging material, not otherwise classified, per study   N1 N

C **A9699** Radiopharmaceutical, therapeutic, not otherwise classified   N
Other carrier priced

D **A9700** Supply of injectable contrast material for use in echocardiography, per study   N
Other carrier priced

C **A9900** Miscellaneous DME supply, accessory, and/or service component of another HCPCS code   Y

C **A9901** DME delivery, set up, and/or dispensing service component of another HCPCS code   A

C **A9999** Miscellaneous DME supply or accessory, not otherwise specified   Y

♂ Male only   ♀ Female only   Ⓐ Age   A2 - Z3 = ASC Payment Indicator   A - Y = APC Status Indicator
ASC = ASC Approved Procedure   **DME** Paid under the DME fee schedule   **PQRS** Physician Quality Reporting System

ENTERAL AND PARENTERAL THERAPY (B4034-B9999)

[D] **B4034** Enteral feeding supply kit; syringe fed, per day, includes but not limited to feeding/flushing syringe, administration set tubing, dressings, tape   Y
Pub: 100-4, Chap. 23, 60.3

[D] **B4035** Enteral feeding supply kit; pump fed, per day, includes but not limited to feeding/flushing syringe, administration set tubing, dressings, tape   Y

[D] **B4036** Enteral feeding supply kit; gravity fed, per day, includes but not limited to feeding/flushing syringe, administration set tubing, dressings, tape   Y

[D] **B4081** Nasogastric tubing with stylet   Y
Pub: 100-4, Chap. 23, 60.3

[D] **B4082** Nasogastric tubing without stylet   Y

[D] **B4083** Stomach tube - Levine type   Y

[C] **B4087** Gastrostomy/jejunostomy tube, standard, any material, any type, each   A

[C] **B4088** Gastrostomy/jejunostomy tube, low-profile, any material, any type, each   A

[M] **B4100** Food thickener, administered orally, per ounce   E
Service not separately priced by Part B

[D] **B4102** Enteral formula, for adults, used to replace fluids and electrolytes (e.g., clear liquids), 500 ml = 1 unit   ◉ Y

[D] **B4103** Enteral formula, for pediatrics, used to replace fluids and electrolytes (e.g., clear liquids), 500 ml = 1 unit   ◉ Y

[D] **B4104** Additive for enteral formula (e.g., fiber)   E
Service not separately priced by Part B

[D] **B4149** Enteral formula, manufactured blenderized natural foods with intact nutrients, includes proteins, fats, carbohydrates, vitamins and minerals, may include fiber, administered through an enteral feeding tube, 100 calories = 1 unit   Y
Pub: 100-4, Chap. 23, 60.3

[D] **B4150** Enteral formula, nutritionally complete with intact nutrients, includes proteins, fats, carbohydrates, vitamins and minerals, may include fiber, administered through an enteral feeding tube, 100 calories = 1 unit   Y

[D] **B4152** Enteral formula, nutritionally complete, calorically dense (equal to or greater than 1.5 kcal/ml) with intact nutrients, includes proteins, fats, carbohydrates, vitamins and minerals, may include fiber, administered through an enteral feeding tube, 100 calories = 1 unit   Y

[D] **B4153** Enteral formula, nutritionally complete, hydrolyzed proteins (amino acids and peptide chain), includes fats, carbohydrates, vitamins and minerals, may include fiber, administered through an enteral feeding tube, 100 calories = 1 unit   Y

[D] **B4154** Enteral formula, nutritionally complete, for special metabolic needs, excludes inherited disease of metabolism, includes altered composition of proteins, fats, carbohydrates, vitamins and/or minerals, may include fiber, administered through an enteral feeding tube, 100 calories = 1 unit   Y

[D] **B4155** Enteral formula, nutritionally incomplete/modular nutrients, includes specific nutrients, carbohydrates (e.g., glucose polymers), proteins/amino acids (e.g., glutamine, arginine), fat (e.g., medium chain triglycerides) or combination, administered through an enteral feeding tube, 100 calories = 1 unit   Y

[D] **B4157** Enteral formula, nutritionally complete, for special metabolic needs for inherited disease of metabolism, includes proteins, fats, carbohydrates, vitamins and minerals, may include fiber, administered through an enteral feeding tube, 100 calories = 1 unit   Y

[D] **B4158** Enteral formula, for pediatrics, nutritionally complete with intact nutrients, includes proteins, fats, carbohydrates, vitamins and minerals, may include fiber and/or iron, administered through an enteral feeding tube, 100 calories = 1 unit   ◉ Y

[D] **B4159** Enteral formula, for pediatrics, nutritionally complete soy based with intact nutrients, includes proteins, fats, carbohydrates, vitamins and minerals, may include fiber and/or iron, administered through an enteral feeding tube, 100 calories = 1 unit   ◉ Y

[D] **B4160** Enteral formula, for pediatrics, nutritionally complete calorically dense (equal to or greater than 0.7 kcal/ml) with intact nutrients, includes proteins, fats, carbohydrates, vitamins and minerals, may include fiber, administered through an enteral feeding tube, 100 calories = 1 unit   ◉ Y

[D] **B4161** Enteral formula, for pediatrics, hydrolyzed/amino acids and peptide chain proteins, includes fats, carbohydrates, vitamins and minerals, may include fiber, administered through an enteral feeding tube, 100 calories = 1 unit   ◉ Y

[D] **B4162** Enteral formula, for pediatrics, special metabolic needs for inherited disease of metabolism, includes proteins, fats, carbohydrates, vitamins and minerals, may include fiber, administered through an enteral feeding tube, 100 calories = 1 unit   ◉ Y

[D] **B4164** Parenteral nutrition solution: carbohydrates (dextrose), 50% or less (500 ml = 1 unit) - homemix   Y

[D] **B4168** Parenteral nutrition solution; amino acid, 3.5%, (500 ml = 1 unit) - homemix   Y

▲ Revised Code   ● New code   [C] Carrier judgment   [D] Special coverage instructions apply
[I] Not payable by Medicare   [M] Non-covered by Medicare   [S] Non-covered by Medicare statute   AHA Coding Clinic®

D **B4172** Parenteral nutrition solution; amino acid, 5.5% through 7%, (500 ml = 1 unit) - homemix   Y

D **B4176** Parenteral nutrition solution; amino acid, 7% through 8.5%, (500 ml = 1 unit) - homemix   Y

D **B4178** Parenteral nutrition solution: amino acid, greater than 8.5% (500 ml = 1 unit) - homemix   Y

D **B4180** Parenteral nutrition solution; carbohydrates (dextrose), greater than 50% (500 ml=1 unit) - homemix   Y

D **B4185** Parenteral nutrition solution, per 10 grams lipids   B

D **B4189** Parenteral nutrition solution; compounded amino acid and carbohydrates with electrolytes, trace elements, and vitamins, including preparation, any strength, 10 to 51 grams of protein - premix   Y

D **B4193** Parenteral nutrition solution; compounded amino acid and carbohydrates with electrolytes, trace elements, and vitamins, including preparation, any strength, 52 to 73 grams of protein - premix   Y

D **B4197** Parenteral nutrition solution; compounded amino acid and carbohydrates with electrolytes, trace elements and vitamins, including preparation, any strength, 74 to 100 grams of protein - premix   Y

D **B4199** Parenteral nutrition solution; compounded amino acid and carbohydrates with electrolytes, trace elements and vitamins, including preparation, any strength, over 100 grams of protein - premix   Y

D **B4216** Parenteral nutrition; additives (vitamins, trace elements, heparin, electrolytes) homemix per day   Y

D **B4220** Parenteral nutrition supply kit; premix, per day   Y

D **B4222** Parenteral nutrition supply kit; home mix, per day   Y

D **B4224** Parenteral nutrition administration kit, per day   Y

D **B5000** Parenteral nutrition solution: compounded amino acid and carbohydrates with electrolytes, trace elements, and vitamins, including preparation, any strength, renal - Amirosyn RF, NephrAmine, RenAmine - premix   Y

D **B5100** Parenteral nutrition solution: compounded amino acid and carbohydrates with electrolytes, trace elements, and vitamins, including preparation, any strength, hepatic - FreAmine HBC, HepAtamine - premix   Y

D **B5200** Parenteral nutrition solution: compounded amino acid and carbohydrates with electrolytes, trace elements, and vitamins, including preparation, any strength, stress - branch chain amino acids - premix   Y

D **B9000** Enteral nutrition infusion pump - without alarm   Y
Pub: 100-4, Chap. 23, 60.3

D **B9002** Enteral nutrition infusion pump - with alarm   Y

D **B9004** Parenteral nutrition infusion pump, portable   Y

D **B9006** Parenteral nutrition infusion pump, stationary   Y

D **B9998** NOC for enteral supplies   Y
Other carrier priced

D **B9999** NOC for parenteral supplies   Y
Other carrier priced

OUTPATIENT PPS (C1300-C9800)

D **C1713** Anchor/screw for opposing bone-to-bone or soft tissue-to-bone (implantable) N1 N
Statute: 1833(T)
Coding Clinic 2005, Q2, P3

D **C1714** Catheter, transluminal atherectomy, directional N1 N
Statute: 1833(T)

D **C1715** Brachytherapy needle N1 N
Statute: 1833(T)

D **C1716** Brachytherapy source, non-stranded, gold-198, per source H2 ASC U
Statute: 1833(T)

D **C1717** Brachytherapy source, non-stranded, high dose rate iridium-192, per source H2 ASC U
Statute: 1833(T)

D **C1719** Brachytherapy source, non-stranded, non-high dose rate iridium-192, per source H2 ASC U
Statute: 1833(T)

D **C1721** Cardioverter-defibrillator, dual chamber (implantable) N1 N
Statute: 1833(T)
Pub: 100-4, Chap. 14, 40.8

D **C1722** Cardioverter-defibrillator, single chamber (implantable) N1 N
Statute: 1833(T)
Coding Clinic 2006, Q2, P9

D **C1724** Catheter, transluminal atherectomy, rotational N1 N
Statute: 1833(T)

D **C1725** Catheter, transluminal angioplasty, non-laser (may include guidance, infusion/perfusion capability) N1 N
Statute: 1833(T)

D **C1726** Catheter, balloon dilatation, non-vascular N1 N
Statute: 1833(T)

Balloon Catheter

D **C1727** Catheter, balloon tissue dissector, non-vascular (insertable) N1 N
Statute: 1833(T)

D **C1728** Catheter, brachytherapy seed administration N1 N
Statute: 1833(T)

D **C1729** Catheter, drainage N1 N
Statute: 1833(T)

D **C1730** Catheter, electrophysiology, diagnostic, other than 3D mapping (19 or fewer electrodes) N1 N
Statute: 1833(T)

D **C1731** Catheter, electrophysiology, diagnostic, other than 3D mapping (20 or more electrodes) N1 N
Statute: 1833(T)

D **C1732** Catheter, electrophysiology, diagnostic/ablation, 3D or vector mapping N1 N
Statute: 1833(T)

D **C1733** Catheter, electrophysiology, diagnostic/ablation, other than 3D or vector mapping, other than cool-tip N1 N
Statute: 1833(T)

D **C1749** Endoscope, retrograde imaging/illumination colonoscope device (implantable) N1 N
Statute: 1833(t)

D **C1750** Catheter, hemodialysis/peritoneal, long-term N1 N
Statute: 1833(T)

D **C1751** Catheter, infusion, inserted peripherally, centrally or midline (other than hemodialysis) N1 N
Statute: 1833(T)

D **C1752** Catheter, hemodialysis/peritoneal, short-term N1 N
Statute: 1833(T)

D **C1753** Catheter, intravascular ultrasound N1 N
Statute: 1833(T)

D **C1754** Catheter, intradiscal N1 N
Statute: 1833(T)

D **C1755** Catheter, intraspinal N1 N
Statute: 1833(T)

D **C1756** Catheter, pacing, transesophageal N1 N
Statute: 1833(T)

D **C1757** Catheter, thrombectomy/embolectomy N1 N
Statute: 1833(T)

D **C1758** Catheter, ureteral N1 N
Statute: 1833(T)

D **C1759** Catheter, intracardiac echocardiography N1 N
Statute: 1833(T)

D **C1760** Closure device, vascular (implantable/insertable) N1 N
Statute: 1833(T)

D **C1762** Connective tissue, human (includes fascia lata) N1 N
Statute: 1833(T)
Coding Clinic 2003, Q3, P12

▲ Revised Code   ● New code   C Carrier judgment   D Special coverage instructions apply
I Not payable by Medicare   M Non-covered by Medicare   S Non-covered by Medicare statute   AHA Coding Clinic®

D **C1763** Connective tissue, non-human (includes synthetic) N1 N

Statute: 1833(T)

Coding Clinic 2010, Q4, P3, QZ, P3;2003, Q3, P12

D **C1764** Event recorder, cardiac (implantable) N1 N

Statute: 1833(T)

Pub: 100-4, Chap. 14, 40.8

D **C1765** Adhesion barrier N1 N

Statute: 1833(T)

D **C1766** Introducer/sheath, guiding, intracardiac electrophysiological, steerable, other than peel-away N1 N

Statute: 1833(T)

D **C1767** Generator, neurostimulator (implantable), non-rechargeable N1 N

Statute: 1833(T)

Coding Clinic 2007, Q1, P8

Pub: 100-4, Chap. 14, 40.8; 100-4, Chap. 32, 40.1

D **C1768** Graft, vascular N1 N

Statute: 1833(T)

D **C1769** Guide wire N1 N

Statute: 1833(T)

Coding Clinic 2007, Q2, P7-8

D **C1770** Imaging coil, magnetic resonance (insertable) N1 N

Statute: 1833(T)

D **C1771** Repair device, urinary, incontinence, with sling graft N1 N

Statute: 1833(T)

Coding Clinic 2008, Q3, P7

Pub: 100-4, Chap. 14, 40.8

D **C1772** Infusion pump, programmable (implantable) N1 N

Statute: 1833(T)

D **C1773** Retrieval device, insertable (used to retrieve fractured medical devices) N1 N

Statute: 1833(T)

D **C1776** Joint device (implantable) N1 N

Statute: 1833(T)

Coding Clinic 2010, Q3, P6;2008, Q4, P10

Pub: 100-4, Chap. 14, 40.8

D **C1777** Lead, cardioverter-defibrillator, endocardial single coil (implantable) N1 N

Statute: 1833(T)

Coding Clinic 2006, Q2, P9

D **C1778** Lead, neurostimulator (implantable) N1 N

Statute: 1833(T)

Coding Clinic 2007, Q1, P8

Pub: 100-4, Chap. 14, 40.8; 100-4, Chap. 32, 40.1

D **C1779** Lead, pacemaker, transvenous VDD single pass N1 N

Statute: 1833(T)

D **C1780** Lens, intraocular (new technology) N1 N

Statute: 1833(T)

D **C1781** Mesh (implantable) N1 N

Statute: 1833(T)

Coding Clinic 2012, Q2, P3;2010, Q2, P2-3

D **C1782** Morcellator N1 N

Statute: 1833(T)

D **C1783** Ocular implant, aqueous drainage assist device N1 N

Statute: 1833(T)

D **C1784** Ocular device, intraoperative, detached retina N1 N

Statute: 1833(T)

D **C1785** Pacemaker, dual chamber, rate-responsive (implantable) N1 N

Statute: 1833(T)

Pub: 100-4, Chap. 14, 40.8

D **C1786** Pacemaker, single chamber, rate-responsive (implantable) N1 N

Statute: 1833(T)

Pub: 100-2, Chap. 1, 40

Pacemaker Insertion

Single chamber

Dual chamber

Biventricular

D **C1787** Patient programmer, neurostimulator N1 N

Statute: 1833(T)

D **C1788** Port, indwelling (implantable) N1 N

Statute: 1833(T)

D **C1789** Prosthesis, breast (implantable) N1 ♀ N

Statute: 1833(T)

D **C1813** Prosthesis, penile, inflatable N1 ♂ N

Statute: 1833(T)

Pub: 100-4, Chap. 14, 40.8

D **C1814** Retinal tamponade device, silicone oil N1 N

Statute: 1833t

Coding Clinic 2006, Q2, P9

♂ Male only   ♀ Female only   🅐 Age   A2 - Z3 = ASC Payment Indicator   A - Y = APC Status Indicator

ASC = ASC Approved Procedure   **DME** Paid under the DME fee schedule   **PQRS** Physician Quality Reporting System

D **C1815** Prosthesis, urinary sphincter
(implantable) N1 N
Statute: 1833(T)
Pub: 100-4, Chap. 14, 40.8

D **C1816** Receiver and/or transmitter, neurostimulator
(implantable) N1 N
Statute: 1833(T)

D **C1817** Septal defect implant system,
intracardiac N1 N
Statute: 1833(T)

D **C1818** Integrated keratoprosthesis N1 N
Statute: 1833T

D **C1819** Surgical tissue localization and excision
device (implantable) N1 N
Statute: 1833T

D **C1820** Generator, neurostimulator (implantable),
with rechargeable battery and charging
system N1 N
Statute: 1833(T)
Pub: 100-4, Chap. 14, 40.8

D **C1821** Interspinous process distraction device
(implantable) N1 N
Statute: 1833(T)

D **C1830** Powered bone marrow biopsy needle N1 H
Statute: 1833(t)

D **C1840** Lens, intraocular (telescopic) N1 H
Statute: 1833(t)

D **C1841** Retinal prosthesis, includes all internal and
external components J7 ASC H
Statute: 1833(t)

D **C1874** Stent, coated/covered, with delivery
system N1 N
Statute: 1833(T)

D **C1875** Stent, coated/covered, without delivery
system N1 N
Statute: 1833(T)

D **C1876** Stent, non-coated/non-covered, with delivery
system N1 N
Statute: 1833(T)

D **C1877** Stent, non-coated/non-covered, without
delivery system N1 N
Statute: 1833(T)

D **C1878** Material for vocal cord medialization,
synthetic (implantable) N1 N
Statute: 1833(T)

D **C1880** Vena cava filter N1 N
Statute: 1833(T)

D **C1881** Dialysis access system (implantable) N1 N
Statute: 1833(T)
Pub: 100-4, Chap. 14, 40.8

D **C1882** Cardioverter-defibrillator, other than single or
dual chamber (implantable) N1 N
Statute: 1833(T)
Coding Clinic 2012, Q2, P9;2006, Q2, P9

D **C1883** Adaptor/extension, pacing lead or
neurostimulator lead (implantable) N1 N
Statute: 1833(T)
Coding Clinic 2007, Q1, P8
Pub: 100-4, Chap. 32, 40.1

D **C1884** Embolization protective system N1 N
Statute: 1833T

D **C1885** Catheter, transluminal angioplasty, laser N1 N
Statute: 1833(T)

D **C1886** Catheter, extravascular tissue ablation, any
modality (insertable) N1 H
Statute: 1833(t)

D **C1887** Catheter, guiding (may include infusion/
perfusion capability) N1 N
Statute: 1833(T)

D **C1888** Catheter, ablation, non-cardiac,
endovascular (implantable) N1 N
Statute: 1833(T)

D **C1891** Infusion pump, non-programmable,
permanent (implantable) N1 N
Statute: 1833(T)
Pub: 100-4, Chap. 14, 40.8

D **C1892** Introducer/sheath, guiding, intracardiac
electrophysiological, fixed-curve,
peel-away N1 N
Statute: 1833(T)

D **C1893** Introducer/sheath, guiding, intracardiac
electrophysiological, fixed-curve, other than
peel-away N1 N
Statute: 1833(T)

D **C1894** Introducer/sheath, other than guiding, other
than intracardiac electrophysiological,
non-laser N1 N
Statute: 1833(T)

D **C1895** Lead, cardioverter-defibrillator, endocardial
dual coil (implantable) N1 N
Statute: 1833(T)
Coding Clinic 2006, Q2, P9

D **C1896** Lead, cardioverter-defibrillator, other than
endocardial single or dual coil
(implantable) N1 N
Statute: 1833(T)

D **C1897** Lead, neurostimulator test kit
(implantable) N1 N
Statute: 1833(T)
Coding Clinic 2007, Q1, P8
Pub: 100-4, Chap. 14, 40.8; 100-4, Chap. 32,
40.1

D **C1898** Lead, pacemaker, other than transvenous
VDD single pass N1 N
Statute: 1833(T)
Coding Clinic 2002, Q3, P8

D **C1899** Lead, pacemaker/cardioverter-defibrillator
combination (implantable) N1 N
Statute: 1833(T)

▲ Revised Code   ● New code   **C** Carrier judgment   **D** Special coverage instructions apply

I Not payable by Medicare   **M** Non-covered by Medicare   **S** Non-covered by Medicare statute   AHA Coding Clinic®

D **C1900** Lead, left ventricular coronary venous system   N1 N
Statute: 1833(T)
Pub: 100-4, Chap. 14, 40.8

D **C2614** Probe, percutaneous lumbar discectomy   N1 N
Statute: 1833(T)

D **C2615** Sealant, pulmonary, liquid   N1 N
Statute: 1833(T)

D **C2616** Brachytherapy source, non-stranded, yttrium-90, per source   H2 ASC U
Statute: 1833(T)

D **C2617** Stent, non-coronary, temporary, without delivery system   N1 N
Statute: 1833(T)

D **C2618** Probe/needle, cryoablation   N1 N
Statute: 1833(T)

D **C2619** Pacemaker, dual chamber, non rate-responsive (implantable)   N1 N
Statute: 1833(T)
Pub: 100-4, Chap. 14, 40.8

D **C2620** Pacemaker, single chamber, non rate-responsive (implantable)   N1 N
Statute: 1833(T)

Pacemaker

D **C2621** Pacemaker, other than single or dual chamber (implantable)   N1 N
Statute: 1833(T)
Coding Clinic 2002, Q3, P8

D **C2622** Prosthesis, penile, non-inflatable   N1 ♂ N
Statute: 1833(T)

● D **C2624** Implantable wireless pulmonary artery pressure sensor with delivery catheter, including all system components

D **C2625** Stent, non-coronary, temporary, with delivery system   N1 N
Statute: 1833(T)

D **C2626** Infusion pump, non-programmable, temporary (implantable)   N1 N
Statute: 1833(T)
Pub: 100-4, Chap. 14, 40.8

D **C2627** Catheter, suprapubic/cystoscopic   N1 N
Statute: 1833(T)

D **C2628** Catheter, occlusion   N1 N
Statute: 1833(T)

D **C2629** Introducer/sheath, other than guiding, other than intracardiac electrophysiological, laser   N1 N
Statute: 1833(T)

D **C2630** Catheter, electrophysiology, diagnostic/ablation, other than 3D or vector mapping, cool-tip   N1 N
Statute: 1833(T)

D **C2631** Repair device, urinary, incontinence, without sling graft   N1 N
Statute: 1833(T)
Pub: 100-4, Chap. 14, 40.8

D **C2634** Brachytherapy source, non-stranded, high activity, iodine-125, greater than 1.01 mCi (NIST), per source   H2 ASC U
Statute: 1833(T)

D **C2635** Brachytherapy source, non-stranded, high activity, paladium-103, greater than 2.2 mCi (NIST), per source   H2 ASC U
Statute: 1833(T)

D **C2636** Brachytherapy linear source, non-stranded, paladium-103, per 1 mm   H2 ASC U
Statute: 1833(T)

D **C2637** Brachytherapy source, non-stranded, ytterbium-169, per source   B
Statute: 1833(T)

D **C2638** Brachytherapy source, stranded, iodine-125, per source   H2 ASC U
Statute: 1833(t)(2)

D **C2639** Brachytherapy source, non-stranded, iodine-125, per source   H2 ASC U
Statute: 1833(t)(2)

D **C2640** Brachytherapy source, stranded, palladium-103, per source   H2 ASC U
Statute: 1833(t)(2)

D **C2641** Brachytherapy source, non-stranded, palladium-103, per source   H2 ASC U
Statute: 1833(t)(2)

D **C2642** Brachytherapy source, stranded, cesium-131, per source   H2 ASC U
Statute: 1833(t)(2)

D **C2643** Brachytherapy source, non-stranded, cesium-131, per source   H2 ASC U
Statute: 1833(t)(2)

● **C2644** Brachytherapy source, cesium-131 chloride solution, per millicurie

D **C2698** Brachytherapy source, stranded, not otherwise specified, per source   H2 ASC U
Statute: 1833(t)(2)

D **C2699** Brachytherapy source, non-stranded, not otherwise specified, per source   H2 ASC U
Statute: 1833(t)(2)

D C5271 Application of low cost skin substitute graft to trunk, arms, legs, total wound surface area up to 100 sq cm; first 25 sq cm or less wound surface area　　　　G2 ASC

Statute: 1833(t)

D C5272 Application of low cost skin substitute graft to trunk, arms, legs, total wound surface area up to 100 sq cm; each additional 25 sq cm wound surface area, or part thereof (list separately in addition to code for primary procedure)　　　　N1

Statute: 1833(t)

D C5273 Application of low cost skin substitute graft to trunk, arms, legs, total wound surface area greater than or equal to 100 sq cm; first 100 sq cm wound surface area, or 1% of body area of infants and children　　G2 ▲ ASC

Statute: 1833(t)

D C5274 Application of low cost skin substitute graft to trunk, arms, legs, total wound surface area greater than or equal to 100 sq cm; each additional 100 sq cm wound surface area, or part thereof, or each additional 1% of body area of infants and children, or part thereof (list separately in addition to code for primary procedure)　　　　N1 ▲

Statute: 1833(t)

D C5275 Application of low cost skin substitute graft to face, scalp, eyelids, mouth, neck, ears, orbits, genitalia, hands, feet, and/or multiple digits, total wound surface area up to 100 sq cm; first 25 sq cm or less wound surface area　G2 ASC

Statute: 1833(t)

D C5276 Application of low cost skin substitute graft to face, scalp, eyelids, mouth, neck, ears, orbits, genitalia, hands, feet, and/or multiple digits, total wound surface area up to 100 sq cm; each additional 25 sq cm wound surface area, or part thereof (list separately in addition to code for primary procedure) N1

Statute: 1833(t)

D C5277 Application of low cost skin substitute graft to face, scalp, eyelids, mouth, neck, ears, orbits, genitalia, hands, feet, and/or multiple digits, total wound surface area greater than or equal to 100 sq cm; first 100 sq cm wound surface area, or 1% of body area of infants and children　　　　G2 ▲ ASC

Statute: 1833(t)

D C5278 Application of low cost skin substitute graft to face, scalp, eyelids, mouth, neck, ears, orbits, genitalia, hands, feet, and/ or multiple digits, total wound surface area greater than or equal to 100 sq cm; each additional 100 sq cm wound surface area, or part thereof, or each additional 1% of body area of infants and children, or part thereof (list separately in addition to code for primary procedure)　　　　N1 ▲

Statute: 1833(t)

D C8900 Magnetic resonance angiography with contrast, abdomen　　　Z2 ASC Q3

Statute: 1833(t)(2)

Pub: 100-4, Chap. 13, 40.1.2

D C8901 Magnetic resonance angiography without contrast, abdomen　　　Z2 ASC Q3

Statute: 1833(t)(2)

Pub: 100-4, Chap. 13, 40.1.2

D C8902 Magnetic resonance angiography without contrast followed by with contrast, abdomen　　　　Z2 ASC Q3

Statute: 1833(t)(2)

Pub: 100-4, Chap. 13, 40.1.2

D C8903 Magnetic resonance imaging with contrast, breast; unilateral　　Z2 ASC Q3

Statute: 1833(t)(2)

D C8904 Magnetic resonance imaging without contrast, breast; unilateral　　Z2 ASC Q3

Statute: 1833(t)(2)

D C8905 Magnetic resonance imaging without contrast followed by with contrast, breast; unilateral　　　　Z2 ASC Q3

Statute: 1833(t)(2)

D C8906 Magnetic resonance imaging with contrast, breast; bilateral　　Z2 ASC Q3

Statute: 1833(t)(2)

D C8907 Magnetic resonance imaging without contrast, breast; bilateral　　Z2 ASC Q3

Statute: 1833(t)(2)

D C8908 Magnetic resonance imaging without contrast followed by with contrast, breast; bilateral　　　　Z2 ASC Q3

Statute: 1833(t)(2)

D C8909 Magnetic resonance angiography with contrast, chest (excluding myocardium)　　Z2 ASC Q3

Statute: 1833(t)(2)

Pub: 100-4, Chap. 13, 40.1.2

D C8910 Magnetic resonance angiography without contrast, chest (excluding myocardium)　　　　Z2 ASC Q3

Statute: 1833(t)(2)

Pub: 100-4, Chap. 13, 40.1.2

D C8911 Magnetic resonance angiography without contrast followed by with contrast, chest (excluding myocardium)　　Z2 ASC Q3

Statute: 1833(t)(2)

Pub: 100-4, Chap. 13, 40.1.2

D C8912 Magnetic resonance angiography with contrast, lower extremity　Z2 ASC Q3

Statute: 1833(t)(2)

Pub: 100-4, Chap. 13, 40.1.2

D C8913 Magnetic resonance angiography without contrast, lower extremity　Z2 ASC Q3

Statute: 1833(t)(2)

Pub: 100-4, Chap. 13, 40.1.2

▲ Revised Code　　● New code　　**C** Carrier judgment　　**D** Special coverage instructions apply

I Not payable by Medicare　　**M** Non-covered by Medicare　　**S** Non-covered by Medicare statute　　AHA Coding Clinic®

D **C8914** Magnetic resonance angiography without contrast followed by with contrast, lower extremity   Z2 ASC Q3
Statute: 1833(t)(2)

Pub: 100-4, Chap. 13, 40.1.2

D **C8918** Magnetic resonance angiography with contrast, pelvis   Z2 ASC Q3
Statute: 430 BIPA

Pub: 100-4, Chap. 13, 40.1.2

D **C8919** Magnetic resonance angiography without contrast, pelvis   Z2 ASC Q3
Statute: 430 BIPA

Pub: 100-4, Chap. 13, 40.1.2

D **C8920** Magnetic resonance angiography without contrast followed by with contrast, pelvis   Z2 ASC Q3
Statute: 430 BIPA

Pub: 100-4, Chap. 13, 40.1.2

D **C8921** Transthoracic echocardiography with contrast, or without contrast followed by with contrast, for congenital cardiac anomalies; complete   S
Statute: 1833(t)(2)

Pub: 100-4, Chap. 4, 200.7.2

D **C8922** Transthoracic echocardiography with contrast, or without contrast followed by with contrast, for congenital cardiac anomalies; follow-up or limited study   S
Statute: 1833(t)(2)

D **C8923** Transthoracic echocardiography with contrast, or without contrast followed by with contrast, real-time with image documentation (2D), includes M-mode recording, when performed, complete, without spectral or color doppler echocardiography   S
Statute: 1833(t)(2)

D **C8924** Transthoracic echocardiography with contrast, or without contrast followed by with contrast, real-time with image documentation (2D), includes M-mode recording, when performed, follow-up or limited study   S
Statute: 1833(t)(2)

D **C8925** Transesophageal echocardiography (TEE) with contrast, or without contrast followed by with contrast, real time with image documentation (2D) (with or without M-mode recording); including probe placement, image acquisition, interpretation and report   S
Statute: 1833(t)(2)

D **C8926** Transesophageal echocardiography (TEE) with contrast, or without contrast followed by with contrast, for congenital cardiac anomalies; including probe placement, image acquisition, interpretation and report   S
Statute: 1833(t)(2)

D **C8927** Transesophageal echocardiography (TEE) with contrast, or without contrast followed by with contrast, for monitoring purposes, including probe placement, real time 2-dimensional image acquisition and interpretation leading to ongoing (continuous) assessment of (dynamically changing) cardiac pumping function and to therapeutic measures on an immediate time basis   S
Statute: 1833(t)(2)

D **C8928** Transthoracic echocardiography with contrast, or without contrast followed by with contrast, real-time with image documentation (2D), includes M-mode recording, when performed, during rest and cardiovascular stress test using treadmill, bicycle exercise and/or pharmacologically induced stress, with interpretation and report   S
Statute: 1833(t)(2)

D **C8929** Transthoracic echocardiography with contrast, or without contrast followed by with contrast, real-time with image documentation (2D), includes M-mode recording, when performed, complete, with spectral doppler echocardiography, and with color flow doppler echocardiography   S
Statute: 1833(t)(2)

D **C8930** Transthoracic echocardiography, with contrast, or without contrast followed by with contrast, real-time with image documentation (2D), includes M-mode recording, when performed, during rest and cardiovascular stress test using treadmill, bicycle exercise and/or pharmacologically induced stress, with interpretation and report; including performance of continuous electrocardiographic monitoring, with physician supervision   S
Statute: 1833(t)(2)

D **C8931** Magnetic resonance angiography with contrast, spinal canal and contents   Z2 ASC Q3
Statute: 1833(t)

D **C8932** Magnetic resonance angiography without contrast, spinal canal and contents   Z2 ASC Q3
Statute: 1833(t)

D **C8933** Magnetic resonance angiography without contrast followed by with contrast, spinal canal and contents   Z2 ASC Q3
Statute: 1833(t)

D **C8934** Magnetic resonance angiography with contrast, upper extremity   Z2 ASC Q3
Statute: 1833(t)

D **C8935** Magnetic resonance angiography without contrast, upper extremity   Z2 ASC Q3
Statute: 1833(t)

D **C8936** Magnetic resonance angiography without contrast followed by with contrast, upper extremity   Z2 ASC Q3
Statute: 1833(t)

♂ Male only   ♀ Female only   **A** Age   A2 - Z3 = ASC Payment Indicator   A - Y = APC Status Indicator
ASC = ASC Approved Procedure   **DME** Paid under the DME fee schedule   **PQRS** Physician Quality Reporting System

D **C8957** Intravenous infusion for therapy/diagnosis; initiation of prolonged infusion (more than 8 hours), requiring use of portable or implantable pump   S

    Value not established 1833(t)

    Coding Clinic 2008, Q3, P8

    Pub: 100-4, Chap. 4, 230.2

C9025 Injection, ramucirumab, 5 mg

C9026 Injection, vedolizumab, 1 mg

● **D** **C9027** Injection, pembrolizumab, 1 mg

● **D** **C9113** Injection, pantoprazole sodium, per vial N1 N

    Statute: 1833(T)

● **D** **C9121** Injection, argatroban, per 5 mg   K2 ASC K

    Statute: 1833(T) Drugs: ARGATROBAN

D **C9132** Prothrombin complex concentrate (human), kcentra, per IU of Factor IX activity K2 ASC G

    Statute: 1833(t) Drugs: KCENTRA

● **D** **C9136** Injection, factor VIII, Fc fusion protein, (recombinant), per IU

D **C9248** Injection, clevidipine butyrate, 1 mg   N1 K

    Statute: 1833(t)

D **C9250** Human plasma fibrin sealant, vapor-heated, solvent-detergent (Artiss), 2ml   K2 ASC K

    Statute: 621MMA Drugs: ARTISS

D **C9254** Injection, lacosamide, 1 mg   N1 N

    Statute: 621MMA

D **C9257** Injection, bevacizumab, 0.25 mg K2 ASC K

    Statute: 1833(t) Drugs: AVASTIN

D **C9275** Injection, hexaminolevulinate hydrochloride, 100 mg, per study dose   N1 N

    Statute: 1833(t)

    Coding Clinic 2011, Q1, P6

D **C9285** Lidocaine 70 mg/tetracaine 70 mg, per patch   N1 G

    Statute: 1833(t)

    Coding Clinic 2011, Q3, P9

D **C9290** Injection, bupivacaine liposome, 1 mg   K2 ASC G

    Statute: 1833(t) Drugs: EXPAREL

D **C9293** Injection, glucarpidase, 10 units   K2 ASC G

    Statute: 1833(t) Drugs: VORAXAZE

● **D** **C9349** Fortaderm, and fortaderm antimicrobial, any type, per square centimeter

D **C9352** Microporous collagen implantable tube (NeuraGen Nerve Guide), per centimeter length   N1 N

    Statute: 621MMA

D **C9353** Microporous collagen implantable slit tube (NeuraWrap Nerve Protector), per centimeter length   N1 N

    Statute: 621MMA

D **C9354** Acellular pericardial tissue matrix of non-human origin (Veritas), per square centimeter   N1 N

    Statute: 621MMA

D **C9355** Collagen nerve cuff (NeuroMatrix), per 0.5 centimeter length   N1 N

    Statute: 621MMA

D **C9356** Tendon, porous matrix of cross-linked collagen and glycosaminoglycan matrix (TenoGlide Tendon Protector Sheet), per square centimeter   N1 N

    Statute: 621 MMA

D **C9358** Dermal substitute, native, non-denatured collagen, fetal bovine origin (SurgiMend Collagen Matrix), per 0.5 square centimeters   N1 K

    Statute: 621 MMA

    Coding Clinic 2012, Q2, P7

D **C9359** Porous purified collagen matrix bone void filler (Integra Mozaik Osteoconductive Scaffold Putty, Integra Os Osteoconductive Scaffold Putty), per 0.5 cc   N1 N

    Statute: 1833(T)

D **C9360** Dermal substitute, native, non-denatured collagen, neonatal bovine origin (SurgiMend Collagen Matrix), per 0.5 square centimeters   N1 K

    Statute: 621MMA

    Coding Clinic 2012, Q2, P7

D **C9361** Collagen matrix nerve wrap (NeuroMend Collagen Nerve Wrap), per 0.5 centimeter length   N1 N

    Statute: 621MMA

D **C9362** Porous purified collagen matrix bone void filler (Integra Mozaik Osteoconductive Scaffold Strip), per 0.5 cc   N1 N

    Statute: 621MMA

    Coding Clinic 2010, Q2, P8

D **C9363** Skin substitute, Integra Meshed Bilayer Wound Matrix, per square centimeter   N1 K

    Statute: 621MMA

    Coding Clinic 2012, Q2, P7;2010, Q2, P8

D **C9364** Porcine implant, Permacol, per square centimeter   N1 N

    Statute: 621MMA

D **C9399** Unclassified drugs or biologicals   K7 ASC A

    Statute: 621MMA

    Coding Clinic 2010, Q3, P8

    Pub: 100-4, Chap. 17, 90.3

● **D** **C9442** Injection, belinostat, 10 mg

● **D** **C9443** Injection, dalbavancin, 10 mg

● **D** **C9444** Injection, oritavancin, 10 mg

● **D** **C9446** Injection, tedizolid phosphate, 1 mg

● **D** **C9447** Injection, phenylephrine and ketorolac, 4 ml vial

D **C9497** Loxapine, inhalation powder, 10 mg K2 ASC

    Statute: 1833(t)

D **C9600** Percutaneous transcatheter placement of drug eluting intracoronary stent(s), with coronary angioplasty when performed; single major coronary artery or branch   T

    Statute: 1833(t)

▲ Revised Code   ● New code   **C** Carrier judgment   **D** Special coverage instructions apply

I Not payable by Medicare   **M** Non-covered by Medicare   **S** Non-covered by Medicare statute   AHA Coding Clinic®

① Build up of cholesterol partially blocking blood flow through the artery.

② Stent with balloon inserted into partially blocked artery.

③ Balloon inflated to expand stent.

④ Balloon removed from expanded stent.

Placement of Intracoronary Stent with Coronary Angioplasty

D **C9601** Percutaneous transcatheter placement of drug-eluting intracoronary stent(s), with coronary angioplasty when performed; each additional branch of a major coronary artery (list separately in addition to code for primary procedure)   T
Statute: 1833(t)

D **C9602** Percutaneous transluminal coronary atherectomy, with drug eluting intracoronary stent, with coronary angioplasty when performed; single major coronary artery or branch   T
Statute: 1833(t)

D **C9603** Percutaneous transluminal coronary atherectomy, with drug-eluting intracoronary stent, with coronary angioplasty when performed; each additional branch of a major coronary artery (list separately in addition to code for primary procedure)   T
Statute: 1833(t)

D **C9604** Percutaneous transluminal revascularization of or through coronary artery bypass graft (internal mammary, free arterial, venous), any combination of drug-eluting intracoronary stent, atherectomy and angioplasty, including distal protection when performed; single vessel   T
Statute: 1833(t)

D **C9605** Percutaneous transluminal revascularization of or through coronary artery bypass graft (internal mammary, free arterial, venous), any combination of drug-eluting intracoronary stent, atherectomy and angioplasty, including distal protection when performed; each additional branch subtended by the bypass graft (list separately in addition to code for primary procedure)   T
Statute: 1833(t)

D **C9606** Percutaneous transluminal revascularization of acute total/subtotal occlusion during acute myocardial infarction, coronary artery or coronary artery bypass graft, any combination of drug-eluting intracoronary stent, atherectomy and angioplasty, including aspiration thrombectomy when performed, single vessel   T
Statute: 1833(t)

D **C9607** Percutaneous transluminal revascularization of chronic total occlusion, coronary artery, coronary artery branch, or coronary artery bypass graft, any combination of drug-eluting intracoronary stent, atherectomy and angioplasty; single vessel   T
Statute: 1833(t)

D **C9608** Percutaneous transluminal revascularization of chronic total occlusion, coronary artery, coronary artery branch, or coronary artery bypass graft, any combination of drug-eluting intracoronary stent, atherectomy and angioplasty; each additional coronary artery, coronary artery branch, or bypass graft (list separately in addition to code for primary procedure)   T
Statute: 1833(t)

D **C9724** Endoscopic full-thickness plication of the stomach using endoscopic plication system (EPS); includes endoscopy   G2 ASC T
Statute: 1833(T)

D **C9725** Placement of endorectal intracavitary applicator for high intensity brachytherapy   G2 ASC T
Statute: 1833(T)

D **C9726** Placement and removal (if performed) of applicator into breast for intraoperative radiation therapy, add-on to primary breast procedure   N1 T
Statute: 1833(T)

D **C9727** Insertion of implants into the soft palate; minimum of three implants   G2 ASC T
Statute: 1833(T)

D **C9728** Placement of interstitial device(s) for radiation therapy/surgery guidance (e.g., fiducial markers, dosimeter), for other than the following sites (any approach): abdomen, pelvis, prostate, retroperitoneum, thorax, single or multiple   R2 ASC X
Statute: 1833(T)

D **C9733** Non-ophthalmic fluorescent vascular angiography   N1 Q2
Statute: 1833(t)
Coding Clinic 2012, Q1, P7

♂ Male only   ♀ Female only   Ⓐ Age   A2 - Z3 = ASC Payment Indicator   A - Y = APC Status Indicator
ASC = ASC Approved Procedure   **DME** Paid under the DME fee schedule   **PQRS** Physician Quality Reporting System

C9734 Focused ultrasound ablation/therapeutic
intervention, other than uterine leiomyomata,
with magnetic resonance (MR) guidance S
Statute: 1833(t)

C9737 Laparoscopy, surgical, esophageal
sphincter augmentation with device (e.g.,
magnetic band) G2 ASC
Statute: 1833(t)

C9739 Cystourethroscopy, with insertion of
transprostatic implant; 1 to 3 implants

C9740 Cystourethroscopy, with insertion of
transprostatic implant; 4 or more implants

C9741 Right heart catheterization with implantation
of wireless pressure sensor in the pulmonary
artery, including any type of measurement,
angiography, imaging supervision,
interpretation, and report

C9742 Laryngoscopy, flexible fiberoptic, with
injection into vocal cord(s), therapeutic,
including diagnostic laryngoscopy, if
performed

C9800 Dermal injection procedure(s) for facial
lipodystrophy syndrome (LDS) and provision
of radiesse or sculptra dermal filler, including
all items and supplies R2 ASC T
Statute: 1833(t)
Coding Clinic 2010, Q3, P8, 10
Pub: 100-3, Chap. 1, Part-4, 250.5; 100-4,
Chap. 32, 260.1; 100-4, Chap. 32, 260.2.1

C9898 Radiolabeled product provided during a
hospital inpatient stay N
Service not separately priced by Part B
Statute: NA

C9899 Implanted prosthetic device, payable only
for inpatients who do not have inpatient
coverage A
Statute: 1833(t)

▲ Revised Code   ● New code   **C** Carrier judgment   **D** Special coverage instructions apply
I Not payable by Medicare   **M** Non-covered by Medicare   **S** Non-covered by Medicare statute   AHA Coding Clinic®

DURABLE MEDICAL EQUIPMENT (E0100-E8002)

D **E0100** Cane, includes canes of all materials, adjustable or fixed, with tip **DME** Y
DME Modifier: NU, RR, UE

D **E0105** Cane, quad or three prong, includes canes of all materials, adjustable or fixed, with tips **DME** Y
DME Modifier: NU, RR, UE

D **E0110** Crutches, forearm, includes crutches of various materials, adjustable or fixed, pair, complete with tips and handgrips **DME** Y
DME Modifier: NU, RR, UE

D **E0111** Crutch forearm, includes crutches of various materials, adjustable or fixed, each, with tip and handgrips **DME** Y
DME Modifier: NU, RR, UE

D **E0112** Crutches underarm, wood, adjustable or fixed, pair, with pads, tips and handgrips **DME** Y
DME Modifier: NU, RR, UE

D **E0113** Crutch underarm, wood, adjustable or fixed, each, with pad, tip and handgrip **DME** Y
DME Modifier: NU, RR, UE

D **E0114** Crutches underarm, other than wood, adjustable or fixed, pair, with pads, tips and handgrips **DME** Y
DME Modifier: NU, RR, UE

D **E0116** Crutch, underarm, other than wood, adjustable or fixed, with pad, tip, handgrip, with or without shock absorber, each **DME** Y
DME Modifier: NU, RR, UE

D **E0117** Crutch, underarm, articulating, spring assisted, each **DME** Y
DME Modifier: NU, RR, UE

C **E0118** Crutch substitute, lower leg platform, with or without wheels, each **E**

D **E0130** Walker, rigid (pickup), adjustable or fixed height **DME** Y
DME Modifier: NU, RR, UE
Pub: 100-4, Chap. 23, 60.3; 100-4, Chap. 36, 50.15

D **E0135** Walker, folding (pickup), adjustable or fixed height **DME** Y
DME Modifier: NU, RR, UE
Pub: 100-4, Chap. 36, 50.15

D **E0140** Walker, with trunk support, adjustable or fixed height, any type **DME** Y
DME Modifier: NU, RR, UE
Pub: 100-4, Chap. 36, 50.15

D **E0141** Walker, rigid, wheeled, adjustable or fixed height **DME** Y
DME Modifier: NU, RR, UE

D **E0143** Walker, folding, wheeled, adjustable or fixed height **DME** Y
DME Modifier: NU, RR, UE

Pub: 100-4, Chap. 36, 50.15

D **E0144** Walker, enclosed, four sided framed, rigid or folding, wheeled with posterior seat **DME** Y
DME Modifier: NU, RR, UE

D **E0147** Walker, heavy duty, multiple braking system, variable wheel resistance **DME** Y
DME Modifier: NU, RR, UE
Pub: 100-4, Chap. 36, 50.15

C **E0148** Walker, heavy duty, without wheels, rigid or folding, any type, each **DME** Y
DME Modifier: NU, RR, UE

C **E0149** Walker, heavy duty, wheeled, rigid or folding, any type **DME** Y
DME Modifier: NU, RR, UE

C **E0153** Platform attachment, forearm crutch, each **DME** Y
DME Modifier: NU, RR, UE

C **E0154** Platform attachment, walker, each **DME** Y
DME Modifier: NU, RR, UE
Pub: 100-4, Chap. 23, 60.3; 100-4, Chap. 36, 50.14; 100-4, Chap. 36, 50.15

C **E0155** Wheel attachment, rigid pick-up walker, per pair **DME** Y
DME Modifier: NU, RR, UE

C **E0156** Seat attachment, walker **DME** Y
DME Modifier: NU, RR, UE
Pub: 100-4, Chap. 36, 50.14

C **E0157** Crutch attachment, walker, each **DME** Y
DME Modifier: NU, RR, UE

C **E0158** Leg extensions for walker, per set of four (4) **DME** Y
DME Modifier: NU, RR, UE

C **E0159** Brake attachment for wheeled walker, replacement, each **DME** Y
DME Modifier: NU, RR, UE

D **E0160** Sitz type bath or equipment, portable, used with or without commode **DME** Y
DME Modifier: NU, RR, UE

D **E0161** Sitz type bath or equipment, portable, used with or without commode, with faucet attachment/s **DME** Y
DME Modifier: NU, RR, UE

D **E0162** Sitz bath chair **DME** Y
DME Modifier: NU, RR, UE

D **E0163** Commode chair, mobile or stationary, with fixed arms **DME** Y
DME Modifier: NU, RR, UE

D **E0165** Commode chair, mobile or stationary, with detachable arms **DME** Y
DME Modifier: RR

D **E0167** Pail or pan for use with commode chair, replacement only **DME** Y
DME Modifier: NU, RR, UE

C **E0168** Commode chair, extra wide and/or heavy duty, stationary or mobile, with or without arms, any type, each `DME` Y
DME Modifier: NU, RR, UE

C **E0170** Commode chair with integrated seat lift mechanism, electric, any type `DME` Y
DME Modifier: RR

C **E0171** Commode chair with integrated seat lift mechanism, non-electric, any type `DME` Y
DME Modifier: RR

S **E0172** Seat lift mechanism placed over or on top of toilet, any type E
Service not separately priced by Part B
Statute: 1861SSA

C **E0175** Foot rest, for use with commode chair, each `DME` Y
DME Modifier: NU, RR, UE

D **E0181** Powered pressure reducing mattress overlay/pad, alternating, with pump, includes heavy duty `DME` Y
DME Modifier: RR

D **E0182** Pump for alternating pressure pad, for replacement only `DME` Y
DME Modifier: RR

D **E0184** Dry pressure mattress `DME` Y
DME Modifier: NU, RR, UE

D **E0185** Gel or gel-like pressure pad for mattress, standard mattress length and width `DME` Y
DME Modifier: NU, RR, UE

D **E0186** Air pressure mattress `DME` Y
DME Modifier: RR

D **E0187** Water pressure mattress `DME` Y
DME Modifier: RR

D **E0188** Synthetic sheepskin pad `DME` Y
DME Modifier: NU, RR, UE

D **E0189** Lambswool sheepskin pad, any size `DME` Y
DME Modifier: NU, RR, UE

D **E0190** Positioning cushion/pillow/wedge, any shape or size, includes all components and accessories E
Service not separately priced by Part B

C **E0191** Heel or elbow protector, each `DME` Y
DME Modifier: NU, RR, UE

C **E0193** Powered air flotation bed (low air loss therapy) `DME` Y
DME Modifier: RR
Pub: 100-4, Chap. 23, 60.3

D **E0194** Air fluidized bed `DME` Y
DME Modifier: RR

D **E0196** Gel pressure mattress `DME` Y
DME Modifier: RR

D **E0197** Air pressure pad for mattress, standard mattress length and width `DME` Y
DME Modifier: NU, RR, UE

D **E0198** Water pressure pad for mattress, standard mattress length and width `DME` Y
DME Modifier: NU, RR, UE

D **E0199** Dry pressure pad for mattress, standard mattress length and width `DME` Y
DME Modifier: NU, RR, UE

D **E0200** Heat lamp, without stand (table model), includes bulb, or infrared element `DME` Y
DME Modifier: NU, RR, UE

C **E0202** Phototherapy (bilirubin) light with photometer `DME` Y
DME Modifier: RR

M **E0203** Therapeutic lightbox, minimum 10, 000 lux, table top model E
Service not separately priced by Part B

D **E0205** Heat lamp, with stand, includes bulb, or infrared element `DME` Y
DME Modifier: NU, RR, UE

D **E0210** Electric heat pad, standard `DME` Y
DME Modifier: NU, RR, UE

D **E0215** Electric heat pad, moist `DME` Y
DME Modifier: NU, RR, UE

D **E0217** Water circulating heat pad with pump `DME` Y
DME Modifier: NU, RR, UE

D **E0218** Water circulating cold pad with pump Y

C **E0221** Infrared heating pad system Y
Service not separately priced by Part B

D **E0225** Hydrocollator unit, includes pads `DME` Y
DME Modifier: NU, RR, UE
Pub: 100-2, Chap. 15, 230

M **E0231** Non-contact wound warming device (temperature control unit, AC adapter and power cord) for use with warming card and wound cover E
Service not separately priced by Part B

M **E0232** Warming card for use with the non contact wound warming device and non contact wound warming wound cover E
Service not separately priced by Part B

D **E0235** Paraffin bath unit, portable (*see* medical supply code A4265 for paraffin) `DME` Y
DME Modifier: RR
Pub: 100-2, Chap. 15, 230

D **E0236** Pump for water circulating pad `DME` Y
DME Modifier: RR

D **E0239** Hydrocollator unit, portable `DME` Y
DME Modifier: NU, RR, UE
Pub: 100-2, Chap. 15, 230

M **E0240** Bath/shower chair, with or without wheels, any size E
Service not separately priced by Part B

M **E0241** Bath tub wall rail, each E
Service not separately priced by Part B

▲ Revised Code   ● New code   C Carrier judgment   D Special coverage instructions apply
I Not payable by Medicare   M Non-covered by Medicare   S Non-covered by Medicare statute   AHA Coding Clinic®

M **E0242** Bath tub rail, floor base   E
Service not separately priced by Part B

M **E0243** Toilet rail, each   E
Service not separately priced by Part B

M **E0244** Raised toilet seat   E
Service not separately priced by Part B

M **E0245** Tub stool or bench   E
Service not separately priced by Part B

C **E0246** Transfer tub rail attachment   E
Service not separately priced by Part B

D **E0247** Transfer bench for tub or toilet with or without commode opening   E
Service not separately priced by Part B

D **E0248** Transfer bench, heavy duty, for tub or toilet with or without commode opening   E
Service not separately priced by Part B

D **E0249** Pad for water circulating heat unit, for replacement only   DME Y
DME Modifier: NU, RR, UE

D **E0250** Hospital bed, fixed height, with any type side rails, with mattress   DME Y
DME Modifier: RR
Pub: 100-4, Chap. 23, 60.3

D **E0251** Hospital bed, fixed height, with any type side rails, without mattress   DME Y
DME Modifier: RR

D **E0255** Hospital bed, variable height, hi-lo, with any type side rails, with mattress   DME Y
DME Modifier: RR

D **E0256** Hospital bed, variable height, hi-lo, with any type side rails, without mattress   DME Y
DME Modifier: RR

D **E0260** Hospital bed, semi-electric (head and foot adjustment), with any type side rails, with mattress   DME Y
DME Modifier: RR

D **E0261** Hospital bed, semi-electric (head and foot adjustment), with any type side rails, without mattress   DME Y
DME Modifier: RR

D **E0265** Hospital bed, total electric (head, foot and height adjustments), with any type side rails, with mattress   DME Y
DME Modifier: RR

D **E0266** Hospital bed, total electric (head, foot and height adjustments), with any type side rails, without mattress   DME Y
DME Modifier: RR

M **E0270** Hospital bed, institutional type includes: oscillating, circulating and stryker frame, with mattress   E
Service not separately priced by Part B

D **E0271** Mattress, innerspring   DME Y
DME Modifier: NU, RR, UE

Pub: 100-4, Chap. 23, 60.3; 100-4, Chap. 36, 50.14

D **E0272** Mattress, foam rubber   DME Y
DME Modifier: NU, RR, UE

M **E0273** Bed board   E
Service not separately priced by Part B

M **E0274** Over-bed table   E
Service not separately priced by Part B

D **E0275** Bed pan, standard, metal or plastic   DME Y
DME Modifier: NU, RR, UE

D **E0276** Bed pan, fracture, metal or plastic   DME Y
DME Modifier: NU, RR, UE

D **E0277** Powered pressure-reducing air mattress   DME Y
DME Modifier: RR
Pub: 100-4, Chap. 23, 60.3

C **E0280** Bed cradle, any type   DME Y
DME Modifier: NU, RR, UE
Pub: 100-4, Chap. 36, 50.14

D **E0290** Hospital bed, fixed height, without side rails, with mattress   DME Y
DME Modifier: RR

D **E0291** Hospital bed, fixed height, without side rails, without mattress   DME Y
DME Modifier: RR

D **E0292** Hospital bed, variable height, hi-lo, without side rails, with mattress   DME Y
DME Modifier: RR

D **E0293** Hospital bed, variable height, hi-lo, without side rails, without mattress   DME Y
DME Modifier: RR

D **E0294** Hospital bed, semi-electric (head and foot adjustment), without side rails, with mattress   DME Y
DME Modifier: RR

D **E0295** Hospital bed, semi-electric (head and foot adjustment), without side rails, without mattress   DME Y
DME Modifier: RR

D **E0296** Hospital bed, total electric (head, foot and height adjustments). without side rails, with mattress   DME Y
DME Modifier: RR

D **E0297** Hospital bed, total electric (head, foot and height adjustments), without side rails, without mattress   DME Y
DME Modifier: RR

C **E0300** Pediatric crib, hospital grade, fully enclosed, with or without top enclosure   DME Ⓐ Y
DME Modifier: NU, RR, UE

D **E0301** Hospital bed, heavy duty, extra wide, with weight capacity greater than 350 pounds, but less than or equal to 600 pounds, with any type side rails, without mattress   DME Y
DME Modifier: RR

♂ Male only   ♀ Female only   Ⓐ Age   A2 - Z3 = ASC Payment Indicator   A - Y = APC Status Indicator
ASC = ASC Approved Procedure   DME Paid under the DME fee schedule   PQRS Physician Quality Reporting System

D E0302 Hospital bed, extra heavy duty, extra wide, with weight capacity greater than 600 pounds, with any type side rails, without mattress   DME Y
DME Modifier: RR

D E0303 Hospital bed, heavy duty, extra wide, with weight capacity greater than 350 pounds, but less than or equal to 600 pounds, with any type side rails, with mattress   DME Y
DME Modifier: RR

D E0304 Hospital bed, extra heavy duty, extra wide, with weight capacity greater than 600 pounds, with any type side rails, with mattress   DME Y
DME Modifier: RR

D E0305 Bed side rails, half length   DME Y
DME Modifier: RR

D E0310 Bed side rails, full length   DME Y
DME Modifier: NU, RR, UE
Pub: 100-4, Chap. 36, 50.14

M E0315 Bed accessory: board, table, or support device, any type   E
Service not separately priced by Part B

C E0316 Safety enclosure frame/canopy for use with hospital bed, any type   DME Y
DME Modifier: RR
Pub: 100-4, Chap. 23, 60.3

D E0325 Urinal; male, jug-type, any material ♂ DME Y
DME Modifier: NU, RR, UE

D E0326 Urinal; female, jug-type, any material ♀ DME Y
DME Modifier: NU, RR, UE

C E0328 Hospital bed, pediatric, manual, 360 degree side enclosures, top of headboard, footboard and side rails up to 24 inches above the spring, includes mattress   Ⓐ Y

C E0329 Hospital bed, pediatric, electric or semi-electric, 360 degree side enclosures, top of headboard, footboard and side rails up to 24 inches above the spring, includes mattress   Ⓐ Y

C E0350 Control unit for electronic bowel irrigation/evacuation system   E
Other carrier priced

C E0352 Disposable pack (water reservoir bag, speculum, valving mechanism and collection bag/box) for use with the electronic bowel irrigation/evacuation system   E
Other carrier priced

C E0370 Air pressure elevator for heel   E
Service not separately priced by Part B

C E0371 Nonpowered advanced pressure reducing overlay for mattress, standard mattress length and width   DME Y
DME Modifier: RR
Pub: 100-4, Chap. 23, 60.3

C E0372 Powered air overlay for mattress, standard mattress length and width   DME Y
DME Modifier: RR

C E0373 Nonpowered advanced pressure reducing mattress   DME Y
DME Modifier: RR

D E0424 Stationary compressed gaseous oxygen system, rental; includes container, contents, regulator, flowmeter, humidifier, nebulizer, cannula or mask, and tubing   DME Y
DME Modifier: RR

D E0425 Stationary compressed gas system, purchase; includes regulator, flowmeter, humidifier, nebulizer, cannula or mask, and tubing   E
Service not separately priced by Part B

D E0430 Portable gaseous oxygen system, purchase; includes regulator, flowmeter, humidifier, cannula or mask, and tubing   E
Service not separately priced by Part B

D E0431 Portable gaseous oxygen system, rental; includes portable container, regulator, flowmeter, humidifier, cannula or mask, and tubing   DME Y
DME Modifier: RR

C E0433 Portable liquid oxygen system, rental; home liquefier used to fill portable liquid oxygen containers, includes portable containers, regulator, flowmeter, humidifier, cannula or mask and tubing, with or without supply reservoir and contents gauge   DME Y
DME Modifier: RR

D E0434 Portable liquid oxygen system, rental; includes portable container, supply reservoir, humidifier, flowmeter, refill adaptor, contents gauge, cannula or mask, and tubing   DME Y
DME Modifier: RR

D E0435 Portable liquid oxygen system, purchase; includes portable container, supply reservoir, flowmeter, humidifier, contents gauge, cannula or mask, tubing and refill adaptor   E
Service not separately priced by Part B

D E0439 Stationary liquid oxygen system, rental; includes container, contents, regulator, flowmeter, humidifier, nebulizer, cannula or mask, & tubing   DME Y
DME Modifier: RR

D E0440 Stationary liquid oxygen system, purchase; includes use of reservoir, contents indicator, regulator, flowmeter, humidifier, nebulizer, cannula or mask, and tubing   E
Service not separately priced by Part B

D E0441 Stationary oxygen contents, gaseous, 1 month's supply = 1 unit   DME Y

D E0442 Stationary oxygen contents, liquid, 1 month's supply = 1 unit   DME Y

D E0443 Portable oxygen contents, gaseous, 1 month's supply = 1 unit   DME Y

▲ Revised Code   ● New code   **C** Carrier judgment   **D** Special coverage instructions apply
I Not payable by Medicare   **M** Non-covered by Medicare   **S** Non-covered by Medicare statute   AHA Coding Clinic®

D **E0444** Portable oxygen contents, liquid, 1 month's supply = 1 unit DME Y

C **E0445** Oximeter device for measuring blood oxygen levels noninvasively N

Service not separately priced by Part B

Pulse Oximeter

M **E0446** Topical oxygen delivery system, not otherwise specified, includes all supplies and accessories E

Service not separately priced by Part B

D **E0450** Volume control ventilator, without pressure support mode, may include pressure control mode, used with invasive interface (e.g., tracheostomy tube) DME Y

DME Modifier: RR

D **E0455** Oxygen tent, excluding croup or pediatric tents Y

I **E0457** Chest shell (cuirass) Y

Service not separately priced by Part B

I **E0459** Chest wrap Y

Service not separately priced by Part B

D **E0460** Negative pressure ventilator; portable or stationary DME Y

DME Modifier: RR

D **E0461** Volume control ventilator, without pressure support mode, may include pressure control mode, used with non-invasive interface (e.g., mask) DME Y

DME Modifier: RR

C **E0462** Rocking bed with or without side rails DME Y

DME Modifier: RR

C **E0463** Pressure support ventilator with volume control mode, may include pressure control mode, used with invasive interface (e.g., tracheostomy tube) DME Y

DME Modifier: RR

C **E0464** Pressure support ventilator with volume control mode, may include pressure control mode, used with non-invasive interface (e.g., mask) DME Y

DME Modifier: RR

D **E0470** Respiratory assist device, bi-level pressure capability, without backup rate feature, used with noninvasive interface, e.g., nasal or facial mask (intermittent assist device with continuous positive airway pressure device) DME Y

DME Modifier: RR

Pub: 100-4, Chap. 23, 60.3

D **E0471** Respiratory assist device, bi-level pressure capability, with back-up rate feature, used with noninvasive interface, e.g., nasal or facial mask (intermittent assist device with continuous positive airway pressure device) DME Y

DME Modifier: RR

D **E0472** Respiratory assist device, bi-level pressure capability, with backup rate feature, used with invasive interface, e.g., tracheostomy tube (intermittent assist device with continuous positive airway pressure device) DME Y

DME Modifier: RR

D **E0480** Percussor, electric or pneumatic, home model DME Y

DME Modifier: RR

M **E0481** Intrapulmonary percussive ventilation system and related accessories E

Service not separately priced by Part B

C **E0482** Cough stimulating device, alternating positive and negative airway pressure DME Y

DME Modifier: RR

C **E0483** High frequency chest wall oscillation air-pulse generator system, (includes hoses and vest), each DME Y

DME Modifier: RR

C **E0484** Oscillatory positive expiratory pressure device, non-electric, any type, each DME Y

DME Modifier: NU, RR, UE

C **E0485** Oral device/appliance used to reduce upper airway collapsibility, adjustable or non-adjustable, prefabricated, includes fitting and adjustment DME Y

DME Modifier: NU, RR, UE

C **E0486** Oral device/appliance used to reduce upper airway collapsibility, adjustable or non-adjustable, custom fabricated, includes fitting and adjustment DME Y

DME Modifier: NU, RR, UE

D **E0487** Spirometer, electronic, includes all accessories N

Service not separately priced by Part B

D **E0500** IPPB machine, all types, with built-in nebulization; manual or automatic valves; internal or external power source DME Y

DME Modifier: RR

D **E0550** Humidifier, durable for extensive supplemental humidification during IPPB treatments or oxygen delivery DME Y

DME Modifier: RR

D **E0555** Humidifier, durable, glass or autoclavable plastic bottle type, for use with regulator or flowmeter Y

D **E0560** Humidifier, durable for supplemental humidification during IPPB treatment or oxygen delivery **DME** Y

DME Modifier: NU, RR, UE

Pub: 100-4, Chap. 23, 60.3

C **E0561** Humidifier, non-heated, used with positive airway pressure device **DME** Y

DME Modifier: NU, RR, UE

Pub: 100-3, Chap. 1, Part-4, 240.4; 100-4, Chap. 36, 50.14

C **E0562** Humidifier, heated, used with positive airway pressure device **DME** Y

DME Modifier: NU, RR, UE

C **E0565** Compressor, air power source for equipment which is not self-contained or cylinder driven **DME** Y

DME Modifier: RR

D **E0570** Nebulizer, with compressor **DME** Y

DME Modifier: RR

C **E0572** Aerosol compressor, adjustable pressure, light duty for intermittent use **DME** Y

DME Modifier: RR

C **E0574** Ultrasonic/electronic aerosol generator with small volume nebulizer **DME** Y

DME Modifier: RR

D **E0575** Nebulizer, ultrasonic, large volume **DME** Y

DME Modifier: RR

D **E0580** Nebulizer, durable, glass or autoclavable plastic, bottle type, for use with regulator or flowmeter **DME** Y

DME Modifier: NU, RR, UE

Pub: 100-4, Chap. 23, 60.3

D **E0585** Nebulizer, with compressor and heater **DME** Y

DME Modifier: RR

Nebulizer

D **E0600** Respiratory suction pump, home model, portable or stationary, electric **DME** Y

DME Modifier: RR

D **E0601** Continuous positive airway pressure (CPAP) device **DME** Y

DME Modifier: RR

Pub: 100-3, Chap. 1, Part-4, 240.4; 100-4, Chap. 23, 60.3

C **E0602** Breast pump, manual, any type ♀ **DME** Y

DME Modifier: NU, RR, UE

C **E0603** Breast pump, electric (AC and/or DC), any type ♀ N

Service not separately priced by Part B

C **E0604** Breast pump, hospital grade, electric (AC and / or DC), any type ♀ A

Service not separately priced by Part B

D **E0605** Vaporizer, room type **DME** Y

DME Modifier: NU, RR, UE

D **E0606** Postural drainage board **DME** Y

DME Modifier: RR

D **E0607** Home blood glucose monitor **DME** Y

DME Modifier: NU, RR, UE

Glucose Monitor

D **E0610** Pacemaker monitor, self-contained, (checks battery depletion, includes audible and visible check systems) **DME** Y

DME Modifier: NU, RR, UE

D **E0615** Pacemaker monitor, self contained, checks battery depletion and other pacemaker components, includes digital/visible check systems **DME** Y

DME Modifier: NU, RR, UE

C **E0616** Implantable cardiac event recorder with memory, activator and programmer N1 N

Service not separately priced by Part B

C **E0617** External defibrillator with integrated electrocardiogram analysis **DME** Y

DME Modifier: RR, KF

C **E0618** Apnea monitor, without recording feature **DME** Y

Service not separately priced by Part B

DME Modifier: RR

C **E0619** Apnea monitor, with recording feature **DME** Y

Service not separately priced by Part B

DME Modifier: RR

C **E0620** Skin piercing device for collection of capillary blood, laser, each **DME** Y

DME Modifier: NU, RR, UE

▲ Revised Code   ● New code   **C** Carrier judgment   **D** Special coverage instructions apply

I Not payable by Medicare   **M** Non-covered by Medicare   **S** Non-covered by Medicare statute   AHA Coding Clinic®

E0621 Sling or seat, patient lift, canvas or nylon `DME` Y
DME Modifier: NU, RR, UE

E0625 Patient lift, bathroom or toilet, not otherwise classified E
Service not separately priced by Part B

E0627 Seat lift mechanism incorporated into a combination lift-chair mechanism `DME` Y
DME Modifier: NU, RR, UE

E0628 Separate seat lift mechanism for use with patient owned furniture-electric `DME` Y
DME Modifier: NU, RR, UE

E0629 Separate seat lift mechanism for use with patient owned furniture-non-electric `DME` Y
DME Modifier: NU, RR, UE

E0630 Patient lift, hydraulic or mechanical, includes any seat, sling, strap(s) or pad(s) `DME` Y
DME Modifier: RR

E0635 Patient lift, electric with seat or sling `DME` Y
DME Modifier: RR

E0636 Multipositional patient support system, with integrated lift, patient accessible controls `DME` Y
DME Modifier: RR

E0637 Combination sit to stand frame/table system, any size including pediatric, with seat lift feature, with or without wheels E
Service not separately priced by Part B

E0638 Standing frame/table system, one position (e.g., upright, supine or prone stander), any size including pediatric, with or without wheels E
Service not separately priced by Part B

E0639 Patient lift, moveable from room to room with disassembly and reassembly, includes all components/accessories E
Service not separately priced by Part B

E0640 Patient lift, fixed system, includes all components/accessories E
Service not separately priced by Part B

E0641 Standing frame/table system, multi-position (e.g., 3-way stander), any size including pediatric, with or without wheels E
Service not separately priced by Part B

E0642 Standing frame/table system, mobile (dynamic stander), any size including pediatric E
Service not separately priced by Part B

E0650 Pneumatic compressor, non-segmental home model `DME` Y
DME Modifier: NU, RR, UE

E0651 Pneumatic compressor, segmental home model without calibrated gradient pressure `DME` Y
DME Modifier: NU, RR, UE

E0652 Pneumatic compressor, segmental home model with calibrated gradient pressure `DME` Y
DME Modifier: NU, RR, UE

E0655 Non-segmental pneumatic appliance for use with pneumatic compressor, half arm `DME` Y
DME Modifier: NU, RR, UE

E0656 Segmental pneumatic appliance for use with pneumatic compressor, trunk `DME` Y
DME Modifier: NU, RR, UE

E0657 Segmental pneumatic appliance for use with pneumatic compressor, chest `DME` Y
DME Modifier: NU, RR, UE

E0660 Non-segmental pneumatic appliance for use with pneumatic compressor, full leg `DME` Y
DME Modifier: NU, RR, UE

E0665 Non-segmental pneumatic appliance for use with pneumatic compressor, full arm `DME` Y
DME Modifier: NU, RR, UE

E0666 Non-segmental pneumatic appliance for use with pneumatic compressor, half leg `DME` Y
DME Modifier: NU, RR, UE

E0667 Segmental pneumatic appliance for use with pneumatic compressor, full leg `DME` Y
DME Modifier: NU, RR, UE

E0668 Segmental pneumatic appliance for use with pneumatic compressor, full arm `DME` Y
DME Modifier: NU, RR, UE

E0669 Segmental pneumatic appliance for use with pneumatic compressor, half leg `DME` Y
DME Modifier: NU, RR, UE

E0670 Segmental pneumatic appliance for use with pneumatic compressor, integrated, 2 full legs and trunk `DME` Y
DME Modifier: NU, RR, UE

E0671 Segmental gradient pressure pneumatic appliance, full leg `DME` Y
DME Modifier: NU, RR, UE

E0672 Segmental gradient pressure pneumatic appliance, full arm `DME` Y
DME Modifier: NU, RR, UE

E0673 Segmental gradient pressure pneumatic appliance, half leg `DME` Y
DME Modifier: NU, RR, UE

E0675 Pneumatic compression device, high pressure, rapid inflation/deflation cycle, for arterial insufficiency (unilateral or bilateral system) `DME` Y
DME Modifier: RR

E0676 Intermittent limb compression device (includes all accessories), not otherwise specified Y
Service not separately priced by Part B

E0691 Ultraviolet light therapy system, includes bulbs/lamps, timer and eye protection; treatment area 2 square feet or less `DME` Y
DME Modifier: NU, RR, UE

♂ Male only ♀ Female only 🅐 Age A2 - Z3 = ASC Payment Indicator A - Y = APC Status Indicator
ASC = ASC Approved Procedure `DME` Paid under the DME fee schedule `PQRS` Physician Quality Reporting System

C **E0692** Ultraviolet light therapy system panel, includes bulbs/lamps, timer and eye protection, 4 foot panel DME Y
DME Modifier: NU, RR, UE

C **E0693** Ultraviolet light therapy system panel, includes bulbs/lamps, timer and eye protection, 6 foot panel DME Y
DME Modifier: NU, RR, UE

C **E0694** Ultraviolet multidirectional light therapy system in 6 foot cabinet, includes bulbs/lamps, timer and eye protection DME Y
DME Modifier: NU, RR, UE

C **E0700** Safety equipment, device or accessory, any type E
Service not separately priced by Part B

D **E0705** Transfer device, any type, each DME B
DME Modifier: NU, RR, UE

C **E0710** Restraints, any type (body, chest, wrist or ankle) E
Other carrier priced

D **E0720** Transcutaneous electrical nerve stimulation (TENS) device, two lead, localized stimulation DME Y
DME Modifier: NU

D **E0730** Transcutaneous electrical nerve stimulation (TENS) device, four or more leads, for multiple nerve stimulation DME Y
DME Modifier: NU
Pub: 100-3, Chap. 1, 10.2; 100-3, Chap. 1, Part 2, 160.7.1; 100-3, Chap. 1, Part 2, 160.27; 100-4, Chap. 20, 30.1.2

D **E0731** Form fitting conductive garment for delivery of TENS or NMES (with conductive fibers separated from the patient's skin by layers of fabric) DME Y
DME Modifier: NU
Pub: 100-3, Chap. 1, 10.2; 100-3, Chap. 1, Part 2, 160.13

D **E0740** Incontinence treatment system, pelvic floor stimulator, monitor, sensor and/or trainer DME Y
DME Modifier: NU, RR, UE

C **E0744** Neuromuscular stimulator for scoliosis DME Y
DME Modifier: RR

D **E0745** Neuromuscular stimulator, electronic shock unit DME Y
DME Modifier: RR

D **E0746** Electromyography (EMG), biofeedback device N
Reasonable charge

D **E0747** Osteogenesis stimulator, electrical, non-invasive, other than spinal applications DME Y
DME Modifier: NU, KF, RR, UE

D **E0748** Osteogenesis stimulator, electrical, non-invasive, spinal applications DME Y
DME Modifier: NU, KF, RR, UE

D **E0749** Osteogenesis stimulator, electrical, surgically implanted N1 DME N
DME Modifier: RR, KF

C **E0755** Electronic salivary reflex stimulator (intra-oral/non-invasive) E
Reasonable charge

C **E0760** Osteogenesis stimulator, low intensity ultrasound, non-invasive DME Y
DME Modifier: NU, KF, RR, UE
Pub: 100-4, Chap. 32, 110.5

D **E0761** Non-thermal pulsed high frequency radiowaves, high peak power electromagnetic energy treatment device E
Service not separately priced by Part B

C **E0762** Transcutaneous electrical joint stimulation device system, includes all accessories DME B
DME Modifier: NU, RR, UE

D **E0764** Functional neuromuscular stimulation, transcutaneous stimulation of sequential muscle groups of ambulation with computer control, used for walking by spinal cord injured, entire system, after completion of training program DME Y
DME Modifier: NU, KF, RR, UE

C **E0765** FDA approved nerve stimulator, with replaceable batteries, for treatment of nausea and vomiting DME Y
DME Modifier: NU, RR, UE

C **E0766** Electrical stimulation device used for cancer treatment, includes all accessories, any type
DME Modifier: RR, KF

D **E0769** Electrical stimulation or electromagnetic wound treatment device, not otherwise classified B
Service not separately priced by Part B
Pub: 100-4, Chap. 32, 11.1

D **E0770** Functional electrical stimulator, transcutaneous stimulation of nerve and/or muscle groups, any type, complete system, not otherwise specified Y

C **E0776** IV pole DME Y
DME Modifier: NU, RR, UE
Pub: 100-4, Chap. 23, 60.3

C **E0779** Ambulatory infusion pump, mechanical, reusable, for infusion 8 hours or greater DME Y
DME Modifier: RR

C **E0780** Ambulatory infusion pump, mechanical, reusable, for infusion less than 8 hours DME Y
DME Modifier: NU

D **E0781** Ambulatory infusion pump, single or multiple channels, electric or battery operated, with administrative equipment, worn by patient DME Y
DME Modifier: RR

D **E0782** Infusion pump, implantable, non-programmable (includes all components, e.g., pump, catheter, connectors, etc.) N1 DME N
DME Modifier: NU, KF, RR, UE

▲ Revised Code   ● New code   C Carrier judgment   D Special coverage instructions apply
I Not payable by Medicare   M Non-covered by Medicare   S Non-covered by Medicare statute   AHA Coding Clinic®

D **E0783** Infusion pump system, implantable, programmable (includes all components, e.g., pump, catheter, connectors, etc.) N1 **DME** N
DME Modifier: NU, KF, RR, UE

D **E0784** External ambulatory infusion pump, insulin **DME** Y
DME Modifier: RR

D **E0785** Implantable intraspinal (epidural/intrathecal) catheter used with implantable infusion pump, replacement N1 **DME** N
DME Modifier: KF

D **E0786** Implantable programmable infusion pump, replacement (excludes implantable intraspinal catheter) N1 **DME** N
DME Modifier: NU, KF, RR, UE

D **E0791** Parenteral infusion pump, stationary, single or multi-channel **DME** Y
DME Modifier: RR

D **E0830** Ambulatory traction device, all types, each N
Service not separately priced by Part B

D **E0840** Traction frame, attached to headboard, cervical traction **DME** Y
DME Modifier: NU, RR, UE

C **E0849** Traction equipment, cervical, free-standing stand/frame, pneumatic, applying traction force to other than mandible **DME** Y
DME Modifier: NU, RR, UE

D **E0850** Traction stand, free standing, cervical traction **DME** Y
DME Modifier: NU, RR, UE

C **E0855** Cervical traction equipment not requiring additional stand or frame **DME** Y
DME Modifier: NU, RR, UE

▲ **C** **E0856** Cervical traction device, with inflatable air bladder(s) **DME** Y
DME Modifier: NU, RR, UE

D **E0860** Traction equipment, overdoor, cervical **DME** Y
DME Modifier: NU, RR, UE

D **E0870** Traction frame, attached to footboard, extremity traction, (e.g., Buck's) **DME** Y
DME Modifier: NU, RR, UE

D **E0880** Traction stand, free standing, extremity traction, (e.g., Buck's) **DME** Y
DME Modifier: NU, RR, UE

D **E0890** Traction frame, attached to footboard, pelvic traction **DME** Y
DME Modifier: NU, RR, UE

D **E0900** Traction stand, free standing, pelvic traction, (e.g., Buck's) **DME** Y
DME Modifier: NU, RR, UE

D **E0910** Trapeze bars, also known as Patient Helper, attached to bed, with grab bar **DME** Y
DME Modifier: RR
Pub: 100-4, Chap. 23, 60.3

D **E0911** Trapeze bar, heavy duty, for patient weight capacity greater than 250 pounds, attached to bed, with grab bar **DME** Y
DME Modifier: RR

D **E0912** Trapeze bar, heavy duty, for patient weight capacity greater than 250 pounds, free standing, complete with grab bar **DME** Y
DME Modifier: RR

D **E0920** Fracture frame, attached to bed, includes weights **DME** Y
DME Modifier: RR

D **E0930** Fracture frame, free standing, includes weights **DME** Y
DME Modifier: RR

D **E0935** Continuous passive motion exercise device for use on knee only **DME** Y
DME Modifier: RR

M **E0936** Continuous passive motion exercise device for use other than knee E
Service not separately priced by Part B

D **E0940** Trapeze bar, free standing, complete with grab bar **DME** Y
DME Modifier: RR
Pub: 100-4, Chap. 23, 60.3

D **E0941** Gravity assisted traction device, any type **DME** Y
DME Modifier: RR

C **E0942** Cervical head harness/halter **DME** Y
DME Modifier: NU, RR, UE

C **E0944** Pelvic belt/harness/boot **DME** Y
DME Modifier: NU, RR, UE

C **E0945** Extremity belt/harness **DME** Y
DME Modifier: NU, RR, UE

D **E0946** Fracture, frame, dual with cross bars, attached to bed, (e.g., balken, 4 poster) **DME** Y
DME Modifier: RR

D **E0947** Fracture frame, attachments for complex pelvic traction **DME** Y
DME Modifier: NU, RR, UE

D **E0948** Fracture frame, attachments for complex cervical traction **DME** Y
DME Modifier: NU, RR, UE

D **E0950** Wheelchair accessory, tray, each **DME** Y
Service not separately priced by Part B
DME Modifier: NU, KE, RR, UE
Pub: 100-4, Chap. 23, 60.3

C **E0951** Heel loop/holder, any type, with or without ankle strap, each **DME** Y
Service not separately priced by Part B
DME Modifier: NU, KE, RR, UE

D **E0952** Toe loop/holder, any type, each **DME** Y
Service not separately priced by Part B
DME Modifier: NU, KE, RR, UE

♂ Male only   ♀ Female only   **A** Age   A2 - Z3 = ASC Payment Indicator   A - Y = APC Status Indicator
ASC = ASC Approved Procedure   **DME** Paid under the DME fee schedule   **PQRS** Physician Quality Reporting System

C **E0955** Wheelchair accessory, headrest, cushioned, any type, including fixed mounting hardware, each `DME` Y

DME Modifier: NU, KE, RR, UE

C **E0956** Wheelchair accessory, lateral trunk or hip support, any type, including fixed mounting hardware, each `DME` Y

DME Modifier: NU, KE, RR, UE

C **E0957** Wheelchair accessory, medial thigh support, any type, including fixed mounting hardware, each `DME` Y

DME Modifier: NU, KE, RR, UE

D **E0958** Manual wheelchair accessory, one-arm drive attachment, each `DME` Y

Service not separately priced by Part B

DME Modifier: RR

C **E0959** Manual wheelchair accessory, adapter for amputee, each `DME` B

Service not separately priced by Part B

DME Modifier: NU, RR, UE

C **E0960** Wheelchair accessory, shoulder harness/straps or chest strap, including any type mounting hardware `DME` Y

DME Modifier: NU, KE, RR, UE

Pub: 100-4, Chap. 23, 60.3

C **E0961** Manual wheelchair accessory, wheel lock brake extension (handle), each `DME` B

Service not separately priced by Part B

DME Modifier: NU, RR, UE

C **E0966** Manual wheelchair accessory, headrest extension, each `DME` B

Service not separately priced by Part B

DME Modifier: NU, RR, UE

D **E0967** Manual wheelchair accessory, hand rim with projections, any type, each `DME` Y

DME Modifier: NU, RR, UE

D **E0968** Commode seat, wheelchair `DME` Y

DME Modifier: RR

D **E0969** Narrowing device, wheelchair `DME` Y

DME Modifier: NU, RR, UE

I **E0970** No.2 footplates, except for elevating leg rest E

Service not separately priced by Part B

C **E0971** Manual wheelchair accessory, anti-tipping device, each `DME` B

Service not separately priced by Part B

DME Modifier: NU, RR, UE

D **E0973** Wheelchair accessory, adjustable height, detachable armrest, complete assembly, each `DME` B

Service not separately priced by Part B

DME Modifier: NU, KE, RR, UE

Pub: 100-4, Chap. 23, 60.3

D **E0974** Manual wheelchair accessory, anti-rollback device, each `DME` B

Service not separately priced by Part B

DME Modifier: NU, RR, UE

C **E0978** Wheelchair accessory, positioning belt/safety belt/pelvic strap, each `DME` B

DME Modifier: NU, KE, RR, UE

Pub: 100-4, Chap. 23, 60.3

C **E0980** Safety vest, wheelchair `DME` Y

DME Modifier: NU, RR, UE

C **E0981** Wheelchair accessory, seat upholstery, replacement only, each `DME` Y

DME Modifier: NU, KE, RR, UE

Pub: 100-4, Chap. 23, 60.3

C **E0982** Wheelchair accessory, back upholstery, replacement only, each `DME` Y

DME Modifier: NU, KE, RR, UE

C **E0983** Manual wheelchair accessory, power add-on to convert manual wheelchair to motorized wheelchair, joystick control `DME` Y

DME Modifier: RR

C **E0984** Manual wheelchair accessory, power add-on to convert manual wheelchair to motorized wheelchair, tiller control `DME` Y

DME Modifier: NU, RR, UE

C **E0985** Wheelchair accessory, seat lift mechanism `DME` Y

DME Modifier: NU, RR, UE

▲ **C** **E0986** Manual wheelchair accessory, push-rim activated power assist system `DME` Y

DME Modifier: NU, RR, UE

C **E0988** Manual wheelchair accessory, lever-activated, wheel drive, pair `DME` Y

DME Modifier: RR

C **E0990** Wheelchair accessory, elevating leg rest, complete assembly, each `DME` B

Service not separately priced by Part B

DME Modifier: NU, KE, RR, UE

Pub: 100-4, Chap. 23, 60.3

C **E0992** Manual wheelchair accessory, solid seat insert `DME` B

DME Modifier: NU, RR, UE

D **E0994** Arm rest, each `DME` Y

DME Modifier: NU, RR, UE

C **E0995** Wheelchair accessory, calf rest/pad, each `DME` B

Service not separately priced by Part B

DME Modifier: NU, KE, RR, UE

Pub: 100-4, Chap. 23, 60.3

C **E1002** Wheelchair accessory, power seating system, tilt only `DME` Y

DME Modifier: NU, KE, RR, UE

Pub: 100-4, Chap. 23, 60.3

C **E1003** Wheelchair accessory, power seating system, recline only, without shear reduction `DME` Y

DME Modifier: NU, KE, RR, UE

▲ Revised Code   ● New code   **C** Carrier judgment   **D** Special coverage instructions apply

I Not payable by Medicare   **M** Non-covered by Medicare   **S** Non-covered by Medicare statute   AHA Coding Clinic®

C **E1004** Wheelchair accessory, power seating system, recline only, with mechanical shear reduction `DME` Y

DME Modifier: NU, KE, RR, UE

C **E1005** Wheelchair accessory, power seatng system, recline only, with power shear reduction `DME` Y

DME Modifier: NU, KE, RR, UE

C **E1006** Wheelchair accessory, power seating system, combination tilt and recline, without shear reduction `DME` Y

DME Modifier: NU, KE, RR, UE

C **E1007** Wheelchair accessory, power seating system, combination tilt and recline, with mechanical shear reduction `DME` Y

DME Modifier: NU, KE, RR, UE

C **E1008** Wheelchair accessory, power seating system, combination tilt and recline, with power shear reduction `DME` Y

DME Modifier: NU, KE, RR, UE

C **E1009** Wheelchair accessory, addition to power seating system, mechanically linked leg elevation system, including pushrod and leg rest, each `DME` Y

DME Modifier: NU, RR, UE

C **E1010** Wheelchair accessory, addition to power seating system, power leg elevation system, including leg rest, pair `DME` Y

DME Modifier: NU, KE, RR, UE

D **E1011** Modification to pediatric size wheelchair, width adjustment package (not to be dispensed with initial chair) `DME` Ⓐ Y

DME Modifier: NU, RR, UE

D **E1014** Reclining back, addition to pediatric size wheelchair `DME` Ⓐ Y

DME Modifier: NU, RR, UE

D **E1015** Shock absorber for manual wheelchair, each `DME` Y

DME Modifier: NU, RR, UE

D **E1016** Shock absorber for power wheelchair, each `DME` Y

DME Modifier: NU, KE, RR, UE

Pub: 100-4, Chap. 23, 60.3

D **E1017** Heavy duty shock absorber for heavy duty or extra heavy duty manual wheelchair, each `DME` Y

DME Modifier: NU, RR, UE

D **E1018** Heavy duty shock absorber for heavy duty or extra heavy duty power wheelchair, each `DME` Y

DME Modifier: NU, RR, UE

D **E1020** Residual limb support system for wheelchair, any type `DME` Y

DME Modifier: NU, KE, RR, UE

Pub: 100-4, Chap. 23, 60.3

C **E1028** Wheelchair accessory, manual swing away, retractable or removable mounting hardware for joystick, other control interface or positioning accessory `DME` Y

DME Modifier: NU, KE, RR, UE

Pub: 100-4, Chap. 23, 60.3

C **E1029** Wheelchair accessory, ventilator tray, fixed `DME` Y

DME Modifier: NU, KE, RR, UE

C **E1030** Wheelchair accessory, ventilator tray, gimbaled `DME` Y

DME Modifier: NU, KE, RR, UE

D **E1031** Rollabout chair, any and all types with castors 5 inch or greater `DME` Y

DME Modifier: RR

D **E1035** Multi-positional patient transfer system, with integrated seat, operated by care giver, patient weight capacity up to and including 300 lbs `DME` Y

DME Modifier: RR

Pub: 100-2, Chap. 15, 110

C **E1036** Multi-positional patient transfer system, extra-wide, with integrated seat, operated by caregiver, patient weight capacity greater than 300 lbs `DME` Y

DME Modifier: RR

D **E1037** Transport chair, pediatric size `DME` Ⓐ Y

DME Modifier: RR

D **E1038** Transport chair, adult size, patient weight capacity up to and including 300 pounds `DME` Ⓐ Y

DME Modifier: RR

C **E1039** Transport chair, adult size, heavy duty, patient weight capacity greater than 300 pounds `DME` Ⓐ Y

DME Modifier: RR

D **E1050** Fully-reclining wheelchair, fixed full length arms, swing away detachable elevating legrests `DME` Y

DME Modifier: RR

D **E1060** Fully-reclining wheelchair, detachable arms, desk or full length, swing away detachable elevating legrests `DME` Y

DME Modifier: RR

D **E1070** Fully-reclining wheelchair, detachable arms (desk or full length) swing away detachable footrest `DME` Y

DME Modifier: RR

D **E1083** Hemi-wheelchair, fixed full length arms, swing away detachable elevating legrest `DME` Y

DME Modifier: RR

D **E1084** Hemi-wheelchair, detachable arms desk or full length arms, swing away detachable elevating legrests `DME` Y

DME Modifier: RR

I **E1085** Hemi-wheelchair, fixed full length arms, swing away detachable footrests   E
Service not separately priced by Part B

I **E1086** Hemi-wheelchair detachable arms desk or full length, swing away detachable footrests E
Service not separately priced by Part B

D **E1087** High strength lightweight wheelchair, fixed full length arms, swing away detachable elevating legrests   `DME` Y
DME Modifier: RR

D **E1088** High strength lightweight wheelchair, detachable arms desk or full length, swing away detachable elevating legrests   `DME` Y
DME Modifier: RR

I **E1089** High strength lightweight wheelchair, fixed length arms, swing away detachable footrest   E
Service not separately priced by Part B

I **E1090** High strength lightweight wheelchair, detachable arms desk or full length, swing away detachable footrests   E
Service not separately priced by Part B

D **E1092** Wide heavy duty wheel chair, detachable arms (desk or full length), swing away detachable elevating legrests   `DME` Y
DME Modifier: RR

D **E1093** Wide heavy duty wheelchair, detachable arms desk or full length arms, swing away detachable footrests   `DME` Y
DME Modifier: RR

D **E1100** Semi-reclining wheelchair, fixed full length arms, swing away detachable elevating legrests   `DME` Y
DME Modifier: RR

D **E1110** Semi-reclining wheelchair, detachable arms (desk or full length) elevating legrest   `DME` Y
DME Modifier: RR

I **E1130** Standard wheelchair, fixed full length arms, fixed or swing away detachable footrests   E
Service not separately priced by Part B

I **E1140** Wheelchair, detachable arms, desk or full length, swing away detachable footrests   E
Service not separately priced by Part B

D **E1150** Wheelchair, detachable arms, desk or full length swing away detachable elevating legrests   `DME` Y
DME Modifier: RR

D **E1160** Wheelchair, fixed full length arms, swing away detachable elevating legrests   `DME` Y
DME Modifier: RR

C **E1161** Manual adult size wheelchair, includes tilt in space   `DME` **Ⓐ** Y
DME Modifier: NU, RR, UE

D **E1170** Amputee wheelchair, fixed full length arms, swing away detachable elevating legrests   `DME` Y
DME Modifier: RR

D **E1171** Amputee wheelchair, fixed full length arms, without footrests or legrest   `DME` Y
DME Modifier: RR

D **E1172** Amputee wheelchair, detachable arms (desk or full length) without footrests or legrest   `DME` Y
DME Modifier: RR

D **E1180** Amputee wheelchair, detachable arms (desk or full length) swing away detachable footrests   `DME` Y
DME Modifier: RR

D **E1190** Amputee wheelchair, detachable arms (desk or full length) swing away detachable elevating legrests   `DME` Y
DME Modifier: RR

D **E1195** Heavy duty wheelchair, fixed full length arms, swing away detachable elevating legrests   `DME` Y
DME Modifier: RR

D **E1200** Amputee wheelchair, fixed full length arms, swing away detachable footrest   `DME` Y
DME Modifier: RR

D **E1220** Wheelchair; specially sized or constructed, (indicate brand name, model number, if any) and justification   Y

D **E1221** Wheelchair with fixed arm, footrests   `DME` Y
DME Modifier: RR

D **E1222** Wheelchair with fixed arm, elevating legrests   `DME` Y
DME Modifier: RR

D **E1223** Wheelchair with detachable arms, footrests   `DME` Y
DME Modifier: RR

D **E1224** Wheelchair with detachable arms, elevating legrests   `DME` Y
DME Modifier: RR

D **E1225** Wheelchair accessory, manual semi-reclining back, (recline greater than 15 degrees, but less than 80 degrees), each   `DME` Y
DME Modifier: RR

D **E1226** Wheelchair accessory, manual fully reclining back, (recline greater than 80 degrees), each   `DME` B
Service not separately priced by Part B
DME Modifier: NU, RR, UE

D **E1227** Special height arms for wheelchair   `DME` Y
DME Modifier: NU, RR, UE

D **E1228** Special back height for wheelchair   `DME` Y
DME Modifier: RR

C **E1229** Wheelchair, pediatric size, not otherwise specified   **Ⓐ** Y

D **E1230** Power operated vehicle (three or four wheel nonhighway) specify brand name and model number   `DME` Y
DME Modifier: NU, RR, UE

▲ Revised Code   ● New code   **C** Carrier judgment   **D** Special coverage instructions apply
I Not payable by Medicare   **M** Non-covered by Medicare   **S** Non-covered by Medicare statute   AHA Coding Clinic®

D **E1231** Wheelchair, pediatric size, tilt-in-space, rigid, adjustable, with seating system `DME` Ⓐ Y
DME Modifier: NU, RR, UE

D **E1232** Wheelchair, pediatric size, tilt-in-space, folding, adjustable, with seating system `DME` Ⓐ Y
DME Modifier: NU, RR, UE

D **E1233** Wheelchair, pediatric size, tilt-in-space, rigid, adjustable, without seating system `DME` Ⓐ Y
DME Modifier: NU, RR, UE

D **E1234** Wheelchair, pediatric size, tilt-in-space, folding, adjustable, without seating system `DME` Ⓐ Y
DME Modifier: NU, RR, UE

D **E1235** Wheelchair, pediatric size, rigid, adjustable, with seating system `DME` Ⓐ Y
DME Modifier: NU, RR, UE

D **E1236** Wheelchair, pediatric size, folding, adjustable, with seating system `DME` Ⓐ Y
DME Modifier: NU, RR, UE

D **E1237** Wheelchair, pediatric size, rigid, adjustable, without seating system `DME` Ⓐ Y
DME Modifier: NU, RR, UE

D **E1238** Wheelchair, pediatric size, folding, adjustable, without seating system `DME` Ⓐ Y
DME Modifier: NU, RR, UE

C **E1239** Power wheelchair, pediatric size, not otherwise specified Ⓐ Y

D **E1240** Lightweight wheelchair, detachable arms, (desk or full length) swing away detachable, elevating legrest `DME` Y
DME Modifier: RR

I **E1250** Lightweight wheelchair, fixed full length arms, swing away detachable footrest E
Service not separately priced by Part B

I **E1260** Lightweight wheelchair, detachable arms (desk or full length) swing away detachable footrest E
Service not separately priced by Part B

D **E1270** Lightweight wheelchair, fixed full length arms, swing away detachable elevating legrests `DME` Y
DME Modifier: RR

D **E1280** Heavy duty wheelchair, detachable arms (desk or full length) elevating legrests `DME` Y
DME Modifier: RR

I **E1285** Heavy duty wheelchair, fixed full length arms, swing away detachable footrest E
Service not separately priced by Part B

I **E1290** Heavy duty wheelchair, detachable arms (desk or full length) swing away detachable footrest E
Service not separately priced by Part B

D **E1295** Heavy duty wheelchair, fixed full length arms, elevating legrest `DME` Y
DME Modifier: RR

D **E1296** Special wheelchair seat height from floor `DME` Y
DME Modifier: NU, RR, UE

D **E1297** Special wheelchair seat depth, by upholstery `DME` Y
DME Modifier: NU, RR, UE

D **E1298** Special wheelchair seat depth and/or width, by construction `DME` Y
DME Modifier: NU, RR, UE

M **E1300** Whirlpool, portable (overtub type) E
Service not separately priced by Part B

D **E1310** Whirlpool, non-portable (built-in type) `DME` Y
DME Modifier: NU, RR, UE

C **E1352** Oxygen accessory, flow regulator capable of positive inspiratory pressure
Service not separately priced by Part B

D **E1353** Regulator `DME` Y
Service not separately priced by Part B
Pub: 100-4, Chap. 23, 60.3

C **E1354** Oxygen accessory, wheeled cart for portable cylinder or portable concentrator, any type, replacement only, each Y
Service not separately priced by Part B

D **E1355** Stand/rack `DME` Y
Service not separately priced by Part B
Pub: 100-4, Chap. 23, 60.3

C **E1356** Oxygen accessory, battery pack/cartridge for portable concentrator, any type, replacement only, each Y
Service not separately priced by Part B

C **E1357** Oxygen accessory, battery charger for portable concentrator, any type, replacement only, each Y
Service not separately priced by Part B

D **E1358** Oxygen accessory, DC power adapter for portable concentrator, any type, replacement only, each Y
Service not separately priced by Part B

D **E1372** Immersion external heater for nebulizer `DME` Y
DME Modifier: NU, RR, UE

D **E1390** Oxygen concentrator, single delivery port, capable of delivering 85 percent or greater oxygen concentration at the prescribed flow rate `DME` Y
DME Modifier: RR

D **E1391** Oxygen concentrator, dual delivery port, capable of delivering 85 percent or greater oxygen concentration at the prescribed flow rate, each `DME` Y
DME Modifier: RR

D **E1392** Portable oxygen concentrator, rental `DME` Y
DME Modifier: RR

C **E1399** Durable medical equipment, miscellaneous Y
Pub: 100-4, Chap. 32, 110.5

♂ Male only   ♀ Female only   Ⓐ Age   A2 - Z3 = ASC Payment Indicator   A - Y = APC Status Indicator
ASC = ASC Approved Procedure   `DME` Paid under the DME fee schedule   `PQRS` Physician Quality Reporting System

DURABLE MEDICAL EQUIPMENT (E0100-E8002)

D **E1405** Oxygen and water vapor enriching system with heated delivery   DME Y
DME Modifier: RR

D **E1406** Oxygen and water vapor enriching system without heated delivery   DME Y
DME Modifier: RR

D **E1500** Centrifuge, for dialysis   A
Reasonable charge

D **E1510** Kidney, dialysate delivery system, kidney machine, pump recirculating, air removal system, flowrate meter, power off, heater and temperature control with alarm, IV poles, pressure gauge, concentrate container   A
Reasonable charge

D **E1520** Heparin infusion pump for hemodialysis   A
Reasonable charge

D **E1530** Air bubble detector for hemodialysis, each, replacement   A
Reasonable charge

D **E1540** Pressure alarm for hemodialysis, each, replacement   A
Reasonable charge

D **E1550** Bath conductivity meter for hemodialysis, each   A
Reasonable charge

D **E1560** Blood leak detector for hemodialysis, each, replacement   A
Reasonable charge

D **E1570** Adjustable chair, for ESRD patients   A
Reasonable charge

D **E1575** Transducer protectors/fluid barriers, for hemodialysis, any size, per 10   A
Reasonable charge

D **E1580** Unipuncture control system for hemodialysis   A
Reasonable charge

D **E1590** Hemodialysis machine   A
Reasonable charge

Hemodialysis Machine

D **E1592** Automatic intermittent peritoneal dialysis system   A
Reasonable charge

D **E1594** Cycler dialysis machine for peritoneal dialysis   A
Reasonable charge

D **E1600** Delivery and/or installation charges for hemodialysis equipment   A
Reasonable charge

D **E1610** Reverse osmosis water purification system, for hemodialysis   A
Reasonable charge

D **E1615** Deionizer water purification system, for hemodialysis   A
Reasonable charge

D **E1620** Blood pump for hemodialysis, replacement   A
Reasonable charge

D **E1625** Water softening system, for hemodialysis   A
Reasonable charge

C **E1630** Reciprocating peritoneal dialysis system   A
Reasonable charge

D **E1632** Wearable artificial kidney, each   A
Reasonable charge

D **E1634** Peritoneal dialysis clamps, each   B
Reasonable charge

D **E1635** Compact (portable) travel hemodialyzer system   A
Reasonable charge

D **E1636** Sorbent cartridges, for hemodialysis, per 10   A
Reasonable charge

D **E1637** Hemostats, each   A
Reasonable charge

D **E1639** Scale, each   A
Reasonable charge

D **E1699** Dialysis equipment, not otherwise specified   A
Reasonable charge

C **E1700** Jaw motion rehabilitation system   DME Y
DME Modifier: NU, RR, UE

C **E1701** Replacement cushions for jaw motion rehabilitation system, pkg. of 6   DME Y

C **E1702** Replacement measuring scales for jaw motion rehabilitation system, pkg. of 200   DME Y

C **E1800** Dynamic adjustable elbow extension/flexion device, includes soft interface material   DME Y
DME Modifier: RR

C **E1801** Static progressive stretch elbow device, extension and/or flexion, with or without range of motion adjustment, includes all components and accessories   DME Y
DME Modifier: RR

C **E1802** Dynamic adjustable forearm pronation/supination device, includes soft interface material   DME Y
DME Modifier: RR

C **E1805** Dynamic adjustable wrist extension / flexion device, includes soft interface material   DME Y
DME Modifier: RR

▲ Revised Code   ● New code   C Carrier judgment   D Special coverage instructions apply
I Not payable by Medicare   M Non-covered by Medicare   S Non-covered by Medicare statute   AHA Coding Clinic®

E1806 Static progressive stretch wrist device, flexion and/or extension, with or without range of motion adjustment, includes all components and accessories **DME** Y
DME Modifier: RR

E1810 Dynamic adjustable knee extension / flexion device, includes soft interface material **DME** Y
DME Modifier: RR

E1811 Static progressive stretch knee device, extension and/or flexion, with or without range of motion adjustment, includes all components and accessories **DME** Y
DME Modifier: RR

E1812 Dynamic knee, extension/flexion device with active resistance control **DME** Y
DME Modifier: RR

E1815 Dynamic adjustable ankle extension/flexion device, includes soft interface material **DME** Y
DME Modifier: RR

E1816 Static progressive stretch ankle device, flexion and/or extension, with or without range of motion adjustment, includes all components and accessories **DME** Y
DME Modifier: RR

E1818 Static progressive stretch forearm pronation / supination device, with or without range of motion adjustment, includes all components and accessories **DME** Y
DME Modifier: RR

E1820 Replacement soft interface material, dynamic adjustable extension/flexion device **DME** Y
DME Modifier: NU, RR, UE

E1821 Replacement soft interface material/cuffs for bi-directional static progressive stretch device **DME** Y
DME Modifier: NU, RR, UE

E1825 Dynamic adjustable finger extension/flexion device, includes soft interface material **DME** Y
DME Modifier: RR

E1830 Dynamic adjustable toe extension/flexion device, includes soft interface material **DME** Y
DME Modifier: RR

E1831 Static progressive stretch toe device, extension and/or flexion, with or without range of motion adjustment, includes all components and accessories **DME** Y
DME Modifier: RR

E1840 Dynamic adjustable shoulder flexion / abduction / rotation device, includes soft interface material **DME** Y
DME Modifier: RR

E1841 Static progressive stretch shoulder device, with or without range of motion adjustment, includes all components and accessories **DME** Y
DME Modifier: RR

E1902 Communication board, non-electronic augmentative or alternative communication device Y
Service not separately priced by Part B

E2000 Gastric suction pump, home model, portable or stationary, electric **DME** Y
DME Modifier: RR

E2100 Blood glucose monitor with integrated voice synthesizer **DME** Y
DME Modifier: NU, RR, UE

E2101 Blood glucose monitor with integrated lancing/blood sample **DME** Y
DME Modifier: NU, RR, UE

E2120 Pulse generator system for tympanic treatment of inner ear endolymphatic fluid **DME** Y
DME Modifier: RR

E2201 Manual wheelchair accessory, nonstandard seat frame, width greater than or equal to 20 inches and less than 24 inches **DME** Y
DME Modifier: NU, RR, UE

E2202 Manual wheelchair accessory, nonstandard seat frame width, 24-27 inches **DME** Y
DME Modifier: NU, RR, UE

E2203 Manual wheelchair accessory, nonstandard seat frame depth, 20 to less than 22 inches **DME** Y
DME Modifier: NU, RR, UE

E2204 Manual wheelchair accessory, nonstandard seat frame depth, 22 to 25 inches **DME** Y
DME Modifier: NU, RR, UE

E2205 Manual wheelchair accessory, handrim without projections (includes ergonomic or contoured), any type, replacement only, each **DME** Y
DME Modifier: NU, RR, UE

E2206 Manual wheelchair accessory, wheel lock assembly, complete, each **DME** Y
DME Modifier: NU, RR, UE

E2207 Wheelchair accessory, crutch and cane holder, each **DME** Y
DME Modifier: NU, RR, UE

E2208 Wheelchair accessory, cylinder tank carrier, each **DME** Y
DME Modifier: NU, KE, RR, UE
Pub: 100-4, Chap. 23, 60.3

E2209 Accessory, arm trough, with or without hand support, each **DME** Y
DME Modifier: NU, KE, RR, UE

E2210 Wheelchair accessory, bearings, any type, replacement only, each **DME** Y
DME Modifier: NU, KE, RR, UE

E2211 Manual wheelchair accessory, pneumatic propulsion tire, any size, each **DME** Y
DME Modifier: NU, RR, UE

♂ Male only   ♀ Female only   Ⓐ Age   A2 - Z3 = ASC Payment Indicator   A - Y = APC Status Indicator
ASC = ASC Approved Procedure   **DME** Paid under the DME fee schedule   **PQRS** Physician Quality Reporting System

E1806 - E2211

DURABLE MEDICAL EQUIPMENT (E0100-E8002)

63

C **E2212** Manual wheelchair accessory, tube for pneumatic propulsion tire, any size, each DME Y
DME Modifier: NU, RR, UE

C **E2213** Manual wheelchair accessory, insert for pneumatic propulsion tire (removable), any type, any size, each DME Y
DME Modifier: NU, RR, UE

C **E2214** Manual wheelchair accessory, pneumatic caster tire, any size, each DME Y
DME Modifier: NU, RR, UE

C **E2215** Manual wheelchair accessory, tube for pneumatic caster tire, any size, each DME Y
DME Modifier: NU, RR, UE

C **E2216** Manual wheelchair accessory, foam filled propulsion tire, any size, each DME Y
DME Modifier: NU, RR, UE

C **E2217** Manual wheelchair accessory, foam filled caster tire, any size, each DME Y
DME Modifier: NU, RR, UE

C **E2218** Manual wheelchair accessory, foam propulsion tire, any size, each DME Y
DME Modifier: NU, RR, UE

C **E2219** Manual wheelchair accessory, foam caster tire, any size, each DME Y
DME Modifier: NU, RR, UE

C **E2220** Manual wheelchair accessory, solid (rubber/plastic) propulsion tire, any size, each DME Y
DME Modifier: NU, RR, UE

C **E2221** Manual wheelchair accessory, solid (rubber/plastic) caster tire (removable), any size, each DME Y
DME Modifier: NU, RR, UE

C **E2222** Manual wheelchair accessory, solid (rubber/plastic) caster tire with integrated wheel, any size, each DME Y
DME Modifier: NU, RR, UE

C **E2224** Manual wheelchair accessory, propulsion wheel excludes tire, any size, each DME Y
DME Modifier: NU, RR, UE

C **E2225** Manual wheelchair accessory, caster wheel excludes tire, any size, replacement only, each DME Y
DME Modifier: NU, RR, UE

C **E2226** Manual wheelchair accessory, caster fork, any size, replacement only, each DME Y
DME Modifier: NU, RR, UE

C **E2227** Manual wheelchair accessory, gear reduction drive wheel, each DME Y
DME Modifier: NU, RR, UE

C **E2228** Manual wheelchair accessory, wheel braking system and lock, complete, each DME Y
DME Modifier: NU, RR, UE

C **E2230** Manual wheelchair accessory, manual standing system E
Service not separately priced by Part B

C **E2231** Manual wheelchair accessory, solid seat support base (replaces sling seat), includes any type mounting hardware DME Y
DME Modifier: NU, RR, UE

C **E2291** Back, planar, for pediatric size wheelchair including fixed attaching hardware A Y

C **E2292** Seat, planar, for pediatric size wheelchair including fixed attaching hardware A Y

C **E2293** Back, contoured, for pediatric size wheelchair including fixed attaching hardware A Y

C **E2294** Seat, contoured, for pediatric size wheelchair including fixed attaching hardware A Y

C **E2295** Manual wheelchair accessory, for pediatric size wheelchair, dynamic seating frame, allows coordinated movement of multiple positioning features A Y

C **E2300** Wheelchair accessory, power seat elevation system, any type Y

C **E2301** Wheelchair accessory, power standing system, any type Y
Service not separately priced by Part B

C **E2310** Power wheelchair accessory, electronic connection between wheelchair controller and one power seating system motor, including all related electronics, indicator feature, mechanical function selection switch, and fixed mounting hardware DME Y
DME Modifier: NU, KE, RR, UE
Pub: 100-4, Chap. 23, 60.3

C **E2311** Power wheelchair accessory, electronic connection between wheelchair controller and two or more power seating system motors, including all related electronics, indicator feature, mechanical function selection switch, and fixed mounting hardware DME Y
DME Modifier: NU, KE, RR, UE

C **E2312** Power wheelchair accessory, hand or chin control interface, mini-proportional remote joystick, proportional, including fixed mounting hardware DME Y
DME Modifier: NU, KC, RR, UE

C **E2313** Power wheelchair accessory, harness for upgrade to expandable controller, including all fasteners, connectors and mounting hardware, each DME Y
DME Modifier: NU, RR, UE

C **E2321** Power wheelchair accessory, hand control interface, remote joystick, nonproportional, including all related electronics, mechanical stop switch, and fixed mounting hardware DME Y
DME Modifier: NU, KC, KE, RR, UE
Pub: 100-4, Chap. 23, 60.3

C **E2322** Power wheelchair accessory, hand control interface, multiple mechanical switches, nonproportional, including all related

---

▲ Revised Code ● New code C Carrier judgment D Special coverage instructions apply
I Not payable by Medicare M Non-covered by Medicare S Non-covered by Medicare statute AHA Coding Clinic®

electronics, mechanical stop switch, and
fixed mounting hardware `DME` Y
DME Modifier: NU, KC, KE, RR, UE

C **E2323** Power wheelchair accessory, specialty
joystick handle for hand control interface,
prefabricated `DME` Y
DME Modifier: NU, KE, RR, UE

C **E2324** Power wheelchair accessory, chin cup for
chin control interface `DME` Y
DME Modifier: NU, KE, RR, UE

C **E2325** Power wheelchair accessory, sip and puff
interface, nonproportional, including all related
electronics, mechanical stop switch, and
manual swingaway mounting hardware `DME` Y
DME Modifier: NU, KE, RR, UE

C **E2326** Power wheelchair accessory, breath tube kit
for sip and puff interface `DME` Y
DME Modifier: NU, KE, RR, UE

C **E2327** Power wheelchair accessory, head
control interface, mechanical, proportional,
including all related electronics, mechanical
direction change switch, and fixed mounting
hardware `DME` Y
DME Modifier: NU, KC, KE, RR, UE

C **E2328** Power wheelchair accessory, head control
or extremity control interface, electronic,
proportional, including all related electronics
and fixed mounting hardware `DME` Y
DME Modifier: NU, KE, RR, UE

C **E2329** Power wheelchair accessory, head control
interface, contact switch mechanism,
nonproportional, including all related
electronics, mechanical stop switch,
mechanical direction change switch, head
array, and fixed mounting hardware `DME` Y
DME Modifier: NU, KE, RR, UE

C **E2330** Power wheelchair accessory, head control
interface, proximity switch mechanism,
nonproportional, including all related
electronics, mechanical stop switch,
mechanical direction change switch, head
array, and fixed mounting hardware `DME` Y
DME Modifier: NU, KE, RR, UE

C **E2331** Power wheelchair accessory, attendant
control, proportional, including all related
electronics and fixed mounting hardware Y

C **E2340** Power wheelchair accessory, nonstandard
seat frame width, 20-23 inches `DME` Y
DME Modifier: NU, RR, UE

C **E2341** Power wheelchair accessory, nonstandard
seat frame width, 24-27 inches `DME` Y
DME Modifier: NU, RR, UE

C **E2342** Power wheelchair accessory, nonstandard
seat frame depth, 20 or 21 inches `DME` Y
DME Modifier: NU, RR, UE

C **E2343** Power wheelchair accessory, nonstandard
seat frame depth, 22-25 inches `DME` Y

DME Modifier: NU, RR, UE

C **E2351** Power wheelchair accessory, electronic
interface to operate speech generating
device using power wheelchair control
interface `DME` Y
DME Modifier: NU, KE, RR, UE
Pub: 100-4, Chap. 23, 60.3

C **E2358** Power wheelchair accessory, group 34 non-
sealed lead acid battery, each Y

C **E2359** Power wheelchair accessory, group 34
sealed lead acid battery, each (e.g., gel cell,
absorbed glassmat) `DME` Y
DME Modifier: NU, RR, UE

C **E2360** Power wheelchair accessory, 22 NF non-
sealed lead acid battery, each `DME` Y
DME Modifier: NU, RR, UE

C **E2361** Power wheelchair accessory, 22 NF sealed
lead acid battery, each, (e.g., gel cell,
absorbed glassmat) `DME` Y
DME Modifier: NU, KE, RR, UE
Pub: 100-4, Chap. 23, 60.3

C **E2362** Power wheelchair accessory, group 24 non-
sealed lead acid battery, each `DME` Y
DME Modifier: NU, RR, UE

C **E2363** Power wheelchair accessory, group 24
sealed lead acid battery, each (e.g., gel cell,
absorbed glassmat) `DME` Y
DME Modifier: NU, KE, RR, UE
Pub: 100-4, Chap. 23, 60.3

C **E2364** Power wheelchair accessory, U-1 non-sealed
lead acid battery, each `DME` Y
DME Modifier: NU, RR, UE

C **E2365** Power wheelchair accessory, U-1 sealed
lead acid battery, each (e.g., gel cell,
absorbed glassmat) `DME` Y
DME Modifier: NU, KE, RR, UE
Pub: 100-4, Chap. 23, 60.3

C **E2366** Power wheelchair accessory,
battery charger, single mode, for use with
only one battery type, sealed or non-sealed,
each `DME` Y
DME Modifier: NU, KE, RR, UE

C **E2367** Power wheelchair accessory, battery charger,
dual mode, for use with either battery type,
sealed or non-sealed, each `DME` Y
DME Modifier: NU, KE, RR, UE

C **E2368** Power wheelchair component, drive wheel
motor, replacement only `DME` Y
DME Modifier: NU, KE, RR, UE

C **E2369** Power wheelchair component, drive wheel
gear box, replacement only `DME` Y
DME Modifier: NU, KE, RR, UE

C **E2370** Power wheelchair component, integrated
drive wheel motor and gear box combination,
replacement only `DME` Y
DME Modifier: NU, KE, RR, UE

E2323 - E2370

DURABLE MEDICAL EQUIPMENT (E0100-E8002)

C **E2371** Power wheelchair accessory, group 27 sealed lead acid battery, (e.g., gel cell, absorbed glassmat), each `DME` Y
DME Modifier: NU, KE, RR, UE

C **E2372** Power wheelchair accessory, group 27 non-sealed lead acid battery, each `DME` Y
DME Modifier: NU, RR, UE

C **E2373** Power wheelchair accessory, hand or chin control interface, compact remote joystick, proportional, including fixed mounting hardware `DME` Y
DME Modifier: NU, KC, KE, RR, UE
Pub: 100-4, Chap. 23, 60.3

D **E2374** Power wheelchair accessory, hand or chin control interface, standard remote joystick (not including controller), proportional, including all related electronics and fixed mounting hardware, replacement only `DME` Y
DME Modifier: NU, KE, RR, UE

D **E2375** Power wheelchair accessory, non-expandable controller, including all related electronics and mounting hardware, replacement only `DME` Y
DME Modifier: NU, KE, RR, UE

D **E2376** Power wheelchair accessory, expandable controller, including all related electronics and mounting hardware, replacement only `DME` Y
DME Modifier: NU, KE, RR, UE

D **E2377** Power wheelchair accessory, expandable controller, including all related electronics and mounting hardware, upgrade provided at initial issue `DME` Y
DME Modifier: NU, KE, RR, UE

C **E2378** Power wheelchair component, actuator, replacement only `DME` Y
DME Modifier: NU, RR, UE

D **E2381** Power wheelchair accessory, pneumatic drive wheel tire, any size, replacement only, each `DME` Y
DME Modifier: NU, KE, RR, UE

D **E2382** Power wheelchair accessory, tube for pneumatic drive wheel tire, any size, replacement only, each `DME` Y
DME Modifier: NU, KE, RR, UE

D **E2383** Power wheelchair accessory, insert for pneumatic drive wheel tire (removable), any type, any size, replacement only, each `DME` Y
DME Modifier: NU, KE, RR, UE

D **E2384** Power wheelchair accessory, pneumatic caster tire, any size, replacement only, each `DME` Y
DME Modifier: NU, KE, RR, UE

D **E2385** Power wheelchair accessory, tube for pneumatic caster tire, any size, replacement only, each `DME` Y
DME Modifier: NU, KE, RR, UE

D **E2386** Power wheelchair accessory, foam filled drive wheel tire, any size, replacement only, each `DME` Y
DME Modifier: NU, KE, RR, UE

D **E2387** Power wheelchair accessory, foam filled caster tire, any size, replacement only, each `DME` Y
DME Modifier: NU, KE, RR, UE

D **E2388** Power wheelchair accessory, foam drive wheel tire, any size, replacement only, each `DME` Y
DME Modifier: NU, KE, RR, UE

D **E2389** Power wheelchair accessory, foam caster tire, any size, replacement only, each `DME` Y
DME Modifier: NU, KE, RR, UE

D **E2390** Power wheelchair accessory, solid (rubber/plastic) drive wheel tire, any size, replacement only, each `DME` Y
DME Modifier: NU, KE, RR, UE

D **E2391** Power wheelchair accessory, solid (rubber/plastic) caster tire (removable), any size, replacement only, each `DME` Y
DME Modifier: NU, KE, RR, UE

D **E2392** Power wheelchair accessory, solid (rubber/plastic) caster tire with integrated wheel, any size, replacement only, each `DME` Y
DME Modifier: NU, KE, RR, UE

D **E2394** Power wheelchair accessory, drive wheel excludes tire, any size, replacement only, each `DME` Y
DME Modifier: NU, KE, RR, UE

D **E2395** Power wheelchair accessory, caster wheel excludes tire, any size, replacement only, each `DME` Y
DME Modifier: NU, KE, RR, UE

D **E2396** Power wheelchair accessory, caster fork, any size, replacement only, each `DME` Y
DME Modifier: NU, KE, RR, UE

C **E2397** Power wheelchair accessory, lithium-based battery, each `DME` Y
DME Modifier: NU, RR, UE

C **E2402** Negative pressure wound therapy electrical pump, stationary or portable `DME` Y
DME Modifier: RR
Pub: 100-4, Chap. 23, 60.3

D **E2500** Speech generating device, digitized speech, using pre-recorded messages, less than or equal to 8 minutes recording time `DME` Y
DME Modifier: NU, RR, UE

D **E2502** Speech generating device, digitized speech, using pre-recorded messages, greater than 8 minutes but less than or equal to 20 minutes recording time `DME` Y
DME Modifier: NU, RR, UE

D **E2504** Speech generating device, digitized speech, using pre-recorded messages, greater than 20 minutes but less than or equal to 40 minutes recording time `DME` Y
DME Modifier: NU, RR, UE

▲ Revised Code　　● New code　　C Carrier judgment　　D Special coverage instructions apply
I Not payable by Medicare　　M Non-covered by Medicare　　S Non-covered by Medicare statute　　AHA Coding Clinic®

D **E2506** Speech generating device, digitized speech, using pre-recorded messages, greater than 40 minutes recording time `DME` Y

DME Modifier: NU, RR, UE

D **E2508** Speech generating device, synthesized speech, requiring message formulation by spelling and access by physical contact with the device `DME` Y

DME Modifier: NU, RR, UE

D **E2510** Speech generating device, synthesized speech, permitting multiple methods of message formulation and multiple methods of device access `DME` Y

DME Modifier: NU, RR, UE

D **E2511** Speech generating software program, for personal computer or personal digital assistant `DME` Y

DME Modifier: NU, RR, UE

D **E2512** Accessory for speech generating device, mounting system `DME` Y

DME Modifier: NU, RR, UE

D **E2599** Accessory for speech generating device, not otherwise classified Y

C **E2601** General use wheelchair seat cushion, width less than 22 inches, any depth `DME` Y

DME Modifier: NU, KE, RR, UE

Pub: 100-4, Chap. 23, 60.3

C **E2602** General use wheelchair seat cushion, width 22 inches or greater, any depth `DME` Y

DME Modifier: NU, KE, RR, UE

C **E2603** Skin protection wheelchair seat cushion, width less than 22 inches, any depth `DME` Y

DME Modifier: NU, KE, RR, UE

C **E2604** Skin protection wheelchair seat cushion, width 22 inches or greater, any depth `DME` Y

DME Modifier: NU, KE, RR, UE

C **E2605** Positioning wheelchair seat cushion, width less than 22 inches, any depth `DME` Y

DME Modifier: NU, KE, RR, UE

C **E2606** Positioning wheelchair seat cushion, width 22 inches or greater, any depth `DME` Y

DME Modifier: NU, KE, RR, UE

C **E2607** Skin protection and positioning wheelchair seat cushion, width less than 22 inches, any depth `DME` Y

DME Modifier: NU, KE, RR, UE

C **E2608** Skin protection and positioning wheelchair seat cushion, width 22 inches or greater, any depth `DME` Y

DME Modifier: NU, KE, RR, UE

C **E2609** Custom fabricated wheelchair seat cushion, any size Y

C **E2610** Wheelchair seat cushion, powered B

C **E2611** General use wheelchair back cushion, width less than 22 inches, any height, including any type mounting hardware `DME` Y

DME Modifier: NU, KE, RR, UE

Pub: 100-4, Chap. 23, 60.3

C **E2612** General use wheelchair back cushion, width 22 inches or greater, any height, including any type mounting hardware `DME` Y

DME Modifier: NU, KE, RR, UE

C **E2613** Positioning wheelchair back cushion, posterior, width less than 22 inches, any height, including any type mounting hardware `DME` Y

DME Modifier: NU, KE, RR, UE

C **E2614** Positioning wheelchair back cushion, posterior, width 22 inches or greater, any height, including any type mounting hardware `DME` Y

DME Modifier: NU, KE, RR, UE

C **E2615** Positioning wheelchair back cushion, posterior-lateral, width less than 22 inches, any height, including any type mounting hardware `DME` Y

DME Modifier: NU, KE, RR, UE

C **E2616** Positioning wheelchair back cushion, posterior-lateral, width 22 inches or greater, any height, including any type mounting hardware `DME` Y

DME Modifier: NU, KE, RR, UE

C **E2617** Custom fabricated wheelchair back cushion, any size, including any type mounting hardware Y

C **E2619** Replacement cover for wheelchair seat cushion or back cushion, each `DME` Y

DME Modifier: NU, KE, RR, UE

Pub: 100-4, Chap. 23, 60.3

C **E2620** Positioning wheelchair back cushion, planar back with lateral supports, width less than 22 inches, any height, including any type mounting hardware `DME` Y

DME Modifier: NU, KE, RR, UE

C **E2621** Positioning wheelchair back cushion, planar back with lateral supports, width 22 inches or greater, any height, including any type mounting hardware `DME` Y

DME Modifier: NU, KE, RR, UE

C **E2622** Skin protection wheelchair seat cushion, adjustable, width less than 22 inches, any depth `DME` Y

DME Modifier: NU, KE, RR, UE

C **E2623** Skin protection wheelchair seat cushion, adjustable, width 22 inches or greater, any depth `DME` Y

DME Modifier: NU, KE, RR, UE

C **E2624** Skin protection and positioning wheelchair seat cushion, adjustable, width less than 22 inches, any depth `DME` Y

DME Modifier: NU, KE, RR, UE

C **E2625** Skin protection and positioning wheelchair seat cushion, adjustable, width 22 inches or greater, any depth DME Y
DME Modifier: NU, KE, RR, UE

C **E2626** Wheelchair accessory, shoulder elbow, mobile arm support attached to wheelchair, balanced, adjustable DME Y
DME Modifier: NU, RR, UE

C **E2627** Wheelchair accessory, shoulder elbow, mobile arm support attached to wheelchair, balanced, adjustable rancho type DME Y
DME Modifier: NU, RR, UE

C **E2628** Wheelchair accessory, shoulder elbow, mobile arm support attached to wheelchair, balanced, reclining DME Y
DME Modifier: NU, RR, UE

C **E2629** Wheelchair accessory, shoulder elbow, mobile arm support attached to wheelchair, balanced, friction arm support (friction dampening to proximal and distal joints) DME Y
DME Modifier: NU, RR, UE

C **E2630** Wheelchair accessory, shoulder elbow, mobile arm support, mono suspension arm and hand support, overhead elbow forearm hand sling support, yoke type suspension support DME Y
DME Modifier: NU, RR, UE

C **E2631** Wheelchair accessory, addition to mobile arm support, elevating proximal arm DME Y
DME Modifier: NU, RR, UE

C **E2632** Wheelchair accessory, addition to mobile arm support, offset or lateral rocker arm with elastic balance control DME Y
DME Modifier: NU, RR, UE

C **E2633** Wheelchair accessory, addition to mobile arm support, supinator DME Y
DME Modifier: NU, RR, UE

I **E8000** Gait trainer, pediatric size, posterior support, includes all accessories and components A E
Service not separately priced by Part B

I **E8001** Gait trainer, pediatric size, upright support, includes all accessories and components A E
Service not separately priced by Part B

I **E8002** Gait trainer, pediatric size, anterior support, includes all accessories and components A E
Service not separately priced by Part B

▲ Revised Code ● New code **C** Carrier judgment **D** Special coverage instructions apply
I Not payable by Medicare **M** Non-covered by Medicare **S** Non-covered by Medicare statute AHA Coding Clinic®

68

PROCEDURES / PROFESSIONAL SERVICES (G0008-G9472)

C **G0008** Administration of influenza virus vaccine   S
Vaccinations
Pub: 100-2, Chap. 12, 40.11; 100-4, Chap. 18, 10.2.1; 100-4, Chap. 18, 10.2.2.1; 100-4, Chap. 18, 10.2.5.2; 100-4, Chap. 18, 10.3.1.1; 100-4, Chap. 18, 10.4.1; 100-4, Chap. 18, 10.4.2; 100-4, Chap. 18, 10.4.3

C **G0009** Administration of pneumococcal vaccine   S
Vaccinations
Pub: 100-4, Chap. 18, 10.2.2.1

C **G0010** Administration of hepatitis B vaccine   S
Vaccinations
Pub: 100-4, Chap. 18, 10.2.2.1

C **G0027** Semen analysis; presence and/or motility of sperm excluding huhner   ♂ A
Price subject to national limitation amount

D **G0101** Cervical or vaginal cancer screening; pelvic and clinical breast examination   ♀ V
Price established using national RVU's
Coding Clinic 2002, Q4, P8

D **G0102** Prostate cancer screening; digital rectal examination   ♂ N
Price established using national RVU's

D **G0103** Prostate cancer screening; prostate specific antigen test (PSA)   ♂ A
Price subject to national limitation amount

D **G0104** Colorectal cancer screening; flexible sigmoidoscopy   P3 ASC S
Price established using national RVU's
Coding Clinic 2011, Q2, P4
Pub: 100-4, Chap. 18, 60.1; 100-4, Chap. 18, 60.2; 100-4, Chap. 18, 60.6

D **G0105** Colorectal cancer screening; colonoscopy on individual at high risk   A2 ASC T
Price established using national RVU's
Coding Clinic 2011, Q2, P4
Pub: 100-4, Chap. 18, 60.1; 100-4, Chap. 18, 60.2; 100-4, Chap. 18, 60.6

D **G0106** Colorectal cancer screening; alternative to G0104, screening sigmoidoscopy, barium enema   S
Price established using national RVU's
Coding Clinic 2011, Q2, P4
Pub: 100-4, Chap. 18, 60.1; 100-4, Chap. 18, 60.2; 100-4, Chap. 18, 60.6

C **G0108** Diabetes outpatient self-management training services, individual, per 30 minutes A
Price established using national RVU's
Pub: 100-2, Chap. 15, 270; 100-2, Chap. 15, 270.4.3; 100-2, Chap. 15, 300; 100-2, Chap. 15, 300.2; 100-2, Chap. 15, 300.3; 100-2, Chap. 15, 300.4; 100-4, Chap. 4, 300.6; 100-4, Chap. 9, 181; 100-4, Chap. 12, 190.3; 100-4, Chap. 12, 190.7; 100-4, Chap. 18, 120.1

C **G0109** Diabetes outpatient self-management training services, group session (2 or more), per 30 minutes   A
Price established using national RVU's
Pub: 100-2, Chap. 15, 300.2; 100-4, Chap. 4, 300.6; 100-4, Chap. 9, 181

C **G0117** Glaucoma screening for high risk patients furnished by an optometrist or ophthalmologist   S
Price established using national RVU's
Pub: 100-2, Chap. 15, 280.1

C **G0118** Glaucoma screening for high risk patient furnished under the direct supervision of an optometrist or ophthalmologist   S
Price established using national RVU's
Pub: 100-2, Chap. 15, 280.1

D **G0120** Colorectal cancer screening; alternative to G0105, screening colonoscopy, barium enema.   S
Price established using national RVU's
Pub: 100-4, Chap. 18, 60.1; 100-4, Chap. 18, 60.2; 100-4, Chap. 18, 60.6

D **G0121** Colorectal cancer screening; colonoscopy on individual not meeting criteria for high risk   A2 ASC T
Price established using national RVU's
Pub: 100-4, Chap. 18, 60.1; 100-4, Chap. 18, 60.2; 100-4, Chap. 18, 60.6

M **G0122** Colorectal cancer screening; barium enema   E
Service not separately priced by Part B
Pub: 100-4, Chap. 18, 60.2; 100-4, Chap. 18, 60.6

D **G0123** Screening cytopathology, cervical or vaginal (any reporting system), collected in preservative fluid, automated thin layer preparation, screening by cytotechnologist under physician supervision   ♀ A
Price subject to national limitation amount

D **G0124** Screening cytopathology, cervical or vaginal (any reporting system), collected in preservative fluid, automated thin layer preparation, requiring interpretation by physician   ♀ B
Price established using national RVU's

D **G0127** Trimming of dystrophic nails, any number   P3 ASC T
Price established using national RVU's
Pub: 100-2, Chap. 15, 290

D **G0128** Direct (face-to-face with patient) skilled nursing services of a registered nurse provided in a comprehensive outpatient rehabilitation facility, each 10 minutes beyond the first 5 minutes   B
Value not established 1833(a)
Pub: 100-2, Chap. 12, 30.1; 100-2, Chap. 12, 40.8; 100-4, Chap. 5, 20.4

C **G0129** Occupational therapy services requiring the skills of a qualified occupational therapist, furnished as a component of a partial hospitalization treatment program, per session (45 minutes or more)   P
Service not separately priced by Part B

D **G0130** Single energy X-ray absorptiometry (SEXA) bone density study, one or more sites; appendicular skeleton (peripheral) (e.g., radius, wrist, heel)   Z3 ASC X
Price established using national RVU's

C **G0141** Screening cytopathology smears, cervical or vaginal, performed by automated system, with manual rescreening, requiring interpretation by physician   ♀ B
Price established using national RVU's

C **G0143** Screening cytopathology, cervical or vaginal (any reporting system), collected in preservative fluid, automated thin layer preparation, with manual screening and rescreening by cytotechnologist under physician supervision   ♀ A
Price subject to national limitation amount

C **G0144** Screening cytopathology, cervical or vaginal (any reporting system), collected in preservative fluid, automated thin layer preparation, with screening by automated system, under physician supervision   ♀ A
Price subject to national limitation amount

C **G0145** Screening cytopathology, cervical or vaginal (any reporting system), collected in preservative fluid, automated thin layer preparation, with screening by automated system and manual rescreening under physician supervision   ♀ A
Price subject to national limitation amount

C **G0147** Screening cytopathology smears, cervical or vaginal, performed by automated system under physician supervision   ♀ A
Price subject to national limitation amount

C **G0148** Screening cytopathology smears, cervical or vaginal, performed by automated system with manual rescreening   ♀ A
Price subject to national limitation amount

C **G0151** Services performed by a qualified physical therapist in the home health or hospice setting, each 15 minutes   B
Service not separately priced by Part B

C **G0152** Services performed by a qualified occupational therapist in the home health or hospice setting, each 15 minutes   B
Service not separately priced by Part B

C **G0153** Services performed by a qualified speech-language pathologist in the home health or hospice setting, each 15 minutes   B
Service not separately priced by Part B

C **G0154** Direct skilled nursing services of a licensed nurse (LPN or RN) in the home health or hospice setting, each 15 minutes   B
Service not separately priced by Part B

C **G0155** Services of clinical social worker in home health or hospice settings, each 15 minutes   B
Service not separately priced by Part B

C **G0156** Services of home health/hospice aide in home health or hospice settings, each 15 minutes   B
Service not separately priced by Part B

C **G0157** Services performed by a qualified physical therapist assistant in the home health or hospice setting, each 15 minutes   B
Service not separately priced by Part B

C **G0158** Services performed by a qualified occupational therapist assistant in the home health or hospice setting, each 15 minutes   B
Service not separately priced by Part B

C **G0159** Services performed by a qualified physical therapist, in the home health setting, in the establishment or delivery of a safe and effective physical therapy maintenance program, each 15 minutes   B
Service not separately priced by Part B

C **G0160** Services performed by a qualified occupational therapist, in the home health setting, in the establishment or delivery of a safe and effective occupational therapy maintenance program, each 15 minutes   B
Service not separately priced by Part B
Pub: 100-4, Chap. 10, 40.2

C **G0161** Services performed by a qualified speech-language pathologist, in the home health setting, in the establishment or delivery of a safe and effective speech-language pathology maintenance program, each 15 minutes   B
Service not separately priced by Part B

C **G0162** Skilled services by a registered nurse (RN) for management and evaluation of the plan of care; each 15 minutes (the patient's underlying condition or complication requires an RN to ensure that essential non-skilled care achieves its purpose in the home health or hospice setting)   B
Service not separately priced by Part B

C **G0163** Skilled services of a licensed nurse (LPN or RN) for the observation and assessment of the patient's condition, each 15 minutes (the change in the patient's condition requires skilled nursing personnel to identify and evaluate the patient's need for possible modification of treatment in the home health or hospice setting)   B
Service not separately priced by Part B

C **G0164** Skilled services of a licensed nurse (LPN or RN), in the training and/or education of a patient or family member, in the home health or hospice setting, each 15 minutes   B
Service not separately priced by Part B

▲ Revised Code   ● New code   C Carrier judgment   D Special coverage instructions apply
I Not payable by Medicare   M Non-covered by Medicare   S Non-covered by Medicare statute   AHA Coding Clinic®

D **G0166** External counterpulsation, per treatment session T

Price established using national RVU's

Pub: 100-4, Chap. 32, 130; 100-4, Chap. 32, 130.1

C **G0168** Wound closure utilizing tissue adhesive(s) only B

Service not separately priced by Part B

Coding Clinic 2005, Q1, P5;2001, Q4, P12;Q3, P13

C **G0175** Scheduled interdisciplinary team conference (minimum of three exclusive of patient care nursing staff) with patient present V

Service not separately priced by Part B

D **G0176** Activity therapy, such as music, dance, art or play therapies not for recreation, related to the care and treatment of patient's disabling mental health problems, per session (45 minutes or more) P

Service not separately priced by Part B

D **G0177** Training and educational services related to the care and treatment of patient's disabling mental health problems per session (45 minutes or more) N

Service not separately priced by Part B

Pub: 100-1, Chap. 3, 30

C **G0179** Physician re-certification for Medicare-covered home health services under a home health plan of care (patient not present), including contacts with home health agency and review of reports of patient status required by physicians to affirm the initial implementation of the plan of care that meets patient's needs, per re-certification period M

Price established using national RVU's

Pub: 100-4, Chap. 11, 40.1.3.1; 100-4, Chap. 12, 180; 100-4, Chap. 12, 180.1

C **G0180** Physician certification for Medicare-covered home health services under a home health plan of care (patient not present), including contacts with home health agency and review of reports of patient status required by physicians to affirm the initial implementation of the plan of care that meets patient's needs, per certification period M

Price established using national RVU's

Pub: 100-4, Chap. 11, 40.1.3.1; 100-4, Chap. 12, 180; 100-4, Chap. 12, 180.1

C **G0181** Physician supervision of a patient receiving Medicare-covered services provided by a participating home health agency (patient not present) requiring complex and multidisciplinary care modalities involving regular physician development and/or revision of care plans, review of subsequent reports of patient status, review of laboratory and other studies, communication (including telephone calls) with other health care professionals involved in the patient's care,

integration of new information into the medical treatment plan and/or adjustment of medical therapy, within a calendar month, 30 minutes or more M

Price established using national RVU's

Pub: 100-4, Chap. 11, 40.1.3.1; 100-4, Chap. 12, 180; 100-4, Chap. 12, 180.1

C **G0182** Physician supervision of a patient under a Medicare-approved hospice (patient not present) requiring complex and multidisciplinary care modalities involving regular physician development and/or revision of care plans, review of subsequent reports of patient status, review of laboratory and other studies, communication (including telephone calls) with other health care professionals involved in the patient's care, integration of new information into the medical treatment plan and/or adjustment of medical therapy, within a calendar month, 30 minutes or more M

Price established using national RVU's

Pub: 100-4, Chap. 11, 40.1.3.1; 100-4, Chap. 12, 180; 100-4, Chap. 12, 180.1

C **G0186** Destruction of localized lesion of choroid (for example, choroidal neovascularization); photocoagulation, feeder vessel technique (one or more sessions) R2 ASC T

Service not separately priced by Part B

C **G0202** Screening mammography, producing direct digital image, bilateral, all views A

Price established using national RVU's

Pub: 100-4, Chap. 18, 20

▲ **C** **G0204** Diagnostic mammography, producing direct 2-d digital image, bilateral, all views A

Price established using national RVU's

Pub: 100-4, Chap. 18, 20; 100-4, Chap. 18, 20.4

▲ **C** **G0206** Diagnostic mammography, producing direct 2-d digital image, unilateral, all views A

Price established using national RVU's

Coding Clinic 2010, Q4, P5

Pub: 100-4, Chap. 18, 20; 100-4, Chap. 18, 20.4

M **G0219** PET imaging whole body; melanoma for non-covered indications E

Service not separately priced by Part B

Coding Clinic 2007, Q1, P6

Pub: 100-3, Chap. 1, Part-4, 220.6.17

M **G0235** PET imaging, any site, not otherwise specified E

Service not separately priced by Part B

Coding Clinic 2007, Q1, P6

Pub: 100-3, Chap. 1, Part-4, 220.6.17; 100-4, Chap. 13, 60

♂ Male only   ♀ Female only   🅐 Age   A2 - Z3 = ASC Payment Indicator   A - Y = APC Status Indicator

ASC = ASC Approved Procedure   **DME** Paid under the DME fee schedule   **PQRS** Physician Quality Reporting System

C **G0237** Therapeutic procedures to increase strength or endurance of respiratory muscles, face to face, one on one, each 15 minutes (includes monitoring)   S

Price established using national RVU's

Pub: 100-2, Chap. 12, 30.1; 100-2, Chap. 12, 40.5

C **G0238** Therapeutic procedures to improve respiratory function, other than described by G0237, one on one, face to face, per 15 minutes (includes monitoring)   S

Price established using national RVU's

Pub: 100-2, Chap. 12, 40.5

C **G0239** Therapeutic procedures to improve respiratory function or increase strength or endurance of respiratory muscles, two or more individuals (includes monitoring)   S

Price established using national RVU's

Pub: 100-2, Chap. 12, 40.5

D **G0245** Initial physician evaluation and management of a diabetic patient with diabetic sensory neuropathy resulting in a loss of protective sensation (LOPS) which must include: (1) the diagnosis of LOPS, (2) a patient history, (3) a physical examination that consists of at least the following elements: (a) visual inspection of the forefoot, hindfoot and toe web spaces, (b) evaluation of a protective sensation, (c) evaluation of foot structure and biomechanics, (d) evaluation of vascular status and skin integrity, and (e) evaluation and recommendation of footwear and (4) patient education   V

Price established using national RVU's

Pub: 100-4, Chap. 32, 80.2; 100-4, Chap. 32, 80.8

D **G0246** Follow-up physician evaluation and management of a diabetic patient with diabetic sensory neuropathy resulting in a loss of protective sensation (LOPS) to include at least the following: (1) a patient history, (2) a physical examination that includes: (a) visual inspection of the forefoot, hindfoot and toe web spaces, (b) evaluation of protective sensation, (c) evaluation of foot structure and biomechanics, (d) evaluation of vascular status and skin integrity, and (e) evaluation and recommendation of footwear, and (3) patient education   V

Price established using national RVU's

Pub: 100-4, Chap. 32, 80.2; 100-4, Chap. 32, 80.8

D **G0247** Routine foot care by a physician of a diabetic patient with diabetic sensory neuropathy resulting in a loss of protective sensation (LOPS) to include, the local care of superficial wounds (i.e. superficial to muscle and fascia) and at least the following if present: (1) local care of superficial wounds, (2) debridement of corns and calluses, and (3) trimming and debridement of nails   P2 ASC T

Price established using national RVU's

Pub: 100-4, Chap. 32, 80.8

D **G0248** Demonstration, prior to initiation of home INR monitoring, for patient with either mechanical heart valve(s), chronic atrial fibrillation, or venous thromboembolism who meets Medicare coverage criteria, under the direction of a physician; includes: face-to-face demonstration of use and care of the INR monitor, obtaining at least one blood sample, provision of instructions for reporting home INR test results, and documentation of patient's ability to perform testing and report results   V

Price established using national RVU's

Pub: 100-3, Chap. 1, Part 3, 190.11; 100-4, Chap. 32, 60.4.1

D **G0249** Provision of test materials and equipment for home INR monitoring of patient with either mechanical heart valve(s), chronic atrial fibrillation, or venous thromboembolism who meets Medicare coverage criteria; includes: provision of materials for use in the home and reporting of test results to physician; testing not occurring more frequently than once a week; testing materials, billing units of service include 4 tests   V

Price established using national RVU's

D **G0250** Physician review, interpretation, and patient management of home INR testing for patient with either mechanical heart valve(s), chronic atrial fibrillation, or venous thromboembolism who meets Medicare coverage criteria; testing not occurring more frequently than once a week; billing units of service include 4 tests   M

Price established using national RVU's

M **G0252** PET imaging, full and partial-ring PET scanners only, for initial diagnosis of breast cancer and/or surgical planning for breast cancer (e.g., initial staging of axillary lymph nodes)   E

Service not separately priced by Part B

Coding Clinic 2007, Q1, P6

Pub: 100-4, Chap. 13, 60

M **G0255** Current perception threshold/sensory nerve conduction test, (SNCT) per limb, any nerve   E

Service not separately priced by Part B

D **G0257** Unscheduled or emergency dialysis treatment for an ESRD patient in a hospital outpatient department that is not certified as an ESRD facility   S

Service not separately priced by Part B

Coding Clinic 2003, Q1, P9

Pub: 100-4, Chap. 4, 200.2; 100-4, Chap. 8, 60.4.7

D **G0259** Injection procedure for sacroiliac joint; arthrograpy   N1 N

Service not separately priced by Part B

D **G0260** Injection procedure for sacroiliac joint; provision of anesthetic, steroid and/or other therapeutic agent, with or without arthrography   A2 ASC T

Service not separately priced by Part B

C **G0268** Removal of impacted cerumen (one or both ears) by physician on same date of service as audiologic function testing   N1 N

Price established using national RVU's

Coding Clinic 2003, Q1, P12

D **G0269** Placement of occlusive device into either a venous or arterial access site, post surgical or interventional procedure (e.g., angioseal plug, vascular plug)   N1 N

Service not separately priced by Part B

Coding Clinic 2011, Q3, P4;2010, Q4, P6

C **G0270** Medical nutrition therapy; reassessment and subsequent intervention(s) following second referral in same year for change in diagnosis, medical condition or treatment regimen (including additional hours needed for renal disease), individual, face to face with the patient, each 15 minutes   A

Price established using national RVU's

Pub: 100-2, Chap. 15, 270; 100-2, Chap. 15, 270.2; 100-4, Chap. 9, 182; 100-4, Chap. 12, 190.3; 100-4, Chap. 12, 190.7

C **G0271** Medical nutrition therapy, reassessment and subsequent intervention(s) following second referral in same year for change in diagnosis, medical condition, or treatment regimen (including additional hours needed for renal disease), group (2 or more individuals), each 30 minutes   A

Price established using national RVU's

Pub: 100-4, Chap. 9, 182

● **D** **G0276** Blinded procedure for lumbar stenosis, percutaneous image-guided lumbar decompression (PILD) or placebo-control, performed in an approved coverage with evidence development (CED) clinical trial

● **D** **G0277** Hyperbaric oxygen under pressure, full body chamber, per 30 minute interval

C **G0278** Iliac and/or femoral artery angiography, non-selective, bilateral or ipsilateral to catheter insertion, performed at the same time as cardiac catheterization and/or coronary angiography, includes positioning or placement of the catheter in the distal aorta or ipsilateral femoral or iliac artery, injection of dye, production of permanent images, and radiologic supervision and interpretation (list separately in addition to primary procedure) N

Price established using national RVU's

Coding Clinic 2011, Q3, P4;2006, Q4, P7

● **C** **G0279** Diagnostic digital breast tomosynthesis, unilateral or bilateral (list separately in addition to G0204 or G0206)

C **G0281** Electrical stimulation, (unattended), to one or more areas, for chronic Stage III and Stage IV pressure ulcers, arterial ulcers, diabetic ulcers, and venous statsis ulcers not demonstrating measurable signs of healing after 30 days of conventional care, as part of a therapy plan of care   A

Price established using national RVU's

Pub: 100-4, Chap. 32, 11.1

M **G0282** Electrical stimulation, (unattended), to one or more areas, for wound care other than described in G0281   E

Service not separately priced by Part B

Pub: 100-4, Chap. 32, 11.1

C **G0283** Electrical stimulation (unattended), to one or more areas for indication(s) other than wound care, as part of a therapy plan of care   A

Price established using national RVU's

C **G0288** Reconstruction, computed tomographic angiography of aorta for surgical planning for vascular surgery   N1 N

Price established using national RVU's

C **G0289** Arthroscopy, knee, surgical, for removal of loose body, foreign body, debridement/shaving of articular cartilage (chondroplasty) at the time of other surgical knee arthroscopy in a different compartment of the same knee   N1 N

Price established using national RVU's

D **G0293** Noncovered surgical procedure(s) using conscious sedation, regional, general or spinal anesthesia in a Medicare qualifying clinical trial, per day   X

Service not separately priced by Part B

D **G0294** Noncovered procedure(s) using either no anesthesia or local anesthesia only, in a Medicare qualifying clinical trial, per day   X

Service not separately priced by Part B

M **G0295** Electromagnetic therapy, to one or more areas, for wound care other than described in G0329 or for other uses   E

Service not separately priced by Part B

C **G0302** Pre-operative pulmonary surgery services for preparation for LVRS, complete course of services, to include a minimum of 16 days of services   S

Service not separately priced by Part B

C **G0303** Pre-operative pulmonary surgery services for preparation for LVRS, 10 to 15 days of services   S

Service not separately priced by Part B

C **G0304** Pre-operative pulmonary surgery services for preparation for LVRS, 1 to 9 days of services   S

Service not separately priced by Part B

♂ Male only   ♀ Female only   **A** Age   A2 - Z3 = ASC Payment Indicator   A - Y = APC Status Indicator

ASC = ASC Approved Procedure   **DME** Paid under the DME fee schedule   **PQRS** Physician Quality Reporting System

G0305 Post-discharge pulmonary surgery services after LVRS, minimum of 6 days of services S

Service not separately priced by Part B

G0306 Complete CBC, automated (HgB, HCT, RBC, WBC, without platelet count) and automated WBC differential count A

Price subject to national limitation amount

G0307 Complete (CBC), automated (HgB, HCT, RBC, WBC; without platelet count) A

Price subject to national limitation amount

G0328 Colorectal cancer screening; fecal occult blood test, immunoassay, 1-3 simultaneous A

Price subject to national limitation amount

Coding Clinic 2012, Q2, P9

G0329 Electromagnetic therapy, to one or more areas for chronic Stage III and Stage IV pressure ulcers, arterial ulcers, diabetic ulcers and venous stasis ulcers not demonstrating measurable signs of healing after 30 days of conventional care as part of a therapy plan of care A

Service not separately priced by Part B

Pub: 100-4, Chap. 32, 11.2

G0333 Pharmacy dispensing fee for inhalation drug(s); initial 30-day supply as a beneficiary M

G0337 Hospice evaluation and counseling services, pre-election B

Price established using national RVU's

Pub: 100-4, Chap. 11, 10.1

G0339 Image-guided robotic linear accelerator-based stereotactic radiosurgery, complete course of therapy in one session or first session of fractionated treatment S

Price established by carriers

Pub: 100-4, Chap. 4, 200.3.4

G0340 Image-guided robotic linear accelerator-based stereotactic radiosurgery, delivery including collimator changes and custom plugging, fractionated treatment, all lesions, per session, second through fifth sessions, maximum five sessions per course of treatment S

Price established by carriers

Pub: 100-4, Chap. 4, 200.3.4

G0341 Percutaneous islet cell transplant, includes portal vein catheterization and infusion C

Price established by carriers

G0342 Laparoscopy for islet cell transplant, includes portal vein catheterization and infusion C

Price established by carriers

G0343 Laparotomy for islet cell transplant, includes portal vein catheterization and infusion C

Price established by carriers

G0364 Bone marrow aspiration performed with bone marrow biopsy through the same incision on the same date of service P3 ASC X

Price established using national RVU's

G0365 Vessel mapping of vessels for hemodialysis access (services for preoperative vessel mapping prior to creation of hemodialysis access using an autogenous hemodialysis conduit, including arterial inflow and venous outflow) P2 ASC S

Price established using national RVU's

G0372 Physician service required to establish and document the need for a power mobility device M

Price established by carriers

Pub: 100-4, Chap. 12, 30.6.15.4

G0378 Hospital observation service, per hour N

Service not separately priced by Part B

Coding Clinic 2007, Q1, P10;2006, Q3, P7-8

Pub: 100-2, Chap. 6, 20.6; 100-4, Chap. 1, 50.3.2; 100-4, Chap. 4, 290.1; 100-4, Chap. 4, 290.2.2; 100-4, Chap. 4, 290.4.1; 100-4, Chap. 4, 290.4.2; 100-4, Chap. 4, 290.4.3; 100-4, Chap. 4, 290.5.1; 100-4, Chap. 4, 290.5.2

G0379 Direct admission of patient for hospital observation care Q3

Service not separately priced by Part B

Coding Clinic 2007, Q1, P7

Pub: 100-2, Chap. 6, 20.6; 100-4, Chap. 4, 290.4.1; 100-4, Chap. 4, 290.4.2; 100-4, Chap. 4, 290.4.3; 100-4, Chap. 4, 290.5.1; 100-4, Chap. 4, 290.5.2

G0380 Level 1 hospital emergency department visit provided in a type B emergency department; (the ED must meet at least one of the following requirements: (1) it is licensed by the state in which it is located under applicable state law as an emergency room or emergency department; (2) it is held out to the public (by name, posted signs, advertising, or other means) as a place that provides care for emergency medical conditions on an urgent basis without requiring a previously scheduled appointment; or (3) during the calendar year immediately preceding the calendar year in which a determination under 42 CFR 489.24 is being made, based on a representative sample of patient visits that occurred during that calendar year, it provides at least one-third of all of its outpatient visits for the treatment of emergency medical conditions on an urgent basis without requiring a previously scheduled appointment) V

Service not separately priced by Part B

Coding Clinic 2009, Q1, P4;2007, Q2, P1

Pub: 100-4, Chap. 4, 160

G0381 Level 2 hospital emergency department visit provided in a type B emergency department; (the ED must meet at least one of the following requirements: (1) it is licensed by the state in which it is located under applicable state law as an emergency room or emergency department; (2) it is held out to the public (by name, posted

signs, advertising, or other means) as a place that provides care for emergency medical conditions on an urgent basis without requiring a previously scheduled appointment; or (3) during the calendar year immediately preceding the calendar year in which a determination under 42 CFR 489.24 is being made, based on a representative sample of patient visits that occurred during that calendar year, it provides at least one-third of all of its outpatient visits for the treatment of emergency medical conditions on an urgent basis without requiring a previously scheduled appointment)   V
Service not separately priced by Part B
Coding Clinic 2009, Q1, P4;2007, Q2, P1
Pub: 100-4, Chap. 4, 160

C G0382 Level 3 hospital emergency department visit provided in a type B emergency department; (the ED must meet at least one of the following requirements: (1) it is licensed by the state in which it is located under applicable state law as an emergency room or emergency department; (2) it is held out to the public (by name, posted signs, advertising, or other means) as a place that provides care for emergency medical conditions on an urgent basis without requiring a previously scheduled appointment; or (3) during the calendar year immediately preceding the calendar year in which a determination under 42 CFR 489.24 is being made, based on a representative sample of patient visits that occurred during that calendar year, it provides at least one-third of all of its outpatient visits for the treatment of emergency medical conditions on an urgent basis without requiring a previously scheduled appointment)   V
Service not separately priced by Part B
Coding Clinic 2009, Q1, P4;2007, Q2, P1
Pub: 100-4, Chap. 4, 160

C G0383 Level 4 hospital emergency department visit provided in a type B emergency department; (the ED must meet at least one of the following requirements: (1) it is licensed by the state in which it is located under applicable state law as an emergency room or emergency department; (2) it is held out to the public (by name, posted signs, advertising, or other means) as a place that provides care for emergency medical conditions on an urgent basis without requiring a previously scheduled appointment; or (3) during the calendar year immediately preceding the calendar year in which a determination under 42 CFR 489.24 is being made, based on a representative sample of patient visits that occurred during that calendar year, it provides at least one-third of all of its outpatient visits for the

treatment of emergency medical conditions on an urgent basis without requiring a previously scheduled appointment)   V
Service not separately priced by Part B
Coding Clinic 2009, Q1, P4;2007, Q2, P1
Pub: 100-4, Chap. 4, 160

C G0384 Level 5 hospital emergency department visit provided in a type B emergency department; (the ED must meet at least one of the following requirements: (1) it is licensed by the state in which it is located under applicable state law as an emergency room or emergency department; (2) it is held out to the public (by name, posted signs, advertising, or other means) as a place that provides care for emergency medical conditions on an urgent basis without requiring a previously scheduled appointment; or (3) during the calendar year immediately preceding the calendar year in which a determination under 42 CFR 489.24 is being made, based on a representative sample of patient visits that occurred during that calendar year, it provides at least one-third of all of its outpatient visits for the treatment of emergency medical conditions on an urgent basis without requiring a previously scheduled appointment)   Q3
Service not separately priced by Part B
Coding Clinic 2009, Q1, P4;2007, Q2, P1
Pub: 100-4, Chap. 4, 160; 100-4, Chap. 4, 290.5.1

D G0389 Ultrasound B-scan and/or real time with image documentation; for abdominal aortic aneurysm (AAA) screening   S
Price established by carriers
Pub: 100-4, Chap. 4, 160

D G0390 Trauma response team associated with hospital critical care service   S
Service not separately priced by Part B
Coding Clinic 2007, Q2, P5
Pub: 100-4, Chap. 4, 160.1

C G0396 Alcohol and/or substance (other than tobacco) abuse structured assessment (e.g., audit, dast), and brief intervention 15 to 30 minutes   S
Price established using national RVU's
Pub: 100-2, Chap. 15, 270; 100-2, Chap. 15, 270.2; 100-4, Chap. 4, 200.6; 100-4, Chap. 12, 190.3; 100-4, Chap. 12, 190.7

C G0397 Alcohol and/or substance (other than tobacco) abuse structured assessment (e.g., audit, dast), and intervention, greater than 30 minutes   S
Price established using national RVU's
Pub: 100-4, Chap. 4, 200.6

♂ Male only   ♀ Female only   Ⓐ Age   A2 - Z3 = ASC Payment Indicator   A - Y = APC Status Indicator
ASC = ASC Approved Procedure   DME Paid under the DME fee schedule   PQRS Physician Quality Reporting System

75

G0398 - G0420

C **G0398** Home sleep study test (HST) with type II portable monitor, unattended; minimum of 7 channels: eeg, eog, emg, ecg/heart rate, airflow, respiratory effort and oxygen saturation   S

Price established by carriers

Pub: 100-3, Chap. 1, Part-4, 240.4

C **G0399** Home sleep test (HST) with type III portable monitor, unattended; minimum of 4 channels: 2 respiratory movement/airflow, 1 ecg/heart rate and 1 oxygen saturation   S

Price established by carriers

C **G0400** Home sleep test (HST) with type IV portable monitor, unattended; minimum of 3 channels   S

Price established by carriers

C **G0402** Initial preventive physical examination; face-to-face visit, services limited to new beneficiary during the first 12 months of Medicare enrollment   PQRS V

Price established using national RVU's

Coding Clinic 2009, Q4, P8

Pub: 100-4, Chap. 9, 150; 100-4, Chap. 12, 80.1; 100-4, Chap. 12, 100.1.1; 100-4, Chap. 18, 80; 100-4, Chap. 18, 80.1; 100-4, Chap. 18, 80.2; 100-4, Chap. 18, 80.3.3; 100-4, Chap. 18, 80.4; 100-4, Chap. 18, 140.6

C **G0403** Electrocardiogram, routine ECG with 12 leads; performed as a screening for the initial preventive physical examination with interpretation and report   M

Price established using national RVU's

C **G0404** Electrocardiogram, routine ECG with 12 leads; tracing only, without interpretation and report, performed as a screening for the initial preventive physical examination   S

Price established using national RVU's

Pub: 100-4, Chap. 18, 80.3.3

C **G0405** Electrocardiogram, routine ECG with 12 leads; interpretation and report only, performed as a screening for the initial preventive physical examination   B

Price established using national RVU's

C **G0406** Follow-up inpatient consultation, limited, physicians typically spend 15 minutes communicating with the patient via telehealth   B

Price established by carriers

Pub: 100-2, Chap. 15, 270; 100-2, Chap. 15, 270.2; 100-4, Chap. 12, 190.3; 100-4, Chap. 12, 190.3.1; 100-4, Chap. 12, 190.3.3; 100-4, Chap. 12, 190.7

C **G0407** Follow-up inpatient consultation, intermediate, physicians typically spend 25 minutes communicating with the patient via telehealth   B

Price established using national RVU's

C **G0408** Follow-up inpatient consultation, complex, physicians typically spend 35 minutes communicating with the patient via telehealth   B

Price established using national RVU's

C **G0409** Social work and psychological services, directly relating to and/or furthering the patient's rehabilitation goals, each 15 minutes, face-to-face; individual (services provided by a CORF-qualified social worker or psychologist in a CORF)   M

Price established by carriers

Pub: 100-2, Chap. 12, 30.1; 100-4, Chap. 5, 100.4; 100-4, Chap. 5, 100.11

C **G0410** Group psychotherapy other than of a multiple-family group, in a partial hospitalization setting, approximately 45 to 50 minutes   P

Price established by carriers

Coding Clinic 2009, Q4, P9, 10

C **G0411** Interactive group psychotherapy, in a partial hospitalization setting, approximately 45 to 50 minutes   P

Price established by carriers

Coding Clinic 2009, Q4, P9, 10

C **G0412** Open treatment of iliac spine(s), tuberosity avulsion, or iliac wing fracture(s), unilateral or bilateral for pelvic bone fracture patterns which do not disrupt the pelvic ring includes internal fixation, when performed   C

Price established by carriers

C **G0413** Percutaneous skeletal fixation of posterior pelvic bone fracture and/or dislocation, for fracture patterns which disrupt the pelvic ring, unilateral or bilateral, (includes ilium, sacroiliac joint and/or sacrum)   T

Price established by carriers

C **G0414** Open treatment of anterior pelvic bone fracture and/or dislocation for fracture patterns which disrupt the pelvic ring, unilateral or bilateral, includes internal fixation when performed (includes pubic symphysis and/or superior/inferior rami)   C

Price established by carriers

C **G0415** Open treatment of posterior pelvic bone fracture and/or dislocation, for fracture patterns which disrupt the pelvic ring, unilateral or bilateral, includes internal fixation, when performed (includes ilium, sacroiliac joint and/or sacrum)   C

Price established by carriers

▲ C **G0416** Surgical pathology, gross and microscopic examinations, for prostate needle biopsy, any method   ♂ X

Price established by carriers

C **G0420** Face-to-face educational services related to the care of chronic kidney disease; individual, per session, per one hour   A

Price established using national RVU's

Pub: 100-2, Chap. 15, 270; 100-2, Chap. 15, 270.2; 100-2, Chap. 15, 310; 100-2, Chap. 15, 310.1; 100-2, Chap. 15, 310.2; 100-2, Chap. 15, 310.3; 100-2, Chap. 15, 310.4; 100-2, Chap. 15, 310.5; 100-4, Chap. 12, 190.3; 100-4, Chap. 12, 190.7

▲ Revised Code   ● New code   C Carrier judgment   D Special coverage instructions apply

I Not payable by Medicare   M Non-covered by Medicare   S Non-covered by Medicare statute   AHA Coding Clinic®

C **G0421** Face-to-face educational services related to the care of chronic kidney disease; group, per session, per one hour   A
Price established using national RVU's

C **G0422** Intensive cardiac rehabilitation; with or without continuous ECG monitoring with exercise, per session   S
Price established using national RVU's
Pub: 100-2, Chap. 15, 232; 100-4, Chap. 32, 140.2.2.1; 100-4, Chap. 32, 140.3; 100-4, Chap. 32, 140.3.1

C **G0423** Intensive cardiac rehabilitation; with or without continuous ECG monitoring; without exercise, per session   S
Price established using national RVU's
Pub: 100-4, Chap. 32, 140.3.1

C **G0424** Pulmonary rehabilitation, including exercise (includes monitoring), one hour, per session, up to two sessions per day   S
Price established using national RVU's
Pub: 100-2, Chap. 15, 231; 100-4, Chap. 32, 140.4; 100-4, Chap. 32, 140.4.1

C **G0425** Telehealth consultation, emergency department or initial inpatient, typically 30 minutes communicating with the patient via telehealth   B
Price established by carriers
Pub: 100-2, Chap. 15, 270; 100-2, Chap. 15, 270.2; 100-4, Chap. 12, 190.3; 100-4, Chap. 12, 190.3.1; 100-4, Chap. 12, 190.3.2; 100-4, Chap. 12, 190.7

C **G0426** Telehealth consultation, emergency department or initial inpatient, typically 50 minutes communicating with the patient via telehealth   B
Price established by carriers

C **G0427** Telehealth consultation, emergency department or initial inpatient, typically 70 minutes or more communicating with the patient via telehealth   B
Price established by carriers

M **G0428** Collagen meniscus implant procedure for filling meniscal defects (e.g., CMI, collagen scaffold, Menaflex)   E
Service not separately priced by Part B
Pub: 100-3, Chap. 1, Part 2, 150.12

C **G0429** Dermal filler injection(s) for the treatment of facial lipodystrophy syndrome (LDS) (e.g., as a result of highly active antiretroviral therapy)   B
Price established by carriers
Coding Clinic 2010, Q3, P8
Pub: 100-3, Chap. 1, Part-4, 250.5; 100-4, Chap. 32, 260.1; 100-4, Chap. 32, 260.2.1; 100-4, Chap. 32, 260.2.2

C **G0431** Drug screen, qualitative; multiple drug classes by high complexity test method (e.g., immunoassay, enzyme assay), per patient encounter   A

Price established by carriers

C **G0432** Infectious agent antibody detection by enzyme immunoassay (EIA) technique, HIV-1 and/or HIV-2, screening   A
Price subject to national limitation amount
Coding Clinic 2010, Q2, P10
Pub: 100-3, Chap. 1, Part 3, 190.14; 100-3, Chap. 1, Part-4, 210.7; 100-4, Chap. 18, 130, 130.1; 100-4, Chap. 18, 130, 130.4

C **G0433** Infectious agent antibody detection by enzyme-linked immunosorbent assay (ELISA) technique, HIV-1 and/or HIV-2, screening   A
Price subject to national limitation amount
Coding Clinic 2010, Q2, P10
Pub: 100-3, Chap. 1, Part-4, 210.7; 100-4, Chap. 16, 70.8; 100-4, Chap. 18, 130, 130.1; 100-4, Chap. 18, 130, 130.4

C **G0434** Drug screen, other than chromatographic; any number of drug classes, by CLIA waived test or moderate complexity test, per patient encounter   A
Price subject to national limitation amount
Coding Clinic 2012, Q2, P9
Pub: 100-4, Chap. 16, 70.8

C **G0435** Infectious agent antibody detection by rapid antibody test, HIV-1 and/or HIV-2, screening   A
Price subject to national limitation amount
Coding Clinic 2010, Q2, P10
Pub: 100-3, Chap. 1, Part-4, 210.7; 100-4, Chap. 18, 130, 130.1; 100-4, Chap. 18, 130, 130.4

C **G0436** Smoking and tobacco cessation counseling visit for the asymptomatic patient; intermediate, greater than 3 minutes, up to 10 minutes   S
Price established by carriers
Coding Clinic 2011, Q1, P5
Pub: 100-2, Chap. 15, 270; 100-2, Chap. 15, 270.2; 100-3, Chap. 1, Part 4, 210.4; 100-4, Chap. 12, 190.3; 100-4, Chap. 12, 190.7; 100-4, Chap. 18, 150.2; 100-4, Chap. 18, 150.4

C **G0437** Smoking and tobacco cessation counseling visit for the asymptomatic patient; intensive, greater than 10 minutes   S
Price established by carriers
Coding Clinic 2011, Q1, P5

C **G0438** Annual wellness visit; includes a personalized prevention plan of service (PPPS), initial visit   **PQRS** A
Price established by carriers
Pub: 100-2, Chap. 15, 280.5; 100-4, Chap. 12, 100.1.1; 100-4, Chap. 18, 140; 100-4, Chap. 18, 140.1; 100-4, Chap. 18, 140.5; 100-4, Chap. 18, 140.6

♂ Male only   ♀ Female only   **A** Age   A2 - Z3 = ASC Payment Indicator   A - Y = APC Status Indicator
ASC = ASC Approved Procedure   **DME** Paid under the DME fee schedule   **PQRS** Physician Quality Reporting System

C **G0439** Annual wellness visit, includes a personalized prevention plan of service (PPPS), subsequent visit   **PQRS** A

Price established by carriers

Pub: 100-2, Chap. 15, 280.5; 100-4, Chap. 18, 140; 100-4, Chap. 18, 140.1; 100-4, Chap. 18, 140.5

C **G0442** Annual alcohol misuse screening, 15 minutes   S

Price established by carriers

Coding Clinic 2012, Q1, P7

Pub: 100-2, Chap. 15, 270; 100-2, Chap. 15, 270.2; 100-3, Chap. 1, Part-4, 210.8; 100-4, Chap. 12, 190.3; 100-4, Chap. 12, 190.7; 100-4, Chap. 18, 180; 100-4, Chap. 18, 180.1; 100-4, Chap. 18, 180.2; 100-4, Chap. 18, 180.3; 100-4, Chap. 18, 180.4; 100-4, Chap. 18, 180.5

C **G0443** Brief face-to-face behavioral counseling for alcohol misuse, 15 minutes   S

Price established by carriers

Coding Clinic 2012, Q1, P7

Pub: 100-4, Chap. 18, 180; 100-4, Chap. 18, 180.1; 100-4, Chap. 18, 180.2; 100-4, Chap. 18, 180.3; 100-4, Chap. 18, 180.4; 100-4, Chap. 18, 180.5

C **G0444** Annual depression screening, 15 minutes   S

Price established by carriers

Pub: 100-4, Chap. 18, 190; 100-4, Chap. 18, 190.1; 100-4, Chap. 18, 190.2; 100-4, Chap. 18, 190.3

C **G0445** High intensity behavioral counseling to prevent sexually transmitted infection; face-to-face, individual, includes: education, skills training and guidance on how to change sexual behavior; performed semi-annually, 30 minutes   S

Price established by carriers

Pub: 100-3, Chap. 1, Part-4, 210.10; 100-4, Chap. 18, 170.1; 100-4, Chap. 18, 170.2; 100-4, Chap. 18, 170.3; 100-4, Chap. 18, 170.4; 100-4, Chap. 18, 170.4.1; 100-4, Chap. 18, 170.5

C **G0446** Annual, face-to-face intensive behavioral therapy for cardiovascular disease, individual, 15 minutes   S

Price established by carriers

Coding Clinic 2012, Q2, P8

Pub: 100-3, Chap. 1, Part-4, 210.11; 100-4, Chap. 18, 160; 100-4, Chap. 18, 160.1; 100-4, Chap. 18, 160.2.1; 100-4, Chap. 18, 160.2.2; 100-4, Chap. 18, 160.3; 100-4, Chap. 18, 160.4; 100-4, Chap. 18, 160.5

C **G0447** Face-to-face behavioral counseling for obesity, 15 minutes   S

Price established by carriers

Coding Clinic 2012, Q1, P8

Pub: 100-3, Chap. 1, Part-4, 210.12; 100-4, Chap. 18, 200; 100-4, Chap. 18, 200.1; 100-4, Chap. 18, 200.2; 100-4, Chap. 18, 200.3; 100-4, Chap. 18, 200.4; 100-4, Chap. 18, 200.5

C **G0448** Insertion or replacement of a permanent pacing cardioverter-defibrillator system with transvenous lead(s), single or dual chamber with insertion of pacing electrode, cardiac venous system, for left ventricular pacing   J8 B

Price established by carriers

C **G0451** Development testing, with interpretation and report, per standardized instrument form   Q3

Price established by carriers

Pub: 100-1, Chap. 3, 30

C **G0452** Molecular pathology procedure; physician interpretation and report   B

Price established by carriers

C **G0453** Continuous intraoperative neurophysiology monitoring, from outside the operating room (remote or nearby), per patient, (attention directed exclusively to one patient) each 15 minutes (list in addition to primary procedure)   N1 N

Price established by carriers

C **G0454** Physician documentation of face-to-face visit for durable medical equipment determination performed by nurse practitioner, physician assistant or clinical nurse specialist   B

Price established by carriers

C **G0455** Preparation with instillation of fecal microbiota by any method, including assessment of donor specimen   X

Price established by carriers

C **G0458** Low dose rate (LDR) prostate brachytherapy services, composite rate   G2 ASC B

Service not separately priced by Part B

C **G0459** Inpatient telehealth pharmacologic management, including prescription, use, and review of medication with no more than minimal medical psychotherapy   B

Price established by carriers

Pub: 100-2, Chap. 15, 270; 100-2, Chap. 15, 270.2; 100-4, Chap. 12, 190.3; 100-4, Chap. 12, 190.7

C **G0460** Autologous platelet rich plasma for chronic wounds/ulcers, including phlebotomy, centrifugation, and all other preparatory procedures, administration and dressings, per treatment   T

Price established by carriers

Pub: 100-3, Chap. 1, Part-4, 270.3; 100-4, Chap. 32, 11.3.1; 100-4, Chap. 32, 11.3.2; 100-4, Chap. 32, 11.3.3; 100-4, Chap. 32, 11.3.4; 100-4, Chap. 32, 11.3.5; 100-4, Chap. 32, 11.3.6

C **G0463** Hospital outpatient clinic visit for assessment and management of a patient

Service not separately priced by Part B

● **C** **G0464** Colorectal cancer screening; stool-based DNA and fecal occult hemoglobin (e.g., KRAS, NDRG4 and BMP3)

▲ Revised Code   ● New code   **C** Carrier judgment   **D** Special coverage instructions apply
I Not payable by Medicare   **M** Non-covered by Medicare   **S** Non-covered by Medicare statute   AHA Coding Clinic®

- **C** **G0466** Federally qualified health center (FQHC) visit, new patient; a medically-necessary, face-to-face encounter (one-on-one) between a new patient and a FQHC practitioner during which time one or more FQHC services are rendered and includes a typical bundle of medicare-covered services that would be furnished per diem to a patient receiving a FQHC visit

- **C** **G0467** Federally qualified health center (FQHC) visit, established patient; a medically-necessary, face-to-face encounter (one-on-one) between an established patient and a FQHC practitioner during which time one or more FQHC services are rendered and includes a typical bundle of medicare-covered services that would be furnished per diem to a patient receiving a FQHC visit

- **C** **G0468** Federally qualified health center (FQHC) visit, ippe or awv; a FQHC visit that includes an initial preventive physical examination (IPPE) or annual wellness visit (AWV) and includes a typical bundle of medicare-covered services that would be furnished per diem to a patient receiving an IPPE or AWV

- **C** **G0469** Federally qualified health center (FQHC) visit, mental health, new patient; a medically-necessary, face-to-face mental health encounter (one-on-one) between a new patient and a FQHC practitioner during which time one or more FQHC services are rendered and includes a typical bundle of medicare-covered services that would be furnished per diem to a patient receiving a mental health visit

- **C** **G0470** Federally qualified health center (FQHC) visit, mental health, established patient; a medically-necessary, face-to-face mental health encounter (one-on-one) between an established patient and a FQHC practitioner during which time one or more FQHC services are rendered and includes a typical bundle of medicare-covered services that would be furnished per diem to a patient receiving a mental health visit

- **C** **G0471** Collection of venous blood by venipuncture or urine sample by catheterization from an individual in a skilled nursing facility (SNF) or by a laboratory on behalf of a home health agency (HHA)

- **D** **G0472** Hepatitis C antibody screening, for individual at high risk and other covered indication(s)

- **C** **G0473** Face-to-face behavioral counseling for obesity, group (2-10), 30 minutes

- **C** **G0913** Improvement in visual function achieved within 90 days following cataract surgery **PQRS** M
  Service not separately priced by Part B

- **C** **G0914** Patient care survey was not completed by patient **PQRS** M
  Service not separately priced by Part B

- **C** **G0915** Improvement in visual function not achieved within 90 days following cataract surgery **PQRS** M
  Service not separately priced by Part B

- **C** **G0916** Satisfaction with care achieved within 90 days following cataract surgery **PQRS** M
  Service not separately priced by Part B

- **C** **G0917** Patient satisfaction survey was not completed by patient **PQRS** M
  Service not separately priced by Part B

- **C** **G0918** Satisfaction with care not achieved within 90 days following cataract surgery **PQRS** M
  Service not separately priced by Part B

- **C** **G3001** Administration and supply of tositumomab, 450 mg S
  Price established by carriers

- **D** **G6001** Ultrasonic guidance for placement of radiation therapy fields

- **C** **G6002** Stereoscopic X-ray guidance for localization of target volume for the delivery of radiation therapy

- **C** **G6003** Radiation treatment delivery, single treatment area, single port or parallel opposed ports, simple blocks or no blocks: up to 5 MeV

- **C** **G6004** Radiation treatment delivery, single treatment area, single port or parallel opposed ports, simple blocks or no blocks: 6-10 MeV

- **C** **G6005** Radiation treatment delivery, single treatment area, single port or parallel opposed ports, simple blocks or no blocks: 11-19 MeV

- **C** **G6006** Radiation treatment delivery, single treatment area, single port or parallel opposed ports, simple blocks or no blocks: 20 MeV or greater

- **C** **G6007** Radiation treatment delivery, 2 separate treatment areas, 3 or more ports on a single treatment area, use of multiple blocks: up to 5 MeV

- **C** **G6008** Radiation treatment delivery, 2 separate treatment areas, 3 or more ports on a single treatment area, use of multiple blocks: 6-10 MeV

- **C** **G6009** Radiation treatment delivery, 2 separate treatment areas, 3 or more ports on a single treatment area, use of multiple blocks: 11-19 MeV

- **C** **G6010** Radiation treatment delivery, 2 separate treatment areas, 3 or more ports on a single treatment area, use of multiple blocks: 20 MeV or greater

- **C** **G6011** Radiation treatment delivery, 3 or more separate treatment areas, custom blocking, tangential ports, wedges, rotational beam, compensators, electron beam; up to 5 MeV

- **C** **G6012** Radiation treatment delivery, 3 or more separate treatment areas, custom blocking, tangential ports, wedges, rotational beam, compensators, electron beam; 6-10 MeV

♂ Male only   ♀ Female only   **A** Age   A2 - Z3 = ASC Payment Indicator   A - Y = APC Status Indicator

ASC = ASC Approved Procedure   **DME** Paid under the DME fee schedule   **PQRS** Physician Quality Reporting System

PROCEDURES / PROFESSIONAL SERVICES (G0008-G9472)   G6013 - G8400

- C **G6013** Radiation treatment delivery, 3 or more separate treatment areas, custom blocking, tangential ports, wedges, rotational beam, compensators, electron beam; 11-19 MeV

- C **G6014** Radiation treatment delivery, 3 or more separate treatment areas, custom blocking, tangential ports, wedges, rotational beam, compensators, electron beam; 20 MeV or greater

- C **G6015** Intensity modulated treatment delivery, single or multiple fields/arcs, via narrow spatially and temporally modulated beams, binary, dynamic MLC, per treatment session

- C **G6016** Compensator-based beam modulation treatment delivery of inverse planned treatment using 3 or more high resolution (milled or cast) compensator, convergent beam modulated fields, per treatment session

- C **G6017** Intra-fraction localization and tracking of target or patient motion during delivery of radiation therapy (e.g., 3D positional tracking, gating, 3D surface tracking), each fraction of treatment

- C **G6018** Ileoscopy, through stoma; with transendoscopic stent placement (includes predilation)

- C **G6019** Colonoscopy through stoma; with ablation of tumor(s), polyp(s), or other lesion(s) not amenable to removal by hot biopsy forceps, bipolar cautery or snare technique

- C **G6020** Colonoscopy through stoma; with transendoscopic stent placement (includes predilation)

- C **G6021** Unlisted procedure, intestine

- C **G6022** Sigmoidoscopy, flexible; with ablation of tumor(s), polyp(s), or other lesions(s) not amenable to removal by hot biopsy forceps, bipolar cautery or snare technique

- C **G6023** Sigmoidoscopy, flexible; with transendoscopic stent placement (includes predilation)

- C **G6024** Colonoscopy, flexible; proximal to splenic flexure; with ablation of tumor(s), polyp(s), or other lesion(s) not amenable to removal by hot biopsy forceps, bipolar cautery or snare technique

- C **G6025** Colonoscopy, flexible, proximal to splenic flexure; with transendoscopic stent placement (includes predilation)

- C **G6027** Anoscopy, high resolution (HRA) (with magnification and chemical agent enhancement); diagnostic, including collection of specimen(s) by brushing or washing when performed

- C **G6028** Anoscopy, high resolution (HRA) (with magnification and chemical agent enhancement); with biopsy(ies)

- C **G6030** Amitriptyline

- C **G6031** Benzodiazepines

- C **G6032** Desipramine

- C **G6034** Doxepin

- C **G6035** Gold

- C **G6036** Assay of imipramine

- C **G6037** Nortriptyline

- C **G6038** Salicylate

- C **G6039** Acetaminophen

- C **G6040** Alcohol (ethanol); any specimen except breath

- C **G6041** Alkaloids, urine, quantitative

- C **G6042** Amphetamine or methamphetamine

- C **G6043** Barbiturates, not elsewhere specified

- C **G6044** Cocaine or metabolite

- C **G6045** Dihydrocodeinone

- C **G6046** Dihydromorphinone

- C **G6047** Dihydrotestosterone

- C **G6048** Dimethadione

- C **G6049** Epiandrosterone

- C **G6050** Ethchlorvynol

- C **G6051** Flurazepam

- C **G6052** Meprobamate

- C **G6053** Methadone

- C **G6054** Methsuximide

- C **G6055** Nicotine

- C **G6056** Opiate(s), drug and metabolites, each procedure

- C **G6057** Phenothiazine

- C **G6058** Drug confirmation, each procedure

C **G8395** Left ventricular ejection fraction (LVEF) >= 40% or documentation as normal or mildly depressed left ventricular systolic function   PQRS M
Service not separately priced by Part B

C **G8396** Left ventricular ejection fraction (LVEF) not performed or documented   PQRS M
Service not separately priced by Part B

C **G8397** Dilated macular or fundus exam performed, including documentation of the presence or absence of macular edema and level of severity of retinopathy   M
Service not separately priced by Part B

C **G8398** Dilated macular or fundus exam not performed   M
Service not separately priced by Part B

C **G8399** Patient with central dual-energy X-ray absorptiometry (DXA) results documented or ordered or pharmacologic therapy (other than minerals/vitamins) for osteoporosis prescribed)   PQRS M
Service not separately priced by Part B

C **G8400** Patient with central dual-energy X-ray absorptiometry (DXA) results not documented or not ordered or pharmacologic therapy (other than minerals/vitamins) for osteoporosis not prescribed, reason not given   PQRS M
Service not separately priced by Part B

▲ Revised Code   ● New code   C Carrier judgment   D Special coverage instructions apply
I Not payable by Medicare   M Non-covered by Medicare   S Non-covered by Medicare statute   AHA Coding Clinic®

C **G8401** Clinician documented that patient was not an eligible candidate for screening or therapy for osteoporosis for women measure ♀ PQRS M
Service not separately priced by Part B

C **G8404** Lower extremity neurological exam performed and documented M
Service not separately priced by Part B

C **G8405** Lower extremity neurological exam not performed M
Service not separately priced by Part B

C **G8410** Footwear evaluation performed and documented M
Service not separately priced by Part B

C **G8415** Footwear evaluation was not performed M
Service not separately priced by Part B

C **G8416** Clinician documented that patient was not an eligible candidate for footwear evaluation measure M
Service not separately priced by Part B

C **G8417** BMI is documented above normal parameters and a follow-up plan is documented PQRS M
Service not separately priced by Part B

C **G8418** BMI is documented below normal parameters and a follow-up plan is documented PQRS M
Service not separately priced by Part B

C **G8419** BMI documented outside normal parameters, no follow-up plan documented, no reason given PQRS M
Service not separately priced by Part B

C **G8420** BMI is documented within normal parameters and no follow-up plan is required PQRS M
Service not separately priced by Part B

C **G8421** BMI not documented and no reason is given PQRS M
Service not separately priced by Part B

C **G8422** BMI not documented, documentation the patient is not eligible for BMI calculation PQRS M
Service not separately priced by Part B

C **G8427** Eligible professional attests to documenting in the medical record they obtained, updated, or reviewed the patient's current medications PQRS M
Service not separately priced by Part B

C **G8428** Current list of medications not documented as obtained, updated, or reviewed by the eligible professional, reason not given PQRS M
Service not separately priced by Part B

C **G8430** Eligible professional attests to documenting in the medical record the patient is not eligible for a current list of medications being obtained, updated, or reviewed by the eligible professional PQRS M
Service not separately priced by Part B

C **G8431** Screening for clinical depression is documented as being positive and a follow-up plan is documented M
Service not separately priced by Part B

C **G8432** Clinical depression screening not documented, reason not given M
Service not separately priced by Part B

C **G8433** Screening for clinical depression not documented, documentation stating the patient is not eligible M
Service not separately priced by Part B

C **G8442** Pain assessment not documented as being performed, documentation the patient is not eligible for a pain assessment using a standardized tool M
Service not separately priced by Part B

C **G8450** Beta-blocker therapy prescribed PQRS M
Service not separately priced by Part B

C **G8451** Beta-blocker therapy for LVEF < 40% not prescribed for reasons documented by the clinician (e.g., low blood pressure, fluid overload, asthma, patients recently treated with an intravenous positive inotropic agent, allergy, intolerance, other medical reasons, patient declined, other patient reasons, or other reasons attributable to the healthcare system) PQRS M
Service not separately priced by Part B

C **G8452** Beta-blocker therapy not prescribed PQRS M
Service not separately priced by Part B

C **G8458** Clinician documented that patient is not an eligible candidate for genotype testing; patient not receiving antiviral treatment for hepatitis C PQRS M
Service not separately priced by Part B

C **G8460** Clinician documented that patient is not an eligible candidate for quantitative RNA testing at week 12; patient not receiving antiviral treatment for hepatitis C PQRS M
Service not separately priced by Part B

▲ C **G8461** Patient receiving antiviral treatment for hepatitis C during the measurement period PQRS M
Service not separately priced by Part B

C **G8465** High risk of recurrence of prostate cancer ♂ M
Service not separately priced by Part B

C **G8473** Angiotensin converting enzyme (ACE) inhibitor or angiotensin receptor blocker (ARB) therapy prescribed M
Service not separately priced by Part B

♂ Male only   ♀ Female only   🅐 Age   A2 - Z3 = ASC Payment Indicator   A - Y = APC Status Indicator
ASC = ASC Approved Procedure   DME Paid under the DME fee schedule   PQRS Physician Quality Reporting System

▲ C **G8474** Angiotensin converting enzyme (ACE) inhibitor or angiotensin receptor blocker (ARB) therapy not prescribed for reasons documented by the clinician (e.g., allergy, intolerance, pregnancy, renal failure due to ACE inhibitor, diseases of the aortic or mitral valve, other medical reasons) or (e.g., patient declined, other patient reasons) or (e.g., lack of drug availability, other reasons attributable to the health care system) M
Service not separately priced by Part B

C **G8475** Angiotensin converting enzyme (ACE) inhibitor or angiotensin receptor blocker (ARB) therapy not prescribed, reason not given M
Service not separately priced by Part B

▲ C **G8476** Most recent blood pressure has a systolic measurement of < 140 mmHg and a diastolic measurement of < 90 mmHg PQRS M
Service not separately priced by Part B

▲ C **G8477** Most recent blood pressure has a systolic measurement of >=140 mmHg and/or a diastolic measurement of >=90 mmHg PQRS M
Service not separately priced by Part B

C **G8478** Blood pressure measurement not performed or documented, reason not given PQRS M
Service not separately priced by Part B

C **G8482** Influenza immunization administered or previously received PQRS M
Service not separately priced by Part B

▲ C **G8483** Influenza immunization was not administered for reasons documented by clinician (e.g., patient allergy or other medical reasons, patient declined or other patient reasons, vaccine not available or other system reasons) PQRS M
Service not separately priced by Part B

▲ C **G8484** Influenza immunization was not administered, reason not given PQRS M
Service not separately priced by Part B

C **G8485** I intend to report the diabetes mellitus (DM) measures group PQRS M
Service not separately priced by Part B

C **G8486** I intend to report the preventive care measures group PQRS M
Service not separately priced by Part B

C **G8487** I intend to report the chronic kidney disease (CKD) measures group PQRS M
Service not separately priced by Part B

C **G8489** I intend to report the coronary artery disease (CAD) measures group PQRS M
Service not separately priced by Part B

C **G8490** I intend to report the rheumatoid arthritis (RA) measures group PQRS M
Service not separately priced by Part B

C **G8491** I intend to report the HIV/AIDS measures group PQRS M
Service not separately priced by Part B

C **G8494** All quality actions for the applicable measures in the diabetes mellitus (DM) measures group have been performed for this patient PQRS M
Service not separately priced by Part B

C **G8495** All quality actions for the applicable measures in the chronic kidney disease (CKD) measures group have been performed for this patient PQRS M
Service not separately priced by Part B

C **G8496** All quality actions for the applicable measures in the preventive care measures group have been performed for this patient PQRS M
Service not separately priced by Part B

C **G8497** All quality actions for the applicable measures in the coronary artery bypass graft (CABG) measures group have been performed for this patient PQRS M
Service not separately priced by Part B

C **G8498** All quality actions for the applicable measures in the coronary artery disease (CAD) measures group have been performed for this patient PQRS M
Service not separately priced by Part B

C **G8499** All quality actions for the applicable measures in the rheumatoid arthritis (RA) measures group have been performed for this patient PQRS M
Service not separately priced by Part B

C **G8500** All quality actions for the applicable measures in the HIV/AIDS measures group have been performed for this patient PQRS M
Service not separately priced by Part B

C **G8506** Patient receiving angiotensin converting enzyme (ACE) inhibitor or angiotensin receptor blocker (ARB) therapy PQRS M
Service not separately priced by Part B

C **G8509** Pain assessment documented as positive using a standardized tool, follow-up plan not documented, reason not given M
Service not separately priced by Part B

C **G8510** Screening for clinical depression is documented as negative, a follow-up plan is not required M
Service not separately priced by Part B

C **G8511** Screening for clinical depression documented as positive, follow up plan not documented, reason not given M
Service not separately priced by Part B

C **G8530** Autogenous AV fistula received M
Service not separately priced by Part B

C **G8531** Clinician documented that patient was not an eligible candidate for autogenous AV fistula M
Service not separately priced by Part B

▲ Revised Code   ● New code   C Carrier judgment   D Special coverage instructions apply

I Not payable by Medicare   M Non-covered by Medicare   S Non-covered by Medicare statute   AHA Coding Clinic®

C **G8532** Clinician documented that patient recevied vascular access other than autogenous AV fistula, reason not given **M**
Service not separately priced by Part B

C **G8535** Elder maltreatment screen not documented; documentation that patient not eligible for the elder maltreatment screen **Ⓐ** **M**
Service not separately priced by Part B

C **G8536** No documentation of an elder maltreatment screen, reason not given **Ⓐ** **M**
Service not separately priced by Part B

C **G8539** Functional outcome assessment documented as positive using a standardized tool and a care plan based on identified deficiencies on the date of functional outcome assessment, is documented **M**
Service not separately priced by Part B

C **G8540** Functional outcome assessment not documented as being performed, documentation the patient is not eligible for a functional outcome assessment using a standardized tool **M**
Service not separately priced by Part B

C **G8541** Functional outcome assessment using a standardized tool not documented, reason not given **M**
Service not separately priced by Part B

C **G8542** Functional outcome assessment using a standardized tool is documented; no functional deficiencies identified, care plan not required **M**
Service not separately priced by Part B

C **G8543** Documentation of a positive functional outcome assessment using a standardized tool; care plan not documented, reason not given **M**
Service not separately priced by Part B

C **G8544** I intend to report the coronary artery bypass graft (CABG) measures group **PQRS** **M**
Service not separately priced by Part B

C **G8545** I intend to report the hepatitis C measures group **PQRS** **M**
Service not separately priced by Part B

C **G8548** I intend to report the heart failure (HF) measures group **PQRS** **M**
Service not separately priced by Part B

C **G8549** All quality actions for the applicable measures in the hepatitis C measures group have been performed for this patient **PQRS** **M**
Service not separately priced by Part B

C **G8551** All quality actions for the applicable measures in the heart failure (HF) measures group have been performed for this patient **PQRS** **M**
Service not separately priced by Part B

C **G8559** Patient referred to a physician (preferably a physician with training in disorders of the ear) for an otologic evaluation **M**
Service not separately priced by Part B

C **G8560** Patient has a history of active drainage from the ear within the previous 90 days **M**
Service not separately priced by Part B

C **G8561** Patient is not eligible for the referral for otologic evaluation for patients with a history of active drainage measure **M**
Service not separately priced by Part B

C **G8562** Patient does not have a history of active drainage from the ear within the previous 90 days **M**
Service not separately priced by Part B

C **G8563** Patient not referred to a physician (preferably a physician with training in disorders of the ear) for an otologic evaluation, reason not given **M**
Service not separately priced by Part B

C **G8564** Patient was referred to a physician (preferably a physician with training in disorders of the ear) for an otologic evaluation, reason not specified) **M**
Service not separately priced by Part B

C **G8565** Verification and documentation of sudden or rapidly progressive hearing loss **M**
Service not separately priced by Part B

C **G8566** Patient is not eligible for the "referral for otologic evaluation for sudden or rapidly progressive hearing loss" measure **M**
Service not separately priced by Part B

C **G8567** Patient does not have verification and documentation of sudden or rapidly progressive hearing loss **M**
Service not separately priced by Part B

C **G8568** Patient was not referred to a physician (preferably a physician with training in disorders of the ear) for an otologic evaluation, reason not given **M**
Service not separately priced by Part B

C **G8569** Prolonged postoperative intubation (> 24 hrs) required **PQRS** **M**
Service not separately priced by Part B

C **G8570** Prolonged postoperative intubation (> 24 hrs) not required **PQRS** **M**
Service not separately priced by Part B

▲ **C** **G8571** Development of deep sternal wound infection/mediastinitis within 30 days postoperatively **PQRS** **M**
Service not separately priced by Part B

▲ **C** **G8572** No deep sternal wound infection/mediastinitis **PQRS** **M**
Service not separately priced by Part B

C **G8573** Stroke following isolated CABG surgery **PQRS** **M**
Service not separately priced by Part B

♂ Male only　　♀ Female only　　**Ⓐ** Age　　A2 - Z3 = ASC Payment Indicator　　A - Y = APC Status Indicator
ASC = ASC Approved Procedure　　**DME** Paid under the DME fee schedule　　**PQRS** Physician Quality Reporting System

G8574 No stroke following isolated CABG surgery [PQRS] M

Service not separately priced by Part B

G8575 Developed postoperative renal failure or required dialysis [PQRS] M

Service not separately priced by Part B

G8576 No postoperative renal failure/dialysis not required [PQRS] M

Service not separately priced by Part B

G8577 Re-exploration required due to mediastinal bleeding with or without tamponade, graft occlusion, valve dysfunction or other cardiac reason [PQRS] M

Service not separately priced by Part B

G8578 Re-exploration not required due to mediastinal bleeding with or without tamponade, graft occlusion, valve dysfunction or other cardiac reason [PQRS] M

Service not separately priced by Part B

G8598 Aspirin or another antithrombotic therapy used [PQRS] M

Service not separately priced by Part B

G8599 Aspirin or another antithrombotic therapy not used, reason not given [PQRS] M

Service not separately priced by Part B

G8600 IV t-PA initiated within three hours (<= 180 minutes) of time last known well M

Service not separately priced by Part B

G8601 IV t-PA not initiated within three hours (<= 180 minutes) of time last known well for reasons documented by clinician M

Service not separately priced by Part B

G8602 IV t-PA not initiated within three hours (<= 180 minutes) of time last known well, reason not given M

Service not separately priced by Part B

G8627 Surgical procedure performed within 30 days following cataract surgery for major complications (e.g., retained nuclear fragments, endophthalmitis, dislocated or wrong power IOL, retinal detachment, or wound dehiscence) [PQRS] M

Service not separately priced by Part B

G8628 Surgical procedure not performed within 30 days following cataract surgery for major complications (e.g., retained nuclear fragments, endophthalmitis, dislocated or wrong power IOL, retinal detachment, or wound dehiscence) [PQRS] M

Service not separately priced by Part B

G8633 Pharmacologic therapy (other than minerals/vitamins) for osteoporosis prescribed M

Service not separately priced by Part B

Healthy bone   Osteoporosis

Osteoporosis

G8634 Clinician documented patient not an eligible candidate to receive pharmacologic therapy for osteoporosis M

Service not separately priced by Part B

G8635 Pharmacologic therapy for osteoporosis was not prescribed, reason not given M

Service not separately priced by Part B

G8645 I intend to report the asthma measures group [PQRS] M

Service not separately priced by Part B

G8646 All quality actions for the applicable measures in the asthma measures group have been performed for this patient [PQRS] M

Service not separately priced by Part B

G8647 Risk-adjusted functional status change residual score for the knee successfully calculated and the score was equal to zero (0) or greater than zero (>0) M

Service not separately priced by Part B

G8648 Risk-adjusted functional status change residual score for the knee successfully calculated and the score was less than zero (<0) M

Service not separately priced by Part B

G8649 Risk-adjusted functional status change residual scores for the knee not measured because the patient did not complete FOTO's functional intake on admission and/or follow up status survey near discharge, patient not eligible/not appropriate M

Service not separately priced by Part B

G8650 Risk-adjusted functional status change residual scores for the knee not measured because the patient did not complete FOTO's functional intake on admission and/or follow up status survey near discharge, reason not given M

Service not separately priced by Part B

C G8651 Risk-adjusted functional status change residual score for the hip successfully calculated and the score was equal to zero (0) or greater than zero (>0)   M
Service not separately priced by Part B

C G8652 Risk-adjusted functional status change residual score for the hip successfully calculated and the score was less than zero (<0)   M
Service not separately priced by Part B

C G8653 Risk-adjusted functional status change residual scores for the hip not measured because the patient did not complete FOTO's functional intake on admission and/or follow up status survey near discharge, patient not eligible/not appropriate   M
Service not separately priced by Part B

C G8654 Risk-adjusted functional status change residual scores for the hip not measured because the patient did not complete FOTO's functional intake on admission and/or follow up status survey near discharge, reason not given   M
Service not separately priced by Part B

C G8655 Risk-adjusted functional status change residual score for the lower leg, foot or ankle successfully calculated and the score was equal to zero (0) or greater than zero(>0)   M
Service not separately priced by Part B

C G8656 Risk-adjusted functional status change residual score for the lower leg, foot or ankle successfully calculated and the score was less than zero (<0)   M
Service not separately priced by Part B

C G8657 Risk-adjusted functional status change residual scores for the lower leg, foot or ankle not measured because the patient did not complete FOTO's functional intake on admission and/or follow up status survey near discharge, patient not eligible/not appropriate   M
Service not separately priced by Part B

C G8658 Risk-adjusted functional status change residual scores for the lower leg, foot or ankle not measured because the patient did not complete FOTO's functional intake on admission and/or follow up status survey near discharge, reason not given   M
Service not separately priced by Part B

C G8659 Risk-adjusted functional status change residual score for the lumbar spine successfully calculated and the score was equal to zero (0) or greater than zero (>0)   M
Service not separately priced by Part B

C G8660 Risk-adjusted functional status change residual score for the lumbar spine successfully calculated and the score was less than zero (<0)   M
Service not separately priced by Part B

C G8661 Risk-adjusted functional status change residual scores for the lumbar spine not measured because the patient did not complete FOTO's functional intake on admission and/or follow up status survey near discharge, patient not eligible/not appropriate   M
Service not separately priced by Part B

C G8662 Risk-adjusted functional status change residual scores for the lumbar spine not measured because the patient did not complete FOTO's functional intake on admission and/or follow up status survey near discharge, reason not given   M
Service not separately priced by Part B

C G8663 Risk-adjusted functional status change residual score for the shoulder successfully calculated and the score was equal to zero (0) or greater than zero (>0)   M
Service not separately priced by Part B

C G8664 Risk-adjusted functional status change residual score for the shoulder successfully calculated and the score was less than zero (<0)   M
Service not separately priced by Part B

C G8665 Risk-adjusted functional status change residual scores for the shoulder not measured because the patient did not complete FOTO's functional intake on admission and/or follow up status survey near discharge, patient not eligible/not appropriate   M
Service not separately priced by Part B

C G8666 Risk-adjusted functional status change residual scores for the shoulder not measured because the patient did not complete FOTO's functional intake on admission and/or follow up status survey near discharge, reason not given   M
Service not separately priced by Part B

C G8667 Risk-adjusted functional status change residual score for the elbow, wrist or hand successfully calculated and the score was equal to zero (0) or greater than zero (>0)   M
Service not separately priced by Part B

C G8668 Risk-adjusted functional status change residual score for the elbow, wrist or hand successfully calculated and the score was less than zero (<0)   M
Service not separately priced by Part B

C G8669 Risk-adjusted functional status change residual scores for the elbow, wrist or hand not measured because the patient did not complete FOTO's functional intake on admission and/or follow up status survey near discharge, patient not eligible/not appropriate   M
Service not separately priced by Part B

♂ Male only   ♀ Female only   **A** Age   A2 - Z3 = ASC Payment Indicator   A - Y = APC Status Indicator
ASC = ASC Approved Procedure   **DME** Paid under the DME fee schedule   **PQRS** Physician Quality Reporting System

C **G8670** Risk-adjusted functional status change residual scores for the elbow, wrist or hand not measured because the patient did not complete FOTO's functional intake on admission and/or follow up status survey near discharge, reason not given M
Service not separately priced by Part B

C **G8671** Risk-adjusted functional status change residual score for the neck, cranium, mandible, thoracic spine, ribs, or other general orthopedic impairment successfully calculated and the score was equal to zero (0) or greater than zero (>0) M
Service not separately priced by Part B

C **G8672** Risk-adjusted functional status change residual score for the neck, cranium, mandible, thoracic spine, ribs, or other general orthopedic impairment successfully calculated and the score was less than zero (<0) M
Service not separately priced by Part B

C **G8673** Risk-adjusted functional status change residual scores for the neck, cranium, mandible, thoracic spine, ribs, or other general orthopedic impairment not measured because the patient did not complete FOTO's functional intake on admission and/or follow up status survey near discharge, patient not eligible/not appropriate M
Service not separately priced by Part B

C **G8674** Risk-adjusted functional status change residual scores for the neck, cranium, mandible, thoracic spine, ribs, or other general orthopedic impairment not measured because the patient did not complete FOTO's functional intake on admission and/or follow up status survey near discharge, reason not given M
Service not separately priced by Part B

C **G8694** Left ventriucular ejection fraction (LVEF) < 40% M
Service not separately priced by Part B

C **G8696** Antithrombotic therapy prescribed at discharge M
Service not separately priced by Part B

C **G8697** Antithrombotic therapy not prescribed for documented reasons (e.g., patients admitted for performance of elective carotid intervention, patient had stroke during hospital stay, patient expired during inpatient stay, other medical reason(s)); (e.g., patient left against medical advice, other patient reason(s)) M
Service not separately priced by Part B

C **G8698** Antithrombotic therapy was not prescribed at discharge, reason not given M
Service not separately priced by Part B

C **G8708** Patient not prescribed or dispensed antibiotic M
Service not separately priced by Part B

C **G8709** Patient prescribed or dispensed antibiotic for documented medical reason(s) (e.g., intestinal infection, pertussis, bacterial infection, lyme disease, otitis media, acute sinusitis, acute pharyngitis, acute tonsillitis, chronic sinusitis, infection of the pharynx/larynx/tonsils/adenoids, prostatitis, cellulitis, mastoiditis, or bone infections, acute lymphadenitis, impetigo, skin staph infections, pneumonia/gonococcal infections, venereal disease (syphilis, chlamydia, inflammatory diseases (female reproductive organs)), infections of the kidney, cystitis or, UTI) M
Service not separately priced by Part B

C **G8710** Patient prescribed or dispensed antibiotic M
Service not separately priced by Part B

C **G8711** Prescribed or dispensed antibiotic M
Service not separately priced by Part B

C **G8712** Antibiotic not prescribed or dispensed M
Service not separately priced by Part B

C **G8713** SpKt/V greater than or equal to 1.2 (single-pool clearance of urea [Kt] / volume [V]) M
Service not separately priced by Part B

C **G8714** Hemodialysis treatment performed exactly three times per week for > 90 days M
Service not separately priced by Part B

C **G8717** SpKt/V less than 1.2 (single-pool clearance of urea [Kt] / volume [V]), reason not given M
Service not separately priced by Part B

C **G8718** Total Kt/V greater than or equal to 1.7 per week (total clearance of urea [Kt] / volume [V]) M
Service not separately priced by Part B

▲ C **G8720** Total Kt/V less than 1.7 per week (total clearance of urea [Kt] / volume [V]) M
Service not separately priced by Part B

C **G8721** pT category (primary tumor), pN category (regional lymph nodes), and histologic grade were documented in pathology report M
Service not separately priced by Part B

C **G8722** Documentation of medical reason(s) for not including the pT category, the pN category or the histologic grade in the pathology report (e.g., re-excision without residual tumor; non-carcinomasanal canal) M
Service not separately priced by Part B

C **G8723** Specimen site is other than anatomic location of primary tumor M
Service not separately priced by Part B

C **G8724** pT category, pN category and histologic grade were not documented in the pathology report, reason not given M
Service not separately priced by Part B

C **G8725** Fasting lipid profile performed (triglycerides, LDL-C, HDL-C and total cholesterol) PQRS M
Service not separately priced by Part B

▲ Revised Code   ● New code   C Carrier judgment   D Special coverage instructions apply
I Not payable by Medicare   M Non-covered by Medicare   S Non-covered by Medicare statute   AHA Coding Clinic®

C **G8726** Clinician has documented reason for not performing fasting lipid profile (e.g., patient declined, other patient reasons) **PQRS** M
Service not separately priced by Part B

C **G8728** Fasting lipid profile not performed, reason not given **PQRS** M
Service not separately priced by Part B

C **G8730** Pain assessment documented as positive using a standardized tool and a follow-up plan is documented M
Service not separately priced by Part B

C **G8731** Pain assessment using a standardized tool is documented as negative, no follow-up plan required M
Service not separately priced by Part B

C **G8732** No documentation of pain assessment, reason not given M
Service not separately priced by Part B

C **G8733** Elder maltreatment screen documented as positive and a follow-up plan is documented Ⓐ M
Service not separately priced by Part B

C **G8734** Elder maltreatment screen documented as negative, no follow-up required Ⓐ M
Service not separately priced by Part B

C **G8735** Elder maltreatment screen documented as positive, follow-up plan not documented, reason not given Ⓐ M
Service not separately priced by Part B

C **G8749** Absence of signs of melanoma (cough, dyspnea, tenderness, localized neurologic signs such as weakness, jaundice or any other sign suggesting systemic spread) or absence of symptoms of melanoma (pain, paresthesia, or any other symptom suggesting the possibility of systemic spread of melanoma) M
Service not separately priced by Part B

C **G8752** Most recent systolic blood pressure < 140 mmHg **PQRS** M
Service not separately priced by Part B

C **G8753** Most recent systolic blood pressure >= 140 mmHg **PQRS** M
Service not separately priced by Part B

C **G8754** Most recent diastolic blood pressure < 90 mmHg **PQRS** M
Service not separately priced by Part B

C **G8755** Most recent diastolic blood pressure >= 90 mmHg **PQRS** M
Service not separately priced by Part B

C **G8756** No documentation of blood pressure measurement, reason not given **PQRS** M
Service not separately priced by Part B

C **G8757** All quality actions for the applicable measures in the chronic obstructive pulmonary disease (COPD) measures group have been performed for this patient **PQRS** M
Service not separately priced by Part B

C **G8758** All quality actions for the applicable measures in the inflammatory bowel disease (IBD) measures group have been performed for this patient **PQRS** M
Service not separately priced by Part B

C **G8759** All quality actions for the applicable measures in the sleep apnea measures group have been performed for this patient **PQRS** M
Service not separately priced by Part B

C **G8761** All quality actions for the applicable measures in the dementia measures group have been performed for this patient **PQRS** M
Service not separately priced by Part B

C **G8762** All quality actions for the applicable measures in the parkinson's disease measures group have been performed for this patient **PQRS** M
Service not separately priced by Part B

C **G8765** All quality actions for the applicable measures in the cataract measures group have been performed for this patient **PQRS** M
Service not separately priced by Part B

C **G8783** Normal blood pressure reading documented, follow-up not required **PQRS** M
Service not separately priced by Part B

C **G8784** Blood pressure reading not documented, documentation the patient is not eligible **PQRS** M
Service not separately priced by Part B

C **G8785** Blood pressure reading not documented, reason not given **PQRS** M
Service not separately priced by Part B

C **G8797** Specimen site other than anatomic location of esophagus M
Service not separately priced by Part B

C **G8798** Specimen site other than anatomic location of prostate M
Service not separately priced by Part B

C **G8806** Performance of trans-abdominal or trans-vaginal ultrasound M
Service not separately priced by Part B

C **G8807** Trans-abdominal or trans-vaginal ultrasound not performed for reasons documented by clinician (e.g., patient has visited the ED multiple times within 72 hours, patient has a documented intrauterine pregnancy [IUP]) M
Service not separately priced by Part B

C **G8808** Performance of trans-abdominal or trans-vaginal ultrasound not ordered, reason not given (e.g., patient has visited the ED multiple times with no documentation of a trans-abdominal or trans-vaginal ultrasound within ED or from referring eligible professional) M
Service not separately priced by Part B

♂ Male only   ♀ Female only   Ⓐ Age   A2 - Z3 = ASC Payment Indicator   A - Y = APC Status Indicator
ASC = ASC Approved Procedure   **DME** Paid under the DME fee schedule   **PQRS** Physician Quality Reporting System

C **G8809** Rh-immunoglobulin (RhoGAM) ordered M
Service not separately priced by Part B

C **G8810** Rh-immunoglobulin (RhoGAM) not ordered for reasons documented by clinician (e.g., patient had prior documented receipt of RhoGAM within 12 weeks, patient refusal) M
Service not separately priced by Part B

C **G8811** Documentation Rh-immunoglobulin (RhoGAM) was not ordered, reason not given M
Service not separately priced by Part B

C **G8815** Statin therapy not prescribed for documented reasons (e.g., medical intolerance to statin, death of patient prior to discharge, transfer of care to another acute care or federal hospital, hospice admission, left against medical advice) M
Service not separately priced by Part B

C **G8816** Statin medication prescribed at discharge M
Service not separately priced by Part B

C **G8817** Statin therapy not prescribed at discharge, reason not given M
Service not separately priced by Part B

C **G8818** Patient discharge to home no later than post-operative day #7 M
Service not separately priced by Part B

C **G8825** Patient not discharged to home by post-operative day #7 M
Service not separately priced by Part B

C **G8826** Patient discharge to home no later than post-operative day #2 following evar M
Service not separately priced by Part B

C **G8833** Patient not discharged to home by post-operative day #2 following evar M
Service not separately priced by Part B

C **G8834** Patient discharged to home no later than post-operative day #2 following CEA M
Service not separately priced by Part B

C **G8838** Patient not discharged to home by post-operative day #2 following CEA M
Service not separately priced by Part B

C **G8839** Sleep apnea symptoms assessed, including presence or absence of snoring and daytime sleepiness PQRS M
Service not separately priced by Part B

▲ C **G8840** Documentation of reason(s) for not documenting an assessment of sleep symptoms (e.g., patient didn't have initial daytime sleepiness, patient visited between initial testing and initiation of therapy) PQRS M
Service not separately priced by Part B

C **G8841** Sleep apnea symptoms not assessed, reason not given PQRS M
Service not separately priced by Part B

C **G8842** Apnea hypopnea index (AHI) or respiratory disturbance index (RDI) measured at the time of initial diagnosis PQRS M
Service not separately priced by Part B

▲ C **G8843** Documentation of reason(s) for not measuring an apnea hypopnea index (AHI) or a respiratory disturbance index (RDI) at the time of initial diagnosis (e.g., psychiatric disease, dementia, patient declined, financial, insurance coverage, test ordered but not yet completed) PQRS M
Service not separately priced by Part B

C **G8844** Apnea hypopnea index (AHI) or respiratory disturbance index (RDI) not measured at the time of initial diagnosis, reason not given PQRS M
Service not separately priced by Part B

C **G8845** Positive airway pressure therapy prescribed PQRS M
Service not separately priced by Part B

C **G8846** Moderate or severe obstructive sleep apnea (apnea hypopnea index (AHI) or respiratory disturbance index (RDI) of 15 or greater) PQRS M
Service not separately priced by Part B

C **G8848** Mild obstructive sleep apnea (apnea hypopnea index (AHI) or respiratory disturbance index (RDI) of less than 15) PQRS M
Service not separately priced by Part B

C **G8849** Documentation of reason(s) for not prescribing positive airway pressure therapy (e.g., patient unable to tolerate, alternative therapies use, patient declined, financial, insurance coverage) PQRS M
Service not separately priced by Part B

C **G8850** Positive airway pressure therapy not prescribed, reason not given PQRS M
Service not separately priced by Part B

C **G8851** Objective measurement of adherence to positive airway pressure therapy, documented PQRS M
Service not separately priced by Part B

C **G8852** Positive airway pressure therapy prescribed PQRS M
Service not separately priced by Part B

C **G8853** Positive airway pressure therapy not prescribed PQRS M
Service not separately priced by Part B

C **G8854** Documentation of reason(s) for not objectively measuring adherence to positive airway pressure therapy (e.g., patient didn't bring data from continuous positive airway pressure [CPAP], therapy not yet initiated, not available on machine) PQRS M
Service not separately priced by Part B

C **G8855** Objective measurement of adherence to positive airway pressure therapy not performed, reason not given **PQRS** M

Service not separately priced by Part B

C **G8856** Referral to a physician for an otologic evaluation performed M

Service not separately priced by Part B

C **G8857** Patient is not eligible for the referral for otologic evaluation measure (e.g., patients who are already under the care of a physician for acute or chronic dizziness) M

Service not separately priced by Part B

C **G8858** Referral to a physician for an otologic evaluation not performed, reason not given M

Service not separately priced by Part B

▲ **C** **G8861** Within the past 2 years, central dual-energy X-ray absorptiometry (DXA) ordered and documented, review of systems and medication history or pharmacologic therapy (other than minerals/vitamins) for osteoporosis prescribed **PQRS** M

Service not separately priced by Part B

C **G8863** Patients not assessed for risk of bone loss, reason not given **PQRS** M

Service not separately priced by Part B

C **G8864** Pneumococcal vaccine administered or previously received **PQRS** M

Service not separately priced by Part B

C **G8865** Documentation of medical reason(s) for not administering or previously receiving pneumococcal vaccine (e.g., patient allergic reaction, potential adverse drug reaction) **PQRS** M

Service not separately priced by Part B

C **G8866** Documentation of patient reason(s) for not administering or previously receiving pneumococcal vaccine (e.g., patient refusal) **PQRS** M

Service not separately priced by Part B

C **G8867** Pneumococcal vaccine not administered or previously received, reason not given **PQRS** M

Service not separately priced by Part B

C **G8868** Patients receiving a first course of anti-TNF therapy **PQRS** M

Service not separately priced by Part B

C **G8869** Patient has documented immunity to hepatitis B and is receiving a first course of anti-TNF therapy **PQRS** M

Service not separately priced by Part B

C **G8870** Hepatitis B vaccine injection administered or previously received and is receiving a first course of anti-TNF therapy **PQRS** M

Service not separately priced by Part B

C **G8871** Patient not receiving a first course of anti-TNF therapy **PQRS** M

Service not separately priced by Part B

C **G8872** Excised tissue evaluated by imaging intraoperatively to confirm successful inclusion of targeted lesion M

Service not separately priced by Part B

C **G8873** Patients with needle localization specimens which are not amenable to intraoperative imaging such as MRI needle wire localization, or targets which are tentatively identified on mammogram or ultrasound which do not contain a biopsy marker but which can be verified on intraoperative inspection or pathology (e.g., needle biopsy site where the biopsy marker is remote from the actual biopsy site) M

Service not separately priced by Part B

C **G8874** Excised tissue not evaluated by imaging intraoperatively to confirm successful inclusion of targeted lesion M

Service not separately priced by Part B

C **G8875** Clinician diagnosed breast cancer preoperatively by a minimally invasive biopsy method M

Service not separately priced by Part B

▲ **C** **G8876** Documentation of reason(s) for not performing minimally invasive biopsy to diagnose breast cancer preoperatively (e.g., lesion too close to skin, implant, chest wall, etc., lesion could not be adequately visualized for needle biopsy, patient condition prevents needle biopsy [weight, breast thickness, etc.], duct excision without imaging abnormality, prophylactic mastectomy, reduction mammoplasty, excisional biopsy performed by another physician) M

Service not separately priced by Part B

C **G8877** Clinician did not attempt to achieve the diagnosis of breast cancer preoperatively by a minimally invasive biopsy method, reason not given M

Service not separately priced by Part B

C **G8878** Sentinel lymph node biopsy procedure performed M

Service not separately priced by Part B

C **G8879** Clinically node negative (T1N0M0 or T3N0M0) invasive breast cancer M

Service not separately priced by Part B

C **G8880** Documentation of reason(s) sentinel lymph node biopsy not performed (e.g., reasons could include but not limited to; non-invasive cancer, incidental discovery of breast cancer on prophylactic mastectomy, incidental discovery of breast cancer on reduction mammoplasty, pre-operative biopsy proven lymph node (LN) metastases, inflammatory carcinoma, Stage 3 locally advanced cancer, recurrent invasive breast cancer, patient refusal after informed consent) M

Service not separately priced by Part B

♂ Male only   ♀ Female only   **A** Age   A2 - Z3 = ASC Payment Indicator   A - Y = APC Status Indicator

ASC = ASC Approved Procedure   **DME** Paid under the DME fee schedule   **PQRS** Physician Quality Reporting System

G8881 Stage of breast cancer is greater than T1N0M0 or T3N0M0 M
Service not separately priced by Part B

G8882 Sentinel lymph node biopsy procedure not performed, reason not given M
Service not separately priced by Part B

G8883 Biopsy results reviewed, communicated, tracked and documented M
Service not separately priced by Part B

G8884 Clinician documented reason that patient's biopsy results were not reviewed M
Service not separately priced by Part B

G8885 Bipsy results not reviewed, communicated, tracked or documented M
Service not separately priced by Part B

G8898 I intend to report the chronic obstructive pulmonary disease (COPD) measures group PQRS M
Service not separately priced by Part B

G8899 I intend to report the inflammatory bowel disease (IBD) measures group PQRS M
Service not separately priced by Part B

G8900 I intend to report the sleep apnea measures group PQRS M
Service not separately priced by Part B

G8902 I intend to report the dementia measures group PQRS M
Service not separately priced by Part B

G8903 I intend to report the parkinson's disease measures group PQRS M
Service not separately priced by Part B

G8906 I intend to report the cataract measures group PQRS M
Service not separately priced by Part B

G8907 Patient documented not to have experienced any of the following events: a burn prior to discharge; a fall within the facility; wrong site/side/patient/procedure/implant event; or a hospital transfer or hospital admission upon discharge from the facility M
Service not separately priced by Part B

G8908 Patient documented to have received a burn prior to discharge M
Service not separately priced by Part B

G8909 Patient documented not to have received a burn prior to discharge M
Service not separately priced by Part B

G8910 Patient documented to have experienced a fall within ASC M
Service not separately priced by Part B

G8911 Patient documented not to have experienced a fall within ambulatory surgical center M
Service not separately priced by Part B

G8912 Patient documented to have experienced a wrong site, wrong side, wrong patient, wrong procedure or wrong implant event M
Service not separately priced by Part B

G8913 Patient documented not to have experienced a wrong site, wrong side, wrong patient, wrong procedure or wrong implant event M
Service not separately priced by Part B

G8914 Patient documented to have experienced a hospital transfer or hospital admission upon discharge from ASC M
Service not separately priced by Part B

G8915 Patient documented not to have experienced a hospital transfer or hospital admission upon discharge from ASC M
Service not separately priced by Part B

G8916 Patient with preoperative order for IV antibiotic surgical site infection (SSI) prophylaxis, antibiotic initiated on time M
Service not separately priced by Part B

G8917 Patient with preoperative order for IV antibiotic surgical site infection (SSI) prophylaxis, antibiotic not initiated on time M
Service not separately priced by Part B

G8918 Patient without preoperative order for IV antibiotic surgical site infection (SSI) prophylaxis M
Service not separately priced by Part B

G8923 Left ventricular ejection fraction (LVEF) < 40% or documentation of moderately or severely depressed left ventricular systolic function PQRS M
Service not separately priced by Part B

▲ **G8924** Spirometry test results demonstrate FEV1/FVC < 60% and patient has COPD symptoms (e.g., dyspnea, cough/sputum, wheezing) M
Service not separately priced by Part B

G8925 Spirometry test results demonstrate FEV1/FVC >=60% or patient does not have COPD symptoms PQRS M
Service not separately priced by Part B

G8926 Spirometry test not performed or documented, reason not given PQRS M
Service not separately priced by Part B

G8927 Adjuvant chemotherapy referred, prescribed or previously received for AJCC Stage III, colon cancer PQRS M
Service not separately priced by Part B

G8928 Adjuvant chemotherapy not prescribed or previously received for documented reasons (e.g., medical co-morbidities, diagnosis date more than 5 years prior to the current visit date, patient's cancer has metastasized, medical contraindication/allergy, poor performance status, other medical reasons, patient refusal, other patient reasons, patient is currently enrolled in a clinical trial that precludes prescription of chemotherapy, other system reasons) PQRS M
Service not separately priced by Part B

▲ Revised Code   ● New code   C Carrier judgment   D Special coverage instructions apply
I Not payable by Medicare   M Non-covered by Medicare   S Non-covered by Medicare statute   AHA Coding Clinic®

G G8929 Adjuvant chemotherapy not prescribed or previously received, reason not specified [PQRS] M
Service not separately priced by Part B

G G8934 Left ventricular ejection fraction (LVEF) <40% or documentation of moderately or severely depressed left ventricular systolic function M
Service not separately priced by Part B

G G8935 Clinician prescribed angiotensin converting enzyme (ACE) inhibitor or angiotensin receptor blocker (ARB) therapy M
Service not separately priced by Part B

▲ **G G8936** Clinician documented that patient was not an eligible candidate for angiotensin converting enzyme (ACE) inhibitor or angiotensin receptor blocker (ARB) therapy (e.g., allergy, intolerance, pregnancy, renal failure due to ACE inhibitor, diseases of the aortic or mitral valve, other medical reasons) or (e.g., patient declined, other patient reasons) or (e.g., lack of drug availability, other reasons attributable to the health care system) M
Service not separately priced by Part B

G G8937 Clinician did not prescribe angiotensin converting enzyme (ACE) inhibitor or angiotensin receptor blocker (ARB) therapy, reason not given M
Service not separately priced by Part B

G G8938 BMI is documented as being outside of normal limits, follow-up plan is not documented, documentation the patient is not eligible [PQRS] M
Service not separately priced by Part B

G G8939 Pain assessment documented as positive, follow-up plan not documented, documentation the patient is not eligible M
Service not separately priced by Part B

G G8940 Screening for clinical depression documented as positive, a follow-up plan not documented, documentation stating the patient is not eligible M
Service not separately priced by Part B

G G8941 Elder maltreatment screen documented as positive, follow-up plan not documented, documentation the patient is not eligible M
Service not separately priced by Part B

G G8942 Functional outcomes assessment using a standardized tool is documented within the previous 30 days and care plan, based on identified deficiencies on the date of the functional outcome assessment, is documented M
Service not separately priced by Part B

G G8944 AJCC melanoma cancer Stage 0 through IIC melanoma M
Service not separately priced by Part B

G G8946 Minimally invasive biopsy method attempted but not diagnostic of breast cancer (e.g., high risk lesion of breast such as atypical ductal hyperplasia, lobular neoplasia, atypical lobular hyperplasia, lobular carcinoma in situ, atypical columnar hyperplasia, flat epithelial atypia, radial scar, complex sclerosing lesion, papillary lesion, or any lesion with spindle cells) M
Service not separately priced by Part B

G G8947 One or more neuropsychiatric symptoms [PQRS] M
Service not separately priced by Part B

G G8948 No neuropsychiatric symptoms [PQRS] M
Service not separately priced by Part B

G G8950 Pre-hypertensive or hypertensive blood pressure reading documented, and the indicated follow-up is documented [PQRS] M
Service not separately priced by Part B

G G8951 Pre-hypertensive or hypertensive blood pressure reading documented, indicated follow-up not documented, documentation the patient is not eligible [PQRS] M
Service not separately priced by Part B

G G8952 Pre-hypertensive or hypertensive blood pressure reading documented, indicated follow-up not documented, reason not given [PQRS] M
Service not separately priced by Part B

G G8953 All quality actions for the applicable measures in the oncology measures group have been performed for this patient [PQRS] M
Service not separately priced by Part B

G G8955 Most recent assessment of adequacy of volume management M
Service not separately priced by Part B

G G8956 Patient receiving maintenance hemodialysis in an outpatient dialysis facility M
Service not separately priced by Part B

G G8958 Assessment of adequacy of volume management not documented, reason not given M
Service not separately priced by Part B

G G8959 Clinician treating major depressive disorder communicates to clinician treating comorbid condition M
Service not separately priced by Part B

G G8960 Clinician treating major depressive disorder did not communicate to clinician treating comorbid condition, reason not given M
Service not separately priced by Part B

G G8961 Cardiac stress imaging test primarily performed on low-risk surgery patient for preoperative evaluation within 30 days preceding this surgery M
Service not separately priced by Part B

G8962 - G8985

PROCEDURES / PROFESSIONAL SERVICES (G0008-G9472)

G G8962 Cardiac stress imaging test performed on patient for any reason including those who did not have low risk surgery or test that was performed more than 30 days preceding low risk surgery M
Service not separately priced by Part B

G G8963 Cardiac stress imaging performed primarily for monitoring of asymptomatic patient who had PCI within 2 years M
Service not separately priced by Part B

G G8964 Cardiac stress imaging test performed primarily for any other reason than monitoring of asymptomatic patient who had PCI within 2 years (e.g., symptomatic patient, patient greater than 2 years since PCI, initial evaluation, etc) M
Service not separately priced by Part B

G G8965 Cardiac stress imaging test primarily performed on low CHD risk patient for initial detection and risk assessment M
Service not separately priced by Part B

G G8966 Cardiac stress imaging test performed on symptomatic or higher than low CHD risk patient or for any reason other than initial detection and risk assessment M
Service not separately priced by Part B

G G8967 Warfarin or another oral anticoagulant that is FDA approved prescribed M
Service not separately priced by Part B

▲ **G** G8968 Documentation of medical reason(s) for not prescribing warfarin or another oral anticoagulant that is FDA approved for the prevention of thromboembolism [e.g., patients with mitral stenosis or prosthetic heart valves, patients with transient or reversible causes of af (e.g., pneumonia, hyperthyroidism, pregnancy, cardiac surgery), allergy, risk of bleeding, other medical reasons] M
Service not separately priced by Part B

G G8969 Documentation of patient reason(s) for not prescribing warfarin or another oral anticoagulant that is FDA approved (e.g., economic, social, and/or religious impediments, noncompliance patient refusal, other patient reasons) M
Service not separately priced by Part B

G G8970 No risk factors or one moderate risk factor for thromboembolism M
Service not separately priced by Part B

G G8971 Warfarin or another oral anticoagulant that is FDA approved not prescribed, reason not given M
Service not separately priced by Part B

G G8972 One or more high risk factors for thromboembolism or more than one moderate risk factor for thromboembolism M
Service not separately priced by Part B

G G8973 Most recent hemoglobin (HgB) level < 10 g/dl M
Service not separately priced by Part B

G G8974 Hemoglobin level measurement not documented, reason not given M
Service not separately priced by Part B

G G8975 Documentation of medical reason(s) for patient having a hemoglobin level < 10 g/dl (e.g., patients who have non-renal etiologies of anemia [e.g., sickle cell anemia or other hemoglobinopathies, hypersplenism, primary bone marrow disease, anemia related to chemotherapy for diagnosis of malignancy, postoperative bleeding, active bloodstream or peritoneal infection], other medical reasons) M
Service not separately priced by Part B

G G8976 Most recent hemoglobin (HgB) level >= 10 g/dl M
Service not separately priced by Part B

G G8977 I intend to report the oncology measures group PQRS M
Service not separately priced by Part B

G G8978 Mobility: walking & moving around functional limitation, current status, at therapy episode outset and at reporting intervals E
Service not separately priced by Part B

G G8979 Mobility: walking & moving around functional limitation, projected goal status, at therapy episode outset, at reporting intervals, and at discharge or to end reporting E
Service not separately priced by Part B

G G8980 Mobility: walking & moving around functional limitation, discharge status, at discharge from therapy or to end reporting E
Service not separately priced by Part B

G G8981 Changing & maintaining body position functional limitation, current status, at therapy episode outset and at reporting intervals E
Service not separately priced by Part B

G G8982 Changing & maintaining body position functional limitation, projected goal status, at therapy episode outset, at reporting intervals, and at discharge or to end reporting E
Service not separately priced by Part B

G G8983 Changing & maintaining body position functional limitation, discharge status, at discharge from therapy or to end reporting E
Service not separately priced by Part B

G G8984 Carrying, moving & handling objects functional limitation, current status, at therapy episode outset and at reporting intervals E
Service not separately priced by Part B

G G8985 Carrying, moving and handling objects, projected goal status, at therapy episode

---

▲ Revised Code   ● New code   **G** Carrier judgment   **D** Special coverage instructions apply
I Not payable by Medicare   **M** Non-covered by Medicare   **S** Non-covered by Medicare statute   AHA Coding Clinic®

outset, at reporting intervals, and at discharge or to end reporting E

Service not separately priced by Part B

C G8986 Carrying, moving & handling objects functional limitation, discharge status, at discharge from therapy or to end reporting E

Service not separately priced by Part B

C G8987 Self care functional limitation, current status, at therapy episode outset and at reporting intervals E

Service not separately priced by Part B

C G8988 Self care functional limitation, projected goal status, at therapy episode outset, at reporting intervals, and at discharge or to end reporting E

Service not separately priced by Part B

C G8989 Self care functional limitation, discharge status, at discharge from therapy or to end reporting E

Service not separately priced by Part B

C G8990 Other physical or occupational therapy primary functional limitation, current status, at therapy episode outset and at reporting intervals E

Service not separately priced by Part B

C G8991 Other physical or occupational therapy primary functional limitation, projected goal status, at therapy episode outset, at reporting intervals, and at discharge or to end reporting E

Service not separately priced by Part B

C G8992 Other physical or occupational therapy primary functional limitation, discharge status, at discharge from therapy or to end reporting E

Service not separately priced by Part B

C G8993 Other physical or occupational therapy subsequent functional limitation, current status, at therapy episode outset and at reporting intervals E

Service not separately priced by Part B

C G8994 Other physical or occupational therapy subsequent functional limitation, projected goal status, at therapy episode outset, at reporting intervals, and at discharge or to end reporting E

Service not separately priced by Part B

C G8995 Other physical or occupational therapy subsequent functional limitation, discharge status, at discharge from therapy or to end reporting E

Service not separately priced by Part B

C G8996 Swallowing functional limitation, current status at therapy episode outset and at reporting intervals E

Service not separately priced by Part B

Pub: 100-4, Chap. 5, 10.6

C G8997 Swallowing functional limitation, projected goal status, at therapy episode outset, at reporting intervals, and at discharge or to end reporting E

Service not separately priced by Part B

C G8998 Swallowing functional limitation, discharge status, at discharge from therapy or to end reporting E

Service not separately priced by Part B

C G8999 Motor speech functional limitation, current status at therapy episode outset and at reporting intervals E

Service not separately priced by Part B

D G9001 Coordinated care fee, initial rate B

Service not separately priced by Part B

D G9002 Coordinated care fee, maintenance rate B

Service not separately priced by Part B

D G9003 Coordinated care fee, risk adjusted high, initial B

Service not separately priced by Part B

D G9004 Coordinated care fee, risk adjusted low, initial B

Service not separately priced by Part B

D G9005 Coordinated care fee, risk adjusted maintenance B

Service not separately priced by Part B

D G9006 Coordinated care fee, home monitoring B

Service not separately priced by Part B

D G9007 Coordinated care fee, scheduled team conference B

Service not separately priced by Part B

D G9008 Coordinated care fee, physician coordinated care oversight services B

Service not separately priced by Part B

D G9009 Coordinated care fee, risk adjusted maintenance, level 3 B

Service not separately priced by Part B

D G9010 Coordinated care fee, risk adjusted maintenance, level 4 B

Service not separately priced by Part B

D G9011 Coordinated care fee, risk adjusted maintenance, level 5 B

Service not separately priced by Part B

D G9012 Other specified case management service not elsewhere classified B

Service not separately priced by Part B

M G9013 ESRD demo basic bundle level I E

Service not separately priced by Part B

M G9014 ESRD demo expanded bundle including venous access and related services E

Service not separately priced by Part B

♂ Male only   ♀ Female only   **A** Age   A2 - Z3 = ASC Payment Indicator   A - Y = APC Status Indicator

ASC = ASC Approved Procedure   **DME** Paid under the DME fee schedule   **PQRS** Physician Quality Reporting System

M **G9016** Smoking cessation counseling, individual, in the absence of or in addition to any other evaluation and management service, per session (6-10 minutes) [demo project code only]　　　　　　　　　　　　　　　E

Service not separately priced by Part B

Pub: 100-3, Chap. 1, Part 4, 210.4

C **G9017** Amantadine hydrochloride, oral, per 100 mg (for use in a Medicare-approved demonstration project)　　　　A

Price established by carriers

C **G9018** Zanamivir, inhalation powder, administered through inhaler, per 10 mg (for use in a Medicare-approved demonstration project) A

Price established by carriers

C **G9019** Oseltamivir phosphate, oral, per 75 mg (for use in a Medicare-approved demonstration project)　　　　　　　A

Price established by carriers

C **G9020** Rimantadine hydrochloride, oral, per 100 mg (for use in a Medicare-approved demonstration project)　　　　A

Price established by carriers

C **G9033** Amantadine hydrochloride, oral brand, per 100 mg (for use in a Medicare-approved demonstration project)　　　　A

Price established by carriers

C **G9034** Zanamivir, inhalation powder, administered through inhaler, brand, per 10 mg (for use in a Medicare-approved demonstration project) A

Service not separately priced by Part B

C **G9035** Oseltamivir phosphate, oral, brand, per 75 mg (for use in a Medicare-approved demonstration project)　　　　　A

Service not separately priced by Part B

C **G9036** Rimantadine hydrochloride, oral, brand, per 100 mg (for use in a Medicare-approved demonstration project)　　　　A

Service not separately priced by Part B

I **G9050** Oncology; primary focus of visit; work-up, evaluation, or staging at the time of cancer diagnosis or recurrence (for use in a Medicare-approved demonstration project) E

Service not separately priced by Part B

I **G9051** Oncology; primary focus of visit; treatment decision-making after disease is staged or restaged, discussion of treatment options, supervising/coordinating active cancer directed therapy or managing consequences of cancer directed therapy (for use in a Medicare-approved demonstration project) E

Service not separately priced by Part B

I **G9052** Oncology; primary focus of visit; surveillance for disease recurrence for patient who has completed definitive cancer-directed therapy and currently lacks evidence of recurrent disease; cancer directed therapy might

be considered in the future (for use in a Medicare-approved demonstration project) E

Service not separately priced by Part B

I **G9053** Oncology; primary focus of visit; expectant management of patient with evidence of cancer for whom no cancer directed therapy is being administered or arranged at present; cancer directed therapy might be considered in the future (for use in a Medicare-approved demonstration project)　　　　E

Service not separately priced by Part B

I **G9054** Oncology; primary focus of visit; supervising, coordinating or managing care of patient with terminal cancer or for whom other medical illness prevents further cancer treatment; includes symptom management, end-of-life care planning, management of palliative therapies (for use in a Medicare-approved demonstration project)　　　　E

Service not separately priced by Part B

I **G9055** Oncology; primary focus of visit; other, unspecified service not otherwise listed (for use in a Medicare-approved demonstration project)　　　　E

Service not separately priced by Part B

I **G9056** Oncology; practice guidelines; management adheres to guidelines (for use in a Medicare-approved demonstration project)　　　E

Service not separately priced by Part B

I **G9057** Oncology; practice guidelines; management differs from guidelines as a result of patient enrollment in an institutional review board approved clinical trial (for use in a Medicare-approved demonstration project)　　　E

Service not separately priced by Part B

I **G9058** Oncology; practice guidelines; management differs from guidelines because the treating physician disagrees with guideline recommendations (for use in a Medicare-approved demonstration project)　　　E

Service not separately priced by Part B

I **G9059** Oncology; practice guidelines; management differs from guidelines because the patient, after being offered treatment consistent with guidelines, has opted for alternative treatment or management, including no treatment (for use in a Medicare-approved demonstration project)　　　E

Service not separately priced by Part B

I **G9060** Oncology; practice guidelines; management differs from guidelines for reason(s) associated with patient comorbid illness or performance status not factored into guidelines (for use in a Medicare-approved demonstration project)　　　E

Service not separately priced by Part B

I **G9061** Oncology; practice guidelines; patient's condition not addressed by available

---

▲ Revised Code　　● New code　　**C** Carrier judgment　　**D** Special coverage instructions apply

I Not payable by Medicare　　**M** Non-covered by Medicare　　**S** Non-covered by Medicare statute　　AHA Coding Clinic®

guidelines (for use in a Medicare-approved demonstration project)   E
Service not separately priced by Part B

I **G9062** Oncology; practice guidelines; management differs from guidelines for other reason(s) not listed (for use in a Medicare-approved demonstration project)   E
Service not separately priced by Part B

C **G9063** Oncology; disease status; limited to non-small cell lung cancer; extent of disease initially established as Stage I (prior to neo-adjuvant therapy, if any) with no evidence of disease progression, recurrence, or metastases (for use in a Medicare-approved demonstration project)   M
Service not separately priced by Part B

C **G9064** Oncology; disease status; limited to non-small cell lung cancer; extent of disease initially established as Stage II (prior to neo-adjuvant therapy, if any) with no evidence of disease progression, recurrence, or metastases (for use in a Medicare-approved demonstration project)   M
Service not separately priced by Part B

C **G9065** Oncology; disease status; limited to non-small cell lung cancer; extent of disease initially established as Stage III A (prior to neo-adjuvant therapy, if any) with no evidence of disease progression, recurrence, or metastases (for use in a Medicare-approved demonstration project)   M
Service not separately priced by Part B

C **G9066** Oncology; disease status; limited to non-small cell lung cancer; Stage III B- IV at diagnosis, metastatic, locally recurrent, or progressive (for use in a Medicare-approved demonstration project)   M
Service not separately priced by Part B

C **G9067** Oncology; disease status; limited to non-small cell lung cancer; extent of disease unknown, staging in progress, or not listed (for use in a Medicare-approved demonstration project)   M
Service not separately priced by Part B

C **G9068** Oncology; disease status; limited to small cell and combined small cell/non-small cell; extent of disease initially established as limited with no evidence of disease progression, recurrence, or metastases (for use in a Medicare-approved demonstration project)   M
Service not separately priced by Part B

C **G9069** Oncology; disease status; small cell lung cancer, limited to small cell and combined small cell/non-small cell; extensive Stage at diagnosis, metastatic, locally recurrent, or progressive (for use in a Medicare-approved demonstration project)   M
Service not separately priced by Part B

C **G9070** Oncology; disease status; small cell lung cancer, limited to small cell and combined small cell/non-small; extent of disease unknown, staging in progress, or not listed (for use in a Medicare-approved demonstration project)   M
Service not separately priced by Part B

C **G9071** Oncology; disease status; invasive female breast cancer (does not include ductal carcinoma in situ); adenocarcinoma as predominant cell type; Stage I or Stage IIA-IIB; or T3, N1, M0; and ER and/or pr positive; with no evidence of disease progression, recurrence, or metastases (for use in a Medicare-approved demonstration project)   ♀ M
Service not separately priced by Part B

C **G9072** Oncology; disease status; invasive female breast cancer (does not include ductal carcinoma in situ); adenocarcinoma as predominant cell type; Stage I, or Stage IIA-IIB; or T3, N1, M0; and ER and PR negative; with no evidence of disease progression, recurrence, or metastases (for use in a Medicare-approved demonstration project)   ♀ M
Service not separately priced by Part B

C **G9073** Oncology; disease status; invasive female breast cancer (does not include ductal carcinoma in situ); adenocarcinoma as predominant cell type; Stage IIIA-IIIB; and not T3, N1, M0; and ER and/or PR positive; with no evidence of disease progression, recurrence, or metastases (for use in a Medicare-approved demonstration project)   ♀ M
Service not separately priced by Part B

C **G9074** Oncology; disease status; invasive female breast cancer (does not include ductal carcinoma in situ); adenocarcinoma as predominant cell type; Stage IIIA-IIIB; and not T3, N1, M0; and ER and PR negative; with no evidence of disease progression, recurrence, or metastases (for use in a Medicare-approved demonstration project)   ♀ M
Service not separately priced by Part B

C **G9075** Oncology; disease status; invasive female breast cancer (does not include ductal carcinoma in situ); adenocarcinoma as predominant cell type; M1 at diagnosis, metastatic, locally recurrent, or progressive (for use in a Medicare-approved demonstration project)   ♀ M
Service not separately priced by Part B

C **G9077** Oncology; disease status; prostate cancer, limited to adenocarcinoma as predominant cell type; T1-T3C and gleason 2-7 and PSA < or equal to 20 at diagnosis with no evidence of disease progression, recurrence, or metastases (for use in a Medicare-approved demonstration project)   ♂ M
Service not separately priced by Part B

♂ Male only   ♀ Female only   **A** Age   A2 - Z3 = ASC Payment Indicator   A - Y = APC Status Indicator
ASC = ASC Approved Procedure   **DME** Paid under the DME fee schedule   **PQRS** Physician Quality Reporting System

G9078 C Oncology; disease status; prostate cancer, limited to adenocarcinoma as predominant cell type; T2 or T3A Gleason 8-10 or PSA > 20 at diagnosis with no evidence of disease progression, recurrence, or metastases (for use in a Medicare-approved demonstration project) ♂ M
Service not separately priced by Part B

G9079 C Oncology; disease status; prostate cancer, limited to adenocarcinoma as predominant cell type; T3B-T4, any N; any T, N1 at diagnosis with no evidence of disease progression, recurrence, or metastases (for use in a Medicare-approved demonstration project) ♂ M
Service not separately priced by Part B

G9080 C Oncology; disease status; prostate cancer, limited to adenocarcinoma; after initial treatment with rising PSA or failure of PSA decline (for use in a Medicare-approved demonstration project) ♂ M
Service not separately priced by Part B

G9083 C Oncology; disease status; prostate cancer, limited to adenocarcinoma; extent of disease unknown, staging in progress, or not listed (for use in a Medicare-approved demonstration project) ♂ M
Service not separately priced by Part B

G9084 C Oncology; disease status; colon cancer, limited to invasive cancer, adenocarcinoma as predominant cell type; extent of disease initially established as T1-3, N0, M0 with no evidence of disease progression, recurrence, or metastases (for use in a Medicare-approved demonstration project) M
Service not separately priced by Part B

G9085 C Oncology; disease status; colon cancer, limited to invasive cancer, adenocarcinoma as predominant cell type; extent of disease initially established as T4, N0, M0 with no evidence of disease progression, recurrence, or metastases (for use in a Medicare-approved demonstration project) M
Service not separately priced by Part B

G9086 C Oncology; disease status; colon cancer, limited to invasive cancer, adenocarcinoma as predominant cell type; extent of disease initially established as T1-4, N1-2, M0 with no evidence of disease progression, recurrence, or metastases (for use in a Medicare-approved demonstration project) M
Service not separately priced by Part B

G9087 C Oncology; disease status; colon cancer, limited to invasive cancer, adenocarcinoma as predominant cell type; M1 at diagnosis, metastatic, locally recurrent, or progressive with current clinical, radiologic, or biochemical evidence of disease (for use in a Medicare-approved demonstration project) M
Service not separately priced by Part B

G9088 C Oncology; disease status; colon cancer, limited to invasive cancer, adenocarcinoma as predominant cell type; M1 at diagnosis, metastatic, locally recurrent, or progressive without current clinical, radiologic, or biochemical evidence of disease (for use in a Medicare-approved demonstration project) M
Service not separately priced by Part B

G9089 C Oncology; disease status; colon cancer, limited to invasive cancer, adenocarcinoma as predominant cell type; extent of disease unknown, staging in progress, or not listed (for use in a Medicare-approved demonstration project) M
Service not separately priced by Part B

G9090 C Oncology; disease status; rectal cancer, limited to invasive cancer, adenocarcinoma as predominant cell type; extent of disease initially established as T1-2, N0, M0 (prior to neo-adjuvant therapy, if any) with no evidence of disease progression, recurrence, or metastases (for use in a Medicare-approved demonstration project) M
Service not separately priced by Part B

G9091 C Oncology; disease status; rectal cancer, limited to invasive cancer, adenocarcinoma as predominant cell type; extent of disease initially established as T3, N0, M0 (prior to neo-adjuvant therapy, if any) with no evidence of disease progression, recurrence, or metastases (for use in a Medicare-approved demonstration project) M
Service not separately priced by Part B

G9092 C Oncology; disease status; rectal cancer, limited to invasive cancer, adenocarcinoma as predominant cell type; extent of disease initially established as T1-3, N1-2, M0 (prior to neo-adjuvant therapy, if any) with no evidence of disease progression, recurrence or metastases (for use in a Medicare-approved demonstration project) M
Service not separately priced by Part B

G9093 C Oncology; disease status; rectal cancer, limited to invasive cancer, adenocarcinoma as predominant cell type; extent of disease initially established as T4, any N, M0 (prior to neo-adjuvant therapy, if any) with no evidence of disease progression, recurrence, or metastases (for use in a Medicare-approved demonstration project) M
Service not separately priced by Part B

G9094 C Oncology; disease status; rectal cancer, limited to invasive cancer, adenocarcinoma as predominant cell type; M1 at diagnosis, metastatic, locally recurrent, or progressive (for use in a Medicare-approved demonstration project) M
Service not separately priced by Part B

G9095 C Oncology; disease status; rectal cancer, limited to invasive cancer, adenocarcinoma

---

▲ Revised Code   ● New code   C Carrier judgment   D Special coverage instructions apply
I Not payable by Medicare   M Non-covered by Medicare   S Non-covered by Medicare statute   AHA Coding Clinic®

as predominant cell type; extent of disease unknown, staging in progress, or not listed (for use in a Medicare-approved demonstration project)　　M
Service not separately priced by Part B

C **G9096** Oncology; disease status; esophageal cancer, limited to adenocarcinoma or squamous cell carcinoma as predominant cell type; extent of disease initially established as T1-T3, N0-N1 or NX (prior to neo-adjuvant therapy, if any) with no evidence of disease progression, recurrence, or metastases (for use in a Medicare-approved demonstration project)　　M
Service not separately priced by Part B

C **G9097** Oncology; disease status; esophageal cancer, limited to adenocarcinoma or squamous cell carcinoma as predominant cell type; extent of disease initially established as T4, any N, M0 (prior to neo-adjuvant therapy, if any) with no evidence of disease progression, recurrence, or metastases (for use in a Medicare-approved demonstration project)　　M
Service not separately priced by Part B

C **G9098** Oncology; disease status; esophageal cancer, limited to adenocarcinoma or squamous cell carcinoma as predominant cell type; M1 at diagnosis, metastatic, locally recurrent, or progressive (for use in a Medicare-approved demonstration project) M
Service not separately priced by Part B

C **G9099** Oncology; disease status; esophageal cancer, limited to adenocarcinoma or squamous cell carcinoma as predominant cell type; extent of disease unknown, staging in progress, or not listed (for use in a Medicare-approved demonstration project) M
Service not separately priced by Part B

C **G9100** Oncology; disease status; gastric cancer, limited to adenocarcinoma as predominant cell type; post R0 resection (with or without neoadjuvant therapy) with no evidence of disease recurrence, progression, or metastases (for use in a Medicare-approved demonstration project)　　M
Service not separately priced by Part B

C **G9101** Oncology; disease status; gastric cancer, limited to adenocarcinoma as predominant cell type; post R1 or R2 resection (with or without neoadjuvant therapy) with no evidence of disease progression, or metastases (for use in a Medicare-approved demonstration project) M
Service not separately priced by Part B

C **G9102** Oncology; disease status; gastric cancer, limited to adenocarcinoma as predominant cell type; clinical or pathologic M0, unresectable with no evidence of disease progression, or metastases (for use in a Medicare-approved demonstration project) M
Service not separately priced by Part B

C **G9103** Oncology; disease status; gastric cancer, limited to adenocarcinoma as predominant cell type; clinical or pathologic M1 at diagnosis, metastatic, locally recurrent, or progressive (for use in a Medicare-approved demonstration project)　　M
Service not separately priced by Part B

C **G9104** Oncology; disease status; gastric cancer, limited to adenocarcinoma as predominant cell type; extent of disease unknown, staging in progress, or not listed (for use in a Medicare-approved demonstration project)　　M
Service not separately priced by Part B

C **G9105** Oncology; disease status; pancreatic cancer, limited to adenocarcinoma as predominant cell type; post R0 resection without evidence of disease progression, recurrence, or metastases (for use in a Medicare-approved demonstration project)　　M
Service not separately priced by Part B

C **G9106** Oncology; disease status; pancreatic cancer, limited to adenocarcinoma; post R1 or R2 resection with no evidence of disease progression, or metastases (for use in a Medicare-approved demonstration project) M
Service not separately priced by Part B

C **G9107** Oncology; disease status; pancreatic cancer, limited to adenocarcinoma; unresectable at diagnosis, M1 at diagnosis, metastatic, locally recurrent, or progressive (for use in a Medicare-approved demonstration project) M
Service not separately priced by Part B

C **G9108** Oncology; disease status; pancreatic cancer, limited to adenocarcinoma; extent of disease unknown, staging in progress, or not listed (for use in a Medicare-approved demonstration project)　　M
Service not separately priced by Part B

C **G9109** Oncology; disease status; head and neck cancer, limited to cancers of oral cavity, pharynx and larynx with squamous cell as predominant cell type; extent of disease initially established as T1-T2 and N0, M0 (prior to neo-adjuvant therapy, if any) with no evidence of disease progression, recurrence, or metastases (for use in a Medicare-approved demonstration project)　　M
Service not separately priced by Part B

C **G9110** Oncology; disease status; head and neck cancer, limited to cancers of oral cavity, pharynx and larynx with squamous cell as predominant cell type; extent of disease initially established as T3-4 and/or N1-3, M0 (prior to neo-adjuvant therapy, if any) with no evidence of disease progression, recurrence, or metastases (for use in a Medicare-approved demonstration project)　　M
Service not separately priced by Part B

C **G9111** Oncology; disease status; head and neck cancer, limited to cancers of oral cavity, pharynx and larynx with squamous cell as predominant cell type; M1 at diagnosis, metastatic, locally recurrent, or progressive (for use in a Medicare-approved demonstration project) M
Service not separately priced by Part B

C **G9112** Oncology; disease status; head and neck cancer, limited to cancers of oral cavity, pharynx and larynx with squamous cell as predominant cell type; extent of disease unknown, staging in progress, or not listed (for use in a Medicare-approved demonstration project) M
Service not separately priced by Part B

C **G9113** Oncology; disease status; ovarian cancer, limited to epithelial cancer; pathologic Stage IA-B (Grade 1) without evidence of disease progression, recurrence, or metastases (for use in a Medicare-approved demonstration project) ♀ M
Service not separately priced by Part B

C **G9114** Oncology; disease status; ovarian cancer, limited to epithelial cancer; pathologic Stage IA-B (Grade 2-3); or Stage IC (all grades); or Stage II; without evidence of disease progression, recurrence, or metastases (for use in a Medicare-approved demonstration project) ♀ M
Service not separately priced by Part B

C **G9115** Oncology; disease status; ovarian cancer, limited to epithelial cancer; pathologic Stage III-IV; without evidence of progression, recurrence, or metastases (for use in a Medicare-approved demonstration project) ♀ M
Service not separately priced by Part B

C **G9116** Oncology; disease status; ovarian cancer, limited to epithelial cancer; evidence of disease progression, or recurrence, and/or platinum resistance (for use in a Medicare-approved demonstration project) ♀ M
Service not separately priced by Part B

C **G9117** Oncology; disease status; ovarian cancer, limited to epithelial cancer; extent of disease unknown, staging in progress, or not listed (for use in a Medicare-approved demonstration project) ♀ M
Service not separately priced by Part B

C **G9123** Oncology; disease status; chronic myelogenous leukemia, limited to Philadelphia chromosome positive and/or BCR-ABL positive; chronic phase not in hematologic, cytogenetic, or molecular remission (for use in a Medicare-approved demonstration project) M
Service not separately priced by Part B

C **G9124** Oncology; disease status; chronic myelogenous leukemia, limited to Philadelphia chromosome positive and/or BCR-ABL positive; accelerated phase not in hematologic cytogenetic, or molecular remission (for use in a Medicare-approved demonstration project) M
Service not separately priced by Part B

C **G9125** Oncology; disease status; chronic myelogenous leukemia, limited to Philadelphia chromosome positive and/or BCR-ABL positive; blast phase not in hematologic, cytogenetic, or molecular remission (for use in a Medicare-approved demonstration project) M
Service not separately priced by Part B

C **G9126** Oncology; disease status; chronic myelogenous leukemia, limited to Philadelphia chromosome positive and/or BCR-ABL positive; in hematologic, cytogenetic, or molecular remission (for use in a Medicare-approved demonstration project) M
Service not separately priced by Part B

C **G9128** Oncology; disease status; limited to multiple myeloma, systemic disease; smoldering, Stage I (for use in a Medicare-approved demonstration project) M
Service not separately priced by Part B

C **G9129** Oncology; disease status; limited to multiple myeloma, systemic disease; Stage II or higher (for use in a Medicare-approved demonstration project) M
Service not separately priced by Part B

C **G9130** Oncology; disease status; limited to multiple myeloma, systemic disease; extent of disease unknown, staging in progress, or not listed (for use in a Medicare-approved demonstration project) M
Service not separately priced by Part B

C **G9131** Oncology; disease status; invasive female breast cancer (does not include ductal carcinoma in situ); adenocarcinoma as predominant cell type; extent of disease unknown, staging in progress, or not listed (for use in a Medicare-approved demonstration project) ♀ M
Service not separately priced by Part B

C **G9132** Oncology; disease status; prostate cancer, limited to adenocarcinoma; hormone-refractory/androgen-independent (e.g., rising PSA on anti-androgen therapy or post-orchiectomy); clinical metastases (for use in a Medicare-approved demonstration project) ♂ M
Service not separately priced by Part B

C **G9133** Oncology; disease status; prostate cancer, limited to adenocarcinoma; hormone-responsive; clinical metastases or M1 at diagnosis (for use in a Medicare-approved demonstration project) ♂ M
Service not separately priced by Part B

▲ Revised Code   ● New code   C Carrier judgment   D Special coverage instructions apply
I Not payable by Medicare   M Non-covered by Medicare   S Non-covered by Medicare statute   AHA Coding Clinic®

C G9134 Oncology; disease status; non-Hodgkin's lymphoma, any cellular classification; Stage i, II at diagnosis, not relapsed, not refractory (for use in a Medicare-approved demonstration project)   M
Service not separately priced by Part B

C G9135 Oncology; disease status; non-Hodgkin's lymphoma, any cellular classification; Stage III, IV, not relapsed, not refractory (for use in a Medicare-approved demonstration project)   M
Service not separately priced by Part B

C G9136 Oncology; disease status; non-Hodgkin's lymphoma, transformed from original cellular diagnosis to a second cellular classification (for use in a Medicare-approved demonstration project)   M
Service not separately priced by Part B

C G9137 Oncology; disease status; non-Hodgkin's lymphoma, any cellular classification; relapsed/refractory (for use in a Medicare-approved demonstration project)   M
Service not separately priced by Part B

C G9138 Oncology; disease status; non-Hodgkin's lymphoma, any cellular classification; diagnostic evaluation, stage not determined, evaluation of possible relapse or non-response to therapy, or not listed (for use in a Medicare-approved demonstration project)   M
Service not separately priced by Part B

C G9139 Oncology; disease status; chronic myelogenous leukemia, limited to Philadelphia chromosome positive and/or BCR-ABL positive; extent of disease unknown, staging in progress, not listed (for use in a Medicare-approved demonstration project)   M
Service not separately priced by Part B

C G9140 Frontier extended stay clinic demonstration; for a patient stay in a clinic approved for the CMS demonstration project; the following measures should be present: the stay must be equal to or greater than 4 hours; weather or other conditions must prevent transfer or the case falls into a category of monitoring and observation cases that are permitted by the rules of the demonstration; there is a maximum frontier extended stay clinic (FESC) visit of 48 hours, except in the case when weather or other conditions prevent transfer; payment is made on each period up to 4 hours, after the first 4 hours   A
Service not separately priced by Part B

C G9143 Warfarin responsiveness testing by genetic technique using any method, any number of specimen(s)   A
Price established by carriers
Coding Clinic 2010, Q2, P10

Pub: 100-3, Chap. 1, Part 2, 90.1; 100-4, Chap. 32, 250.1; 100-4, Chap. 32, 250.2

M G9147 Outpatient intravenous insulin treatment (OIVIT) either pulsatile or continuous, by any means, guided by the results of measurements for: respiratory quotient; and/or, urine urea nitrogen (UUN); and/or, arterial, venous or capillary glucose; and/or potassium concentration   E
Service not separately priced by Part B
Coding Clinic 2010, Q2, P10

Pub: 100-3, Chap. 1, Part 1, 40.7; 100-4, Chap. 4, 320.1; 100-4, Chap. 4, 320.2

C G9148 National Committee for Quality Assurance - Level 1 medical home   M
Service not separately priced by Part B

C G9149 National Committee for Quality Assurance - Level 2 medical home   M
Service not separately priced by Part B

C G9150 National Committee for Quality Assurance - Level 3 medical home   M
Service not separately priced by Part B

C G9151 MAPCP Demonstration - state provided services   M
Service not separately priced by Part B

C G9152 MAPCP Demonstration - Community Health Teams   M
Service not separately priced by Part B

C G9153 MAPCP Demonstration - Physician Incentive Pool   M
Service not separately priced by Part B

C G9156 Evaluation for wheelchair requiring face to face visit with physician   M
Service not separately priced by Part B

C G9157 Transesophageal Doppler use for cardiac monitoring   B
Service not separately priced by Part B
Pub: 100-4, Chap. 32, 310; 100-4, Chap. 32, 310.2

C G9158 Motor speech functional limitation, discharge status, at discharge from therapy or to end reporting   E
Service not separately priced by Part B
Pub: 100-4, Chap. 5, 10.6

C G9159 Spoken language comprehension functional limitation, current status at therapy episode outset and at reporting intervals   E
Service not separately priced by Part B

▲ **C G9160** Spoken language comprehension functional limitation, projected goal status at therapy episode outset, at reporting intervals, and at discharge or to end reporting   E
Service not separately priced by Part B

C G9161 Spoken language comprehension functional limitation, discharge status, at discharge from therapy or to end reporting   E
Service not separately priced by Part B

♂ Male only   ♀ Female only   **A** Age   A2 - Z3 = ASC Payment Indicator   A - Y = APC Status Indicator
ASC = ASC Approved Procedure   **DME** Paid under the DME fee schedule   **PQRS** Physician Quality Reporting System

99

G9162-G9197

PROCEDURES / PROFESSIONAL SERVICES (G0008-G9472)

C **G9162** Spoken language expression functional limitation, current status at therapy episode outset and at reporting intervals   E

Service not separately priced by Part B

▲ **C** **G9163** Spoken language expression functional limitation, projected goal status at therapy episode outset, at reporting intervals, and at discharge or to end reporting   E

Service not separately priced by Part B

C **G9164** Spoken language expression functional limitation, discharge status at discharge from therapy or to end reporting   E

Service not separately priced by Part B

C **G9165** Attention functional limitation, current status at therapy episode outset and at reporting intervals   E

Service not separately priced by Part B

▲ **C** **G9166** Attention functional limitation, projected goal status at therapy episode outset, at reporting intervals, and at discharge or to end reporting   E

Service not separately priced by Part B

C **G9167** Attention functional limitation, discharge status at discharge from therapy or to end reporting   E

Service not separately priced by Part B

C **G9168** Memory functional limitation, current status at therapy episode outset and at reporting intervals   E

Service not separately priced by Part B

▲ **C** **G9169** Memory functional limitation, projected goal status at therapy episode outset, at reporting intervals, and at discharge or to end reporting   E

Service not separately priced by Part B

C **G9170** Memory functional limitation, discharge status at discharge from therapy or to end reporting   E

Service not separately priced by Part B

C **G9171** Voice functional limitation, current status at therapy episode outset and at reporting intervals   E

Service not separately priced by Part B

▲ **C** **G9172** Voice functional limitation, projected goal status at therapy episode outset, at reporting intervals, and at discharge or to end reporting   E

Service not separately priced by Part B

C **G9173** Voice functional limitation, discharge status at discharge from therapy or to end reporting   E

Service not separately priced by Part B

C **G9174** Other speech language pathology functional limitation, current status at therapy episode outset and at reporting intervals   E

Service not separately priced by Part B

▲ **C** **G9175** Other speech language pathology functional limitation, projected goal status at therapy episode outset, at reporting intervals, and at discharge or to end reporting   E

Service not separately priced by Part B

C **G9176** Other speech language pathology functional limitation, discharge status at discharge from therapy or to end reporting   E

Service not separately priced by Part B

▲ **C** **G9186** Motor speech functional limitation, projected goal status at therapy episode outset, at reporting intervals, and at discharge or to end reporting   E

Service not separately priced by Part B

Pub: 100-4, Chap. 5, 10.6

C **G9187** Bundled payments for care improvement initiative home visit for patient assessment performed by a qualified health care professional for individuals not considered homebound including, but not limited to, assessment of safety, falls, clinical status, fluid status, medication reconciliation/ management, patient compliance with orders/plan of care, performance of activities of daily living, appropriateness of care setting; (for use only in the Medicare-approved bundled payments for care improvement initiative); may not be billed for a 30-day period covered by a transitional care management code   E

Price established by carriers

C **G9188** Beta-blocker therapy not prescribed, reason not given

Service not separately priced by Part B

C **G9189** Beta-blocker therapy prescribed or currently being taken

Service not separately priced by Part B

C **G9190** Documentation of medical reason(s) for not prescribing beta-blocker therapy (e.g., allergy, intolerance, other medical reasons)

Service not separately priced by Part B

C **G9191** Documentation of patient reason(s) for not prescribing beta-blocker therapy (e.g., patient declined, other patient reasons)

Service not separately priced by Part B

C **G9192** Documentation of system reason(s) for not prescribing beta-blocker therapy (e.g., other reasons attributable to the health care system)

Service not separately priced by Part B

C **G9196** Documentation of medical reason(s) for not ordering first or second generation cephalosporin for antimicrobial prophylaxis **PQRS**

Service not separately priced by Part B

C **G9197** Documentation of order for first or second generation cephalosporin for antimicrobial prophylaxis **PQRS**

Service not separately priced by Part B

C **G9198** Order for first or second generation cephalosporin for antimicrobial prophylaxis was not documented, reason not given `PQRS`
Service not separately priced by Part B

C **G9203** RNA testing for hepatitis C documented as performed within 12 months prior to initiation of antiviral treatment for hepatitis C `PQRS`
Service not separately priced by Part B

C **G9204** RNA testing for hepatitis C was not documented as performed within 12 months prior to initiation of antiviral treatment for hepatitis C, reason not given `PQRS`
Service not separately priced by Part B

C **G9205** Patient starting antiviral treatment for hepatitis C during the measurement period `PQRS`
Service not separately priced by Part B

C **G9206** Patient starting antiviral treatment for hepatitis C during the measurement period `PQRS`
Service not separately priced by Part B

C **G9207** Hepatitis C genotype testing documented as performed within 12 months prior to initiation of antiviral treatment for hepatitis C `PQRS`
Service not separately priced by Part B

C **G9208** Hepatitis C genotype testing was not documented as performed within 12 months prior to initiation of antiviral treatment for hepatitis C, reason not given `PQRS`
Service not separately priced by Part B

C **G9209** Hepatitis C quantitative RNA testing documented as performed between 4-12 weeks after the initiation of antiviral treatment `PQRS`
Service not separately priced by Part B

▲ **C** **G9210** Hepatitis C quantitative RNA testing not performed between 4-12 weeks after the initiation of antiviral treatment for documented reason(s) (e.g., patients whose treatment was discontinued during the testing period prior to testing, other medical reasons, patient declined, other patient reasons) `PQRS`
Service not separately priced by Part B

C **G9211** Hepatitis C quantitative RNA testing was not documented as performed between 4-12 weeks after the initiation of antiviral treatment, reason not given `PQRS`
Service not separately priced by Part B

C **G9212** DSM-IVTM criteria for major depressive disorder documented at the initial evaluation
Service not separately priced by Part B

C **G9213** DSM-IV-TR criteria for major depressive disorder not documented at the initial evaluation, reason not otherwise specified
Service not separately priced by Part B

C **G9217** PCP prophylaxis was not prescribed within 3 months of low CD4+ cell count below 200 cells/mm3, reason not given `PQRS`
Service not separately priced by Part B

C **G9219** Pneumocystis jiroveci pneumonia prophylaxis not prescribed within 3 months of low CD4+ cell count below 200 cells/mm3 for medical reason (i.e., patient's CD4+ cell count above threshold within 3 months after CD4+ cell count below threshold, indicating that the patient's CD4+ levels are within an acceptable range and the patient does not require PCP prophylaxis)
Service not separately priced by Part B

C **G9222** Pneumocystis jiroveci pneumonia prophylaxis prescribed wthin 3 months of low CD4+ cell count below 200 cells/mm3 `PQRS`
Service not separately priced by Part B

C **G9223** Pneumocystis jiroveci pneumonia prophylaxis prescribed within 3 months of low CD4+ cell count below 500 cells/mm3 or a CD4 percentage below 15%
Service not separately priced by Part B

C **G9225** Foot exam was not performed, reason not given `PQRS`
Service not separately priced by Part B

C **G9226** Foot examination performed (includes examination through visual inspection, sensory exam with monofilament, and pulse exam - report when all of the 3 components are completed) `PQRS`
Service not separately priced by Part B

C **G9227** Functional outcome assessment documented, care plan not documented, documentation the patient is not eligible for a care plan
Service not separately priced by Part B

C **G9228** Chlamydia, gonorrhea and syphilis screening results documented (report when results are present for all of the 3 screenings) `PQRS`
Service not separately priced by Part B

C **G9229** Chlamydia, gonorrhea, and syphilis not screened, due to documented reason (patient refusal is the only allowed exclusion) `PQRS`
Service not separately priced by Part B

C **G9230** Chlamydia, gonorrhea, and syphilis not screened, reason not given `PQRS`
Service not separately priced by Part B

C **G9231** Documentation of end stage renal disease (ESRD), dialysis, renal transplant or pregnancy `PQRS`
Service not separately priced by Part B

C **G9232** Clinician treating major depressive disorder did not communicate to clinician treating comorbid condition for specified patient reason
Service not separately priced by Part B

♂ Male only   ♀ Female only   🅐 Age   A2 - Z3 = ASC Payment Indicator   A - Y = APC Status Indicator
ASC = ASC Approved Procedure   `DME` Paid under the DME fee schedule   `PQRS` Physician Quality Reporting System

G9198 - G9232

PROCEDURES / PROFESSIONAL SERVICES (G0008-G9472)

101

G9233 - G9264

PROCEDURES / PROFESSIONAL SERVICES (G0008-G9472)

C **G9233** All quality actions for the applicable measures in the total knee replacement measures group have been performed for this patient `PQRS`
Service not separately priced by Part B

C **G9234** I intend to report the total knee replacement measures group `PQRS`
Service not separately priced by Part B

C **G9235** All quality actions for the applicable measures in the general surgery measures group have been performed for this patient `PQRS`
Service not separately priced by Part B

C **G9236** All quality actions for the applicable measures in the optimizing patient exposure to ionizing radiation measures group have been performed for this patient `PQRS`
Service not separately priced by Part B

C **G9237** I intend to report the general surgery measures group `PQRS`
Service not separately priced by Part B

C **G9238** I intend to report the optimizing patient exposure to ionizing radiation measures group `PQRS`
Service not separately priced by Part B

C **G9239** Documentation of reasons for patient initiating maintenance hemodialysis with a catheter as the mode of vascular access (e.g., patient has a maturing AVF/AVG, time-limited trial of hemodialysis, patients undergoing palliative dialysis, other medical reasons, patient declined AVF/AVG, other patient reasons, patient followed by reporting nephrologist for fewer than 90 days, other system reasons)
Service not separately priced by Part B

C **G9240** Patient whose mode of vascular access is a catheter at the time maintenance hemodialysis is initiated
Service not separately priced by Part B

C **G9241** Patient whose mode of vascular access is not a catheter at the time maintenance hemodialysis is initiated
Service not separately priced by Part B

▲ C **G9242** Documentation of viral load equal to or greater than 200 copies/ml or viral load not performed `PQRS`
Service not separately priced by Part B

C **G9243** Documentation of viral load less than 200 copies/ml `PQRS`
Service not separately priced by Part B

C **G9244** Antiretroviral therapy not prescribed `PQRS`
Service not separately priced by Part B

C **G9245** Antiretroviral therapy prescribed `PQRS`
Service not separately priced by Part B

C **G9246** Patient did not have at least one medical visit in each 6 month period of the 24 month measurement period, with a minimum of 60 days between medical visits `PQRS`
Service not separately priced by Part B

C **G9247** Patient had at least one medical visit in each 6 month period of the 24 month measurement period, with a minimum of 60 days between medical visits `PQRS`
Service not separately priced by Part B

C **G9250** Documentation of patient pain brought to a comfortable level within 48 hours from initial assessment
Service not separately priced by Part B

C **G9251** Documentation of patient with pain not brought to a comfortable level within 48 hours from initial assessment
Service not separately priced by Part B

C **G9254** Documentation of patient discharged to home later than post-operative day 2 following CAS
Service not separately priced by Part B

C **G9255** Documentation of patient discharged to home no later than post operative day 2 following CAS
Service not separately priced by Part B

C **G9256** Documentation of patient death following CAS
Service not separately priced by Part B

C **G9257** Documentation of patient stroke following CAS
Service not separately priced by Part B

C **G9258** Documentation of patient stroke following CEA
Service not separately priced by Part B

C **G9259** Documentation of patient survival and absence of stroke following CAS
Service not separately priced by Part B

C **G9260** Documentation of patient death following CEA
Service not separately priced by Part B

C **G9261** Documentation of patient survival and absence of stroke following CEA
Service not separately priced by Part B

C **G9262** Documentation of patient death in the hospital following endovascular AAA repair
Service not separately priced by Part B

C **G9263** Documentation of patient survival in the hospital following endovascular AAA repair
Service not separately priced by Part B

C **G9264** Documentation of patient receiving maintenance hemodialysis for greater than or equal to 90 days with a catheter for documented reasons (e.g., patient is undergoing palliative dialysis with a catheter, patient approved by a qualified transplant program and scheduled to receive a living donor kidney transplant, other medical reasons, patient declined AVF/AVG, other patient reasons)
Service not separately priced by Part B

▲ Revised Code   ● New code   C Carrier judgment   D Special coverage instructions apply
I Not payable by Medicare   M Non-covered by Medicare   S Non-covered by Medicare statute   AHA Coding Clinic®

C **G9265** Patient receiving maintenance hemodialysis for greater than or equal to 90 days with a catheter as the mode of vascular access
Service not separately priced by Part B

C **G9266** Patient receiving maintenance hemodialysis for greater than or equal to 90 days without a catheter as the mode of vascular access
Service not separately priced by Part B

C **G9267** Documentation of patient with one or more complications or mortality within 30 days
Service not separately priced by Part B

C **G9268** Documentation of patient with one or more complications within 90 days
Service not separately priced by Part B

C **G9269** Documentation of patient without one or more complications and without mortality within 30 days
Service not separately priced by Part B

C **G9270** Documentation of patient without one or more complications within 90 days
Service not separately priced by Part B

C **G9273** Blood pressure has a systolic value of < 140 and a diastolic value of < 90
Service not separately priced by Part B

C **G9274** Blood pressure has a systolic value of =140 and a diastolic value of = 90 or systolic value < 140 and diastolic value = 90 or systolic value = 140 and diastolic value < 90
Service not separately priced by Part B

C **G9275** Documentation that patient is a current non-tobacco user
Service not separately priced by Part B

C **G9276** Documentation that patient is a current tobacco user
Service not separately priced by Part B

▲ C **G9277** Documentation that the patient is on daily aspirin or anti-platelet or has documentation of a valid contraindication to aspirin/anti-platelet. automatic contraindications include anti-coagulant use, allergy, and history of gastrointestinal bleed. additionally, any reason documented by the physician as a reason for not taking daily aspirin or anti-platelet is acceptable (examples include non-steroidal anti-inflammatory agents, risk for drug interaction, or uncontrolled hypertension defined as > 180 systolic or > 110 diastolic
Service not separately priced by Part B

▲ C **G9278** Documentation that the patient is not on daily aspirin or anti-platelet regimen
Service not separately priced by Part B

C **G9279** Pneumococcal screening performed and documentation of vaccination received prior to discharge
Service not separately priced by Part B

C **G9280** Pneumococcal vaccination not administered prior to discharge, reason not specified
Service not separately priced by Part B

C **G9281** Screening performed and documentation that vaccination not indicated/patient refusal
Service not separately priced by Part B

C **G9282** Documentation of medical reason(s) for not reporting the histological type or NSCLC-NOS classification with an explanation (e.g., biopsy taken for other purposes in a patient with a history of non-small cell lung cancer or other documented medical reasons)
Service not separately priced by Part B

C **G9283** Non small cell lung cancer biopsy and cytology specimen report documents classification into specific histologic type or classified as NSCLC-NOS with an explanation
Service not separately priced by Part B

C **G9284** Non small cell lung cancer biopsy and cytology specimen report does not document classification into specific histologic type or classified as NSCLC-NOS with an explanation
Service not separately priced by Part B

C **G9285** Specimen site other than anatomic location of lung or is not classified as non small cell lung cancer
Service not separately priced by Part B

C **G9286** Documentation of antibiotic regimen prescribed within 7 days of diagnosis or within 10 days after onset of symptoms
Service not separately priced by Part B

C **G9287** No antibiotic regimen prescribed within 7 days of diagnosis or within 10 days after onset of symptoms
Service not separately priced by Part B

C **G9288** Documentation of medical reason(s) for not reporting the histological type or NSCLC-NOS classification with an explanation (e.g., a solitary fibrous tumor in a person with a history of non-small cell carcinoma or other documented medical reasons)
Service not separately priced by Part B

C **G9289** Non small cell lung cancer biopsy and cytology specimen report documents classification into specific histologic type or classified as NSCLC-NOS with an explanation
Service not separately priced by Part B

C **G9290** Non small cell lung cancer biopsy and cytology specimen report does not document classification into specific histologic type or classified as NSCLC-NOS with an explanation
Service not separately priced by Part B

♂ Male only   ♀ Female only   Ⓐ Age   A2 - Z3 = ASC Payment Indicator   A - Y = APC Status Indicator
ASC = ASC Approved Procedure   **DME** Paid under the DME fee schedule   **PQRS** Physician Quality Reporting System

C **G9291** Specimen site other than anatomic location of lung, is not classified as non small cell lung cancer or classified as NSCLC-NOS
Service not separately priced by Part B

C **G9292** Documentation of medical reason(s) for not reporting pt category and a statement on thickness and ulceration and for PT1, mitotic rate (e.g., negative skin biopsies in a patient with a history of melanoma or other documented medical reasons)
Service not separately priced by Part B

C **G9293** Pathology report does not include the pt category and a statement on thickness and ulceration and for PT1, mitotic rate
Service not separately priced by Part B

C **G9294** Pathology report includes the pt category and a statement on thickness and ulceration and for PT1, mitotic rate
Service not separately priced by Part B

C **G9295** Specimen site other than anatomic cutaneous location
Service not separately priced by Part B

▲ C **G9296** Patients with documented shared decision-making including discussion of conservative (non-surgical) therapy (e.g., nsaids, analgesics, weight loss, exercise, injections) prior to the procedure PQRS
Service not separately priced by Part B

▲ C **G9297** Shared decision-making including discussion of conservative (non-surgical) therapy (e.g., nsaids, analgesics, weight loss, exercise, injections) prior to the procedure, not documented, reason not given PQRS
Service not separately priced by Part B

▲ C **G9298** Patients who are evaluated for venous thromboembolic and cardiovascular risk factors within 30 days prior to the procedure (e.g., history of DVT, PE, MI, arrhythmia and stroke) PQRS
Service not separately priced by Part B

▲ C **G9299** Patients who are not evaluated for venous thromboembolic and cardiovascular risk factors within 30 days prior to the procedure including (e.g., history of DVT, PE, MI, arrhythmia and stroke, reason not given) PQRS
Service not separately priced by Part B

C **G9300** Documentation of medical reason(s) for not completely infusing the prophylactic antibiotic prior to the inflation of the proximal tourniquet (e.g., a tourniquet was not used) PQRS
Service not separately priced by Part B

C **G9301** Patients who had the prophylactic antibiotic completely infused prior to the inflation of the proximal tourniquet PQRS
Service not separately priced by Part B

C **G9302** Prophylactic antibiotic not completely infused prior to the inflation of the proximal tourniquet, reason not given PQRS
Service not separately priced by Part B

▲ C **G9303** Operative report does not identify the prosthetic implant specifications including the prosthetic implant manufacturer, the brand name of the prosthetic implant and the size of each prosthetic implant, reason not given PQRS
Service not separately priced by Part B

▲ C **G9304** Operative report identifies the prosthetic implant specifications including the prosthetic implant manufacturer, the brand name of the prosthetic implant and the size of each prosthetic implant PQRS
Service not separately priced by Part B

C **G9305** Intervention for presence of leak of endoluminal contents through an anastomosis not required PQRS
Service not separately priced by Part B

C **G9306** Intervention for presence of leak of endoluminal contents through an anastomosis required PQRS
Service not separately priced by Part B

C **G9307** No return to the operating room for a surgical procedure, for any reason, within 30 days of the principal operative procedure PQRS
Service not separately priced by Part B

C **G9308** Unplanned return to the operating room for a surgical procedure, for any reason, within 30 days of the principal operative procedure PQRS
Service not separately priced by Part B

C **G9309** No unplanned hospital readmission within 30 days of principal procedure PQRS
Service not separately priced by Part B

C **G9310** Unplanned hospital readmission within 30 days of principal procedure PQRS
Service not separately priced by Part B

C **G9311** No surgical site infection PQRS
Service not separately priced by Part B

C **G9312** Surgical site infection PQRS
Service not separately priced by Part B

C **G9313** Amoxicillin, with or without clavulanate, not prescribed as first line antibiotic at the time of diagnosis for documented reason (e.g., cystic fibrosis, immotile cilia disorders, ciliary dyskinesia, immune deficiency, prior history of sinus surgery within the past 12 months, and anatomic abnormalities, such as deviated nasal septum, resistant organisms, allergy to medication, recurrent sinusitis, chronic sinusitis, or other reasons)
Service not separately priced by Part B

C **G9314** Amoxicillin, with or without clavulanate, not prescribed as first line antibiotic at the time of diagnosis, reason not given
Service not separately priced by Part B

▲ Revised Code   ● New code   C Carrier judgment   D Special coverage instructions apply
I Not payable by Medicare   M Non-covered by Medicare   S Non-covered by Medicare statute   AHA Coding Clinic®

C **G9315** Documentation amoxicillin, with or without clavulanate, prescribed as a first line antibiotic at the time of diagnosis

Service not separately priced by Part B

C **G9316** Documentation of patient-specific risk assessment with a risk calculator based on multi-institutional clinical data, the specific risk calculator used, and communication of risk assessment from risk calculator with the patient or family `PQRS`

Service not separately priced by Part B

C **G9317** Documentation of patient-specific risk assessment with a risk calculator based on multi-institutional clinical data, the specific risk calculator used, and communication of risk assessment from risk calculator with the patient or family not completed `PQRS`

Service not separately priced by Part B

C **G9318** Imaging study named according to standardized nomenclature `PQRS`

Service not separately priced by Part B

C **G9319** Imaging study not named according to standardized nomenclature, reason not given `PQRS`

Service not separately priced by Part B

C **G9320** Documentation of medical reason(s) for not naming CT studies according to a standardized nomenclature provided (e.g., CT studies performed for radiation treatment planning or image-guided radiation treatment delivery) `PQRS`

Service not separately priced by Part B

C **G9321** Count of previous ct (any type of ct) and cardiac nuclear medicine (myocardial perfusion) studies documented in the 12-month period prior to the current study `PQRS`

Service not separately priced by Part B

C **G9322** Count of previous CT and cardiac nuclear medicine (myocardial perfusion) studies not documented in the 12-month period prior to the current study, reason not given `PQRS`

Service not separately priced by Part B

C **G9323** Documentation of medical reason(s) for not counting previous ct and cardiac nuclear medicine (myocardial perfusion) studies (e.g., CT studies performed for radiation treatment planning or image-guided radiation treatment delivery) `PQRS`

Service not separately priced by Part B

C **G9324** All necessary data elements not included, reason not given `PQRS`

Service not separately priced by Part B

C **G9325** CT studies not reported to a radiation dose index registry due to medical reasons (e.g., CT studies performed for radiation treatment planning or image-guided radiation treatment delivery) `PQRS`

Service not separately priced by Part B

C **G9326** CT studies performed not reported to a radiation dose index registry, reason not given `PQRS`

Service not separately priced by Part B

C **G9327** CT studies performed reported to a radiation dose index registry with all necessary data elements `PQRS`

Service not separately priced by Part B

C **G9328** Dicom format image data availability not documented in final report due to medical reasons (e.g., CT studies performed for radiation treatment planning or image-guided radiation treatment delivery) `PQRS`

Service not separately priced by Part B

▲ C **G9329** Dicom format image data available to non-affiliated external healthcare facilities or entities on a secure, media free, reciprocally searchable basis with patient authorization for at least a 12-month period after the study not documented in final report, reason not given `PQRS`

Service not separately priced by Part B

▲ C **G9340** Final report documented that dicom format image data available to non-affiliated external healthcare facilities or entities on a secure, media free, reciprocally searchable basis with patient authorization for at least a 12-month period after the study `PQRS`

Service not separately priced by Part B

▲ C **G9341** Search conducted for prior patient CT studies completed at non-affiliated external healthcare facilities or entities within the past 12-months and are available through a secure, authorized, media-free, shared archive prior to an imaging study being performed `PQRS`

Service not separately priced by Part B

▲ C **G9342** Search not conducted prior to an imaging study being performed for prior patient CT studies completed at non-affiliated external healthcare facilities or entities within the past 12-months and are available through a secure, authorized, media-free, shared archive, reason not given `PQRS`

Service not separately priced by Part B

▲ C **G9343** Due to medical reasons, search not conducted for dicom format images for prior patient CT imaging studies completed at non-affiliated external healthcare facilities or entities within the past 12 months that are available through a secure, authorized, media-free, shared archive (e.g., CT studies performed for radiation treatment planning or image-guided radiation treatment delivery) `PQRS`

Service not separately priced by Part B

♂ Male only   ♀ Female only   ⓐ Age   A2 - Z3 = ASC Payment Indicator   A - Y = APC Status Indicator
ASC = ASC Approved Procedure   `DME` Paid under the DME fee schedule   `PQRS` Physician Quality Reporting System

▲ C **G9344** Due to system reasons search not conducted for dicom format images for prior patient CT imaging studies completed at non-affiliated external healthcare facilities or entities within the past 12 months that are available through a secure, authorized, media-free, shared archive (e.g., non-affiliated external healthcare facilities or entities does not have archival abilities through a shared archival system) [PQRS]
Service not separately priced by Part B

▲ C **G9345** Follow-up recommendations documented according to recommended guidelines for incidentally detected pulmonary nodules (e.g., follow-up CT imaging studies needed or that no follow-up is needed) based at a minimum on nodule size and patient risk factors [PQRS]
Service not separately priced by Part B

▲ C **G9346** Follow-up recommendations not documented according to recommended guidelines for incidentally detected pulmonary nodules due to medical reasons (e.g., patients with known malignant disease, patients with unexplained fever, CT studies performed for radiation treatment planning or image-guided radiation treatment delivery) [PQRS]
Service not separately priced by Part B

▲ C **G9347** Follow-up recommendations not documented according to recommended guidelines for incidentally detected pulmonary nodules, reason not given [PQRS]
Service not separately priced by Part B

C **G9348** CT scan of the paranasal sinuses ordered at the time of diagnosis for documented reasons (e.g., persons with sinusitis symptoms lasting at least 7 to 10 days, antibiotic resistance, immunocompromised, recurrent sinusitis, acute frontal sinusitis, acute sphenoid sinusitis, periorbital cellulitis, or other medical)
Service not separately priced by Part B

C **G9349** Documentation of a CT scan of the paranasal sinuses ordered at the time of diagnosis or received within 28 days after date of diagnosis
Service not separately priced by Part B

C **G9350** CT scan of the paranasal sinuses not ordered at the time of diagnosis or received within 28 days after date of diagnosis
Service not separately priced by Part B

C **G9351** More than one CT scan of the paranasal sinuses ordered or received within 90 days after diagnosis
Service not separately priced by Part B

C **G9352** More than one CT scan of the paranasal sinuses ordered or received within 90 days after the date of diagnosis, reason not given
Service not separately priced by Part B

C **G9353** More than one CT scan of the paranasal sinuses ordered or received within 90 days after the date of diagnosis for documented reasons (e.g., patients with complications, second CT obtained prior to surgery, other medical reasons)
Service not separately priced by Part B

C **G9354** More than one CT scan of the paranasal sinuses not ordered within 90 days after the date of diagnosis
Service not separately priced by Part B

C **G9355** Elective delivery or early induction not performed ♀
Service not separately priced by Part B

C **G9356** Elective delivery or early induction performed ♀
Service not separately priced by Part B

C **G9357** Post-partum screenings, evaluations and education performed ♀
Service not separately priced by Part B

C **G9358** Post-partum screenings, evaluations and education not performed ♀
Service not separately priced by Part B

C **G9359** Documentation of negative or managed positive TB screen with further evidence that TB is not active
Service not separately priced by Part B

C **G9360** No documentation of negative or managed positive TB screen
Service not separately priced by Part B

● C **G9361** Medical indication for induction (documentation of reason(s) for elective delivery or early induction (e.g., hemorrhage and placental complications, hypertension, preeclampsia and eclampsia, rupture of membranes-premature, prolonged maternal conditions complicating pregnancy/delivery, fetal conditions complicating pregnancy/delivery, malposition and malpresentation of fetus, late pregnancy, prior uterine surgery, or participation in clinical trial))

● C **G9362** Duration of monitored anesthesia care (MAC) or peripheral nerve block (PNB) without the use of general anesthesia during an applicable procedure 60 minutes or longer, as documented in the anesthesia record

● C **G9363** Duration of monitored anesthesia care (MAC) or peripheral nerve block (PNB) without the use of general anesthesia during an applicable procedure or general or neuraxial anesthesia less than 60 minutes, as documented in the anesthesia record

● C **G9364** Sinusitis caused by, or presumed to be caused by, bacterial infection

● C **G9365** One high-risk medication ordered

● C **G9366** One high-risk medication not ordered

▲ Revised Code ● New code C Carrier judgment D Special coverage instructions apply
I Not payable by Medicare M Non-covered by Medicare S Non-covered by Medicare statute AHA Coding Clinic®

- C **G9367** At least two different high-risk medications ordered

- C **G9368** At least two different high-risk medications not ordered

- C **G9369** Individual filled at least two prescriptions for any antipsychotic medication and had a proportion of days covered (PDC) of 0.8 or greater

- C **G9370** Individual who did not fill at least two prescriptions for any antipsychotic medication or did not have a Individual who did not fill at least two prescriptions for any antipsychotic medication or did not have a proportion of days covered (PDC) of 0.8 or greater of 0.8 or greater

- C **G9376** Patient continued to have the retina attached at the 6 months follow up visit (+/- 1 month) following only one surgery

- C **G9377** Patient did not have the retina attached after 6 months following only one surgery

- C **G9378** Patient continued to have the retina attached at the 6 months follow up visit (+/- 1 month)

- C **G9379** Patient did not achieve flat retinas six months post surgery

- C **G9380** Patient offered assistance with end of life issues during the measurement period

- C **G9381** Documentation of medical reason(s) for not offering assistance with end of life issues (e.g., patient in hospice and in terminal phase) during the measurement period

- C **G9382** Patient not offered assistance with end of life issues during the measurement period

- C **G9383** Patient received screening for HCV infection within the 12 month reporting period

- C **G9384** Documentation of medical reason(s) for not receiving screening for HCV infection within the 12 month reporting period (e.g., decompensated cirrhosis including advanced disease [ie, ascites, esophageal variceal bleeding, hepatic encephalopathy], hepatocellular carcinoma, or waitlist for organ transplant, limited life expectancy, other medical reasons)

- C **G9385** Documentation of patient reason(s) for not receiving screening for HCV infection within the 12 month reporting period (e.g., patient declined, other patient reasons)

- C **G9386** Screening for HCV infection not received within the 12 month reporting period, reason not given

- C **G9389** Unplanned rupture of the posterior capsule requiring vitrectomy

- C **G9390** No unplanned rupture of the posterior capsule requiring vitrectomy

- C **G9391** Patient achieves refraction +-1 D for the eye that underwent cataract surgery, measured at the one month follow up visit

- C **G9392** Patient does not achieve refraction +-1 D for the eye that underwent cataract surgery, measured at the one month follow up visit

- C **G9393** Patient with an initial PHQ-9 score greater than nine who achieves remission at twelve months as demonstrated by a twelve month (+/- 30 days) PHQ-9 score of less than five

- C **G9394** Patient who had a diagnosis of bipolar disorder or personality disorder, death, permanent nursing home resident or receiving hospice or palliative care any time during the measurement or assessment period

- C **G9395** Patient with an initial PHQ-9 score greater than nine who did not achieve remission at twelve months as demonstrated by a twelve month (+/- 30 days) PHQ-9 score greater than or equal to five

- C **G9396** Patient with an initial PHQ-9 score greater than nine who was not assessed for remission at twelve months (+/- 30 days)

- C **G9399** Documentation in the patient record of a discussion between the physician/clinician and the patient that includes all of the following: treatment choices appropriate to genotype, risks and benefits, evidence of effectiveness, and patient preferences toward the outcome of the treatment

- C **G9400** Documentation of medical or patient reason(s) for not discussing treatment options; medical reasons: patient is not a candidate for treatment due to advanced physical or mental health comorbidity (including active substance use); currently receiving antiviral treatment; successful antiviral treatment (with sustained virologic response) prior to reporting period; other documented medical reasons; patient reasons: patient unable or unwilling to participate in the discussion or other patient reasons

- C **G9401** No documentation of a discussion in the patient record of a discussion between the physician or other qualified healthcare professional and the patient that includes all of the following: treatment choices appropriate to genotype, risks and benefits, evidence of effectiveness, and patient preferences toward treatment

- C **G9402** Patient received follow-up on the date of discharge or within 30 days after discharge

- C **G9403** Clinician documented reason patient was not able to complete 30 day follow-up from acute inpatient setting discharge (e.g., patient death prior to follow-up visit, patient non-compliant for visit follow-up)

- C **G9404** Patient did not receive follow-up on the date of discharge or within 30 days after discharge

- C **G9405** Patient received follow-up within 7 days from discharge

♂ Male only   ♀ Female only   **A** Age   A2 - Z3 = ASC Payment Indicator   A - Y = APC Status Indicator

ASC = ASC Approved Procedure   **DME** Paid under the DME fee schedule   **PQRS** Physician Quality Reporting System

- C **G9406** Clinician documented reason patient was not able to complete 7 day follow-up from acute inpatient setting discharge (i.e patient death prior to follow-up visit, patient non-compliance for visit follow-up)

- C **G9407** Patient did not receive follow-up on or within 7 days after discharge

- C **G9408** Patients with cardiac tamponade and/or pericardiocentesis occurring within 30 days

- C **G9409** Patients without cardiac tamponade and/or pericardiocentesis occurring within 30 days

- C **G9410** Patient admitted within 180 days, status post cied implantation, replacement, or revision with an infection requiring device removal or surgical revision

- C **G9411** Patient not admitted within 180 days, status post cied implantation, replacement, or revision with an infection requiring device removal or surgical revision

- C **G9412** Patient admitted within 180 days, status post cied implantation, replacement, or revision with an infection requiring device removal or surgical revision

- C **G9413** Patient not admitted within 180 days, status post cied implantation, replacement, or revision with an infection requiring device removal or surgical revision

- C **G9414** Patient had one dose of meningococcal vaccine on or between the patient's 11th and 13th birthdays

- C **G9415** Patient did not have one dose of meningococcal vaccine on or between the patient's 11th and 13th birthdays

- C **G9416** Patient had one tetanus, diphtheria toxoids and acellular pertussis vaccine (TDAP) or one tetanus, diphtheria toxoids vaccine (TD) on or between the patient's 10th and 13th birthdays or one tetanus and one diphtheria vaccine on or between the patient's 10th and 13th birthdays

- C **G9417** Patient did not have one tetanus, diphtheria toxoids and acellular pertussis vaccine (TDAP) or one tetanus, diphtheria toxoids vaccine (TD) on or between the patient's 10th and 13th birthdays or one tetanus and one diphtheria vaccine on or between the patient's 10th and 13th birthdays

- C **G9418** Primary non-small cell lung cancer biopsy and cytology specimen report documents classification into specific histologic type or classified as NSCLC-NOS with an explanation

- C **G9419** Documentation of medical reason(s) for not reporting the histological type or NSCLC-NOS classification with an explanation (e.g., biopsy taken for other purposes in a patient with a history of primary non-small cell lung cancer or other documented medical reasons)

- C **G9420** Specimen site other than anatomic location of lung or is not classified as primary non-small cell lung cancer

- C **G9421** Primary non-small cell lung cancer biopsy and cytology specimen report does not document classification into specific histologic type or classified as NSCLC-NOS with an explanation

- C **G9422** Non-small cell lung cancer biopsy and cytology specimen report documents classification into specific histologic type or classified as NSCLC-NOS with an explanation

- C **G9423** Documentation of medical reason(s) for not reporting the histological type or NSCLC-NOS classification with an explanation (e.g., a solitary fibrous tumor in a person with a history of non-small cell carcinoma or other documented medical reasons)

- C **G9424** Specimen site other than anatomic location of lung, is not classified as non-small cell lung cancer or classified as NSCLC-NOS

- C **G9425** Non small cell lung cancer biopsy and cytology specimen report does not document classification into specific histologic type or classified as NSCLC-NOS with an explanation

- C **G9426** Improvement in median time from ED arrival to initial ED oral or parenteral pain medication administration performed for ED admitted patients

- C **G9427** Improvement in median time from ED arrival to initial ED oral or parenteral pain medication administration not performed for ED admitted patients

- C **G9428** Pathology report includes the Pt category and a statement on thickness and ulceration and for pT1, mitotic rate

- C **G9429** Documentation of medical reason(s) for not reporting Pt category and a statement on thickness and ulceration and for pT1, mitotic rate (e.g., negative skin biopsies in a patient with a history of melanoma or other documented medical reasons)

- C **G9430** Specimen site other than anatomic cutaneous location

- C **G9431** Pathology report does not include the Pt category and a statement on thickness and ulceration and for pT1, mitotic rate

- C **G9432** Asthma well-controlled based on the ACT, C-ACT, ACQ, or ATAQ score and results documented

- C **G9433** Death, permanent nursing home resident or receiving hospice or palliative care any time during the measurement period

- C **G9434** Asthma not well-controlled based on the ACT, C-ACT, ACQ, or ATAQ score, or specified asthma control tool not used, reason not given

- C **G9435** Aspirin prescribed at discharge

▲ Revised Code   ● New code   C Carrier judgment   D Special coverage instructions apply
I Not payable by Medicare   M Non-covered by Medicare   S Non-covered by Medicare statute   AHA Coding Clinic®

- C **G9436** Aspirin not prescribed for documented reasons (e.g., allergy, medical intolerance, history of bleed)
- C **G9437** Aspirin not prescribed at discharge
- C **G9438** P2Y inhibitor prescribed at discharge
- C **G9439** P2Y inhibitor not prescribed for documented reasons (e.g., allergy, medical intolerance, history of bleed)
- C **G9440** P2Y inhibitor not prescribed at discharge
- C **G9441** Statin prescribed at discharge
- C **G9442** Statin not prescribed for documented reasons (e.g., allergy, medical intolerance)
- C **G9443** Statin not prescribed at discharge
- C **G9448** Patients who were born in the years 1945-1965
- C **G9449** History of receiving blood transfusions prior to 1992
- C **G9450** History of injection drug use
- C **G9451** Patient received one-time screening for HCV infection
- C **G9452** Documentation of medical reason(s) for not receiving one-time screening for HCV infection (e.g., decompensated cirrhosis indicating advanced disease [ie, ascites, esophageal variceal bleeding, hepatic encephalopathy], hepatocellular carcinoma, waitlist for organ transplant, limited life expectancy, other medical reasons)
- C **G9453** Documentation of patient reason(s) for not receiving one-time screening for HCV infection (e.g., patient declined, other patient reasons)
- C **G9454** One-time screening for HCV infection not received within 12 month reporting period and no documentation of prior screening for HCV infection, reason not given
- C **G9455** Patient underwent abdominal imaging with ultrasound, contrast enhanced CT or contrast MRI for HCC
- C **G9456** Documentation of medical or patient reason(s) for not ordering or performing screening for HCC. medical reason: comorbid medical conditions with expected survival < 5 years, hepatic decompensation and not a candidate for liver transplantation, or other medical reasons; patient reasons: patient declined or other patient reasons (e.g., cost of tests, time related to accessing testing equipment)
- C **G9457** Patient did not undergo abdominal imaging and did not have a documented reason for not undergoing abdominal imaging in the reporting period
- C **G9458** Patient documented as tobacco user and received tobacco cessation intervention (must include at least one of the following: advice given to quit smoking or tobacco use, counseling on the benefits of quitting smoking or tobacco use, assistance with

or referral to external smoking or tobacco cessation support programs, or current enrollment in smoking or tobacco use cessation program) if identified as a tobacco user
- C **G9459** Currently a tobacco non-user
- C **G9460** Tobacco assessment or tobacco cessation intervention not performed, reason not otherwise specified
- C **G9463** I intend to report the sinusitis measures group
- C **G9464** All quality actions for the applicable measures in the sinusitis measures group have been performed for this patient
- C **G9465** I intend to report the acute otitis externa (AOE) measures group
- C **G9466** All quality actions for the applicable measures in the AOE measures group have been performed for this patient
- C **G9467** Patient who have received or are receiving corticosteroids greater than or equal to 10 mg/day of prednisone equivalents for 60 or greater consecutive days or a single prescription equating to 600 mg prednisone or greater for all fills
- C **G9468** Patient not receiving corticosteroids greater than or equal to 10 mg/day of prednisone equivalents for 60 or greater consecutive days or a single prescription equating to 600 mg prednisone or greater for all fills
- C **G9469** Patients who have received or are receiving corticosteroids greater than or equal to 10 mg/day of prednisone equivalents for 60 or greater consecutive days or a single prescription equating to 600 mg prednisone or greater for all fills
- C **G9470** Patients not receiving corticosteroids greater than or equal to 10 mg/day of prednisone equivalents for 60 or greater consecutive days or a single prescription equating to 600mg prednisone or greater for all fills
- C **G9471** Within the past 2 years, central dual-energy X-ray absorptiometry (DXA) not ordered or documented
- C **G9472** Within the past 2 years, central dual-energy X-ray absorptiometry (DXA) not ordered and documented, no review of systems and no medication history or pharmacologic therapy (other than minerals/vitamins) for osteoporosis prescribed

ALCOHOL AND DRUG ABUSE TREATMENT (H0001-H2037)

▯ **H0001** Alcohol and/or drug assessment
Service not separately priced by Part B

▯ **H0002** Behavioral health screening to determine eligibility for admission to treatment program
Service not separately priced by Part B

▯ **H0003** Alcohol and/or drug screening; laboratory analysis of specimens for presence of alcohol and/or drugs
Service not separately priced by Part B

▯ **H0004** Behavioral health counseling and therapy, per 15 minutes
Service not separately priced by Part B

▯ **H0005** Alcohol and/or drug services; group counseling by a clinician
Service not separately priced by Part B

▯ **H0006** Alcohol and/or drug services; case management
Service not separately priced by Part B

▯ **H0007** Alcohol and/or drug services; crisis intervention (outpatient)
Service not separately priced by Part B

▯ **H0008** Alcohol and/or drug services; sub-acute detoxification (hospital inpatient)
Service not separately priced by Part B

▯ **H0009** Alcohol and/or drug services; acute detoxification (hospital inpatient)
Service not separately priced by Part B

▯ **H0010** Alcohol and/or drug services; sub-acute detoxification (residential addiction program inpatient)
Service not separately priced by Part B

▯ **H0011** Alcohol and/or drug services; acute detoxification (residential addiction program inpatient)
Service not separately priced by Part B

▯ **H0012** Alcohol and/or drug services; sub-acute detoxification (residential addiction program outpatient)
Service not separately priced by Part B

▯ **H0013** Alcohol and/or drug services; acute detoxification (residential addiction program outpatient)
Service not separately priced by Part B

▯ **H0014** Alcohol and/or drug services; ambulatory detoxification
Service not separately priced by Part B

▯ **H0015** Alcohol and/or drug services; intensive outpatient (treatment program that operates at least 3 hours/day and at least 3 days/week and is based on an individualized treatment plan), including assessment, counseling; crisis intervention, and activity therapies or education

Service not separately priced by Part B

▯ **H0016** Alcohol and/or drug services; medical/somatic (medical intervention in ambulatory setting)
Service not separately priced by Part B

▯ **H0017** Behavioral health; residential (hospital residential treatment program), without room and board, per diem
Service not separately priced by Part B

▯ **H0018** Behavioral health; short-term residential (non-hospital residential treatment program), without room and board, per diem
Service not separately priced by Part B

▯ **H0019** Behavioral health; long-term residential (non-medical, non-acute care in a residential treatment program where stay is typically longer than 30 days), without room and board, per diem
Service not separately priced by Part B

▯ **H0020** Alcohol and/or drug services; methadone administration and/or service (provision of the drug by a licensed program)
Service not separately priced by Part B

▯ **H0021** Alcohol and/or drug training service (for staff and personnel not employed by providers)
Service not separately priced by Part B

▯ **H0022** Alcohol and/or drug intervention service (planned facilitation)
Service not separately priced by Part B

▯ **H0023** Behavioral health outreach service (planned approach to reach a targeted population)
Service not separately priced by Part B

▯ **H0024** Behavioral health prevention information dissemination service (one-way direct or non-direct contact with service audiences to affect knowledge and attitude)
Service not separately priced by Part B

▯ **H0025** Behavioral health prevention education service (delivery of services with target population to affect knowledge, attitude and/or behavior)
Service not separately priced by Part B

▯ **H0026** Alcohol and/or drug prevention process service, community-based (delivery of services to develop skills of impactors)
Service not separately priced by Part B

▯ **H0027** Alcohol and/or drug prevention environmental service (broad range of external activities geared toward modifying systems in order to mainstream prevention through policy and law)
Service not separately priced by Part B

▯ **H0028** Alcohol and/or drug prevention problem identification and referral service (e.g., student assistance and employee assistance programs), does not include assessment
Service not separately priced by Part B

▲ Revised Code ● New code 🅲 Carrier judgment 🅳 Special coverage instructions apply
▯ Not payable by Medicare 🅼 Non-covered by Medicare 🆂 Non-covered by Medicare statute AHA Coding Clinic®

H0029 Alcohol and/or drug prevention alternatives service (services for populations that exclude alcohol and other drug use e.g. alcohol free social events)
Service not separately priced by Part B

H0030 Behavioral health hotline service
Service not separately priced by Part B

H0031 Mental health assessment, by non-physician
Service not separately priced by Part B

H0032 Mental health service plan development by non-physician
Service not separately priced by Part B

H0033 Oral medication administration, direct observation
Service not separately priced by Part B

H0034 Medication training and support, per 15 minutes
Service not separately priced by Part B

H0035 Mental health partial hospitalization, treatment, less than 24 hours
Service not separately priced by Part B

H0036 Community psychiatric supportive treatment, face-to-face, per 15 minutes
Service not separately priced by Part B

H0037 Community psychiatric supportive treatment program, per diem
Service not separately priced by Part B

H0038 Self-help/peer services, per 15 minutes
Service not separately priced by Part B

H0039 Assertive community treatment, face-to-face, per 15 minutes
Service not separately priced by Part B

H0040 Assertive community treatment program, per diem
Service not separately priced by Part B

H0041 Foster care, child, non-therapeutic, per diem Ⓐ
Service not separately priced by Part B

H0042 Foster care, child, non-therapeutic, per month Ⓐ
Service not separately priced by Part B

H0043 Supported housing, per diem
Service not separately priced by Part B

H0044 Supported housing, per month
Service not separately priced by Part B

H0045 Respite care services, not in the home, per diem
Service not separately priced by Part B

H0046 Mental health services, not otherwise specified
Service not separately priced by Part B

H0047 Alcohol and/or other drug abuse services, not otherwise specified
Service not separately priced by Part B

H0048 Alcohol and/or other drug testing: collection and handling only, specimens other than blood
Service not separately priced by Part B

H0049 Alcohol and/or drug screening
Service not separately priced by Part B

H0050 Alcohol and/or drug services, brief intervention, per 15 minutes
Service not separately priced by Part B

H1000 Prenatal care, at-risk assessment ♀
Service not separately priced by Part B

H1001 Prenatal care, at-risk enhanced service; antepartum management ♀
Service not separately priced by Part B

H1002 Prenatal care, at risk enhanced service; care coordination ♀
Service not separately priced by Part B

H1003 Prenatal care, at-risk enhanced service; education ♀
Service not separately priced by Part B

H1004 Prenatal care, at-risk enhanced service; follow-up home visit ♀
Service not separately priced by Part B

H1005 Prenatal care, at-risk enhanced service package (includes H1001-H1004) ♀
Service not separately priced by Part B

H1010 Non-medical family planning education, per session
Service not separately priced by Part B

H1011 Family assessment by licensed behavioral health professional for state defined purposes
Service not separately priced by Part B

H2000 Comprehensive multidisciplinary evaluation
Service not separately priced by Part B

H2001 Rehabilitation program, per 1/2 day
Service not separately priced by Part B

H2010 Comprehensive medication services, per 15 minutes
Service not separately priced by Part B

H2011 Crisis intervention service, per 15 minutes
Service not separately priced by Part B

H2012 Behavioral health day treatment, per hour
Service not separately priced by Part B

H2013 Psychiatric health facility service, per diem
Service not separately priced by Part B

H2014 Skills training and development, per 15 minutes
Service not separately priced by Part B

H2015 Comprehensive community support services, per 15 minutes
Service not separately priced by Part B

♂ Male only   ♀ Female only   Ⓐ Age   A2 - Z3 = ASC Payment Indicator   A - Y = APC Status Indicator
ASC = ASC Approved Procedure   **DME** Paid under the DME fee schedule   **PQRS** Physician Quality Reporting System

H2016 Comprehensive community support services, per diem

Service not separately priced by Part B

H2017 Psychosocial rehabilitation services, per 15 minutes

Service not separately priced by Part B

H2018 Psychosocial rehabilitation services, per diem

Service not separately priced by Part B

H2019 Therapeutic behavioral services, per 15 minutes

Service not separately priced by Part B

H2020 Therapeutic behavioral services, per diem

Service not separately priced by Part B

H2021 Community-based wrap-around services, per 15 minutes

Service not separately priced by Part B

H2022 Community-based wrap-around services, per diem

Service not separately priced by Part B

H2023 Supported employment, per 15 minutes

Service not separately priced by Part B

H2024 Supported employment, per diem

Service not separately priced by Part B

H2025 Ongoing support to maintain employment, per 15 minutes

Service not separately priced by Part B

H2026 Ongoing support to maintain employment, per diem

Service not separately priced by Part B

H2027 Psychoeducational service, per 15 minutes

Service not separately priced by Part B

H2028 Sexual offender treatment service, per 15 minutes

Service not separately priced by Part B

H2029 Sexual offender treatment service, per diem

Service not separately priced by Part B

H2030 Mental health clubhouse services, per 15 minutes

Service not separately priced by Part B

H2031 Mental health clubhouse services, per diem

Service not separately priced by Part B

H2032 Activity therapy, per 15 minutes

Service not separately priced by Part B

H2033 Multisystemic therapy for juveniles, per 15 minutes

Service not separately priced by Part B

H2034 Alcohol and/or drug abuse halfway house services, per diem

Service not separately priced by Part B

H2035 Alcohol and/or other drug treatment program, per hour

Service not separately priced by Part B

H2036 Alcohol and/or other drug treatment program, per diem

Service not separately priced by Part B

H2037 Developmental delay prevention activities, dependent child of client, per 15 minutes Ⓐ

Service not separately priced by Part B

▲ Revised Code   ● New code   **C** Carrier judgment   **D** Special coverage instructions apply

I Not payable by Medicare   **M** Non-covered by Medicare   **S** Non-covered by Medicare statute   AHA Coding Clinic®

DRUGS ADMINISTERED OTHER THAN ORAL METHOD (J0120-J8999)

D J0120 Injection, tetracycline, up to 250 mg   N1 N

C J0129 Injection, abatacept, 10 mg (code may be used for Medicare when drug administered under the direct supervision of a physician, not for use when drug is self administered)   K2 ASC K
Drugs: ABATACEPT

D J0130 Injection abciximab, 10 mg   K2 ASC K
Drugs: REOPRO

C J0131 Injection, acetaminophen, 10 mg   N1 G:
Coding Clinic 2012, Q1, P9

C J0132 Injection, acetylcysteine, 100 mg K2 ASC K
Drugs: ACETYLCYSTEINE, ACETADOTE

C J0133 Injection, acyclovir, 5 mg   N1 N
Drugs: ACYCLOVIR SODIUM

C J0135 Injection, adalimumab, 20 mg   K2 ASC K
Drugs: HUMIRA

● **D** J0153 Injection, adenosine, 1 mg (not to be used to report any adenosine phosphate compounds)

D J0171 Injection, Adrenalin, epinephrine, 0.1 mg N1 N
Drugs: EPINEPHRINE, EPINEPHRINE HCL, ADRENALIN
Coding Clinic 2011, Q1, P8

C J0178 Injection, aflibercept, 1 mg   K2 ASC G
Drugs: EYLEA

C J0180 Injection, agalsidase beta, 1 mg K2 ASC K
Drugs: FABRAZYME

D J0190 Injection, biperiden lactate, per 5 mg   E:

D J0200 Injection, alatrofloxacin mesylate, 100 mg   N1 N

D J0205 Injection, alglucerase, per 10 units   ASC K:

D J0207 Injection, amifostine, 500 mg   K2 ASC K
Drugs: AMIFOSTINE FOR INJECTION, ETHYOL

D J0210 Injection, methyldopate HCl, up to 250 mg   N1 K
Drugs: METHYLDOPATE HCL

C J0215 Injection, alefacept, 0.5 mg   K2 ASC K
Drugs: AMEVIVE

C J0220 Injection, alglucosidase alfa, 10 mg, not otherwise specified   K2 ASC K
Drugs: MYOZYME
Coding Clinic 2012, Q1, P9

C J0221 Injection, alglucosidase alfa, (Lumizyme), 10 mg   K2 ASC K
Drugs: LUMIZYME

D J0256 Injection, alpha 1 proteinase inhibitor (human), not otherwise specified, 10 mg   K2 ASC K
Drugs: ZEMAIRA, ARALAST NP, PROLASTIN, PROLASTIN-C

Coding Clinic 2012, Q1, P9

D J0257 Injection, alpha 1 proteinase inhibitor (human), (GLASSIA), 10 mg   K2 ASC K
Drugs: GLASSIA
Coding Clinic 2012, Q1, P8

D J0270 Injection, alprostadil, 1.25 mcg (code may be used for Medicare when drug administered under the direct supervision of a physician, not for use when drug is self administered) B:

D J0275 Alprostadil urethral suppository (code may be used for Medicare when drug administered under the direct supervision of a physician, not for use when drug is self administered)   B:

C J0278 Injection, amikacin sulfate, 100 mg   N1 N
Drugs: AMIKACIN SULFATE

D J0280 Injection, aminophyllin, up to 250 mg   N1 N
Drugs: AMINOPHYLLINE

D J0282 Injection, amiodarone hydrochloride, 30 mg   N1 N

D J0285 Injection, amphotericin B, 50 mg   N1 N
Drugs: AMPHOTERICIN B

D J0287 Injection, amphotericin B lipid complex, 10 mg   K2 ASC K
Drugs: ABELCET

D J0288 Injection, amphotericin B cholesteryl sulfate complex, 10 mg   N1 K:

D J0289 Injection, amphotericin B liposome, 10 mg   K2 ASC K
Drugs: AMBISOME

D J0290 Injection, ampicillin sodium, 500 mg   N1 N
Drugs: AMPICILLIN SODIUM, AMPICILLIN FOR INJECTION

D J0295 Injection, ampicillin sodium/sulbactam sodium, per 1.5 gm   N1 N
Drugs: UNASYN 1.5GM, UNASYN 3GM, UNASYN 1.5GM PIGGYBACK, UNASYN 3GM PIGGYBACK, UNASYN 15GM, AMPICILLIN-SULBACTAM

D J0300 Injection, amobarbital, up to 125 mg K2 ASC K:

D J0330 Injection, succinylcholine chloride, up to 20 mg   N1 N

C J0348 Injection, anidulafungin, 1 mg   N1 K
Drugs: ERAXIS

D J0350 Injection, anistreplase, per 30 units   N

D J0360 Injection, hydralazine HCl, up to 20 mg N1 N
Drugs: HYDRALAZINE HCL

C J0364 Injection, apomorphine hydrochloride, 1 mg   N1 N
Drugs: APOKYN

D J0365 Injection, aprotinin, 10, 000 kiu   K2 ASC K

D J0380 Injection, metaraminol bitartrate, per 10 mg   N1 N

D J0390 Injection, chloroquine hydrochloride, up to 250 mg   N1 N

♂ Male only   ♀ Female only   **Ⓐ** Age   A2 - Z3 = ASC Payment Indicator   A - Y = APC Status Indicator
ASC = ASC Approved Procedure   **DME** Paid under the DME fee schedule   **PQRS** Physician Quality Reporting System

D	J0395	Injection, arbutamine HCl, 1 mg	K
C	J0400	Injection, aripiprazole, intramuscular, 0.25 mg	N1 N
		Drugs: ARIPIPRAZOLE IM INJ	
C	J0401	Injection, aripiprazole, extended release, 1 mg	K2 ASC
D	J0456	Injection, azithromycin, 500 mg	N1 N
		Drugs: ZITHROMAX, AZITHROMYCIN	
D	J0461	Injection, atropine sulfate, 0.01 mg	N1 N
		Drugs: ATROPINE SULFATE	
D	J0470	Injection, dimercaprol, per 100 mg	N1 N
		Drugs: BAL IN OIL	
D	J0475	Injection, baclofen, 10 mg	K2 ASC K
		Drugs: GABLOFEN, LIORESAL	
D	J0476	Injection, baclofen, 50 mcg for intrathecal trial	K2 ASC K
		Drugs: GABLOFEN, LIORESAL	
D	J0480	Injection, basiliximab, 20 mg	K2 ASC K
		Drugs: SIMULECT	
C	J0485	Injection, belatacept, 1 mg	K2 ASC G
		Drugs: NULOJIX	
C	J0490	Injection, belimumab, 10 mg	K2 ASC G
		Drugs: BENLYSTA	
		Coding Clinic 2012, Q1, P9	
D	J0500	Injection, dicyclomine HCl, up to 20 mg	N1 N
		Drugs: BENTYL	
D	J0515	Injection, benztropine mesylate, per 1 mg	N1 N
		Drugs: COGENTIN, BENZTROPINE	
D	J0520	Injection, bethanechol chloride, myotonachol or urecholine, up to 5 mg	N1 N
C	J0558	Injection, penicillin G benzathine and penicillin G procaine, 100, 000 units	N1 N
		Drugs: BICILLIN C-R, BICILLIN C-R 900/300 (1.2MILLION UNITS/SYR), BICILLIN CR PEDIATRIC	
		Coding Clinic 2011, Q1, P8	
D	J0561	Injection, penicillin G benzathine, 100, 000 units	N1 N
		Drugs: BICILLIN L-A	
		Coding Clinic 2011, Q1, P8	
● D	J0571	Buprenorphine, oral, 1 mg	
● D	J0572	Buprenorphine/naloxone, oral, less than or equal to 3 mg	
● D	J0573	Buprenorphine/naloxone, oral, greater than 3 mg, but less than or equal to 6 mg	
● D	J0574	Buprenorphine/naloxone, oral, greater than 6 mg, but less than or equal to 10 mg	
● D	J0575	Buprenorphine/naloxone, oral, greater than 10 mg	
C	J0583	Injection, bivalirudin, 1 mg	K2 ASC K
		Drugs: ANGIOMAX	
D	J0585	Injection, onabotulinumtoxinA, 1 unit	K2 ASC K
		Drugs: BOTOX, BOTOX COSMETIC	

C	J0586	Injection, abobotulinumtoxin A, 5 units	K2 ASC K
		Drugs: DYSPORT	
D	J0587	Injection, rimabotulinumtoxinb B, 100 units	K2 ASC K
		Drugs: MYOBLOC	
C	J0588	Injection, incobotulinumtoxin A, 1 unit	K2 ASC K
		Drugs: XEOMIN	
		Coding Clinic 2012, Q1, P9	
D	J0592	Injection, buprenorphine hydrochloride, 0.1 mg	N1 N
		Drugs: BUPRENORPHINE HCL, BUPRENORPHINE HCL INJECTION	
C	J0594	Injection, Busulfan, 1 mg	K2 ASC K
		Drugs: BUSULFAN	
C	J0595	Injection, butorphanol tartrate, 1 mg	N1 N
		Drugs: STADOL, BUTORPHANOL TARTRATE	
C	J0597	Injection, C-1 esterase inhibitor (human), Berinert, 10 units	K2 ASC K
		Drugs: BERINERT	
		Coding Clinic 2011, Q1, P7	
C	J0598	Injection, C-1 esterase inhibitor (human), Cinryze, 10 units	K2 ASC K
		Drugs: CINRYZE	
D	J0600	Injection, edetate calcium disodium, up to 1000 mg	K2 ASC K
		Drugs: CALCIUM DISODIUM VERSENATE (EDETATE CALCIUM DISODIUM)	
D	J0610	Injection, calcium gluconate, per 10 ml	N1 N
		Drugs: CALCIUM GLUCONATE	
D	J0620	Injection, calcium glycerophosphate and calcium lactate, per 10 ml	N1 N
D	J0630	Injection, calcitonin salmon, up to 400 units	K2 ASC K
		Drugs: MIACALCIN	
		Pub: 100-4, Chap. 10, 90 .1	
D	J0636	Injection, calcitriol, 0.1 mcg	N1 N
		Drugs: CALCIJEX, CALCITRIOL	
C	J0637	Injection, caspofungin acetate, 5 mg	K2 ASC K
		Drugs: CANCIDAS	
C	J0638	Injection, canakinumab, 1 mg	K2 ASC G
		Drugs: ILARIS	
D	J0640	Injection, leucovorin calcium, per 50 mg	N1 N
		Drugs: CALCIUM FOLINATE (HUNGARIAN IMPORT), LEUCOVORIN CALCIUM	
		Coding Clinic 2009, Q1, P10	
D	J0641	Injection, levoleucovorin calcium, 0.5 mg	K2 ASC K
		Drugs: LEVOLEUCOVORIN CALCIUM (IMPORT VERSION), LEVOLEUCOVORIN CALCIUM	
D	J0670	Injection, mepivacaine hydrochloride, per 10 ml	N1 N
		Drugs: MEPIVACAINE HCL, POLOCAINE-MPF, POLOCAINE	

▲ Revised Code ● New code C Carrier judgment D Special coverage instructions apply

I Not payable by Medicare M Non-covered by Medicare S Non-covered by Medicare statute AHA Coding Clinic®

D **J0690** Injection, cefazolin sodium, 500 mg N1 N
Drugs: CEFAZOLIN FOR INJECTION USP, CEFAZOLIN SODIUM, CEFAZOLIN SODIUM IN DEXTROSE

C **J0692** Injection, cefepime hydrochloride, 500 mg N1 N
Drugs: CEFEPIME HCL IN DEXTROSE, CEFEPIME HCL, MAXIPIME

D **J0694** Injection, cefoxitin sodium, 1 gm N1 N
Drugs: CEFOXITIN SODIUM, MEFOXIN

D **J0696** Injection, ceftriaxone sodium, per 250 mg N1 N
Drugs: ROCEPHIN, CEFTRIAXONE FOR INJECTION USP, CEFTRIAXONE, CEFTRIAXONE, CEFTRIAXONE IN D5W, CEFTRIAXONE SODIUM

D **J0697** Injection, sterile cefuroxime sodium, per 750 mg N1 N
Drugs: ZINACEF, ZINACEF IN D5W, ZINACEF IN STERILE WATER, CEFUROXIME SODIUM, CEFUROXIME-DEXTROSE, ZINACEF (FROZEN)

D **J0698** Injection, cefotaxime sodium, per gm N1 N
Drugs: CLAFORAN, CLAFORAN IN D5W, CEFOTAXIME FOR INJECTION, CEFOTAXIME SODIUM

D **J0702** Injection, betamethasone acetate 3 mg and betamethasone sodium phosphate 3 mg N1 N
Drugs: CELESTONE SOLUSPAN

C **J0706** Injection, Caffeine Citrate, 5 mg N1 N
Drugs: CAFFEINE CITRATE

D **J0710** Injection, cephapirin sodium, up to 1 gm N1 N

C **J0712** Injection, ceftaroline fosamil, 10 mg N1 G
Drugs: TEFLARO
Coding Clinic 2012, Q1, P9

D **J0713** Injection, ceftazidime, per 500 mg N1 N
Drugs: CEFTAZIDIME, FORTAZ, FORTAZ IN D5W, TAZICEF, FORTAZ (FROZEN), FORTAZ ADD-V, FORTAZ (ADD-V)

D **J0715** Injection, ceftizoxime sodium, per 500 mg N1 N

C **J0716** Injection, centruroides immune f(ab)2, up to 120 milligrams K2 ASC G

C **J0717** Injection, certolizumab pegol, 1 mg (code may be used for Medicare when drug administered under the direct supervision of a physician, not for use when drug is self administered) K2
Drugs: CIMZIA

D **J0720** Injection, chloramphenicol sodium succinate, up to 1 gm N1 N
Drugs: CHLORAMPHENICOL SOD SUCCINATE

D **J0725** Injection, chorionic gonadotropin, per 1, 000 USP units N1 N
Drugs: NOVAREL, CHORIONIC GONADOTROPIN

D **J0735** Injection, clonidine hydrochloride, 1 mg N1 N
Drugs: CLONIDINE HYDROCHLORIDE INJECTION, CLONIDINE HYDROCHLORIDE, DURACLON

D **J0740** Injection, cidofovir, 375 mg K2 ASC K
Drugs: CIDOFOVIR, VISTIDE

D **J0743** Injection, cilastatin sodium; imipenem, per 250 mg N1 N
Drugs: PRIMAXIN IV, IMIPENEM AND CILASTATIN

C **J0744** Injection, ciprofloxacin for intravenous infusion, 200 mg N1 N
Drugs: CIPROFLOXACIN, CIPROFLOXACIN IN DEXTROSE

D **J0745** Injection, codeine phosphate, per 30 mg N1 N

D **J0760** Injection, colchicine, per 1 mg N1 N

D **J0770** Injection, colistimethate sodium, up to 150 mg N1 N
Drugs: COLISTIMETHATE SODIUM, COLY-MYCIN M PARENTERAL

C **J0775** Injection, collagenase, clostridium histolyticum, 0.01 mg K2 ASC K
Drugs: XIAFLEX (COLLAGENASE CLOSTRIDIUM HISTOLYTICUM)
Coding Clinic 2011, Q1, P7

D **J0780** Injection, prochlorperazine, up to 10 mg N1 N
Drugs: PROCHLORPERAZINE EDISYLATE

D **J0795** Injection, corticorelin ovine triflutate, 1 microgram K2 ASC K
Drugs: ACTHREL

D **J0800** Injection, corticotropin, up to 40 units K2 ASC K
Drugs: ACTHAR HP, H.P. ACTHAR

C **J0833** Injection, cosyntropin, not otherwise specified, 0.25 mg K2 ASC K:

C **J0834** Injection, cosyntropin (Cortrosyn), 0.25 mg N1 N
Drugs: CORTROSYN, COSYNTROPIN, COSYNTROPIN (CORTROSYN GENERIC), COSYNTROPIN NOVAPLUS (CORTROSYN GENERIC)

C **J0840** Injection, crotalidae polyvalent immune FAB(Ovine), up to 1 gram K2 ASC K
Drugs: CROFAB POWDER FOR SOLUTION
Coding Clinic 2012, Q1, P9

D **J0850** Injection, cytomegalovirus immune globulin intravenous (human), per vial K2 ASC K
Drugs: CYTOGAM

C **J0878** Injection, daptomycin, 1 mg K2 ASC K
Drugs: CUBICIN

D **J0881** Injection, darbepoetin alfa, 1 microgram (non-ESRD use) K2 ASC K
Drugs: ARANESP

♂ Male only   ♀ Female only   🅐 Age   A2 - Z3 = ASC Payment Indicator   A - Y = APC Status Indicator
ASC = ASC Approved Procedure   **DME** Paid under the DME fee schedule   **PQRS** Physician Quality Reporting System

D **J0882** Injection, darbepoetin alfa, 1 microgram (for ESRD on dialysis) A

Other carrier priced Drugs: ARANESP

Pub: 100-4, Chap. 8, 60.4; 100-4, Chap. 8, 60.4.1; 100-4, Chap. 8, 60.4.4.1; 100-4, Chap. 8, 60.4.4.2; 100-4, Chap. 8, 60.4.5.1; 100-4, Chap. 8, 60.4.6.3; 100-4, Chap. 8, 60.4.6.4; 100-4, Chap. 8, 60.4.6.5; 100-4, Chap. 8, 60.4.7

D **J0885** Injection, epoetin alfa, (for non-ESRD use), 1000 units K2 ASC K

Drugs: EPOGEN, PROCRIT

Coding Clinic 2006, Q2, P5

D **J0886** Injection, epoetin alfa, 1000 units (for ESRD on dialysis) A

Other carrier priced Drugs: EPOGEN, PROCRIT

Coding Clinic 2006, Q2, P5

Pub: 100-4, Chap. 8, 60.4; 100-4, Chap. 8, 60.4.1; 100-4, Chap. 8, 60.4.4.1; 100-4, Chap. 8, 60.4.4.2; 100-4, Chap. 8, 60.4.5.1

● **D** **J0887** Injection, epoetin beta, 1 microgram, (for ESRD on dialysis)

● **D** **J0888** Injection, epoetin beta, 1 microgram, (for Non ESRD use)

C **J0890** Injection, peginesatide, 0.1 mg (for ESRD on dialysis) A

Pub: 100-4, Chap. 8, 60.4; 100-4, Chap. 8, 60.4.1; 100-4, Chap. 8, 60.4.4.1; 100-4, Chap. 8, 60.4.4.2; 100-4, Chap. 8, 60.4.5.1; 100-4, Chap. 8, 60.4.7

C **J0894** Injection, decitabine, 1 mg K2 ASC K

Drugs: DECITABINE

D **J0895** Injection, deferoxamine mesylate, 500 mg N1 N

Drugs: DESFERAL, DEFEROXAMINE MESYLATE

C **J0897** Injection, denosumab, 1 mg K2 ASC K

Drugs: PROLIA, XGEVA

Coding Clinic 2012, Q1, P9

D **J0945** Injection, brompheniramine maleate, per 10 mg N1 N

D **J1000** Injection, depo-estradiol cypionate, up to 5 mg N1 N

Drugs: DEPO-ESTRADIOL

D **J1020** Injection, methylprednisolone acetate, 20 mg N1 N

Drugs: DEPO-MEDROL, METHYLPREDNISOLONE ACETATE USP, METHYLPRED

Coding Clinic 2005, Q3, P10

D **J1030** Injection, methylprednisolone acetate, 40 mg N1 N

Drugs: DEPO-MEDROL, METHYLPREDNISOLONE ACETATE USP

Coding Clinic 2005, Q3, P10

D **J1040** Injection, methylprednisolone acetate, 80 mg N1 N

Drugs: DEPO-MEDROL, METHYLPREDNISOLONE ACETATE

C **J1050** Injection, medroxyprogesterone acetate, 1 mg N1 N

Drugs: DEPO-PROVERA

● **D** **J1071** Injection, testosterone cypionate, 1 mg

D **J1094** Injection, dexamethasone acetate, 1 mg N1 N

D **J1100** Injection, dexamethasone sodium phosphate, 1 mg N1 N

Drugs: DEXAMETHASONE SODIUM PHOSPHATE

D **J1110** Injection, dihydroergotamine mesylate, per 1 mg N1 N

Drugs: DIHYDROERGOTAMINE MESYLATE, D.H.E. 45

D **J1120** Injection, acetazolamide sodium, up to 500 mg N1 N

Drugs: ACETAZOLAMIDE SODIUM

D **J1160** Injection, digoxin, up to 0.5 mg N1 N

Drugs: LANOXIN, DIGOXIN, LANOXIN INJ

D **J1162** Injection, digoxin immune FAB(Ovine), per vial K2 ASC K

Drugs: DIGIFAB

D **J1165** Injection, phenytoin sodium, per 50 mg N1 N

Drugs: PHENYTOIN, PHENYTOIN SODIUM

D **J1170** Injection, hydromorphone, up to 4 mg N1 N

Drugs: HYDROMORPHONE HCL, HYDROMORPHONE HYDROCHLORIDE, HYDROMORPHONE

D **J1180** Injection, dyphylline, up to 500 mg N

D **J1190** Injection, dexrazoxane hydrochloride, per 250 mg K2 ASC K

Drugs: ZINECARD, TOTECT, DEXRAZOXANE

D **J1200** Injection, diphenhydramine HCl, up to 50 mg N1 N

Drugs: DIPHENHYDRAMINE HCL, BENADRYL

D **J1205** Injection, chlorothiazide sodium, per 500 mg K2 ASC K

Drugs: CHLOROTHIAZIDE SODIUM, DIURIL IV

D **J1212** Injection, DMSO, dimethyl sulfoxide, 50%, 50 ml N1 K

Drugs: RIMSO-50

D **J1230** Injection, methadone HCl, up to 10 mg N1 N

Drugs: METHADONE HCL

D **J1240** Injection, dimenhydrinate, up to 50 mg N1 N

Drugs: DIMENHYDRINATE

D **J1245** Injection, dipyridamole, per 10 mg N1 N

Drugs: DIPYRIDAMOLE

D **J1250** Injection, Dobutamine hydrochloride, per 250 mg N1 N

Drugs: DOBUTAMINE HCL

D **J1260** Injection, dolasetron mesylate, 10 mg N1 N

Drugs: ANZEMET

C **J1265** Injection, dopamine HCl, 40 mg N1 N

Drugs: DOPAMINE IN D5W, DOPAMINE 200MG/5ML, DOPAMINE HCL 200MGIN 5%

▲ Revised Code ● New code **C** Carrier judgment **D** Special coverage instructions apply

I Not payable by Medicare **M** Non-covered by Medicare **S** Non-covered by Medicare statute AHA Coding Clinic®

DEXTROSE LIFECARE 250ML, DOPAMINE HCL 400MGIN 5% DEXTROSE LIFECARE 500ML, DOPAMINE HCL 400MGIN 5% DEXTROSE LIFECARE 250ML, DOPAMINE HCL

C **J1267** Injection, doripenem, 10 mg   N1 N
     Drugs: DORIBAX

C **J1270** Injection, doxercalciferol, 1 mcg   N1 N
     Drugs: HECTOROL

C **J1290** Injection, ecallantide, 1 mg   K2 ASC K
     Drugs: KALBITOR®
     Coding Clinic 2011, Q1, P7

C **J1300** Injection, eculizumab, 10 mg   K2 ASC K
     Drugs: SOLIRIS

D **J1320** Injection, amitriptyline HCl, up to 20 mg   N1 N

● **C** **J1322** Injection, elosulfase alfa, 1 mg

C **J1324** Injection, enfuvirtide, 1 mg   K2 ASC K:

D **J1325** Injection, epoprostenol, 0.5 mg   N1 N
     Drugs: FLOLAN, EPOPROSTENOL, EPOPROSTENOL (VELETRI)

D **J1327** Injection, eptifibatide, 5 mg   K2 ASC K
     Drugs: INTEGRILIN

D **J1330** Injection, ergonovine maleate, up to 0.2 mg   N1 N

C **J1335** Injection, ertapenem sodium, 500 mg   N1 N
     Drugs: INVANZ

D **J1364** Injection, erythromycin lactobionate, per 500 mg   N1 N
     Drugs: ERYTHROMYCIN LACTOBIONATE, ERYTHROMYCIN

D **J1380** Injection, estradiol valerate, up to 10 mg   N1 N
     Drugs: ESTRADIOL VALERATE, DELESTROGEN
     Coding Clinic 2011, Q1, P8

D **J1410** Injection, estrogen conjugated, per 25 mg   K2 ASC K
     Drugs: PREMARIN

D **J1430** Injection, ethanolamine oleate, 100 mg   K2 ASC K
     Drugs: ETHANOLAMINE OLEATE

D **J1435** Injection, estrone, per 1 mg   K:

D **J1436** Injection, etidronate disodium, per 300 mg   N1 N

D **J1438** Injection, etanercept, 25 mg (code may be used for Medicare when drug administered under the direct supervision of a physician, not for use when drug is self administered)   K2 ASC K
     Drugs: ENBREL, ENBREL (ETANERCEPT)

● **C** **J1439** Injection, ferric carboxymaltose, 1 mg

D **J1442** Injection, filgrastim (G-CSF), 1 microgram   K2 ASC
     Drugs: NEUPOGEN

D **J1446** Injection, TBO-filgrastim, 5 micrograms   K2 ASC:

D **J1450** Injection fluconazole, 200 mg   N1 N

Drugs: DIFLUCAN IN SODIUM CHLORIDE, DIFLUCAN IV, FLUCONAZOLE INJECTION, FLUCONAZOLE IN DEXTROSE, FLUCONAZOLE IN SODIUM CHLORIDE, DIFLUCAN, NOVAPLUS FLUCONAZOLE, FLUCONAZOLE, FLUCONAZOLE INJECTION IN PVC FLEXIBLE CON

Pub: 100-2, Chap. 15, 50.2

D **J1451** Injection, fomepizole, 15 mg   K2 ASC K
     Drugs: FOMEPIZOLE, ANTIZOL

D **J1452** Injection, fomivirsen sodium, intraocular, 1.65 mg   N1 K
     Pub: 100-2, Chap. 15, 50.4.2

C **J1453** Injection, fosaprepitant, 1 mg   K2 ASC K
     Drugs: EMEND FOR INJECTION, EMEND FOR INJECTION 150MG

D **J1455** Injection, foscarnet sodium, per 1000 mg   K2 ASC N

C **J1457** Injection, gallium nitrate, 1 mg   N1 N

C **J1458** Injection, galsulfase, 1 mg   K2 ASC K
     Drugs: NAGLAZYME

C **J1459** Injection, immune globulin (Privigen), intravenous, non-lyophilized (e.g., liquid), 500 mg   K2 ASC K
     Drugs: PRIVIGEN

D **J1460** Injection, gamma globulin, intramuscular, 1 cc   K2 ASC K
     Drugs: GAMASTAN S/D, GAMASTAN 10ML 532 PACK LF 13MM
     Coding Clinic 2011, Q1, P8

C **J1556** Injection, immune globulin (bivigam), 500 mg   K2 ASC
     Drugs: BIVIGAM

C **J1557** Injection, immune globulin, (Gammaplex), intravenous, non-lyophilized (e.g., liquid), 500 mg   K2 ASC K
     Drugs: GAMMAPLEX
     Coding Clinic 2012, Q1, P9

C **J1559** Injection, immune globulin (Hizentra), 100 mg   K2 ASC K
     Drugs: HIZENTRA
     Coding Clinic 2011, Q1, P6

D **J1560** Injection, gamma globulin, intramuscular, over 10 cc   K2 ASC K
     Drugs: GAMASTAN S/D, GAMASTAN 10ML 532 PACK LF 13MM

D **J1561** Injection, immune globulin, (Gamunex-C/Gammaked), non-lyophilized (e.g., liquid), 500 mg   K2 ASC K
     Drugs: GAMUNEX, GAMUNEX-C, GAMMAKED
     Coding Clinic 2012, Q1, P9

C **J1562** Injection, immune globulin (Vivaglobin), 100 mg   ASC K:

D **J1566** Injection, immune globulin, intravenous, lyophilized (e.g., powder), not otherwise specified, 500 mg   K2 ASC K
     Drugs: GAMMAGARD S/D, CARIMUNE NF

♂ Male only   ♀ Female only   **A** Age   A2 - Z3 = ASC Payment Indicator   A - Y = APC Status Indicator

ASC = ASC Approved Procedure   **DME** Paid under the DME fee schedule   **PQRS** Physician Quality Reporting System

C **J1568** Injection, immune globulin, (Octagam), intravenous, non-lyophilized (e.g., liquid), 500 mg   K2 ASC K

    Drugs: OCTAGAM, OCTAGAM 5%, 25 G IN 500 ML, OCTAGAM 5%, 1 G IN 20 ML, OCTAGAM 5%, 2.5 G IN 50 ML, OCTAGAM 5%, 5 G IN 100 ML

D **J1569** Injection, immune globulin, (Gammagard liquid), non-lyophilized, (e.g., liquid), 500 mg   K2 ASC K

    Drugs: GAMMAGARD LIQUID

D **J1570** Injection, ganciclovir sodium, 500 mg   K2 ASC K

    Drugs: CYTOVENE

D **J1571** Injection, hepatitis B immune globulin (HepaGam B), intramuscular, 0.5 ml K2 ASC K

    Drugs: CBI HEPAGAM B 5 ML, CBI HEPAGAM B 1 ML, NOVA HEPAGAM B 1 ML, NOVA HEPAGAM B 5 ML, HEPAGAM B - IV

    Coding Clinic 2008, Q3, P7-8

D **J1572** Injection, immune globulin, (Flebogamma/ Flebogamma Dif), intravenous, non-lyophilized (e.g., liquid), 500 mg   K2 ASC G

    Drugs: FLEBOGAMMA, FLEBOGAMMA DIF, FLEBOGAMMA 10% DIF

C **J1573** Injection, hepatitis B immune globulin (HepaGam B), intravenous, 0.5 ml K2 ASC K

    Drugs: CBI HEPAGAM B 5 ML, CBI HEPAGAM B 1 ML, NOVA HEPAGAM B 1 ML, NOVA HEPAGAM B 5 ML, HEPAGAM B - IV

    Coding Clinic 2008, Q3, P8

D **J1580** Injection, garamycin, gentamicin, up to 80 mg   N1 N

    Drugs: GENTAMICIN SULFATE

C **J1590** Injection, gatifloxacin, 10 mg   N1 K

    Pub: 100-4, Chap. 4, 10.4

D **J1595** Injection, glatiramer acetate, 20 mg   K2 ASC K

C **J1599** Injection, immune globulin, intravenous, non-lyophilized (e.g., liquid), not otherwise specified, 500 mg   N1 N

    Coding Clinic 2011, Q6, P1

D **J1600** Injection, gold sodium thiomalate, up to 50 mg   N1 N

    Drugs: MYOCHRYSINE

    Pub: 100-4, Chap. 4, 10.4

C **J1602** Injection, golimumab, 1 mg, for intravenous use   K2

D **J1610** Injection, glucagon hydrochloride, per 1 mg   K2 ASC K

    Drugs: GLUCAGON EMERGENCY, GLUCAGON HYDROCHLORIDE, GLUCAGEN HYPOKIT, GLUCAGEN

D **J1620** Injection, gonadorelin hydrochloride, per 100 mcg   K:

D **J1626** Injection, granisetron hydrochloride, 100 mcg   N1 N

    Drugs: GRANISETRON HCL

    Pub: 100-4, Chap. 4, 10.4

D **J1630** Injection, haloperidol, up to 5 mg   N1 N

    Drugs: HALOPERIDOL LACTATE, HALDOL

    Pub: 100-4, Chap. 4, 10.4

D **J1631** Injection, haloperidol decanoate, per 50 mg   N1 N

    Drugs: HALOPERIDOL DECANOATE, HALDOL DECANOATE

D **J1640** Injection, hemin, 1 mg   K2 ASC K

    Drugs: PANHEMATIN

D **J1642** Injection, heparin sodium, (heparin lock flush), per 10 units   N1 N

    Drugs: HEPARIN LOCK FLUSH, HEPARIN SODIUM FLUSH, HEPARIN (PORCINE) LOCK FLUSH

    Pub: 100-4, Chap. 4, 10.4

D **J1644** Injection, heparin sodium, per 1000 units   N1 N

    Drugs: HEPARIN SODIUM (PORCINE), HEPARIN (PORCINE) IN D5W, HEPARIN (PORCINE) IN NACL, HEPARIN SODIUM, HEPARIN SODIUM IN NACL

    Pub: 100-4, Chap. 4, 10.4

D **J1645** Injection, dalteparin sodium, per 2500 IU   N1 N

    Drugs: FRAGMIN

C **J1650** Injection, enoxaparin sodium, 10 mg   N1 N

    Drugs: LOVENOX, ENOXAPARIN SODIUM

    Pub: 100-4, Chap. 4, 10.4

D **J1652** Injection, fondaparinux sodium, 0.5 mg N1 N

    Drugs: ARIXTRA, FONDAPARINUX SODIUM

C **J1655** Injection, tinzaparin sodium, 1000 IU   N1 N

    Pub: 100-4, Chap. 4, 10.4

D **J1670** Injection, tetanus immune globulin, human, up to 250 units   K2 ASC K

    Drugs: HYPERTET S/D

D **J1675** Injection, histrelin acetate, 10 micrograms   B

D **J1700** Injection, hydrocortisone acetate, up to 25 mg   N1 N

    Pub: 100-4, Chap. 4, 10.4

D **J1710** Injection, hydrocortisone sodium phosphate, up to 50 mg   N1 N

    Pub: 100-4, Chap. 4, 10.4

D **J1720** Injection, hydrocortisone sodium succinate, up to 100 mg   N1 N

    Drugs: SOLU-CORTEF, SOLU-CORTEF 500 MG 4ML

    Pub: 100-4, Chap. 4, 10.4

C **J1725** Injection, hydroxyprogesterone caproate, 1 mg   K2 ASC K

    Coding Clinic :2012, Q1, P9

D **J1730** Injection, diazoxide, up to 300 mg   K

C **J1740** Injection, ibandronate sodium, 1 mg   K2 ASC K

    Drugs: IBANDRONATE SODIUM, BONIVA

▲ Revised Code   ● New code   C Carrier judgment   D Special coverage instructions apply

I Not payable by Medicare   M Non-covered by Medicare   S Non-covered by Medicare statute   AHA Coding Clinic®

C	**J1741** Injection, ibuprofen, 100 mg	N1 N
D	**J1742** Injection, ibutilide fumarate, 1 mg	K2 ASC K
	Drugs: CORVERT, IBUTILIDE FUMARATE	
C	**J1743** Injection, idursulfase, 1 mg	K2 ASC K
	Drugs: ELAPRASE	
C	**J1744** Injection, icatibant, 1 mg	K2 ASC K
D	**J1745** Injection infliximab, 10 mg	K2 ASC K
	Drugs: REMICADE	
D	**J1750** Injection, iron dextran, 50 mg	K2 ASC K
	Drugs: DEXFERRUM, INFED	
C	**J1756** Injection, iron sucrose, 1 mg	N1 N
	Drugs: VENOFER	
D	**J1786** Injection, imiglucerase, 10 units	K2 ASC K
	Drugs: CEREZYME	
	Coding Clinic :2011, Q1, P8	

J1790 Injection, droperidol, up to 5 mg — N1 N
Drugs: DROPERIDOL, INAPSINE
Pub: 100-4, Chap. 4, 10.4

J1800 Injection, propranolol HCl, up to 1 mg — N1 N
Drugs: PROPRANOLOL, PROPRANOLOL HCL
Pub: 100-4, Chap. 4, 10.4

J1810 Injection, droperidol and fentanyl Citrate, up to 2 ml ampule — E

J1815 Injection, insulin, per 5 units — N1 N
Drugs: HUMALOG, HUMALOG MIX 50/50, HUMULIN R, HUMULIN R , HUMULIN N, HUMALOG PEN, NOVOLIN R, NOVOLIN N, NOVOLIN 70/30, NOVOLOG PENFILL, NOVOLOG FLEXPEN, NOVOLOG, LANTUS
Pub: 100-4, Chap. 4, 10.4

J1817 Insulin for administration through DME (i.e., insulin pump) per 50 units — N1 N
Drugs: HUMALOG, HUMULIN R, HUMULIN R , HUMALOG PEN, NOVOLIN R, NOVOLOG PENFILL, NOVOLOG FLEXPEN, NOVOLOG

J1826 Injection, interferon beta-1a, 30 mcg — E
Service not separately priced by Part B
Coding Clinic :2011 , Q2, P9;Q1, P8

J1830 Injection interferon beta-1b, 0.25 mg (code may be used for Medicare when drug administered under the direct supervision of a physician, not for use when drug is self administered) — K2 ASC K

J1835 Injection, itraconazole, 50 mg — K
Pub: 100-4, Chap. 4, 10.4

J1840 Injection, kanamycin sulfate, up to 500 mg — N1 N
Drugs: KANAMYCIN SULFATE
Pub: 100-4, Chap. 4, 10.4

J1850 Injection, kanamycin sulfate, up to 75 mg — N1 N
Drugs: KANAMYCIN SULFATE
Pub: 100-4, Chap. 4, 10.4

J1885 Injection, ketorolac tromethamine, per 15 mg — N1 N
Drugs: KETOROLAC TROMETHAMINE
Pub: 100-4, Chap. 4, 10.4

J1890 Injection, cephalothin sodium, up to 1 gram — N1 N
Pub: 100-4, Chap. 4, 10.4

J1930 Injection, lanreotide, 1 mg — K2 K
Drugs: SOMATULINE DEPOT

J1931 Injection, laronidase, 0.1 mg — K2 ASC K
Drugs: ALDURAZYME

J1940 Injection, furosemide, up to 20 mg — N1 N
Drugs: FUROSEMIDE
Pub: 100-4, Chap. 4, 10.4

J1945 Injection, lepirudin, 50 mg — K2 ASC K

J1950 Injection, leuprolide acetate (for depot suspension), per 3.75 mg — K2 ASC K
Drugs: LUPRON DEPOT-PED 11.25MG, LUPRON DEPOT 3.75MG , LUPRON DEPOT 3-MONTH, 11.25MG , LUPRON DEPOT-PED 3-MONTH, 11.25MG , LUPRON DEPOT-PED 3-MONTH, 30 MG

J1953 Injection, levetiracetam, 10 mg — N1 N
Drugs: LEVETIRACETAM, LEVETIRACETAM (KEPPRA)

J1955 Injection, levocarnitine, per 1 gm — B
Drugs: LEVOCARNITINE, CARNITOR

J1956 Injection, levofloxacin, 250 mg — N1 N
Drugs: LEVOFLOXACIN, LEVAQUIN
Pub: 100-4, Chap. 4, 10.4

J1960 Injection, levorphanol tartrate, up to 2 mg — N1 N
Pub: 100-4, Chap. 4, 10.4

J1980 Injection, hyoscyamine sulfate, up to 0.25 mg — N1 N
Drugs: LEVSIN INJECTION .5 MG/ML
Pub: 100-4, Chap. 4, 10.4

J1990 Injection, chlordiazepoxide HCl, up to 100 mg — N1 N
Pub: 100-4, Chap. 4, 10.4

J2001 Injection, lidocaine HCl for intravenous infusion, 10 mg — N1 N
Drugs: LIDOCAINE IN D5W
Pub: 100-4, Chap. 4, 10.4

J2010 Injection, lincomycin HCl, up to 300 mg — N1 N
Drugs: LINCOCIN
Pub: 100-4, Chap. 4, 10.4

J2020 Injection, linezolid, 200 mg — K2 ASC K
Drugs: ZYVOX

J2060 Injection, lorazepam, 2 mg — N1 N
Drugs: LORAZEPAM, ATIVAN
Pub: 100-4, Chap. 4, 10.4

J2150 Injection, mannitol, 25% in 50 ml — N1 N
Drugs: MANNITOL
Pub: 100-4, Chap. 4, 10.4

♂ Male only   ♀ Female only   Ⓐ Age   A2 - Z3 = ASC Payment Indicator   A - Y = APC Status Indicator
ASC = ASC Approved Procedure   **DME** Paid under the DME fee schedule   **PQRS** Physician Quality Reporting System

C **J2170** Injection, mecasermin, 1 mg   N1 N
Pub: 100-4, Chap. 4, 10.4

D **J2175** Injection, meperidine hydrochloride, per 100
mg   N1 N
Drugs: DEMEROL, MEPERIDINE HCL
Pub: 100-4, Chap. 4, 10.4

D **J2180** Injection, meperidine and promethazine HCl,
up to 50 mg   N1 N
Pub: 100-4, Chap. 4, 10.4

C **J2185** Injection, meropenem, 100 mg   N1 N
Drugs: MERREM, NOVAPLUS MERREM,
MEROPENEM
Pub: 100-4, Chap. 4, 10.4

D **J2210** Injection, methylergonovine maleate, up to
0.2 mg   N1 N
Drugs: METHERGINE,
METHYLERGONOVINE MALEATE
Pub: 100-4, Chap. 4, 10.4

C **J2212** Injection, methylnaltrexone, 0.1 mg K2 ASC K

C **J2248** Injection, micafungin sodium, 1 mg K2 ASC K
Drugs: MICAFUNGIN SODIUM (MYCAMINE)

D **J2250** Injection, midazolam hydrochloride,
per 1 mg   N1 N
Drugs: MIDAZOLAM HCL
Pub: 100-4, Chap. 4, 10.4

D **J2260** Injection, milrinone lactate, 5 mg   N1 N
Drugs: MILRINONE IN DEXTROSE,
MILRINONE LACTATE
Pub: 100-4, Chap. 4, 10.4

C **J2265** Injection, minocycline hydrochloride,
1 mg   N1 K

D **J2270** Injection, morphine sulfate, up to 10 mg N1 N
Drugs: MORPHINE SULFATE
Pub: 100-4, Chap. 4, 10.4

● D **J2274** Injection, morphine sulfate, preservative-free
for epidural or intrathecal use, 10 mg

D **J2278** Injection, ziconotide, 1 microgram K2 ASC K
Drugs: PRIALT

C **J2280** Injection, moxifloxacin, 100 mg   N1 N
Drugs: AVELOX
Pub: 100-4, Chap. 4, 10.4

D **J2300** Injection, nalbuphine hydrochloride, per 10
mg   N1 N
Drugs: NALBUPHINE HCL
Pub: 100-4, Chap. 4, 10.4

D **J2310** Injection, naloxone hydrochloride,
per 1 mg   N1 N
Drugs: NALOXONE HCL

C **J2315** Injection, naltrexone, depot form,
1 mg   K2 ASC K
Drugs: VIVITROL

D **J2320** Injection, nandrolone decanoate, up to 50
mg   N1 N
Coding Clinic :2011, Q1, P8

C **J2323** Injection, natalizumab, 1 mg   K2 ASC K
Drugs: NATALIZUMAB, TYSABRI

D **J2325** Injection, nesiritide, 0.1 mg   K2 ASC K
Drugs: NATRECOR

C **J2353** Injection, octreotide, depot form for
intramuscular injection, 1 mg   K2 ASC K
Drugs: SANDOSTATIN LAR DEPOT

C **J2354** Injection, octreotide, non-depot form for
subcutaneous or intravenous injection, 25
mcg   N1 N
Drugs: SANDOSTATIN, OCTREOTIDE
ACETATE

D **J2355** Injection, oprelvekin, 5 mg   K2 ASC K
Drugs: NEUMEGA

C **J2357** Injection, omalizumab, 5 mg   K2 ASC K
Drugs: XOLAIR

C **J2358** Injection, olanzapine, long-acting,
1 mg   K2 ASC K
Drugs: ZYPREXA RELPREVV
Coding Clinic :2011, Q1, P6

D **J2360** Injection, orphenadrine citrate, up to
60 mg   N1 N
Drugs: ORPHENADRINE CITRATE,
ORPHENADRINE CITRATE INJECTION

D **J2370** Injection, phenylephrine HCl, up to 1 ml N1 N
Drugs: PHENYLEPHRINE HCL

D **J2400** Injection, chloroprocaine hydrochloride, per
30 ml   N1 N
Drugs: CHLOROPROCAINE HCL,
NESACAINE, NESACAINE-MPF

D **J2405** Injection, ondansetron hydrochloride, per 1
mg   N1 N
Drugs: ONDANSETRON HCL, ZOFRAN,
ONDANSETRON

D **J2410** Injection, oxymorphone HCl, up to 1 mg N1 N
Drugs: OPANA

C **J2425** Injection, palifermin,
50 micrograms   K2 ASC K
Drugs: KEPIVANCE, KEPIVANCE/
PALIFERMIN

C **J2426** Injection, paliperidone palmitate extended
release, 1 mg   K2 ASC K
Drugs: INVEGA SUSTENNA
Coding Clinic :2011, Q1, P7

D **J2430** Injection, pamidronate disodium,
per 30 mg   N1 N
Drugs: PAMIDRONATE DISODIUM

D **J2440** Injection, papaverine HCl, up to 60 mg N1 N

D **J2460** Injection, oxytetracycline HCl, up to 50 mg N

C **J2469** Injection, palonosetron HCl,
25 mcg   K2 ASC K
Drugs: ALOXI

D **J2501** Injection, paricalcitol, 1 mcg   N1 N
Drugs: ZEMPLAR

▲ Revised Code   ● New code   C Carrier judgment   D Special coverage instructions apply
I Not payable by Medicare   M Non-covered by Medicare   S Non-covered by Medicare statute   AHA Coding Clinic®

C J2503 Injection, pegaptanib sodium,
0.3 mg   K2 ASC K
      Drugs: MACUGEN

D J2504 Injection, pegademase bovine,
25 IU   K2 ASC K
      Drugs: ADAGEN

C J2505 Injection, pegfilgrastim, 6 mg   K2 ASC K
      Statute: NEULASTA

C J2507 Injection, pegloticase, 1 mg   K2 ASC G
      Drugs: KRYSTEXXA
      Coding Clinic :2012, Q1, P9

D J2510 Injection, penicillin G procaine, aqueous, up
to 600, 000 units   N1 N
      Drugs: PENICILLIN G PROCAINE

D J2513 Injection, pentastarch, 10% solution,
100 ml   N1 N

D J2515 Injection, pentobarbital sodium,
per 50 mg   K2 ASC N
      Drugs: NEMBUTAL

D J2540 Injection, penicillin G potassium, up to 600,
000 units   N1 N
      Drugs: PFIZERPEN-G, PENICILLIN G POT IN
      DEXTROSE, PENICILLIN G POTASSIUM

D J2543 Injection, piperacillin sodium/tazobactam
sodium, 1 gram/0.125 grams
(1.125 grams)   N1 N
      Drugs: ZOSYN, NOVAPLUS ZOSYN,
      PIPERACILLIN SODIUM-TAZOBACTAM
      SODIUM, PIPERACILLIN SODIUM/ TAZO
      (ADD-VANTAGE), PIPERACILLIN SODIUM/
      TAZO, PIPERACILLIN AND TAZOBACTAM

D J2545 Pentamidine isethionate, inhalation
solution, FDA-approved final product, non-
compounded, administered through DME,
unit dose form, per 300 mg   B
      Drugs: NEBUPENT

D J2550 Injection, promethazine HCl, up to
50 mg   N1 N
      Drugs: PROMETHAZINE, PROMETHAZINE
      HCL, PHENERGAN

D J2560 Injection, phenobarbital sodium,
up to 120 mg   N1 N
      Drugs: PHENOBARBITAL SODIUM

C J2562 Injection, plerixafor, 1 mg   K2 ASC K
      Drugs: MOZOBIL (PLERIXAFOR)

D J2590 Injection, oxytocin, up to 10 units   N1 N
      Drugs: OXYTOCIN, PITOCIN

D J2597 Injection, desmopressin acetate,
per 1 mcg   K2 ASC K
      Drugs: DDAVP, DESMOPRESSIN ACETATE

D J2650 Injection, prednisolone acetate,
up to 1 ml   N1 N

D J2670 Injection, tolazoline HCl,
up to 25 mg   K2 ASC E

D J2675 Injection, progesterone, per 50 mg   N1 N
      Drugs: PROGESTERONE

D J2680 Injection, fluphenazine decanoate, up to 25
mg   N1 N
      Drugs: FLUPHENAZINE DECANOATE

D J2690 Injection, procainamide HCl,
up to 1 gm   N1 ♀ N
      Drugs: PROCAINAMIDE HCL

D J2700 Injection, oxacillin sodium, up to 250 mg   N1 K
      Drugs: BACTOCILL IN DEXTROSE,
      OXACILLIN SODIUM, OXACILLIN

● **C** J2704 Injection, propofol, 10 mg

D J2710 Injection, neostigmine methylsulfate, up to
0.5 mg   N1 N

D J2720 Injection, protamine sulfate, per 10 mg   N1 N
      Drugs: PROTAMINE SULFATE

C J2724 Injection, protein C concentrate, intravenous,
human, 10 IU   K2 ASC K
      Drugs: CEPROTIN

D J2725 Injection, protirelin, per 250 mcg   K

D J2730 Injection, pralidoxime chloride,
up to 1 gm   K2 ASC K
      Drugs: PROTOPAM CHLORIDE

D J2760 Injection, phentolamine mesylate,
up to 5 mg   K2 ASC N
      Drugs: PHENTOLAMINE MESYLATE

D J2765 Injection, metoclopramide HCl, up to
10 mg   N1 N
      Drugs: METOCLOPRAMIDE HCL, REGLAN

D J2770 Injection, quinupristin/dalfopristin, 500 mg
(150/350)   K2 ASC K
      Drugs: SYNERCID

C J2778 Injection, ranibizumab, 0.1 mg   K2 ASC K
      Drugs: RANIBIZUMAB

D J2780 Injection, ranitidine hydrochloride, 25 mg   N1 N
      Drugs: ZANTAC, ZANTAC IN NACL, ZANTAC
      INJECTION, ZANTAC INJECTION PREMIXED,
      RANITIDINE

C J2783 Injection, rasburicase, 0.5 mg   K2 ASC K
      Drugs: ELITEK

C J2785 Injection, regadenoson, 0.1 mg   N1 K
      Drugs: REGADENOSON

D J2788 Injection, Rho D immune globulin, human,
minidose, 50 micrograms (250 IU)   N1 K
      Drugs: MICRHOGAM, MICRHOGAM UF
      PLUS, BAYRHO-D

D J2790 Injection, Rho D immune globulin, human,
full dose, 300 micrograms (1500 IU)   N1 K
      Drugs: RHOGAM ULTRA-FILTERED PLUS,
      HYPERRHO S/D

D J2791 Injection, Rho D immune globulin (human),
(Rhophylac), intramuscular or intravenous,
100 IU   K2 ASC K
      Drugs: RHOPHYLAC

D J2792 Injection, Rho D immune globulin,
intravenous, human, solvent detergent, 100
IU   K2 ASC K
      Drugs: WINRHO SDF

♂ Male only   ♀ Female only   **A** Age   A2 - Z3 = ASC Payment Indicator   A - Y = APC Status Indicator

ASC = ASC Approved Procedure   **DME** Paid under the DME fee schedule   **PQRS** Physician Quality Reporting System

D **J2793** Injection, rilonacept, 1 mg   K2 ASC K

C **J2794** Injection, risperidone, long acting, 0.5 mg   K2 ASC K
Drugs: RISPERDAL CONSTA

C **J2795** Injection, ropivacaine hydrochloride, 1 mg   N1 N
Drugs: NAROPIN, NAROPIN , NAROPIN (NOVAPLUS)

C **J2796** Injection, romiplostim, 10 micrograms   K2 ASC K
Drugs: NPLATE

D **J2800** Injection, methocarbamol, up to 10 ml   N1 N
Drugs: ROBAXIN

C **J2805** Injection, sincalide, 5 micrograms   N1 N
Drugs: SINCALIDE INJ

D **J2810** Injection, theophylline, per 40 mg   N1 N
Drugs: THEOPHYLLINE IN D5W

D **J2820** Injection, sargramostim (GM-CSF), 50 mcg   K2 ASC K
Drugs: LEUKINE

D **J2850** Injection, secretin, synthetic, human, 1 microgram   K2 ASC K
Drugs: CHIRHOSTIM

D **J2910** Injection, aurothioglucose, up to 50 mg   N1 N

D **J2916** Injection, sodium ferric gluconate complex in sucrose injection, 12.5 mg   N1 N
Drugs: FERRLECIT, SODIUM FERRIC GLUCONATE COMPLEX IN SUCROSE, NULECIT

D **J2920** Injection, methylprednisolone sodium succinate, up to 40 mg   N1 N
Drugs: SOLU-MEDROL, METHYLPRED SODIUM SUCCINATE, METHYLPREDNISOLONE SODIUM SUCC

D **J2930** Injection, methylprednisolone sodium succinate, up to 125 mg   N1 N
Drugs: SOLU-MEDROL, METHYLPRED SODIUM SUCCINATE, METHYLPREDNISOLONE SODIUM SUCC

D **J2940** Injection, somatrem, 1 mg   E
Statute: 1861s2b

D **J2941** Injection, somatropin, 1 mg   N1 K
Statute: 1861s2b

D **J2950** Injection, promazine HCl, up to 25 mg   N1 N

D **J2993** Injection, reteplase, 18.1 mg   K2 ASC K
Drugs: RETAVASE HALF KIT, RETAVASE KIT

D **J2995** Injection, streptokinase, per 250, 000 IU   N1 N

D **J2997** Injection, alteplase recombinant, 1 mg   K2 ASC K
Drugs: CATHFLO ACTIVASE, ACTIVASE

D **J3000** Injection, streptomycin, up to 1 gm   N1 N
Drugs: STREPTOMYCIN SULFATE

D **J3010** Injection, fentanyl Citrate, 0.1 mg   N1 N
Drugs: FENTANYL CITRATE, SUBLIMAZE

D **J3030** Injection, sumatriptan succinate, 6 mg (code may be used for Medicare when drug administered under the direct supervision of a physician, not for use when drug is self administered)   N1 N

● **C** **J3060** Injection, taliglucerase alfa, 10 units K2 ASC
Drugs: ELELYSO

D **J3070** Injection, pentazocine, 30 mg   N1 N
Drugs: TALWIN LACTATE

C **J3095** Injection, telavancin, 10 mg   K2 ASC K
Drugs: VIBATIV
Coding Clinic :2011, Q1, P7

C **J3101** Injection, tenecteplase, 1 mg   K2 ASC K
Drugs: TNKASE

D **J3105** Injection, terbutaline sulfate, up to 1 mg N1 N
Drugs: TERBUTALINE, TERBUTALINE SULFATE, TERBUTALINE SULFATE INJECTION USP

D **J3110** Injection, teriparatide, 10 mcg   B

● **D** **J3121** Injection, testosterone enanthate, 1 mg

● **D** **J3145** Injection, testosterone undecanoate, 1 mg

D **J3230** Injection, chlorpromazine HCl, up to 50 mg   N1 N
Drugs: CHLORPROMAZINE HCL

D **J3240** Injection, thyrotropin alpha, 0.9 mg, provided in 1.1 mg vial   K2 ASC K
Drugs: THYROGEN

C **J3243** Injection, tigecycline, 1 mg   K2 ASC K
Drugs: TIGECYCLINE

C **J3246** Injection, tirofiban HCl, 0.25mg   K2 ASC K
Drugs: AGGRASTAT

D **J3250** Injection, trimethobenzamide HCl, up to 200 mg   N1 N
Drugs: TIGAN, TRIMETHOBENZAMIDE HCL

D **J3260** Injection, tobramycin sulfate, up to 80 mg   N1 N
Drugs: TOBRAMYCIN INJECTION, TOBRAMYCIN SULFATE IN SALINE, TOBRAMYCIN SULFATE

C **J3262** Injection, tocilizumab, 1 mg   K2 ASC K
Drugs: ACTEMRA
Coding Clinic :2011, Q1, P7

D **J3265** Injection, torsemide, 10 mg/ml   N1 N

D **J3280** Injection, thiethylperazine maleate, up to 10 mg   N1 N

C **J3285** Injection, treprostinil, 1 mg   K2 ASC K
Drugs: REMODULIN

D **J3300** Injection, triamcinolone acetonide, preservative free, 1 mg   K2 ASC K
Drugs: TRIAMCINOLONE ACETONIDE, PRESERVATIVE FREE

D **J3301** Injection, triamcinolone acetonide, not otherwise specified, 10 mg   N1 N
Drugs: KENALOG, TRIAMCINOLONE ACETONIDE, KENALOG-40

D **J3302** Injection, triamcinolone diacetate, per 5 mg   N1 N

▲ Revised Code   ● New code   **C** Carrier judgment   **D** Special coverage instructions apply
I Not payable by Medicare   **M** Non-covered by Medicare   **S** Non-covered by Medicare statute   AHA Coding Clinic®

D	J3303	Injection, triamcinolone hexacetonide, per 5 mg	N1 N

Drugs: ARISTOSPAN INTRALESIONAL, ARISTOSPAN INTRA-ARTICULAR

D	J3305	Injection, trimetrexate glucuronate, per 25 mg	E
D	J3310	Injection, perphenazine, up to 5 mg	N1 N
D	J3315	Injection, triptorelin pamoate, 3.75 mg	K2 ASC K

Drugs: TRELSTAR

D	J3320	Injection, spectinomycin dihydrochloride, up to 2 gm	E
D	J3350	Injection, urea, up to 40 gm	K2 ASC N
D	J3355	Injection, urofollitropin, 75 IU	K2 ASC K

Drugs: BRAVELLE

C	J3357	Injection, ustekinumab, 1 mg	K2 ASC K

Drugs: STELARA

Coding Clinic :2012, Q1, P7

D	J3360	Injection, diazepam, up to 5 mg	N1 N

Drugs: DIAZEPAM

Coding Clinic :2007, Q2, P6-7

D	J3364	Injection, urokinase, 5000 IU vial	N1 N
D	J3365	Injection, IV, urokinase, 250, 000 IU vial	ASC K
D	J3370	Injection, vancomycin HCl, 500 mg	N1 N

Drugs: VANCOMYCIN HCL, VANCOCIN HCL, VANCOMYCIN HYDROCHLORIDE

C	J3385	Injection, velaglucerase alfa, 100 units	K2 ASC K

Drugs: VPRIV

Coding Clinic :2011, Q1, P7

D	J3396	Injection, verteporfin, 0.1 mg	K2 ASC K

Drugs: VISUDYNE

Pub: 100-3, Chap. 1, Part 1, 80.2; 100-3, Chap. 1, Part 1, 80.2.1; 100-3, Chap. 1, Part 1, 80.3; 100-3, Chap. 1, Part 1, 80.3.1; 100-4, Chap. 32, 300; 100-4, Chap. 32, 300.1; 100-4, Chap. 32, 300.2

D	J3400	Injection, triflupromazine HCl, up to 20 mg	N1 N
D	J3410	Injection, hydroxyzine HCl, up to 25 mg	N1 N

Drugs: HYDROXYZINE HCL

C	J3411	Injection, thiamine HCl, 100 mg	N1 N

Drugs: THIAMINE HCL

C	J3415	Injection, pyridoxine HCl, 100 mg	N1 N

Drugs: PYRIDOXINE HCL

D	J3420	Injection, vitamin B-12 cyanocobalamin, up to 1000 mcg	N1 N

Drugs: CYANOCOBALAMIN

D	J3430	Injection, phytonadione (vitamin K), per 1 mg	N1 N

Drugs: VITAMIN K1

D	J3465	Injection, voriconazole, 10 mg	K2 ASC K

Drugs: VFEND IV, VORICONAZOLE

D	J3470	Injection, hyaluronidase, up to 150 units	N1 N
D	J3471	Injection, hyaluronidase, ovine, preservative free, per 1 USP unit (up to 999 USP units)	N1 N

D	J3472	Injection, hyaluronidase, ovine, preservative free, per 1000 USP units	N1 N
D	J3473	Injection, hyaluronidase, recombinant, 1 USP unit	N1 N

Drugs: HYALURONIDASE

D	J3475	Injection, magnesium sulfate, per 500 mg	N1 N

Drugs: MAGNESIUM SULFATE

D	J3480	Injection, potassium chloride, per 2 mEq	N1 N

Drugs: POTASSIUM CHLORIDE, POTASSIUM CHLORIDE/DEXTROSE, POTASSIUM CHLORIDE/SODIUM CHLORIDE

D	J3485	Injection, zidovudine, 10 mg	N1 N

Drugs: RETROVIR

C	J3486	Injection, ziprasidone mesylate, 10 mg	N1 N

Drugs: GEODON

C	J3489	Injection, zoledronic acid, 1 mg	K2 ASC

Drugs: ZOMETA, RECLAST, ZOLEDRONIC ACID

D	J3490	Unclassified drugs	N1 N
M	J3520	Edetate disodium, per 150 mg	E

Service not separately priced by Part B

D	J3530	Nasal vaccine inhalation	N1 N
M	J3535	Drug administered through a metered dose inhaler	E

Service not separately priced by Part B

M	J3570	Laetrile, amygdalin, vitamin B17	E

Service not separately priced by Part B

C	J3590	Unclassified biologics	N1 N
D	J7030	Infusion, normal saline solution, 1000 cc	N1 N

Drugs: SODIUM CHLORIDE

D	J7040	Infusion, normal saline solution, sterile (500 ml=1 unit)	N1 N

Drugs: SODIUM CHLORIDE

D	J7042	5% dextrose/normal saline (500 ml = 1 unit)	N1 N

Drugs: DEXTROSE-NACL

D	J7050	Infusion, normal saline solution , 250 cc	N1 N

Drugs: SODIUM CHLORIDE

D	J7060	5% dextrose/water (500 ml = 1 unit)	N1 N

Drugs: DEXTROSE, DEXTROSE 5%

D	J7070	Infusion, D5W, 1000 cc	N1 N

Drugs: DEXTROSE

D	J7100	Infusion, dextran 40, 500 ml	N1 N

Drugs: LMD 10% IN 0.9% SODIUM CHL INJECTION 500ML

D	J7110	Infusion, dextran 75, 500 ml	N1 N
D	J7120	Ringers lactate infusion, up to 1000 cc	N1 N

Drugs: LACTATED RINGERS, LACTATED RINGER'S

D	J7131	Hypertonic saline solution, 1 ml	N1 N

Coding Clinic :2012, Q1, P9

C	J7178	Injection, human fibrinogen concentrate, 1 mg	K2 K

C **J7180** Injection, factor XIII (antihemophilic factor, human), 1 IU K2 ASC G

Coding Clinic :2012, Q1, P9

● C **J7181** Injection, factor XIII a-subunit, (recombinant), per IU

● C **J7182** Injection, factor VIII, (antihemophilic factor, recombinant), (Novoeight), per IU

D **J7183** Injection, von Willebrand factor complex (human), wilate, 1 IU VWF:RCo K2 ASC K

Drugs: WILATE

Coding Clinic :2012, Q1, P9

C **J7185** Injection, factor VIII (antihemophilic factor, recombinant) (XYNTHA), per IU K2 ASC K

Drugs: XYNTHA

D **J7186** Injection, antihemophilic factor VIII/von Willebrand factor complex (human), per factor VIII IU K2 ASC K

Drugs: ALPHANATE /VON WILLEBRAND FACTOR COMPLEX

Pub: 100-4, Chap. 17, 80.4.1

D **J7187** Injection, von Willebrand factor complex (Humate-P), per IU VWF:RCo K2 ASC K

Drugs: HUMATE-P LOW DILUENT

Pub: 100-4, Chap. 17, 80.4.1

D **J7189** Factor VIIa (antihemophilic factor, recombinant), per 1 microgram K2 ASC K

Drugs: NOVOSEVEN RT

Pub: 100-4, Chap. 17, 80.4.1

D **J7190** Factor VIII (antihemophilic factor, human) per IU K2 ASC K

Drugs: MONOCLATE-P, HEMOFIL M, KOATE-DVI, ALPHANATE /VON WILLEBRAND FACTOR COMPLEX

Pub: 100-4, Chap. 17, 80.4.1

D **J7191** Factor VIII (antihemophilic factor (porcine)), per IU K2 ASC N

Pub: 100-4, Chap. 17, 80.4.1

D **J7192** Factor VIII (antihemophilic factor, recombinant) per IU, not otherwise specified K2 ASC K

Drugs: KOGENATE FS FIXED POLY CLASSIC, KOGENATE FS, KOGENATE FS 3000 , KOGENATE FS FIXED POLY BIO-SET, KOGENATE FS BIO-SET, KOGENATE FS 3000 BIO-SET, HELIXATE FS, HELIXATE FS 3000, RECOMBINATE, ADVATE

Pub: 100-4, Chap. 17, 80.4.1

D **J7193** Factor IX (antihemophilic factor, purified, non-recombinant) per IU K2 ASC K

Drugs: MONONINE, ALPHANINE SD, ALPHANINE®SD VF 500 IU M2V USA, ALPHANINE®SD VF 1000 IU M2V USA, ALPHANINE®SD VF 1500 IU M2V USA

Pub: 100-4, Chap. 17, 80.4.1

D **J7194** Factor IX, complex, per IU K2 ASC K

Drugs: BEBULIN, PROFILNINE SD, PROFILNINE® SD FIX SD(1000), PROFILNINE® SD FIX SD(1500),

PROFILNINE® SD FIX SD M2V(500), PROFILNINE® SD FIX SD M2V(1000), PROFILNINE® SD FIX SD M2V(1500)

Pub: 100-4, Chap. 17, 80.4.1

▲ D **J7195** Injection, factor IX (antihemophilic factor, recombinant) per IU, not otherwise specified K2 ASC K

Drugs: BENEFIX

Pub: 100-4, Chap. 17, 80.4.1

C **J7196** Injection, antithrombin recombinant, 50 IU K2 ASC K

Coding Clinic :2011, Q1, P6

D **J7197** Antithrombin III (human), per IU K2 ASC K

Drugs: THROMBATE III

D **J7198** Anti-inhibitor, per IU K2 ASC K

Drugs: FEIBA NF

Pub: 100-4, Chap. 17, 80.4.1

D **J7199** Hemophilia clotting factor, not otherwise classified B

Pub: 100-4, Chap. 17, 80.4.1

● D **J7200** Injection, factor IX, (antihemophilic factor, recombinant), Rixubis, per IU

● D **J7201** Injection, factor IX, fc fusion protein (recombinant), per IU

S **J7300** Intrauterine copper contraceptive E

Service not separately priced by Part B
Statute: 1862a1

▲ S **J7301** Levonorgestrel-releasing intrauterine contraceptive system, 13.5 mg ♀

Service not separately priced by Part B
Statute: 1862(a)(1)

S **J7302** Levonorgestrel-releasing intrauterine contraceptive system, 52 mg ♀ E

Service not separately priced by Part B
Statute: 1862a1

S **J7303** Contraceptive supply, hormone containing vaginal ring, each ♀ E

Service not separately priced by Part B
Statute: 1862.1

S **J7304** Contraceptive supply, hormone containing patch, each ♀ E

Service not separately priced by Part B
Statute: 1862.1

I **J7306** Levonorgestrel (contraceptive) implant system, including implants and supplies E

Service not separately priced by Part B

I **J7307** Etonogestrel (contraceptive) implant system, including implant and supplies E

Service not separately priced by Part B

C **J7308** Aminolevulinic acid HCl for topical administration, 20%, single unit dosage form (354 mg) K2 ASC K

Drugs: LEVULAN KERASTICK

D **J7309** Methyl aminolevulinate (MAL) for topical administration, 16.8%, 1 gram K2 ASC K

Drugs: METVIXIA

Coding Clinic :2011, Q1, P6

▲ Revised Code   ● New code   C Carrier judgment   D Special coverage instructions apply
I Not payable by Medicare   M Non-covered by Medicare   S Non-covered by Medicare statute   AHA Coding Clinic®

D J7310 Ganciclovir, 4.5 mg, long-acting
implant   K2 ASC K
Drugs: VITRASERT

C J7311 Fluocinolone acetonide, intravitreal
implant   K2 ASC K
Drugs: FLUOCINOLONE ACETONIDE IMPLT
(RETISERT)

C J7312 Injection, dexamethasone, intravitreal
implant, 0.1 mg   K2 ASC K
Drugs: OZURDEX
Coding Clinic :2011, Q1, P7

C J7315 Mitomycin, ophthalmic, 0.2 mg   K2 ASC G

C J7316 Injection, ocriplasmin, 0.125 mg   K2 ASC
Drugs: JETREA

C J7321 Hyaluronan or derivative, Hyalgan or
supartz, for intra-articular injection,
per dose   K2 ASC K
Drugs: HYALGAN, SUPARTZ

C J7323 Hyaluronan or derivative, Euflexxa, for intra-
articular injection, per dose   K2 ASC K
Drugs: EUFLEXXA

C J7324 Hyaluronan or derivative, Orthovisc, for intra-
articular injection, per dose   K2 ASC K
Drugs: ORTHOVISC

C J7325 Hyaluronan or derivative, Synvisc or
Synvisc-One, for intra-articular injection, 1
mg   K2 ASC K
Drugs: SYNVISC, SYNVISCONE

C J7326 Hyaluronan or derivative, Gel-One, for intra-
articular injection, per dose   K2 ASC K
Drugs: GEL-ONE
Coding Clinic :2012, Q1, P8

● **C** J7327 Hyaluronan or derivative, monovisc, for intra-
articular injection, per dose

C J7330 Autologous cultured chondrocytes, implant B
Other carrier priced Drugs: CARTICEL
Coding Clinic :2010, Q4, P3

● **C** J7336 Capsaicin 8% patch, per square centimeter

D J7500 Azathioprine, oral, 50 mg   N1 N
Drugs: AZATHIOPRINE, AZASAN
Pub: 100-2, Chap. 15, 50

D J7501 Azathioprine, parenteral, 100 mg   K2 ASC K
Drugs: AZATHIOPRINE SODIUM

D J7502 Cyclosporine, oral, 100 mg   N1 N
Other carrier priced Drugs: GENGRAF,
SANDIMMUNE, NEORAL, CYCLOSPORINE,
CYCLOSPORINE MODIFIED

D J7504 Lymphocyte immune globulin,
antithymocyte globulin, equine, parenteral,
250 mg   K2 ASC K
Drugs: ATGAM

D J7505 Muromonab-CD3, parenteral, 5 mg K2 ASC K

D J7506 Prednisone, oral, per 5 mg   N1 N
Drugs: PREDNISONE INTENSOL,
PREDNISONE, PREDNISONE (PAK)

D J7507 Tacrolimus, immediate release, oral,
1 mg   N1 N
Drugs: TACROLIMUS, PROGRAF,
TACROLIMUS, ORAL

D J7508 Tacrolimus, extended release, oral,
0.1 mg   K2 ASC
Drugs: ASTAGRAF XL

D J7509 Methylprednisolone oral, per 4 mg   N1 N
Drugs: MEDROL, MEDROL (PAK),
METHYLPREDNISOLONE (PAK),
METHYLPREDNISOLONE

D J7510 Prednisolone oral, per 5 mg   N1 N
Drugs: PREDNISOLONE

C J7511 Lymphocyte immune globulin, antithymocyte
globulin, rabbit, parenteral, 25 mg K2 ASC K
Drugs: THYMOGLOBULIN

D J7513 Daclizumab, parenteral, 25 mg   K2 ASC K

C J7515 Cyclosporine, oral, 25 mg   N1 N
Drugs: GENGRAF, SANDIMMUNE, NEORAL,
CYCLOSPORINE, CYCLOSPORINE
MODIFIED

C J7516 Cyclosporin, parenteral, 250 mg   N1 N
Drugs: SANDIMMUNE, CYCLOSPORINE

C J7517 Mycophenolate mofetil, oral, 250 mg   N1 N
Drugs: CELLCEPT, MYCOPHENOLATE
MOFETIL

D J7518 Mycophenolic acid, oral, 180 mg   N1 N
Drugs: MYFORTIC

D J7520 Sirolimus, oral, 1 mg   N1 N
Drugs: RAPAMUNE

D J7525 Tacrolimus, parenteral, 5 mg   K2 ASC K
Drugs: PROGRAF

D J7527 Everolimus, oral, 0.25 mg   N1 K
Drugs: ZORTRESS

D J7599 Immunosuppressive drug, not otherwise
classified   N1 N

C J7604 Acetylcysteine, inhalation solution,
compounded product, administered through
DME, unit dose form, per gram   M

C J7605 Arformoterol, inhalation solution, FDA
approved final product, non-compounded,
administered through DME, unit dose form,
15 micrograms   M
Drugs: ARFORMOTEROL

C J7606 Formoterol fumarate, inhalation solution,
FDA approved final product, non-
compounded, administered through DME,
unit dose form, 20 micrograms   M
Drugs: PERFOROMIST

C J7607 Levalbuterol, inhalation solution,
compounded product, administered through
DME, concentrated form, 0.5 mg   M

D J7608 Acetylcysteine, inhalation solution, FDA-
approved final product, non-compounded,
administered through DME, unit dose form,
per gram   M
Drugs: ACETYLCYSTEINE

♂ Male only   ♀ Female only   **A** Age   A2 - Z3 = ASC Payment Indicator   A - Y = APC Status Indicator
ASC = ASC Approved Procedure   **DME** Paid under the DME fee schedule   **PQRS** Physician Quality Reporting System

C **J7609** Albuterol, inhalation solution, compounded product, administered through DME, unit dose, 1 mg   M

Inhaler

C **J7610** Albuterol, inhalation solution, compounded product, administered through DME, concentrated form, 1 mg   M

D **J7611** Albuterol, inhalation solution, FDA-approved final product, non-compounded, administered through DME, concentrated form, 1 mg   M
Service not separately priced by Part B
Drugs: ALBUTEROL SULFATE

D **J7612** Levalbuterol, inhalation solution, FDA-approved final product, non-compounded, administered through DME, concentrated form, 0.5 mg   M
Service not separately priced by Part B
Drugs: LEVALBUTEROL INHALATION SOLUTION CONCENTRATED, XOPENEX

D **J7613** Albuterol, inhalation solution, FDA-approved final product, non-compounded, administered through DME, unit dose, 1 mg   M
Service not separately priced by Part B
Drugs: ALBUTEROL SULFATE, ACCUNEB

D **J7614** Levalbuterol, inhalation solution, FDA-approved final product, non-compounded, administered through DME, unit dose, 0.5 mg   M
Service not separately priced by Part B
Drugs: LEVALBUTEROL, XOPENEX

C **J7615** Levalbuterol, inhalation solution, compounded product, administered through DME, unit dose, 0.5 mg   M

D **J7620** Albuterol, up to 2.5 mg and ipratropium bromide, up to 0.5 mg, FDA-approved final product, non-compounded, administered through DME   M
Drugs: ALBUTEROL IPRATROPIUM, DUONEB

C **J7622** Beclomethasone, inhalation solution, compounded product, administered through DME, unit dose form, per milligram   M

C **J7624** Betamethasone, inhalation solution, compounded product, administered through DME, unit dose form, per milligram   M

C **J7626** Budesonide, inhalation solution, FDA-approved final product, non-compounded, administered through DME, unit dose form, up to 0.5 mg   M
Drugs: BUDESONIDE, PULMICORT

C **J7627** Budesonide, inhalation solution, compounded product, administered through DME, unit dose form, up to 0.5 mg   M

D **J7628** Bitolterol mesylate, inhalation solution, compounded product, administered through DME, concentrated form, per milligram   M

D **J7629** Bitolterol mesylate, inhalation solution, compounded product, administered through DME, unit dose form, per milligram   M

D **J7631** Cromolyn sodium, inhalation solution, FDA-approved final product, non-compounded, administered through DME, unit dose form, per 10 milligrams   M
Drugs: CROMOLYN SODIUM

C **J7632** Cromolyn sodium, inhalation solution, compounded product, administered through DME, unit dose form, per 10 milligrams   M

C **J7633** Budesonide, inhalation solution, FDA-approved final product, non-compounded, administered through DME, concentrated form, per 0.25 milligram   M

C **J7634** Budesonide, inhalation solution, compounded product, administered through DME, concentrated form, per 0.25 milligram   M

D **J7635** Atropine, inhalation solution, compounded product, administered through DME, concentrated form, per milligram   M

D **J7636** Atropine, inhalation solution, compounded product, administered through DME, unit dose form, per milligram   M

D **J7637** Dexamethasone, inhalation solution, compounded product, administered through DME, concentrated form, per milligram   M

D **J7638** Dexamethasone, inhalation solution, compounded product, administered through DME, unit dose form, per milligram   M

D **J7639** Dornase alfa, inhalation solution, FDA-approved final product, non-compounded, administered through DME, unit dose form, per milligram   M
Drugs: PULMOZYME

C **J7640** Formoterol, inhalation solution, compounded product, administered through DME, unit dose form, 12 micrograms   E
Service not separately priced by Part B

C **J7641** Flunisolide, inhalation solution, compounded product, administered through DME, unit dose, per milligram   M

D **J7642** Glycopyrrolate, inhalation solution, compounded product, administered through DME, concentrated form, per milligram   M

D **J7643** Glycopyrrolate, inhalation solution, compounded product, administered through DME, unit dose form, per milligram   M

D **J7644** Ipratropium bromide, inhalation solution, FDA-approved final product, non-compounded, administered through DME, unit dose form, per milligram   M
Drugs: IPRATROPIUM BROMIDE

C **J7645** Ipratropium bromide, inhalation solution, compounded product, administered through DME, unit dose form, per milligram   M

C **J7647** Isoetharine HCl, inhalation solution, compounded product, administered through DME, concentrated form, per milligram   M

D **J7648** Isoetharine HCl, inhalation solution, FDA-approved final product, non-compounded, administered through DME, concentrated form, per milligram   M

D **J7649** Isoetharine HCl, inhalation solution, FDA-approved final product, non-compounded, administered through DME, unit dose form, per milligram   M

C **J7650** Isoetharine HCl, inhalation solution, compounded product, administered through DME, unit dose form, per milligram   M

C **J7657** Isoproterenol HCl, inhalation solution, compounded product, administered through DME, concentrated form, per milligram   M

D **J7658** Isoproterenol HCl, inhalation solution, FDA-approved final product, non-compounded, administered through DME, concentrated form, per milligram   M

D **J7659** Isoproterenol HCl, inhalation solution, FDA-approved final product, non-compounded, administered through DME, unit dose form, per milligram   M

C **J7660** Isoproterenol HCl, inhalation solution, compounded product, administered through DME, unit dose form, per milligram   M

C **J7665** Mannitol, administered through an inhaler, 5 mg   N1 N
Drugs: ARIDOL

C **J7667** Metaproterenol sulfate, inhalation solution, compounded product, concentrated form, per 10 milligrams   M

D **J7668** Metaproterenol sulfate, inhalation solution, FDA-approved final product, non-compounded, administered through DME, concentrated form, per 10 milligrams   M

D **J7669** Metaproterenol sulfate, inhalation solution, FDA-approved final product, non-compounded, administered through DME, unit dose form, per 10 milligrams   M

C **J7670** Metaproterenol sulfate, inhalation solution, compounded product, administered through DME, unit dose form, per 10 milligrams   M

C **J7674** Methacholine chloride administered as inhalation solution through a nebulizer, per 1 mg   N1 N
Drugs: PROVOCHOLINE

C **J7676** Pentamidine isethionate, inhalation solution, compounded product, administered through DME, unit dose form, per 300 mg   M

D **J7680** Terbutaline sulfate, inhalation solution, compounded product, administered through DME, concentrated form, per milligram   M

D **J7681** Terbutaline sulfate, inhalation solution, compounded product, administered through DME, unit dose form, per milligram   M

D **J7682** Tobramycin, inhalation solution, FDA-approved final product, non-compounded, unit dose form, administered through DME, per 300 milligrams   M
Drugs: TOBI

D **J7683** Triamcinolone, inhalation solution, compounded product, administered through DME, concentrated form, per milligram   M

D **J7684** Triamcinolone, inhalation solution, compounded product, administered through DME, unit dose form, per milligram   M

C **J7685** Tobramycin, inhalation solution, compounded product, administered through DME, unit dose form, per 300 milligrams   M

C **J7686** Treprostinil, inhalation solution, FDA-approved final product, non-compounded, administered through DME, unit dose form, 1.74 mg   M
Drugs: TYVASO (STARTER KIT), TYVASO (REFILL KIT), TYVASO

D **J7699** Noc drugs, inhalation solution administered through DME   M

D **J7799** Noc drugs, other than inhalation drugs, administered through DME   N1 N

D **J8498** Antiemetic drug, rectal/suppository, not otherwise specified   B
Statute: 1861s2T

M **J8499** Prescription drug, oral, non chemotherapeutic, NOS   E
Service not separately priced by Part B

D **J8501** Aprepitant, oral, 5 mg   K2 ASC K
Drugs: EMEND BI-PACK, EMEND, EMEND TRI-FOLD

D **J8510** Busulfan; oral, 2 mg   N1 K
Drugs: MYLERAN

M **J8515** Cabergoline, oral, 0.25 mg   E
Service not separately priced by Part B

D **J8520** Capecitabine, oral, 150 mg   K2 ASC K
Drugs: XELODA

D **J8521** Capecitabine, oral, 500 mg   K2 ASC K
Drugs: XELODA

♂ Male only   ♀ Female only   Ⓐ Age   A2 - Z3 = ASC Payment Indicator   A - Y = APC Status Indicator
ASC = ASC Approved Procedure   DME Paid under the DME fee schedule   PQRS Physician Quality Reporting System

D	**J8530**	Cyclophosphamide; oral, 25 mg	N1 N
		Drugs: CYCLOPHOSPHAMIDE	
D	**J8540**	Dexamethasone, oral, 0.25 mg	N1 N
		Statute: 1861(s)2T	
		Drugs: DEXAMETHASONE	
D	**J8560**	Etoposide; oral, 50 mg	K2 ASC K
		Drugs: ETOPOSIDE	
C	**J8562**	Fludarabine phosphate, oral, 10 mg	N1 K
		Coding Clinic: 2011, Q1, P9	
D	**J8565**	Gefitinib, oral, 250 mg	E
		Service not separately priced by Part B	
D	**J8597**	Antiemetic drug, oral, not otherwise specified	N1 N
		Statute: 1861s2T	
D	**J8600**	Melphalan; oral, 2 mg	N1 N
		Drugs: ALKERAN	
D	**J8610**	Methotrexate; oral, 2.5 mg	N1 N
		Drugs: METHOTREXATE, METHOTRAXATE, TREXALL, RHEUMATREX	
C	**J8650**	Nabilone, oral, 1 mg	K2 ASC K
D	**J8700**	Temozolomide, oral, 5 mg	K2 ASC K
		Drugs: TEMODAR, TEMOZOLOMIDE	
C	**J8705**	Topotecan, oral, 0.25 mg	K2 ASC K
		Drugs: TOPOTECAN, ORAL	
D	**J8999**	Prescription drug, oral, chemotherapeutic, NOS	B

▲ Revised Code   ● New code   C Carrier judgment   D Special coverage instructions apply

I Not payable by Medicare   M Non-covered by Medicare   S Non-covered by Medicare statute   AHA Coding Clinic®

CHEMOTHERAPY DRUGS (J9000-J9999)

D J9000 Injection, doxorubicin hydrochloride, 10 mg   N1 N
Drugs: DOXORUBICIN HCL, ADRIAMYCIN
Coding Clinic: 2007, Q4, P5

I J9010 Injection, alemtuzumab, 10 mg   K2 ASC K
Statute: 1833T

D J9015 Injection, aldesleukin, per single use vial   K2 ASC K
Drugs: PROLEUKIN

C J9017 Injection, arsenic trioxide, 1 mg   K2 ASC K
Drugs: TRISENOX

D J9019 Injection, asparaginase (Erwinaze), 1, 000 IU   K2 ASC G
Drugs: ERWINAZE

D J9020 Injection, asparaginase, not otherwise specified, 10, 000 units   K2 ASC K
Drugs: ELSPAR

C J9025 Injection, azacitidine, 1 mg   K2 ASC K
Drugs: AZACITIDINE, AZACITIDINE (VIDAZA)

C J9027 Injection, clofarabine, 1 mg   K2 ASC K
Drugs: CLOLAR

D J9031 BCG (intravesical) per instillation   K2 ASC K
Drugs: TICE BCG, THERACYS

C J9033 Injection, bendamustine HCl, 1 mg K2 ASC K
Drugs: TREANDA

C J9035 Injection, bevacizumab, 10 mg   K2 ASC K
Drugs: AVASTIN

D J9040 Injection, bleomycin sulfate, 15 units   N1 N
Drugs: BLEOMYCIN SULFATE, BLEOMYCIN

C J9041 Injection, bortezomib, 0.1 mg   K2 ASC K
Drugs: VELCADE

C J9042 Injection, brentuximab vedotin, 1 mg   K2 ASC G
Drugs: ADCETRIS

C J9043 Injection, cabazitaxel, 1 mg   K2 ASC K
Drugs: JEVTANA
Coding Clinic: 2012, Q1, P9

D J9045 Injection, carboplatin, 50 mg   N1 N
Drugs: CARBOPLATIN

C J9047 Injection, carfilzomib, 1 mg   K2 ASC
Drugs: KYPROLIS

D J9050 Injection, carmustine, 100 mg   K2 ASC K
Drugs: BICNU

C J9055 Injection, cetuximab, 10 mg   K2 ASC K
Drugs: ERBITUX

D J9060 Injection, cisplatin, powder or solution, 10 mg   N1 N
Drugs: CISPLATIN
Coding Clinic: 2011, Q1, P8

D J9065 Injection, cladribine, per 1 mg   K2 ASC K
Drugs: CLADRIBINE, LEUSTATIN

D J9070 Cyclophosphamide, 100 mg   K2 ASC K
Drugs: CYCLOPHOSPHAMIDE
Coding Clinic: 2011, Q1, P8-9

C J9098 Injection, cytarabine liposome, 10 mg   K2 ASC K
Drugs: DEPOCYT

D J9100 Injection, cytarabine, 100 mg   N1 N
Drugs: CYTARABINE
Coding Clinic: 2011, Q1, P9

D J9120 Injection, dactinomycin, 0.5 mg   K2 ASC K
Drugs: DACTINOMYCIN, COSMEGEN

D J9130 Dacarbazine, 100 mg   N1 N
Drugs: DACARBAZINE
Coding Clinic: 2011, Q1, P9

D J9150 Injection, daunorubicin, 10 mg   K2 ASC K
Drugs: DAUNORUBICIN HCL, CERUBIDINE

D J9151 Injection, daunorubicin Citrate, liposomal formulation, 10 mg   K2 ASC K

C J9155 Injection, degarelix, 1 mg   K2 ASC K
Drugs: FIRMAGON

C J9160 Injection, denileukin diftitox, 300 micrograms   ASC K
Drugs: ONTAK

D J9165 Injection, diethylstilbestrol diphosphate, 250 mg   E

D J9171 Injection, docetaxel, 1 mg   K2 ASC K
Drugs: TAXOTERE, DOCETAXEL, DOCEFREZ
Coding Clinic: 2012, Q1, P9

D J9175 Injection, Elliotts' B solution, 1 ml   N1 N
Drugs: ELLIOTTS B

C J9178 Injection, epirubicin HCl, 2 mg   N1 K
Drugs: ELLENCE, EPIRUBICIN

C J9179 Injection, eribulin mesylate, 0.1 mg   K2 ASC G
Drugs: HALAVEN

D J9181 Injection, etoposide, 10 mg   N1 N
Drugs: ETOPOPHOS, ETOPOSIDE, TOPOSAR

D J9185 Injection, fludarabine phosphate, 50 mg   K2 ASC K
Drugs: FLUDARABINE PHOSPHATE, FLUDARA

D J9190 Injection, fluorouracil, 500 mg   N1 N
Drugs: ADRUCIL, FLUOROURACIL

D J9200 Injection, floxuridine, 500 mg   K2 ASC K
Drugs: FLOXURIDINE

D J9201 Injection, gemcitabine hydrochloride, 200 mg   N1 K
Drugs: GEMZAR, GEMCITABINE HYDROCHLORIDE, GEMCITABINE, GEMCITABINE HCL

D J9202 Goserelin acetate implant, per 3.6 mg   K2 ASC K
Drugs: ZOLADEX

♂ Male only   ♀ Female only   **A** Age   A2 - Z3 = ASC Payment Indicator   A - Y = APC Status Indicator
ASC = ASC Approved Procedure   **DME** Paid under the DME fee schedule   **PQRS** Physician Quality Reporting System

D **J9206** Injection, irinotecan, 20 mg   N1 N
Drugs: CAMPTOSAR, IRINOTECAN HCL

C **J9207** Injection, ixabepilone, 1 mg   K2 ASC K
Drugs: IXABEPILONE

D **J9208** Injection, ifosfamide, 1 gram   K2 ASC K
Drugs: IFOSFAMIDE, IFEX

D **J9209** Injection, mesna, 200 mg   N1 N
Drugs: MESNEX, MESNA

D **J9211** Injection, idarubicin hydrochloride, 5 mg   K2 ASC K
Drugs: IDAMYCIN PFS, IDARUBICIN

D **J9212** Injection, interferon alfacon-1, recombinant, 1 microgram   N1 K

D **J9213** Injection, interferon, alfa-2a, recombinant, 3 million units   K2 ASC N

D **J9214** Injection, interferon, alfa-2b, recombinant, 1 million units   K2 ASC K
Drugs: INTRON-A

D **J9215** Injection, interferon, alfa-N3, (human leukocyte derived), 250, 000 IU   K2 N

D **J9216** Injection, interferon, gamma 1-b, 3 million units   K2 ASC K

D **J9217** Leuprolide acetate (for depot suspension), 7.5 mg   K2 ASC K
Drugs: ELIGARD, LUPRON DEPOT-PED 7.5 MG, LUPRON DEPOT-PED 15MG, LUPRON DEPOT-3 MONTH 22.5 MG KIT, LUPRON DEPOT 6-MONTH, 45MG , LUPRON DEPOT 7.5 MG KIT, LUPRON DEPOT 4-MONTH, 30MG

D **J9218** Leuprolide acetate, per 1 mg   K2 ASC K
Drugs: LEUPROLIDE ACETATE, LEUPROLIDE ACETATE INJ

D **J9219** Leuprolide acetate implant, 65 mg   ASC K

D **J9225** Histrelin implant (Vantas), 50 mg   K2 ASC K
Drugs: VANTAS IMPLANT

D **J9226** Histrelin implant (Supprelin LA), 50 mg   K2 ASC K
Drugs: SUPPRELIN LA IMPLANT

C **J9228** Injection, ipilimumab, 1 mg   K2 ASC G
Drugs: YERVOY
Coding Clinic: 2012, Q1, P9

D **J9230** Injection, mechlorethamine hydrochloride, (nitrogen mustard), 10 mg   K2 ASC K
Drugs: MUSTARGEN

D **J9245** Injection, melphalan hydrochloride, 50 mg   K2 ASC K
Drugs: ALKERAN, MELPHALAN

D **J9250** Methotrexate sodium, 5 mg   N1 N
Drugs: METHOTREXATE SODIUM, METHOTREXATE, METHOTREXATE POWDER 1GM IN 50ML SD VIAL (P.F.)

D **J9260** Methotrexate sodium, 50 mg   N1 N
Drugs: METHOTREXATE SODIUM, METHOTREXATE, METHOTREXATE POWDER 1GM IN 50ML SD VIAL (P.F.)

C **J9261** Injection, nelarabine, 50 mg   K2 ASC K
Drugs: ARRANON

C **J9262** Injection, omacetaxine mepesuccinate, 0.01 mg   K2 ASC

C **J9263** Injection, oxaliplatin, 0.5 mg   K2 ASC K
Drugs: ELOXATIN, OXALIPLATIN
Coding Clinic: 2009, Q1, P10

C **J9264** Injection, paclitaxel protein-bound particles, 1 mg   K2 ASC K
Drugs: ABRAXANE

D **J9266** Injection, pegaspargase, per single dose vial   K2 ASC K
Drugs: ONCASPAR

● D **J9267** Injection, paclitaxel, 1 mg

D **J9268** Injection, pentostatin, 10 mg   K2 ASC K
Drugs: NIPENT, PENTOSTATIN

D **J9270** Injection, plicamycin, 2.5 mg   N1 N

D **J9280** Injection, mitomycin, 5 mg   K2 ASC K
Drugs: MITOMYCIN
Coding Clinic: 2011, Q1, P9

D **J9293** Injection, mitoxantrone hydrochloride, per 5 mg   K2 ASC K
Drugs: MITOXANTRONE HYDROCHLORIDE

C **J9300** Injection, gemtuzumab ozogamicin, 5 mg   ASC K
Drugs: MYLOTARG

● C **J9301** Injection, obinutuzumab, 10 mg

C **J9302** Injection, ofatumumab, 10 mg   K2 ASC K
Drugs: ARZERRA
Coding Clinic: 2011, Q1, P7

C **J9303** Injection, panitumumab, 10 mg   K2 ASC K
Drugs: PANITUMUMAB

C **J9305** Injection, pemetrexed, 10 mg   K2 ASC K
Drugs: ALIMTA

C **J9306** Injection, pertuzumab, 1 mg   K2 ASC
Drugs: PERJETA

C **J9307** Injection, pralatrexate, 1 mg   K2 ASC K
Drugs: FOLOTYN
Coding Clinic: 2011, Q1, P7

D **J9310** Injection, rituximab, 100 mg   K2 ASC K
Drugs: RITUXAN

C **J9315** Injection, romidepsin, 1 mg   K2 ASC K
Drugs: ISTODAX (ROMIDEPSIN)
Coding Clinic: 2011, Q1, P7

D **J9320** Injection, streptozocin, 1 gram   K2 ASC K
Drugs: ZANOSAR

C **J9328** Injection, temozolomide, 1 mg   K2 ASC K
Drugs: TEMODAR IV

C **J9330** Injection, temsirolimus, 1 mg   K2 ASC K
Drugs: TEMSIROLIMUS

D **J9340** Injection, thiotepa, 15 mg   K2 ASC K

▲ Revised Code   ● New code   C Carrier judgment   D Special coverage instructions apply
I Not payable by Medicare   M Non-covered by Medicare   S Non-covered by Medicare statute   AHA Coding Clinic®

C **J9351** Injection, topotecan, 0.1 mg   K2 ASC K
    Drugs: HYCAMTIN, TOPOTECAN, TOPOTECAN HCL
    Coding Clinic: 2011, Q1, P9

C **J9354** Injection, ado-trastuzumab emtansine, 1 mg   K2 ASC
    Drugs: KADCYLA

C **J9355** Injection, trastuzumab, 10 mg   K2 ASC K
    Drugs: HERCEPTIN

D **J9357** Injection, valrubicin, intravesical, 200 mg   K2 ASC K
    Drugs: VALSTAR

D **J9360** Injection, vinblastine sulfate, 1 mg   N1 N
    Drugs: VINBLASTINE SULFATE

D **J9370** Vincristine sulfate, 1 mg   N1 N
    Drugs: VINCRISTINE SULFATE
    Coding Clinic: 2011, Q1, P9

C **J9371** Injection, vincristine sulfate liposome, 1 mg   K2 ASC

D **J9390** Injection, vinorelbine tartrate, 10 mg   N1 ASC N
    Drugs: VINORELBINE TARTRATE, NAVELBINE

C **J9395** Injection, fulvestrant, 25 mg   K2 ASC K
    Drugs: FASLODEX

C **J9400** Injection, ziv-aflibercept, 1 mg   K2 ASC
    Drugs: ZALTRAP

D **J9600** Injection, porfimer sodium, 75 mg   K2 ASC K

D **J9999** Not otherwise classified, antineoplastic drugs   N1 N

J9351 - J9999

CHEMOTHERAPY DRUGS (J9000-J9999)

DURABLE MEDICAL EQUIPMENT (DME) MEDICARE ADMINISTRATIVE CONTRACTORS (MACS) (K0001-K9999)

C **K0001** Standard wheelchair `DME` Y
DME Modifier: RR

C **K0002** Standard hemi (low seat) wheelchair `DME` Y
DME Modifier: RR

C **K0003** Lightweight wheelchair `DME` Y
DME Modifier: RR

C **K0004** High strength, lightweight wheelchair `DME` Y
DME Modifier: RR

C **K0005** Ultralightweight wheelchair `DME` Y
DME Modifier: NU, RR, UE

C **K0006** Heavy duty wheelchair `DME` Y
DME Modifier: RR

C **K0007** Extra heavy duty wheelchair `DME` Y
DME Modifier: RR

D **K0008** Custom manual wheelchair/base Y

C **K0009** Other manual wheelchair/base `DME` Y
DME Modifier: RR

C **K0010** Standard - weight frame motorized/power wheelchair `DME` Y
DME Modifier: RR

C **K0011** Standard - weight frame motorized/power wheelchair with programmable control parameters for speed adjustment, tremor dampening, acceleration control and braking `DME` Y
DME Modifier: RR, KF

C **K0012** Lightweight portable motorized/power wheelchair `DME` Y
DME Modifier: RR

D **K0013** Custom motorized/power wheelchair base Y

C **K0014** Other motorized/power wheelchair base Y

C **K0015** Detachable, non-adjustable height armrest, each `DME` Y
DME Modifier: NU, KE, RR, UE
Pub: 100-4, Chap. 23, 60.3

C **K0017** Detachable, adjustable height armrest, base, each `DME` Y
DME Modifier: NU, KE, RR, UE

C **K0018** Detachable, adjustable height armrest, upper portion, each `DME` Y
DME Modifier: NU, KE, RR, UE

C **K0019** Arm pad, each `DME` Y
DME Modifier: NU, KE, RR, UE

C **K0020** Fixed, adjustable height armrest, pair `DME` Y
DME Modifier: NU, KE, RR, UE

C **K0037** High mount flip-up footrest, each `DME` Y
DME Modifier: NU, KE, RR, UE

C **K0038** Leg strap, each `DME` Y
DME Modifier: NU, KE, RR, UE

C **K0039** Leg strap, H style, each `DME` Y
DME Modifier: NU, KE, RR, UE

C **K0040** Adjustable angle footplate, each `DME` Y
DME Modifier: NU, KE, RR, UE

C **K0041** Large size footplate, each `DME` Y
DME Modifier: NU, KE, RR, UE

C **K0042** Standard size footplate, each `DME` Y
DME Modifier: NU, KE, RR, UE

C **K0043** Footrest, lower extension tube, each `DME` Y
DME Modifier: NU, KE, RR, UE

C **K0044** Footrest, upper hanger bracket, each `DME` Y
DME Modifier: NU, KE, RR, UE

C **K0045** Footrest, complete assembly `DME` Y
DME Modifier: NU, KE, RR, UE

C **K0046** Elevating legrest, lower extension tube, each `DME` Y

C **K0047** Elevating legrest, upper hanger bracket, each `DME` Y
DME Modifier: NU, KE, RR, UE

C **K0050** Ratchet assembly `DME` Y
DME Modifier: NU, KE, RR, UE

C **K0051** Cam release assembly, footrest or legrest, each `DME` Y
DME Modifier: NU, KE, RR, UE

C **K0052** Swingaway, detachable footrests, each `DME` Y
DME Modifier: NU, KE, RR, UE

C **K0053** Elevating footrests, articulating (telescoping), each `DME` Y
DME Modifier: NU, KE, RR, UE

C **K0056** Seat height less than 17 inch or equal to or greater than 21 inch for a high strength, lightweight, or ultralightweight wheelchair `DME` Y
DME Modifier: NU, RR, UE

C **K0065** Spoke protectors, each `DME` Y
DME Modifier: NU, RR, UE

C **K0069** Rear wheel assembly, complete, with solid tire, spokes or molded, each `DME` Y
DME Modifier: NU, RR, UE

C **K0070** Rear wheel assembly, complete, with pneumatic tire, spokes or molded, each `DME` Y
DME Modifier: NU, RR, UE

C **K0071** Front caster assembly, complete, with pneumatic tire, each `DME` Y
DME Modifier: NU, RR, UE

C **K0072** Front caster assembly, complete, with semi-pneumatic tire, each `DME` Y
DME Modifier: NU, RR, UE

C **K0073** Caster pin lock, each `DME` Y
DME Modifier: NU, RR, UE

C **K0077** Front caster assembly, complete, with solid tire, each `DME` Y
DME Modifier: NU, RR, UE

C **K0098** Drive belt for power wheelchair `DME` Y
DME Modifier: NU, KE, RR, UE

▲ Revised Code   ● New code   **C** Carrier judgment   **D** Special coverage instructions apply

I Not payable by Medicare   **M** Non-covered by Medicare   **S** Non-covered by Medicare statute   AHA Coding Clinic®

C **K0105** IV hanger, each `DME` Y
DME Modifier: NU, RR, UE

C **K0108** Wheelchair component or accessory, not otherwise specified Y

D **K0195** Elevating leg rests, pair (for use with capped rental wheelchair base) `DME` Y
DME Modifier: RR, KE

Pub: 100-4, Chap. 23, 60.3

D **K0455** Infusion pump used for uninterrupted parenteral administration of medication, (e.g., epoprostenol or treprostinol) `DME` Y
DME Modifier: RR

Infusion Pump

D **K0462** Temporary replacement for patient owned equipment being repaired, any type Y

D **K0552** Supplies for external drug infusion pump, syringe type cartridge, sterile, each `DME` Y

C **K0601** Replacement battery for external infusion pump owned by patient, silver oxide, 1.5 volt, each `DME` Y
DME Modifier: NU

C **K0602** Replacement battery for external infusion pump owned by patient, silver oxide, 3 volt, each `DME` Y
DME Modifier: NU

C **K0603** Replacement battery for external infusion pump owned by patient, alkaline, 1.5 volt, each `DME` Y
DME Modifier: NU

C **K0604** Replacement battery for external infusion pump owned by patient, lithium, 3.6 volt, each `DME` Y
DME Modifier: NU

C **K0605** Replacement battery for external infusion pump owned by patient, lithium, 4.5 volt, each `DME` Y
DME Modifier: NU

C **K0606** Automatic external defibrillator, with integrated electrocardiogram analysis, garment type `DME` Y
DME Modifier: RR, KF

C **K0607** Replacement battery for automated external defibrillator, garment type only, each `DME` Y
DME Modifier: NU, KF, RR, UE

C **K0608** Replacement garment for use with automated external defibrillator, each `DME` Y
DME Modifier: NU, KF, RR, UE

C **K0609** Replacement electrodes for use with automated external defibrillator, garment type only, each `DME` Y
DME Modifier: KF

C **K0669** Wheelchair accessory, wheelchair seat or back cushion, does not meet specific code criteria or no written coding verification from DME PDAC Y

C **K0672** Addition to lower extremity orthosis, removable soft interface, all components, replacement only, each `DME` A

C **K0730** Controlled dose inhalation drug delivery system `DME` Y
DME Modifier: NU, RR, UE

C **K0733** Power wheelchair accessory, 12 to 24 amp hour sealed lead acid battery, each (e.g., gel cell, absorbed glassmat) `DME` Y
DME Modifier: NU, KE, RR, UE

Pub: 100-4, Chap. 23, 60.3

C **K0738** Portable gaseous oxygen system, rental; home compressor used to fill portable oxygen cylinders; includes portable containers, regulator, flowmeter, humidifier, cannula or mask, and tubing `DME` Y
DME Modifier: RR

C **K0739** Repair or nonroutine service for durable medical equipment other than oxygen equipment requiring the skill of a technician, labor component, per 15 minutes Y

M **K0740** Repair or nonroutine service for oxygen equipment requiring the skill of a technician, labor component, per 15 minutes E
Service not separately priced by Part B

C **K0743** Suction pump, home model, portable, for use on wounds Y

C **K0744** Absorptive wound dressing for use with suction pump, home model, portable, pad size 16 square inches or less A

C **K0745** Absorptive wound dressing for use with suction pump, home model, portable, pad size more than 16 square inches but less than or equal to 48 square inches A

C **K0746** Absorptive wound dressing for use with suction pump, home model, portable, pad size greater than 48 square inches A

C **K0800** Power operated vehicle, group 1 standard, patient weight capacity up to and including 300 pounds `DME` Y
DME Modifier: NU, RR, UE

Pub: 100-4, Chap. 12, 30.6.15.4; 100-4, Chap. 23, 60.3

C **K0801** Power operated vehicle, group 1 heavy duty, patient weight capacity 301 to 450 pounds `DME` Y
DME Modifier: NU, RR, UE

C **K0802** Power operated vehicle, group 1 very heavy duty, patient weight capacity 451 to 600 pounds `DME` Y
DME Modifier: NU, RR, UE

C **K0806** Power operated vehicle, group 2 standard, patient weight capacity up to and including 300 pounds `DME` Y
DME Modifier: NU, RR, UE

C **K0807** Power operated vehicle, group 2 heavy duty, patient weight capacity 301 to 450 pounds `DME` Y
DME Modifier: NU, RR, UE

C **K0808** Power operated vehicle, group 2 very heavy duty, patient weight capacity 451 to 600 pounds `DME` Y
DME Modifier: NU, RR, UE

C **K0812** Power operated vehicle, not otherwise classified Y

C **K0813** Power wheelchair, group 1 standard, portable, sling/solid seat and back, patient weight capacity up to and including 300 pounds `DME` Y
DME Modifier: RR

C **K0814** Power wheelchair, group 1 standard, portable, captains chair, patient weight capacity up to and including 300 pounds `DME` Y
DME Modifier: RR

C **K0815** Power wheelchair, group 1 standard, sling/solid seat and back, patient weight capacity up to and including 300 pounds `DME` Y
DME Modifier: RR

C **K0816** Power wheelchair, group 1 standard, captains chair, patient weight capacity up to and including 300 pounds `DME` Y
DME Modifier: RR

C **K0820** Power wheelchair, group 2 standard, portable, sling/solid seat/back, patient weight capacity up to and including 300 pounds `DME` Y
DME Modifier: RR

C **K0821** Power wheelchair, group 2 standard, portable, captains chair, patient weight capacity up to and including 300 pounds `DME` Y
DME Modifier: RR

C **K0822** Power wheelchair, group 2 standard, sling/solid seat/back, patient weight capacity up to and including 300 pounds `DME` Y
DME Modifier: RR

C **K0823** Power wheelchair, group 2 standard, captains chair, patient weight capacity up to and including 300 pounds `DME` Y
DME Modifier: RR

C **K0824** Power wheelchair, group 2 heavy duty, sling/solid seat/back, patient weight capacity 301 to 450 pounds `DME` Y
DME Modifier: RR

C **K0825** Power wheelchair, group 2 heavy duty, captains chair, patient weight capacity 301 to 450 pounds `DME` Y
DME Modifier: RR

C **K0826** Power wheelchair, group 2 very heavy duty, sling/solid seat/back, patient weight capacity 451 to 600 pounds `DME` Y
DME Modifier: RR

C **K0827** Power wheelchair, group 2 very heavy duty, captains chair, patient weight capacity 451 to 600 pounds `DME` Y
DME Modifier: RR

C **K0828** Power wheelchair, group 2 extra heavy duty, sling/solid seat/back, patient weight capacity 601 pounds or more `DME` Y
DME Modifier: RR

C **K0829** Power wheelchair, group 2 extra heavy duty, captains chair, patient weight 601 pounds or more `DME` Y
DME Modifier: RR

C **K0830** Power wheelchair, group 2 standard, seat elevator, sling/solid seat/back, patient weight capacity up to and including 300 pounds Y

C **K0831** Power wheelchair, group 2 standard, seat elevator, captains chair, patient weight capacity up to and including 300 pounds Y

C **K0835** Power wheelchair, group 2 standard, single power option, sling/solid seat/back, patient weight capacity up to and including 300 pounds `DME` Y
DME Modifier: RR

C **K0836** Power wheelchair, group 2 standard, single power option, captains chair, patient weight capacity up to and including 300 pounds `DME` Y
DME Modifier: RR

C **K0837** Power wheelchair, group 2 heavy duty, single power option, sling/solid seat/back, patient weight capacity 301 to 450 pounds `DME` Y
DME Modifier: RR

C **K0838** Power wheelchair, group 2 heavy duty, single power option, captains chair, patient weight capacity 301 to 450 pounds `DME` Y
DME Modifier: RR

C **K0839** Power wheelchair, group 2 very heavy duty, single power option sling/solid seat/back, patient weight capacity 451 to 600 pounds `DME` Y
DME Modifier: RR

C **K0840** Power wheelchair, group 2 extra heavy duty, single power option, sling/solid seat/back, patient weight capacity 601 pounds or more `DME` Y
DME Modifier: RR

▲ Revised Code   ● New code   **C** Carrier judgment   **D** Special coverage instructions apply
I Not payable by Medicare   **M** Non-covered by Medicare   **S** Non-covered by Medicare statute   AHA Coding Clinic®

C K0841 Power wheelchair, group 2 standard, multiple power option, sling/solid seat/back, patient weight capacity up to and including 300 pounds **DME** Y

DME Modifier: RR

C K0842 Power wheelchair, group 2 standard, multiple power option, captains chair, patient weight capacity up to and including 300 pounds **DME** Y

DME Modifier: RR

C K0843 Power wheelchair, group 2 heavy duty, multiple power option, sling/solid seat/back, patient weight capacity 301 to 450 pounds **DME** Y

DME Modifier: RR

C K0848 Power wheelchair, group 3 standard, sling/solid seat/back, patient weight capacity up to and including 300 pounds **DME** Y

DME Modifier: RR

C K0849 Power wheelchair, group 3 standard, captains chair, patient weight capacity up to and including 300 pounds **DME** Y

DME Modifier: RR

C K0850 Power wheelchair, group 3 heavy duty, sling/solid seat/back, patient weight capacity 301 to 450 pounds **DME** Y

DME Modifier: RR

C K0851 Power wheelchair, group 3 heavy duty, captains chair, patient weight capacity 301 to 450 pounds **DME** Y

DME Modifier: RR

C K0852 Power wheelchair, group 3 very heavy duty, sling/solid seat/back, patient weight capacity 451 to 600 pounds **DME** Y

DME Modifier: RR

C K0853 Power wheelchair, group 3 very heavy duty, captains chair, patient weight capacity 451 to 600 pounds **DME** Y

DME Modifier: RR

C K0854 Power wheelchair, group 3 extra heavy duty, sling/solid seat/back, patient weight capacity 601 pounds or more **DME** Y

DME Modifier: RR

C K0855 Power wheelchair, group 3 extra heavy duty, captains chair, patient weight capacity 601 pounds or more **DME** Y

DME Modifier: RR

C K0856 Power wheelchair, group 3 standard, single power option, sling/solid seat/back, patient weight capacity up to and including 300 pounds **DME** Y

DME Modifier: RR

C K0857 Power wheelchair, group 3 standard, single power option, captains chair, patient weight capacity up to and including 300 pounds **DME** Y

DME Modifier: RR

C K0858 Power wheelchair, group 3 heavy duty, single power option, sling/solid seat/back, patient weight 301 to 450 pounds **DME** Y

DME Modifier: RR

C K0859 Power wheelchair, group 3 heavy duty, single power option, captains chair, patient weight capacity 301 to 450 pounds **DME** Y

DME Modifier: RR

C K0860 Power wheelchair, group 3 very heavy duty, single power option, sling/solid seat/back, patient weight capacity 451 to 600 pounds **DME** Y

DME Modifier: RR

C K0861 Power wheelchair, group 3 standard, multiple power option, sling/solid seat/back, patient weight capacity up to and including 300 pounds **DME** Y

DME Modifier: RR, KF

C K0862 Power wheelchair, group 3 heavy duty, multiple power option, sling/solid seat/back, patient weight capacity 301 to 450 pounds **DME** Y

DME Modifier: RR

C K0863 Power wheelchair, group 3 very heavy duty, multiple power option, sling/solid seat/back, patient weight capacity 451 to 600 pounds **DME** Y

DME Modifier: RR

C K0864 Power wheelchair, group 3 extra heavy duty, multiple power option, sling/solid seat/back, patient weight capacity 601 pounds or more **DME** Y

DME Modifier: RR

C K0868 Power wheelchair, group 4 standard, sling/solid seat/back, patient weight capacity up to and including 300 pounds Y

C K0869 Power wheelchair, group 4 standard, captains chair, patient weight capacity up to and including 300 pounds Y

C K0870 Power wheelchair, group 4 heavy duty, sling/solid seat/back, patient weight capacity 301 to 450 pounds Y

C K0871 Power wheelchair, group 4 very heavy duty, sling/solid seat/back, patient weight capacity 451 to 600 pounds Y

C K0877 Power wheelchair, group 4 standard, single power option, sling/solid seat/back, patient weight capacity up to and including 300 pounds Y

C K0878 Power wheelchair, group 4 standard, single power option, captains chair, patient weight capacity up to and including 300 pounds Y

C K0879 Power wheelchair, group 4 heavy duty, single power option, sling/solid seat/back, patient weight capacity 301 to 450 pounds Y

C K0880 Power wheelchair, group 4 very heavy duty, single power option, sling/solid seat/back, patient weight 451 to 600 pounds Y

♂ Male only   ♀ Female only   Ⓐ Age   A2 - Z3 = ASC Payment Indicator   A - Y = APC Status Indicator

ASC = ASC Approved Procedure   **DME** Paid under the DME fee schedule   **PQRS** Physician Quality Reporting System

C **K0884** Power wheelchair, group 4 standard, multiple power option, sling/solid seat/back, patient weight capacity up to and including 300 pounds Y

C **K0885** Power wheelchair, group 4 standard, multiple power option, captains chair, patient weight capacity up to and including 300 pounds Y

C **K0886** Power wheelchair, group 4 heavy duty, multiple power option, sling/solid seat/back, patient weight capacity 301 to 450 pounds Y

C **K0890** Power wheelchair, group 5 pediatric, single power option, sling/solid seat/back, patient weight capacity up to and including 125 pounds Ⓐ Y

C **K0891** Power wheelchair, group 5 pediatric, multiple power option, sling/solid seat/back, patient weight capacity up to and including 125 pounds Ⓐ Y

C **K0898** Power wheelchair, not otherwise classified Y

C **K0899** Power mobility device, not coded by DME PDAC or does not meet criteria Y

Pub: 100-4, Chap. 12, 30.6.15.4

D **K0900** Customized durable medical equipment, other than wheelchair Y

● **K0901** Knee orthosis (KO), single upright, thigh and calf, with adjustable flexion and extension joint (unicentric or polycentric), medial-lateral and rotation control, with or without varus/valgus adjustment, prefabricated, off-the-shelf

● **K0902** Knee orthosis (KO), double upright, thigh and calf, with adjustable flexion and extension joint (unicentric or polycentric), medial-lateral and rotation control, with or without varus/valgus adjustment, prefabricated, off-the-shelf

ORTHOTIC PROCEDURES AND SERVICES (L0112-L4631)

C L0112 Cranial cervical orthosis, congenital torticollis type, with or without soft interface material, adjustable range of motion joint, custom fabricated `DME` A

C L0113 Cranial cervical orthosis, torticollis type, with or without joint, with or without soft interface material, prefabricated, includes fitting and adjustment `DME` A

C L0120 Cervical, flexible, non-adjustable, prefabricated, off-the-shelf (foam collar) `DME` A

C L0130 Cervical, flexible, thermoplastic collar, molded to patient `DME` A

C L0140 Cervical, semi-rigid, adjustable (plastic collar) `DME` A

C L0150 Cervical, semi-rigid, adjustable molded chin cup (plastic collar with mandibular/occipital piece) `DME` A

C L0160 Cervical, semi-rigid, wire frame occipital/mandibular support, prefabricated, off-the-shelf `DME` A

C L0170 Cervical, collar, molded to patient model `DME` A

C L0172 Cervical, collar, semi-rigid thermoplastic foam, two-piece, prefabricated, off-the-shelf `DME` A

C L0174 Cervical, collar, semi-rigid, thermoplastic foam, two piece with thoracic extension, prefabricated, off-the-shelf `DME` A

C L0180 Cervical, multiple post collar, occipital/mandibular supports, adjustable `DME` A

C L0190 Cervical, multiple post collar, occipital/mandibular supports, adjustable cervical bars (SOMI, Guilford, Taylor types) `DME` A

C L0200 Cervical, multiple post collar, occipital/mandibular supports, adjustable cervical bars, and thoracic extension `DME` A

C L0220 Thoracic, rib belt, custom fabricated `DME` A

C L0450 Thoracic-lumbar-sacral orthosis (TLSO), flexible, provides trunk support, upper thoracic region, produces intracavitary pressure to reduce load on the intervertebral disks with rigid stays or panel(s), includes shoulder straps and closures, prefabricated, off-the-shelf `DME` A

C L0452 Thoracic-lumbar-sacral orthosis (TLSO), flexible, provides trunk support, upper thoracic region, produces intracavitary pressure to reduce load on the intervertebral disks with rigid stays or panel(s), includes shoulder straps and closures, custom fabricated `DME` A

C L0454 Thoracic-lumbar-sacral orthosis (TLSO) flexible, provides trunk support, extends from sacrococcygeal junction to above T-9 vertebra, restricts gross trunk motion in the sagittal plane, produces intracavitary pressure to reduce load on the intervertebral disks with rigid stays or panel(s), includes shoulder straps and closures, prefabricated item that has been trimmed, bent, molded, assembled, or otherwise customized to fit a specific patient by an individual with expertise `DME` A

C L0455 Thoracic-lumbar-sacral orthosis (TLSO), flexible, provides trunk support, extends from sacrococcygeal junction to above T-9 vertebra, restricts gross trunk motion in the sagittal plane, produces intracavitary pressure to reduce load on the intervertebral disks with rigid stays or panel(s), includes shoulder straps and closures, prefabricated, off-the-shelf `DME`

C L0456 Thoracic-lumbar-sacral orthosis (TLSO), flexible, provides trunk support, thoracic region, rigid posterior panel and soft anterior apron, extends from the sacrococcygeal junction and terminates just inferior to the scapular spine, restricts gross trunk motion in the sagittal plane, produces intracavitary pressure to reduce load on the intervertebral disks, includes straps and closures, prefabricated item that has been trimmed, bent, molded, assembled, or otherwise customized to fit a specific patient by an individual with expertise `DME` A

C L0457 Thoracic-lumbar-sacral orthosis (TLSO), flexible, provides trunk support, thoracic region, rigid posterior panel and soft anterior apron, extends from the sacrococcygeal junction and terminates just inferior to the scapular spine, restricts gross trunk motion in the sagittal plane, produces intracavitary pressure to reduce load on the intervertebral disks, includes straps and closures, prefabricated, off-the-shelf `DME`

C L0458 Thoracic-lumbar-sacral orthosis (TLSO), triplanar control, modular segmented spinal system, two rigid plastic shells, posterior extends from the sacrococcygeal junction and terminates just inferior to the scapular spine, anterior extends from the symphysis pubis to the xiphoid, soft liner, restricts gross trunk motion in the sagittal, coronal, and transverse planes, lateral strength is provided by overlapping plastic and stabilizing closures, includes straps and closures, prefabricated, includes fitting and adjustment `DME` A

♂ Male only ♀ Female only Ⓐ Age A2 - Z3 = ASC Payment Indicator A - Y = APC Status Indicator
ASC = ASC Approved Procedure `DME` Paid under the DME fee schedule `PQRS` Physician Quality Reporting System

C L0460 Thoracic-lumbar-sacral orthosis (TLSO), triplanar control, modular segmented spinal system, two rigid plastic shells, posterior extends from the sacrococcygeal junction and terminates just inferior to the scapular spine, anterior extends from the symphysis pubis to the sternal notch, soft liner, restricts gross trunk motion in the sagittal, coronal, and transverse planes, lateral strength is provided by overlapping plastic and stabilizing closures, includes straps and closures, prefabricated item that has been trimmed, bent, molded, assembled, or otherwise customized to fit a specific patient by an individual with expertise **DME** A

C L0462 Thoracic-lumbar-sacral orthosis (TLSO), triplanar control, modular segmented spinal system, three rigid plastic shells, posterior extends from the sacrococcygeal junction and terminates just inferior to the scapular spine, anterior extends from the symphysis pubis to the sternal notch, soft liner, restricts gross trunk motion in the sagittal, coronal, and transverse planes, lateral strength is provided by overlapping plastic and stabilizing closures, includes straps and closures, prefabricated, includes fitting and adjustment **DME** A

C L0464 Thoracic-lumbar-sacral orthosis (TLSO), triplanar control, modular segmented spinal system, four rigid plastic shells, posterior extends from sacrococcygeal junction and terminates just inferior to scapular spine, anterior extends from symphysis pubis to the sternal notch, soft liner, restricts gross trunk motion in sagittal, coronal, and transverse planes, lateral strength is provided by overlapping plastic and stabilizing closures, includes straps and closures, prefabricated, includes fitting and adjustment **DME** A

C L0466 Thoracic-lumbar-sacral orthosis (TLSO), sagittal control, rigid posterior frame and flexible soft anterior apron with straps, closures and padding, restricts gross trunk motion in sagittal plane, produces intracavitary pressure to reduce load on intervertebral disks, prefabricated item that has been trimmed, bent, molded, assembled, or otherwise customized to fit a specific patient by an individual with expertise **DME** A

C L0467 Thoracic-lumbar-sacral orthosis (TLSO), sagittal control, rigid posterior frame and flexible soft anterior apron with straps, closures and padding, restricts gross trunk motion in sagittal plane, produces intracavitary pressure to reduce load on intervertebral disks, prefabricated, off-the-shelf **DME**

C L0468 Thoracic-lumbar-sacral orthosis (TLSO), sagittal-coronal control, rigid posterior frame and flexible soft anterior apron with straps, closures and padding, extends from sacrococcygeal junction over scapulae, lateral strength provided by pelvic, thoracic, and lateral frame pieces, restricts gross trunk motion in sagittal, and coronal planes, produces intracavitary pressure to reduce load on intervertebral disks, prefabricated item that has been trimmed, bent, molded, assembled, or otherwise customized to fit a specific patient by an individual with expertise **DME** A

C L0469 Thoracic-lumbar-sacral orthosis (TLSO), sagittal-coronal control, rigid posterior frame and flexible soft anterior apron with straps, closures and padding, extends from sacrococcygeal junction over scapulae, lateral strength provided by pelvic, thoracic, and lateral frame pieces, restricts gross trunk motion in sagittal and coronal planes, produces intracavitary pressure to reduce load on intervertebral disks, prefabricated, off-the-shelf **DME**

C L0470 Thoracic-lumbar-sacral orthosis (TLSO), triplanar control, rigid posterior frame and flexible soft anterior apron with straps, closures and padding extends from sacrococcygeal junction to scapula, lateral strength provided by pelvic, thoracic, and lateral frame pieces, rotational strength provided by subclavicular extensions, restricts gross trunk motion in sagittal, coronal, and transverse planes, provides intracavitary pressure to reduce load on the intervertebral disks, includes fitting and shaping the frame, prefabricated, includes fitting and adjustment **DME** A

C L0472 Thoracic-lumbar-sacral orthosis (TLSO), triplanar control, hyperextension, rigid anterior and lateral frame extends from symphysis pubis to sternal notch with two anterior components (one pubic and one sternal), posterior and lateral pads with straps and closures, limits spinal flexion, restricts gross trunk motion in sagittal, coronal, and transverse planes, includes fitting and shaping the frame, prefabricated, includes fitting and adjustment **DME** A

C L0480 Thoracic-lumbar-sacral orthosis (TLSO), triplanar control, one piece rigid plastic shell without interface liner, with multiple straps and closures, posterior extends from sacrococcygeal junction and terminates just inferior to scapular spine, anterior extends from symphysis pubis to sternal notch, anterior or posterior opening, restricts gross trunk motion in sagittal, coronal, and transverse planes, includes a carved plaster or CAD-CAM model, custom fabricated **DME** A

C L0482 Thoracic-lumbar-sacral orthosis (TLSO), triplanar control, one piece rigid plastic shell with interface liner, multiple straps and closures, posterior extends from sacrococcygeal junction and terminates

---

▲ Revised Code   ● New code   **C** Carrier judgment   **D** Special coverage instructions apply

I Not payable by Medicare   **M** Non-covered by Medicare   **S** Non-covered by Medicare statute   AHA Coding Clinic®

just inferior to scapular spine, anterior extends from symphysis pubis to sternal notch, anterior or posterior opening, restricts gross trunk motion in sagittal, coronal, and transverse planes, includes a carved plaster or CAD-CAM model, custom fabricated **DME** A

C **L0484** Thoracic-lumbar-sacral orthosis (TLSO), triplanar control, two piece rigid plastic shell without interface liner, with multiple straps and closures, posterior extends from sacrococcygeal junction and terminates just inferior to scapular spine, anterior extends from symphysis pubis to sternal notch, lateral strength is enhanced by overlapping plastic, restricts gross trunk motion in the sagittal, coronal, and transverse planes, includes a carved plaster or CAD-CAM model, custom fabricated **DME** A

C **L0486** Thoracic-lumbar-sacral orthosis (TLSO), triplanar control, two piece rigid plastic shell with interface liner, multiple straps and closures, posterior extends from sacrococcygeal junction and terminates just inferior to scapular spine, anterior extends from symphysis pubis to sternal notch, lateral strength is enhanced by overlapping plastic, restricts gross trunk motion in the sagittal, coronal, and transverse planes, includes a carved plaster or CAD-CAM model, custom fabricated **DME** A

C **L0488** Thoracic-lumbar-sacral orthosis (TLSO), triplanar control, one piece rigid plastic shell with interface liner, multiple straps and closures, posterior extends from sacrococcygeal junction and terminates just inferior to scapular spine, anterior extends from symphysis pubis to sternal notch, anterior or posterior opening, restricts gross trunk motion in sagittal, coronal, and transverse planes, prefabricated, includes fitting and adjustment **DME** A

C **L0490** Thoracic-lumbar-sacral orthosis (TLSO), sagittal-coronal control, one piece rigid plastic shell, with overlapping reinforced anterior, with multiple straps and closures, posterior extends from sacrococcygeal junction and terminates at or before the T-9 vertebra, anterior extends from symphysis pubis to xiphoid, anterior opening, restricts gross trunk motion in sagittal and coronal planes, prefabricated, includes fitting and adjustment **DME** A

C **L0491** Thoracic-lumbar-sacral orthosis (TLSO), sagittal-coronal control, modular segmented spinal system, two rigid plastic shells, posterior extends from the sacrococcygeal junction and terminates just inferior to the scapular spine, anterior extends from the symphysis pubis to the xiphoid, soft liner, restricts gross trunk motion in the sagittal and coronal planes, lateral strength is provided by overlapping plastic and

stabilizing closures, includes straps and closures, prefabricated, includes fitting and adjustment **DME** A

C **L0492** Thoracic-lumbar-sacral orthosis (TLSO), sagittal-coronal control, modular segmented spinal system, three rigid plastic shells, posterior extends from the sacrococcygeal junction and terminates just inferior to the scapular spine, anterior extends from the symphysis pubis to the xiphoid, soft liner, restricts gross trunk motion in the sagittal and coronal planes, lateral strength is provided by overlapping plastic and stabilizing closures, includes straps and closures, prefabricated, includes fitting and adjustment **DME** A

C **L0621** Sacroiliac orthosis (SO), flexible, provides pelvic-sacral support, reduces motion about the sacroiliac joint, includes straps, closures, may include pendulous abdomen design, prefabricated, off-the-shelf **DME** A

C **L0622** Sacroiliac orthosis (SO), flexible, provides pelvic-sacral support, reduces motion about the sacroiliac joint, includes straps, closures, may include pendulous abdomen design, custom fabricated **DME** A

C **L0623** Sacroiliac orthosis (SO), provides pelvic-sacral support, with rigid or semi-rigid panels over the sacrum and abdomen, reduces motion about the sacroiliac joint, includes straps, closures, may include pendulous abdomen design, prefabricated, off-the-shelf **DME** A

C **L0624** Sacroiliac orthosis (SO), provides pelvic-sacral support, with rigid or semi-rigid panels placed over the sacrum and abdomen, reduces motion about the sacroiliac joint, includes straps, closures, may include pendulous abdomen design, custom fabricated **DME** A

C **L0625** Lumbar orthosis (LO), flexible, provides lumbar support, posterior extends from L-1 to below L-5 vertebra, produces intracavitary pressure to reduce load on the intervertebral discs, includes straps, closures, may include pendulous abdomen design, shoulder straps, stays, prefabricated, off-the-shelf **DME** A

C **L0626** Lumbar orthosis (LO), sagittal control, with rigid posterior panel(s), posterior extends from L-1 to below L-5 vertebra, produces intracavitary pressure to reduce load on the intervertebral discs, includes straps, closures, may include padding, stays, shoulder straps, pendulous abdomen design, prefabricated item that has been trimmed, bent, molded, assembled, or otherwise customized to fit a specific patient by an individual with expertise **DME** A

C **L0627** Lumbar orthosis (LO), sagittal control, with rigid anterior and posterior panels, posterior extends from L-1 to below L-5 vertebra, produces intracavitary pressure to reduce load on the intervertebral discs, includes straps, closures, may include padding, shoulder straps, pendulous abdomen design, prefabricated item that has been trimmed, bent, molded, assembled, or otherwise customized to fit a specific patient by an individual with expertise DME A

C **L0628** Lumbar-sacral orthosis (LSO), flexible, provides lumbo-sacral support, posterior extends from sacrococcygeal junction to T-9 vertebra, produces intracavitary pressure to reduce load on the intervertebral discs, includes straps, closures, may include stays, shoulder straps, pendulous abdomen design, prefabricated, off-the-shelf DME A

Lumbar-Sacral Orthosis

C **L0629** Lumbar-sacral orthosis (LSO), flexible, provides lumbo-sacral support, posterior extends from sacrococcygeal junction to T-9 vertebra, produces intracavitary pressure to reduce load on the intervertebral discs, includes straps, closures, may include stays, shoulder straps, pendulous abdomen design, custom fabricated DME A

C **L0630** Lumbar-sacral orthosis (LSO), sagittal control, with rigid posterior panel(s), posterior extends from sacrococcygeal junction to T-9 vertebra, produces intracavitary pressure to reduce load on the intervertebral discs, includes straps, closures, may include padding, stays, shoulder straps, pendulous abdomen design, prefabricated item that has been trimmed, bent, molded, assembled, or otherwise customized to fit a specific patient by an individual with expertise DME A

C **L0631** Lumbar-sacral orthosis (LSO), sagittal control, with rigid anterior and posterior panels, posterior extends from sacrococcygeal junction to T-9 vertebra, produces intracavitary pressure to reduce

load on the intervertebral discs, includes straps, closures, may include padding, shoulder straps, pendulous abdomen design, prefabricated item that has been trimmed, bent, molded, assembled, or otherwise customized to fit a specific patient by an individual with expertise DME A

C **L0632** Lumbar-sacral orthosis (LSO), sagittal control, with rigid anterior and posterior panels, posterior extends from sacrococcygeal junction to T-9 vertebra, produces intracavitary pressure to reduce load on the intervertebral discs, includes straps, closures, may include padding, shoulder straps, pendulous abdomen design, custom fabricated DME A

C **L0633** Lumbar-sacral orthosis (LSO), sagittal-coronal control, with rigid posterior frame/panel(s), posterior extends from sacrococcygeal junction to T-9 vertebra, lateral strength provided by rigid lateral frame/panels, produces intracavitary pressure to reduce load on intervertebral discs, includes straps, closures, may include padding, stays, shoulder straps, pendulous abdomen design, prefabricated item that has been trimmed, bent, molded, assembled, or otherwise customized to fit a specific patient by an individual with expertise DME A

C **L0634** Lumbar-sacral orthosis (LSO), sagittal-coronal control, with rigid posterior frame/panel(s), posterior extends from sacrococcygeal junction to T-9 vertebra, lateral strength provided by rigid lateral frame/panel(s), produces intracavitary pressure to reduce load on intervertebral discs, includes straps, closures, may include padding, stays, shoulder straps, pendulous abdomen design, custom fabricated DME A

C **L0635** Lumbar-sacral orthosis (LSO), sagittal-coronal control, lumbar flexion, rigid posterior frame/panel(s), lateral articulating design to flex the lumbar spine, posterior extends from sacrococcygeal junction to T-9 vertebra, lateral strength provided by rigid lateral frame/panel(s), produces intracavitary pressure to reduce load on intervertebral discs, includes straps, closures, may include padding, anterior panel, pendulous abdomen design, prefabricated, includes fitting and adjustment DME A

C **L0636** Lumbar-sacral orthosis (LSO), sagittal-coronal control, lumbar flexion, rigid posterior frame/panels, lateral articulating design to flex the lumbar spine, posterior extends from sacrococcygeal junction to T-9 vertebra, lateral strength provided by rigid lateral frame/panels, produces intracavitary pressure to reduce load on intervertebral discs, includes straps, closures, may include padding, anterior panel, pendulous abdomen design, custom fabricated DME A

▲ Revised Code ● New code C Carrier judgment D Special coverage instructions apply
I Not payable by Medicare M Non-covered by Medicare S Non-covered by Medicare statute AHA Coding Clinic®

C **L0637** Lumbar-sacral orthosis (LSO), sagittal-coronal control, with rigid anterior and posterior frame/panels, posterior extends from sacrococcygeal junction to T-9 vertebra, lateral strength provided by rigid lateral frame/panels, produces intracavitary pressure to reduce load on intervertebral discs, includes straps, closures, may include padding, shoulder straps, pendulous abdomen design, prefabricated item that has been trimmed, bent, molded, assembled, or otherwise customized to fit a specific patient by an individual with expertise `DME` A

C **L0638** Lumbar-sacral orthosis (LSO), sagittal-coronal control, with rigid anterior and posterior frame/panels, posterior extends from sacrococcygeal junction to T-9 vertebra, lateral strength provided by rigid lateral frame/panels, produces intracavitary pressure to reduce load on intervertebral discs, includes straps, closures, may include padding, shoulder straps, pendulous abdomen design, custom fabricated `DME` A

C **L0639** Lumbar-sacral orthosis (LSO), sagittal-coronal control, rigid shell(s)/panel(s), posterior extends from sacrococcygeal junction to T-9 vertebra, anterior extends from symphysis pubis to xyphoid, produces intracavitary pressure to reduce load on the intervertebral discs, overall strength is provided by overlapping rigid material and stabilizing closures, includes straps, closures, may include soft interface, pendulous abdomen design, prefabricated item that has been trimmed, bent, molded, assembled, or otherwise customized to fit a specific patient by an individual with expertise `DME` A

C **L0640** Lumbar-sacral orthosis (LSO), sagittal-coronal control, rigid shell(s)/panel(s), posterior extends from sacrococcygeal junction to T-9 vertebra, anterior extends from symphysis pubis to xiphoid, produces intracavitary pressure to reduce load on the intervertebral discs, overall strength is provided by overlapping rigid material and stabilizing closures, includes straps, closures, may include soft interface, pendulous abdomen design, custom fabricated `DME` A

C **L0641** Lumbar orthosis (LO), sagittal control, with rigid posterior panel(s), posterior extends from L-1 to below L-5 vertebra, produces intracavitary pressure to reduce load on the intervertebral discs, includes straps, closures, may include padding, stays, shoulder straps, pendulous abdomen design, prefabricated, off-the-shelf `DME`

C **L0642** Lumbar orthosis (LO), sagittal control, with rigid anterior and posterior panels, posterior extends from L-1 to below L-5 vertebra, produces intracavitary pressure to reduce load on the intervertebral discs, includes straps, closures, may include padding, shoulder straps, pendulous abdomen design, prefabricated, off-the-shelf `DME`

C **L0643** Lumbar-sacral orthosis (LSO), sagittal control, with rigid posterior panel(s), posterior extends from sacrococcygeal junction to T-9 vertebra, produces intracavitary pressure to reduce load on the intervertebral discs, includes straps, closures, may include padding, stays, shoulder straps, pendulous abdomen design, prefabricated, off-the-shelf `DME`

C **L0648** Lumbar-sacral orthosis (LSO), sagittal control, with rigid anterior and posterior panels, posterior extends from sacrococcygeal junction to T-9 vertebra, produces intracavitary pressure to reduce load on the intervertebral discs, includes straps, closures, may include padding, shoulder straps, pendulous abdomen design, prefabricated, off-the-shelf `DME`

C **L0649** Lumbar-sacral orthosis (LSO), sagittal-coronal control, with rigid posterior frame/panel(s), posterior extends from sacrococcygeal junction to T-9 vertebra, lateral strength provided by rigid lateral frame/panels, produces intracavitary pressure to reduce load on intervertebral discs, includes straps, closures, may include padding, stays, shoulder straps, pendulous abdomen design, prefabricated, off-the-shelf `DME`

C **L0650** Lumbar-sacral orthosis (LSO), sagittal-coronal control, with rigid anterior and posterior frame/panel(s), posterior extends from sacrococcygeal junction to T-9 vertebra, lateral strength provided by rigid lateral frame/panel(s), produces intracavitary pressure to reduce load on intervertebral discs, includes straps, closures, may include padding, shoulder straps, pendulous abdomen design, prefabricated, off-the-shelf `DME`

C **L0651** Lumbar-sacral orthosis (LSO), sagittal-coronal control, rigid shell(s)/panel(s), posterior extends from sacrococcygeal junction to T-9 vertebra, anterior extends from symphysis pubis to xyphoid, produces intracavitary pressure to reduce load on the intervertebral discs, overall strength is provided by overlapping rigid material and stabilizing closures, includes straps, closures, may include soft interface, pendulous abdomen design, prefabricated, off-the-shelf `DME`

C **L0700** Cervical-thoracic-lumbar-sacral-orthoses (CTLSO), anterior-posterior-lateral control, molded to patient model (Minerva type) `DME` A

C **L0710** Cervical-thoracic-lumbar-sacral-orthoses (CTLSO), anterior-posterior-lateral-control, molded to patient model, with interface material (Minerva type) `DME` A

C **L0810** Halo procedure, cervical halo incorporated into jacket vest `DME` A

L0820 Halo procedure, cervical halo incorporated into plaster body jacket `DME` A

L0830 Halo procedure, cervical halo incorporated into Milwaukee type orthosis `DME` A

L0859 Addition to halo procedure, magnetic resonance image compatible systems, rings and pins, any material `DME` A

L0861 Addition to halo procedure, replacement liner/interface material `DME` A

L0970 Thoracic-lumbar-sacral orthosis (TLSO), corset front `DME` A

L0972 Lumbar-sacral orthosis (LSO), corset front `DME` A

L0974 Thoracic-lumbar-sacral orthosis (TLSO), full corset `DME` A

L0976 Lumbar-sacral orthotic (LSO), full corset `DME` A

L0978 Axillary crutch extension `DME` A

L0980 Peroneal straps, prefabricated, off-the-shelf, pair `DME` A

L0982 Stocking supporter grips, prefabricated, off-the-shelf, set of four (4) `DME` A

L0984 Protective body sock, prefabricated, off-the-shelf, each `DME` A

L0999 Addition to spinal orthosis, not otherwise specified A

L1000 Cervical-thoracic-lumbar-sacral orthosis (CTLSO) (Milwaukee), inclusive of furnishing initial orthosis, including model `DME` A

L1001 Cervical-thoracic-lumbar-sacral orthosis (CTLSO), immobilizer, infant size, prefabricated, includes fitting and adjustment `DME` A

L1005 Tension based scoliosis orthosis and accessory pads, includes fitting and adjustment `DME` A

L1010 Addition to Cervical-thoracic-lumbar-sacral orthosis (CTLSO) or scoliosis orthosis, axilla sling `DME` A

L1020 Addition to Cervical-thoracic-lumbar-sacral orthosis (CTLSO) or scoliosis orthosis, kyphosis pad `DME` A

L1025 Addition to Cervical-thoracic-lumbar-sacral orthosis (CTLSO) or scoliosis orthosis, kyphosis pad, floating `DME` A

L1030 Addition to Cervical-thoracic-lumbar-sacral orthosis (CTLSO) or scoliosis orthosis, lumbar bolster pad `DME` A

L1040 Addition to Cervical-thoracic-lumbar-sacral orthosis (CTLSO) or scoliosis orthosis, lumbar or lumbar rib pad `DME` A

L1050 Addition to Cervical-thoracic-lumbar-sacral orthosis (CTLSO) or scoliosis orthosis, sternal pad `DME` A

L1060 Addition to Cervical-thoracic-lumbar-sacral orthosis (CTLSO) or scoliosis orthosis, thoracic pad `DME` A

L1070 Addition to Cervical-thoracic-lumbar-sacral orthosis (CTLSO) or scoliosis orthosis, trapezius sling `DME` A

L1080 Addition to Cervical-thoracic-lumbar-sacral orthosis (CTLSO) or scoliosis orthosis, outrigger `DME` A

L1085 Addition to Cervical-thoracic-lumbar-sacral orthosis (CTLSO) or scoliosis orthosis, outrigger, bilateral with vertical extensions `DME` A

L1090 Addition to Cervical-thoracic-lumbar-sacral orthosis (CTLSO) or scoliosis orthosis, lumbar sling `DME` A

L1100 Addition to Cervical-thoracic-lumbar-sacral orthosis (CTLSO) or scoliosis orthosis, ring flange, plastic or leather `DME` A

L1110 Addition to Cervical-thoracic-lumbar-sacral orthosis (CTLSO) or scoliosis orthosis, ring flange, plastic or leather, molded to patient model `DME` A

L1120 Addition to Cervical-thoracic-lumbar-sacral orthosis (CTLSO), scoliosis orthosis, cover for upright, each `DME` A

L1200 Thoracic-lumbar-sacral-orthosis (TLSO), inclusive of furnishing initial orthosis only `DME` A

L1210 Addition to Thoracic-lumbar-sacral-orthosis (TLSO), (low profile), lateral thoracic extension `DME` A

L1220 Addition to Thoracic-lumbar-sacral orthosis (TLSO), (low profile), anterior thoracic extension `DME` A

L1230 Addition to Thoracic-lumbar-sacral orthosis (TLSO), (low profile), Milwaukee type superstructure `DME` A

L1240 Addition to Thoracic-lumbar-sacral orthosis (TLSO), (low profile), lumbar derotation pad `DME` A

L1250 Addition to Thoracic-lumbar-sacral orthosis (TLSO), (low profile), anterior asis pad `DME` A

L1260 Addition to Thoracic-lumbar-sacral orthosis (TLSO), (low profile), anterior thoracic derotation pad `DME` A

L1270 Addition to Thoracic-lumbar-sacral orthosis (TLSO), (low profile), abdominal pad `DME` A

L1280 Addition to Thoracic-lumbar-sacral orthosis (TLSO), (low profile), rib gusset (elastic), each `DME` A

L1290 Addition to Thoracic-lumbar-sacral orthosis (TLSO), (low profile), lateral trochanteric pad `DME` A

L1300 Other scoliosis procedure, body jacket molded to patient model `DME` A

L1310 Other scoliosis procedure, post-operative body jacket `DME` A

L1499 Spinal orthosis, not otherwise specified A

L1600 Hip orthosis, abduction control of hip joints, flexible, Frejka type with cover, prefabricated item that has been trimmed, bent, molded, assembled, or otherwise customized to fit a specific patient by an individual with expertise `DME` A

▲ Revised Code   ● New code   **C** Carrier judgment   **D** Special coverage instructions apply
I Not payable by Medicare   **M** Non-covered by Medicare   **S** Non-covered by Medicare statute   AHA Coding Clinic®

C **L1610** Hip orthosis, abduction control of hip joints, flexible, (Frejka cover only), prefabricated item that has been trimmed, bent, molded, assembled, or otherwise customized to fit a specific patient by an individual with expertise ▪DME▪ A

C **L1620** Hip orthosis, abduction control of hip joints, flexible, (Pavlik harness), prefabricated item that has been trimmed, bent, molded, assembled, or otherwise customized to fit a specific patient by an individual with expertise ▪DME▪ A

C **L1630** Hip orthosis (HO), abduction control of hip joints, semi-flexible (Von Rosen type), custom-fabricated ▪DME▪ A

C **L1640** Hip orthosis (HO), abduction control of hip joints, static, pelvic band or spreader bar, thigh cuffs, custom-fabricated ▪DME▪ A

C **L1650** Hip orthosis (HO), abduction control of hip joints, static, adjustable, (Ilfled type), prefabricated, includes fitting and adjustment ▪DME▪ A

C **L1652** Hip orthosis (HO), bilateral thigh cuffs with adjustable abductor spreader bar, adult size, prefabricated, includes fitting and adjustment, any type ▪DME▪ A

C **L1660** Hip orthosis (HO), abduction control of hip joints, static, plastic, prefabricated, includes fitting and adjustment ▪DME▪ A

C **L1680** Hip orthosis (HO), abduction control of hip joints, dynamic, pelvic control, adjustable hip motion control, thigh cuffs (Rancho hip action type), custom fabricated ▪DME▪ A

C **L1685** Hip orthosis (HO), abduction control of hip joint, postoperative hip abduction type, custom fabricated ▪DME▪ A

C **L1686** Hip orthosis (HO), abduction control of hip joint, postoperative hip abduction type, prefabricated, includes fitting and adjustment ▪DME▪ A

C **L1690** Combination, bilateral, lumbo-sacral, hip, femur orthosis providing adduction and internal rotation control, prefabricated, includes fitting and adjustment ▪DME▪ A

C **L1700** Legg perthes orthosis, (Toronto type), custom-fabricated ▪DME▪ A

C **L1710** Legg perthes orthosis, (Newington type), custom fabricated ▪DME▪ A

C **L1720** Legg perthes orthosis, trilateral, (Tachdijan type), custom-fabricated ▪DME▪ A

C **L1730** Legg perthes orthosis, (Scottish Rite type), custom-fabricated ▪DME▪ A

C **L1755** Legg perthes orthosis, (Patten bottom type), custom-fabricated ▪DME▪ A

C **L1810** Knee orthosis (KO), elastic with joints, prefabricated item that has been trimmed, bent, molded, assembled, or otherwise customized to fit a specific patient by an individual with expertise ▪DME▪ A

C **L1812** Knee orthosis (KO), elastic with joints, prefabricated, off-the-shelf ▪DME▪

C **L1820** Knee orthosis (KO), elastic with condylar pads and joints, with or without patellar control, prefabricated, includes fitting and adjustment ▪DME▪ A

C **L1830** Knee orthosis (KO), immobilizer, canvas longitudinal, prefabricated, off-the-shelf ▪DME▪ A

Knee Orthosis

C **L1831** Knee orthosis (KO), locking knee joint(s), positional orthosis, prefabricated, includes fitting and adjustment ▪DME▪ A

C **L1832** Knee orthosis (KO), adjustable knee joints (unicentric or polycentric), positional orthosis, rigid support, prefabricated item that has been trimmed, bent, molded, assembled, or otherwise customized to fit a specific patient by an individual with expertise ▪DME▪ A

C **L1833** Knee orthosis (KO), adjustable knee joints (unicentric or polycentric), positional orthosis, rigid support, prefabricated, off-the shelf ▪DME▪

C **L1834** Knee orthosis (KO), without knee joint, rigid, custom-fabricated ▪DME▪ A

C **L1836** Knee orthosis (KO), rigid, without joint(s), includes soft interface material, prefabricated, off-the-shelf ▪DME▪ A

C **L1840** Knee orthosis (KO), derotation, medial-lateral, anterior cruciate ligament, custom fabricated ▪DME▪ A

C **L1843** Knee orthosis (KO), single upright, thigh and calf, with adjustable flexion and extension joint (unicentric or polycentric), medial-lateral and rotation control, with or without varus/valgus adjustment, prefabricated item that has been trimmed, bent, molded, assembled, or otherwise customized to fit a specific patient by an individual with expertise ▪DME▪ A

C **L1844** Knee orthosis (KO), single upright, thigh and calf, with adjustable flexion and extension joint (unicentric or polycentric), medial-lateral and rotation control, with or without varus/valgus adjustment, custom fabricated ▪DME▪ A

C **L1845** Knee orthosis (KO), double upright, thigh and calf, with adjustable flexion and extension joint (unicentric or polycentric), medial-lateral and rotation control, with or without varus/valgus adjustment, prefabricated item that has been trimmed, bent, molded, assembled, or otherwise customized to fit a specific patient by an individual with expertise DME A

C **L1846** Knee orthosis (KO), double upright, thigh and calf, with adjustable flexion and extension joint (unicentric or polycentric), medial-lateral and rotation control, with or without varus/valgus adjustment, custom fabricated DME A

C **L1847** Knee orthosis (KO), double upright with adjustable joint, with inflatable air support chamber(s), prefabricated item that has been trimmed, bent, molded, assembled, or otherwise customized to fit a specific patient by an individual with expertise DME A

C **L1848** Knee orthosis (KO), double upright with adjustable joint, with inflatable air support chamber(s), prefabricated, off-the-shelf DME

C **L1850** Knee orthosis (KO), swedish type, prefabricated, off-the-shelf DME A

C **L1860** Knee orthosis (KO), modification of supracondylar prosthetic socket, custom-fabricated (SK) DME A

C **L1900** Ankle foot orthosis (AFO), spring wire, dorsiflexion assist calf band, custom-fabricated DME A

C **L1902** Ankle foot orthosis (AFO), ankle gauntlet, prefabricated, off-the-shelf DME A

C **L1904** Ankle orthosis, ankle gauntlet, custom-fabricated DME A

C **L1906** Ankle foot orthosis (AFO), multiligamentus ankle support, prefabricated, off-the-shelf DME A

C **L1907** Ankle orthosis, supramalleolar with straps, with or without interface/pads, custom fabricated DME A

C **L1910** Ankle foot orthosis (AFO), posterior, single bar, clasp attachment to shoe counter, prefabricated, includes fitting and adjustment DME A

Ankle Foot Orthosis

C **L1920** Ankle foot orthosis (AFO), single upright with static or adjustable stop (phelps or perlstein type), custom-fabricated DME A

C **L1930** Ankle foot orthosis (AFO), plastic or other material, prefabricated, includes fitting and adjustment DME A

C **L1932** Ankle foot orthosis (AFO), rigid anterior tibial section, total carbon fiber or equal material, prefabricated, includes fitting and adjustment DME A

C **L1940** Ankle foot orthosis (AFO), plastic or other material, custom-fabricated DME A

C **L1945** Ankle foot orthosis (AFO), plastic, rigid anterior tibial section (floor reaction), custom-fabricated DME A

C **L1950** Ankle foot orthosis (AFO), spiral, (institute of rehabilitative medicine type), plastic, custom-fabricated DME A

C **L1951** Ankle foot orthosis (AFO), spiral, (institute of rehabilitative medicine type), plastic or other material, prefabricated, includes fitting and adjustment DME A

C **L1960** Ankle foot orthosis (AFO), posterior solid ankle, plastic, custom-fabricated DME A

C **L1970** Ankle foot orthosis (AFO), plastic with ankle joint, custom-fabricated DME A

C **L1971** Ankle foot orthosis (AFO), plastic or other material with ankle joint, prefabricated, includes fitting and adjustment DME A

C **L1980** Ankle foot orthosis (AFO), single upright free plantar dorsiflexion, solid stirrup, calf band/cuff (single bar 'BK' orthosis), custom-fabricated DME A

C **L1990** Ankle foot orthosis (AFO), double upright free plantar dorsiflexion, solid stirrup, calf band/cuff (double bar 'BK' orthosis), custom-fabricated DME A

C **L2000** Knee ankle foot orthosis (KAFO), single upright, free knee, free ankle, solid stirrup, thigh and calf bands/cuffs (single bar 'AK' orthosis), custom-fabricated DME A

C **L2005** Knee ankle foot orthosis (KAFO), any material, single or double upright, stance control, automatic lock and swing phase release, any type activation, includes ankle joint, any type, custom fabricated DME A

C **L2010** Knee ankle foot orthosis (KAFO), single upright, free ankle, solid stirrup, thigh and calf bands/cuffs (single bar 'AK' orthosis), without knee joint, custom-fabricated DME A

C **L2020** Knee ankle foot orthosis (KAFO), double upright, free ankle, solid stirrup, thigh and calf bands/cuffs (double bar 'AK' orthosis), custom-fabricated DME A

C **L2030** Knee ankle foot orthosis (KAFO), double upright, free ankle, solid stirrup, thigh and calf bands/cuffs, (double bar 'AK' orthosis), without knee joint, custom fabricated DME A

C **L2034** Knee ankle foot orthosis (KAFO), full plastic, single upright, with or without free motion

---

▲ Revised Code ● New code C Carrier judgment D Special coverage instructions apply

I Not payable by Medicare M Non-covered by Medicare S Non-covered by Medicare statute AHA Coding Clinic®

knee, medial lateral rotation control, with or without free motion ankle, custom fabricated `DME` A

C **L2035** Knee ankle foot orthosis (KAFO), full plastic, static (pediatric size), without free motion ankle, prefabricated, includes fitting and adjustment `DME` Ⓐ A

C **L2036** Knee ankle foot orthosis, full plastic, double upright, with or without free motion knee, with or without free motion ankle, custom fabricated `DME` A

C **L2037** Knee ankle foot orthosis (KAFO), full plastic, single upright, with or without free motion knee, with or without free motion ankle, custom fabricated `DME` A

C **L2038** Knee ankle foot orthosis (KAFO), full plastic, with or without free motion knee, multi-axis ankle, custom fabricated `DME` A

C **L2040** Hip knee ankle foot orthosis (HKAFO), torsion control, bilateral rotation straps, pelvic band/belt, custom fabricated `DME` A

C **L2050** Hip knee ankle foot orthosis (HKAFO), torsion control, bilateral torsion cables, hip joint, pelvic band/belt, custom-fabricated `DME` A

C **L2060** Hip knee ankle foot orthosis (HKAFO), torsion control, bilateral torsion cables, ball bearing hip joint, pelvic band/ belt, custom-fabricated `DME` A

C **L2070** Hip knee ankle foot orthosis (HKAFO), torsion control, unilateral rotation straps, pelvic band/belt, custom fabricated `DME` A

C **L2080** Hip knee ankle foot orthosis (HKAFO), torsion control, unilateral torsion cable, hip joint, pelvic band/belt, custom-fabricated `DME` A

C **L2090** Hip knee ankle foot orthosis (HKAFO), torsion control, unilateral torsion cable, ball bearing hip joint, pelvic band/ belt, custom-fabricated `DME` A

C **L2106** Ankle foot orthosis (AFO), fracture orthosis, tibial fracture cast orthosis, thermoplastic type casting material, custom-fabricated `DME` A

C **L2108** Ankle foot orthosis (AFO), fracture orthosis, tibial fracture cast orthosis, custom-fabricated `DME` A

C **L2112** Ankle foot orthosis (AFO), fracture orthosis, tibial fracture orthosis, soft, prefabricated, includes fitting and adjustment `DME` A

C **L2114** Ankle foot orthosis (AFO), fracture orthosis, tibial fracture orthosis, semi-rigid, prefabricated, includes fitting and adjustment `DME` A

C **L2116** Ankle foot orthosis (AFO), fracture orthosis, tibial fracture orthosis, rigid, prefabricated, includes fitting and adjustment `DME` A

C **L2126** Knee ankle foot orthosis (KAFO), fracture orthosis, femoral fracture cast orthosis, thermoplastic type casting material, custom-fabricated `DME` A

C **L2128** Knee ankle foot orthosis(KAFO), fracture orthosis, femoral fracture cast orthosis, custom-fabricated `DME` A

C **L2132** Knee ankle foot orthosis(KAFO), fracture orthosis, femoral fracture cast orthosis, soft, prefabricated, includes fitting and adjustment `DME` A

C **L2134** Knee ankle foot orthosis(KAFO), fracture orthosis, femoral fracture cast orthosis, semi-rigid, prefabricated, includes fitting and adjustment `DME` A

C **L2136** Knee ankle foot orthosis(KAFO), fracture orthosis, femoral fracture cast orthosis, rigid, prefabricated, includes fitting and adjustment `DME` A

C **L2180** Addition to lower extremity fracture orthosis, plastic shoe insert with ankle joints `DME` A

C **L2182** Addition to lower extremity fracture orthosis, drop lock knee joint `DME` A

C **L2184** Addition to lower extremity fracture orthosis, limited motion knee joint `DME` A

C **L2186** Addition to lower extremity fracture orthosis, adjustable motion knee joint, lerman type `DME` A

C **L2188** Addition to lower extremity fracture orthosis, quadrilateral brim `DME` A

C **L2190** Addition to lower extremity fracture orthosis, waist belt `DME` A

C **L2192** Addition to lower extremity fracture orthosis, hip joint, pelvic band, thigh flange, and pelvic belt `DME` A

C **L2200** Addition to lower extremity, limited ankle motion, each joint `DME` A

C **L2210** Addition to lower extremity, dorsiflexion assist (plantar flexion resist), each joint `DME` A

C **L2220** Addition to lower extremity, dorsiflexion and plantar flexion assist/resist, each joint `DME` A

C **L2230** Addition to lower extremity, split flat caliper stirrups and plate attachment `DME` A

C **L2232** Addition to lower extremity orthosis, rocker bottom for total contact ankle foot orthosis (AFO), for custom fabricated orthosis only `DME` A

C **L2240** Addition to lower extremity, round caliper and plate attachment `DME` A

C **L2250** Addition to lower extremity, foot plate, molded to patient model, stirrup attachment `DME` A

C **L2260** Addition to lower extremity, reinforced solid stirrup (Scott-Craig type) `DME` A

C **L2265** Addition to lower extremity, long tongue stirrup `DME` A

C **L2270** Addition to lower extremity, varus/valgus correction ('T') strap, padded/lined or malleolus pad `DME` A

C **L2275** Addition to lower extremity, varus/valgus correction, plastic modification, padded/lined `DME` A

♂ Male only   ♀ Female only   Ⓐ Age   A2 - Z3 = ASC Payment Indicator   A - Y = APC Status Indicator

ASC = ASC Approved Procedure   `DME` Paid under the DME fee schedule   `PQRS` Physician Quality Reporting System

C **L2280** Addition to lower extremity, molded inner boot DME A

C **L2300** Addition to lower extremity, abduction bar (bilateral hip involvement), jointed, adjustable DME A

C **L2310** Addition to lower extremity, abduction bar-straight DME A

C **L2320** Addition to lower extremity, non-molded lacer, for custom fabricated orthosis only DME A

C **L2330** Addition to lower extremity, lacer molded to patient model, for custom fabricated orthosis only DME A

C **L2335** Addition to lower extremity, anterior swing band DME A

C **L2340** Addition to lower extremity, pre-tibial shell, molded to patient model DME A

C **L2350** Addition to lower extremity, prosthetic type, (BK) socket, molded to patient model, (used for 'PTB' 'AFO' orthoses) DME A

C **L2360** Addition to lower extremity, extended steel shank DME A

C **L2370** Addition to lower extremity, Patten bottom DME A

C **L2375** Addition to lower extremity, torsion control, ankle joint and half solid stirrup DME A

C **L2380** Addition to lower extremity, torsion control, straight knee joint, each joint DME A

C **L2385** Addition to lower extremity, straight knee joint, heavy duty, each joint DME A

C **L2387** Addition to lower extremity, polycentric knee joint, for custom fabricated knee ankle foot orthosis (KAFO), each joint DME A

C **L2390** Addition to lower extremity, offset knee joint, each joint DME A

C **L2395** Addition to lower extremity, offset knee joint, heavy duty, each joint DME A

C **L2397** Addition to lower extremity orthosis, suspension sleeve DME A

C **L2405** Addition to knee joint, drop lock, each DME A

C **L2415** Addition to knee lock with integrated release mechanism (bail, cable, or equal), any material, each joint DME A

C **L2425** Addition to knee joint, disc or dial lock for adjustable knee flexion, each joint DME A

C **L2430** Addition to knee joint, ratchet lock for active and progressive knee extension, each joint DME A

C **L2492** Addition to knee joint, lift loop for drop lock ring DME A

C **L2500** Addition to lower extremity, thigh/weight bearing, gluteal/ ischial weight bearing, ring DME A

C **L2510** Addition to lower extremity, thigh/weight bearing, quadri- lateral brim, molded to patient model DME A

C **L2520** Addition to lower extremity, thigh/weight bearing, quadri- lateral brim, custom fitted DME A

C **L2525** Addition to lower extremity, thigh/weight bearing, ischial containment/narrow M-L brim molded to patient model DME A

C **L2526** Addition to lower extremity, thigh/weight bearing, ischial containment/narrow M-L brim, custom fitted DME A

C **L2530** Addition to lower extremity, thigh-weight bearing, lacer, non-molded DME A

C **L2540** Addition to lower extremity, thigh/weight bearing, lacer, molded to patient model DME A

C **L2550** Addition to lower extremity, thigh/weight bearing, high roll cuff DME A

C **L2570** Addition to lower extremity, pelvic control, hip joint, Clevis type two position joint, each DME A

C **L2580** Addition to lower extremity, pelvic control, pelvic sling DME A

C **L2600** Addition to lower extremity, pelvic control, hip joint, Clevis type, or thrust bearing, free, each DME A

C **L2610** Addition to lower extremity, pelvic control, hip joint, Clevis type or thrust bearing, lock, each DME A

C **L2620** Addition to lower extremity, pelvic control, hip joint, heavy duty, each DME A

C **L2622** Addition to lower extremity, pelvic control, hip joint, adjustable flexion, each DME A

C **L2624** Addition to lower extremity, pelvic control, hip joint, adjustable flexion, extension, abduction control, each DME A

C **L2627** Addition to lower extremity, pelvic control, plastic, molded to patient model, reciprocating hip joint and cables DME A

C **L2628** Addition to lower extremity, pelvic control, metal frame, reciprocating hip joint and cables DME A

C **L2630** Addition to lower extremity, pelvic control, band and belt, unilateral DME A

C **L2640** Addition to lower extremity, pelvic control, band and belt, bilateral DME A

C **L2650** Addition to lower extremity, pelvic and thoracic control, gluteal pad, each DME A

C **L2660** Addition to lower extremity, thoracic control, thoracic band DME A

C **L2670** Addition to lower extremity, thoracic control, paraspinal uprights DME A

C **L2680** Addition to lower extremity, thoracic control, lateral support uprights DME A

C **L2750** Addition to lower extremity orthosis, plating chrome or nickel, per bar DME A

C **L2755** Addition to lower extremity orthosis, high strength, lightweight material, all hybrid lamination/prepreg composite, per segment, for custom fabricated orthosis only DME A

C **L2760** Addition to lower extremity orthosis, extension, per extension, per bar (for lineal adjustment for growth) DME A

▲ Revised Code   ● New code   C Carrier judgment   D Special coverage instructions apply

I Not payable by Medicare   M Non-covered by Medicare   S Non-covered by Medicare statute   AHA Coding Clinic®

C **L2768** Orthotic side bar disconnect device, per bar DME A

C **L2780** Addition to lower extremity orthosis, non-corrosive finish, per bar DME A

C **L2785** Addition to lower extremity orthosis, drop lock retainer, each DME A

C **L2795** Addition to lower extremity orthosis, knee control, full kneecap DME A

C **L2800** Addition to lower extremity orthosis, knee control, knee cap, medial or lateral pull, for use with custom fabricated orthosis only DME A

C **L2810** Addition to lower extremity orthosis, knee control, condylar pad DME A

C **L2820** Addition to lower extremity orthosis, soft interface for molded plastic, below knee section DME A

C **L2830** Addition to lower extremity orthosis, soft interface for molded plastic, above knee section DME A

C **L2840** Addition to lower extremity orthosis, tibial length sock, fracture or equal, each DME A

C **L2850** Addition to lower extremity orthosis, femoral length sock, fracture or equal, each DME A

I **L2861** Addition to lower extremity joint, knee or ankle, concentric adjustable torsion style mechanism for custom fabricated orthotics only, each E
    Service not separately priced by Part B

C **L2999** Lower extremity orthoses, not otherwise specified A

D **L3000** Foot, insert, removable, molded to patient model, 'UCB' type, Berkeley Shell, each DME A
    Service not separately priced by Part B
    Pub: 100-2, Chap. 15, 290

D **L3001** Foot, insert, removable, molded to patient model, Spenco, each DME A
    Service not separately priced by Part B
    Pub: 100-2, Chap. 15, 290

D **L3002** Foot, insert, removable, molded to patient model, Plastazote or equal, each DME A
    Service not separately priced by Part B
    Pub: 100-2, Chap. 15, 290

D **L3003** Foot, insert, removable, molded to patient model, silicone gel, each DME A
    Service not separately priced by Part B
    Pub: 100-2, Chap. 15, 290

D **L3010** Foot, insert, removable, molded to patient model, longitudinal arch support, each DME A
    Service not separately priced by Part B
    Pub: 100-2, Chap. 15, 290

D **L3020** Foot, insert, removable, molded to patient model, longitudinal/ metatarsal support, each DME A
    Service not separately priced by Part B
    Pub: 100-2, Chap. 15, 290

D **L3030** Foot, insert, removable, formed to patient foot, each DME A
    Service not separately priced by Part B
    Pub: 100-2, Chap. 15, 290

C **L3031** Foot, insert/plate, removable, addition to lower extremity orthosis, high strength, lightweight material, all hybrid lamination/ prepreg composite, each DME A
    Service not separately priced by Part B

D **L3040** Foot, arch support, removable, premolded, longitudinal, each DME A
    Service not separately priced by Part B
    Pub: 100-2, Chap. 15, 290

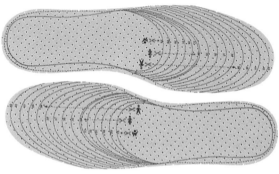

Arch Support

D **L3050** Foot, arch support, removable, premolded, metatarsal, each DME A
    Service not separately priced by Part B
    Pub: 100-2, Chap. 15, 290

D **L3060** Foot, arch support, removable, premolded, longitudinal/ metatarsal, each DME A
    Service not separately priced by Part B
    Pub: 100-2, Chap. 15, 290

D **L3070** Foot, arch support, non-removable attached to shoe, longitudinal, each DME A
    Service not separately priced by Part B
    Pub: 100-2, Chap. 15, 290

D **L3080** Foot, arch support, non-removable attached to shoe, metatarsal, each DME A
    Service not separately priced by Part B
    Pub: 100-2, Chap. 15, 290

D **L3090** Foot, arch support, non-removable attached to shoe, longitudinal/metatarsal, each DME A
    Service not separately priced by Part B
    Pub: 100-2, Chap. 15, 290

♂ Male only   ♀ Female only   Ⓐ Age   A2 - Z3 = ASC Payment Indicator   A - Y = APC Status Indicator
ASC = ASC Approved Procedure   DME Paid under the DME fee schedule   PQRS Physician Quality Reporting System

147

L2768 - L3090

ORTHOTIC PROCEDURES AND SERVICES (L0112-L4631)

D **L3100** Hallus-valgus night dynamic splint, prefabricated, off-the-shelf   **DME** A

Service not separately priced by Part B

Pub: 100-2, Chap. 15, 290

Hallux Valgus Splint

D **L3140** Foot, abduction rotation bar, including shoes   **DME** A

Service not separately priced by Part B

Pub: 100-2, Chap. 15, 290

D **L3150** Foot, abduction rotatation bar, without shoes   **DME** A

Service not separately priced by Part B

Pub: 100-2, Chap. 15, 290

C **L3160** Foot, adjustable shoe-styled positioning device   A

Service not separately priced by Part B

D **L3170** Foot, plastic, silicone or equal, heel stabilizer, prafabricated, off-the-shelf, each   **DME** A

Service not separately priced by Part B

Pub: 100-2, Chap. 15, 290

D **L3201** Orthopedic shoe, Oxford with supinator or pronator, infant   Ⓐ A

Service not separately priced by Part B

Pub: 100-2, Chap. 15, 290

D **L3202** Orthopedic shoe, Oxford with supinator or pronator, child   Ⓐ A

Service not separately priced by Part B

Pub: 100-2, Chap. 15, 290

D **L3203** Orthopedic shoe, Oxford with supinator or pronator, junior   Ⓐ A

Service not separately priced by Part B

Pub: 100-2, Chap. 15, 290

D **L3204** Orthopedic shoe, hightop with supinator or pronator, infant   Ⓐ A

Service not separately priced by Part B

Pub: 100-2, Chap. 15, 290

D **L3206** Orthopedic shoe, hightop with supinator or pronator, child   Ⓐ A

Service not separately priced by Part B

Pub: 100-2, Chap. 15, 290

D **L3207** Orthopedic shoe, hightop with supinator or pronator, junior   Ⓐ A

Service not separately priced by Part B

Pub: 100-2, Chap. 15, 290

D **L3208** Surgical boot, each, infant   Ⓐ A

Service not separately priced by Part B

D **L3209** Surgical boot, each, child   Ⓐ A

Service not separately priced by Part B

D **L3211** Surgical boot, each, junior   Ⓐ A

Service not separately priced by Part B

D **L3212** Benesch boot, pair, infant   Ⓐ A

Service not separately priced by Part B

D **L3213** Benesch boot, pair, child   Ⓐ A

Service not separately priced by Part B

D **L3214** Benesch boot, pair, junior   Ⓐ A

Service not separately priced by Part B

S **L3215** Orthopedic footwear, ladies shoe, Oxford, each   ♀ E

Service not separately priced by Part B
Statute: 1862A8

S **L3216** Orthopedic footwear, ladies shoe, depth inlay, each   ♀ E

Service not separately priced by Part B
Statute: 1862A8

S **L3217** Orthopedic footwear, ladies shoe, hightop, depth inlay, each   ♀ E

Service not separately priced by Part B
Statute: 1862A8

S **L3219** Orthopedic footwear, mens shoe, Oxford, each   ♂ E

Service not separately priced by Part B
Statute: 1862A8

S **L3221** Orthopedic footwear, mens shoe, depth inlay, each   ♂ E

Service not separately priced by Part B
Statute: 1862A8

S **L3222** Orthopedic footwear, mens shoe, hightop, depth inlay, each   ♂ E

Service not separately priced by Part B
Statute: 1862A8

D **L3224** Orthopedic footwear, woman's shoe, Oxford, used as an integral part of a brace (orthosis)   ♀ **DME** A

Pub: 100-2, Chap. 15, 290

D **L3225** Orthopedic footwear, man's shoe, Oxford, used as an integral part of a brace (orthosis)   ♂ **DME** A

Pub: 100-2, Chap. 15, 290

D **L3230** Orthopedic footwear, custom shoe, depth inlay, each   A

Service not separately priced by Part B

Pub: 100-2, Chap. 15, 290

▲ Revised Code   ● New code   **C** Carrier judgment   **D** Special coverage instructions apply

I Not payable by Medicare   **M** Non-covered by Medicare   **S** Non-covered by Medicare statute   AHA Coding Clinic®

D **L3250** Orthopedic footwear, custom molded shoe, removable inner mold, prosthetic shoe, each   A
Service not separately priced by Part B
Pub: 100-2, Chap. 15, 290

D **L3251** Foot, shoe molded to patient model, silicone shoe, each   A
Service not separately priced by Part B
Pub: 100-2, Chap. 15, 290

D **L3252** Foot, shoe molded to patient model, Plastazote (or similar), custom fabricated, each   A
Service not separately priced by Part B
Pub: 100-2, Chap. 15, 290

D **L3253** Foot, molded shoe Plastazote (or similar) custom fitted, each   A
Service not separately priced by Part B
Pub: 100-2, Chap. 15, 290

D **L3254** Non-standard size or width   A
Service not separately priced by Part B
Pub: 100-2, Chap. 15, 290

D **L3255** Non-standard size or length   A
Service not separately priced by Part B
Pub: 100-2, Chap. 15, 290

D **L3257** Orthopedic footwear, additional charge for split size   A
Service not separately priced by Part B
Pub: 100-2, Chap. 15, 290

D **L3260** Surgical boot/shoe, each   E
Service not separately priced by Part B

C **L3265** Plastazote sandal, each   A
Service not separately priced by Part B

D **L3300** Lift, elevation, heel, tapered to metatarsals, per inch   `DME` A
Service not separately priced by Part B
Pub: 100-2, Chap. 15, 290

D **L3310** Lift, elevation, heel and sole, neoprene, per inch   `DME` A
Service not separately priced by Part B
Pub: 100-2, Chap. 15, 290

D **L3320** Lift, elevation, heel and sole, cork, per inch   A
Service not separately priced by Part B
Pub: 100-2, Chap. 15, 290

D **L3330** Lift, elevation, metal extension (skate) `DME` A
Service not separately priced by Part B
Pub: 100-2, Chap. 15, 290

D **L3332** Lift, elevation, inside shoe, tapered, up to one-half inch   `DME` A
Service not separately priced by Part B
Pub: 100-2, Chap. 15, 290

D **L3334** Lift, elevation, heel, per inch   `DME` A
Service not separately priced by Part B
Pub: 100-2, Chap. 15, 290

D **L3340** Heel wedge, SACH   `DME` A
Service not separately priced by Part B
Pub: 100-2, Chap. 15, 290

D **L3350** Heel wedge   `DME` A
Service not separately priced by Part B
Pub: 100-2, Chap. 15, 290

D **L3360** Sole wedge, outside sole   `DME` A
Service not separately priced by Part B
Pub: 100-2, Chap. 15, 290

D **L3370** Sole wedge, between sole   `DME` A
Service not separately priced by Part B
Pub: 100-2, Chap. 15, 290

D **L3380** Clubfoot wedge   `DME` A
Service not separately priced by Part B
Pub: 100-2, Chap. 15, 290

D **L3390** Outflare wedge   `DME` A
Service not separately priced by Part B
Pub: 100-2, Chap. 15, 290

D **L3400** Metatarsal bar wedge, rocker   `DME` A
Service not separately priced by Part B
Pub: 100-2, Chap. 15, 290

D **L3410** Metatarsal bar wedge, between sole `DME` A
Service not separately priced by Part B
Pub: 100-2, Chap. 15, 290

D **L3420** Full sole and heel wedge, between sole   `DME` A
Service not separately priced by Part B
Pub: 100-2, Chap. 15, 290

D **L3430** Heel, counter, plastic reinforced   `DME` A
Service not separately priced by Part B
Pub: 100-2, Chap. 15, 290

D **L3440** Heel, counter, leather reinforced   `DME` A
Service not separately priced by Part B
Pub: 100-2, Chap. 15, 290

D **L3450** Heel, SACH cushion type   `DME` A
Service not separately priced by Part B
Pub: 100-2, Chap. 15, 290

D **L3455** Heel, new leather, standard   `DME` A
Service not separately priced by Part B
Pub: 100-2, Chap. 15, 290

D **L3460** Heel, new rubber, standard   `DME` A
Service not separately priced by Part B
Pub: 100-2, Chap. 15, 290

D **L3465** Heel, Thomas with wedge   `DME` A
Service not separately priced by Part B
Pub: 100-2, Chap. 15, 290

D **L3470** Heel, Thomas extended to ball   `DME` A
Service not separately priced by Part B
Pub: 100-2, Chap. 15, 290

D **L3480** Heel, pad and depression for spur   `DME` A
Service not separately priced by Part B
Pub: 100-2, Chap. 15, 290

♂ Male only   ♀ Female only   **A** Age   A2 - Z3 = ASC Payment Indicator   A - Y = APC Status Indicator
ASC = ASC Approved Procedure   `DME` Paid under the DME fee schedule   `PQRS` Physician Quality Reporting System

L3485 - L3720 *(side tab)*

ORTHOTIC PROCEDURES AND SERVICES (L0112-L4631) *(side tab)*

D **L3485** Heel, pad, removable for spur   A
Service not separately priced by Part B
Pub: 100-2, Chap. 15, 290

D **L3500** Orthopedic shoe addition, insole, leather   **DME** A
Service not separately priced by Part B
Pub: 100-2, Chap. 15, 290

D **L3510** Orthopedic shoe addition, insole, rubber   **DME** A
Service not separately priced by Part B
Pub: 100-2, Chap. 15, 290

D **L3520** Orthopedic shoe addition, insole, felt covered with leather   **DME** A
Service not separately priced by Part B
Pub: 100-2, Chap. 15, 290

D **L3530** Orthopedic shoe addition, sole, half   **DME** A
Service not separately priced by Part B
Pub: 100-2, Chap. 15, 290

D **L3540** Orthopedic shoe addition, sole, full   **DME** A
Service not separately priced by Part B
Pub: 100-2, Chap. 15, 290

D **L3550** Orthopedic shoe addition, toe tap standard   **DME** A
Service not separately priced by Part B
Pub: 100-2, Chap. 15, 290

D **L3560** Orthopedic shoe addition, toe tap, horseshoe   **DME** A
Service not separately priced by Part B
Pub: 100-2, Chap. 15, 290

D **L3570** Orthopedic shoe addition, special extension to instep (leather with eyelets)   **DME** A
Service not separately priced by Part B
Pub: 100-2, Chap. 15, 290

D **L3580** Orthopedic shoe addition, convert instep to velcro closure   **DME** A
Service not separately priced by Part B
Pub: 100-2, Chap. 15, 290

D **L3590** Orthopedic shoe addition, convert firm shoe counter to soft counter   **DME** A
Service not separately priced by Part B
Pub: 100-2, Chap. 15, 290

D **L3595** Orthopedic shoe addition, March bar   **DME** A
Service not separately priced by Part B
Pub: 100-2, Chap. 15, 290

D **L3600** Transfer of an orthosis from one shoe to another, caliper plate, existing   **DME** A
Service not separately priced by Part B
Pub: 100-2, Chap. 15, 290

D **L3610** Transfer of an orthosis from one shoe to another, caliper plate, new   **DME** A
Service not separately priced by Part B
Pub: 100-2, Chap. 15, 290

D **L3620** Transfer of an orthosis from one shoe to another, solid stirrup, existing   **DME** A
Service not separately priced by Part B
Pub: 100-2, Chap. 15, 290

D **L3630** Transfer of an orthosis from one shoe to another, solid stirrup, new   **DME** A
Service not separately priced by Part B
Pub: 100-2, Chap. 15, 290

D **L3640** Transfer of an orthosis from one shoe to another, dennis browne splint (Riveton), both shoes   **DME** A
Service not separately priced by Part B
Pub: 100-2, Chap. 15, 290

D **L3649** Orthopedic shoe, modification, addition or transfer, not otherwise specified   A
Service not separately priced by Part B
Pub: 100-2, Chap. 15, 290

C **L3650** Shoulder orthosis (SO), figure of eight design abduction restrainer, prefabricated, off-the-shelf   **DME** A

C **L3660** Shoulder orthosis (SO), figure of eight design abduction restrainer, canvas and webbing, prefabricated, off-the-shelf   **DME** A

C **L3670** Shoulder orthosis (SO), acromio/clavicular (canvas and webbing type), prefabricated, off-the-shelf   **DME** A

C **L3671** Shoulder orthosis (SO), shoulder joint design, without joints, may include soft interface, straps, custom fabricated, includes fitting and adjustment   **DME** A

C **L3674** Shoulder orthosis (SO), abduction positioning (airplane design), thoracic component and support bar, with or without nontorsion joint/turnbuckle, may include soft interface, straps, custom fabricated, includes fitting and adjustment   **DME** A

C **L3675** Shoulder orthosis (SO), vest type abduction restrainer, canvas webbing type or equal, prefabricated, off-the-shelf   **DME** A

D **L3677** Shoulder orthosis (SO), shoulder joint design, without joints, may include soft interface, straps, prefabricated item that has been trimmed, bent, molded, assembled, or otherwise customized to fit a specific patient by an individual with expertise   A
Service not separately priced by Part B

C **L3678** Shoulder orthosis (SO), shoulder joint design, without joints, may include soft interface, straps, prefabricated, off-the-shelf

C **L3702** Elbow orthosis (EO), without joints, may include soft interface, straps, custom fabricated, includes fitting and adjustment   **DME** A

C **L3710** Elbow orthosis (EO), elastic with metal joints, prefabricated, off-the-shelf   **DME** A

C **L3720** Elbow orthosis (EO), double upright with forearm/arm cuffs, free motion, custom-fabricated   **DME** A

▲ Revised Code   ● New code   **C** Carrier judgment   **D** Special coverage instructions apply
I Not payable by Medicare   **M** Non-covered by Medicare   **S** Non-covered by Medicare statute   AHA Coding Clinic®

C **L3730** Elbow orthosis (EO), double upright with forearm/arm cuffs, extension/ flexion assist, custom-fabricated `DME` A

C **L3740** Elbow orthosis (EO), double upright with forearm/arm cuffs, adjustable position lock with active control, custom-fabricated `DME` A

C **L3760** Elbow orthosis (EO), with adjustable position locking joint(s), prefabricated, includes fitting and adjustments, any type `DME` A

C **L3762** Elbow orthosis (EO), rigid, without joints, includes soft interface material, prefabricated, off-the-shelf `DME` A

C **L3763** Elbow wrist hand orthosis (EWHO), rigid, without joints, may include soft interface, straps, custom fabricated, includes fitting and adjustment `DME` A

C **L3764** Elbow wrist hand orthosis (EWHO), includes one or more nontorsion joints, elastic bands, turnbuckles, may include soft interface, straps, custom fabricated, includes fitting and adjustment `DME` A

C **L3765** Elbow wrist hand finger orthosis (EWHFO), rigid, without joints, may include soft interface, straps, custom fabricated, includes fitting and adjustment `DME` A

C **L3766** Elbow wrist hand finger orthosis (EWHFO), includes one or more nontorsion joints, elastic bands, turnbuckles, may include soft interface, straps, custom fabricated, includes fitting and adjustment `DME` A

C **L3806** Wrist hand finger orthosis (WHFO), includes one or more nontorsion joint(s), turnbuckles, elastic bands/springs, may include soft interface material, straps, custom fabricated, includes fitting and adjustment `DME` A

C **L3807** Wrist hand finger orthosis (WHFO), without joint(s), prefabricated item that has been trimmed, bent, molded, assembled, or otherwise customized to fit a specific patient by an individual with expertise `DME` A

C **L3808** Wrist hand finger orthosis (WHFO), rigid without joints, may include soft interface material; straps, custom fabricated, includes fitting and adjustment `DME` A

C **L3809** Wrist hand finger orthosis (WHFO), without joint(s), prefabricated, off-the-shelf, any type `DME`

I **L3891** Addition to upper extremity joint, wrist or elbow, concentric adjustable torsion style mechanism for custom fabricated orthotics only, each E

Service not separately priced by Part B

C **L3900** Wrist hand finger orthosis (WHFO), dynamic flexor hinge, reciprocal wrist extension/ flexion, finger flexion/extension, wrist or finger driven, custom-fabricated `DME` A

C **L3901** Wrist hand finger orthosis (WHFO), dynamic flexor hinge, reciprocal wrist extension/ flexion, finger flexion/extension, cable driven, custom-fabricated `DME` A

C **L3904** Wrist hand finger orthosis (WHFO), external powered, electric, custom-fabricated `DME` A

C **L3905** Wrist hand orthosis (WHO), includes one or more nontorsion joints, elastic bands, turnbuckles, may include soft interface, straps, custom fabricated, includes fitting and adjustment `DME` A

C **L3906** Wrist hand orthosis (WHO), without joints, may include soft interface, straps, custom fabricated, includes fitting and adjustment `DME` A

C **L3908** Wrist hand orthosis (WHO), wrist extension control cock-up, non molded, prefabricated, off-the-shelf `DME` A

C **L3912** Hand finger orthosis (HFO), flexion glove with elastic finger control, prefabricated, off-the-shelf `DME` A

C **L3913** Hand finger orthosis (HFO), without joints, may include soft interface, straps, custom fabricated, includes fitting and adjustment `DME` A

C **L3915** Wrist hand orthosis (WHO), includes one or more nontorsion joint(s), elastic bands, turnbuckles, may include soft interface, straps, prefabricated item that has been trimmed, bent, molded, assembled, or otherwise customized to fit a specific patient by an individual with expertise `DME` A

C **L3916** Wrist hand orthosis (WHO), includes one or more nontorsion joint(s), elastic bands, turnbuckles, may include soft interface, straps, prefabricated, off-the-shelf `DME`

C **L3917** Hand orthosis (HO), metacarpal fracture orthosis, prefabricated item that has been trimmed, bent, molded, assembled, or otherwise customized to fit a specific patient by an individual with expertise `DME` A

C **L3918** Hand orthosis (HO), metacarpal fracture orthosis, prefabricated, off-the-shelf `DME`

C **L3919** Hand orthosis (HO), without joints, may include soft interface, straps, custom fabricated, includes fitting and adjustment `DME` A

C **L3921** Hand finger orthosis (HFO), includes one or more nontorsion joints, elastic bands, turnbuckles, may include soft interface, straps, custom fabricated, includes fitting and adjustment `DME` A

C **L3923** Hand finger orthosis (HFO), without joints, may include soft interface, straps, prefabricated item that has been trimmed, bent, molded, assembled, or otherwise customized to fit a specific patient by an individual with expertise `DME` A

C **L3924** Hand finger orthosis (HFO), without joints, may include soft interface, straps, prefabricated, off-the-shelf `DME`

C **L3925** Finger orthosis (FO), proximal interphalangeal (PIP)/distal interphalangeal (DIP), non torsion joint/spring, extension/ flexion, may include soft interface material, prefabricated, off-the-shelf `DME` A

♂ Male only   ♀ Female only   Ⓐ Age   A2 - Z3 = ASC Payment Indicator   A - Y = APC Status Indicator

ASC = ASC Approved Procedure   `DME` Paid under the DME fee schedule   `PQRS` Physician Quality Reporting System

C L3927 Finger orthosis (FO), proximal interphalangeal (PIP)/distal interphalangeal (DIP), without joint/spring, extension/flexion (e.g., static or ring type), may include soft interface material, prefabricated, off-the-shelf **DME** A

C L3929 Hand finger orthosis (HFO), includes one or more nontorsion joint(s), turnbuckles, elastic bands/springs, may include soft interface material, straps, prefabricated item that has been trimmed, bent, molded, assembled, or otherwise customized to fit a specific patient by an individual with expertise **DME** A

C L3930 Hand finger orthosis (HFO), includes one or more nontorsion joint(s), turnbuckles, elastic bands/springs, may include soft interface material, straps, prefabricated, off-the-shelf **DME**

C L3931 Wrist hand finger orthosis (WHFO), includes one or more nontorsion joint(s), turnbuckles, elastic bands/springs, may include soft interface material, straps, prefabricated, includes fitting and adjustment **DME** A

C L3933 Finger orthosis (FO), without joints, may include soft interface, custom fabricated, includes fitting and adjustment **DME** A

C L3935 Finger orthosis (FO), nontorsion joint, may include soft interface, custom fabricated, includes fitting and adjustment **DME** A

C L3956 Addition of joint to upper extremity orthosis, any material; per joint **DME** A

C L3960 Shoulder elbow wrist hand orthosis (SEWHO), abduction positioning, airplane design, prefabricated, includes fitting and adjustment **DME** A

C L3961 Shoulder elbow wrist hand orthosis (SEWHO), shoulder cap design, without joints, may include soft interface, straps, custom fabricated, includes fitting and adjustment **DME** A

C L3962 Shoulder elbow wrist hand orthosis (SEWHO), abduction positioning, erbs palsey design, prefabricated, includes fitting and adjustment **DME** A

C L3967 Shoulder elbow wrist hand orthosis (SEWHO), abduction positioning (airplane design), thoracic component and support bar, without joints, may include soft interface, straps, custom fabricated, includes fitting and adjustment **DME** A

C L3971 Shoulder elbow wrist hand orthosis (SEWHO), shoulder cap design, includes one or more nontorsion joints, elastic bands, turnbuckles, may include soft interface, straps, custom fabricated, includes fitting and adjustment **DME** A

C L3973 Shoulder elbow wrist hand orthosis (SEWHO), abduction positioning (airplane design), thoracic component and support bar, includes one or more nontorsion joints, elastic bands, turnbuckles, may include soft interface, straps, custom fabricated, includes fitting and adjustment **DME** A

C L3975 Shoulder elbow wrist hand finger orthosis, shoulder cap design, without joints, may include soft interface, straps, custom fabricated, includes fitting and adjustment **DME** A

C L3976 Shoulder elbow wrist hand finger orthosis, abduction positioning (airplane design), thoracic component and support bar, without joints, may include soft interface, straps, custom fabricated, includes fitting and adjustment **DME** A

C L3977 Shoulder elbow wrist hand finger orthosis, shoulder cap design, includes one or more nontorsion joints, elastic bands, turnbuckles, may include soft interface, straps, custom fabricated, includes fitting and adjustment **DME** A

C L3978 Shoulder elbow wrist hand finger orthosis, abduction positioning (airplane design), thoracic component and support bar, includes one or more nontorsion joints, elastic bands, turnbuckles, may include soft interface, straps, custom fabricated, includes fitting and adjustment **DME** A

C L3980 Upper extremity fracture orthosis, humeral, prefabricated, includes fitting and adjustment **DME** A

● **C L3981** Upper extremity fracture orthosis, humeral, prefabricated, includes shoulder cap design, with or without joints, forearm section, may include soft interface, straps, includes fitting and adjustments

C L3982 Upper extremity fracture orthosis, radius/ulnar, prefabricated, includes fitting and adjustment **DME** A

C L3984 Upper extremity fracture orthosis, wrist, prefabricated, includes fitting and adjustment **DME** A

C L3995 Addition to upper extremity orthosis, sock, fracture or equal, each **DME** A

C L3999 Upper limb orthosis, not otherwise specified A

C L4000 Replace girdle for spinal orthosis (Cervical-thoracic-lumbar-sacral orthosis (CTLSO) or Shoulder orthosis (SO)) **DME** A

C L4002 Replacement strap, any orthosis, includes all components, any length, any type **DME** A

C L4010 Replace trilateral socket brim **DME** A

C L4020 Replace quadrilateral socket brim, molded to patient model **DME** A

C L4030 Replace quadrilateral socket brim, custom fitted **DME** A

C L4040 Replace molded thigh lacer, for custom fabricated orthosis only **DME** A

C L4045 Replace non-molded thigh lacer, for custom fabricated orthosis only **DME** A

▲ Revised Code ● New code **C** Carrier judgment **D** Special coverage instructions apply
I Not payable by Medicare **M** Non-covered by Medicare **S** Non-covered by Medicare statute AHA Coding Clinic®

152

C **L4050** Replace molded calf lacer, for custom fabricated orthosis only `DME` A

C **L4055** Replace non-molded calf lacer, for custom fabricated orthosis only `DME` A

C **L4060** Replace high roll cuff `DME` A

C **L4070** Replace proximal and distal upright for KAFO `DME` A

C **L4080** Replace metal bands KAFO, proximal thigh `DME` A

C **L4090** Replace metal bands KAFO-AFO, calf or distal thigh `DME` A

C **L4100** Replace leather cuff KAFO, proximal thigh `DME` A

C **L4110** Replace leather cuff KAFO-AFO, calf or distal thigh `DME` A

C **L4130** Replace pretibial shell `DME` A

D **L4205** Repair of orthotic device, labor component, per 15 minutes A

D **L4210** Repair of orthotic device, repair or replace minor parts A

C **L4350** Ankle control orthosis, stirrup style, rigid, includes any type interface (e.g., pneumatic, gel), prefabricated, off-the-shelf `DME` A

C **L4360** Walking boot, pneumatic and/or vacuum, with or without joints, with or without interface material, prefabricated item that has been trimmed, bent, molded, assembled, or otherwise customized to fit a specific patient by an individual with expertise `DME` A

C **L4361** Walking boot, pneumatic and/or vacuum, with or without joints, with or without interface material, prefabricated, off-the-shelf `DME`

C **L4370** Pneumatic full leg splint, prefabricated, off-the-shelf `DME` A

C **L4386** Walking boot, non-pneumatic, with or without joints, with or without interface material, prefabricated item that has been trimmed, bent, molded, assembled, or otherwise customized to fit a specific patient by an individual with expertise `DME` A

C **L4387** Walking boot, non-pneumatic, with or without joints, with or without interface material, prefabricated, off-the-shelf `DME`

C **L4392** Replacement, soft interface material, static AFO `DME` A

C **L4394** Replace soft interface material, foot drop splint `DME` A

C **L4396** Static or dynamic ankle foot orthosis, including soft interface material, adjustable for fit, for positioning, may be used for minimal ambulation, prefabricated item that has been trimmed, bent, molded, assembled, or otherwise customized to fit a specific patient by an individual with expertise `DME` A

C **L4397** Static or dynamic ankle foot orthosis, including soft interface material, adjustable for fit, for positioning, may be used for minimal ambulation, prefabricated, off-the-shelf `DME`

C **L4398** Foot drop splint, recumbent positioning device, prefabricated, off-the-shelf `DME` A

C **L4631** Ankle foot orthosis (AFO), walking boot type, varus/valgus correction, rocker bottom, anterior tibial shell, soft interface, custom arch support, plastic or other material, includes straps and closures, custom fabricated `DME` A

PROSTHETIC PROCEDURES (L5000-L9900)

D **L5000** Partial foot, shoe insert with longitudinal arch, toe filler **DME** A

D **L5010** Partial foot, molded socket, ankle height, with toe filler **DME** A
Pub: 100-2, Chap. 15, 290

D **L5020** Partial foot, molded socket, tibial tubercle height, with toe filler **DME** A
Pub: 100-2, Chap. 15, 290

C **L5050** Ankle, Symes, molded socket, SACH foot **DME** A

C **L5060** Ankle, Symes, metal frame, molded leather socket, articulated ankle/foot **DME** A

C **L5100** Below knee, molded socket, shin, SACH foot **DME** A

C **L5105** Below knee, plastic socket, joints and thigh lacer, SACH foot **DME** A

C **L5150** Knee disarticulation (or through knee), molded socket, external knee joints, shin, SACH foot **DME** A

C **L5160** Knee disarticulation (or through knee), molded socket, bent knee configuration, external knee joints, shin, SACH foot **DME** A

C **L5200** Above knee, molded socket, single axis constant friction knee, shin, SACH foot **DME** A

C **L5210** Above knee, short prosthesis, no knee joint ('stubbies'), with foot blocks, no ankle joints, each **DME** A

C **L5220** Above knee, short prosthesis, no knee joint ('stubbies'), with articulated ankle/foot, dynamically aligned, each **DME** A

C **L5230** Above knee, for proximal femoral focal deficiency, constant friction knee, shin, SACH foot **DME** A

C **L5250** Hip disarticulation, Canadian type; molded socket, hip joint, single axis constant friction knee, shin, SACH foot **DME** A

C **L5270** Hip disarticulation, tilt table type; molded socket, locking hip joint, single axis constant friction knee, shin, SACH foot **DME** A

C **L5280** Hemipelvectomy, Canadian type; molded socket, hip joint, single axis constant friction knee, shin, SACH foot **DME** A

C **L5301** Below knee, molded socket, shin, SACH foot, endoskeletal system **DME** A

C **L5312** Knee disarticulation (or through knee), molded socket, single axis knee, pylon, SACH foot, endoskeletal system **DME** A

C **L5321** Above knee, molded socket, open end, SACH foot, endoskeletal system, single axis knee **DME** A

C **L5331** Hip disarticulation, Canadian type, molded socket, endoskeletal system, hip joint, single axis knee, SACH foot **DME** A

C **L5341** Hemipelvectomy, Canadian type, molded socket, endoskeletal system, hip joint, single axis knee, SACH foot **DME** A

C **L5400** Immediate post surgical or early fitting, application of initial rigid dressing, including fitting, alignment, suspension, and one cast change, below knee **DME** A

C **L5410** Immediate post surgical or early fitting, application of initial rigid dressing, including fitting, alignment and suspension, below knee, each additional cast change and realignment **DME** A

C **L5420** Immediate post surgical or early fitting, application of initial rigid dressing, including fitting, alignment and suspension and one cast change 'AK' or knee disarticulation **DME** A

C **L5430** Immediate post surgical or early fitting, application of initial rigid dressing, incl. fitting, alignment and suspension, 'AK' or knee disarticulation, each additional cast change and realignment **DME** A

C **L5450** Immediate post surgical or early fitting, application of non-weight bearing rigid dressing, below knee **DME** A

C **L5460** Immediate post surgical or early fitting, application of non-weight bearing rigid dressing, above knee **DME** A

C **L5500** Initial, below knee 'PTB' type socket, non-alignable system, pylon, no cover, SACH foot, plaster socket, direct formed **DME** A
Pub: 100-2, Chap. 1, 40

C **L5505** Initial, above knee - knee disarticulation, ischial level socket, non-alignable system, pylon, no cover, SACH foot, plaster socket, direct formed **DME** A
Pub: 100-2, Chap. 1, 40

C **L5510** Preparatory, below knee 'PTB' type socket, non-alignable system, pylon, no cover, SACH foot, plaster socket, molded to model **DME** A

C **L5520** Preparatory, below knee 'PTB' type socket, non-alignable system, pylon, no cover, SACH foot, thermoplastic or equal, direct formed **DME** A

C **L5530** Preparatory, below knee 'PTB' type socket, non-alignable system, pylon, no cover, SACH foot, thermoplastic or equal, molded to model **DME** A

C **L5535** Preparatory, below knee 'PTB' type socket, non-alignable system, no cover, SACH foot, prefabricated, adjustable open end socket **DME** A

C **L5540** Preparatory, below knee 'PTB' type socket, non-alignable system, pylon, no cover, SACH foot, laminated socket, molded to model **DME** A

C **L5560** Preparatory, above knee- knee disarticulation, ischial level socket, non-alignable system, pylon, no cover, SACH foot, plaster socket, molded to model **DME** A

C **L5570** Preparatory, above knee - knee disarticulation, ischial level socket, non-alignable system, pylon, no cover, SACH foot, thermoplastic or equal, direct formed **DME** A

▲ Revised Code   ● New code   **C** Carrier judgment   **D** Special coverage instructions apply
I Not payable by Medicare   **M** Non-covered by Medicare   **S** Non-covered by Medicare statute   AHA Coding Clinic®

C **L5580** Preparatory, above knee - knee disarticulation ischial level socket, non-alignable system, pylon, no cover, SACH foot, thermoplastic or equal, molded to model DME A

C **L5585** Preparatory, above knee - knee disarticulation, ischial level socket, non-alignable system, pylon, no cover, SACH foot, prefabricated adjustable open end socket DME A

C **L5590** Preparatory, above knee - knee disarticulation ischial level socket, non-alignable system, pylon no cover, SACH foot, laminated socket, molded to model DME A

C **L5595** Preparatory, hip disarticulation-hemipelvectomy, pylon, no cover, SACH foot, thermoplastic or equal, molded to patient model DME A

C **L5600** Preparatory, hip disarticulation-hemipelvectomy, pylon, no cover, SACH foot, laminated socket, molded to patient model DME A

C **L5610** Addition to lower extremity, endoskeletal system, above knee, hydracadence system DME A

C **L5611** Addition to lower extremity, endoskeletal system, above knee-knee disarticulation, 4 bar linkage, with friction swing phase control DME A

C **L5613** Addition to lower extremity, endoskeletal system, above knee-knee disarticulation, 4 bar linkage, with hydraulic swing phase control DME A

C **L5614** Addition to lower extremity, exoskeletal system, above knee-knee disarticulation, 4 bar linkage, with pneumatic swing phase control DME A

C **L5616** Addition to lower extremity, endoskeletal system, above knee, universal multiplex system, friction swing phase control DME A

C **L5617** Addition to lower extremity, quick change self-aligning unit, above knee or below knee, each DME A

C **L5618** Addition to lower extremity, test socket, Symes DME A

C **L5620** Addition to lower extremity, test socket, below knee DME A

C **L5622** Addition to lower extremity, test socket, knee disarticulation DME A

C **L5624** Addition to lower extremity, test socket, above knee DME A

C **L5626** Addition to lower extremity, test socket, hip disarticulation DME A

C **L5628** Addition to lower extremity, test socket, hemipelvectomy DME A

C **L5629** Addition to lower extremity, below knee, acrylic socket DME A

C **L5630** Addition to lower extremity, Symes type, expandable wall socket DME A

C **L5631** Addition to lower extremity, above knee or knee disarticulation, acrylic socket DME A

C **L5632** Addition to lower extremity, Symes type, 'PTB' brim design socket DME A

C **L5634** Addition to lower extremity, Symes type, posterior opening (Canadian) socket DME A

C **L5636** Addition to lower extremity, Symes type, medial opening socket DME A

C **L5637** Addition to lower extremity, below knee, total contact DME A

C **L5638** Addition to lower extremity, below knee, leather socket DME A

C **L5639** Addition to lower extremity, below knee, wood socket DME A

C **L5640** Addition to lower extremity, knee disarticulation, leather socket DME A

C **L5642** Addition to lower extremity, above knee, leather socket DME A

C **L5643** Addition to lower extremity, hip disarticulation, flexible inner socket, external frame DME A

C **L5644** Addition to lower extremity, above knee, wood socket DME A

C **L5645** Addition to lower extremity, below knee, flexible inner socket, external frame DME A

C **L5646** Addition to lower extremity, below knee, air, fluid, gel or equal, cushion socket DME A

C **L5647** Addition to lower extremity, below knee suction socket DME A

C **L5648** Addition to lower extremity, above knee, air, fluid, gel or equal, cushion socket DME A

C **L5649** Addition to lower extremity, ischial containment/narrow M-L socket DME A

C **L5650** Additions to lower extremity, total contact, above knee or knee disarticulation socket DME A

C **L5651** Addition to lower extremity, above knee, flexible inner socket, external frame DME A

C **L5652** Addition to lower extremity, suction suspension, above knee or knee disarticulation socket DME A

C **L5653** Addition to lower extremity, knee disarticulation, expandable wall socket DME A

C **L5654** Addition to lower extremity, socket insert, Symes, (Kemblo, Pelite, Aliplast, Plastazote or equal) DME A

C **L5655** Addition to lower extremity, socket insert, below knee (Kemblo, Pelite, Aliplast, Plastazote or equal) DME A

C **L5656** Addition to lower extremity, socket insert, knee disarticulation (Kemblo, Pelite, Aliplast, Plastazote or equal) DME A

C **L5658** Addition to lower extremity, socket insert, above knee (Kemblo, Pelite, Aliplast, Plastazote or equal) DME A

C **L5661** Addition to lower extremity, socket insert, multi-durometer Symes DME A

♂ Male only   ♀ Female only   Ⓐ Age   A2 - Z3 = ASC Payment Indicator   A - Y = APC Status Indicator
ASC = ASC Approved Procedure   DME Paid under the DME fee schedule   PQRS Physician Quality Reporting System

155

C **L5665** Addition to lower extremity, socket insert, multi-durometer, below knee DME A

C **L5666** Addition to lower extremity, below knee, cuff suspension DME A

C **L5668** Addition to lower extremity, below knee, molded distal cushion DME A

C **L5670** Addition to lower extremity, below knee, molded supracondylar suspension ('PTS' or similar) DME A

C **L5671** Addition to lower extremity, below knee / above knee suspension locking mechanism (shuttle, lanyard or equal), excludes socket insert DME A

C **L5672** Addition to lower extremity, below knee, removable medial brim suspension DME A

C **L5673** Addition to lower extremity, below knee/ above knee, custom fabricated from existing mold or prefabricated, socket insert, silicone gel, elastomeric or equal, for use with locking mechanism DME A

C **L5676** Additions to lower extremity, below knee, knee joints, single axis, pair DME A

C **L5677** Additions to lower extremity, below knee, knee joints, polycentric, pair DME A

C **L5678** Additions to lower extremity, below knee, joint covers, pair DME A

C **L5679** Addition to lower extremity, below knee/ above knee, custom fabricated from existing mold or prefabricated, socket insert, silicone gel, elastomeric or equal, not for use with locking mechanism DME A

C **L5680** Addition to lower extremity, below knee, thigh lacer, nonmolded DME A

C **L5681** Addition to lower extremity, below knee/ above knee, custom fabricated socket insert for congenital or atypical traumatic amputee, silicone gel, elastomeric or equal, for use with or without locking mechanism, initial only (for other than initial, use code L5673 or L5679) DME A

C **L5682** Addition to lower extremity, below knee, thigh lacer, gluteal/ischial, molded DME A

C **L5683** Addition to lower extremity, below knee/ above knee, custom fabricated socket insert for other than congenital or atypical traumatic amputee, silicone gel, elastomeric or equal, for use with or without locking mechanism, initial only (for other than initial, use code L5673 or L5679) DME A

C **L5684** Addition to lower extremity, below knee, fork strap DME A

C **L5685** Addition to lower extremity prosthesis, below knee, suspension/sealing sleeve, with or without valve, any material, each DME A

C **L5686** Addition to lower extremity, below knee, back check (extension control) DME A

C **L5688** Addition to lower extremity, below knee, waist belt, webbing DME A

C **L5690** Addition to lower extremity, below knee, waist belt, padded and lined DME A

C **L5692** Addition to lower extremity, above knee, pelvic control belt, light DME A

C **L5694** Addition to lower extremity, above knee, pelvic control belt, padded and lined DME A

C **L5695** Addition to lower extremity, above knee, pelvic control, sleeve suspension, neoprene or equal, each DME A

C **L5696** Addition to lower extremity, above knee or knee disarticulation, pelvic joint DME A

C **L5697** Addition to lower extremity, above knee or knee disarticulation, pelvic band DME A

C **L5698** Addition to lower extremity, above knee or knee disarticulation, Silesian bandage DME A

C **L5699** All lower extremity prostheses, shoulder harness DME A

C **L5700** Replacement, socket, below knee, molded to patient model DME A

C **L5701** Replacement, socket, above knee/knee disarticulation, including attachment plate, molded to patient model DME A

C **L5702** Replacement, socket, hip disarticulation, including hip joint, molded to patient model DME A

C **L5703** Ankle, Symes, molded to patient model, socket without solid ankle cushion heel (SACH) foot, replacement only DME A

C **L5704** Custom shaped protective cover, below knee DME A

C **L5705** Custom shaped protective cover, above knee DME A

C **L5706** Custom shaped protective cover, knee disarticulation DME A

C **L5707** Custom shaped protective cover, hip disarticulation DME A

C **L5710** Addition, exoskeletal knee-shin system, single axis, manual lock DME A

C **L5711** Additions exoskeletal knee-shin system, single axis, manual lock, ultra-light material DME A

C **L5712** Addition, exoskeletal knee-shin system, single axis, friction swing and stance phase control (safety knee) DME A

C **L5714** Addition, exoskeletal knee-shin system, single axis, variable friction swing phase control DME A

C **L5716** Addition, exoskeletal knee-shin system, polycentric, mechanical stance phase lock DME A

C **L5718** Addition, exoskeletal knee-shin system, polycentric, friction swing and stance phase control DME A

C **L5722** Addition, exoskeletal knee-shin system, single axis, pneumatic swing, friction stance phase control DME A

C **L5724** Addition, exoskeletal knee-shin system, single axis, fluid swing phase control DME A

▲ Revised Code ● New code C Carrier judgment D Special coverage instructions apply
I Not payable by Medicare M Non-covered by Medicare S Non-covered by Medicare statute AHA Coding Clinic®

C **L5726** Addition, exoskeletal knee-shin system, single axis, external joints fluid swing phase control `DME` A

C **L5728** Addition, exoskeletal knee-shin system, single axis, fluid swing and stance phase control `DME` A

C **L5780** Addition, exoskeletal knee-shin system, single axis, pneumatic/hydra pneumatic swing phase control `DME` A

C **L5781** Addition to lower limb prosthesis, vacuum pump, residual limb volume management and moisture evacuation system `DME` A

C **L5782** Addition to lower limb prosthesis, vacuum pump, residual limb volume management and moisture evacuation system, heavy duty `DME` A

C **L5785** Addition, exoskeletal system, below knee, ultra-light material (titanium, carbon fiber or equal) `DME` A

C **L5790** Addition, exoskeletal system, above knee, ultra-light material (titanium, carbon fiber or equal) `DME` A

C **L5795** Addition, exoskeletal system, hip disarticulation, ultra-light material (titanium, carbon fiber or equal) `DME` A

C **L5810** Addition, endoskeletal knee-shin system, single axis, manual lock `DME` A

C **L5811** Addition, endoskeletal knee-shin system, single axis, manual lock, ultra-light material `DME` A

C **L5812** Addition, endoskeletal knee-shin system, single axis, friction swing and stance phase control (safety knee) `DME` A

C **L5814** Addition, endoskeletal knee-shin system, polycentric, hydraulic swing phase control, mechanical stance phase lock `DME` A

C **L5816** Addition, endoskeletal knee-shin system, polycentric, mechanical stance phase lock `DME` A

C **L5818** Addition, endoskeletal knee-shin system, polycentric, friction swing, and stance phase control `DME` A

C **L5822** Addition, endoskeletal knee-shin system, single axis, pneumatic swing, friction stance phase control `DME` A

C **L5824** Addition, endoskeletal knee-shin system, single axis, fluid swing phase control `DME` A

C **L5826** Addition, endoskeletal knee-shin system, single axis, hydraulic swing phase control, with miniature high activity frame `DME` A

C **L5828** Addition, endoskeletal knee-shin system, single axis, fluid swing and stance phase control `DME` A

C **L5830** Addition, endoskeletal knee-shin system, single axis, pneumatic/ swing phase control `DME` A

C **L5840** Addition, endoskeletal knee/shin system, 4-bar linkage or multiaxial, pneumatic swing phase control `DME` A

C **L5845** Addition, endoskeletal, knee-shin system, stance flexion feature, adjustable `DME` A

C **L5848** Addition to endoskeletal knee-shin system, fluid stance extension, dampening feature, with or without adjustability `DME` A

C **L5850** Addition, endoskeletal system, above knee or hip disarticulation, knee extension assist `DME` A

C **L5855** Addition, endoskeletal system, hip disarticulation, mechanical hip extension assist `DME` A

C **L5856** Addition to lower extremity prosthesis, endoskeletal knee-shin system, microprocessor control feature, swing and stance phase, includes electronic sensor(s), any type `DME` A

C **L5857** Addition to lower extremity prosthesis, endoskeletal knee-shin system, microprocessor control feature, swing phase only, includes electronic sensor(s), any type `DME` A

C **L5858** Addition to lower extremity prosthesis, endoskeletal knee shin system, microprocessor control feature, stance phase only, includes electronic sensor(s), any type `DME` A

C **L5859** Addition to lower extremity prosthesis, endoskeletal knee-shin system, powered and programmable flexion/extension assist control, includes any type motor(s) `DME` A

C **L5910** Addition, endoskeletal system, below knee, alignable system `DME` A

C **L5920** Addition, endoskeletal system, above knee or hip disarticulation, alignable system `DME` A

C **L5925** Addition, endoskeletal system, above knee, knee disarticulation or hip disarticulation, manual lock `DME` A

C **L5930** Addition, endoskeletal system, high activity knee control frame `DME` A

C **L5940** Addition, endoskeletal system, below knee, ultra-light material (titanium, carbon fiber or equal) `DME` A

C **L5950** Addition, endoskeletal system, above knee, ultra-light material (titanium, carbon fiber or equal) `DME` A

C **L5960** Addition, endoskeletal system, hip disarticulation, ultra-light material (titanium, carbon fiber or equal) `DME` A

C **L5961** Addition, endoskeletal system, polycentric hip joint, pneumatic or hydraulic control, rotation control, with or without flexion and/or extension control `DME` A

C **L5962** Addition, endoskeletal system, below knee, flexible protective outer surface covering system `DME` A

C **L5964** Addition, endoskeletal system, above knee, flexible protective outer surface covering system `DME` A

C **L5966** Addition, endoskeletal system, hip disarticulation, flexible protective outer surface covering system `DME` A

L5726 - L5966

PROSTHETIC PROCEDURES (L5000-L9900)

C **L5968** Addition to lower limb prosthesis, multiaxial ankle with swing phase active dorsiflexion feature DME A

C **L5969** Addition, endoskeletal ankle-foot or ankle system, power assist, includes any type motor(s)

C **L5970** All lower extremity prostheses, foot, external keel, solid ankle cushion heel (SACH) foot DME A

C **L5971** All lower extremity prosthesis, solid ankle cushion heel (SACH) foot, replacement only DME A

C **L5972** All lower extremity prostheses, foot, flexible keel DME A

C **L5973** Endoskeletal ankle foot system, microprocessor controlled feature, dorsiflexion and/or plantar flexion control, includes power source DME A

C **L5974** All lower extremity prostheses, foot, single axis ankle/foot DME A

C **L5975** All lower extremity prosthesis, combination single axis ankle and flexible keel foot DME A

C **L5976** All lower extremity prostheses, energy storing foot (seattle carbon copy II or equal) DME A

C **L5978** All lower extremity prostheses, foot, multiaxial ankle/foot DME A

C **L5979** All lower extremity prosthesis, multi-axial ankle, dynamic response foot, one piece system DME A

C **L5980** All lower extremity prostheses, flex foot system DME A

C **L5981** All lower extremity prostheses, flex-walk system or equal DME A

C **L5982** All exoskeletal lower extremity prostheses, axial rotation unit DME A

C **L5984** All endoskeletal lower extremity prosthesis, axial rotation unit, with or without adjustability DME A

C **L5985** All endoskeletal lower extremity prostheses, dynamic prosthetic pylon DME A

C **L5986** All lower extremity prostheses, multi-axial rotation unit ('MCP' or equal) DME A

C **L5987** All lower extremity prosthesis, shank foot system with vertical loading pylon DME A

C **L5988** Addition to lower limb prosthesis, vertical shock reducing pylon feature DME A

C **L5990** Addition to lower extremity prosthesis, user adjustable heel height DME A

C **L5999** Lower extremity prosthesis, not otherwise specified A

C **L6000** Partial hand, thumb remaining DME A

C **L6010** Partial hand, little and/or ring finger remaining DME A

C **L6020** Partial hand, no finger remaining DME A

● C **L6026** Transcarpal/metacarpal or partial hand disarticulation prosthesis, external power, self-suspended, inner socket with removable

forearm section, electrodes and cables, two batteries, charger, myoelectric control of terminal device, excludes terminal device(s)

C **L6050** Wrist disarticulation, molded socket, flexible elbow hinges, triceps pad DME A

C **L6055** Wrist disarticulation, molded socket with expandable interface, flexible elbow hinges, triceps pad DME A

C **L6100** Below elbow, molded socket, flexible elbow hinge, triceps pad DME A

C **L6110** Below elbow, molded socket, (Muenster or Northwestern suspension types) DME A

C **L6120** Below elbow, molded double wall split socket, step-up hinges, half cuff DME A

C **L6130** Below elbow, molded double wall split socket, stump activated locking hinge, half cuff DME A

C **L6200** Elbow disarticulation, molded socket, outside locking hinge, forearm DME A

C **L6205** Elbow disarticulation, molded socket with expandable interface, outside locking hinges, forearm DME A

C **L6250** Above elbow, molded double wall socket, internal locking elbow, forearm DME A

C **L6300** Shoulder disarticulation, molded socket, shoulder bulkhead, humeral section, internal locking elbow, forearm DME A

C **L6310** Shoulder disarticulation, passive restoration (complete prosthesis) DME A

C **L6320** Shoulder disarticulation, passive restoration (shoulder cap only) DME A

C **L6350** Interscapular thoracic, molded socket, shoulder bulkhead, humeral section, internal locking elbow, forearm DME A

C **L6360** Interscapular thoracic, passive restoration (complete prosthesis) DME A

C **L6370** Interscapular thoracic, passive restoration (shoulder cap only) DME A

C **L6380** Immediate post surgical or early fitting, application of initial rigid dressing, including fitting alignment and suspension of components, and one cast change, wrist disarticulation or below elbow DME A

C **L6382** Immediate post surgical or early fitting, application of initial rigid dressing including fitting alignment and suspension of components, and one cast change, elbow disarticulation or above elbow DME A

C **L6384** Immediate post surgical or early fitting, application of initial rigid dressing including fitting alignment and suspension of components, and one cast change, shoulder disarticulation or interscapular thoracic DME A

C **L6386** Immediate post surgical or early fitting, each additional cast change and realignment DME A

C **L6388** Immediate post surgical or early fitting, application of rigid dressing only DME A

C **L6400** Below elbow, molded socket, endoskeletal system, including soft prosthetic tissue shaping **DME** A

C **L6450** Elbow disarticulation, molded socket, endoskeletal system, including soft prosthetic tissue shaping **DME** A

C **L6500** Above elbow, molded socket, endoskeletal system, including soft prosthetic tissue shaping **DME** A

C **L6550** Shoulder disarticulation, molded socket, endoskeletal system, including soft prosthetic tissue shaping **DME** A

C **L6570** Interscapular thoracic, molded socket, endoskeletal system, including soft prosthetic tissue shaping **DME** A

C **L6580** Preparatory, wrist disarticulation or below elbow, single wall plastic socket, friction wrist, flexible elbow hinges, figure of eight harness, humeral cuff, Bowden cable control, USMC or equal pylon, no cover, molded to patient model **DME** A

C **L6582** Preparatory, wrist disarticulation or below elbow, single wall socket, friction wrist, flexible elbow hinges, figure of eight harness, humeral cuff, Bowden cable control, USMC or equal pylon, no cover, direct formed **DME** A

C **L6584** Preparatory, elbow disarticulation or above elbow, single wall plastic socket, friction wrist, locking elbow, figure of eight harness, fair lead cable control, USMC or equal pylon, no cover, molded to patient model **DME** A

C **L6586** Preparatory, elbow disarticulation or above elbow, single wall socket, friction wrist, locking elbow, figure of eight harness, fair lead cable control, USMC or equal pylon, no cover, direct formed **DME** A

C **L6588** Preparatory, shoulder disarticulation or interscapular thoracic, single wall plastic socket, shoulder joint, locking elbow, friction wrist, chest strap, fair lead cable control, USMC or equal pylon, no cover, molded to patient model **DME** A

C **L6590** Preparatory, shoulder disarticulation or interscapular thoracic, single wall socket, shoulder joint, locking elbow, friction wrist, chest strap, fair lead cable control, USMC or equal pylon, no cover, direct formed **DME** A

C **L6600** Upper extremity additions, polycentric hinge, pair **DME** A

C **L6605** Upper extremity additions, single pivot hinge, pair **DME** A

C **L6610** Upper extremity additions, flexible metal hinge, pair **DME** A

C **L6611** Addition to upper extremity prosthesis, external powered, additional switch, any type **DME** A

C **L6615** Upper extremity addition, disconnect locking wrist unit **DME** A

C **L6616** Upper extremity addition, additional disconnect insert for locking wrist unit, each **DME** A

C **L6620** Upper extremity addition, flexion/extension wrist unit, with or without friction **DME** A

C **L6621** Upper extremity prosthesis addition, flexion/extension wrist with or without friction, for use with external powered terminal device **DME** A

C **L6623** Upper extremity addition, spring assisted rotational wrist unit with latch release **DME** A

C **L6624** Upper extremity addition, flexion/extension and rotation wrist unit **DME** A

C **L6625** Upper extremity addition, rotation wrist unit with cable lock **DME** A

C **L6628** Upper extremity addition, quick disconnect hook adapter, Otto Bock or equal **DME** A

C **L6629** Upper extremity addition, quick disconnect lamination collar with coupling piece, Otto Bock or equal **DME** A

C **L6630** Upper extremity addition, stainless steel, any wrist **DME** A

C **L6632** Upper extremity addition, latex suspension sleeve, each **DME** A

C **L6635** Upper extremity addition, lift assist for elbow **DME** A

C **L6637** Upper extremity addition, nudge control elbow lock **DME** A

C **L6638** Upper extremity addition to prosthesis, electric locking feature, only for use with manually powered elbow **DME** A

C **L6640** Upper extremity additions, shoulder abduction joint, pair **DME** A

C **L6641** Upper extremity addition, excursion amplifier, pulley type **DME** A

C **L6642** Upper extremity addition, excursion amplifier, lever type **DME** A

C **L6645** Upper extremity addition, shoulder flexion-abduction joint, each **DME** A

C **L6646** Upper extremity addition, shoulder joint, multipositional locking, flexion, adjustable abduction friction control, for use with body powered or external powered system **DME** A

C **L6647** Upper extremity addition, shoulder lock mechanism, body powered actuator **DME** A

C **L6648** Upper extremity addition, shoulder lock mechanism, external powered actuator **DME** A

C **L6650** Upper extremity addition, shoulder universal joint, each **DME** A

C **L6655** Upper extremity addition, standard control cable, extra **DME** A

C **L6660** Upper extremity addition, heavy duty control cable **DME** A

C **L6665** Upper extremity addition, Teflon, or equal, cable lining **DME** A

C **L6670** Upper extremity addition, hook to hand, cable adapter **DME** A

C **L6672** Upper extremity addition, harness, chest or shoulder, saddle type **DME** A

♂ Male only   ♀ Female only   **A** Age   A2 - Z3 = ASC Payment Indicator   A - Y = APC Status Indicator

ASC = ASC Approved Procedure   **DME** Paid under the DME fee schedule   **PQRS** Physician Quality Reporting System

L6675 - L6890

C **L6675** Upper extremity addition, harness, (e.g., figure of eight type), single cable design   **DME** A

C **L6676** Upper extremity addition, harness, (e.g., figure of eight type), dual cable design   **DME** A

C **L6677** Upper extremity addition, harness, triple control, simultaneous operation of terminal device and elbow   **DME** A

C **L6680** Upper extremity addition, test socket, wrist disarticulation or below elbow   **DME** A

C **L6682** Upper extremity addition, test socket, elbow disarticulation or above elbow   **DME** A

C **L6684** Upper extremity addition, test socket, shoulder disarticulation or interscapular thoracic   **DME** A

C **L6686** Upper extremity addition, suction socket   **DME** A

C **L6687** Upper extremity addition, frame type socket, below elbow or wrist disarticulation   **DME** A

C **L6688** Upper extremity addition, frame type socket, above elbow or elbow disarticulation   **DME** A

C **L6689** Upper extremity addition, frame type socket, shoulder disarticulation   **DME** A

C **L6690** Upper extremity addition, frame type socket, interscapular-thoracic   **DME** A

C **L6691** Upper extremity addition, removable insert, each   **DME** A

C **L6692** Upper extremity addition, silicone gel insert or equal, each   **DME** A

C **L6693** Upper extremity addition, locking elbow, forearm counterbalance   **DME** A

C **L6694** Addition to upper extremity prosthesis, below elbow/above elbow, custom fabricated from existing mold or prefabricated, socket insert, silicone gel, elastomeric or equal, for use with locking mechanism   **DME** A

C **L6695** Addition to upper extremity prosthesis, below elbow/above elbow, custom fabricated from existing mold or prefabricated, socket insert, silicone gel, elastomeric or equal, not for use with locking mechanism   **DME** A

C **L6696** Addition to upper extremity prosthesis, below elbow/above elbow, custom fabricated socket insert for congenital or atypical traumatic amputee, silicone gel, elastomeric or equal, for use with or without locking mechanism, initial only (for other than initial, use code L6694 or L6695)   **DME** A

C **L6697** Addition to upper extremity prosthesis, below elbow/above elbow, custom fabricated socket insert for other than congenital or atypical traumatic amputee, silicone gel, elastomeric or equal, for use with or without locking mechanism, initial only (for other than initial, use code L6694 or L6695)   **DME** A

C **L6698** Addition to upper extremity prosthesis, below elbow/above elbow, lock mechanism, excludes socket insert   **DME** A

C **L6703** Terminal device, passive hand/mitt, any material, any size   **DME** A

C **L6704** Terminal device, sport/recreational/work attachment, any material, any size   **DME** A

C **L6706** Terminal device, hook, mechanical, voluntary opening, any material, any size, lined or unlined   **DME** A

C **L6707** Terminal device, hook, mechanical, voluntary closing, any material, any size, lined or unlined   **DME** A

C **L6708** Terminal device, hand, mechanical, voluntary opening, any material, any size   **DME** A

C **L6709** Terminal device, hand, mechanical, voluntary closing, any material, any size   **DME** A

C **L6711** Terminal device, hook, mechanical, voluntary opening, any material, any size, lined or unlined, pediatric   **DME** Ⓐ A

C **L6712** Terminal device, hook, mechanical, voluntary closing, any material, any size, lined or unlined, pediatric   **DME** Ⓐ A

C **L6713** Terminal device, hand, mechanical, voluntary opening, any material, any size, pediatric **DME** Ⓐ A

C **L6714** Terminal device, hand, mechanical, voluntary closing, any material, any size, pediatric   **DME** Ⓐ A

C **L6715** Terminal device, multiple articulating digit, includes motor(s), initial issue or replacement   **DME** A

C **L6721** Terminal device, hook or hand, heavy duty, mechanical, voluntary opening, any material, any size, lined or unlined   **DME** A

C **L6722** Terminal device, hook or hand, heavy duty, mechanical, voluntary closing, any material, any size, lined or unlined   **DME** A

D **L6805** Addition to terminal device, modifier wrist unit   **DME** A

D **L6810** Addition to terminal device, precision pinch device   **DME** A

C **L6880** Electric hand, switch or myoelectric controlled, independently articulating digits, any grasp pattern or combination of grasp patterns, includes motor(s)   **DME** A

C **L6881** Automatic grasp feature, addition to upper limb electric prosthetic terminal device **DME** A

D **L6882** Microprocessor control feature, addition to upper limb prosthetic terminal device   **DME** A

C **L6883** Replacement socket, below elbow/wrist disarticulation, molded to patient model, for use with or without external power   **DME** A

C **L6884** Replacement socket, above elbow/elbow disarticulation, molded to patient model, for use with or without external power   **DME** A

C **L6885** Replacement socket, shoulder disarticulation/interscapular thoracic, molded to patient model, for use with or without external power   **DME** A

C **L6890** Addition to upper extremity prosthesis, glove for terminal device, any material, prefabricated, includes fitting and adjustment   **DME**

▲ Revised Code   ● New code   **C** Carrier judgment   **D** Special coverage instructions apply

I Not payable by Medicare   **M** Non-covered by Medicare   **S** Non-covered by Medicare statute   AHA Coding Clinic®

C **L6895** Addition to upper extremity prosthesis, glove for terminal device, any material, custom fabricated   DME A

C **L6900** Hand restoration (casts, shading and measurements included), partial hand, with glove, thumb or one finger remaining   DME A

C **L6905** Hand restoration (casts, shading and measurements included), partial hand, with glove, multiple fingers remaining   DME A

C **L6910** Hand restoration (casts, shading and measurements included), partial hand, with glove, no fingers remaining   DME A

C **L6915** Hand restoration (shading, and measurements included), replacement glove for above   DME A

C **L6920** Wrist disarticulation, external power, self-suspended inner socket, removable forearm shell, Otto Bock or equal, switch, cables, two batteries and one charger, switch control of terminal device   DME A

C **L6925** Wrist disarticulation, external power, self-suspended inner socket, removable forearm shell, Otto Bock or equal electrodes, cables, two batteries and one charger, myoelectronic control of terminal device   DME A

C **L6930** Below elbow, external power, self-suspended inner socket, removable forearm shell, Otto Bock or equal switch, cables, two batteries and one charger, switch control of terminal device   DME A

C **L6935** Below elbow, external power, self-suspended inner socket, removable forearm shell, Otto Bock or equal electrodes, cables, two batteries and one charger, myoelectronic control of terminal device   DME A

C **L6940** Elbow disarticulation, external power, molded inner socket, removable humeral shell, outside locking hinges, forearm, Otto Bock or equal switch, cables, two batteries and one charger, switch control of terminal device   DME A

C **L6945** Elbow disarticulation, external power, molded inner socket, removable humeral shell, outside locking hinges, forearm, Otto Bock or equal electrodes, cables, two batteries and one charger, myoelectronic control of terminal device   DME A

C **L6950** Above elbow, external power, molded inner socket, removable humeral shell, internal locking elbow, forearm, Otto Bock or equal switch, cables, two batteries and one charger, switch control of terminal device   DME A

C **L6955** Above elbow, external power, molded inner socket, removable humeral shell, internal locking elbow, forearm, Otto Bock or equal electrodes, cables, two batteries and one charger, myoelectronic control of terminal device   DME A

C **L6960** Shoulder disarticulation, external power, molded inner socket, removable shoulder shell, shoulder bulkhead, humeral section, mechanical elbow, forearm, Otto Bock or equal switch, cables, two batteries and one charger, switch control of terminal device   DME A

C **L6965** Shoulder disarticulation, external power, molded inner socket, removable shoulder shell, shoulder bulkhead, humeral section, mechanical elbow, forearm, Otto Bock or equal electrodes, cables, two batteries and one charger, myoelectronic control of terminal device   DME A

C **L6970** Interscapular-thoracic, external power, molded inner socket, removable shoulder shell, shoulder bulkhead, humeral section, mechanical elbow, forearm, Otto Bock or equal switch, cables, two batteries and one charger, switch control of terminal device   DME A

C **L6975** Interscapular-thoracic, external power, molded inner socket, removable shoulder shell, shoulder bulkhead, humeral section, mechanical elbow, forearm, Otto Bock or equal electrodes, cables, two batteries and one charger, myoelectronic control of terminal device   DME A

C **L7007** Electric hand, switch or myoelectric controlled, adult   DME A A

C **L7008** Electric hand, switch or myoelectric, controlled, pediatric   DME A A

C **L7009** Electric hook, switch or myoelectric controlled, adult   DME A A

C **L7040** Prehensile actuator, switch controlled   DME A

C **L7045** Electric hook, switch or myoelectric controlled, pediatric   DME A A

C **L7170** Electronic elbow, Hosmer or equal, switch controlled   DME A

C **L7180** Electronic elbow, microprocessor sequential control of elbow and terminal device   DME A

C **L7181** Electronic elbow, microprocessor simultaneous control of elbow and terminal device   DME A

C **L7185** Electronic elbow, adolescent, Variety Village or equal, switch controlled   DME A

C **L7186** Electronic elbow, child, Variety Village or equal, switch controlled   DME A A

C **L7190** Electronic elbow, adolescent, Variety Village or equal, myoelectronically controlled   DME A

C **L7191** Electronic elbow, child, Variety Village or equal, myoelectronically controlled   DME A A

● C **L7259** Electronic wrist rotator, any type

C **L7360** Six volt battery, each   DME A

C **L7362** Battery charger, six volt, each   DME A

C **L7364** Twelve volt battery, each   DME A

C **L7366** Battery charger, twelve volt, each   DME A

▲ C **L7367** Lithium ion battery, rechargeable, replacement   DME A

L7368 - L8420

PROSTHETIC PROCEDURES (L5000-L9900)

C **L7368** Lithium ion battery charger, replacement only **DME** A

C **L7400** Addition to upper extremity prosthesis, below elbow/wrist disarticulation, ultralight material (titanium, carbon fiber or equal) **DME** A

Arm Prosthesis

C **L7401** Addition to upper extremity prosthesis, above elbow disarticulation, ultralight material (titanium, carbon fiber or equal) **DME** A

C **L7402** Addition to upper extremity prosthesis, shoulder disarticulation/interscapular thoracic, ultralight material (titanium, carbon fiber or equal) **DME** A

C **L7403** Addition to upper extremity prosthesis, below elbow/wrist disarticulation, acrylic material **DME** A

C **L7404** Addition to upper extremity prosthesis, above elbow disarticulation, acrylic material **DME** A

C **L7405** Addition to upper extremity prosthesis, shoulder disarticulation/interscapular thoracic, acrylic material **DME** A

C **L7499** Upper extremity prosthesis, not otherwise specified A

D **L7510** Repair of prosthetic device, repair or replace minor parts A

C **L7520** Repair prosthetic device, labor component, per 15 minutes A

S **L7600** Prosthetic donning sleeve, any material, each E
Service not separately priced by Part B
Statute: 1862(1)(a)

C **L7900** Male vacuum erection system ♂ **DME** A

C **L7902** Tension ring, for vacuum erection device, any type, replacement only, each **DME** A

D **L8000** Breast prosthesis, mastectomy bra, without integrated breast prosthesis form, any size, any type ♀ **DME** A

D **L8001** Breast prosthesis, mastectomy bra, with integrated breast prosthesis form, unilateral, any size, any type ♀ **DME** A

D **L8002** Breast prosthesis, mastectomy bra, with integrated breast prosthesis form, bilateral, any size, any type ♀ **DME** A

D **L8010** Breast prosthesis, mastectomy sleeve ♀ A
Service not separately priced by Part B

D **L8015** External breast prosthesis garment, with mastectomy form, post mastectomy ♀ **DME** A

D **L8020** Breast prosthesis, mastectomy form ♀ **DME** A

D **L8030** Breast prosthesis, silicone or equal, without integral adhesive ♀ **DME** A

D **L8031** Breast prosthesis, silicone or equal, with integral adhesive ♀ **DME** A

C **L8032** Nipple prosthesis, reusable, any type, each ♀ **DME** A

D **L8035** Custom breast prosthesis, post mastectomy, molded to patient model ♀ **DME** A

C **L8039** Breast prosthesis, not otherwise specified ♀ A

C **L8040** Nasal prosthesis, provided by a non-physician **DME** A
DME Modifier: KM, KN

C **L8041** Midfacial prosthesis, provided by a non-physician **DME** A
DME Modifier: KM, KN

C **L8042** Orbital prosthesis, provided by a non-physician **DME** A
DME Modifier: KM, KN

C **L8043** Upper facial prosthesis, provided by a non-physician **DME** A
DME Modifier: KM, KN

C **L8044** Hemi-facial prosthesis, provided by a non-physician **DME** A
DME Modifier: KM, KN

C **L8045** Auricular prosthesis, provided by a non-physician **DME** A
DME Modifier: KM, KN

C **L8046** Partial facial prosthesis, provided by a non-physician **DME** A
DME Modifier: KM, KN

C **L8047** Nasal septal prosthesis, provided by a non-physician **DME** A
DME Modifier: KM, KN

C **L8048** Unspecified maxillofacial prosthesis, by report, provided by a non-physician A

C **L8049** Repair or modification of maxillofacial prosthesis, labor component, 15 minute increments, provided by a non-physician A

D **L8300** Truss, single with standard pad **DME** A

D **L8310** Truss, double with standard pads **DME** A

D **L8320** Truss, addition to standard pad, water pad **DME** A

D **L8330** Truss, addition to standard pad, scrotal pad ♂ **DME** A

D **L8400** Prosthetic sheath, below knee, each **DME** A

D **L8410** Prosthetic sheath, above knee, each **DME** A

D **L8415** Prosthetic sheath, upper limb, each **DME** A

C **L8417** Prosthetic sheath/sock, including a gel cushion layer, below knee or above knee, each **DME** A

D **L8420** Prosthetic sock, multiple ply, below knee, each **DME** A

▲ Revised Code ● New code **C** Carrier judgment **D** Special coverage instructions apply

I Not payable by Medicare **M** Non-covered by Medicare **S** Non-covered by Medicare statute AHA Coding Clinic®

D **L8430** Prosthetic sock, multiple ply, above knee, each `DME` A

D **L8435** Prosthetic sock, multiple ply, upper limb, each `DME` A

D **L8440** Prosthetic shrinker, below knee, each `DME` A

D **L8460** Prosthetic shrinker, above knee, each `DME` A

D **L8465** Prosthetic shrinker, upper limb, each `DME` A

D **L8470** Prosthetic sock, single ply, fitting, below knee, each `DME` A

D **L8480** Prosthetic sock, single ply, fitting, above knee, each `DME` A

D **L8485** Prosthetic sock, single ply, fitting, upper limb, each `DME` A

C **L8499** Unlisted procedure for miscellaneous prosthetic services A

D **L8500** Artificial larynx, any type `DME` A

D **L8501** Tracheostomy speaking valve `DME` A

C **L8505** Artificial larynx replacement battery / accessory, any type A

C **L8507** Tracheo-esophageal voice prosthesis, patient inserted, any type, each `DME` A

C **L8509** Tracheo-esophageal voice prosthesis, inserted by a licensed health care provider, any type `DME` A

D **L8510** Voice amplifier `DME` A

C **L8511** Insert for indwelling tracheoesophageal prosthesis, with or without valve, replacement only, each `DME` A

C **L8512** Gelatin capsules or equivalent, for use with tracheoesophageal voice prosthesis, replacement only, per 10 `DME` A

C **L8513** Cleaning device used with tracheoesophageal voice prosthesis, pipet, brush, or equal, replacement only, each `DME` A

C **L8514** Tracheoesophageal puncture dilator, replacement only, each `DME` A

C **L8515** Gelatin capsule, application device for use with tracheoesophageal voice prosthesis, each `DME` A

D **L8600** Implantable breast prosthesis, silicone or equal N1 ♀ `DME` N

Breast Prosthesis

D **L8603** Injectable bulking agent, collagen implant, urinary tract, 2.5 ml syringe, includes shipping and necessary supplies N1 `DME` N

C **L8604** Injectable bulking agent, dextranomer/ hyaluronic acid copolymer implant, urinary tract, 1 ml, includes shipping and necessary supplies N1 N

Service not separately priced by Part B

C **L8605** Injectable bulking agent, dextranomer/ hyaluronic acid copolymer implant, anal canal, 1 ml, includes shipping and necessary supplies `DME` N

D **L8606** Injectable bulking agent, synthetic implant, urinary tract, 1 ml syringe, includes shipping and necessary supplies N1 `DME` N

C **L8609** Artificial cornea N1 `DME` N

D **L8610** Ocular implant N1 `DME` N

D **L8612** Aqueous shunt N1 `DME` N

D **L8613** Ossicula implant N1 `DME` N

D **L8614** Cochlear device, includes all internal and external components N1 `DME` N
Pub: 100-4, Chap. 14, 40.8

D **L8615** Headset/headpiece for use with cochlear implant device, replacement `DME` A

D **L8616** Microphone for use with cochlear implant device, replacement `DME` A

D **L8617** Transmitting coil for use with cochlear implant device, replacement `DME` A

D **L8618** Transmitter cable for use with cochlear implant device, replacement `DME` A

D **L8619** Cochlear implant, external speech processor and controller, integrated system, replacement `DME` A

C **L8621** Zinc air battery for use with cochlear implant device, replacement, each `DME` A

C **L8622** Alkaline battery for use with cochlear implant device, any size, replacement, each `DME` A

C **L8623** Lithium ion battery for use with cochlear implant device speech processor, other than ear level, replacement, each `DME` A

C **L8624** Lithium ion battery for use with cochlear implant device speech processor, ear level, replacement, each `DME` A

D **L8627** Cochlear implant, external speech processor, component, replacement `DME` A

D **L8628** Cochlear implant, external controller component, replacement `DME` A

D **L8629** Transmitting coil and cable, integrated, for use with cochlear implant device, replacement `DME` A

D **L8630** Metacarpophalangeal joint implant N1 `DME` N

D **L8631** Metacarpal phalangeal joint replacement, two or more pieces, metal (e.g., stainless steel or cobalt chrome), ceramic-like material (e.g., pyrocarbon), for surgical implantation (all sizes, includes entire system) N1 `DME` N

D **L8641** Metatarsal joint implant N1 `DME` N

D **L8642** Hallux implant N1 `DME` N

D **L8658** Interphalangeal joint spacer, silicone or equal, each N1 `DME` N

♂ Male only   ♀ Female only   Ⓐ Age   A2 - Z3 = ASC Payment Indicator   A - Y = APC Status Indicator

ASC = ASC Approved Procedure   `DME` Paid under the DME fee schedule   `PQRS` Physician Quality Reporting System

PROSTHETIC PROCEDURES (L5000-L9900)

D **L8659** Interphalangeal finger joint replacement, 2 or more pieces, metal (e.g., stainless steel or cobalt chrome), ceramic-like material (e.g., pyrocarbon) for surgical implantation, any size   N1 `DME` N

D **L8670** Vascular graft material, synthetic, implant   `DME` N

D **L8679** Implantable neurostimulator, pulse generator, any type   `DME`

I **L8680** Implantable neurostimulator electrode, each   N

D **L8681** Patient programmer (external) for use with implantable programmable neurostimulator pulse generator, replacement only   `DME` A

D **L8682** Implantable neurostimulator radiofrequency receiver   `DME` N

D **L8683** Radiofrequency transmitter (external) for use with implantable neurostimulator radiofrequency receiver   `DME` A

D **L8684** Radiofrequency transmitter (external) for use with implantable sacral root neurostimulator receiver for bowel and bladder management, replacement   `DME` A

I **L8685** Implantable neurostimulator pulse generator, single array, rechargeable, includes extension   N

  Service not separately priced by Part B

I **L8686** Implantable neurostimulator pulse generator, single array, non-rechargeable, includes extension   N

  Service not separately priced by Part B

I **L8687** Implantable neurostimulator pulse generator, dual array, rechargeable, includes extension   N

  Service not separately priced by Part B

I **L8688** Implantable neurostimulator pulse generator, dual array, non-rechargeable, includes extension   N

  Service not separately priced by Part B

D **L8689** External recharging system for battery (internal) for use with implantable neurostimulator, replacement only   `DME` A

C **L8690** Auditory osseointegrated device, includes all internal and external components   N1 `DME` N
  Pub: 100-4, Chap. 14, 40.8

C **L8691** Auditory osseointegrated device, external sound processor, replacement   `DME` A

S **L8692** Auditory osseointegrated device, external sound processor, used without osseointegration, body worn, includes headband or other means of external attachment   E

  Service not separately priced by Part B
  Statute: 1862(a)(7)

C **L8693** Auditory osseointegrated device abutment, any length, replacement only   `DME` A

D **L8695** External recharging system for battery (external) for use with implantable neurostimulator, replacement only   `DME` A

● **D** **L8696** Antenna (external) for use with implantable diaphragmatic/phrenic nerve stimulation device, replacement, each

C **L8699** Prosthetic implant, not otherwise specified   N1 N

C **L9900** Orthotic and prosthetic supply, accessory, and/or service component of another HCPCS "L" code   N1 N

▲ Revised Code　　● New code　　**C** Carrier judgment　　**D** Special coverage instructions apply

I Not payable by Medicare　　**M** Non-covered by Medicare　　**S** Non-covered by Medicare statute　　AHA Coding Clinic®

MEDICAL SERVICES (M0064-M0301)

[M] **M0075** Cellular therapy   E

Service not separately priced by Part B

[M] **M0076** Prolotherapy   E

Service not separately priced by Part B

[M] **M0100** Intragastric hypothermia using gastric
freezing   E

Service not separately priced by Part B

[M] **M0300** IV chelation therapy (chemical
endarterectomy)   E

Service not separately priced by Part B

Pub: 100-3, Chap. 1, 20.21; 100-3, Chap. 1,
20.22

[M] **M0301** Fabric wrapping of abdominal aneurysm   E

Service not separately priced by Part B

♂ Male only   ♀ Female only   **Ⓐ** Age   A2 - Z3 = ASC Payment Indicator   A - Y = APC Status Indicator
ASC = ASC Approved Procedure   **DME** Paid under the DME fee schedule   **PQRS** Physician Quality Reporting System

PATHOLOGY AND LABORATORY SERVICES
(P2028-P9615)

D **P2028** Cephalin flocculation, blood A
Other carrier priced

D **P2029** Congo red, blood A
Other carrier priced

M **P2031** Hair analysis (excluding arsenic) E
Service not separately priced by Part B

D **P2033** Thymol turbidity, blood A
Other carrier priced

D **P2038** Mucoprotein, blood (seromucoid) (medical
necessity procedure) A
Price subject to national limitation amount

D **P3000** Screening Papanicolaou smear, cervical or
vaginal, up to three smears, by technician
under physician supervision ♀ A
Price subject to national limitation amount

D **P3001** Screening Papanicolaou smear, cervical
or vaginal, up to three smears, requiring
interpretation by physician ♀ B
Price established using national RVU's

I **P7001** Culture, bacterial, urine; quantitative,
sensitivity study E
Service not separately priced by Part B

D **P9010** Blood (whole), for transfusion, per unit R
Reasonable charge
Pub: 100-1, Chap. 3, 20.5; 100-1, Chap. 3,
20.5.2; 100-1, Chap. 3, 20.5.3; 100-2, Chap. 1,
10; 100-4, Chap. 3, 40.2.2

D **P9011** Blood, split unit R
Reasonable charge
Pub: 100-1, Chap. 3, 20.5; 100-1, Chap. 3,
20.5.2; 100-1, Chap. 3, 20.5.3; 100-2, Chap.
1, 10; 100-4, Chap. 3, 40.2.2; 100-4, Chap. 4,
231.4

D **P9012** Cryoprecipitate, each unit R
Reasonable charge
Pub: 100-2, Chap. 1, 10; 100-4, Chap. 3, 40.2.2

D **P9016** Red blood cells, leukocytes reduced,
each unit R
Reasonable charge
Pub: 100-2, Chap. 1, 10; 100-4, Chap. 3, 40.2.2

D **P9017** Fresh frozen plasma (single donor), frozen
within 8 hours of collection, each unit R
Reasonable charge
Pub: 100-2, Chap. 1, 10; 100-4, Chap. 3, 40.2.2

D **P9019** Platelets, each unit R
Reasonable charge
Pub: 100-2, Chap. 1, 10; 100-4, Chap. 3, 40.2.2

D **P9020** Platelet rich plasma, each unit R
Reasonable charge
Pub: 100-4, Chap. 3, 40.2.2

D **P9021** Red blood cells, each unit R
Reasonable charge

Pub: 100-1, Chap. 3, 20.5; 100-1, Chap. 3,
20.5.2; 100-1, Chap. 3, 20.5.3; 100-2, Chap. 1,
10; 100-4, Chap. 3, 40.2.2

D **P9022** Red blood cells, washed, each unit R
Reasonable charge
Pub: 100-1, Chap. 3, 20.5; 100-1, Chap. 3,
20.5.2; 100-1, Chap. 3, 20.5.3; 100-2, Chap. 1,
10; 100-4, Chap. 3, 40.2.2

D **P9023** Plasma, pooled multiple donor, solvent/
detergent treated, frozen, each unit R
Reasonable charge
Pub: 100-2, Chap. 1, 10; 100-4, Chap. 3, 40.2.2

D **P9031** Platelets, leukocytes reduced, each unit R
Reasonable charge
Pub: 100-2, Chap. 1, 10; 100-4, Chap. 3, 40.2.2

D **P9032** Platelets, irradiated, each unit R
Reasonable charge
Pub: 100-2, Chap. 1, 10; 100-4, Chap. 3, 40.2.2

D **P9033** Platelets, leukocytes reduced, irradiated,
each unit R
Reasonable charge
Pub: 100-2, Chap. 1, 10; 100-4, Chap. 3, 40.2.2

D **P9034** Platelets, pheresis, each unit R
Reasonable charge
Pub: 100-2, Chap. 1, 10; 100-4, Chap. 3, 40.2.2

D **P9035** Platelets, pheresis, leukocytes reduced,
each unit R
Reasonable charge
Pub: 100-2, Chap. 1, 10; 100-4, Chap. 3, 40.2.2

D **P9036** Platelets, pheresis, irradiated, each unit R
Reasonable charge
Pub: 100-2, Chap. 1, 10; 100-4, Chap. 3, 40.2.2

D **P9037** Platelets, pheresis, leukocytes reduced,
irradiated, each unit R
Reasonable charge
Pub: 100-2, Chap. 1, 10; 100-4, Chap. 3, 40.2.2

D **P9038** Red blood cells, irradiated, each unit R
Reasonable charge
Pub: 100-1, Chap. 3, 20.5; 100-1, Chap. 3,
20.5.2; 100-1, Chap. 3, 20.5.3; 100-2, Chap. 1,
10; 100-4, Chap. 3, 40.2.2

D **P9039** Red blood cells, deglycerolized, each unit R
Reasonable charge
Pub: 100-2, Chap. 1, 10; 100-4, Chap. 3, 40.2.2

D **P9040** Red blood cells, leukocytes reduced,
irradiated, each unit R
Reasonable charge
Pub: 100-2, Chap. 1, 10; 100-4, Chap. 3, 40.2.2

C **P9041** Infusion, albumin (human), 5%,
50 ml K2 ASC K
Reasonable charge
Pub: 100-2, Chap. 1, 10; 100-4, Chap. 3, 40.2.2

D **P9043** Infusion, plasma protein fraction (human),
5%, 50 ml R
Reasonable charge

▲ Revised Code   ● New code   **C** Carrier judgment   **D** Special coverage instructions apply
I Not payable by Medicare   **M** Non-covered by Medicare   **S** Non-covered by Medicare statute   AHA Coding Clinic®

Pub: 100-2, Chap. 1, 10; 100-4, Chap. 3, 40.2.2

D **P9044** Plasma, cryoprecipitate reduced, each unit R

Reasonable charge

Pub: 100-2, Chap. 1, 10; 100-4, Chap. 3, 40.2.2

C **P9045** Infusion, albumin (human), 5%,
250 ml K2 ASC K

Reasonable charge

Pub: 100-2, Chap. 1, 10; 100-4, Chap. 3, 40.2.2

C **P9046** Infusion, albumin (human), 25%,
20 ml K2 ASC K

Reasonable charge

Pub: 100-2, Chap. 1, 10; 100-4, Chap. 3, 40.2.2

C **P9047** Infusion, albumin (human), 25%,
50 ml K2 ASC K

Reasonable charge

Pub: 100-2, Chap. 1, 10; 100-4, Chap. 3, 40.2.2

C **P9048** Infusion, plasma protein fraction (human),
5%, 250ml R

Reasonable charge

Pub: 100-2, Chap. 1, 10; 100-4, Chap. 3, 40.2.2

C **P9050** Granulocytes, pheresis, each unit R

Reasonable charge

Pub: 100-2, Chap. 1, 10; 100-4, Chap. 3, 40.2.2

D **P9051** Whole blood or red blood cells, leukocytes
reduced, CMV-negative, each unit R

Reasonable charge Statute: 1833T

Pub: 100-2, Chap. 1, 10; 100-4, Chap. 3, 40.2.2

D **P9052** Platelets, HLA-matched leukocytes reduced,
apheresis/pheresis, each unit R

Reasonable charge Statute: 1833T

Pub: 100-2, Chap. 1, 10; 100-4, Chap. 3, 40.2.2

D **P9053** Platelets, pheresis, leukocytes reduced,
CMV-negative, irradiated, each unit R

Reasonable charge Statute: 1833T

Pub: 100-2, Chap. 1, 10; 100-4, Chap. 3, 40.2.2

D **P9054** Whole blood or red blood cells, leukocytes
reduced, frozen, deglycerol, washed, each
unit R

Reasonable charge Statute: 1833T

Pub: 100-2, Chap. 1, 10; 100-4, Chap. 3, 40.2.2

D **P9055** Platelets, leukocytes reduced, CMV-
negative, apheresis/pheresis, each unit R

Reasonable charge Statute: 1833T

Pub: 100-2, Chap. 1, 10; 100-4, Chap. 3, 40.2.2

D **P9056** Whole blood, leukocytes reduced, irradiated,
each unit R

Reasonable charge Statute: 1833T

Pub: 100-2, Chap. 1, 10; 100-4, Chap. 3, 40.2.2

D **P9057** Red blood cells, frozen/deglycerolized/
washed, leukocytes reduced, irradiated,
each unit R

Reasonable charge Statute: 1833T

Pub: 100-2, Chap. 1, 10; 100-4, Chap. 3, 40.2.2

D **P9058** Red blood cells, leukocytes reduced, CMV-
negative, irradiated, each unit R

Reasonable charge Statute: 1833T

Pub: 100-2, Chap. 1, 10; 100-4, Chap. 3, 40.2.2

D **P9059** Fresh frozen plasma between 8-24 hours of
collection, each unit R

Reasonable charge Statute: 1833T

Pub: 100-2, Chap. 1, 10; 100-4, Chap. 3, 40.2.2

D **P9060** Fresh frozen plasma, donor retested, each
unit R

Reasonable charge Statute: 1833T

Pub: 100-2, Chap. 1, 10; 100-4, Chap. 3, 40.2.2

D **P9603** Travel allowance one way in connection with
medically necessary laboratory specimen
collection drawn from home bound or nursing
home bound patient; prorated miles actually
travelled A

Price established by carriers

Pub: 100-4, Chap. 16, 60.2

D **P9604** Travel allowance one way in connection with
medically necessary laboratory specimen
collection drawn from home bound or nursing
home bound patient; prorated trip charge. A

Price established by carriers

Pub: 100-4, Chap. 16, 60.2

D **P9612** Catheterization for collection of specimen,
single patient, all places of service A

Other carrier priced

D **P9615** Catheterization for collection of specimen (s)
(multiple patients) N

Other carrier priced

Pub: 100-4, Chap. 16, 60.1.4

♂ Male only   ♀ Female only   **A** Age   A2 - Z3 = ASC Payment Indicator   A - Y = APC Status Indicator

ASC = ASC Approved Procedure   **DME** Paid under the DME fee schedule   **PQRS** Physician Quality Reporting System

TEMPORARY CODES (Q0035-Q9999)

D **Q0035** Cardiokymography   X
Price established using national RVU's

D **Q0081** Infusion therapy, using other than chemotherapeutic drugs, per visit   B
Service not separately priced by Part B
Coding Clinic: 2004, Q2, P11;Q1, P5, 8;2002, Q2, P10;Q1, P7

C **Q0083** Chemotherapy administration by other than infusion technique only e.g., subcutaneous, intramuscular, push), per visit   B
Service not separately priced by Part B
Coding Clinic: 2002, Q1, P7

D **Q0084** Chemotherapy administration by infusion technique only, per visit   B
Service not separately priced by Part B
Coding Clinic: 2004, Q2, P11;2002, Q1, P7

C **Q0085** Chemotherapy administration by both infusion technique and other technique(s) e.g., subcutaneous, intramuscular, push), per visit   B
Service not separately priced by Part B
Coding Clinic: 2012, Q1, P7

D **Q0091** Screening Papanicolaou smear; obtaining, preparing and conveyance of cervical or vaginal smear to laboratory   ♀ T
Price established using national RVU's
Coding Clinic: 2002, Q4, P8

D **Q0092** Set-up portable X-ray equipment   N
Price established using national RVU's

C **Q0111** Wet mounts, including preparations of vaginal, cervical or skin specimens   A
Price subject to national limitation amount

C **Q0112** All potassium hydroxide (KOH) preparations   A
Price subject to national limitation amount

C **Q0113** Pinworm examinations   A
Price subject to national limitation amount

C **Q0114** Fern test   ♀ A
Price subject to national limitation amount

C **Q0115** Post-coital direct, qualitative examinations of vaginal or cervical mucous   ♀ A
Price subject to national limitation amount

C **Q0138** Injection, ferumoxytol, for treatment of iron deficiency anemia, 1 mg (non-ESRD use)   K2 ASC K
Drugs: FERAHEME

C **Q0139** Injection, ferumoxytol, for treatment of iron deficiency anemia, 1 mg (for ESRD on dialysis)   A
Drugs: FERAHEME

M **Q0144** Azithromycin dihydrate, oral, capsules/powder, 1 gram   E
Service not separately priced by Part B

C **Q0161** Chlorpromazine hydrochloride, 5 mg, oral, FDA approved prescription anti-emetic, for use as a complete therapeutic substitute for an IV anti-emetic at the time of chemotherapy treatment, not to exceed a 48 hour dosage regimen   N1:

D **Q0162** Ondansetron 1 mg, oral, FDA approved prescription anti-emetic, for use as a complete therapeutic substitute for an IV anti-emetic at the time of chemotherapy treatment, not to exceed a 48 hour dosage regimen   N1 N
Statute: 4557 Drugs: ONDANSETRON HCL, ONDANSETRON, ZOFRAN, ZOFRAN ODT, ONDANSETRON ODT
Coding Clinic: 2012, Q1, P9

D **Q0163** Diphenhydramine hydrochloride, 50 mg, oral, FDA approved prescription anti-emetic, for use as a complete therapeutic substitute for an IV anti-emetic at time of chemotherapy treatment not to exceed a 48 hour dosage regimen   N1 N
Statute: 4557 Drugs: DIPHENHYDRAMINE HCL
Coding Clinic: 2012, Q2, P10

D **Q0164** Prochlorperazine maleate, 5 mg, oral, FDA approved prescription anti-emetic, for use as a complete therapeutic substitute for an IV anti-emetic at the time of chemotherapy treatment, not to exceed a 48 hour dosage regimen   N1 N
Statute: 4557 Drugs: PROCHLORPERAZINE MALEATE
Coding Clinic: 2012, Q2, P10

D **Q0166** Granisetron hydrochloride, 1 mg, oral, FDA approved prescription anti-emetic, for use as a complete therapeutic substitute for an IV anti-emetic at the time of chemotherapy treatment, not to exceed a 24 hour dosage regimen   N1 N
Statute: 4557 Drugs: GRANISETRON HCL
Coding Clinic: 2012, Q2, P10

D **Q0167** Dronabinol, 2.5 mg, oral, FDA approved prescription anti-emetic, for use as a complete therapeutic substitute for an IV anti-emetic at the time of chemotherapy treatment, not to exceed a 48 hour dosage regimen   N1 N
Statute: 4557 Drugs: MARINOL, DRONABINOL
Coding Clinic: 2012, Q2, P10

D **Q0169** Promethazine hydrochloride, 12.5 mg, oral, FDA approved prescription anti-emetic, for use as a complete therapeutic substitute for an IV anti-emetic at the time of chemotherapy treatment, not to exceed a 48 hour dosage regimen   N1 N
Statute: 4557 Drugs: PROMETHAZINE HCL
Coding Clinic: 2012, Q2, P11

D **Q0173** Trimethobenzamide hydrochloride, 250 mg, oral, FDA approved prescription anti-emetic, for use as a complete therapeutic substitute for an IV anti-emetic at the time of chemotherapy treatment, not to exceed a 48 hour dosage regimen N1 N

Statute: 4557

Coding Clinic: 2012, Q2, P15

D **Q0174** Thiethylperazine maleate, 10 mg, oral, FDA approved prescription anti-emetic, for use as a complete therapeutic substitute for an IV anti-emetic at the time of chemotherapy treatment, not to exceed a 48 hour dosage regimen N1 N

Statute: 4557

Coding Clinic: 2012, Q2, P16

D **Q0175** Perphenazine, 4 mg, oral, FDA approved prescription anti-emetic, for use as a complete therapeutic substitute for an IV anti-emetic at the time of chemotherapy treatment, not to exceed a 48 hour dosage regimen N1 N

Statute: 4557

Coding Clinic: 2012, Q2, P17

D **Q0177** Hydroxyzine pamoate, 25 mg, oral, FDA approved prescription anti-emetic, for use as a complete therapeutic substitute for an IV anti-emetic at the time of chemotherapy treatment, not to exceed a 48 hour dosage regimen N1 N

Statute: 4557

Coding Clinic: 2012, Q2, P19

D **Q0180** Dolasetron mesylate, 100 mg, oral, FDA approved prescription anti-emetic, for use as a complete therapeutic substitute for an IV anti-emetic at the time of chemotherapy treatment, not to exceed a 24 hour dosage regimen N1 N

Statute: 4557 Drugs: ANZEMET

Coding Clinic: 2012, Q2, P21

D **Q0181** Unspecified oral dosage form, FDA approved prescription anti-emetic, for use as a complete therapeutic substitute for a IV anti-emetic at the time of chemotherapy treatment, not to exceed a 48 hour dosage regimen N1 E

Statute: 4557

Coding Clinic: 2012, Q2, P22

D **Q0478** Power adapter for use with electric or electric/pneumatic ventricular assist device, vehicle type **DME** A

D **Q0479** Power module for use with electric or electric/pneumatic ventricular assist device, replacement only **DME** A

D **Q0480** Driver for use with pneumatic ventricular assist device, replacement only **DME** A

D **Q0481** Microprocessor control unit for use with electric ventricular assist device, replacement only **DME** A

D **Q0482** Microprocessor control unit for use with electric/pneumatic combination ventricular assist device, replacement only **DME** A

D **Q0483** Monitor/display module for use with electric ventricular assist device, replacement only **DME** A

D **Q0484** Monitor/display module for use with electric or electric/pneumatic ventricular assist device, replacement only **DME** A

D **Q0485** Monitor control cable for use with electric ventricular assist device, replacement only **DME** A

D **Q0486** Monitor control cable for use with electric/pneumatic ventricular assist device, replacement only **DME** A

D **Q0487** Leads (pneumatic/electrical) for use with any type electric/pneumatic ventricular assist device, replacement only **DME** A

D **Q0488** Power pack base for use with electric ventricular assist device, replacement only A

D **Q0489** Power pack base for use with electric/pneumatic ventricular assist device, replacement only **DME** A

D **Q0490** Emergency power source for use with electric ventricular assist device, replacement only **DME** A

D **Q0491** Emergency power source for use with electric/pneumatic ventricular assist device, replacement only **DME** A

D **Q0492** Emergency power supply cable for use with electric ventricular assist device, replacement only **DME** A

D **Q0493** Emergency power supply cable for use with electric/pneumatic ventricular assist device, replacement only **DME** A

D **Q0494** Emergency hand pump for use with electric or electric/pneumatic ventricular assist device, replacement only **DME** A

D **Q0495** Battery/power pack charger for use with electric or electric/pneumatic ventricular assist device, replacement only **DME** A

D **Q0496** Battery, other than lithium-ion, for use with electric or electric/pneumatic ventricular assist device, replacement only **DME** A

D **Q0497** Battery clips for use with electric or electric/pneumatic ventricular assist device, replacement only **DME** A

D **Q0498** Holster for use with electric or electric/pneumatic ventricular assist device, replacement only **DME** A

D **Q0499** Belt/vest/bag for use to carry external peripheral components of any type ventricular assist device, replacement only **DME** A

♂ Male only   ♀ Female only   🅐 Age   A2 - Z3 = ASC Payment Indicator   A - Y = APC Status Indicator
ASC = ASC Approved Procedure   **DME** Paid under the DME fee schedule   **PQRS** Physician Quality Reporting System

D **Q0500** Filters for use with electric or electric/ pneumatic ventricular assist device, replacement only   DME A

D **Q0501** Shower cover for use with electric or electric/pneumatic ventricular assist device, replacement only   DME A

D **Q0502** Mobility cart for pneumatic ventricular assist device, replacement only   DME A

D **Q0503** Battery for pneumatic ventricular assist device, replacement only, each   DME A

D **Q0504** Power adapter for pneumatic ventricular assist device, replacement only, vehicle type   DME A

D **Q0506** Battery, lithium-ion, for use with electric or electric/pneumatic ventricular assist device, replacement only   DME A

D **Q0507** Miscellaneous supply or accessory for use with an external ventricular assist device   N1 A

D **Q0508** Miscellaneous supply or accessory for use with an implanted ventricular assist device   N1 A

D **Q0509** Miscellaneous supply or accessory for use with any implanted ventricular assist device for which payment was not made under Medicare Part A   N1 A

D **Q0510** Pharmacy supply fee for initial immunosuppressive drug(s), first month following transplant   B

D **Q0511** Pharmacy supply fee for oral anti-cancer, oral anti-emetic or immunosuppressive drug(s); for the first prescription in a 30-day period   B

D **Q0512** Pharmacy supply fee for oral anti-cancer, oral anti-emetic or immunosuppressive drug(s); for a subsequent prescription in a 30-day period   B

D **Q0513** Pharmacy dispensing fee for inhalation drug(s); per 30 days   B

D **Q0514** Pharmacy dispensing fee for inhalation drug(s); per 90 days   B

D **Q0515** Injection, sermorelin acetate, 1 microgram   ASC K

D **Q1004** New technology intraocular lens category 4 as defined in Federal Register notice   E
Other carrier priced

D **Q1005** New technology intraocular lens category 5 as defined in Federal Register notice   E
Other carrier priced

D **Q2004** Irrigation solution for treatment of bladder calculi, for example renacidin, per 500 ml   N1 N
Statute: 1861S2B

D **Q2009** Injection, fosphenytoin, 50 mg phenytoin equivalent   N1 N
Statute: 1861S2B Drugs: FOSPHENYTOIN, FOSPHENYTOIN SODIUM

D **Q2017** Injection, teniposide, 50 mg   K2 ASC K
Statute: 1861S2B Drugs: VUMON, TENIPOSIDE

D **Q2026** Injection, Radiesse, 0.1 ml   B
Coding Clinic: 2010, Q3, P8
Pub: 100-4, Chap. 32, 260.2.2

D **Q2028** Injection, sculptra, 0.5 mg

D **Q2034** Influenza virus vaccine, split virus, for intramuscular use (Agriflu)   L1 L
Vaccinations

D **Q2035** Influenza virus vaccine, split virus, when administered to individuals 3 years of age and older, for intramuscular use (Afluria)   L1 Ⓐ L
Vaccinations
Coding Clinic: 2011, Q1, P7;2010, Q4, P8-9
Pub: 100-2, Chap. 15, 50.4.4.2

D **Q2036** Influenza virus vaccine, split virus, when administered to individuals 3 years of age and older, for intramuscular use (Flulaval)   L1 Ⓐ L
Vaccinations
Coding Clinic: 2011, Q1, P7;2010, Q4, P8-9

D **Q2037** Influenza virus vaccine, split virus, when administered to individuals 3 years of age and older, for intramuscular use (Fluvirin)   L1 Ⓐ L
Vaccinations
Coding Clinic: 2011, Q1, P7;2010, Q4, P8-9

D **Q2038** Influenza virus vaccine, split virus, when administered to individuals 3 years of age and older, for intramuscular use (Fluzone)   L1 Ⓐ L
Vaccinations
Coding Clinic: 2011, Q1, P7;2010, Q4, P8-9

D **Q2039** Influenza virus vaccine, split virus, when administered to individuals 3 years of age and older, for intramuscular use (not otherwise specified)   L1 Ⓐ L
Vaccinations
Coding Clinic: 2011, Q1, P7;2010, Q4, P8-9

D **Q2043** Sipuleucel-T, minimum of 50 million autologous CD54+ cells activated with PAP-GM-CSF, including leukapheresis and all other preparatory procedures, per infusion   K2 ASC K
Statute: PROVENGE®
Coding Clinic: 2012, Q2, P7;Q1, P7, 9;2011, Q3, P9

C **Q2049** Injection, doxorubicin hydrochloride, liposomal, imported Lipodox, 10 mg   K2 ASC K
Drugs: LIPODOX, LIPODOX 50

D **Q2050** Injection, doxorubicin hydrochloride, liposomal, not otherwise specified, 10 mg   K2 ASC K
Drugs: DOXORUBICIN HCL, LIPOSOMAL, , DOXIL

D **Q2052** Services, supplies and accessories used in the home under the Medicare intravenous immune globulin (IVIG) demonstration
Other carrier priced

▲ Revised Code   ● New code   C Carrier judgment   D Special coverage instructions apply
I Not payable by Medicare   M Non-covered by Medicare   S Non-covered by Medicare statute   AHA Coding Clinic®

D **Q3001** Radioelements for brachytherapy, any type, each   B
Other carrier priced

C **Q3014** Telehealth originating site facility fee   A
Pub: 100-4, Chap. 12, 190.6

D **Q3027** Injection, interferon beta-1a, 1 mcg for intramuscular use   K2 ASC
Drugs: AVONEX

I **Q3028** Injection, interferon beta-1a, 1 mcg for subcutaneous use
Service not separately priced by Part B

D **Q3031** Collagen skin test   N1 N
Price established using national RVU's

C **Q4001** Casting supplies, body cast adult, with or without head, plaster   Ⓐ B
Reasonable charge

C **Q4002** Cast supplies, body cast adult, with or without head, fiberglass   Ⓐ B
Reasonable charge

C **Q4003** Cast supplies, shoulder cast, adult (11 years +), plaster   Ⓐ B
Reasonable charge

C **Q4004** Cast supplies, shoulder cast, adult (11 years +), fiberglass   Ⓐ B
Reasonable charge

C **Q4005** Cast supplies, long arm cast, adult (11 years +), plaster   Ⓐ B
Reasonable charge

C **Q4006** Cast supplies, long arm cast, adult (11 years +), fiberglass   Ⓐ B
Reasonable charge

C **Q4007** Cast supplies, long arm cast, pediatric (0-10 years), plaster   Ⓐ B
Reasonable charge

C **Q4008** Cast supplies, long arm cast, pediatric (0-10 years), fiberglass   Ⓐ B
Reasonable charge

C **Q4009** Cast supplies, short arm cast, adult (11 years +), plaster   Ⓐ B
Reasonable charge

C **Q4010** Cast supplies, short arm cast, adult (11 years +), fiberglass   Ⓐ B
Reasonable charge

C **Q4011** Cast supplies, short arm cast, pediatric (0-10 years), plaster   Ⓐ B
Reasonable charge

C **Q4012** Cast supplies, short arm cast, pediatric (0-10 years), fiberglass   Ⓐ B
Reasonable charge

C **Q4013** Cast supplies, gauntlet cast (includes lower forearm and hand), adult (11 years +), plaster   Ⓐ B
Reasonable charge

C **Q4014** Cast supplies, gauntlet cast (includes lower forearm and hand), adult (11 years +), fiberglass   Ⓐ B
Reasonable charge

C **Q4015** Cast supplies, gauntlet cast (includes lower forearm and hand), pediatric (0-10 years), plaster   Ⓐ B
Reasonable charge

C **Q4016** Cast supplies, gauntlet cast (includes lower forearm and hand), pediatric (0-10 years), fiberglass   Ⓐ B
Reasonable charge

C **Q4017** Cast supplies, long arm splint, adult (11 years +), plaster   Ⓐ B
Reasonable charge

C **Q4018** Cast supplies, long arm splint, adult (11 years +), fiberglass   Ⓐ B
Reasonable charge

C **Q4019** Cast supplies, long arm splint, pediatric (0-10 years), plaster   Ⓐ B
Reasonable charge

C **Q4020** Cast supplies, long arm splint, pediatric (0-10 years), fiberglass   Ⓐ B
Reasonable charge

C **Q4021** Cast supplies, short arm splint, adult (11 years +), plaster   Ⓐ B
Reasonable charge

C **Q4022** Cast supplies, short arm splint, adult (11 years +), fiberglass   Ⓐ B
Reasonable charge

C **Q4023** Cast supplies, short arm splint, pediatric (0-10 years), plaster   Ⓐ B
Reasonable charge

C **Q4024** Cast supplies, short arm splint, pediatric (0-10 years), fiberglass   Ⓐ B
Reasonable charge

C **Q4025** Cast supplies, hip spica (one or both legs), adult (11 years +), plaster   Ⓐ B
Reasonable charge

C **Q4026** Cast supplies, hip spica (one or both legs), adult (11 years +), fiberglass   Ⓐ B
Reasonable charge

C **Q4027** Cast supplies, hip spica (one or both legs), pediatric (0-10 years), plaster   Ⓐ B
Reasonable charge

C **Q4028** Cast supplies, hip spica (one or both legs), pediatric (0-10 years), fiberglass   Ⓐ B
Reasonable charge

C **Q4029** Cast supplies, long leg cast, adult (11 years +), plaster   Ⓐ B
Reasonable charge

C **Q4030** Cast supplies, long leg cast, adult (11 years +), fiberglass   Ⓐ B
Reasonable charge

♂ Male only   ♀ Female only   Ⓐ Age   A2 - Z3 = ASC Payment Indicator   A - Y = APC Status Indicator
ASC = ASC Approved Procedure   **DME** Paid under the DME fee schedule   **PQRS** Physician Quality Reporting System

Q4031 - Q4105

TEMPORARY CODES (Q0035-Q9999)

C **Q4031** Cast supplies, long leg cast, pediatric (0-10 years), plaster   **A** B
Reasonable charge

C **Q4032** Cast supplies, long leg cast, pediatric (0-10 years), fiberglass   **A** B
Reasonable charge

C **Q4033** Cast supplies, long leg cylinder cast, adult (11 years +), plaster   **A** B
Reasonable charge

C **Q4034** Cast supplies, long leg cylinder cast, adult (11 years +), fiberglass   **A** B
Reasonable charge

C **Q4035** Cast supplies, long leg cylinder cast, pediatric (0-10 years), plaster   **A** B
Reasonable charge

C **Q4036** Cast supplies, long leg cylinder cast, pediatric (0-10 years), fiberglass   **A** B
Reasonable charge

C **Q4037** Cast supplies, short leg cast, adult (11 years +), plaster   **A** B
Reasonable charge

C **Q4038** Cast supplies, short leg cast, adult (11 years +), fiberglass   **A** B
Reasonable charge

C **Q4039** Cast supplies, short leg cast, pediatric (0-10 years), plaster   **A** B
Reasonable charge

C **Q4040** Cast supplies, short leg cast, pediatric (0-10 years), fiberglass   **A** B
Reasonable charge

C **Q4041** Cast supplies, long leg splint, adult (11 years +), plaster   **A** B
Reasonable charge

C **Q4042** Cast supplies, long leg splint, adult (11 years +), fiberglass   **A** B
Reasonable charge

C **Q4043** Cast supplies, long leg splint, pediatric (0-10 years), plaster   **A** B
Reasonable charge

C **Q4044** Cast supplies, long leg splint, pediatric (0-10 years), fiberglass   **A** B
Reasonable charge

C **Q4045** Cast supplies, short leg splint, adult (11 years +), plaster   **A** B
Reasonable charge

C **Q4046** Cast supplies, short leg splint, adult (11 years +), fiberglass   **A** B
Reasonable charge

C **Q4047** Cast supplies, short leg splint, pediatric (0-10 years), plaster   **A** B
Reasonable charge

C **Q4048** Cast supplies, short leg splint, pediatric (0-10 years), fiberglass   **A** B
Reasonable charge

C **Q4049** Finger splint, static   B
Reasonable charge

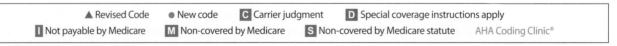

Finger Splint

C **Q4050** Cast supplies, for unlisted types and materials of casts   B
Other carrier priced

C **Q4051** Splint supplies, miscellaneous (includes thermoplastics, strapping, fasteners, padding and other supplies)   B
Other carrier priced

C **Q4074** Iloprost, inhalation solution, Food and Drug Administration (FDA)-approved final product, non-compounded, administered through DME, unit dose form, up to 20 micrograms   Y
Drugs: VENTAVIS

D **Q4081** Injection, epoetin alfa, 100 units (for ESRD on dialysis)   A
Other carrier priced Drugs: EPOGEN, PROCRIT
Pub: 100-4, Chap. 8, 60.4; 100-4, Chap. 8, 60.4.1; 100-4, Chap. 8, 60.4.4.1: 100-4, Chap. 8, 60.4.4.2 ; 100-4, Chap. 8, 60.4.5.1

C **Q4082** Drug or biological, not otherwise classified, Part B drug competitive acquisition program (CAP)   B

C **Q4100** Skin substitute, not otherwise specified   N1 N
Coding Clinic 2012, Q2, P7

C **Q4101** Apligraf, per square centimeter   N1 K
Drugs: APLIGRAF
Coding Clinic 2012, Q2, P7;2011, Q1, P9

C **Q4102** Oasis wound matrix, per square centimeter   N1 K
Drugs: OASIS ULTRA TRI-LAYER MATRIX, OASIS WOUND MATRIX
Coding Clinic 2012, Q2, P7;2011, Q1, P9

C **Q4103** Oasis burn matrix, per square centimeter   N1 K
Drugs: OASIS ULTRA TRI-LAYER MATRIX
Coding Clinic 2012, Q2, P7;2011, Q1, P9

C **Q4104** Integra bilayer matrix wound dressing (BMWD), per square centimeter   N1 K
Drugs: INTEGRA - BMWD
Coding Clinic 2012, Q2, P7;2011, Q1, P9;2010, Q2, P8

C **Q4105** Integra dermal regeneration template (DRT), per square centimeter   N1 K
Drugs: INTEGRA - DRT

▲ Revised Code   ● New code   **C** Carrier judgment   **D** Special coverage instructions apply
I Not payable by Medicare   **M** Non-covered by Medicare   **S** Non-covered by Medicare statute   AHA Coding Clinic®

Coding Clinic 2012, Q2, P7;2011, Q1, P9;2010, Q2, P8

C **Q4106** Dermagraft, per square centimeter N1 K

Drugs: DERMAGRAFT

Coding Clinic 2012, Q2, P7;2011, Q1, P9

C **Q4107** GRAFTJACKET, per square centimeter N1 K

Drugs: MAXFORCE THICK, HANDJACKET SCAFFOLD THIN, ULCERJACKET SCAFFOLD, ULTRA MAXFORCE, GRAFTJACKET STD, GRAFTJACKET SMALL LIGAMENT REPAIR MATRIX, GRAFTJACKET MAXSTRIP

Coding Clinic 2012, Q2, P7;2011, Q1, P9

C **Q4108** Integra matrix, per square centimeter N1 K

Drugs: INTEGRA MATRIX WOUND DRESSING

Coding Clinic 2012, Q2, P7;2011, Q1, P9;2010, Q2, P8

C **Q4110** PriMatrix, per square centimeter N1 K

Drugs: PRIMATRIX, PRIMATRIX 4 X 4 CM, MESHED; 1 EACH, PRIMATRIX 6 X 6 CM, MESHED; 1 EACH, PRIMATRIX 8 X 8 CM, MESHED; 1 EACH, PRIMATRIX 8 X 12 CM, MESHED; 1 EACH

Coding Clinic 2012, Q2, P7;2011, Q1, P9

C **Q4111** GammaGraft, per square centimeter N1 K

Drugs: GAMMAGRAFT

Coding Clinic 2012, Q2, P7;2011, Q1, P9

C **Q4112** Cymetra, injectable, 1cc N1 K

Drugs: CYMETRA

Coding Clinic 2012, Q2, P7;2011, Q1, P9

C **Q4113** GRAFTJACKET XPRESS, injectable, 1cc N1 K

Drugs: GRAFTJACKET® FLOWABLE SOFT 2CC, GRAFTJACKET XPRESS

Coding Clinic 2012, Q2, P7;2011, Q1, P9

C **Q4114** Integra flowable wound matrix, injectable, 1cc N1 K

Drugs: FLOWABLE WOUND MATRIX

Coding Clinic 2012, Q2, P7;2010, Q2, P8

C **Q4115** AlloSkin, per square centimeter N1 K

Drugs: ALLOSKIN

Coding Clinic 2012, Q2, P7;2011, Q1, P9

C **Q4116** AlloDerm, per square centimeter N1 K

Drugs: ALLODERM

Coding Clinic 2012, Q2, P7;2011, Q1, P9

C **Q4117** HYALOMATRIX, per square centimeter E

C **Q4118** MatriStem micromatrix, 1 mg N1 K

Coding Clinic 2012, Q2, P7;2011, Q1, P6

▲ **C** **Q4119** MatriStem Wound Matrix, per square centimetre N1 K

Coding Clinic 2012, Q2, P7;2011, Q1, P6

C **Q4120** MatriStem burn matrix, per square centimeter E

C **Q4121** TheraSkin, per square centimeter K2 K

Drugs: THERASKIN

Coding Clinic 2012, Q2, P7;2011, Q1, P6

C **Q4122** DermACELL, per square centimeter K2 ASC G

Coding Clinic 2012, Q2, P7;Q1, P8

C **Q4123** AlloSkin RT, per square centimeter N1 K

Drugs: ALLOSKIN RT

C **Q4124** OASIS ultra tri-layer wound matrix, per square centimeter N1 G

Coding Clinic 2012, Q2, P7;Q1, P9

C **Q4125** Arthroflex, per square centimeter N1 K

C **Q4126** MemoDerm, DermaSpan, TranZgraft or InteguPly, per square centimeter K

C **Q4127** Talymed, per square centimeter K2 ASC G

C **Q4128** FlexHD, AllopatchHD, or MatrixHD, per square centimeter N1 K

C **Q4129** Unite biomatrix, per square centimeter E

C **Q4130** Strattice TM, per square centimeter N1 N

Coding Clinic 2012, Q2, P7

C **Q4131** EpiFix, per square centimeter K2 ASC G

C **Q4132** Grafix core, per square centimeter K2 ASC G

C **Q4133** Grafix prime, per square centimeter K2 ASC G

C **Q4134** Hmatrix, per square centimeter K

C **Q4135** Mediskin, per square centimeter K

C **Q4136** E-Z Derm, per square centimeter K

C **Q4137** AMNIOEXCEL or BioDExCel, per square centimeter N1

C **Q4138** BioDFence dryflex, per square centimeter N1

C **Q4139** AmnioMatrix or biodmatrix, injectable, 1 cc N1

C **Q4140** Biodfence, per square centimeter N1

C **Q4141** AlloSkin AC, per square centimeter N1

C **Q4142** XCM BIOLOGIC tissue matrix, per square centimeter N1

C **Q4143** Repriza, per square centimeter N1

C **Q4145** EpiFix, injectable, 1 mg N1

C **Q4146** Tensix, per square centimeter N1

▲ **C** **Q4147** Architect, Architect PX, or Architect FX, extracellular matrix, per square centimeter N1

C **Q4148** Neox 1k, per square centimeter N1

C **Q4149** Excellagen, 0.1 cc N1

● **C** **Q4150** Allowrap DS or Dry, per square centimeter

● **C** **Q4151** AmnioBand or Guardian, per square centimeter

● **C** **Q4152** DermaPure, per square centimeter

● **C** **Q4153** Dermavest, per square centimeter

● **C** **Q4154** Biovance, per square centimeter

● **C** **Q4155** NeoxFlo or clarixFlo, 1 mg

● **C** **Q4156** Neox 100, per square centimeter

● **C** **Q4157** Revitalon, per square centimeter

● **C** **Q4158** MariGen, per square centimeter

● **C** **Q4159** Affinity, per square centimeter

● **C** **Q4160** NuShield, per square centimeter

D **Q5001** Hospice or home health care provided in patient's home/residence B

Service not separately priced by Part B

Pub: 100-4, Chap. 10, 40.2; 100-4, Chap. 11, 30.3

Coding Clinic 2012, Q2, P7;2011, Q1, P6

♂ Male only   ♀ Female only   **Ⓐ** Age   A2 - Z3 = ASC Payment Indicator   A - Y = APC Status Indicator

ASC = ASC Approved Procedure   **DME** Paid under the DME fee schedule   **PQRS** Physician Quality Reporting System

D	**Q5002**	Hospice or home health care provided in assisted living facility	B

Service not separately priced by Part B

D	**Q5003**	Hospice care provided in nursing long term care facility (LTC) or non-skilled nursing facility (NF)	B

Service not separately priced by Part B

D	**Q5004**	Hospice care provided in skilled nursing facility (SNF)	B

Service not separately priced by Part B

D	**Q5005**	Hospice care provided in inpatient hospital	B

Service not separately priced by Part B

D	**Q5006**	Hospice care provided in inpatient hospice facility	B

Service not separately priced by Part B

D	**Q5007**	Hospice care provided in long term care facility	B

Service not separately priced by Part B

D	**Q5008**	Hospice care provided in inpatient psychiatric facility	B

Service not separately priced by Part B

D	**Q5009**	Hospice or home health care provided in place not otherwise specified (NOS)	B

Service not separately priced by Part B

Pub: 100-4, Chap. 10, 40.2

D	**Q5010**	Hospice home care provided in a hospice facility	B

Service not separately priced by Part B

D	**Q9951**	Low osmolar contrast material, 400 or greater mg/ml iodine concentration, per ml	N1 N

Pub: 100-4, Chap. 13, 40

D	**Q9953**	Injection, iron-based magnetic resonance contrast agent, per ml	N1 N

Other carrier priced

D	**Q9954**	Oral magnetic resonance contrast agent, per 100 ml	N1 N

Other carrier priced

C	**Q9955**	Injection, perflexane lipid microspheres, per ml	N1 N

Other carrier priced

C	**Q9956**	Injection, octafluoropropane microspheres, per ml	N1 N

Other carrier priced Drugs: OPTISON

C	**Q9957**	Injection, perflutren lipid microspheres, per ml	N1 N

Other carrier priced Drugs: DEFINITY

D	**Q9958**	High osmolar contrast material, up to 149 mg/ml iodine concentration, per ml	N1 N

Drugs: CYSTO-CONRAY II, CONRAY 30, CYSTOGRAFIN, RENO-DIP, CYSTOGRAFIN-DILUTE

Coding Clinic 2007, Q1, P6

D	**Q9959**	High osmolar contrast material, 150-199 mg/ml iodine concentration, per ml	N1 N

Coding Clinic 2007, Q1, P6

D	**Q9960**	High osmolar contrast material, 200-249 mg/ml iodine concentration, per ml	N1 N

Drugs: CONRAY 43

Coding Clinic 2007, Q1, P6

D	**Q9961**	High osmolar contrast material, 250-299 mg/ml iodine concentration, per ml	N1 N

Drugs: CONRAY, CHOLOGRAFIN MEGLUMINE

Coding Clinic 2007, Q1, P6

D	**Q9962**	High osmolar contrast material, 300-349 mg/ml iodine concentration, per ml	N1 N

Coding Clinic 2007, Q1, P6

D	**Q9963**	High osmolar contrast material, 350-399 mg/ml iodine concentration, per ml	N1 N

Drugs: MD-76R, MD GASTROVIEW, GASTROGRAFIN, SINOGRAFIN

Coding Clinic 2007, Q1, P6

D	**Q9964**	High osmolar contrast material, 400 or greater mg/ml iodine concentration, per ml	N1 N

Coding Clinic 2007, Q1, P6

D	**Q9965**	Low osmolar contrast material, 100-199 mg/ml iodine concentration, per ml	N1 N

Drugs: OMNIPAQUE 140, OMNIPAQUE 180, ULTRAVIST 150

D	**Q9966**	Low osmolar contrast material, 200-299 mg/ml iodine concentration, per ml	N1 N

Drugs: OPTIRAY 240, ISOVUE-200, ISOVUE-250, ISOVUE-250 MULTIPACK, ISOVUE-M-200, OMNIPAQUE 240, OMNIPAQUE, OMNIPAQUE 300, VISIPAQUE 270, VISIPAQUE, ULTRAVIST 240

D	**Q9967**	Low osmolar contrast material, 300-399 mg/ml iodine concentration, per ml	N1 N

Drugs: OPTIRAY 320, OPTIRAY 300, OXILAN 350, OPTIRAY 350, HEXABRIX 320, ISOVUE-300, ISOVUE-300 MULTI PACK, ISOVUE-300 PREFILLED SYRINGES, ISOVUE 300, ISOVUE-370, ISOVUE-370 MULTI PACK, ISOVUE-370 PREFILLED SYRINGES, ISO

C	**Q9968**	Injection, non-radioactive, non-contrast, visualization adjunct (e.g., methylene blue, isosulfan blue), 1 mg	N1 K

D	**Q9969**	Tc-99m from non-highly enriched uranium source, full cost recovery add-on, per study dose	K

Statute:

▲ Revised Code   ● New code   **C** Carrier judgment   **D** Special coverage instructions apply

I Not payable by Medicare   **M** Non-covered by Medicare   **S** Non-covered by Medicare statute   AHA Coding Clinic®

DIAGNOSTIC RADIOLOGY SERVICES (R0070-R0076)

D **R0070** Transportation of portable X-ray equipment and personnel to home or nursing home, per trip to facility or location, one patient seen B
Price established by carriers

D **R0075** Transportation of portable X-ray equipment and personnel to home or nursing home, per trip to facility or location, more than one patient seen B
Price established by carriers

D **R0076** Transportation of portable EKG to facility or location, per patient B
Price established by carriers

♂ Male only   ♀ Female only   **A** Age   A2 - Z3 = ASC Payment Indicator   A - Y = APC Status Indicator
ASC = ASC Approved Procedure   **DME** Paid under the DME fee schedule   **PQRS** Physician Quality Reporting System

175

TEMPORARY NATIONAL CODES (NON-MEDICARE) (S0012-S9999)

S0012 Butorphanol tartrate, nasal spray, 25 mg
Service not separately priced by Part B

S0014 Tacrine hydrochloride, 10 mg
Service not separately priced by Part B

S0017 Injection, aminocaproic acid, 5 grams
Service not separately priced by Part B

S0020 Injection, bupivacaine hydrochloride, 30 ml
Service not separately priced by Part B

S0021 Injection, cefoperazone sodium, 1 gram
Service not separately priced by Part B

S0023 Injection, cimetidine hydrochloride, 300 mg
Service not separately priced by Part B

S0028 Injection, famotidine, 20 mg
Service not separately priced by Part B

S0030 Injection, metronidazole, 500 mg
Service not separately priced by Part B

S0032 Injection, nafcillin sodium, 2 grams
Service not separately priced by Part B

S0034 Injection, ofloxacin, 400 mg
Service not separately priced by Part B

S0039 Injection, sulfamethoxazole and trimethoprim, 10 ml
Service not separately priced by Part B

S0040 Injection, ticarcillin disodium and clavulanate potassium, 3.1 grams
Service not separately priced by Part B

S0073 Injection, aztreonam, 500 mg
Service not separately priced by Part B

S0074 Injection, cefotetan disodium, 500 mg
Service not separately priced by Part B

S0077 Injection, clindamycin phosphate, 300 mg
Service not separately priced by Part B

S0078 Injection, fosphenytoin sodium, 750 mg
Service not separately priced by Part B

S0080 Injection, pentamidine isethionate, 300 mg
Service not separately priced by Part B

S0081 Injection, piperacillin sodium, 500 mg
Service not separately priced by Part B

S0088 Imatinib, 100 mg
Service not separately priced by Part B

S0090 Sildenafil citrate, 25 mg
Service not separately priced by Part B

S0091 Granisetron hydrochloride, 1 mg (for circumstances falling under the Medicare statute, use Q0166)
Service not separately priced by Part B

S0092 Injection, hydromorphone hydrochloride, 250 mg (loading dose for infusion pump)
Service not separately priced by Part B

S0093 Injection, morphine sulfate, 500 mg (loading dose for infusion pump)
Service not separately priced by Part B

S0104 Zidovudine, oral, 100 mg
Service not separately priced by Part B

S0106 Bupropion HCL sustained release tablet, 150 mg, per bottle of 60 tablets
Service not separately priced by Part B

S0108 Mercaptopurine, oral, 50 mg
Service not separately priced by Part B

S0109 Methadone, oral, 5 mg
Service not separately priced by Part B

S0117 Tretinoin, topical, 5 grams
Service not separately priced by Part B

S0119 Ondansetron, oral, 4 mg (for circumstances falling under the Medicare statute, use HCPCS Q code)
Service not separately priced by Part B

S0122 Injection, menotropins, 75 IU
Service not separately priced by Part B

S0126 Injection, follitropin alfa, 75 IU ♀
Service not separately priced by Part B

S0128 Injection, follitropin beta, 75 IU
Service not separately priced by Part B

S0132 Injection, ganirelix acetate, 250 mcg ♀
Service not separately priced by Part B

S0136 Clozapine, 25 mg
Service not separately priced by Part B

S0137 Didanosine (ddi), 25 mg
Service not separately priced by Part B

S0138 Finasteride, 5 mg ♂
Service not separately priced by Part B

S0139 Minoxidil, 10 mg
Service not separately priced by Part B

S0140 Saquinavir, 200 mg
Service not separately priced by Part B

S0142 Colistimethate sodium, inhalation solution administered through DME, concentrated form, per mg
Service not separately priced by Part B

S0145 Injection, pegylated interferon alfa-2a, 180 mcg per ml
Service not separately priced by Part B

S0148 Injection, pegylated interferon alfa-2b, 10 mcg
Service not separately priced by Part B

S0155 Sterile dilutant for epoprostenol, 50ml
Service not separately priced by Part B

S0156 Exemestane, 25 mg
Service not separately priced by Part B

S0157 Becaplermin gel 0.01%, 0.5 gm
Service not separately priced by Part B

S0160 Dextroamphetamine sulfate, 5 mg
Service not separately priced by Part B

▲ Revised Code   ● New code   **C** Carrier judgment   **D** Special coverage instructions apply
I Not payable by Medicare   **M** Non-covered by Medicare   **S** Non-covered by Medicare statute   AHA Coding Clinic®

S0164 Injection, pantoprazole sodium, 40 mg
Service not separately priced by Part B

S0166 Injection, olanzapine, 2.5 mg
Service not separately priced by Part B

S0169 Calcitrol, 0.25 microgram
Service not separately priced by Part B

S0170 Anastrozole, oral, 1 mg
Service not separately priced by Part B

S0171 Injection, bumetanide, 0.5 mg
Service not separately priced by Part B

S0172 Chlorambucil, oral, 2 mg
Service not separately priced by Part B

S0174 Dolasetron mesylate, oral 50 mg (for circumstances falling under the Medicare statute, use Q0180)
Service not separately priced by Part B

S0175 Flutamide, oral, 125 mg
Service not separately priced by Part B

S0176 Hydroxyurea, oral, 500 mg
Service not separately priced by Part B

S0177 Levamisole hydrochloride, oral, 50 mg
Service not separately priced by Part B

S0178 Lomustine, oral, 10 mg
Service not separately priced by Part B

S0179 Megestrol acetate, oral, 20 mg
Service not separately priced by Part B

S0182 Procarbazine hydrochloride, oral, 50 mg
Service not separately priced by Part B

▲ **S0183** Prochlorperazine maleate, oral, 5 mg (for circumstances falling under the medicare statute, use Q0164)
Service not separately priced by Part B

S0187 Tamoxifen citrate, oral, 10 mg
Service not separately priced by Part B

S0189 Testosterone pellet, 75 mg
Service not separately priced by Part B

S0190 Mifepristone, oral, 200 mg ♀
Service not separately priced by Part B

S0191 Misoprostol, oral, 200 mcg
Service not separately priced by Part B

S0194 Dialysis/stress vitamin supplement, oral, 100 capsules
Service not separately priced by Part B

S0195 Pneumococcal conjugate vaccine, polyvalent, intramuscular, for children from five years to nine years of age who have not previously received the vaccine Ⓐ
Service not separately priced by Part B

S0197 Prenatal vitamins, 30-day supply ♀
Service not separately priced by Part B

S0199 Medically induced abortion by oral ingestion of medication including all associated services and supplies (e.g., patient counseling, office visits, confirmation of pregnancy by HCG, ultrasound to confirm duration of pregnancy, ultrasound to confirm completion of abortion) except drugs ♀
Service not separately priced by Part B

S0201 Partial hospitalization services, less than 24 hours, per diem
Service not separately priced by Part B

S0207 Paramedic intercept, non-hospital-based ALS service (non-voluntary), non-transport
Service not separately priced by Part B

S0208 Paramedic intercept, hospital-based ALS service (non-voluntary), non-transport
Service not separately priced by Part B

S0209 Wheelchair van, mileage, per mile
Service not separately priced by Part B

S0215 Non-emergency transportation; mileage, per mile
Service not separately priced by Part B

S0220 Medical conference by a physician with interdisciplinary team of health professionals or representatives of community agencies to coordinate activities of patient care (patient is present); approximately 30 minutes
Service not separately priced by Part B

S0221 Medical conference by a physician with interdisciplinary team of health professionals or representatives of community agencies to coordinate activities of patient care (patient is present); approximately 60 minutes
Service not separately priced by Part B

S0250 Comprehensive geriatric assessment and treatment planning performed by assessment team Ⓐ
Service not separately priced by Part B

S0255 Hospice referral visit (advising patient and family of care options) performed by nurse, social worker, or other designated staff
Service not separately priced by Part B

S0257 Counseling and discussion regarding advance directives or end of life care planning and decisions, with patient and/or surrogate (list separately in addition to code for appropriate evaluation and management service)
Service not separately priced by Part B

S0260 History and physical (outpatient or office) related to surgical procedure (list separately in addition to code for appropriate evaluation and management service)
Service not separately priced by Part B

S0265 Genetic counseling, under physician supervision, each 15 minutes
Service not separately priced by Part B

S0270 Physician management of patient home care, standard monthly case rate (per 30 days)
Service not separately priced by Part B

♂ Male only   ♀ Female only   Ⓐ Age   A2 - Z3 = ASC Payment Indicator   A - Y = APC Status Indicator
ASC = ASC Approved Procedure   DME Paid under the DME fee schedule   PQRS Physician Quality Reporting System

S0164 - S0270

TEMPORARY NATIONAL CODES (NON-MEDICARE) (S0012-S9999)

177

S0271	Physician management of patient home care, hospice monthly case rate (per 30 days)
	Service not separately priced by Part B

S0272	Physician management of patient home care, episodic care monthly case rate (per 30 days)
	Service not separately priced by Part B

S0273	Physician visit at member's home, outside of a capitation arrangement
	Service not separately priced by Part B

S0274	Nurse practitioner visit at member's home, outside of a capitation arrangement
	Service not separately priced by Part B

S0280	Medical home program, comprehensive care coordination and planning, initial plan
	Service not separately priced by Part B

S0281	Medical home program, comprehensive care coordination and planning, maintenance of plan
	Service not separately priced by Part B

S0302	Completed early periodic screening diagnosis and treatment (EPSDT) service (list in addition to code for appropriate evaluation and management service) Ⓐ
	Service not separately priced by Part B

S0310	Hospitalist services (list separately in addition to code for appropriate evaluation and management service)
	Service not separately priced by Part B

S0315	Disease management program; initial assessment and initiation of the program
	Service not separately priced by Part B

S0316	Disease management program, follow-up/reassessment
	Service not separately priced by Part B

S0317	Disease management program; per diem
	Service not separately priced by Part B

S0320	Telephone calls by a registered nurse to a disease management program member for monitoring purposes; per month
	Service not separately priced by Part B

S0340	Lifestyle modification program for management of coronary artery disease, including all supportive services; first quarter / stage
	Service not separately priced by Part B

S0341	Lifestyle modification program for management of coronary artery disease, including all supportive services; second or third quarter / stage
	Service not separately priced by Part B

S0342	Lifestyle modification program for management of coronary artery disease, including all supportive services; fourth quarter / stage
	Service not separately priced by Part B

S0353	Treatment planning and care coordination management for cancer, initial treatment
	Service not separately priced by Part B

S0354	Treatment planning and care coordination management for cancer, established patient with a change of regimen
	Service not separately priced by Part B

S0390	Routine foot care; removal and/or trimming of corns, calluses and/or nails and preventive maintenance in specific medical conditions (e.g., diabetes), per visit
	Service not separately priced by Part B

S0395	Impression casting of a foot performed by a practitioner other than the manufacturer of the orthotic
	Service not separately priced by Part B

S0400	Global fee for extracorporeal shock wave lithotripsy treatment of kidney stone(s)
	Service not separately priced by Part B

S0500	Disposable contact lens, per lens
	Service not separately priced by Part B

S0504	Single vision prescription lens (safety, athletic, or sunglass), per lens
	Service not separately priced by Part B

S0506	Bifocal vision prescription lens (safety, athletic, or sunglass), per lens
	Service not separately priced by Part B

S0508	Trifocal vision prescription lens (safety, athletic, or sunglass), per lens
	Service not separately priced by Part B

S0510	Non-prescription lens (safety, athletic, or sunglass), per lens
	Service not separately priced by Part B

S0512	Daily wear specialty contact lens, per lens
	Service not separately priced by Part B

S0514	Color contact lens, per lens
	Service not separately priced by Part B

S0515	Scleral lens, liquid bandage device, per lens
	Service not separately priced by Part B

S0516	Safety eyeglass frames
	Service not separately priced by Part B

S0518	Sunglasses frames
	Service not separately priced by Part B

S0580	Polycarbonate lens (list this code in addition to the basic code for the lens)
	Service not separately priced by Part B

S0581	Nonstandard lens (list this code in addition to the basic code for the lens)
	Service not separately priced by Part B

S0590	Integral lens service, miscellaneous services reported separately
	Service not separately priced by Part B

S0592	Comprehensive contact lens evaluation
	Service not separately priced by Part B

▲ Revised Code   ● New code   C Carrier judgment   D Special coverage instructions apply

I Not payable by Medicare   M Non-covered by Medicare   S Non-covered by Medicare statute   AHA Coding Clinic®

S0595 Dispensing new spectacle lenses for patient supplied frame
Service not separately priced by Part B

S0596 Phakic intraocular lens for correction of refractive error
Service not separately priced by Part B

S0601 Screening proctoscopy
Service not separately priced by Part B

S0610 Annual gynecological examination, new patient ♀
Service not separately priced by Part B

S0612 Annual gynecological examination, established patient ♀
Service not separately priced by Part B

S0613 Annual gynecological examination; clinical breast examination without pelvic evaluation ♀
Service not separately priced by Part B

S0618 Audiometry for hearing aid evaluation to determine the level and degree of hearing loss
Service not separately priced by Part B

S0620 Routine ophthalmological examination including refraction; new patient
Service not separately priced by Part B

S0621 Routine ophthalmological examination including refraction; established patient
Service not separately priced by Part B

S0622 Physical exam for college, new or established patient (list separately in addition to appropriate evaluation and management code) Ⓐ
Service not separately priced by Part B

S0630 Removal of sutures; by a physician other than the physician who originally closed the wound
Service not separately priced by Part B

S0800 Laser in situ keratomileusis (LASIK)
Service not separately priced by Part B

S0810 Photorefractive keratectomy (PRK)
Service not separately priced by Part B

Phototherapeutic Keratectomy

S0812 Phototherapeutic keratectomy (PTK)
Service not separately priced by Part B

S1001 Deluxe item, patient aware (list in addition to code for basic item)
Service not separately priced by Part B
Pub: 100-2, Chap. 1, 10.1.4

S1002 Customized item (list in addition to code for basic item)
Service not separately priced by Part B

S1015 IV tubing extension set
Service not separately priced by Part B

S1016 Non-PVC (polyvinyl chloride) intravenous administration set, for use with drugs that are not stable in PVC e.g. paclitaxel
Service not separately priced by Part B

S1030 Continuous noninvasive glucose monitoring device, purchase (for physician interpretation of data, use CPT® code)
Service not separately priced by Part B

S1031 Continuous noninvasive glucose monitoring device, rental, including sensor, sensor replacement, and download to monitor (for physician interpretation of data, use CPT® code)
Service not separately priced by Part B

● **S1034** Artificial pancreas device system (e.g., low glucose suspend (LGS) feature) including continuous glucose monitor, blood glucose device, insulin pump and computer algorithm that communicates with all of the devices

● **S1035** Sensor; invasive (e.g., subcutaneous), disposable, for use with artificial pancreas device system

● **S1036** Transmitter; external, for use with artificial pancreas device system

● **S1037** Receiver (monitor); external, for use with artificial pancreas device system

S1040 Cranial remolding orthosis, pediatric, rigid, with soft interface material, custom fabricated, includes fitting and adjustment(s) Ⓐ
Service not separately priced by Part B

S1090 Mometasone furoate sinus implant, 370 micrograms
Service not separately priced by Part B

S2053 Transplantation of small intestine and liver allografts
Service not separately priced by Part B

S2054 Transplantation of multivisceral organs
Service not separately priced by Part B

S2055 Harvesting of donor multivisceral organs, with preparation and maintenance of allografts; from cadaver donor
Service not separately priced by Part B

S2060 Lobar lung transplantation
Service not separately priced by Part B

S2061 Donor lobectomy (lung) for transplantation, living donor
Service not separately priced by Part B

♂ Male only   ♀ Female only   Ⓐ Age   A2 - Z3 = ASC Payment Indicator   A - Y = APC Status Indicator
ASC = ASC Approved Procedure   **DME** Paid under the DME fee schedule   **PQRS** Physician Quality Reporting System

Ⅰ S2065 Simultaneous pancreas kidney transplantation

Service not separately priced by Part B

Ⅰ S2066 Breast reconstruction with gluteal artery perforator (GAP) flap, including harvesting of the flap, microvascular transfer, closure of donor site and shaping the flap into a breast, unilateral ♀

Service not separately priced by Part B

Ⅰ S2067 Breast reconstruction of a single breast with "stacked" deep inferior epigastric perforator (DIEP) flap(s) and/or gluteal artery perforator (GAP) flap(s), including harvesting of the flap(s), microvascular transfer, closure of donor site(s) and shaping the flap into a breast, unilateral ♀

Service not separately priced by Part B

Ⅰ S2068 Breast reconstruction with deep inferior epigastric perforator (DIEP) flap or superficial inferior epigastric artery (SIEA) flap, including harvesting of the flap, microvascular transfer, closure of donor site and shaping the flap into a breast, unilateral ♀

Service not separately priced by Part B

Ⅰ S2070 Cystourethroscopy, with ureteroscopy and/or pyeloscopy; with endoscopic laser treatment of ureteral calculi (includes ureteral catheterization)

Service not separately priced by Part B

Ⅰ S2079 Laparoscopic esophagomyotomy (Heller type)

Service not separately priced by Part B

Ⅰ S2080 Laser-assisted uvulopalatoplasty (LAUP)

Service not separately priced by Part B

Ⅰ S2083 Adjustment of gastric band diameter via subcutaneous port by injection or aspiration of saline

Service not separately priced by Part B

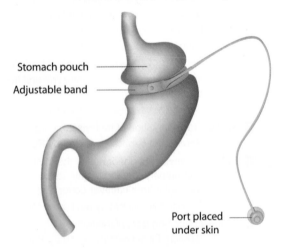

Stomach pouch

Adjustable band

Port placed under skin

Gastric Band

Ⅰ S2095 Transcatheter occlusion or embolization for tumor destruction, percutaneous, any method, using yttrium-90 microspheres

Service not separately priced by Part B

Ⅰ S2102 Islet cell tissue transplant from pancreas; allogeneic

Service not separately priced by Part B

Ⅰ S2103 Adrenal tissue transplant to brain

Service not separately priced by Part B

Ⅰ S2107 Adoptive immunotherapy i.e. development of specific anti-tumor reactivity (e.g., tumor-infiltrating lymphocyte therapy) per course of treatment

Service not separately priced by Part B

Ⅰ S2112 Arthroscopy, knee, surgical for harvesting of cartilage (chondrocyte cells)

Service not separately priced by Part B

Ⅰ S2115 Osteotomy, periacetabular, with internal fixation

Service not separately priced by Part B

Ⅰ S2117 Arthroereisis, subtalar

Service not separately priced by Part B

Ⅰ S2118 Metal-on-metal total hip resurfacing, including acetabular and femoral components

Service not separately priced by Part B

Ⅰ S2120 Low density lipoprotein (LDL) apheresis using heparin-induced extracorporeal LDL precipitation

Service not separately priced by Part B

Ⅰ S2140 Cord blood harvesting for transplantation, allogeneic

Service not separately priced by Part B

Ⅰ S2142 Cord blood-derived stem-cell transplantation, allogeneic

Service not separately priced by Part B

Ⅰ S2150 Bone marrow or blood-derived stem cells (peripheral or umbilical), allogeneic or autologous, harvesting, transplantation, and related complications; including: pheresis and cell preparation/storage; marrow ablative therapy; drugs, supplies, hospitalization with outpatient follow-up; medical/surgical, diagnostic, emergency, and rehabilitative services; and the number of days of pre-and post-transplant care in the global definition

Service not separately priced by Part B

Ⅰ S2152 Solid organ(s), complete or segmental, single organ or combination of organs; deceased or living donor (s), procurement, transplantation, and related complications; including: drugs; supplies; hospitalization with outpatient follow-up; medical/surgical, diagnostic, emergency, and rehabilitative services, and the number of days of pre- and post-transplant care in the global definition

Service not separately priced by Part B

▲ Revised Code   ● New code   **C** Carrier judgment   **D** Special coverage instructions apply

Ⅰ Not payable by Medicare   **M** Non-covered by Medicare   **S** Non-covered by Medicare statute   AHA Coding Clinic®

S2202 Echosclerotherapy
Service not separately priced by Part B

S2205 Minimally invasive direct coronary artery bypass surgery involving mini-thoracotomy or mini-sternotomy surgery, performed under direct vision; using arterial graft(s), single coronary arterial graft
Service not separately priced by Part B

S2206 Minimally invasive direct coronary artery bypass surgery involving mini-thoracotomy or mini-sternotomy surgery, performed under direct vision; using arterial graft(s), two coronary arterial grafts
Service not separately priced by Part B

S2207 Minimally invasive direct coronary artery bypass surgery involving mini-thoracotomy or mini-sternotomy surgery, performed under direct vision; using venous graft only, single coronary venous graft
Service not separately priced by Part B

S2208 Minimally invasive direct coronary artery bypass surgery involving mini-thoracotomy or mini-sternotomy surgery, performed under direct vision; using single arterial and venous graft(s), single venous graft
Service not separately priced by Part B

S2209 Minimally invasive direct coronary artery bypass surgery involving mini-thoracotomy or mini-sternotomy surgery, performed under direct vision; using two arterial grafts and single venous graft
Service not separately priced by Part B

S2225 Myringotomy, laser-assisted
Service not separately priced by Part B

S2230 Implantation of magnetic component of semi-implantable hearing device on ossicles in middle ear
Service not separately priced by Part B

S2235 Implantation of auditory brain stem implant
Service not separately priced by Part B

S2260 Induced abortion, 17 to 24 weeks ♀
Service not separately priced by Part B

S2265 Induced abortion, 25 to 28 weeks ♀
Service not separately priced by Part B

S2266 Induced abortion, 29 to 31 weeks ♀
Service not separately priced by Part B

S2267 Induced abortion, 32 weeks or greater ♀
Service not separately priced by Part B

S2300 Arthroscopy, shoulder, surgical; with thermally-induced capsulorrhaphy
Service not separately priced by Part B

S2325 Hip core decompression
Service not separately priced by Part B

S2340 Chemodenervation of abductor muscle(s) of vocal cord
Service not separately priced by Part B

S2341 Chemodenervation of adductor muscle(s) of vocal cord
Service not separately priced by Part B

S2342 Nasal endoscopy for post-operative debridement following functional endoscopic sinus surgery, nasal and/or sinus cavity(s), unilateral or bilateral
Service not separately priced by Part B

S2348 Decompression procedure, percutaneous, of nucleus pulposus of intervertebral disc, using radiofrequency energy, single or multiple levels, lumbar
Service not separately priced by Part B

S2350 Diskectomy, anterior, with decompression of spinal cord and/or nerve root(s), including osteophytectomy; lumbar, single interspace
Service not separately priced by Part B

S2351 Diskectomy, anterior, with decompression of spinal cord and/or nerve root(s), including osteophytectomy; lumbar, each additional interspace (list separately in addition to code for primary procedure)
Service not separately priced by Part B

S2360 Percutaneous vertebroplasty, one vertebral body, unilateral or bilateral injection; cervical
Service not separately priced by Part B

S2361 Each additional cervical vertebral body (list separately in addition to code for primary procedure)
Service not separately priced by Part B

S2400 Repair, congenital diaphragmatic hernia in the fetus using temporary tracheal occlusion, procedure performed in utero ♀ Ⓐ
Service not separately priced by Part B

S2401 Repair, urinary tract obstruction in the fetus, procedure performed in utero ♀ Ⓐ
Service not separately priced by Part B

S2402 Repair, congenital cystic adenomatoid malformation in the fetus, procedure performed in utero ♀ Ⓐ
Service not separately priced by Part B

S2403 Repair, extralobar pulmonary sequestration in the fetus, procedure performed in utero ♀ Ⓐ
Service not separately priced by Part B

S2404 Repair, myelomeningocele in the fetus, procedure performed in utero ♀ Ⓐ
Service not separately priced by Part B

S2405 Repair of sacrococcygeal teratoma in the fetus, procedure performed in utero ♀ Ⓐ
Service not separately priced by Part B

S2409 Repair, congenital malformation of fetus, procedure performed in utero, not otherwise classified ♀ Ⓐ
Service not separately priced by Part B

S2411 Fetoscopic laser therapy for treatment of twin-to-twin transfusion syndrome Ⓐ
Service not separately priced by Part B

S2900 Surgical techniques requiring use of robotic surgical system (list separately in addition to code for primary procedure)
Service not separately priced by Part B

S3000 Diabetic indicator; retinal eye exam, dilated, bilateral
Service not separately priced by Part B

S3005 Performance measurement, evaluation of patient self assessment, depression
Service not separately priced by Part B

S3600 STAT laboratory request (situations other than S3601)
Service not separately priced by Part B

S3601 Emergency STAT laboratory charge for patient who is homebound or residing in a nursing facility
Service not separately priced by Part B

S3620 Newborn metabolic screening panel, includes test kit, postage and the laboratory tests specified by the state for inclusion in this panel (e.g., galactose; hemoglobin, electrophoresis; hydroxyprogesterone, 17-D; phenylanine (PKU); and thyroxine, total) Ⓐ
Service not separately priced by Part B

S3630 Eosinophil count, blood, direct
Service not separately priced by Part B

S3645 HIV-1 antibody testing of oral mucosal transudate
Service not separately priced by Part B

S3650 Saliva test, hormone level; during menopause ♀
Service not separately priced by Part B

S3652 Saliva test, hormone level; to assess preterm labor risk ♀
Service not separately priced by Part B

S3655 Antisperm antibodies test (immunobead) ♀
Service not separately priced by Part B

S3708 Gastrointestinal fat absorption study
Service not separately priced by Part B

S3721 Prostate cancer antigen 3 (PCA3) testing ♂
Service not separately priced by Part B

S3722 Dose optimization by area under the curve (AUC) analysis, for infusional 5-fluorouracil
Service not separately priced by Part B

S3800 Genetic testing for amyotrophic lateral sclerosis (ALS)
Service not separately priced by Part B

S3840 DNA analysis for germline mutations of the RET proto-oncogene for susceptibility to multiple endocrine neoplasia type 2
Service not separately priced by Part B

S3841 Genetic testing for retinoblastoma
Service not separately priced by Part B

S3842 Genetic testing for Von Hippel-Lindau disease

Service not separately priced by Part B

S3844 DNA analysis of the connexin 26 gene (GJB2) for susceptibility to congenital, profound deafness
Service not separately priced by Part B

S3845 Genetic testing for alpha-thalassemia
Service not separately priced by Part B

S3846 Genetic testing for hemoglobin E beta-thalassemia
Service not separately priced by Part B

S3849 Genetic testing for niemann-pick disease
Service not separately priced by Part B

S3850 Genetic testing for sickle cell anemia
Service not separately priced by Part B

S3852 DNA analysis for APOE epsilon 4 allele for susceptibility to alzheimer's disease
Service not separately priced by Part B

S3853 Genetic testing for myotonic muscular dystrophy
Service not separately priced by Part B

S3854 Gene expression profiling panel for use in the management of breast cancer treatment ♀

Service not separately priced by Part B

S3861 Genetic testing, sodium channel, voltage-gated, type V, alpha subunit (SCN5A) and variants for suspected brugada syndrome
Service not separately priced by Part B

S3865 Comprehensive gene sequence analysis for hypertrophic cardiomyopathy
Service not separately priced by Part B

S3866 Genetic analysis for a specific gene mutation for hypertrophic cardiomyopathy (HCM) in an individual with a known HCM mutation in the family
Service not separately priced by Part B

S3870 Comparative genomic hybridization (CGH) microarray testing for developmental delay, autism spectrum disorder and/or intellectual disability
Service not separately priced by Part B

S3890 DNA analysis, fecal, for colorectal cancer screening
Service not separately priced by Part B

S3900 Surface electromyography (EMG)
Service not separately priced by Part B

S3902 Ballistocardiogram
Service not separately priced by Part B

S3904 Masters two step
Service not separately priced by Part B

S4005 Interim labor facility global (labor occurring but not resulting in delivery) ♀
Service not separately priced by Part B

S4011 In vitro fertilization; including but not limited to identification and incubation of mature

---

▲ Revised Code ● New code Ⓒ Carrier judgment Ⓓ Special coverage instructions apply

Ⓘ Not payable by Medicare Ⓜ Non-covered by Medicare Ⓢ Non-covered by Medicare statute AHA Coding Clinic®

oocytes, fertilization with sperm, incubation of embryo(s), and subsequent visualization for determination of development ♀
Service not separately priced by Part B

S4013 Complete cycle, gamete intrafallopian transfer (GIFT), case rate ♀
Service not separately priced by Part B

S4014 Complete cycle, zygote intrafallopian transfer (ZIFT), case rate ♀
Service not separately priced by Part B

S4015 Complete in vitro fertilization cycle, not otherwise specified, case rate ♀
Service not separately priced by Part B

S4016 Frozen in vitro fertilization cycle, case rate ♀
Service not separately priced by Part B

S4017 Incomplete cycle, treatment cancelled prior to stimulation, case rate ♀
Service not separately priced by Part B

S4018 Frozen embryo transfer procedure cancelled before transfer, case rate ♀
Service not separately priced by Part B

S4020 In vitro fertilization procedure cancelled before aspiration, case rate ♀
Service not separately priced by Part B

S4021 In vitro fertilization procedure cancelled after aspiration, case rate ♀
Service not separately priced by Part B

S4022 Assisted oocyte fertilization, case rate ♀
Service not separately priced by Part B

S4023 Donor egg cycle, incomplete, case rate ♀
Service not separately priced by Part B

S4025 Donor services for in vitro fertilization (sperm or embryo), case rate ♀
Service not separately priced by Part B

S4026 Procurement of donor sperm from sperm bank ♂
Service not separately priced by Part B

S4027 Storage of previously frozen embryos ♀
Service not separately priced by Part B

S4028 Microsurgical epididymal sperm aspiration (MESA) ♂
Service not separately priced by Part B

S4030 Sperm procurement and cryopreservation services; initial visit ♂
Service not separately priced by Part B

S4031 Sperm procurement and cryopreservation services; subsequent visit ♂
Service not separately priced by Part B

S4035 Stimulated intrauterine insemination (IUI), case rate ♀
Service not separately priced by Part B

S4037 Cryopreserved embryo transfer, case rate ♀
Service not separately priced by Part B

S4040 Monitoring and storage of cryopreserved embryos, per 30 days ♀
Service not separately priced by Part B

S4042 Management of ovulation induction (interpretation of diagnostic tests and studies, non-face-to-face medical management of the patient), per cycle ♀
Service not separately priced by Part B

S4981 Insertion of levonorgestrel-releasing intrauterine system ♀
Service not separately priced by Part B

S4989 Contraceptive intrauterine device (e.g., Progestacert IUD), including implants and supplies ♀
Service not separately priced by Part B

Intrauterine Device

S4990 Nicotine patches, legend
Service not separately priced by Part B

S4991 Nicotine patches, non-legend
Service not separately priced by Part B

S4993 Contraceptive pills for birth control ♀
Service not separately priced by Part B

S4995 Smoking cessation gum
Service not separately priced by Part B

S5000 Prescription drug, generic
Service not separately priced by Part B

S5001 Prescription drug, brand name
Service not separately priced by Part B

S5010 5% dextrose and 0.45% normal saline, 1000 ml
Service not separately priced by Part B

S5011 5% dextrose in lactated ringer's, 1000 ml
Service not separately priced by Part B

S5012 5% dextrose with potassium chloride, 1000 ml
Service not separately priced by Part B

S5013 5% dextrose/0.45% normal saline with potassium chloride and magnesium sulfate, 1000 ml
Service not separately priced by Part B

S5014 5% dextrose/0.45% normal saline with potassium chloride and magnesium sulfate, 1500 ml
Service not separately priced by Part B

♂ Male only   ♀ Female only   🅐 Age   A2 - Z3 = ASC Payment Indicator   A - Y = APC Status Indicator
ASC = ASC Approved Procedure   **DME** Paid under the DME fee schedule   **PQRS** Physician Quality Reporting System

I S5035 Home infusion therapy, routine service of infusion device (e.g., pump maintenance)
Service not separately priced by Part B

I S5036 Home infusion therapy, repair of infusion device (e.g., pump repair)
Service not separately priced by Part B

I S5100 Day care services, adult; per 15 minutes Ⓐ
Service not separately priced by Part B

I S5101 Day care services, adult; per half day Ⓐ
Service not separately priced by Part B

I S5102 Day care services, adult; per diem Ⓐ
Service not separately priced by Part B

I S5105 Day care services, center-based; services not included in program fee, per diem
Service not separately priced by Part B

I S5108 Home care training to home care client, per 15 minutes
Service not separately priced by Part B

I S5109 Home care training to home care client, per session
Service not separately priced by Part B

I S5110 Home care training, family; per 15 minutes
Service not separately priced by Part B

I S5111 Home care training, family; per session
Service not separately priced by Part B

I S5115 Home care training, non-family; per 15 minutes
Service not separately priced by Part B

I S5116 Home care training, non-family; per session
Service not separately priced by Part B

I S5120 Chore services; per 15 minutes
Service not separately priced by Part B

I S5121 Chore services; per diem
Service not separately priced by Part B

I S5125 Attendant care services; per 15 minutes
Service not separately priced by Part B

I S5126 Attendant care services; per diem
Service not separately priced by Part B

I S5130 Homemaker service, NOS; per 15 minutes
Service not separately priced by Part B

I S5131 Homemaker service, NOS; per diem
Service not separately priced by Part B

I S5135 Companion care, adult (e.g., IADL/ADL); per 15 minutes Ⓐ
Service not separately priced by Part B

I S5136 Companion care, adult (e.g., IADL/ADL); per diem Ⓐ
Service not separately priced by Part B

I S5140 Foster care, adult; per diem Ⓐ
Service not separately priced by Part B

I S5141 Foster care, adult; per month Ⓐ
Service not separately priced by Part B

I S5145 Foster care, therapeutic, child; per diem Ⓐ
Service not separately priced by Part B

I S5146 Foster care, therapeutic, child; per month Ⓐ
Service not separately priced by Part B

I S5150 Unskilled respite care, not hospice; per 15 minutes
Service not separately priced by Part B

I S5151 Unskilled respite care, not hospice; per diem
Service not separately priced by Part B

I S5160 Emergency response system; installation and testing
Service not separately priced by Part B

I S5161 Emergency response system; service fee, per month (excludes installation and testing)
Service not separately priced by Part B

I S5162 Emergency response system; purchase only
Service not separately priced by Part B

I S5165 Home modifications; per service
Service not separately priced by Part B

I S5170 Home delivered meals, including preparation; per meal
Service not separately priced by Part B

I S5175 Laundry service, external, professional; per order
Service not separately priced by Part B

I S5180 Home health respiratory therapy, initial evaluation
Service not separately priced by Part B

I S5181 Home health respiratory therapy, NOS, per diem
Service not separately priced by Part B

I S5185 Medication reminder service, non-face-to-face; per month
Service not separately priced by Part B

I S5190 Wellness assessment, performed by non-physician
Service not separately priced by Part B

I S5199 Personal care item, NOS, each
Service not separately priced by Part B

I S5497 Home infusion therapy, catheter care / maintenance, not otherwise classified; includes administrative services, professional pharmacy services, care coordination, and all necessary supplies and equipment (drugs and nursing visits coded separately), per diem
Service not separately priced by Part B

I S5498 Home infusion therapy, catheter care / maintenance, simple (single lumen), includes administrative services, professional pharmacy services, care coordination and all necessary supplies and equipment, (drugs and nursing visits coded separately), per diem
Service not separately priced by Part B

I S5501 Home infusion therapy, catheter care / maintenance, complex (more than one lumen), includes administrative services, professional pharmacy services, care coordination, and all necessary supplies and equipment (drugs and nursing visits coded separately), per diem
Service not separately priced by Part B

▲ Revised Code ● New code C Carrier judgment D Special coverage instructions apply
I Not payable by Medicare M Non-covered by Medicare S Non-covered by Medicare statute AHA Coding Clinic®

▯ **S5502** Home infusion therapy, catheter care / maintenance, implanted access device, includes administrative services, professional pharmacy services, care coordination and all necessary supplies and equipment, (drugs and nursing visits coded separately), per diem (use this code for interim maintenance of vascular access not currently in use)
Service not separately priced by Part B

▯ **S5517** Home infusion therapy, all supplies necessary for restoration of catheter patency or declotting
Service not separately priced by Part B

▯ **S5518** Home infusion therapy, all supplies necessary for catheter repair
Service not separately priced by Part B

▯ **S5520** Home infusion therapy, all supplies (including catheter) necessary for a peripherally inserted central venous catheter (PICC) line insertion
Service not separately priced by Part B

▯ **S5521** Home infusion therapy, all supplies (including catheter) necessary for a midline catheter insertion
Service not separately priced by Part B

▯ **S5522** Home infusion therapy, insertion of peripherally inserted central venous catheter (PICC), nursing services only (no supplies or catheter included)
Service not separately priced by Part B

▯ **S5523** Home infusion therapy, insertion of midline venous catheter, nursing services only (no supplies or catheter included)
Service not separately priced by Part B

▯ **S5550** Insulin, rapid onset, 5 units
Service not separately priced by Part B

▯ **S5551** Insulin, most rapid onset (Lispro or Aspart); 5 units
Service not separately priced by Part B

▯ **S5552** Insulin, intermediate acting (NPH or LENTE); 5 units
Service not separately priced by Part B

▯ **S5553** Insulin, long acting; 5 units
Service not separately priced by Part B

▯ **S5560** Insulin delivery device, reusable pen; 1.5 ml size
Service not separately priced by Part B

▯ **S5561** Insulin delivery device, reusable pen; 3 ml size
Service not separately priced by Part B

▯ **S5565** Insulin cartridge for use in insulin delivery device other than pump; 150 units
Service not separately priced by Part B

▯ **S5566** Insulin cartridge for use in insulin delivery device other than pump; 300 units
Service not separately priced by Part B

▯ **S5570** Insulin delivery device, disposable pen (including insulin); 1.5 ml size
Service not separately priced by Part B

▯ **S5571** Insulin delivery device, disposable pen (including insulin); 3 ml size
Service not separately priced by Part B

▯ **S8030** Scleral application of tantalum ring(s) for localization of lesions for proton beam therapy
Service not separately priced by Part B

● **S8032** Low-dose Computed Tomography For Lung Cancer Screening

▯ **S8035** Magnetic source imaging
Service not separately priced by Part B

▯ **S8037** Magnetic resonance cholangiopancreatography (MRCP)
Service not separately priced by Part B

▯ **S8040** Topographic brain mapping
Service not separately priced by Part B

▯ **S8042** Magnetic resonance imaging (MRI), low-field
Service not separately priced by Part B

▯ **S8055** Ultrasound guidance for multifetal pregnancy reduction(s), technical component (only to be used when the physician doing the reduction procedure does not perform the ultrasound, guidance is included in the CPT® code for multifetal pregnancy reduction) ♀
Service not separately priced by Part B

▯ **S8080** Scintimammography (radioimmunoscintigraphy of the breast), unilateral, including supply of radiopharmaceutical ♀
Service not separately priced by Part B

▯ **S8085** Fluorine-18 fluorodeoxyglucose (F-18 FDG) imaging using dual-head coincidence detection system (non-dedicated PET scan)
Service not separately priced by Part B

▯ **S8092** Electron beam computed tomography (also known as ultrafast CT, cine CT)
Service not separately priced by Part B

CT Scanner

I **S8096** Portable peak flow meter
Service not separately priced by Part B

I **S8097** Asthma kit (including but not limited to portable peak expiratory flow meter, instructional video, brochure, and/or spacer)
Service not separately priced by Part B

I **S8100** Holding chamber or spacer for use with an inhaler or nebulizer; without mask
Service not separately priced by Part B

I **S8101** Holding chamber or spacer for use with an inhaler or nebulizer; with mask
Service not separately priced by Part B

I **S8110** Peak expiratory flow rate (physician services)
Service not separately priced by Part B

I **S8120** Oxygen contents, gaseous, 1 unit equals 1 cubic foot
Service not separately priced by Part B

I **S8121** Oxygen contents, liquid, 1 unit equals 1 pound
Service not separately priced by Part B

I **S8130** Interferential current stimulator, 2 channel
Service not separately priced by Part B

I **S8131** Interferential current stimulator, 4 channel
Service not separately priced by Part B

I **S8185** Flutter device
Service not separately priced by Part B

I **S8186** Swivel adaptor
Service not separately priced by Part B

I **S8189** Tracheostomy supply, not otherwise classified
Service not separately priced by Part B

I **S8210** Mucus trap
Service not separately priced by Part B

I **S8262** Mandibular orthopedic repositioning device, each
Service not separately priced by Part B

I **S8265** Haberman feeder for cleft lip/palate
Service not separately priced by Part B

I **S8270** Enuresis alarm, using auditory buzzer and/or vibration device
Service not separately priced by Part B

I **S8301** Infection control supplies, not otherwise specified
Service not separately priced by Part B

I **S8415** Supplies for home delivery of infant   A
Service not separately priced by Part B

I **S8420** Gradient pressure aid (sleeve and glove combination), custom made
Service not separately priced by Part B

I **S8421** Gradient pressure aid (sleeve and glove combination), ready made
Service not separately priced by Part B

I **S8422** Gradient pressure aid (sleeve), custom made, medium weight
Service not separately priced by Part B

I **S8423** Gradient pressure aid (sleeve), custom made, heavy weight
Service not separately priced by Part B

I **S8424** Gradient pressure aid (sleeve), ready made
Service not separately priced by Part B

I **S8425** Gradient pressure aid (glove), custom made, medium weight
Service not separately priced by Part B

I **S8426** Gradient pressure aid (glove), custom made, heavy weight
Service not separately priced by Part B

I **S8427** Gradient pressure aid (glove), ready made
Service not separately priced by Part B

I **S8428** Gradient pressure aid (gauntlet), ready made
Service not separately priced by Part B

I **S8429** Gradient pressure exterior wrap
Service not separately priced by Part B

I **S8430** Padding for compression bandage, roll
Service not separately priced by Part B

I **S8431** Compression bandage, roll
Service not separately priced by Part B

I **S8450** Splint, prefabricated, digit (specify digit by use of modifier)
Service not separately priced by Part B

I **S8451** Splint, prefabricated, wrist or ankle
Service not separately priced by Part B

I **S8452** Splint, prefabricated, elbow
Service not separately priced by Part B

I **S8460** Camisole, post-mastectomy
Service not separately priced by Part B

I **S8490** Insulin syringes (100 syringes, any size)
Service not separately priced by Part B

I **S8930** Electrical stimulation of auricular acupuncture points; each 15 minutes of personal one-on-one contact with the patient
Service not separately priced by Part B

I **S8940** Equestrian/hippotherapy, per session
Service not separately priced by Part B

I **S8948** Application of a modality (requiring constant provider attendance) to one or more areas; low-level laser; each 15 minutes
Service not separately priced by Part B

I **S8950** Complex lymphedema therapy, each 15 minutes
Service not separately priced by Part B

I **S8990** Physical or manipulative therapy performed for maintenance rather than restoration
Service not separately priced by Part B

I **S8999** Resuscitation bag (for use by patient on artificial respiration during power failure or other catastrophic event)
Service not separately priced by Part B

▲ Revised Code   ● New code   C Carrier judgment   D Special coverage instructions apply
I Not payable by Medicare   M Non-covered by Medicare   S Non-covered by Medicare statute   AHA Coding Clinic®

S9001 Home uterine monitor with or without associated nursing services ♀
Service not separately priced by Part B

S9007 Ultrafiltration monitor
Service not separately priced by Part B

S9015 Automated EEG monitoring
Service not separately priced by Part B

S9024 Paranasal sinus ultrasound
Service not separately priced by Part B

S9025 Omnicardiogram/cardiointegram
Service not separately priced by Part B

S9034 Extracorporeal shockwave lithotripsy for gall stones
Service not separately priced by Part B

Extracorporeal Shock Wave Lithotripsy

S9055 Procuren or other growth factor preparation to promote wound healing
Service not separately priced by Part B

S9056 Coma stimulation per diem
Service not separately priced by Part B

S9061 Home administration of aerosolized drug therapy (e.g., pentamidine); administrative services, professional pharmacy services, care coordination, all necessary supplies and equipment (drugs and nursing visits coded separately), per diem
Service not separately priced by Part B

S9083 Global fee urgent care centers
Service not separately priced by Part B

S9088 Services provided in an urgent care center (list in addition to code for service)
Service not separately priced by Part B

S9090 Vertebral axial decompression, per session
Service not separately priced by Part B

S9097 Home visit for wound care
Service not separately priced by Part B

S9098 Home visit, phototherapy services (e.g., Bili-lite), including equipment rental, nursing services, blood draw, supplies, and other services, per diem
Service not separately priced by Part B

S9110 Telemonitoring of patient in their home, including all necessary equipment; computer system, connections, and software; maintenance; patient education and support; per month
Service not separately priced by Part B

S9117 Back school, per visit
Service not separately priced by Part B

S9122 Home health aide or certified nurse assistant, providing care in the home; per hour
Service not separately priced by Part B

S9123 Nursing care, in the home; by registered nurse, per hour
Service not separately priced by Part B

S9124 Nursing care, in the home; by licensed practical nurse, per hour
Service not separately priced by Part B

S9125 Respite care, in the home, per diem
Service not separately priced by Part B

S9126 Hospice care, in the home, per diem
Service not separately priced by Part B

S9127 Social work visit, in the home, per diem
Service not separately priced by Part B

S9128 Speech therapy, in the home, per diem
Service not separately priced by Part B

S9129 Occupational therapy, in the home, per diem
Service not separately priced by Part B

S9131 Physical therapy; in the home, per diem
Service not separately priced by Part B

S9140 Diabetic management program, follow-up visit to non-MD provider
Service not separately priced by Part B

S9141 Diabetic management program, follow-up visit to MD provider
Service not separately priced by Part B

S9145 Insulin pump initiation, instruction in initial use of pump (pump not included)
Service not separately priced by Part B

S9150 Evaluation by ocularist
Service not separately priced by Part B

S9152 Speech therapy, re-evaluation
Service not separately priced by Part B

S9208 Home management of preterm labor, including administrative services, professional pharmacy services, care coordination, and all necessary supplies or equipment (drugs and nursing visits coded separately), per diem (do not use this code with any home infusion per diem code) ♀
Service not separately priced by Part B

♂ Male only   ♀ Female only   🅐 Age   A2 - Z3 = ASC Payment Indicator   A - Y = APC Status Indicator
ASC = ASC Approved Procedure   **DME** Paid under the DME fee schedule   **PQRS** Physician Quality Reporting System

I **S9209** Home management of preterm premature rupture of membranes (PPROM), including administrative services, professional pharmacy services, care coordination, and all necessary supplies or equipment (drugs and nursing visits coded separately), per diem (do not use this code with any home infusion per diem code) ♀
Service not separately priced by Part B

I **S9211** Home management of gestational hypertension, includes administrative services, professional pharmacy services, care coordination and all necessary supplies and equipment (drugs and nursing visits coded separately); per diem (do not use this code with any home infusion per diem code) ♀
Service not separately priced by Part B

I **S9212** Home management of postpartum hypertension, includes administrative services, professional pharmacy services, care coordination, and all necessary supplies and equipment (drugs and nursing visits coded separately), per diem (do not use this code with any home infusion per diem code) ♀
Service not separately priced by Part B

I **S9213** Home management of preeclampsia, includes administrative services, professional pharmacy services, care coordination, and all necessary supplies and equipment (drugs and nursing services coded separately); per diem (do not use this code with any home infusion per diem code) ♀
Service not separately priced by Part B

I **S9214** Home management of gestational diabetes, includes administrative services, professional pharmacy services, care coordination, and all necessary supplies and equipment (drugs and nursing visits coded separately); per diem (do not use this code with any home infusion per diem code) ♀
Service not separately priced by Part B

I **S9325** Home infusion therapy, pain management infusion; administrative services, professional pharmacy services, care coordination, and all necessary supplies and equipment, (drugs and nursing visits coded separately), per diem (do not use this code with S9326, S9327 or S9328)
Service not separately priced by Part B

I **S9326** Home infusion therapy, continuous (twenty-four hours or more) pain management infusion; administrative services, professional pharmacy services, care coordination and all necessary supplies and equipment (drugs and nursing visits coded separately), per diem
Service not separately priced by Part B

I **S9327** Home infusion therapy, intermittent (less than twenty-four hours) pain management infusion; administrative services,

professional pharmacy services, care coordination, and all necessary supplies and equipment (drugs and nursing visits coded separately), per diem
Service not separately priced by Part B

I **S9328** Home infusion therapy, implanted pump pain management infusion; administrative services, professional pharmacy services, care coordination, and all necessary supplies and equipment (drugs and nursing visits coded separately), per diem
Service not separately priced by Part B

I **S9329** Home infusion therapy, chemotherapy infusion; administrative services, professional pharmacy services, care coordination, and all necessary supplies and equipment (drugs and nursing visits coded separately), per diem (do not use this code with S9330 or S9331)
Service not separately priced by Part B

I **S9330** Home infusion therapy, continuous (twenty-four hours or more) chemotherapy infusion; administrative services, professional pharmacy services, care coordination, and all necessary supplies and equipment (drugs and nursing visits coded separately), per diem
Service not separately priced by Part B

I **S9331** Home infusion therapy, intermittent (less than twenty-four hours) chemotherapy infusion; administrative services, professional pharmacy services, care coordination, and all necessary supplies and equipment (drugs and nursing visits coded separately), per diem
Service not separately priced by Part B

I **S9335** Home therapy, hemodialysis; administrative services, professional pharmacy services, care coordination, and all necessary supplies and equipment (drugs and nursing services coded separately), per diem
Service not separately priced by Part B

I **S9336** Home infusion therapy, continuous anticoagulant infusion therapy (e.g., Heparin), administrative services, professional pharmacy services, care coordination and all necessary supplies and equipment (drugs and nursing visits coded separately), per diem
Service not separately priced by Part B

I **S9338** Home infusion therapy, immunotherapy, administrative services, professional pharmacy services, care coordination, and all necessary supplies and equipment (drugs and nursing visits coded separately), per diem
Service not separately priced by Part B

I **S9339** Home therapy; peritoneal dialysis, administrative services, professional pharmacy services, care coordination and all necessary supplies and equipment (drugs and nursing visits coded separately), per diem

Service not separately priced by Part B

▯ **S9340** Home therapy; enteral nutrition; administrative services, professional pharmacy services, care coordination, and all necessary supplies and equipment (enteral formula and nursing visits coded separately), per diem

Service not separately priced by Part B

▯ **S9341** Home therapy; enteral nutrition via gravity; administrative services, professional pharmacy services, care coordination, and all necessary supplies and equipment (enteral formula and nursing visits coded separately), per diem

Service not separately priced by Part B

▯ **S9342** Home therapy; enteral nutrition via pump; administrative services, professional pharmacy services, care coordination, and all necessary supplies and equipment (enteral formula and nursing visits coded separately), per diem

Service not separately priced by Part B

▯ **S9343** Home therapy; enteral nutrition via bolus; administrative services, professional pharmacy services, care coordination, and all necessary supplies and equipment (enteral formula and nursing visits coded separately), per diem

Service not separately priced by Part B

▯ **S9345** Home infusion therapy, anti-hemophilic agent infusion therapy (e.g., factor VIII); administrative services, professional pharmacy services, care coordination, and all necessary supplies and equipment (drugs and nursing visits coded separately), per diem

Service not separately priced by Part B

▯ **S9346** Home infusion therapy, alpha-1-proteinase inhibitor (e.g., Prolastin); administrative services, professional pharmacy services, care coordination, and all necessary supplies and equipment (drugs and nursing visits coded separately), per diem

Service not separately priced by Part B

▯ **S9347** Home infusion therapy, uninterrupted, long-term, controlled rate intravenous or subcutaneous infusion therapy (e.g., epoprostenol); administrative services, professional pharmacy services, care coordination, and all necessary supplies and equipment (drugs and nursing visits coded separately), per diem

Service not separately priced by Part B

▯ **S9348** Home infusion therapy, sympathomimetic/ inotropic agent infusion therapy (e.g., Dobutamine); administrative services,

professional pharmacy services, care coordination, all necessary supplies and equipment (drugs and nursing visits coded separately), per diem

Service not separately priced by Part B

▯ **S9349** Home infusion therapy, tocolytic infusion therapy; administrative services, professional pharmacy services, care coordination, and all necessary supplies and equipment (drugs and nursing visits coded separately), per diem

Service not separately priced by Part B

▯ **S9351** Home infusion therapy, continuous or intermittent anti-emetic infusion therapy; administrative services, professional pharmacy services, care coordination, and all necessary supplies and equipment (drugs and visits coded separately), per diem

Service not separately priced by Part B

▯ **S9353** Home infusion therapy, continuous insulin infusion therapy; administrative services, professional pharmacy services, care coordination, and all necessary supplies and equipment (drugs and nursing visits coded separately), per diem

Service not separately priced by Part B

▯ **S9355** Home infusion therapy, chelation therapy; administrative services, professional pharmacy services, care coordination, and all necessary supplies and equipment (drugs and nursing visits coded separately), per diem

Service not separately priced by Part B

▯ **S9357** Home infusion therapy, enzyme replacement intravenous therapy; (e.g., Imiglucerase); administrative services, professional pharmacy services, care coordination, and all necessary supplies and equipment (drugs and nursing visits coded separately), per diem

Service not separately priced by Part B

▯ **S9359** Home infusion therapy, anti-tumor necrosis factor intravenous therapy; (e.g., Infliximab); administrative services, professional pharmacy services, care coordination, and all necessary supplies and equipment (drugs and nursing visits coded separately), per diem

Service not separately priced by Part B

▯ **S9361** Home infusion therapy, diuretic intravenous therapy; administrative services, professional pharmacy services, care coordination, and all necessary supplies and equipment (drugs and nursing visits coded separately), per diem

Service not separately priced by Part B

I **S9363** Home infusion therapy, anti-spasmotic therapy; administrative services, professional pharmacy services, care coordination, and all necessary supplies and equipment (drugs and nursing visits coded separately), per diem

Service not separately priced by Part B

I **S9364** Home infusion therapy, total parenteral nutrition (TPN); administrative services, professional pharmacy services, care coordination, and all necessary supplies and equipment including standard TPN formula (lipids, specialty amino acid formulas, drugs other than in standard formula and nursing visits coded separately), per diem (do not use with home infusion codes S9365-S9368 using daily volume scales)

Service not separately priced by Part B

I **S9365** Home infusion therapy, total parenteral nutrition (TPN); one liter per day, administrative services, professional pharmacy services, care coordination, and all necessary supplies and equipment including standard TPN formula (lipids, specialty amino acid formulas, drugs other than in standard formula and nursing visits coded separately), per diem

Service not separately priced by Part B

I **S9366** Home infusion therapy, total parenteral nutrition (TPN); more than one liter but no more than two liters per day, administrative services, professional pharmacy services, care coordination, and all necessary supplies and equipment including standard TPN formula (lipids, specialty amino acid formulas, drugs other than in standard formula and nursing visits coded separately), per diem

Service not separately priced by Part B

I **S9367** Home infusion therapy, total parenteral nutrition (TPN); more than two liters but no more than three liters per day, administrative services, professional pharmacy services, care coordination, and all necessary supplies and equipment including standard TPN formula (lipids, specialty amino acid formulas, drugs other than in standard formula and nursing visits coded separately), per diem

Service not separately priced by Part B

I **S9368** Home infusion therapy, total parenteral nutrition (TPN); more than three liters per day, administrative services, professional pharmacy services, care coordination, and all necessary supplies and equipment including standard TPN formula (lipids, specialty amino acid formulas, drugs other than in standard formula and nursing visits coded separately), per diem

Service not separately priced by Part B

I **S9370** Home therapy, intermittent anti-emetic injection therapy; administrative services, professional pharmacy services, care coordination, and all necessary supplies and equipment (drugs and nursing visits coded separately), per diem

Service not separately priced by Part B

I **S9372** Home therapy; intermittent anticoagulant injection therapy (e.g., Heparin); administrative services, professional pharmacy services, care coordination, and all necessary supplies and equipment (drugs and nursing visits coded separately), per diem (do not use this code for flushing of infusion devices with Heparin to maintain patency)

Service not separately priced by Part B

I **S9373** Home infusion therapy, hydration therapy; administrative services, professional pharmacy services, care coordination, and all necessary supplies and equipment (drugs and nursing visits coded separately), per diem (do not use with hydration therapy codes S9374-S9377 using daily volume scales)

Service not separately priced by Part B

I **S9374** Home infusion therapy, hydration therapy; one liter per day, administrative services, professional pharmacy services, care coordination, and all necessary supplies and equipment (drugs and nursing visits coded separately), per diem

Service not separately priced by Part B

I **S9375** Home infusion therapy, hydration therapy; more than one liter but no more than two liters per day, administrative services, professional pharmacy services, care coordination, and all necessary supplies and equipment (drugs and nursing visits coded separately), per diem

Service not separately priced by Part B

I **S9376** Home infusion therapy, hydration therapy; more than two liters but no more than three liters per day, administrative services, professional pharmacy services, care coordination, and all necessary supplies and equipment (drugs and nursing visits coded separately), per diem

Service not separately priced by Part B

I **S9377** Home infusion therapy, hydration therapy; more than three liters per day, administrative services, professional pharmacy services, care coordination, and all necessary supplies (drugs and nursing visits coded separately), per diem

Service not separately priced by Part B

I **S9379** Home infusion therapy, infusion therapy, not otherwise classified; administrative services, professional pharmacy services, care coordination, and all necessary supplies and

equipment (drugs and nursing visits coded separately), per diem
Service not separately priced by Part B

S9381 Delivery or service to high risk areas requiring escort or extra protection, per visit
Service not separately priced by Part B

S9401 Anticoagulation clinic, inclusive of all services except laboratory tests, per session
Service not separately priced by Part B

S9430 Pharmacy compounding and dispensing services
Service not separately priced by Part B

S9433 Medical food nutritionally complete, administered orally, providing 100% of nutritional intake
Service not separately priced by Part B

S9434 Modified solid food supplements for inborn errors of metabolism
Service not separately priced by Part B

S9435 Medical foods for inborn errors of metabolism
Service not separately priced by Part B

S9436 Childbirth preparation/lamaze classes, non-physician provider, per session ♀
Service not separately priced by Part B

S9437 Childbirth refresher classes, non-physician provider, per session ♀
Service not separately priced by Part B

S9438 Cesarean birth classes, non-physician provider, per session ♀
Service not separately priced by Part B

S9439 VBAC (vaginal birth after cesarean) classes, non-physician provider, per session ♀
Service not separately priced by Part B

S9441 Asthma education, non-physician provider, per session
Service not separately priced by Part B

S9442 Birthing classes, non-physician provider, per session ♀
Service not separately priced by Part B

S9443 Lactation classes, non-physician provider, per session ♀
Service not separately priced by Part B

S9444 Parenting classes, non-physician provider, per session
Service not separately priced by Part B

S9445 Patient education, not otherwise classified, non-physician provider, individual, per session
Service not separately priced by Part B

S9446 Patient education, not otherwise classified, non-physician provider, group, per session
Service not separately priced by Part B

S9447 Infant safety (including CPR) classes, non-physician provider, per session
Service not separately priced by Part B

S9449 Weight management classes, non-physician provider, per session
Service not separately priced by Part B

S9451 Exercise classes, non-physician provider, per session
Service not separately priced by Part B

S9452 Nutrition classes, non-physician provider, per session
Service not separately priced by Part B

S9453 Smoking cessation classes, non-physician provider, per session
Service not separately priced by Part B

S9454 Stress management classes, non-physician provider, per session
Service not separately priced by Part B

S9455 Diabetic management program, group session
Service not separately priced by Part B

S9460 Diabetic management program, nurse visit
Service not separately priced by Part B

S9465 Diabetic management program, dietitian visit
Service not separately priced by Part B

S9470 Nutritional counseling, dietitian visit
Service not separately priced by Part B

S9472 Cardiac rehabilitation program, non-physician provider, per diem
Service not separately priced by Part B

S9473 Pulmonary rehabilitation program, non-physician provider, per diem
Service not separately priced by Part B

S9474 Enterostomal therapy by a registered nurse certified in enterostomal therapy, per diem
Service not separately priced by Part B

S9475 Ambulatory setting substance abuse treatment or detoxification services, per diem
Service not separately priced by Part B

S9476 Vestibular rehabilitation program, non-physician provider, per diem
Service not separately priced by Part B

S9480 Intensive outpatient psychiatric services, per diem
Service not separately priced by Part B

S9482 Family stabilization services, per 15 minutes
Service not separately priced by Part B

S9484 Crisis intervention mental health services, per hour
Service not separately priced by Part B

S9485 Crisis intervention mental health services, per diem
Service not separately priced by Part B

S9490 Home infusion therapy, corticosteroid infusion; administrative services, professional pharmacy services, care coordination, and all necessary supplies and equipment (drugs and nursing visits coded separately), per diem
Service not separately priced by Part B

♂ Male only   ♀ Female only   Ⓐ Age   A2 - Z3 = ASC Payment Indicator   A - Y = APC Status Indicator
ASC = ASC Approved Procedure   **DME** Paid under the DME fee schedule   **PQRS** Physician Quality Reporting System

▍ **S9494** Home infusion therapy, antibiotic, antiviral, or antifungal therapy; administrative services, professional pharmacy services, care coordination, and all necessary supplies and equipment (drugs and nursing visits coded separately), per diem (do not use this code with home infusion codes for hourly dosing schedules S9497-S9504)
Service not separately priced by Part B

▍ **S9497** Home infusion therapy, antibiotic, antiviral, or antifungal therapy; once every 3 hours; administrative services, professional pharmacy services, care coordination, and all necessary supplies and equipment (drugs and nursing visits coded separately), per diem
Service not separately priced by Part B

▍ **S9500** Home infusion therapy, antibiotic, antiviral, or antifungal therapy; once every 24 hours; administrative services, professional pharmacy services, care coordination, and all necessary supplies and equipment (drugs and nursing visits coded separately), per diem
Service not separately priced by Part B

▍ **S9501** Home infusion therapy, antibiotic, antiviral, or antifungal therapy; once every 12 hours; administrative services, professional pharmacy services, care coordination, and all necessary supplies and equipment (drugs and nursing visits coded separately), per diem
Service not separately priced by Part B

▍ **S9502** Home infusion therapy, antibiotic, antiviral, or antifungal therapy; once every 8 hours, administrative services, professional pharmacy services, care coordination, and all necessary supplies and equipment (drugs and nursing visits coded separately), per diem
Service not separately priced by Part B

▍ **S9503** Home infusion therapy, antibiotic, antiviral, or antifungal; once every 6 hours; administrative services, professional pharmacy services, care coordination, and all necessary supplies and equipment (drugs and nursing visits coded separately), per diem
Service not separately priced by Part B

▍ **S9504** Home infusion therapy, antibiotic, antiviral, or antifungal; once every 4 hours; administrative services, professional pharmacy services, care coordination, and all necessary supplies and equipment (drugs and nursing visits coded separately), per diem
Service not separately priced by Part B

▍ **S9529** Routine venipuncture for collection of specimen(s), single home bound, nursing home, or skilled nursing facility patient
Service not separately priced by Part B

▍ **S9537** Home therapy; hematopoietic hormone injection therapy (e.g., erythropoietin, G-CSF, GM-CSF); administrative services, professional pharmacy services, care coordination, and all necessary supplies and equipment (drugs and nursing visits coded separately), per diem
Service not separately priced by Part B

▍ **S9538** Home transfusion of blood product(s); administrative services, professional pharmacy services, care coordination and all necessary supplies and equipment (blood products, drugs, and nursing visits coded separately), per diem
Service not separately priced by Part B

▍ **S9542** Home injectable therapy, not otherwise classified, including administrative services, professional pharmacy services, care coordination, and all necessary supplies and equipment (drugs and nursing visits coded separately), per diem
Service not separately priced by Part B

▍ **S9558** Home injectable therapy; growth hormone, including administrative services, professional pharmacy services, care coordination, and all necessary supplies and equipment (drugs and nursing visits coded separately), per diem
Service not separately priced by Part B

▍ **S9559** Home injectable therapy, interferon, including administrative services, professional pharmacy services, care coordination, and all necessary supplies and equipment (drugs and nursing visits coded separately), per diem
Service not separately priced by Part B

▍ **S9560** Home injectable therapy; hormonal therapy (e.g.; leuprolide, goserelin), including administrative services, professional pharmacy services, care coordination, and all necessary supplies and equipment (drugs and nursing visits coded separately), per diem
Service not separately priced by Part B

▍ **S9562** Home injectable therapy, palivizumab, including administrative services, professional pharmacy services, care coordination, and all necessary supplies and equipment (drugs and nursing visits coded separately), per diem
Service not separately priced by Part B

▍ **S9590** Home therapy, irrigation therapy (e.g., sterile irrigation of an organ or anatomical cavity); including administrative services, professional pharmacy services, care coordination, and all necessary supplies and equipment (drugs and nursing visits coded separately), per diem
Service not separately priced by Part B

▲ Revised Code   ● New code   **C** Carrier judgment   **D** Special coverage instructions apply
▍ Not payable by Medicare   **M** Non-covered by Medicare   **S** Non-covered by Medicare statute   AHA Coding Clinic®

▮ **S9810** Home therapy; professional pharmacy services for provision of infusion, specialty drug administration, and/or disease state management, not otherwise classified, per hour (do not use this code with any per diem code)

Service not separately priced by Part B

▮ **S9900** Services by a Journal-listed Christian science practitioner for the purpose of healing, per diem

Service not separately priced by Part B

▮ **S9901** Services by a journal-listed christian science nurse, per hour

▮ **S9960** Ambulance service, conventional air services, nonemergency transport, one way (fixed wing)

Service not separately priced by Part B

▮ **S9961** Ambulance service, conventional air service, nonemergency transport, one way (rotary wing)

Service not separately priced by Part B

▮ **S9970** Health club membership, annual

Service not separately priced by Part B

▮ **S9975** Transplant related lodging, meals and transportation, per diem

Service not separately priced by Part B

▮ **S9976** Lodging, per diem, not otherwise classified

Service not separately priced by Part B

▮ **S9977** Meals, per diem, not otherwise specified

Service not separately priced by Part B

▮ **S9981** Medical records copying fee, administrative

Service not separately priced by Part B

▮ **S9982** Medical records copying fee, per page

Service not separately priced by Part B

▮ **S9986** Not medically necessary service (patient is aware that service not medically necessary)

Service not separately priced by Part B

▮ **S9988** Services provided as part of a Phase I clinical trial

Service not separately priced by Part B

▮ **S9989** Services provided outside of the United States of America (list in addition to code(s) for services(s))

Service not separately priced by Part B

▮ **S9990** Services provided as part of a Phase II clinical trial

Service not separately priced by Part B

▮ **S9991** Services provided as part of a Phase III clinical trial

Service not separately priced by Part B

▮ **S9992** Transportation costs to and from trial location and local transportation costs (e.g., fares for taxicab or bus) for clinical trial participant and one caregiver/companion

Service not separately priced by Part B

▮ **S9994** Lodging costs (e.g., hotel charges) for clinical trial participant and one caregiver/companion

Service not separately priced by Part B

▮ **S9996** Meals for clinical trial participant and one caregiver/companion

Service not separately priced by Part B

▮ **S9999** Sales tax

Service not separately priced by Part B

♂ Male only   ♀ Female only   Ⓐ Age   A2 - Z3 = ASC Payment Indicator   A - Y = APC Status Indicator

ASC = ASC Approved Procedure   **DME** Paid under the DME fee schedule   **PQRS** Physician Quality Reporting System

NATIONAL CODES ESTABLISHED FOR STATE MEDICAID AGENCIES (T1000-T5999)

T1000 Private duty / independent nursing service(s) - licensed, up to 15 minutes
Service not separately priced by Part B

T1001 Nursing assessment / evaluation
Service not separately priced by Part B

T1002 RN services, up to 15 minutes
Service not separately priced by Part B

T1003 LPN/LVN services, up to 15 minutes
Service not separately priced by Part B

T1004 Services of a qualified nursing aide, up to 15 minutes
Service not separately priced by Part B

T1005 Respite care services, up to 15 minutes
Service not separately priced by Part B

T1006 Alcohol and/or substance abuse services, family/couple counseling
Service not separately priced by Part B

T1007 Alcohol and/or substance abuse services, treatment plan development and/or modification
Service not separately priced by Part B

T1009 Child sitting services for children of the individual receiving alcohol and/or substance abuse services
Service not separately priced by Part B

T1010 Meals for individuals receiving alcohol and/or substance abuse services (when meals not included in the program)
Service not separately priced by Part B

T1012 Alcohol and/or substance abuse services, skills development
Service not separately priced by Part B

T1013 Sign language or oral interpretive services, per 15 minutes
Service not separately priced by Part B

T1014 Telehealth transmission, per minute, professional services bill separately
Service not separately priced by Part B

T1015 Clinic visit/encounter, all-inclusive
Service not separately priced by Part B

T1016 Case management, each 15 minutes
Service not separately priced by Part B

T1017 Targeted case management, each 15 minutes
Service not separately priced by Part B

T1018 School-based individualized education program (IEP) services, bundled
Service not separately priced by Part B

T1019 Personal care services, per 15 minutes, not for an inpatient or resident of a hospital, nursing facility, ICF/MR or IMD, part of the individualized plan of treatment (code may not be used to identify services provided by home health aide or certified nurse assistant)
Service not separately priced by Part B

T1020 Personal care services, per diem, not for an inpatient or resident of a hospital, nursing facility, ICF/MR or IMD, part of the individualized plan of treatment (code may not be used to identify services provided by home health aide or certified nurse assistant)
Service not separately priced by Part B

T1021 Home health aide or certified nurse assistant, per visit
Service not separately priced by Part B

T1022 Contracted home health agency services, all services provided under contract, per day
Service not separately priced by Part B

T1023 Screening to determine the appropriateness of consideration of an individual for participation in a specified program, project or treatment protocol, per encounter
Service not separately priced by Part B

T1024 Evaluation and treatment by an integrated, specialty team contracted to provide coordinated care to multiple or severely handicapped children, per encounter Ⓐ
Service not separately priced by Part B

T1025 Intensive, extended multidisciplinary services provided in a clinic setting to children with complex medical, physical, mental and psychosocial impairments, per diem Ⓐ
Service not separately priced by Part B

T1026 Intensive, extended multidisciplinary services provided in a clinic setting to children with complex medical, physical, medical and psychosocial impairments, per hour Ⓐ
Service not separately priced by Part B

T1027 Family training and counseling for child development, per 15 minutes
Service not separately priced by Part B

T1028 Assessment of home, physical and family environment, to determine suitability to meet patient's medical needs
Service not separately priced by Part B

T1029 Comprehensive environmental lead investigation, not including laboratory analysis, per dwelling
Service not separately priced by Part B

T1030 Nursing care, in the home, by registered nurse, per diem
Service not separately priced by Part B

T1031 Nursing care, in the home, by licensed practical nurse, per diem
Service not separately priced by Part B

T1502 Administration of oral, intramuscular and/or subcutaneous medication by health care agency/professional, per visit
Service not separately priced by Part B

▲ Revised Code ● New code Ⓒ Carrier judgment Ⓓ Special coverage instructions apply
Ⓘ Not payable by Medicare Ⓜ Non-covered by Medicare Ⓢ Non-covered by Medicare statute AHA Coding Clinic®

▯ **T1503** Administration of medication, other than oral and/or injectable, by a health care agency/ professional, per visit
Service not separately priced by Part B

▯ **T1505** Electronic medication compliance management device, includes all components and accessories, not otherwise classified
Service not separately priced by Part B

▯ **T1999** Miscellaneous therapeutic items and supplies, retail purchases, not otherwise classified; identify product in "remarks"
Service not separately priced by Part B

▯ **T2001** Non-emergency transportation; patient attendant/escort
Service not separately priced by Part B

▯ **T2002** Non-emergency transportation; per diem
Service not separately priced by Part B

▯ **T2003** Non-emergency transportation; encounter/ trip
Service not separately priced by Part B

▯ **T2004** Non-emergency transport; commercial carrier, multi-pass
Service not separately priced by Part B

▯ **T2005** Non-emergency transportation; stretcher van
Service not separately priced by Part B

▯ **T2007** Transportation waiting time, air ambulance and non-emergency vehicle, one-half (1/2) hour increments
Service not separately priced by Part B

▯ **T2010** Preadmission screening and resident review (PASRR) level I identification screening, per screen
Service not separately priced by Part B

▯ **T2011** Preadmission screening and resident review (PASRR) level II evaluation, per evaluation
Service not separately priced by Part B

▯ **T2012** Habilitation, educational; waiver, per diem
Service not separately priced by Part B

▯ **T2013** Habilitation, educational, waiver; per hour
Service not separately priced by Part B

▯ **T2014** Habilitation, prevocational, waiver; per diem
Service not separately priced by Part B

▯ **T2015** Habilitation, prevocational, waiver; per hour
Service not separately priced by Part B

▯ **T2016** Habilitation, residential, waiver; per diem
Service not separately priced by Part B

▯ **T2017** Habilitation, residential, waiver; 15 minutes
Service not separately priced by Part B

▯ **T2018** Habilitation, supported employment, waiver; per diem
Service not separately priced by Part B

▯ **T2019** Habilitation, supported employment, waiver; per 15 minutes
Service not separately priced by Part B

▯ **T2020** Day habilitation, waiver; per diem
Service not separately priced by Part B

▯ **T2021** Day habilitation, waiver; per 15 minutes
Service not separately priced by Part B

▯ **T2022** Case management, per month
Service not separately priced by Part B

▯ **T2023** Targeted case management; per month
Service not separately priced by Part B

▯ **T2024** Service assessment/plan of care development, waiver
Service not separately priced by Part B

▯ **T2025** Waiver services; not otherwise specified (NOS)
Service not separately priced by Part B

▯ **T2026** Specialized childcare, waiver; per diem
Service not separately priced by Part B

▯ **T2027** Specialized childcare, waiver; per 15 minutes
Service not separately priced by Part B

▯ **T2028** Specialized supply, not otherwise specified, waiver
Service not separately priced by Part B

▯ **T2029** Specialized medical equipment, not otherwise specified, waiver
Service not separately priced by Part B

▯ **T2030** Assisted living, waiver; per month
Service not separately priced by Part B

▯ **T2031** Assisted living; waiver, per diem
Service not separately priced by Part B

▯ **T2032** Residential care, not otherwise specified (NOS), waiver; per month
Service not separately priced by Part B

▯ **T2033** Residential care, not otherwise specified (NOS), waiver; per diem
Service not separately priced by Part B

▯ **T2034** Crisis intervention, waiver; per diem
Service not separately priced by Part B

▯ **T2035** Utility services to support medical equipment and assistive technology/devices, waiver
Service not separately priced by Part B

▯ **T2036** Therapeutic camping, overnight, waiver; each session
Service not separately priced by Part B

▯ **T2037** Therapeutic camping, day, waiver; each session
Service not separately priced by Part B

▯ **T2038** Community transition, waiver; per service
Service not separately priced by Part B

▯ **T2039** Vehicle modifications, waiver; per service
Service not separately priced by Part B

▯ **T2040** Financial management, self-directed, waiver; per 15 minutes
Service not separately priced by Part B

▯ **T2041** Supports brokerage, self-directed, waiver; per 15 minutes
Service not separately priced by Part B

I T2042 Hospice routine home care; per diem
Service not separately priced by Part B

I T2043 Hospice continuous home care; per hour
Service not separately priced by Part B

I T2044 Hospice inpatient respite care; per diem
Service not separately priced by Part B

I T2045 Hospice general inpatient care; per diem
Service not separately priced by Part B

I T2046 Hospice long term care, room and board only; per diem
Service not separately priced by Part B

I T2048 Behavioral health; long-term care residential (non-acute care in a residential treatment program where stay is typically longer than 30 days), with room and board, per diem
Service not separately priced by Part B

I T2049 Non-emergency transportation; stretcher van, mileage; per mile
Service not separately priced by Part B

I T2101 Human breast milk processing, storage and distribution only ♀
Service not separately priced by Part B

M T4521 Adult sized disposable incontinence product, brief/diaper, small, each
Service not separately priced by Part B

M T4522 Adult sized disposable incontinence product, brief/diaper, medium, each
Service not separately priced by Part B

M T4523 Adult sized disposable incontinence product, brief/diaper, large, each
Service not separately priced by Part B

M T4524 Adult sized disposable incontinence product, brief/diaper, extra large, each
Service not separately priced by Part B

M T4525 Adult sized disposable incontinence product, protective underwear/pull-on, small size, each
Service not separately priced by Part B

M T4526 Adult sized disposable incontinence product, protective underwear/pull-on, medium size, each
Service not separately priced by Part B

M T4527 Adult sized disposable incontinence product, protective underwear/pull-on, large size, each
Service not separately priced by Part B

M T4528 Adult sized disposable incontinence product, protective underwear/pull-on, extra large size, each
Service not separately priced by Part B

M T4529 Pediatric sized disposable incontinence product, brief/diaper, small/medium size, each Ⓐ
Service not separately priced by Part B

M T4530 Pediatric sized disposable incontinence product, brief/diaper, large size, each Ⓐ
Service not separately priced by Part B

M T4531 Pediatric sized disposable incontinence product, protective underwear/pull-on, small/medium size, each Ⓐ
Service not separately priced by Part B

M T4532 Pediatric sized disposable incontinence product, protective underwear/pull-on, large size, each Ⓐ
Service not separately priced by Part B

M T4533 Youth sized disposable incontinence product, brief/diaper, each
Service not separately priced by Part B

M T4534 Youth sized disposable incontinence product, protective underwear/pull-on, each
Service not separately priced by Part B

M T4535 Disposable liner/shield/guard/pad/undergarment, for incontinence, each
Service not separately priced by Part B

M T4536 Incontinence product, protective underwear/pull-on, reusable, any size, each
Service not separately priced by Part B

M T4537 Incontinence product, protective underpad, reusable, bed size, each
Service not separately priced by Part B

M T4538 Diaper service, reusable diaper, each diaper
Service not separately priced by Part B

M T4539 Incontinence product, diaper/brief, reusable, any size, each
Service not separately priced by Part B

M T4540 Incontinence product, protective underpad, reusable, chair size, each
Service not separately priced by Part B

I T4541 Incontinence product, disposable underpad, large, each
Service not separately priced by Part B

I T4542 Incontinence product, disposable underpad, small size, each
Service not separately priced by Part B

M T4543 Adult sized disposable incontinence product, protective brief/diaper, above extra large, each
Service not separately priced by Part B

M T4544 Adult sized disposable incontinence product, protective underwear/pull-on, above extra large, each Ⓐ
Service not separately priced by Part B

I T5001 Positioning seat for persons with special orthopedic needs
Service not separately priced by Part B

I T5999 Supply, not otherwise specified
Service not separately priced by Part B

▲ Revised Code   ● New code   **C** Carrier judgment   **D** Special coverage instructions apply

I Not payable by Medicare   **M** Non-covered by Medicare   **S** Non-covered by Medicare statute   AHA Coding Clinic®

VISION SERVICES (V2020-V2799)

D **V2020** Frames, purchases `DME` A

M **V2025** Deluxe frame E

Service not separately priced by Part B

C **V2100** Sphere, single vision, plano to plus or minus 4.00, per lens `DME` A

C **V2101** Sphere, single vision, plus or minus 4.12 to plus or minus 7.00d, per lens `DME` A

C **V2102** Sphere, single vision, plus or minus 7.12 to plus or minus 20.00d, per lens `DME` A

C **V2103** Spherocylinder, single vision, plano to plus or minus 4.00d sphere, .12 to 2.00d cylinder, per lens `DME` A

C **V2104** Spherocylinder, single vision, plano to plus or minus 4.00d sphere, 2.12 to 4.00d cylinder, per lens `DME` A

C **V2105** Spherocylinder, single vision, plano to plus or minus 4.00d sphere, 4.25 to 6.00d cylinder, per lens `DME` A

C **V2106** Spherocylinder, single vision, plano to plus or minus 4.00d sphere, over 6.00d cylinder, per lens `DME` A

C **V2107** Spherocylinder, single vision, plus or minus 4.25 to plus or minus 7.00 sphere, .12 to 2.00d cylinder, per lens `DME` A

C **V2108** Spherocylinder, single vision, plus or minus 4.25d to plus or minus 7.00d sphere, 2.12 to 4.00d cylinder, per lens `DME` A

C **V2109** Spherocylinder, single vision, plus or minus 4.25 to plus or minus 7.00d sphere, 4.25 to 6.00d cylinder, per lens `DME` A

C **V2110** Spherocylinder, single vision, plus or minus 4.25 to 7.00d sphere, over 6.00d cylinder, per lens `DME` A

C **V2111** Spherocylinder, single vision, plus or minus 7.25 to plus or minus 12.00d sphere, .25 to 2.25d cylinder, per lens `DME` A

C **V2112** Spherocylinder, single vision, plus or minus 7.25 to plus or minus 12.00d sphere, 2.25d to 4.00d cylinder, per lens `DME` A

C **V2113** Spherocylinder, single vision, plus or minus 7.25 to plus or minus 12.00d sphere, 4.25 to 6.00d cylinder, per lens `DME` A

C **V2114** Spherocylinder, single vision, sphere over plus or minus 12.00d, per lens `DME` A

C **V2115** Lenticular, (myodisc), per lens, single vision `DME` A

C **V2118** Aniseikonic lens, single vision `DME` A

D **V2121** Lenticular lens, per lens, single `DME` A

C **V2199** Not otherwise classified, single vision lens A

C **V2200** Sphere, bifocal, plano to plus or minus 4.00d, per lens `DME` A

C **V2201** Sphere, bifocal, plus or minus 4.12 to plus or minus 7.00d, per lens `DME` A

C **V2202** Sphere, bifocal, plus or minus 7.12 to plus or minus 20.00d, per lens `DME` A

C **V2203** Spherocylinder, bifocal, plano to plus or minus 4.00d sphere, 0.12 to 2.00d cylinder, per lens `DME` A

C **V2204** Spherocylinder, bifocal, plano to plus or minus 4.00d sphere, 2.12 to 4.00d cylinder, per lens `DME` A

C **V2205** Spherocylinder, bifocal, plano to plus or minus 4.00d sphere, 4.25 to 6.00d cylinder, per lens `DME` A

C **V2206** Spherocylinder, bifocal, plano to plus or minus 4.00d sphere, over 6.00d cylinder, per lens `DME` A

C **V2207** Spherocylinder, bifocal, plus or minus 4.25 to plus or minus 7.00d sphere, .12 to 2.00d cylinder, per lens `DME` A

C **V2208** Spherocylinder, bifocal, plus or minus 4.25 to plus or minus 7.00d sphere, 2.12 to 4.00d cylinder, per lens `DME` A

C **V2209** Spherocylinder, bifocal, plus or minus 4.25 to plus or minus 7.00d sphere, 4.25 to 6.00d cylinder, per lens `DME` A

C **V2210** Spherocylinder, bifocal, plus or minus 4.25 to plus or minus 7.00d sphere, over 6.00d cylinder, per lens `DME` A

C **V2211** Spherocylinder, bifocal, plus or minus 7.25 to plus or minus 12.00d sphere, .25 to 2.25d cylinder, per lens `DME` A

C **V2212** Spherocylinder, bifocal, plus or minus 7.25 to plus or minus 12.00d sphere, 2.25 to 4.00d cylinder, per lens `DME` A

C **V2213** Spherocylinder, bifocal, plus or minus 7.25 to plus or minus 12.00d sphere, 4.25 to 6.00d cylinder, per lens `DME` A

C **V2214** Spherocylinder, bifocal, sphere over plus or minus 12.00d, per lens `DME` A

C **V2215** Lenticular (myodisc), per lens, bifocal `DME` A

C **V2218** Aniseikonic, per lens, bifocal `DME` A

C **V2219** Bifocal seg width over 28mm `DME` A

C **V2220** Bifocal add over 3.25d `DME` A

D **V2221** Lenticular lens, per lens, bifocal `DME` A

C **V2299** Specialty bifocal (by report) A

C **V2300** Sphere, trifocal, plano to plus or minus 4.00d, per lens `DME` A

C **V2301** Sphere, trifocal, plus or minus 4.12 to plus or minus 7.00d, per lens `DME` A

C **V2302** Sphere, trifocal, plus or minus 7.12 to plus or minus 20.00, per lens `DME` A

C **V2303** Spherocylinder, trifocal, plano to plus or minus 4.00d sphere, .12-2.00d cylinder, per lens `DME` A

C **V2304** Spherocylinder, trifocal, plano to plus or minus 4.00d sphere, 2.25-4.00d cylinder, per lens `DME` A

C **V2305** Spherocylinder, trifocal, plano to plus or minus 4.00d sphere, 4.25 to 6.00 cylinder, per lens `DME` A

♂ Male only   ♀ Female only   **A** Age   A2 - Z3 = ASC Payment Indicator   A - Y = APC Status Indicator

ASC = ASC Approved Procedure   `DME` Paid under the DME fee schedule   `PQRS` Physician Quality Reporting System

V2306 - V2781

VISION SERVICES (V2020-V2799)

C	**V2306** Spherocylinder, trifocal, plano to plus or minus 4.00d sphere, over 6.00d cylinder, per lens	DME A
C	**V2307** Spherocylinder, trifocal, plus or minus 4.25 to plus or minus 7.00d sphere, .12 to 2.00d cylinder, per lens	DME A
C	**V2308** Spherocylinder, trifocal, plus or minus 4.25 to plus or minus 7.00d sphere, 2.12 to 4.00d cylinder, per lens	DME A
C	**V2309** Spherocylinder, trifocal, plus or minus 4.25 to plus or minus 7.00d sphere, 4.25 to 6.00d cylinder, per lens	DME A
C	**V2310** Spherocylinder, trifocal, plus or minus 4.25 to plus or minus 7.00d sphere, over 6.00d cylinder, per lens	DME A
C	**V2311** Spherocylinder, trifocal, plus or minus 7.25 to plus or minus 12.00d sphere, .25 to 2.25d cylinder, per lens	DME A
C	**V2312** Spherocylinder, trifocal, plus or minus 7.25 to plus or minus 12.00d sphere, 2.25 to 4.00d cylinder, per lens	DME A
C	**V2313** Spherocylinder, trifocal, plus or minus 7.25 to plus or minus 12.00d sphere, 4.25 to 6.00d cylinder, per lens	DME A
C	**V2314** Spherocylinder, trifocal, sphere over plus or minus 12 .00d, per lens	DME A
C	**V2315** Lenticular, (myodisc), per lens, trifocal	DME A
C	**V2318** Aniseikonic lens, trifocal	DME A
C	**V2319** Trifocal seg width over 28 mm	DME A
C	**V2320** Trifocal add over 3.25d	DME A
D	**V2321** Lenticular lens, per lens, trifocal	DME A
C	**V2399** Specialty trifocal (by report)	A
C	**V2410** Variable asphericity lens, single vision, full field, glass or plastic, per lens	DME A
C	**V2430** Variable asphericity lens, bifocal, full field, glass or plastic, per lens	DME A
C	**V2499** Variable sphericity lens, other type	A
C	**V2500** Contact lens, PMMA, spherical, per lens	DME A
C	**V2501** Contact lens, PMMA, toric or prism ballast, per lens	DME A
C	**V2502** Contact lens, PMMA, bifocal, per lens	DME A
C	**V2503** Contact lens, PMMA, color vision deficiency, per lens	DME A
C	**V2510** Contact lens, gas permeable, spherical, per lens	DME A
C	**V2511** Contact lens, gas permeable, toric, prism ballast, per lens	DME A
C	**V2512** Contact lens, gas permeable, bifocal, per lens	DME A
C	**V2513** Contact lens, gas permeable, extended wear, per lens	DME A
D	**V2520** Contact lens, hydrophilic, spherical, per lens	DME A
D	**V2521** Contact lens, hydrophilic, toric, or prism ballast, per lens	DME A
D	**V2522** Contact lens, hydrophillic, bifocal, per lens	DME A

D	**V2523** Contact lens, hydrophilic, extended wear, per lens	DME A
C	**V2530** Contact lens, scleral, gas impermeable, per lens	DME A
D	**V2531** Contact lens, scleral, gas permeable, per lens	DME A
C	**V2599** Contact lens, other type	A
C	**V2600** Hand held low vision aids and other nonspectacle mounted aids	A
C	**V2610** Single lens spectacle mounted low vision aids	A
C	**V2615** Telescopic and other compound lens system, including distance vision telescopic, near vision telescopes and compound microscopic lens system	A
D	**V2623** Prosthetic eye, plastic, custom	DME A
C	**V2624** Polishing/resurfacing of ocular prosthesis	DME A
C	**V2625** Enlargement of ocular prosthesis	DME A
C	**V2626** Reduction of ocular prosthesis	DME A
D	**V2627** Scleral cover shell	DME A
C	**V2628** Fabrication and fitting of ocular conformer	DME A
C	**V2629** Prosthetic eye, other type	A
D	**V2630** Anterior chamber intraocular lens	N1 N
	Reasonable charge	
D	**V2631** Iris supported intraocular lens	N1 N
	Reasonable charge	
D	**V2632** Posterior chamber intraocular lens	N1 N
	Reasonable charge	
	Pub: 100-4, Chap. 32, 120.2	
C	**V2700** Balance lens, per lens	DME A
M	**V2702** Deluxe lens feature	E
	Service not separately priced by Part B	
C	**V2710** Slab off prism, glass or plastic, per lens	DME A
C	**V2715** Prism, per lens	DME A
C	**V2718** Press-on lens, Fresnell prism, per lens	DME A
C	**V2730** Special base curve, glass or plastic, per lens	DME A
D	**V2744** Tint, photochromatic, per lens	DME A
D	**V2745** Addition to lens; tint, any color, solid, gradient or equal, excludes photochromatic, any lens material, per lens	DME A
D	**V2750** Anti-reflective coating, per lens	DME A
D	**V2755** U-V lens, per lens	DME A
C	**V2756** Eye glass case	E
	Service not separately priced by Part B	
C	**V2760** Scratch resistant coating, per lens	DME A
D	**V2761** Mirror coating, any type, solid, gradient or equal, any lens material, per lens	B
D	**V2762** Polarization, any lens material, per lens	DME A
C	**V2770** Occluder lens, per lens	DME A
C	**V2780** Oversize lens, per lens	DME A
C	**V2781** Progressive lens, per lens	B
	Service not separately priced by Part B	

D **V2782** Lens, index 1.54 to 1.65 plastic or 1.60 to 1.79 glass, excludes polycarbonate, per lens `DME` A

D **V2783** Lens, index greater than or equal to 1.66 plastic or greater than or equal to 1.80 glass, excludes polycarbonate, per lens `DME` A

D **V2784** Lens, polycarbonate or equal, any index, per lens `DME` A

C **V2785** Processing, preserving and transporting corneal tissue F4 ASC F

Pub: 100-4, Chap. 4, 200.1

D **V2786** Specialty occupational multifocal lens, per lens `DME` A

S **V2787** Astigmatism correcting function of intraocular lens E

Service not separately priced by Part B
Statute: 1862(a)(7)

Pub: 100-4, Chap. 32, 120.1; 100-4, Chap. 32, 120.2

S **V2788** Presbyopia correcting function of intraocular lens E

Service not separately priced by Part B
Statute: 1862(a)(7)

Pub: 100-4, Chap. 32, 120.1; 100-4, Chap. 32, 120.2

C **V2790** Amniotic membrane for surgical reconstruction, per procedure N1 N

Other carrier priced

Pub: 100-4, Chap. 4, 200.4

C **V2797** Vision supply, accessory and/or service component of another HCPCS vision code A

Service not separately priced by Part B

▲ C **V2799** Vision item or service, miscellaneous A

HEARING SERVICES (V5008-V5364)

M **V5008** Hearing screening   E
      Service not separately priced by Part B

S **V5010** Assessment for hearing aid   E
      Service not separately priced by Part B
      Statute: 1862A7

S **V5011** Fitting/orientation/checking of hearing aid   E
      Service not separately priced by Part B
      Statute: 1862A7

S **V5014** Repair/modification of a hearing aid   E
      Service not separately priced by Part B
      Statute: 1862A7

S **V5020** Conformity evaluation   E
      Service not separately priced by Part B
      Statute: 1862A7

S **V5030** Hearing aid, monaural, body worn, air conduction   E
      Service not separately priced by Part B
      Statute: 1862A7

S **V5040** Hearing aid, monaural, body worn, bone conduction   E
      Service not separately priced by Part B
      Statute: 1862A7

S **V5050** Hearing aid, monaural, in the ear   E
      Service not separately priced by Part B
      Statute: 1862A7

S **V5060** Hearing aid, monaural, behind the ear   E
      Service not separately priced by Part B
      Statute: 1862A7

S **V5070** Glasses, air conduction   E
      Service not separately priced by Part B
      Statute: 1862A7

S **V5080** Glasses, bone conduction   E
      Service not separately priced by Part B
      Statute: 1862A7

S **V5090** Dispensing fee, unspecified hearing aid   E
      Service not separately priced by Part B
      Statute: 1862A7

S **V5095** Semi-implantable middle ear hearing prosthesis   E
      Service not separately priced by Part B
      Statute: 1862A7

S **V5100** Hearing aid, bilateral, body worn   E
      Service not separately priced by Part B
      Statute: 1862A7

S **V5110** Dispensing fee, bilateral   E
      Service not separately priced by Part B
      Statute: 1862A7

S **V5120** Binaural, body   E
      Service not separately priced by Part B
      Statute: 1862A7

S **V5130** Binaural, in the ear   E
      Service not separately priced by Part B
      Statute: 1862A7

S **V5140** Binaural, behind the ear   E
      Service not separately priced by Part B
      Statute: 1862A7

S **V5150** Binaural, glasses   E
      Service not separately priced by Part B
      Statute: 1862A7

S **V5160** Dispensing fee, binaural   E
      Service not separately priced by Part B
      Statute: 1862A7

S **V5170** Hearing aid, CROS, in the ear   E
      Service not separately priced by Part B
      Statute: 1862A7

S **V5180** Hearing aid, CROS, behind the ear   E
      Service not separately priced by Part B
      Statute: 1862A7

S **V5190** Hearing aid, CROS, glasses   E
      Service not separately priced by Part B
      Statute: 1862A7

S **V5200** Dispensing fee, CROS   E
      Service not separately priced by Part B
      Statute: 1862A7

S **V5210** Hearing aid, BICROS, in the ear   E
      Service not separately priced by Part B
      Statute: 1862A7

S **V5220** Hearing aid, BICROS, behind the ear   E
      Service not separately priced by Part B
      Statute: 1862A7

S **V5230** Hearing aid, BICROS, glasses   E
      Service not separately priced by Part B
      Statute: 1862A7

S **V5240** Dispensing fee, BICROS   E
      Service not separately priced by Part B
      Statute: 1862A7

S **V5241** Dispensing fee, monaural hearing aid, any type   E
      Service not separately priced by Part B
      Statute: 1862A7

S **V5242** Hearing aid, analog, monaural, CIC (completely in the ear canal)   E
      Service not separately priced by Part B
      Statute: 1862A7

S **V5243** Hearing aid, analog, monaural, ITC (in the canal)   E
      Service not separately priced by Part B
      Statute: 1862A7

S **V5244** Hearing aid, digitally programmable analog, monaural, CIC   E
      Service not separately priced by Part B
      Statute: 1862A7

S **V5245** Hearing aid, digitally programmable, analog, monaural, ITC   E
      Service not separately priced by Part B
      Statute: 1862A7

S **V5246** Hearing aid, digitally programmable analog, monaural, ITE (in the ear)   E
      Service not separately priced by Part B
      Statute: 1862A7

▲ Revised Code   ● New code   C Carrier judgment   D Special coverage instructions apply

I Not payable by Medicare   M Non-covered by Medicare   S Non-covered by Medicare statute   AHA Coding Clinic®

S **V5247** Hearing aid, digitally programmable analog, monaural, BTE (behind the ear)   E
Service not separately priced by Part B
Statute: 1862A7

S **V5248** Hearing aid, analog, binaural, CIC   E
Service not separately priced by Part B
Statute: 1862A7

S **V5249** Hearing aid, analog, binaural, ITC   E
Service not separately priced by Part B
Statute: 1862A7

S **V5250** Hearing aid, digitally programmable analog, binaural, CIC   E
Service not separately priced by Part B
Statute: 1862A7

S **V5251** Hearing aid, digitally programmable analog, binaural, ITC   E
Service not separately priced by Part B
Statute: 1862A7

S **V5252** Hearing aid, digitally programmable, binaural, ITE   E
Service not separately priced by Part B
Statute: 1862A7

S **V5253** Hearing aid, digitally programmable, binaural, BTE   E
Service not separately priced by Part B
Statute: 1862A7

S **V5254** Hearing aid, digital, monaural, CIC   E
Service not separately priced by Part B
Statute: 1862A7

S **V5255** Hearing aid, digital, monaural, ITC   E
Service not separately priced by Part B
Statute: 1862A7

S **V5256** Hearing aid, digital, monaural, ITE   E
Service not separately priced by Part B
Statute: 1862A7

S **V5257** Hearing aid, digital, monaural, BTE   E
Service not separately priced by Part B
Statute: 1862A7

S **V5258** Hearing aid, digital, binaural, CIC   E
Service not separately priced by Part B
Statute: 1862A7

S **V5259** Hearing aid, digital, binaural, ITC   E
Service not separately priced by Part B
Statute: 1862A7

S **V5260** Hearing aid, digital, binaural, ITE   E
Service not separately priced by Part B
Statute: 1862A7

S **V5261** Hearing aid, digital, binaural, BTE   E
Service not separately priced by Part B
Statute: 1862A7

S **V5262** Hearing aid, disposable, any type, monaural   E
Service not separately priced by Part B
Statute: 1862A7

S **V5263** Hearing aid, disposable, any type, binaural   E
Service not separately priced by Part B
Statute: 1862A7

S **V5264** Ear mold/insert, not disposable, any type   E
Service not separately priced by Part B
Statute: 1862A7

S **V5265** Ear mold/insert, disposable, any type   E
Service not separately priced by Part B
Statute: 1862A7

S **V5266** Battery for use in hearing device   E
Service not separately priced by Part B
Statute: 1862A7

S **V5267** Hearing aid or assistive listening device/supplies/accessories, not otherwise specified   E
Service not separately priced by Part B
Statute: 1862A7

S **V5268** Assistive listening device, telephone amplifier, any type   E
Service not separately priced by Part B
Statute: 1862A7

S **V5269** Assistive listening device, alerting, any type   E
Service not separately priced by Part B
Statute: 1862A7

S **V5270** Assistive listening device, television amplifier, any type   E
Service not separately priced by Part B
Statute: 1862A7

S **V5271** Assistive listening device, television caption decoder   E
Service not separately priced by Part B
Statute: 1862A7

S **V5272** Assistive listening device, TDD   E
Service not separately priced by Part B
Statute: 1862A7

S **V5273** Assistive listening device, for use with cochlear implant   E
Service not separately priced by Part B
Statute: 1862A7

S **V5274** Assistive listening device, not otherwise specified   E
Service not separately priced by Part B
Statute: 1862A7

S **V5275** Ear impression, each   E
Service not separately priced by Part B
Statute: 1862A7

S **V5281** Assistive listening device, personal FM/DM system, monaural, (1 receiver, transmitter, microphone), any type   E
Service not separately priced by Part B
Statute: 1862A7

S **V5282** Assistive listening device, personal FM/DM system, binaural, (2 receivers, transmitter, microphone), any type   E
Service not separately priced by Part B
Statute: 1862A7

S **V5283** Assistive listening device, personal FM/DM neck, loop induction receiver   E
Service not separately priced by Part B
Statute: 1862A7

V5284 - V5364

S **V5284** Assistive listening device, personal FM/DM, ear level receiver   E

Service not separately priced by Part B
Statute: 1862A7

S **V5285** Assistive listening device, personal FM/DM, direct audio input receiver   E

Service not separately priced by Part B
Statute: 1862A7

S **V5286** Assistive listening device, personal blue tooth FM/DM receiver   E

Service not separately priced by Part B
Statute: 1862A7

S **V5287** Assistive listening device, personal FM/DM receiver, not otherwise specified   E

Service not separately priced by Part B
Statute: 1862A7

S **V5288** Assistive listening device, personal FM/DM transmitter assistive listening device   E

Service not separately priced by Part B
Statute: 1862A7

S **V5289** Assistive listening device, personal FM/DM adapter/boot coupling device for receiver, any type   E

Service not separately priced by Part B
Statute: 1862A7

S **V5290** Assistive listening device, transmitter microphone, any type   E

Service not separately priced by Part B
Statute: 1862A7

S **V5298** Hearing aid, not otherwise classified   E

Service not separately priced by Part B
Statute: 1862A7

D **V5299** Hearing service, miscellaneous   B

Price established by carriers

S **V5336** Repair/modification of augmentative communicative system or device (excludes adaptive hearing aid)   E

Service not separately priced by Part B
Statute: 1862A7

S **V5362** Speech screening   E

Service not separately priced by Part B
Statute: 1862(a)(7)

S **V5363** Language screening   E

Service not separately priced by Part B
Statute: 1862(a)(7)

S **V5364** Dysphagia screening   E

Service not separately priced by Part B
Statute: 1862(a)(7)

Index to Dental Services and Procedures

Coronectomy - Fistula

Coronectomy D7251
Coronoidectomy D7991
Counseling
  Nutritional D1310
  Oral hygiene D1330
  Tobacco D1320
Crevicular antimicrobial agents D4381
Crown
  Abutment (on implant) supported D6058 – D6064, D6094
  Implant supported D6065 – D6067
  Individual restorations (indirect) D2710 – D2799
  Prefabricated D2929 – D2934
  Provisional D2799
  Re-cement D2920
  Repair D2980
  Resin-based composite, anterior, direct D2390
  Temporary (fractured tooth) D2970
  Under existing removable partial D2971
Crown exposure D4230, D4231
Crown lengthening, hard tissue D4249
Crown repair D2980
Cryosurgery D7465
Culture and sensitivity test D0415
Culture, viral D0416
Curettage
  Open flap
    Four or more D4240
    One to three D4241
  Without flap
    Four or more D4341
    One to three D4342
Cytologic smears D0480
Cytology sample collection D7287

D

Debridement
  Endodontic D3221
  Full mouth D4355
  Peri-implant D6101 – D6102
Dentures, removable
  Adjustments D5410 – D5422
  Complete D5110 – D5120
  Immediate, complete D5130, D5140
  Implant/abutment supported, complete D6110, D6111
  Implant/abutment supported, partial D6112, D6113
  Modification of removable prosthesis following implant surgery D5875
  Overdenture D5863 – D5866
  Partial D5211 – D5281
  Precision attachment D5862
  Rebase D5710 – D5721
  Reline D5730 – D5761
  Repairs, complete and partial D5510, D5520, D5610 – D5671
  Temporary/interim D5810 – D5821
Dentures
  Implant/abutment supported, full D6114, D6115
  Implant/abutment supported, partial D6116, D6117
Desensitizing medicament D9910
Desensitizing resin D9911
Destruction of lesion D7465
Diagnostic D0100 – D0999
Diagnostic casts D0470
Diagnostic imaging
  Bitewing
    Four Image D0274

Single Image D0270
  Two Image D0272
  Three Image D0273
  Cephalometric image D0340
  Ertical bitewings - 7 to 8 Image D0277
  Extraoral D0250-D0260
  Image capture and interpretation D0210 – D0371
  Image capture only D0380 – D0386
  Interpretation and report only D0391
  Intraoral D0120-D0240
  Post processing image or image sets D0393 – D0395
  Posterior-anterior D0290
  Sialography D0310
Disc repair Temporomandibular joint D7852
Dietary planning D1310
Distal/proximal wedge D4274
Dressing change, periodontal, unscheduled D4920
Drugs
  Other D9630
  Therapeutic parenteral, single administration D9610
  Therapeutic parental, two or more administrations D9612
Dry socket/localized osteitis D9930

E

Emergency treatment D0140, D9110
Enamel microabrasion D9970
Enameloplasty D9971
Endodontics
  Apexification/recalcification apexification/recalcification D3351-D3353
  Retreatment of previous root canal therapy D3346 -D3348
Endodontic endosseous implant D3460
Equilibration D9951, D9952
Eruption of teeth
  Mobilization, surgical D7282
  Placement of device to aid eruption D7283
Evaluations
  Oral
    Comprehensive, new or established patient D0150
    Comprehensive periodontal evaluation - new or established patient D0180
    Detailed and extensive, problem focused D0160
    Limited, problem focused D0140
    Periodic, established patient D0120
    Re-evaluation - limited, (established patient; not post-operative visit) D0170
    Re-evaluation – post-operative office visit D0171
    Under three years of age D0145
Excision
  Benign lesion D7410 – D7412
  Malignant lesion/tumor D7413 – D7415, D7440, D7441
  Salivary gland D7981
Exfoliative cytological smear D0480
Extraoral Images D0250, D0260
Extractions D7111, D7140
  Surgical D7210 – D7250

F

Facial Bone Survey D0290
Fiberotomy, transseptal D7291
Fibroma D7410, D7411
Fissurotomy *See* Odontoplasty
Fistula
  Oroantral D7260
  Salivary D7983

Fixation device, not in conjunction with fracture D7998
Fixed partial dentures
    Pontics D6205 – D6253
    Re-cementation D6930
    Repair D6980
    Retainers
        Crowns D6710 – D6794
        Implant/abutment supported D6068 – D6077, D6194
        Inlay/onlay D6600 – D6634
        Maryland Bridge D6545, D6548, D6549
        Pediatric D6985
    Sectioning D9120
Flaps
    Apically positioned D4245
    Gingival D4240, D4241
Flexible base partial denture D5225, D5226
Fluoride
    Dispensing for home use D9630
    Gel carrier D5986
    Topical D1208
    Varnish D1206
Fractures, treatment of
    Alveolus D7670, D7770
    Facial bone D7680, D7780
    Malar/zygomatic arch D7650, D7660, D7750, D7760
    Mandible
        Compound closed reduction D7740
        Compound open reduction D7730
        Simple closed reduction D7640
        Simple open reduction D7630
    Maxilla
        Compound closed reduction D7720
        Compound open reduction D7710
        Simple closed reduction D7620
        Simple open reduction D7610
    No incision required D7650 – D7660
    Surgical incision required D7750 – D7760
Frenectomy/frenotomy D7960
Frenuloplasty D7963
Full mouth series D0210

G

Genetic test D0421
Gingiva, pericoronal, removal of D7971
Gingival flap D4240, D4241
Gingival Irrigation D4921
Gingivectomy/gingivoplasty D4210-D4212
Glass ionomers D2330 – D2394
Gold Foil Restorations
    One surface D2410
    Two surfaces D2420
    Three surfaces D2430
Graft
    Bone replacement D4263, D4264, D6103, D6104, D7953
    Combined connective tissue and double pedicle D4276
    Free soft tissue D4277 – D4278
    Maxillofacial soft/hard tissue D7955
    Osseous, osteoperiosteal, or cartilage D7950
    Pedicle soft tissue D4270
    Periradicular D3428, D3429
    Sinus augmentation D7951
    Skin D7920
    Soft tissue D4270 – D4273
    Subepithelial connective tissue D4273
    Synthetic D7955
Guided tissue regeneration D4266, D4267
    In conjunction with periradicular surgery D3432

H

Harvest of bone D7295
Hemisection D3920
Hospital call, Ambulatory surgical centre call D9420
House call, extended care facility D9410
Hyperplastic tissue removal D7970

I

Images, facial/oral D0350
Immediate denture
    Maxillary D5130
    Mandibular D5140
Impacted tooth, removal of
    Completely bony D7240
    Completely bony, with unusual surgical
        complications D7241
    Partially bony D7230
    Soft tissue D7220
Implant
    Abutments D6056, D6057, D6051
    Chin D7995
    Endodontic D3460
    Endosteal/endosseous D6010
    Eposteal/subperiosteal D6040
    Interim implant D6012
    Maintenance D6080
    Mandible D7996
    Mini D6013
    Modification of removable prosthesis D5875
    Other implant services D6080 – D6199
    Peri-implant defect D6103
    Radiographic/surgical implant index D6190
    Re-cement D6092, D6093
    Removal D6100
    Repair D6090, D6091, D6095
    Second stage surgery D6011
    Transosteal/transosseous D6050
Implant Services D6000 – D6199
Incision and drainage
    Extraoral soft tissue D7520-D7521
    Intraoral soft tissue D7510-D7511
Inlay
    Fixed partial denture retainer
        Metallic D2510 – D2530
        Metallic D6602 – D6607, D6624
        Porcelain/ceramic D6600 – D6601
        Porcelain/ceramic D2610 – D2630
        Resin-based composite D2650 – D2652
        Re-cement D2910
Intentional re-implantation D3470
Interceptive orthodontics D8050, D8060
Interim abutment D6051
Interim complete denture D5810, D5811
Interim partial denture D5820, D5821
Internal root repair D3333
Interpretation of diagnostic image D0391
Intravenous moderate (conscious) sedation/analgesia
    Each additional 15 minutes D9242
    First 30 minutes D9241
Irrigation, gingival D4921

J

Joint reconstruction D7858

L

Labial veneer
Chairside D2960
Laboratory D2961
Porcelain D2962
Lateral exostosis D7471
LeFort I
Maxilla - total D7946
Maxilla - segmented D7947
LeFort II; LeFort III
Without bone graft D7948
With bone graft D7949
Lesions, surgical excision
Intra-osseous lesions D7440 – D7461
Soft tissue D7410 – D7415, D7465
Limited orthodontic treatment D8010 – D8040
Localized osteitis/dry socket D9930

M

Maintenance and cleaning of prosthesis D5993
Malar bone, repair of fracture
Simple
Closed reduction D7660
Open reduction D7650
Compound
Closed reduction D7760
Open reduction D7750
Mandible, fracture of D7630 – D7640, D7730 – D7740
Maryland Bridge
Pontic D6210 – D6252
Retainer/abutment D6545, D6548, D6549
Maxilla, repair of fracture
Closed reduction, teeth immobilized D7620
Open reduction, teeth immobilized D7610
Closed reduction D7720Open reduction D7710
Maxillofacial defect D7955
Maxillofacial MRI
Capture and interpretation D0369
Image capture (only) D0385
Maxillofacial prosthetics
Auricular D5914
Cranial D5924
Facial D5919, D5925, D5929
Feeding aid D5951
Maintenance and cleaning D5993
Mandibular resection D5934, D5935
Nasal D5913, D5922, D5926
Obturator D5931 – D5933, D5936
Ocular D5916
Orbital D5915
Palatal D5954 – D5959
Speech aid D5952, D5953, D5960
Maxillofacial ultrasound
Capture and interpretation D0370
Image capture (only) D0386
Microabrasion, enamel D9970
Microorganisms, culture and sensitivity D0415
Missed appointment D9987
Moulage, facial D5911, D5912
Moderate sedation D9241, D9242, D9248
Mouthguard, athletic D9941

Mucosal abnormalities, pre-diagnostic test D0431
Myotomy D7856

N

Neoplasms, removal of D7410 – D7465
Nightguard D9940
Nitrous oxide, analgesia D9230
Non-intravenous moderate (conscious) sedation D9248
Non-odontogenic cyst D7460, D7461
Nutritional counseling D1310

O

Obturator
Post-surgical D5932
Refitting D5933
Surgical D5931
Occlusal adjustment
Complete D9952
Limited D9951
Occlusal guard D9940
Reline or repair D9942
Occlusal orthotic device D7880
Occlusion analysis D9950
Odontogenic cyst D7450, D7451
Odontoplasty D9971
Office visit D9430, D9440
Onlay
Fixed partial denture retainers, metallic D6610 – D6615, D6634
Metallic D2542 – D2544
Porcelain/ceramic D2642 – D2644
Resin-based composite D2662 – D2664
Operculectomy D7971
Oral & Maxillofacial Surgery D7000 – D7999
Oral hygiene instructions D1330
Oral pathology
Accession of tissue D0472 – D0474; D0480, D0486
Consultation, slides D0484, D0485
Cytology D0480
Decalcification procedure D0475
Electron microscopy D0481
Immunofluorescence
Direct D0482
Indirect D0483
Immunohistochemical stains D0478
Other oral pathology procedures D0502
Special stains
For microorganisms D0476
Not for microorganisms D0477
Tissue hybridization D0479
Orthodontics D8000 – D8999
Orthodontic treatment D8000 – D8999
Orthotic appliance D7880
Osseous surgery/graft D4260 – D4264
Ostectomy, partial D7550
Osteitis, localized; dry socket D9930
Osteoplasty D7940
Osteotomy D7941 – D7945
Overdenture
Dental implant supported fixed
Edentulous arch – mandibular D6115
Edentulous arch – maxillary D6114
Partially edentulous arch – mandibular D6117
Partially edentulous arch – maxillary D6116
Dental implant supported removable

P

R

Resin-based composite, direct - Tongue thrusting appliance

Occlusal guard D9942
Onlay D2982
Orthodontic appliance D8691
Orthodontic fixed retainer D8693, D8694
Precision or semi-precision attachment D5867, D6052
Removable partial dentures D5610 - D5671
Sealant D1353
Veneer D2983

Resin-based composite, direct
Anterior D2330 – D2335
Crown D2390
Posterior D2391 – D2394
Veneers D2960

Resin-based composite, indirect
Crown D2710
Fixed partial denture abutment D6710
Pontic D6205
Veneers D2961

Restorative
Amalgam D2140-D2161
Crown D2710-D2794
Gold foil D2410-D2430
Inlay/onlay D2510 – D2664, D6600 – D6634
Other restorative services D2910-D2990
Resin-based composite D2330-D2394

Restorative foundation for indirect restoration D2949

Retainers
Fixed partial denture
Crowns D6710 – D6794
Implant abutment supported D6068 – D6074, D6194
Implant supported D6075 – D6077
Inlays/onlays D6600 – D6634
Orthodontic D8680, D8691, D8692
Resin bonded D6545, D6548, D6549

Removal
Cysts D7410 – D7465
Exostosis
Lateral exostosis D7471
Osseous tuberosity D7485
Surgical reduction of fibrous tuberosity D7972
Torus mandibularis D7473
Torus palatinus D7472
Foreign bodies D7530, D7540

Retrograde filling D3430
Revision, periodontal surgery D4268
Ridge augmentation (grafting) D7950
Root
Planing D4341
Removal D7140, D7250
Resection/amputation D3450

Root canal
Incomplete D3332
Obstruction D3331
Therapy D3310 – D3353

Rubber dam, surgical isolation D3910

S

Sales tax D9985
Saliva
Analysis of sample D0418
Sample collection D0417

Salivary gland
Excision D7981
Fistula closure D7983

Scaling and root planing D4341, D4342
Screening of a patient D0190

Sealant
Placement D1351
Repair D1353

Section of fixed partial denture D9120
Sedation
Intravenous, moderate (conscious) D9241, D9242
Non-intravenous, moderate (conscious) D9248

Sedative filling *See* **Protective Restoration**
Semi-precision attachment abutment D6052
Sequestrectomy D7550
Sialodochoplasty D7982
Sialoendoscopy capture and interpretation D0371
Sialography D0310
Sialolithotomy D7980
Sinus augmentation
Via lateral open approach D7951
Via vertical approach D7952

Sinus perforation, closure D7261
Sinusotomy D7560
Skin graft D7920
Sleep apnea appliance D5999
Space maintainer D1510 – D1550
Re-cement D1550
Removal (by dentist who did not place appliance) D1555

Speech aid
Adult D5953
Pediatric D5952

Splinting
Commissure D5987
Provisional
Extracoronal D4321
Intracoronal D4320
Surgical D5988

Stainless steel crown D2930, D2931, D2933, D2934
Stayplate D5820, D5821
Stent D5982
Stress breaker D6940
Supra crestal fiberotomy D7291
Surgical, ambulatory center D9420
Suturing
Complicated D7911, D7912
Simple D7910

Synovectomy D7854

T

Temporomandibular joint
Manipulation D7830
Radiographs D0320, D0321
Reduction D7810 – D7820
Surgical discectomy D7850
Treatment D7810 – D7899

Thumb sucking appliance D8210, D8220
Tissue conditioning D5850, D5851
Tissue, excision of hyperplastic D7970
Titanium
Crown, FPD retainer D6794
Crown, single unit D2794
Implant abutment supported D6094
Implant abutment supported for FPD D6194
Implant supported D6065
Implant supported for FPD D6067
Inlay, FPD retainer D6624
Onlay, FPD retainer D6634

Tobacco counseling D1320
Tomographic survey D0322
Tongue thrusting appliance D8210, D8220

Tooth, natural
    Caries susceptibility test D0425
    Extraction D7111, D7140, D7210 – D7250
    Impacted, removal of D7220 – D7241
    Intentional re-implantation D3470
    Pulp vitality test D0460
    Re-implantation, evulsed/displaced D7270
    Surgical access D7280
    Surgical repositioning D7290
    Transplantation D7272
Tooth, reattach fragment D2921
Topical medicament carrier D5991
Torus (removal of)
    Mandibularis D7473
    Palatinus D7472
Tracheotomy, emergency D7990
Transplantation, tooth D7272
Transseptal fiberotomy D7291
Trismus appliance D5937
Tuberosity
    Fibrous D7972
    Surgical reduction D7485
Tumors, (removal of) D7440 – D7465

U

Un-erupted tooth, surgical access D7280
Unilateral removable partial denture D5281

V

Veneers
    Chairside D2960
    Laboratory D2961
    Porcelain D2962
Vertical bitewings D0277
Vestibuloplasty D7340, D7350
Viral culture D0416

W

Wax-up (diagnostic) D9950
Whitening *See* **Bleaching**
Wounds, treatment of D7910 – D7912

X

X-rays *See* **Diagnostic Imaging**

Z

Zygomatic arch
    Simple fracture treatment
        Closed reduction D7660
        Open reduction D7650
    Compound fracture treatment
        Closed reduction D7760
        Open reduction D7750

209

Tabular List of Dental Codes

DIAGNOSTIC

CLINICAL ORAL EVALUATIONS

D0120 Periodic oral evaluation - established patient

An evaluation performed on a patient of record to determine any changes in the patient's dental and medical health status since a previous comprehensive or periodic evaluation. This includes an oral cancer evaluation and periodontal screening where indicated, and may require interpretation of information acquired through additional diagnostic procedures. Report additional diagnostic procedures separately.

D0140 Limited oral evaluation - problem focused

An evaluation limited to a specific oral health problem or complaint. This may require interpretation of information acquired through additional diagnostic procedures. Report additional diagnostic procedures separately. Definitive procedures may be required on the same date as the evaluation. Typically, patients receiving this type of evaluation present with a specific problem and/or dental emergencies, trauma, acute infections, etc.

D0145 Oral evaluation for a patient under three years of age and counseling with primary caregiver

Diagnostic services performed for a child under the age of three, preferably within the first six months of the eruption of the first primary tooth, including recording the oral and physical health history, evaluation of caries susceptibility, development of an appropriate preventive oral health regimen and communication with and counseling of the child's parent, legal guardian and/or primary caregiver.

D0150 Comprehensive oral evaluation - new or established patient

Used by a general dentist and/or a specialist when evaluating a patient comprehensively. This applies to new patients; established patients who have had a significant change in health conditions or other unusual circumstances, by report, or established patients who have been absent from active treatment for three or more years. It is a thorough evaluation and recording of the extraoral and intraoral hard and soft tissues. It may require interpretation of information acquired through additional diagnostic procedures. Additional diagnostic procedures should be reported separately. This includes an evaluation for oral cancer where indicated, the evaluation and recording of the patient's dental and medical history and a general health assessment. It may include the evaluation and recording of dental caries, missing or unerupted teeth, restorations, existing prostheses, occlusal relationships, periodontal conditions (including periodontal screening and/or charting), hard and soft tissue anomalies, etc.

D0160 Detailed and extensive oral evaluation - problem focused, by report

A detailed and extensive problem focused evaluation entails extensive diagnostic and cognitive modalities based on the findings of a comprehensive oral evaluation. Integration of more extensive diagnostic modalities to develop a treatment plan for a specific problem is required. The condition requiring this type of evaluation should be described and documented. Examples of conditions requiring this type of evaluation may include dentofacial anomalies, complicated perio-prosthetic conditions, complex temporomandibular dysfunction, facial pain of unknown origin, conditions requiring multi-disciplinary consultation, etc.

D0170 Re-evaluation - limited, problem focused (established patient; not post-operative visit)

Assessing the status of a previously existing condition. For example: - a traumatic injury where no treatment was rendered but patient needs follow-up monitoring; - evaluation for undiagnosed continuing pain; - soft tissue lesion requiring follow-up evaluation.

● **D0171** Re-evaluation – post-operative office visit

D0180 Comprehensive periodontal evaluation - new or established patient

This procedure is indicated for patients showing signs or symptoms of periodontal disease and for patients with risk factors such as smoking or diabetes. It includes evaluation of periodontal conditions, probing and charting, evaluation and recording of the patient's dental and medical history and general health assessment. It may include the evaluation and recording of dental caries, missing or unerupted teeth, restorations, occlusal relationships and oral cancer evaluation.

PRE-DIAGNOSTIC SERVICES

D0190 Screening of a patient

A screening, including state or federally mandated screenings, to determine an individual's need to be seen by a dentist for diagnosis.

D0191 Assessment of a patient

A limited clinical inspection that is performed to identify possible signs of oral or systemic disease, malformation, or injury, and the potential need for referral for diagnosis and treatment.

▲ Revised Code   ● New code   ~~Strikethrough~~ Deleted Code

DIAGNOSTIC IMAGING

D0210 Intraoral - complete series of radiographic images

A radiographic survey of the whole mouth, usually consisting of 14-22 periapical and posterior bitewing images intended to display the crowns and roots of all teeth, periapical areas and alveolar bone.

D0220 Intraoral - periapical first radiographic image

D0230 Intraoral - periapical each additional radiographic image

D0240 Intraoral - occlusal radiographic image

D0250 Extraoral - first radiographic image

D0260 Extraoral - each additional radiographic image

D0270 Bitewing - single radiographic image

D0272 Bitewings - two radiographic images

D0273 Bitewings - three radiographic images

D0274 Bitewings - four radiographic images

D0277 Vertical bitewings - 7 to 8 radiographic images

This does not constitute a full mouth intraoral radiographic series.

D0290 Posterior-anterior or lateral skull and facial bone survey radiographic image

D0310 Sialography

D0320 Temporomandibular joint arthrogram, including injection

D0321 Other temporomandibular joint radiographic images, by report

D0322 Tomographic survey

D0330 Panoramic radiographic image

D0340 Cephalometric radiographic image

▲ **D0350** 2D oral/facial photographic image obtained intra-orally or extra-orally

● **D0351** 3D photographic image

This procedure is for dental or maxillofacial diagnostic purposes. Not applicable for a CAD-CAM procedure.

D0364 Cone beam CT capture and interpretation with limited field of view – less than one whole jaw

D0365 Cone beam CT capture and interpretation with field of view of one full dental arch – mandible

D0366 Cone beam CT capture and interpretation with field of view of one full dental arch – maxilla, with or without cranium

D0367 Cone beam CT capture and interpretation with field of view of both jaws; with or without cranium

D0368 Cone beam CT capture and interpretation for TMJ series including two or more exposures

D0369 Maxillofacial MRI capture and interpretation

D0370 Maxillofacial ultrasound capture and interpretation

D0371 Sialoendoscopy capture and interpretation

D0380 Cone beam CT image capture with limited field of view – less than one whole jaw

D0381 Cone beam CT image capture with field of view of one full dental arch – mandible

D0382 Cone beam CT image capture with field of view of one full dental arch – maxilla, with or without cranium

D0383 Cone beam CT image capture with field of view of both jaws; with or without cranium

D0384 Cone beam CT image capture for TMJ series including two or more exposures

D0385 Maxillofacial MRI image capture

D0386 Maxillofacial ultrasound image capture

D0391 Interpretation of diagnostic image by a practitioner not associated with capture of the image, including report

D0393 Treatment simulation using 3D image volume

The use of 3D image volumes for simulation of treatment including, but not limited to, dental implant placement, orthognathic surgery and orthodontic tooth movement.

D0394 Digital subtraction of two or more images or image volumes of the same modality

To demonstrate changes that have occurred over time.

D0395 Fusion of two or more 3D image volumes of one or more modalities

TESTS AND EXAMINATIONS

D0415 Collection of microorganisms for culture and sensitivity

D0416 Viral culture

A diagnostic test to identify viral organisms, most often herpes virus.

D0417 Collection and preparation of saliva sample for laboratory diagnostic testing

D0418 Analysis of saliva sample

Chemical or biological analysis of saliva sample for diagnostic purposes.

D0421 Genetic test for susceptibility to oral diseases

Sample collection for the purpose of certified laboratory analysis to detect specific genetic variations associated with increased susceptibility for oral diseases such as severe periodontal disease.

D0425 Caries susceptibility tests

Not to be used for carious dentin staining.

D0431 Adjunctive pre-diagnostic test that aids in detection of mucosal abnormalities including premalignant and malignant lesions, not to include cytology or biopsy procedures

D0460 Pulp vitality tests

Includes multiple teeth and contra lateral comparison(s), as indicated.

D0470 Diagnostic casts

Also known as diagnostic models or study models.

▲ Revised Code   ● New code   ~~Strikethrough~~ Deleted Code

ORAL PATHOLOGY LABORATORY (USE CODES D0472 - D0502)

D0472 Accession of tissue, gross examination, preparation and transmission of written report

To be used in reporting architecturally intact tissue obtained by invasive means.

D0473 Accession of tissue, gross and microscopic examination, preparation and transmission of written report

To be used in reporting architecturally intact tissue obtained by invasive means.

D0474 Accession of tissue, gross and microscopic examination, including assessment of surgical margins for presence of disease, preparation and transmission of written report

To be used in reporting architecturally intact tissue obtained by invasive means.

D0475 Decalcification procedure

Procedure in which hard tissue is processed in order to allow sectioning and subsequent microscopic examination.

D0476 Special stains for microorganisms

Procedure in which additional stains are applied to biopsy or surgical specimen in order to identify microorganisms.

D0477 Special stains, not for microorganisms

Procedure in which additional stains are applied to a biopsy or surgical specimen in order to identify such things as melanin, mucin, iron, glycogen, etc.

D0478 Immunohistochemical stains

A procedure in which specific antibody based reagents are applied to tissue samples in order to facilitate diagnosis.

D0479 Tissue in-situ hybridization, including interpretation

A procedure which allows for the identification of nucleic acids, DNA and RNA, in the tissue sample in order to aid in the diagnosis of microorganisms and tumors.

D0480 Accession of exfoliative cytologic smears, microscopic examination, preparation and transmission of written report

To be used in reporting disaggregated, non-transepithelial cell cytology sample via mild scraping of the oral mucosa.

▲ **D0481** Electron microscopy

D0482 Direct immunofluorescence

A technique used to identify immunoreactants which are localized to the patient's skin or mucous membranes.

D0483 Indirect immunofluorescence

A technique used to identify circulating immunoreactants.

D0484 Consultation on slides prepared elsewhere

A service provided in which microscopic slides of a biopsy specimen prepared at another laboratory are evaluated to aid in the diagnosis of a difficult case or to offer a consultative opinion at the patient's request. The findings are delivered by written report.

D0485 Consultation, including preparation of slides from biopsy material supplied by referring source

A service that requires the consulting pathologist to prepare the slides as well as render a written report. The slides are evaluated to aid in the diagnosis of a difficult case or to offer a consultative opinion at the patient's request.

D0486 Laboratory accession of transepithelial cytologic sample, microscopic examination, preparation and transmission of written report

Analysis, and written report of findings, of cytologic sample of disaggregated transepithelial cells.

D0502 Other oral pathology procedures, by report

TESTS AND EXAMINATIONS

D0601 Caries risk assessment and documentation, with a finding of low risk

Using recognized assessment tools.

D0602 Caries risk assessment and documentation, with a finding of moderate risk

Using recognized assessment tools.

D0603 Caries risk assessment and documentation, with a finding of high risk

Using recognized assessment tools.

NONE

D0999 Unspecified diagnostic procedure, by report

Used for procedure that is not adequately described by a code. Describe procedure.

▲ Revised Code   ● New code   ~~Strikethrough~~ Deleted Code

PREVENTIVE

DENTAL PROPHYLAXIS

D1110 Prophylaxis - adult

Removal of plaque, calculus and stains from the tooth structures in the permanent and transitional dentition. It is intended to control local irritational factors.

D1120 Prophylaxis - child

Removal of plaque, calculus and stains from the tooth structures in the primary and transitional dentition. It is intended to control local irritational factors.

TOPICAL FLUORIDE TREATMENT (OFFICE PROCEDURE)

D1206 Topical application of fluoride varnish

▲ **D1208** Topical application of fluoride – excluding varnish

OTHER PREVENTIVE SERVICES

D1310 Nutritional counseling for control of dental disease

Counseling on food selection and dietary habits as a part of treatment and control of periodontal disease and caries.

D1320 Tobacco counseling for the control and prevention of oral disease

Tobacco prevention and cessation services reduce patient risks of developing tobacco-related oral diseases and conditions and improves prognosis for certain dental therapies.

D1330 Oral hygiene instructions

This may include instructions for home care. Examples include tooth brushing technique, flossing, use of special oral hygiene aids.

D1351 Sealant - per tooth

Mechanically and/or chemically prepared enamel surface sealed to prevent decay.

D1352 Preventive resin restoration in a moderate to high caries risk patient – permanent tooth

Conservative restoration of an active cavitated lesion in a pit or fissure that does not extend into dentin; includes placement of a sealant in any radiating non-carious fissures or pits.

● **D1353** Sealant repair – per tooth

SPACE MAINTENANCE (PASSIVE APPLIANCES)

D1510 Space maintainer - fixed - unilateral

D1515 Space maintainer - fixed - bilateral

D1520 Space maintainer - removable - unilateral

D1525 Space maintainer - removable - bilateral

▲ **D1550** Re-cement or re-bond space maintainer

D1555 Removal of fixed space maintainer

Procedure delivered by dentist who did not originally place the appliance, or by the practice where the appliance was originally delivered to the patient.

NONE

D1999 Unspecified preventive procedure, by report

▲ Revised Code   ● New code   ~~Strikethrough~~ Deleted Code

RESTORATIVE

AMALGAM RESTORATIONS (INCLUDING POLISHING)

D2140 Amalgam - one surface, primary or permanent

D2150 Amalgam - two surfaces, primary or permanent

D2160 Amalgam - three surfaces, primary or permanent

D2161 Amalgam - four or more surfaces, primary or permanent

RESIN-BASED COMPOSITE RESTORATIONS - DIRECT

D2330 Resin-based composite - one surface, anterior

D2331 Resin-based composite - two surfaces, anterior

D2332 Resin-based composite - three surfaces, anterior

D2335 Resin-based composite - four or more surfaces or involving incisal angle (anterior)

Incisal angle to be defined as one of the angles formed by the junction of the incisal and the mesial or distal surface of an anterior tooth.

D2390 Resin-based composite crown, anterior

Full resin-based composite coverage of tooth.

D2391 Resin-based composite - one surface, posterior

Used to restore a carious lesion into the dentin or a deeply eroded area into the dentin. Not a preventive procedure.

D2392 Resin-based composite - two surfaces, posterior

D2393 Resin-based composite - three surfaces, posterior

D2394 Resin-based composite - four or more surfaces, posterior

GOLD FOIL RESTORATIONS

D2410 Gold foil - one surface

D2420 Gold foil - two surfaces

D2430 Gold foil - three surfaces

INLAY/ONLAY RESTORATIONS

D2510 Inlay - metallic - one surface

D2520 Inlay - metallic - two surfaces

D2530 Inlay - metallic - three or more surfaces

D2542 Onlay - metallic - two surfaces

D2543 Onlay - metallic - three surfaces

D2544 Onlay - metallic - four or more surfaces

D2610 Inlay - porcelain/ceramic - one surface

D2620 Inlay - porcelain/ceramic - two surfaces

D2630 Inlay - porcelain/ceramic - three or more surfaces

D2642 Onlay - porcelain/ceramic - two surfaces

D2643 Onlay - porcelain/ceramic - three surfaces

D2644 Onlay - porcelain/ceramic - four or more surfaces

D2650 Inlay - resin-based composite - one surface

D2651 Inlay - resin-based composite - two surfaces

D2652 Inlay - resin-based composite - three or more surfaces

D2662 Onlay - resin-based composite - two surfaces

D2663 Onlay - resin-based composite - three surfaces

D2664 Onlay - resin-based composite - four or more surfaces

CROWNS - SINGLE RESTORATIONS ONLY

D2710 Crown - resin-based composite (indirect)

D2712 Crown - ¾ resin-based composite (indirect)

This code does not include facial veneers.

D2720 Crown - resin with high noble metal

D2721 Crown - resin with predominantly base metal

D2722 Crown - resin with noble metal

D2740 Crown - porcelain/ceramic substrate

D2750 Crown - porcelain fused to high noble metal

D2751 Crown - porcelain fused to predominantly base metal

D2752 Crown - porcelain fused to noble metal

D2780 Crown - 3/4 cast high noble metal

D2781 Crown - 3/4 cast predominantly base metal

D2782 Crown - 3/4 cast noble metal

D2783 Crown - 3/4 porcelain/ceramic

This code does not include facial veneers.

D2790 Crown - full cast high noble metal

D2791 Crown - full cast predominantly base metal

D2792 Crown - full cast noble metal

D2794 Crown - titanium

D2799 Provisional crown– further treatment or completion of diagnosis necessary prior to final impression

Not to be used as a temporary crown for a routine prosthetic restoration.

OTHER RESTORATIVE SERVICES

▲ **D2910** Re-cement or re-bond inlay, onlay, veneer or partial coverage restoration

▲ **D2915** Re-cement or re-bond indirectly fabricated or prefabricated post and core

▲ **D2920** Re-cement or re-bond crown

D2921 Reattachment of tooth fragment, incisal edge or cusp

D2929 Prefabricated porcelain/ceramic crown – primary tooth

D2930 Prefabricated stainless steel crown - primary tooth

D2931 Prefabricated stainless steel crown - permanent tooth

D2932 Prefabricated resin crown

D2933 Prefabricated stainless steel crown with resin window

Open-face stainless steel crown with aesthetic resin facing or veneer.

D2934 Prefabricated esthetic coated stainless steel crown - primary tooth

Stainless steel primary crown with exterior esthetic coating.

▲ Revised Code   ● New code   ~~Strikethrough~~ Deleted Code

D2940 Protective restoration

Direct placement of a restorative material to protect tooth and/or tissue form. This procedure may be used to relieve pain, promote healing, or prevent further deterioration. Not to be used for endodontic access closure, or as a base or liner under a restoration.

D2941 Interim therapeutic restoration – primary dentition

Placement of an adhesive restorative material following caries debridement by hand or other method for the management of early childhood caries. Not considered a definitive restoration.

D2949 Restorative foundation for an indirect restoration

Placement of restorative material to yield a more ideal form, including elimination of undercuts.

D2950 Core buildup, including any pins when required

Refers to building up of coronal structure when there is insufficient retention for a separate extracoronal restorative procedure. A core buildup is not a filler to eliminate any undercut, box form, or concave irregularity in a preparation.

D2951 Pin retention - per tooth, in addition to restoration

D2952 Post and core in addition to crown, indirectly fabricated

Post and core are custom fabricated as a single unit.

D2953 Each additional indirectly fabricated post - same tooth

To be used with D2952.

D2954 Prefabricated post and core in addition to crown

Core is built around a prefabricated post. This procedure includes the core material.

D2955 Post removal

D2957 Each additional prefabricated post - same tooth

To be used with D2954.

D2960 Labial veneer (resin laminate) - chairside

Refers to labial/facial direct resin bonded veneers.

D2961 Labial veneer (resin laminate) - laboratory

Refers to labial/facial indirect resin bonded veneers.

D2962 Labial veneer (porcelain laminate) - laboratory

Refers also to facial veneers that extend interproximally and/or cover the incisal edge. Porcelain/ceramic veneers presently include all ceramic and porcelain veneers.

D2970 Temporary crown (fractured tooth)

Usually a preformed artificial crown, which is fitted over a damaged tooth as an immediate protective device. This is not to be used as temporization during crown fabrication.

D2971 Additional procedures to construct new crown under existing partial denture framework

To be reported in addition to a crown code.

▲ **D2975** Coping

A thin covering of the coronal portion of a tooth, usually devoid of anatomic contour, that can be used as a definitive restoration.

D2980 Crown repair necessitated by restorative material failure

D2981 Inlay repair necessitated by restorative material failure

D2982 Onlay repair necessitated by restorative material failure

D2983 Veneer repair necessitated by restorative material failure

D2990 Resin infiltration of incipient smooth surface lesions

Placement of an infiltrating resin restoration for strengthening, stabilizing and/or limiting the progression of the lesion.

NONE

D2999 Unspecified restorative procedure, by report

Use for procedure that is not adequately described by a code. Describe procedure.

▲ Revised Code   ● New code   ~~Strikethrough~~ Deleted Code

ENDODONTICS

PULP CAPPING

D3110 Pulp cap - direct (excluding final restoration)

Procedure in which the exposed pulp is covered with a dressing or cement that protects the pulp and promotes healing and repair.

D3120 Pulp cap - indirect (excluding final restoration)

Procedure in which the nearly exposed pulp is covered with a protective dressing to protect the pulp from additional injury and to promote healing and repair via formation of secondary dentin. This code is not to be used for bases and liners when all caries has been removed.

PULPOTOMY

D3220 Therapeutic pulpotomy (excluding final restoration) - removal of pulp coronal to the dentinocemental junction and application of medicament

Pulpotomy is the surgical removal of a portion of the pulp with the aim of maintaining the vitality of the remaining portion by means of an adequate dressing.– To be performed on primary or permanent teeth.– This is not to be construed as the first stage of root canal therapy.– Not to be used for apexogenesis.

D3221 Pulpal debridement, primary and permanent teeth

Pulpal debridement for the relief of acute pain prior to conventional root canal therapy. This procedure is not to be used when endodontic treatment is completed on the same day.

D3222 Partial pulpotomy for apexogenesis - permanent tooth with incomplete root development

Removal of a portion of the pulp and application of a medicament with the aim of maintaining the vitality of the remaining portion to encourage continued physiological development and formation of the root. This procedure is not to be construed as the first stage of root canal therapy.

ENDODONTIC THERAPY ON PRIMARY TEETH

D3230 Pulpal therapy (resorbable filling) - anterior, primary tooth (excluding final restoration)

Primary incisors and cuspids.

D3240 Pulpal therapy (resorbable filling) - posterior, primary tooth (excluding final restoration)

Primary first and second molars.

ENDODONTIC THERAPY (INCLUDING TREATMENT PLAN, CLINICAL PROCEDURES AND FOLLOW-UP CARE)

D3310 Endodontic therapy, anterior tooth (excluding final restoration)

D3320 Endodontic therapy, bicuspid tooth (excluding final restoration)

D3330 Endodontic therapy, molar (excluding final restoration)

D3331 Treatment of root canal obstruction; non-surgical access

In lieu of surgery, the formation of a pathway to achieve an apical seal without surgical intervention because of a non-negotiable root canal blocked by foreign bodies, including but not limited to separated instruments, broken posts or calcification of 50% or more of the length of the tooth root.

D3332 Incomplete endodontic therapy; inoperable, unrestorable or fractured tooth

Considerable time is necessary to determine diagnosis and/or provide initial treatment before the fracture makes the tooth unretainable.

D3333 Internal root repair of perforation defects

Non-surgical seal of perforation caused by resorption and/or decay but not iatrogenic by provider filing claim.

ENDODONTIC RETREATMENT

D3346 Retreatment of previous root canal therapy - anterior

D3347 Retreatment of previous root canal therapy - bicuspid

D3348 Retreatment of previous root canal therapy - molar

APEXIFICATION/RECALCIFICATION

▲ **D3351** Apexification/recalcification – initial visit (apical closure / calcific repair of perforations, root resorption, etc.)

Includes opening tooth, preparation of canal spaces, first placement of medication and necessary radiographs. (This procedure may include first phase of complete root canal therapy.)

D3352 Apexification/recalcification – interim medication replacement

For visits in which the intra-canal medication is replaced with new medication. Includes any necessary radiographs.

D3353 Apexification/recalcification - final visit (includes completed root canal therapy - apical closure/ calcific repair of perforations, root resorption, etc.)

Includes removal of intra-canal medication and procedures necessary to place final root canal filling material including necessary radiographs. (This procedure includes last phase of complete root canal therapy.)

PULPAL REGENERATION

D3355 Pulpal regeneration - initial visit

Includes opening tooth, preparation of canal spaces, placement of medication.

▲ Revised Code	● New code	~~Strikethrough~~ Deleted Code

D3356 Pulpal regeneration - interim medication replacement

D3357 Pulpal regeneration - completion of treatment

Does not include final restoration.

APICOECTOMY/PERIRADICULAR SERVICES

D3410 Apicoectomy - anterior

For surgery on root of anterior tooth. Does not include placement of retrograde filling material.

D3421 Apicoectomy - bicuspid (first root)

For surgery on one root of a bicuspid. Does not include placement of retrograde filling material. If more than one root is treated, *see* D3426.

D3425 Apicoectomy - molar (first root)

For surgery on one root of a molar tooth. Does not include placement of retrograde filling material. If more than one root is treated, *see* D3426.

D3426 Apicoectomy (each additional root)

Typically used for bicuspids and molar surgeries when more than one root is treated during the same procedure. This does not include retrograde filling material placement.

D3427 Periradicular surgery without apicoectomy

D3428 Bone graft in conjunction with periradicular surgery – per tooth, single site

Includes non-autogenous graft material.

D3429 Bone graft in conjunction with periradicular surgery – each additional contiguous tooth in the same surgical site

Includes non-autogenous graft material.

D3430 Retrograde filling - per root

For placement of retrograde filling material during periradicular surgery procedures. If more than one filling is placed in one root - report as D3999 and describe.

D3431 Biologic materials to aid in soft and osseous tissue regeneration in conjunction with periradicular surgery

D3432 Guided tissue regeneration, resorbable barrier, per site, in conjunction with periradicular surgery

D3450 Root amputation - per root

Root resection of a multi-rooted tooth while leaving the crown. If the crown is sectioned, *see* D3920.

D3460 Endodontic endosseous implant

Placement of implant material, which extends from a pulpal space into the bone beyond the end of the root.

D3470 Intentional reimplantation (including necessary splinting)

For the intentional removal, inspection and treatment of the root and replacement of a tooth into its own socket. This does not include necessary retrograde filling material placement.

OTHER ENDODONTIC PROCEDURES

D3910 Surgical procedure for isolation of tooth with rubber dam

D3920 Hemisection (including any root removal), not including root canal therapy

Includes separation of a multi-rooted tooth into separate sections containing the root and the overlying portion of the crown. It may also include the removal of one or more of those sections.

D3950 Canal preparation and fitting of preformed dowel or post

Should not be reported in conjunction with D2952, D2953, D2954 or D2957 by the same practitioner.

NONE

D3999 Unspecified endodontic procedure, by report

Used for procedure that is not adequately described by a code. Describe procedure.

▲ Revised Code   ● New code   ~~Strikethrough~~ Deleted Code

PERIODONTICS

SURGICAL SERVICES (INCLUDING USUAL POSTOPERATIVE CARE)

D4210 Gingivectomy or gingivoplasty - four or more contiguous teeth or tooth bounded spaces per quadrant

It is performed to eliminate suprabony pockets or to restore normal architecture when gingival enlargements or asymmetrical or unaesthetic topography is evident with normal bony configuration.

D4211 Gingivectomy or gingivoplasty - one to three contiguous teeth or tooth bounded spaces per quadrant

It is performed to eliminate suprabony pockets or to restore normal architecture when gingival enlargements or asymmetrical or unaesthetic topography is evident with normal bony configuration.

D4212 Gingivectomy or gingivoplasty to allow access for restorative procedure, per tooth

D4230 Anatomical crown exposure - four or more contiguous teeth per quadrant

This procedure is utilized in an otherwise periodontally healthy area to remove enlarged gingival tissue and supporting bone (ostectomy) to provide an anatomically correct gingival relationship.

D4231 Anatomical crown exposure - one to three teeth per quadrant

This procedure is utilized in an otherwise periodontally healthy area to remove enlarged gingival tissue and supporting bone (ostectomy) to provide an anatomically correct gingival relationship.

D4240 Gingival flap procedure, including root planing - four or more contiguous teeth or tooth bounded spaces per quadrant

A soft tissue flap is reflected or resected to allow debridement of the root surface and the removal of granulation tissue. Osseous recontouring is not accomplished in conjunction with this procedure. May include open flap curettage, reverse bevel flap surgery, modified Kirkland flap procedure, and modified Widman surgery. This procedure is performed in the presence of moderate to deep probing depths, loss of attachment, need to maintain esthetics, need for increased access to the root surface and alveolar bone, or to determine the presence of a cracked tooth, fractured root, or external root resorption. Other procedures may be required concurrent to D4240 and should be reported separately using their own unique codes

D4241 Gingival flap procedure, including root planing - one to three contiguous teeth or tooth bounded spaces per quadrant

A soft tissue flap is reflected or resected to allow debridement of the root surface and the removal of granulation tissue. Osseous recontouring

is not accomplished in conjunction with this procedure. May include open flap curettage, reverse bevel flap surgery, modified Kirkland flap procedure, and modified Widman surgery. This procedure is performed in the presence of moderate to deep probing depths, loss of attachment, need to maintain esthetics, need for increased access to the root surface and alveolar bone, or to determine the presence of a cracked tooth, fractured root, or external root resorption. Other procedures may be required concurrent to D4241 and should be reported separately using their own unique codes.

D4245 Apically positioned flap

Procedure is used to preserve keratinized gingiva in conjunction with osseous resection and second stage implant procedure. Procedure may also be used to preserve keratinized/attached gingiva during surgical exposure of labially impacted teeth, and may be used during treatment of peri-implantitis.

▲ **D4249** Clinical crown lengthening – hard tissue

This procedure is employed to allow a restorative procedure on a tooth with little or no tooth structure exposed to the oral cavity. Crown lengthening requires reflection of a full thickness flap and removal of bone, altering the crown to root ratio. It is performed in a healthy periodontal environment, as opposed to osseous surgery, which is performed in the presence of periodontal disease.

▲ **D4260** Osseous surgery (including elevation of a full thickness flap and closure) – four or more contiguous teeth or tooth bounded spaces per quadrant

This procedure modifies the bony support of the teeth by reshaping the alveolar process to achieve a more physiologic form during the surgical procedure. This must include the removal of supporting bone (ostectomy) and/or non-supporting bone (osteoplasty). Other procedures may be required concurrent to D4260 and should be reported using their own unique codes.

▲ **D4261** Osseous surgery (including elevation of a full thickness flap and closure) – one to three contiguous teeth or tooth bounded spaces per quadrant

This procedure modifies the bony support of the teeth by reshaping the alveolar process to achieve a more physiologic form during the surgical procedure. This must include the removal of supporting bone (ostectomy) and/or non-supporting bone (osteoplasty). Other procedures may be required concurrent to D4261 and should be reported using their own unique codes.

▲ Revised Code   ● New code   ~~Strikethrough~~ Deleted Code

D4263 Bone replacement graft - first site in quadrant

This procedure involves the use of grafts to stimulate periodontal regeneration when the disease process has led to a deformity of the bone. This procedure does not include flap entry and closure, wound debridement, osseous contouring, or the placement of biologic materials to aid in osseous tissue regeneration or barrier membranes. Other separate procedures delivered concurrently are documented with their own codes.

D4264 Bone replacement graft - each additional site in quadrant

This procedure involves the use of grafts to stimulate periodontal regeneration when the disease process has led to a deformity of the bone. This procedure does not include flap entry and closure, wound debridement, osseous contouring, or the placement of biologic materials to aid in osseous tissue regeneration or barrier membranes. This procedure is performed concurrently with one or more bone replacement grafts to document the number of sites involved.

D4265 Biologic materials to aid in soft and osseous tissue regeneration

Biologic materials may be used alone or with other regenerative substrates such as bone and barrier membranes, depending upon their formulation and the presentation of the periodontal defect. This procedure does not include surgical entry and closure, wound debridement, osseous contouring, or the placement of graft materials and/or barrier membranes. Other separate procedures may be required concurrent to D4265 and should be reported using their own unique codes.

D4266 Guided tissue regeneration - resorbable barrier, per site

This procedure does not include flap entry and closure, or, when indicated, wound debridement, osseous contouring, bone replacement grafts, and placement of biologic materials to aid in osseous regeneration. This procedure can be used for periodontal and peri-implant defects.

D4267 Guided tissue regeneration - nonresorbable barrier, per site (includes membrane removal)

This procedure does not include flap entry and closure, or, when indicated, wound debridement, osseous contouring, bone replacement grafts, and placement of biologic materials to aid in osseous regeneration. This procedure can be used for periodontal and peri-implant defects.

D4268 Surgical revision procedure, per tooth

This procedure is to refine the results of a previously provided surgical procedure. This may require a surgical procedure to modify the irregular contours of hard or soft tissue. A mucoperiosteal flap may be elevated to allow access to reshape alveolar bone. The flaps are replaced or repositioned and sutured.

D4270 Pedicle soft tissue graft procedure

A pedicle flap of gingiva can be raised from an edentulous ridge, adjacent teeth, or from the existing gingiva on the tooth and moved laterally or coronally to replace alveolar mucosa as marginal tissue. The procedure can be used to cover an exposed root or to eliminate a gingival defect if the root is not too prominent in the arch.

D4273 Subepithelial connective tissue graft procedures, per tooth

This procedure is performed to create or augment gingiva, to obtain root coverage to eliminate sensitivity and to prevent root caries, to eliminate frenum pull, to extend the vestibular fornix, to augment collapsed ridges, to provide an adequate gingival interface with a restoration or to cover bone or ridge regeneration sites when adequate gingival tissues are not available for effective closure. There are two surgical sites. The recipient site utilizes a split thickness incision, retaining the overlying flap of gingiva and/or mucosa. The connective tissue is dissected from the donor site leaving an epithelialized flap for closure. After the graft is placed on the recipient site, it is covered with the retained overlying flap.

D4274 Distal or proximal wedge procedure (when not performed in conjunction with surgical procedures in the same anatomical area)

This procedure is performed in an edentulous area adjacent to a periodontally involved tooth. Gingival incisions are utilized to allow removal of a tissue wedge to gain access and correct the underlying osseous defect and to permit close flap adaptation.

D4275 Soft tissue allograft

Procedure is performed to create or augment the gingiva, with or without root coverage. This may be used to eliminate the pull of the frena and muscle attachments, to extend the vestibular fornix, and correct localized gingival recession. There is no donor site.

D4276 Combined connective tissue and double pedicle graft, per tooth

Advanced gingival recession often cannot be corrected with a single procedure. Combined tissue grafting procedures are needed to achieve the desired outcome.

D4277 Free soft tissue graft procedure (including donor site surgery), first tooth or edentulous tooth position in graft

D4278 Free soft tissue graft procedure (including donor site surgery), each additional contiguous tooth or edentulous tooth position in same graft site

NON-SURGICAL PERIODONTAL SERVICE

D4320 Provisional splinting - intracoronal

This is an interim stabilization of mobile teeth. A variety of methods and appliances may be employed for this purpose. Identify the teeth involved.

▲ Revised Code   ● New code   ~~Strikethrough~~ Deleted Code

D4321 Provisional splinting - extracoronal

This is an interim stabilization of mobile teeth. A variety of methods and appliances may be employed for this purpose. Identify the teeth involved.

D4341 Periodontal scaling and root planing - four or more teeth per quadrant

This procedure involves instrumentation of the crown and root surfaces of the teeth to remove plaque and calculus from these surfaces. It is indicated for patients with periodontal disease and is therapeutic, not prophylactic, in nature. Root planing is the definitive procedure designed for the removal of cementum and dentin that is rough, and/or permeated by calculus or contaminated with toxins or microorganisms. Some soft tissue removal occurs. This procedure may be used as a definitive treatment in some stages of periodontal disease and/or as a part of pre-surgical procedures in others.

D4342 Periodontal scaling and root planing - one to three teeth per quadrant

This procedure involves instrumentation of the crown and root surfaces of the teeth to remove plaque and calculus from these surfaces. It is indicated for patients with periodontal disease and is therapeutic, not prophylactic, in nature. Root planing is the definitive procedure designed for the removal of cementum and dentin that is rough, and/or permeated by calculus or contaminated with toxins or microorganisms. Some soft tissue removal occurs. This procedure may be used as a definitive treatment in some stages of periodontal disease and/or as a part of pre-surgical procedures in others.

D4355 Full mouth debridement to enable comprehensive evaluation and diagnosis

The gross removal of plaque and calculus that interfere with the ability of the dentist to perform a comprehensive oral evaluation. This preliminary procedure does not preclude the need for additional procedures.

D4381 Localized delivery of antimicrobial agents via a controlled release vehicle into diseased crevicular tissue, per tooth

FDA approved subgingival delivery devices containing antimicrobial medication(s) are inserted into periodontal pockets to suppress the pathogenic microbiota. These devices slowly release the pharmacological agents so they can remain at the intended site of action in a therapeutic concentration for a sufficient length of time.

OTHER PERIODONTAL SERVICES

D4910 Periodontal maintenance

This procedure is instituted following periodontal therapy and continues at varying intervals, determined by the clinical evaluation of the dentist, for the life of the dentition or any implant replacements. It includes removal of the bacterial plaque and calculus from supragingival and subgingival regions, site specific scaling and root planing where indicated, and polishing the teeth. If new or recurring periodontal disease appears, additional diagnostic and treatment procedures must be considered.

D4920 Unscheduled dressing change (by someone other than treating dentist or their staff)

D4921 Gingival irrigation – per quadrant

Irrigation of gingival pockets with medicinal agent. Not to be used to report use of mouth rinses or non-invasive chemical debridement.

NONE

D4999 Unspecified periodontal procedure, by report

Use for procedure that is not adequately described by a code. Describe procedure.

PROSTHODONTICS (REMOVABLE)

COMPLETE DENTURES (INCLUDING ROUTINE POST-DELIVERY CARE)

D5110 Complete denture - maxillary

D5120 Complete denture - mandibular

D5130 Immediate denture - maxillary

Includes limited follow-up care only; does not include required future rebasing/relining procedure(s) or a complete new denture.

D5140 Immediate denture - mandibular

Includes limited follow-up care only; does not include required future rebasing/relining procedure(s) or a complete new denture.

PARTIAL DENTURES (INCLUDING ROUTINE POST-DELIVERY CARE)

D5211 Maxillary partial denture - resin base (including any conventional clasps, rests and teeth)

Includes acrylic resin base denture with resin or wrought wire clasps.

D5212 Mandibular partial denture - resin base (including any conventional clasps, rests and teeth)

Includes acrylic resin base denture with resin or wrought wire clasps.

D5213 Maxillary partial denture - cast metal framework with resin denture bases (including any conventional clasps, rests and teeth)

D5214 Mandibular partial denture - cast metal framework with resin denture bases (including any conventional clasps, rests and teeth)

D5225 Maxillary partial denture - flexible base (including any clasps, rests and teeth)

D5226 Mandibular partial denture - flexible base (including any clasps, rests and teeth)

D5281 Removable unilateral partial denture - one piece cast metal (including clasps and teeth)

ADJUSTMENTS TO DENTURES

D5410 Adjust complete denture - maxillary

D5411 Adjust complete denture - mandibular

D5421 Adjust partial denture - maxillary

D5422 Adjust partial denture - mandibular

REPAIRS TO COMPLETE DENTURES

D5510 Repair broken complete denture base

D5520 Replace missing or broken teeth - complete denture (each tooth)

REPAIRS TO PARTIAL DENTURES

D5610 Repair resin denture base

D5620 Repair cast framework

D5630 Repair or replace broken clasp

D5640 Replace broken teeth - per tooth

D5650 Add tooth to existing partial denture

D5660 Add clasp to existing partial denture

D5670 Replace all teeth and acrylic on cast metal framework (maxillary)

D5671 Replace all teeth and acrylic on cast metal framework (mandibular)

DENTURE REBASE PROCEDURES

D5710 Rebase complete maxillary denture

D5711 Rebase complete mandibular denture

D5720 Rebase maxillary partial denture

D5721 Rebase mandibular partial denture

DENTURE RELINE PROCEDURES

D5730 Reline complete maxillary denture (chairside)

D5731 Reline complete mandibular denture (chairside)

D5740 Reline maxillary partial denture (chairside)

D5741 Reline mandibular partial denture (chairside)

D5750 Reline complete maxillary denture (laboratory)

D5751 Reline complete mandibular denture (laboratory)

D5760 Reline maxillary partial denture (laboratory)

D5761 Reline mandibular partial denture (laboratory)

INTERIM PROSTHESIS

D5810 Interim complete denture (maxillary)

D5811 Interim complete denture (mandibular)

D5820 Interim partial denture (maxillary)

Includes any necessary clasps and rests.

D5821 Interim partial denture (mandibular)

Includes any necessary clasps and rests.

OTHER REMOVABLE PROSTHETIC SERVICES

D5850 Tissue conditioning, maxillary

Treatment reline using materials designed to heal unhealthy ridges prior to more definitive final restoration.

D5851 Tissue conditioning, mandibular

Treatment reline using materials designed to heal unhealthy ridges prior to more definitive final restoration.

D5862 Precision attachment, by report

Each set of male and female components should be reported as one precision attachment. Describe the type of attachment used.

D5863 Overdenture – complete maxillary

D5864 Overdenture – partial maxillary

D5865 Overdenture – complete mandibular

D5866 Overdenture – partial mandibular

D5867 Replacement of replaceable part of semi-precision or precision attachment (male or female component)

D5875 Modification of removable prosthesis following implant surgery

▲ Revised Code   ● New code   ~~Strikethrough~~ Deleted Code

The modification of existing removable prosthesis is sometimes necessary at the time of implant placement and bone graft surgery and is always necessary at the time of the placement of the healing caps. This code could also be used to report the modification of an existing prosthesis when the abutments are placed and retentive elements are placed into the removable prosthesis, thereby reducing the need for a new prosthesis.

NONE

D5899 Unspecified removable prosthodontic procedure, by report

Use for a procedure that is not adequately described by a code. Describe procedure.

MAXILLOFACIAL PROSTHETICS

NONE

D5911 Facial moulage (sectional)

A sectional facial moulage impression is a procedure used to record the soft tissue contours of a portion of the face. Occasionally several separate sectional impressions are made, then reassembled to provide a full facial contour cast. The impression is utilized to create a partial facial moulage and generally is not reusable.

D5912 Facial moulage (complete)

Synonymous terminology: facial impression, face mask impression. A complete facial moulage impression is a procedure used to record the soft tissue contours of the whole face. The impression is utilized to create a facial moulage and generally is not reusable.

D5913 Nasal prosthesis

Synonymous terminology: artificial nose. A removable prosthesis attached to the skin, which artificially restores part or all of the nose. Fabrication of a nasal prosthesis requires creation of an original mold. Additional prostheses usually can be made from the same mold, and assuming no further tissue changes occur, the same mold can be utilized for extended periods of time. When a new prosthesis is made from the existing mold, this procedure is termed a nasal prosthesis replacement.

D5914 Auricular prosthesis

Synonymous terminology: artificial ear, ear prosthesis. A removable prosthesis, which artificially restores part or all of the natural ear. Usually, replacement prostheses can be made from the original mold if tissue bed changes have not occurred. Creation of an auricular prosthesis requires fabrication of a mold, from which additional prostheses usually can be made, as needed later (auricular prosthesis, replacement).

D5915 Orbital prosthesis

A prosthesis, which artificially restores the eye, eyelids, and adjacent hard and soft tissue, lost as a result of trauma or surgery. Fabrication of an orbital prosthesis requires creation of an original mold. Additional prostheses usually can be made from the same mold, and assuming no further tissue changes occur, the same mold can be utilized for extended periods of time. When a new prosthesis is made from the existing mold, this procedure is termed an orbital prosthesis replacement.

D5916 Ocular prosthesis

Synonymous terminology: artificial eye, glass eye. A prosthesis, which artificially replaces an eye missing as a result of trauma, surgery or congenital absence. The prosthesis does not replace missing eyelids or adjacent skin, mucosa or muscle. Ocular prostheses require semiannual or annual cleaning and polishing.

Also, occasional revisions to re-adapt the prosthesis to the tissue bed may be necessary. Glass eyes are rarely made and cannot be re-adapted.

D5919 Facial prosthesis

Synonymous terminology: prosthetic dressing. A removable prosthesis, which artificially replaces a portion of the face, lost due to surgery, trauma or congenital absence. Flexion of natural tissues may preclude adaptation and movement of the prosthesis to match the adjacent skin. Salivary leakage, when communicating with the oral cavity, adversely affects retention.

D5922 Nasal septal prosthesis

Synonymous terminology: Septal plug, septal button. Removable prosthesis to occlude (obturate) a hole within the nasal septal wall. Adverse chemical degradation in this moist environment may require frequent replacement. Silicone prostheses are occasionally subject to fungal invasion.

D5923 Ocular prosthesis, interim

Synonymous terminology: Eye shell, shell, ocular conformer, conformer. A temporary replacement generally made of clear acrylic resin for an eye lost due to surgery or trauma. No attempt is made to re-establish esthetics. Fabrication of an interim ocular prosthesis generally implies subsequent fabrication of an aesthetic ocular prosthesis.

D5924 Cranial prosthesis

Synonymous terminology: Skull plate, cranioplasty prosthesis, cranial implant. A biocompatible, permanently implanted replacement of a portion of the skull bones; an artificial replacement for a portion of the skull bone.

D5925 Facial augmentation implant prosthesis

Synonymous terminology: facial implant. An implantable biocompatible material generally onlayed upon an existing bony area beneath the skin tissue to fill in or collectively raise portions of the overlaying facial skin tissues to create acceptable contours. Although some forms of pre-made surgical implants are commercially available, the facial augmentation is usually custom made for surgical implantation for each individual patient due to the irregular or extensive nature of the facial deficit.

D5926 Nasal prosthesis, replacement

Synonymous terminology: replacement nose. An artificial nose produced from a previously made mold. A replacement prosthesis does not require fabrication of a new mold. Generally, several prostheses can be made from the same mold assuming no changes occur in the tissue bed due to surgery or age related topographical variations.

▲ Revised Code   ● New code   ~~Strikethrough~~ Deleted Code

D5927 Auricular prosthesis, replacement

Synonymous terminology: replacement ear. An artificial ear produced from a previously made mold. A replacement prosthesis does not require fabrication of a new mold. Generally, several prostheses can be made from the same mold assuming no changes occur in the tissue bed due to surgery or age related topographical variations.

D5928 Orbital prosthesis, replacement

A replacement for a previously made orbital prosthesis. A replacement prosthesis does not require fabrication of a new mold. Generally, several prostheses can be made from the same mold assuming no changes occur in the tissue bed due to surgery or age related topographical variations.

D5929 Facial prosthesis, replacement

A replacement facial prosthesis made from the original mold. A replacement prosthesis does not require fabrication of a new mold. Generally, several prostheses can be made from the same mold assuming no changes occur in the tissue bed due to further surgery or age related topographical variations.

D5931 Obturator prosthesis, surgical

Synonymous terminology: Obturator, surgical stayplate, immediate temporary obturator. A temporary prosthesis inserted during or immediately following surgical or traumatic loss of a portion or all of one or both maxillary bones and contiguous alveolar structures (e.g., gingival tissue, teeth). Frequent revisions of surgical obturators are necessary during the ensuing healing phase (approximately six months). Some dentists prefer to replace many or all teeth removed by the surgical procedure in the surgical obturator, while others do not replace any teeth. Further surgical revisions may require fabrication of another surgical obturator (e.g., an initially planned small defect may be revised and greatly enlarged after the final pathology report indicates margins are not free of tumor).

D5932 Obturator prosthesis, definitive

Synonymous terminology: obturator. A prosthesis, which artificially replaces part or all of the maxilla and associated teeth, lost due to surgery, trauma or congenital defects. A definitive obturator is made when it is deemed that further tissue changes or recurrence of tumor are unlikely and a more permanent prosthetic rehabilitation can be achieved; it is intended for long-term use.

D5933 Obturator prosthesis, modification

Synonymous terminology: adjustment, denture adjustment, temporary or office reline. Revision or alteration of an existing obturator (surgical, interim, or definitive); possible modifications include relief of the denture base due to tissue compression, augmentation of the seal or peripheral areas to affect adequate sealing or separation between the nasal and oral cavities.

D5934 Mandibular resection prosthesis with guide flange

Synonymous terminology: resection device, resection appliance. A prosthesis which guides the remaining portion of the mandible, left after a partial resection, into a more normal relationship with the maxilla. This allows for some tooth-to-tooth or an improved tooth contact. It may also artificially replace missing teeth and thereby increase masticatory efficiency.

D5935 Mandibular resection prosthesis without guide flange

A prosthesis which helps guide the partially resected mandible to a more normal relation with the maxilla allowing for increased tooth contact. It does not have a flange or ramp, however, to assist in directional closure. It may replace missing teeth and thereby increase masticatory efficiency. Dentists who treat mandibulectomy patients may prefer to replace some, all or none of the teeth in the defect area. Frequently, the defect's margins preclude even partial replacement. Use of a guide (a mandibular resection prosthesis with a guide flange) may not be possible due to anatomical limitations or poor patient tolerance. Ramps, extended occlusal arrangements and irregular occlusal positioning relative to the denture foundation frequently preclude stability of the prostheses, and thus some prostheses are poorly tolerated under such adverse circumstances.

D5936 Obturator prosthesis, interim

Synonymous terminology: immediate postoperative obturator. A prosthesis which is made following completion of the initial healing after a surgical resection of a portion or all of one or both the maxillae; frequently many or all teeth in the defect area are replaced by this prosthesis. This prosthesis replaces the surgical obturator, which is usually inserted at, or immediately following the resection. Generally, an interim obturator is made to facilitate closure of the resultant defect after initial healing has been completed. Unlike the surgical obturator, which usually is made prior to surgery and frequently revised in the operating room during surgery, the interim obturator is made when the defect margins are clearly defined and further surgical revisions are not planned. It is a provisional prosthesis, which may replace some or all lost teeth, and other lost bone and soft tissue structures. Also, it frequently must be revised (termed an obturator prosthesis modification) during subsequent dental procedures (e.g., restorations, gingival surgery) as well as to compensate for further tissue shrinkage before a definitive obturator prosthesis is made.

D5937 Trismus appliance (not for TMD treatment)

Synonymous terminology: occlusal device for mandibular trismus, dynamic bite opener. A prosthesis, which assists the patient in increasing their oral aperture width in order to eat as well as maintain oral hygiene. Several versions and designs are possible, all intending to ease the severe lack of oral opening experienced by many patients immediately following extensive intraoral surgical procedures.

D5951   Feeding aid

Synonymous terminology: feeding prosthesis. A prosthesis, which maintains the right and left maxillary segments of an infant cleft palate patient in their proper orientation until surgery is performed to repair the cleft. It closes the oral-nasal cavity defect, thus enhancing sucking and swallowing. Used on an interim basis, this prosthesis achieves separation of the oral and nasal cavities in infants born with wide clefts necessitating delayed closure. It is eliminated if surgical closure can be affected or, alternatively, with eruption of the deciduous dentition a pediatric speech aid may be made to facilitate closure of the defect.

D5952   Speech aid prosthesis, pediatric

Synonymous terminology: nasopharyngeal obturator, speech appliance, obturator, cleft palate appliance, prosthetic speech aid, speech bulb. A temporary or interim prosthesis used to close a defect in the hard and/or soft palate. It may replace tissue lost due to developmental or surgical alterations. It is necessary for the production of intelligible speech. Normal lateral growth of the palatal bones necessitates occasional replacement of this prosthesis. Intermittent revisions of the obturator section can assist in maintenance of palatalpharyngeal closure (termed a speech aid prosthesis modification). Frequently, such prostheses are not fabricated before the deciduous dentition is fully erupted since clasp retention is often essential.

D5953   Speech aid prosthesis, adult

Synonymous terminology: prosthetic speech appliance, speech aid, speech bulb. A definitive prosthesis, which can improve speech in adult cleft palate patients either by obturating (sealing off) a palatal cleft or fistula, or occasionally by assisting an incompetent soft palate. Both mechanisms are necessary to achieve velopharyngeal competency. Generally, this prosthesis is fabricated when no further growth is anticipated and the objective is to achieve long-term use. Hence, more precise materials and techniques are utilized. Occasionally such procedures are accomplished in conjunction with precision attachments in crown work undertaken on some or all maxillary teeth to achieve improved aesthetics.

D5954   Palatal augmentation prosthesis

Synonymous terminology: superimposed prosthesis, maxillary glossectomy prosthesis, maxillary speech prosthesis, palatal drop prosthesis. A removable prosthesis which alters the hard and/or soft palate's topographical form adjacent to the tongue.

D5955   Palatal lift prosthesis, definitive

A prosthesis which elevates the soft palate superiorly and aids in restoration of soft palate functions which may be lost due to an acquired, congenital or developmental defect. A definitive palatal lift is usually made for patients whose experience with an interim palatal lift has been successful, especially if surgical alterations are deemed unwarranted.

D5958   Palatal lift prosthesis, interim

Synonymous terminology: diagnostic palatal lift. A prosthesis which elevates and assists in restoring soft palate function which may be lost due to clefting, surgery, trauma or unknown paralysis. It is intended for interim use to determine its usefulness in achieving palatalpharyngeal competency or enhance swallowing reflexes. This prosthesis is intended for interim use as a diagnostic aid to assess the level of possible improvement in speech intelligibility. Some clinicians believe use of a palatal lift on an interim basis may stimulate an otherwise flaccid soft palate to increase functional activity, subsequently lessening its need.

D5959   Palatal lift prosthesis, modification

Synonymous terminology: revision of lift, adjustment. Alterations in the adaptation, contour, form or function of an existing palatal lift necessitated due to tissue impingement, lack of function, poor clasp adaptation or the like.

D5960   Speech aid prosthesis, modification

Synonymous terminology: adjustment, repair, revision. Any revision of a pediatric or adult speech aid not necessitating its replacement. Frequently, revisions of the obturating section of any speech aid is required to facilitate enhanced speech intelligibility. Such revisions or repairs do not require complete remaking of the prosthesis, thus extending its longevity.

D5982   Surgical stent

Synonymous terminology: periodontal stent, skin graft stent, columellar stent. Stents are utilized to apply pressure to soft tissues to facilitate healing and prevent cicatrization or collapse. A surgical stent may be required in surgical and post-surgical revisions to achieve close approximation of tissues. Usually such materials as temporary or interim soft denture liners, gutta percha, or dental modeling impression compound may be used.

CARRIERS

D5983   Radiation carrier

Synonymous terminology: radiotherapy prosthesis, carrier prosthesis, radiation applicator, radium carrier, intracavity carrier, intracavity applicator. A device used to administer radiation to confined areas by means of capsules, beads or needles of radiation emitting materials such as radium or cesium. Its function is to hold the radiation source

---

▲ Revised Code   ● New code   ~~Strikethrough~~ Deleted Code

securely in the same location during the entire period of treatment. Radiation oncologists occasionally request these devices to achieve close approximation and controlled application of radiation to a tumor deemed amiable to eradication.

NONE

D5984 Radiation shield

Synonymous terminology: radiation stent, tongue protector, lead shield. An intraoral prosthesis designed to shield adjacent tissues from radiation during orthovoltage treatment of malignant lesions of the head and neck region.

NONE

D5985 Radiation cone locator

Synonymous terminology: docking device, cone locator. A prosthesis utilized to direct and reduplicate the path of radiation to an oral tumor during a split course of irradiation.

CARRIERS

D5986 Fluoride gel carrier

Synonymous terminology: fluoride applicator. A prosthesis, which covers the teeth in either dental arch and is used to apply topical fluoride in close proximity to tooth enamel and dentin for several minutes daily.

NONE

D5987 Commissure splint

Synonymous terminology: lip splint. A device placed between the lips, which assists in achieving increased opening between the lips. Use of such devices enhances opening where surgical, chemical or electrical alterations of the lips has resulted in severe restriction or contractures.

D5988 Surgical splint

Synonymous terminology: Gunning splint, modified Gunning splint, labiolingual splint, fenestrated splint, Kingsley splint, cast metal splint. Splints are designed to utilize existing teeth and/or alveolar processes as points of anchorage to assist in stabilization and immobilization of broken bones during healing. They are used to re-establish, as much as possible, normal occlusal relationships during the process of immobilization. Frequently, existing prostheses (e.g., a patient's complete dentures) can be modified to serve as surgical splints. Frequently, surgical splints have arch bars added to facilitate intermaxillary fixation. Rubber elastics may be used to assist in this process. Circummandibular eyelet hooks can be utilized for enhanced stabilization with wiring to adjacent bone.

CARRIERS

D5991 Vesiculobullous disease medicament carrier

A custom fabricated carrier that covers the teeth and alveolar mucosa, or alveolar mucosa alone, and is used to deliver prescription medicaments for treatment of immunologically mediated vesiculobullous disease.

NONE

D5992 Adjust maxillofacial prosthetic appliance, by report

D5993 Maintenance and cleaning of a maxillofacial prosthesis (extra or intraoral) other than required adjustments, by report

Maintenance and cleaning of a maxillofacial prosthesis.

CARRIERS

D5994 Periodontal medicament carrier with peripheral seal – laboratory processed

A custom fabricated, laboratory processed carrier that covers the teeth and alveolar mucosa. Used as a vehicle to deliver prescribed medicaments for sustained contact with the gingiva, alveolar mucosa, and into the periodontal sulcus or pocket.

NONE

D5999 Unspecified maxillofacial prosthesis, by report

Used for procedure that is not adequately described by a code. Describe procedure.

▲ Revised Code ● New code ~~Strikethrough~~ Deleted Code

IMPLANT SERVICES

SURGICAL SERVICES

D6010 Surgical placement of implant body: endosteal implant

D6011 Second stage implant surgery

Surgical access to an implant body for placement of a healing cap or to enable placement of an abutment.

D6012 Surgical placement of interim implant body for transitional prosthesis: endosteal implant

Includes removal during later therapy to accommodate the definitive restoration, which may include placement of other implants.

D6013 Surgical placement of mini implant

D6040 Surgical placement: eposteal implant

An eposteal (subperiosteal) framework of a biocompatible material designed and fabricated to fit on the surface of the bone of the mandible or maxilla with permucosal extensions which provide support and attachment of a prosthesis. This may be a complete arch or unilateral appliance. Eposteal implants rest upon the bone and under the periosteum.

D6050 Surgical placement: transosteal implant

A transosteal (transosseous) biocompatible device with threaded posts penetrating both the superior and inferior cortical bone plates of the mandibular symphysis and exiting through the permucosa providing support and attachment for a dental prosthesis. Transosteal implants are placed completely through the bone and into the oral cavity from extraoral or intraoral.

IMPLANT SUPPORTED PROSTHETICS

D6051 Interim abutment

Includes placement and removal. A healing cap is not an interim abutment.

D6052 Semi-precision attachment abutment

Includes placement of keeper assembly.

~~**D6053** Implant/abutment supported removable denture for completely edentulous arch~~

~~**D6054** Implant/abutment supported removable denture for partially edentulous arch~~

D6055 Connecting bar – implant supported or abutment supported

Utilized to stabilize and anchor a prosthesis.

D6056 Prefabricated abutment – includes modification and placement

Modification of a prefabricated abutment may be necessary.

D6057 Custom fabricated abutment – includes placement

Created by a laboratory process, specific for an individual application.

▲ **D6058** Abutment supported porcelain/ceramic crown

A single crown restoration that is retained, supported and stabilized by an abutment on an implant.

▲ **D6059** Abutment supported porcelain fused to metal crown (high noble metal)

A single metal-ceramic crown restoration that is retained, supported and stabilized by an abutment on an implant.

▲ **D6060** Abutment supported porcelain fused to metal crown (predominantly base metal)

A single metal-ceramic crown restoration that is retained, supported and stabilized by an abutment on an implant.

▲ **D6061** Abutment supported porcelain fused to metal crown (noble metal)

A single metal-ceramic crown restoration that is retained, supported and stabilized by an abutment on an implant.

▲ **D6062** Abutment supported cast metal crown (high noble metal)

A single cast metal crown restoration that is retained, supported and stabilized by an abutment on an implant.

▲ **D6063** Abutment supported cast metal crown (predominantly base metal)

A single cast metal crown restoration that is retained, supported and stabilized by an abutment on an implant.

▲ **D6064** Abutment supported cast metal crown (noble metal)

A single cast metal crown restoration that is retained, supported and stabilized by an abutment on an implant.

▲ **D6065** Implant supported porcelain/ceramic crown

A single crown restoration that is retained, supported and stabilized by an implant.

▲ **D6066** Implant supported porcelain fused to metal crown (titanium, titanium alloy, high noble metal)

A single metal-ceramic crown restoration that is retained, supported and stabilized by an implant.

▲ **D6067** Implant supported metal crown (titanium, titanium alloy, high noble metal)

A single cast metal or milled crown restoration that is retained, supported and stabilized by an implant.

▲ **D6068** Abutment supported retainer for porcelain/ceramic FPD

A ceramic retainer for a fixed partial denture that gains retention, support and stability from an abutment on an implant.

▲ **D6069** Abutment supported retainer for porcelain fused to metal FPD (high noble metal)

A metal-ceramic retainer for a fixed partial denture that gains retention, support and stability from an abutment on an implant.

▲ Revised Code   ● New code   ~~Strikethrough~~ Deleted Code

▲ **D6070** Abutment supported retainer for porcelain fused to metal FPD (predominantly base metal)

A metal-ceramic retainer for a fixed partial denture that gains retention, support and stability from an abutment on an implant.

▲ **D6071** Abutment supported retainer for porcelain fused to metal FPD (noble metal)

A metal-ceramic retainer for a fixed partial denture that gains retention, support and stability from an abutment on an implant.

▲ **D6072** Abutment supported retainer for cast metal FPD (high noble metal)

A cast metal retainer for a fixed partial denture that gains retention, support and stability from an abutment on an implant.

▲ **D6073** Abutment supported retainer for cast metal FPD (predominantly base metal)

A cast metal retainer for a fixed partial denture that gains retention, support and stability from an abutment on an implant.

▲ **D6074** Abutment supported retainer for cast metal FPD (noble metal)

A cast metal retainer for a fixed partial denture that gains retention, support and stability from an abutment on an implant.

▲ **D6075** Implant supported retainer for ceramic FPD

A ceramic retainer for a fixed partial denture that gains retention, support and stability from an implant.

▲ **D6076** Implant supported retainer for porcelain fused to metal FPD (titanium, titanium alloy, or high noble metal)

A metal-ceramic retainer for a fixed partial denture that gains retention, support and stability from an implant.

▲ **D6077** Implant supported retainer for cast metal FPD (titanium, titanium alloy, or high noble metal)

A cast metal retainer for a fixed partial denture that gains retention, support and stability from an implant.

~~**D6078** Implant/abutment supported fixed denture for completely edentulous arch~~

~~A prosthesis that is retained, supported and stabilized by implants or abutments placed on implants but does not have specific relationships between implant positions and replacement teeth; may be screw retained or cemented; commonly referred to as a "hybrid prosthesis."~~

~~**D6079** Implant/abutment supported fixed denture for partially edentulous arch~~

~~A prosthesis that is retained, supported and stabilized by implants or abutments placed on implants but does not have specific relationship between implant positions and replacement teeth; may be screw retained or cemented; commonly referred to as a "hybrid prosthesis"~~

OTHER IMPLANT SERVICES

D6080 Implant maintenance procedures when prostheses are removed and reinserted, including cleansing of prostheses and abutments

This procedure includes active debriding of the implant(s) and examination of all aspects of the implant system(s), including the occlusion and stability of the superstructure. The patient is also instructed in thorough daily cleansing of the implant(s). This is not a per implant code, and is indicated for implant supported fixed prostheses.

D6090 Repair implant supported prosthesis, by report

This procedure involves the repair or replacement of any part of the implant supported prosthesis.

D6091 Replacement of semi-precision or precision attachment (male or female component) of implant/abutment supported prosthesis, per attachment

This procedure applies to the replaceable male or female component of the attachment.

▲ **D6092** Re-cement or re-bond implant/abutment supported crown

▲ **D6093** Re-cement or re-bond implant/abutment supported fixed partial denture

IMPLANT SUPPORTED PROSTHETICS

▲ **D6094** Abutment supported crown - (titanium)

A single crown restoration that is retained, supported and stabilized by an abutment on an implant. May be cast or milled.

OTHER IMPLANT SERVICES

D6095 Repair implant abutment, by report

This procedure involves the repair or replacement of any part of the implant abutment.

SURGICAL SERVICES

D6100 Implant removal, by report

This procedure involves the surgical removal of an implant. Describe procedure.

▲ **D6101** Debridement of a peri-implant defect or defects surrounding a single implant, and surface cleaning of the exposed implant surfaces, including flap entry and closure

▲ **D6102** Debridement and osseous contouring of a peri-implant defect or defects surrounding a single implant and includes surface cleaning of the exposed implant surfaces, including flap entry and closure

▲ **D6103** Bone graft for repair of peri-implant defect – does not include flap entry and closure. Placement of a barrier membrane or biologic materials to aid in osseous regeneration are reported separately

---

▲ Revised Code   ● New code   ~~Strikethrough~~ Deleted Code

229

D6104 Bone graft at time of implant placement

Placement of a barrier membrane, or biologic materials to aid in osseous regeneration are reported separately.

IMPLANT SUPPORTED PROSTHETICS

- **D6110** Implant /abutment supported removable denture for edentulous arch – maxillary
- **D6111** Implant /abutment supported removable denture for edentulous arch – mandibular
- **D6112** Implant /abutment supported removable denture for partially edentulous arch – maxillary
- **D6113** Implant /abutment supported removable denture for partially edentulous arch – mandibular
- **D6114** Implant /abutment supported fixed denture for edentulous arch – maxillary
- **D6115** Implant /abutment supported fixed denture for edentulous arch – mandibular
- **D6116** Implant /abutment supported fixed denture for partially edentulous arch – maxillary
- **D6117** Implant /abutment supported fixed denture for partially edentulous arch – mandibular

PRE-SURGICAL SERVICES

D6190 Radiographic/surgical implant index, by report

An appliance, designed to relate osteotomy or fixture position to existing anatomic structures, to be utilized during radiographic exposure for treatment planning and/or during osteotomy creation for fixture installation.

IMPLANT SUPPORTED PROSTHETICS

▲ **D6194** Abutment supported retainer crown for FPD (titanium)

A retainer for a fixed partial denture that gains retention, support and stability from an abutment on an implant. May be cast or milled.

NONE

D6199 Unspecified implant procedure, by report

Use for procedure that is not adequately described by a code. Describe procedure.

▲ Revised Code   ● New code   ~~Strikethrough~~ Deleted Code

PROSTHODONTICS, FIXED

FIXED PARTIAL DENTURE PONTICS

D6205 Pontic - indirect resin based composite

Not to be used as a temporary or provisional prosthesis.

D6210 Pontic - cast high noble metal

D6211 Pontic - cast predominantly base metal

D6212 Pontic - cast noble metal

D6214 Pontic - titanium

D6240 Pontic - porcelain fused to high noble metal

D6241 Pontic - porcelain fused to predominantly base metal

D6242 Pontic - porcelain fused to noble metal

D6245 Pontic - porcelain/ceramic

D6250 Pontic - resin with high noble metal

D6251 Pontic - resin with predominantly base metal

D6252 Pontic - resin with noble metal

D6253 Provisional pontic - further treatment or completion of diagnosis necessary prior to final impression

Not to be used as a temporary pontic for routine prosthetic fixed partial dentures.

D6545 Retainer - cast metal for resin bonded fixed prosthesis

D6548 Retainer - porcelain/ceramic for resin bonded fixed prosthesis

● **D6549** Resin retainer – for resin bonded fixed prosthesis

D6600 Inlay - porcelain/ceramic, two surfaces

D6601 Inlay - porcelain/ceramic, three or more surfaces

D6602 Inlay - cast high noble metal, two surfaces

D6603 Inlay - cast high noble metal, three or more surfaces

D6604 Inlay - cast predominantly base metal, two surfaces

D6605 Inlay - cast predominantly base metal, three or more surfaces

D6606 Inlay - cast noble metal, two surfaces

D6607 Inlay - cast noble metal, three or more surfaces

D6608 Onlay - porcelain/ceramic, two surfaces

D6609 Onlay - porcelain/ceramic, three or more surfaces

D6610 Onlay - cast high noble metal, two surfaces

D6611 Onlay - cast high noble metal, three or more surfaces

D6612 Onlay - cast predominantly base metal, two surfaces

D6613 Onlay - cast predominantly base metal, three or more surfaces

D6614 Onlay - cast noble metal, two surfaces

D6615 Onlay - cast noble metal, three or more surfaces

D6624 Inlay - titanium

D6634 Onlay - titanium

D6710 Crown - indirect resin based composite

Not to be used as a temporary or provisional prosthesis.

D6720 Crown - resin with high noble metal

D6721 Crown - resin with predominantly base metal

D6722 Crown - resin with noble metal

D6740 Crown - porcelain/ceramic

D6750 Crown - porcelain fused to high noble metal

D6751 Crown - porcelain fused to predominantly base metal

D6752 Crown - porcelain fused to noble metal

D6780 Crown - 3/4 cast high noble metal

D6781 Crown - 3/4 cast predominantly base metal

D6782 Crown - 3/4 cast noble metal

D6783 Crown - 3/4 porcelain/ceramic

D6790 Crown - full cast high noble metal

D6791 Crown - full cast predominantly base metal

D6792 Crown - full cast noble metal

D6793 Provisional retainer crown - further treatment or completion of diagnosis necessary prior to final impression

Not to be used as a temporary retainer crown for routine prosthetic fixed partial dentures.

D6794 Crown - titanium

OTHER FIXED PARTIAL DENTURE SERVICES

D6920 Connector bar

A device attached to fixed partial denture retainer or coping which serves to stabilize and anchor a removable overdenture prosthesis.

▲ **D6930** Re-cement or re-bond fixed partial denture

D6940 Stress breaker

A non-rigid connector.

D6950 Precision attachment

A male and female pair constitutes one precision attachment, and is separate from the prosthesis.

~~D6975~~ ~~Coping~~

~~To be used as a definitive restoration when coping is an integral part of a fixed prosthesis.~~

D6980 Fixed partial denture repair necessitated by restorative material failure

D6985 Pediatric partial denture, fixed

This prosthesis is used primarily for aesthetic purposes.

NONE

D6999 Unspecified fixed prosthodontic procedure, by report

Used for procedure that is not adequately described by a code. Describe procedure.

▲ Revised Code　　● New code　　~~Strikethrough~~ Deleted Code

ORAL & MAXILLOFACIAL SURGERY

EXTRACTIONS (INCLUDES LOCAL ANESTHESIA, SUTURING, IF NEEDED, AND ROUTINE POSTOPERATIVE CARE)

D7111 Extraction, coronal remnants - deciduous tooth

Removal of soft tissue-retained coronal remnants.

D7140 Extraction, erupted tooth or exposed root (elevation and/or forceps removal)

Includes routine removal of tooth structure, minor smoothing of socket bone, and closure, as necessary.

SURGICAL EXTRACTIONS (INCLUDES LOCAL ANESTHESIA, SUTURING, IF NEEDED, AND ROUTINE POSTOPERATIVE CARE)

D7210 Surgical removal of erupted tooth requiring removal of bone and/or sectioning of tooth, and including elevation of mucoperiosteal flap if indicated

Includes related cutting of gingiva and bone, removal of tooth structure, minor smoothing of socket bone and closure.

D7220 Removal of impacted tooth - soft tissue

Occlusal surface of tooth covered by soft tissue; requires mucoperiosteal flap elevation.

D7230 Removal of impacted tooth - partially bony

Part of crown covered by bone; requires mucoperiosteal flap elevation and bone removal.

D7240 Removal of impacted tooth - completely bony

Most or all of crown covered by bone; requires mucoperiosteal flap elevation and bone removal.

D7241 Removal of impacted tooth - completely bony, with unusual surgical complications

Most or all of crown covered by bone; unusually difficult or complicated due to factors such as nerve dissection required, separate closure of maxillary sinus required or aberrant tooth position.

D7250 Surgical removal of residual tooth roots (cutting procedure)

Includes cutting of soft tissue and bone, removal of tooth structure, and closure.

D7251 Coronectomy – intentional partial tooth removal

Intentional partial tooth removal is performed when a neurovascular complication is likely if the entire impacted tooth is removed.

OTHER SURGICAL PROCEDURES

D7260 Oroantral fistula closure

Excision of fistulous tract between maxillary sinus and oral cavity and closure by advancement flap.

D7261 Primary closure of a sinus perforation

Subsequent to surgical removal of tooth, exposure of sinus requiring repair, or immediate closure of oroantral or oral nasal communication in absence of fistulous tract.

D7270 Tooth reimplantation and/or stabilization of accidentally evulsed or displaced tooth

Includes splinting and/or stabilization.

D7272 Tooth transplantation (includes reimplantation from one site to another and splinting and/or stabilization)

D7280 Surgical access of an unerupted tooth

An incision is made and the tissue is reflected and bone removed as necessary to expose the crown of an impacted tooth not intended to be extracted.

D7282 Mobilization of erupted or malpositioned tooth to aid eruption

To move/luxate teeth to eliminate ankylosis; not in conjunction with an extraction.

D7283 Placement of device to facilitate eruption of impacted tooth

Placement of an orthodontic bracket, band or other device on an unerupted tooth, after its exposure, to aid in its eruption. Report the surgical exposure separately using D7280.

▲ **D7285** Incisional biopsy of oral tissue-hard (bone, tooth)

For partial removal of specimen only. This procedure involves biopsy of osseous lesions and is not used for apicoectomy/periradicular surgery. This procedure does not entail an excision.

▲ **D7286** Incisional biopsy of oral tissue-soft

For partial removal of an architecturally intact specimen only. This procedure is not used at the same time as codes for apicoectomy/periradicular curettage. This procedure does not entail an excision.

D7287 Exfoliative cytological sample collection

For collection of non-transepithelial cytology sample via mild scraping of the oral mucosa.

D7288 Brush biopsy - transepithelial sample collection

For collection of oral disaggregated transepithelial cells via rotational brushing of the oral mucosa.

D7290 Surgical repositioning of teeth

Grafting procedure(s) is/are additional.

D7291 Transseptal fiberotomy/supra crestal fiberotomy, by report

The supraosseous connective tissue attachment is surgically severed around the involved teeth. Where there are adjacent teeth, the transseptal fiberotomy of a single tooth will involve a minimum of three teeth. Since the incisions are within the gingival sulcus and tissue and the root surface is not instrumented, this procedure heals by the reunion of connective tissue with the root surface on which viable periodontal tissue is present (reattachment).

▲ Revised Code ● New code ~~Strikethrough~~ Deleted Code

▲ **D7292** Surgical placement of temporary anchorage device [screw retained plate] requiring flap; includes device removal

▲ **D7293** Surgical placement of temporary anchorage device requiring flap; includes device removal

▲ **D7294** Surgical placement of temporary anchorage device without flap; includes device removal

D7295 Harvest of bone for use in autogenous grafting procedure

Reported in addition to those autogenous graft placement procedures that do not include harvesting of bone.

ALVEOLOPLASTY - SURGICAL PREPARATION OF RIDGE

D7310 Alveoloplasty in conjunction with extractions - four or more teeth or tooth spaces, per quadrant

The alveoloplasty is distinct (separate procedure) from extractions and/or surgical extractions. Usually in preparation for a prosthesis or other treatments such as radiation therapy and transplant surgery.

D7311 Alveoloplasty in conjunction with extractions - one to three teeth or tooth spaces, per quadrant

The alveoloplasty is distinct (separate procedure) from extractions and/or surgical extractions. Usually in preparation for a prosthesis or other treatments such as radiation therapy and transplant surgery.

D7320 Alveoloplasty not in conjunction with extractions - four or more teeth or tooth spaces, per quadrant

No extractions performed in an edentulous area. See D7310 if teeth are being extracted concurrently with the alveoloplasty. Usually in preparation for a prosthesis or other treatments such as radiation therapy and transplant surgery.

D7321 Alveoloplasty not in conjunction with extractions - one to three teeth or tooth spaces, per quadrant

No extractions performed in an edentulous area. See D7311 if teeth are being extracted concurrently with the alveoloplasty. Usually in preparation for a prosthesis or other treatments such as radiation therapy and transplant surgery.

VESTIBULOPLASTY

D7340 Vestibuloplasty - ridge extension (secondary epithelialization)

D7350 Vestibuloplasty - ridge extension (including soft tissue grafts, muscle reattachment, revision of soft tissue attachment and management of hypertrophied and hyperplastic tissue)

SURGICAL EXCISION OF SOFT TISSUE LESIONS

D7410 Excision of benign lesion up to 1.25 cm

D7411 Excision of benign lesion greater than 1.25 cm

D7412 Excision of benign lesion, complicated

Requires extensive undermining with advancement or rotational flap closure.

D7413 Excision of malignant lesion up to 1.25 cm

D7414 Excision of malignant lesion greater than 1.25 cm

D7415 Excision of malignant lesion, complicated

Requires extensive undermining with advancement or rotational flap closure.

D7440 Excision of malignant tumor - lesion diameter up to 1.25 cm

D7441 Excision of malignant tumor - lesion diameter greater than 1.25 cm

D7450 Removal of benign odontogenic cyst or tumor - lesion diameter up to 1.25 cm

D7451 Removal of benign odontogenic cyst or tumor - lesion diameter greater than 1.25 cm

D7460 Removal of benign nonodontogenic cyst or tumor - lesion diameter up to 1.25 cm

D7461 Removal of benign nonodontogenic cyst or tumor - lesion diameter greater than 1.25 cm

D7465 Destruction of lesion(s) by physical or chemical method, by report

Examples include using cryo, laser or electro surgery.

EXCISION OF BONE TISSUE

D7471 Removal of lateral exostosis (maxilla or mandible)

D7472 Removal of torus palatinus

D7473 Removal of torus mandibularis

D7485 Surgical reduction of osseous tuberosity

D7490 Radical resection of maxilla or mandible

Partial resection of maxilla or mandible; removal of lesion and defect with margin of normal appearing bone. Reconstruction and bone grafts should be reported separately.

SURGICAL INCISION

D7510 Incision and drainage of abscess - intraoral soft tissue

Involves incision through mucosa, including periodontal origins.

D7511 Incision and drainage of abscess - intraoral soft tissue - complicated (includes drainage of multiple fascial spaces)

Incision is made intraorally and dissection is extended into adjacent fascial space(s) to provide adequate drainage of abscess/cellulitis.

D7520 Incision and drainage of abscess - extraoral soft tissue

Involves incision through skin.

D7521 Incision and drainage of abscess - extraoral soft tissue - complicated (includes drainage of multiple fascial spaces)

▲ Revised Code   ● New code   ~~Strikethrough~~ Deleted Code

Incision is made extraorally and dissection is extended into adjacent fascial space(s) to provide adequate drainage of abscess/cellulitis.

D7530 Removal of foreign body from mucosa, skin, or subcutaneous alveolar tissue

D7540 Removal of reaction producing foreign bodies, musculoskeletal system

May include, but is not limited to, removal of splinters, pieces of wire, etc., from muscle and/or bone.

D7550 Partial ostectomy/sequestrectomy for removal of non-vital bone

Removal of loose or sloughed-off dead bone caused by infection or reduced blood supply.

D7560 Maxillary sinusotomy for removal of tooth fragment or foreign body

TREATMENT OF FRACTURES - SIMPLE

D7610 Maxilla - open reduction (teeth immobilized, if present)

Teeth may be wired, banded or splinted together to prevent movement. Surgical incision required for interosseous fixation.

D7620 Maxilla - closed reduction (teeth immobilized, if present)

No incision required to reduce fracture. *See* D7610 if interosseous fixation is applied.

D7630 Mandible - open reduction (teeth immobilized, if present)

Teeth may be wired, banded or splinted together to prevent movement. Surgical incision required to reduce fracture.

D7640 Mandible - closed reduction (teeth immobilized, if present)

No incision required to reduce fracture. *See* D7630 if interosseous fixation is applied.

D7650 Malar and/or zygomatic arch - open reduction

D7660 Malar and/or zygomatic arch - closed reduction

D7670 Alveolus - closed reduction, may include stabilization of teeth

Teeth may be wired, banded or splinted together to prevent movement.

D7671 Alveolus - open reduction, may include stabilization of teeth

Teeth may be wired, banded or splinted together to prevent movement.

D7680 Facial bones - complicated reduction with fixation and multiple surgical approaches

Facial bones include upper and lower jaw, cheek, and bones around eyes, nose, and ears.

D7710 Maxilla - open reduction

Surgical incision required to reduce fracture.

D7720 Maxilla - closed reduction

D7730 Mandible - open reduction

Surgical incision required to reduce fracture.

D7740 Mandible - closed reduction

D7750 Malar and/or zygomatic arch - open reduction

Surgical incision required to reduce fracture.

D7760 Malar and/or zygomatic arch - closed reduction

D7770 Alveolus - open reduction stabilization of teeth

Fractured bone(s) are exposed to mouth or outside the face. Surgical incision required to reduce fracture.

D7771 Alveolus, closed reduction stabilization of teeth

Fractured bone(s) are exposed to mouth or outside the face.

D7780 Facial bones - complicated reduction with fixation and multiple surgical approaches

Surgical incision required to reduce fracture. Facial bones include upper and lower jaw, cheek, and bones around eyes, nose, and ears.

REDUCTION OF DISLOCATION AND MANAGEMENT OF OTHER TEMPOROMANDIBULAR JOINT DYSFUNCTIONS

D7810 Open reduction of dislocation

Access to TMJ via surgical opening.

D7820 Closed reduction of dislocation

Joint manipulated into place; no surgical exposure.

D7830 Manipulation under anesthesia

Usually done under general anesthesia or intravenous sedation.

D7840 Condylectomy

Surgical removal of all or portion of the mandibular condyle (separate procedure).

D7850 Surgical discectomy, with/without implant

Excision of the intra-articular disc of a joint.

D7852 Disc repair

Repositioning and/or sculpting of disc; repair of perforated posterior attachment.

D7854 Synovectomy

Excision of a portion or all of the synovial membrane of a joint.

D7856 Myotomy

Cutting of muscle for therapeutic purposes (separate procedure).

D7858 Joint reconstruction

Reconstruction of osseous components including or excluding soft tissues of the joint with autogenous, homologous, or alloplastic materials.

D7860 Arthrotomy

Cutting into joint (separate procedure).

D7865 Arthroplasty

Reduction of osseous components of the joint to create a pseudoarthrosis or eliminate an irregular remodeling pattern (osteophytes).

D7870 Arthrocentesis

Withdrawal of fluid from a joint space by aspiration.

D7871 Non-arthroscopic lysis and lavage

▲ Revised Code   ● New code   ~~Strikethrough~~ Deleted Code

Inflow and outflow catheters are placed into the joint space. The joint is lavaged and manipulated as indicated in an effort to release minor adhesions and synovial vacuum phenomenon as well as to remove inflammation products from the joint space.

D7872 Arthroscopy - diagnosis, with or without biopsy

D7873 Arthroscopy - surgical: lavage and lysis of adhesions

Removal of adhesions using the arthroscope and lavage of the joint cavities.

D7874 Arthroscopy - surgical: disc repositioning and stabilization

Repositioning and stabilization of disc using arthroscopic techniques.

D7875 Arthroscopy - surgical: synovectomy

Removal of inflamed and hyperplastic synovium (partial/complete) via an arthroscopic technique.

D7876 Arthroscopy - surgical: discectomy

Removal of disc and remodeled posterior attachment via the arthroscope.

D7877 Arthroscopy - surgical: debridement

Removal of pathologic hard and/or soft tissue using the arthroscope.

D7880 Occlusal orthotic device, by report

Presently includes splints provided for treatment of temporomandibular joint dysfunction.

D7899 Unspecified TMD therapy, by report

Used for procedure that is not adequately described by a code. Describe procedure.

REPAIR OF TRAUMATIC WOUNDS

D7910 Suture of recent small wounds up to 5 cm

COMPLICATED SUTURING (RECONSTRUCTION REQUIRING DELICATE HANDLING OF TISSUES AND WIDE UNDERMINING FOR METICULOUS CLOSURE)

D7911 Complicated suture - up to 5 cm
D7912 Complicated suture - greater than 5 cm

OTHER REPAIR PROCEDURES

D7920 Skin graft (identify defect covered, location and type of graft)

D7921 Collection and application of autologous blood concentrate product

D7940 Osteoplasty - for orthognathic deformities

Reconstruction of jaws for correction of congenital, developmental or acquired traumatic or surgical deformity.

D7941 Osteotomy - mandibular rami

D7943 Osteotomy - mandibular rami with bone graft; includes obtaining the graft

D7944 Osteotomy - segmented or subapical

Report by range of tooth numbers within segment.

D7945 Osteotomy - body of mandible

Surgical section of lower jaw. This includes the surgical exposure, bone cut, fixation, routine wound closure and normal post-operative follow-up care.

D7946 LeFort I (maxilla - total)

Surgical section of the upper jaw. This includes the surgical exposure, bone cuts, downfracture, repositioning, fixation, routine wound closure and normal post-operative follow-up care.

D7947 LeFort I (maxilla - segmented)

When reporting a surgically assisted palatal expansion without downfracture, this code would entail a reduced service and should be "by report."

D7948 LeFort II or LeFort III (osteoplasty of facial bones for midface hypoplasia or retrusion) - without bone graft

Surgical section of upper jaw. This includes the surgical exposure, bone cuts, downfracture, segmentation of maxilla, repositioning, fixation, routine wound closure and normal post-operative follow-up care.

D7949 LeFort II or LeFort III - with bone graft

Includes obtaining autografts.

D7950 Osseous, osteoperiosteal, or cartilage graft of the mandible or maxilla - autogenous or nonautogenous, by report

This procedure is for ridge augmentation or reconstruction to increase height, width and/or volume of residual alveolar ridge. It includes obtaining graft material. Placement of a barrier membrane, if used, should be reported separately.

D7951 Sinus augmentation with bone or bone substitutes via a lateral open approach

The augmentation of the sinus cavity to increase alveolar height for reconstruction of edentulous portions of the maxilla. This procedure is performed via a lateral open approach. This includes obtaining the bone or bone substitutes. Placement of a barrier membrane if used should be reported separately.

D7952 Sinus augmentation via a vertical approach

The augmentation of the sinus to increase alveolar height by vertical access through the ridge crest by raising the floor of the sinus and grafting as necessary. This includes obtaining the bone or bone substitutes.

D7953 Bone replacement graft for ridge preservation - per site

Graft is placed in an extraction or implant removal site at the time of the extraction or removal to preserve ridge integrity (e.g., clinically indicated in preparation for implant reconstruction or where alveolar contour is critical to planned prosthetic reconstruction). Does not include obtaining graft material. Membrane, if used should be reported separately.

▲ Revised Code   ● New code   ~~Strikethrough~~ Deleted Code

D7955 Repair of maxillofacial soft and/or hard tissue defect

Reconstruction of surgical, traumatic, or congenital defects of the facial bones, including the mandible, may utilize graft materials in conjunction with soft tissue procedures to repair and restore the facial bones to form and function. This does not include obtaining the graft and these procedures may require multiple surgical approaches. This procedure does not include edentulous maxilla and mandibular reconstruction for prosthetic considerations.

D7960 Frenulectomy - also known as frenectomy or frenotomy - separate procedure not incidental to another procedure

Surgical removal or release of mucosal and muscle elements of a buccal, labial or lingual frenum that is associated with a pathological condition, or interferes with proper oral development or treatment.

D7963 Frenuloplasty

Excision of frenum with accompanying excision or repositioning of aberrant muscle and z-plasty or other local flap closure.

D7970 Excision of hyperplastic tissue - per arch

D7971 Excision of pericoronal gingiva

Surgical removal of inflammatory or hypertrophied tissues surrounding partially erupted/impacted teeth.

D7972 Surgical reduction of fibrous tuberosity

D7980 Sialolithotomy

Surgical procedure by which a stone within a salivary gland or its duct is removed, either intraorally or extraorally.

D7981 Excision of salivary gland, by report

D7982 Sialodochoplasty

Surgical procedure for the repair of a defect and/or restoration of a portion of a salivary gland duct.

D7983 Closure of salivary fistula

Surgical closure of an opening between a salivary duct and/or gland and the cutaneous surface, or an opening into the oral cavity through other than the normal anatomic pathway.

D7990 Emergency tracheotomy

Surgical formation of a tracheal opening usually below the cricoid cartilage to allow for respiratory exchange.

D7991 Coronoidectomy

Surgical removal of the coronoid process of the mandible.

D7995 Synthetic graft - mandible or facial bones, by report

Includes allogenic material.

D7996 Implant-mandible for augmentation purposes (excluding alveolar ridge), by report

D7997 Appliance removal (not by dentist who placed appliance), includes removal of archbar

D7998 Intraoral placement of a fixation device not in conjunction with a fracture

The placement of intermaxillary fixation appliance for documented medically accepted treatments not in association with fractures.

NONE

D7999 Unspecified oral surgery procedure, by report

Used for procedure that is not adequately described by a code. Describe procedure.

▲ Revised Code   ● New code   ~~Strikethrough~~ Deleted Code

ORTHODONTICS

LIMITED ORTHODONTIC TREATMENT

D8010 Limited orthodontic treatment of the primary dentition

D8020 Limited orthodontic treatment of the transitional dentition

D8030 Limited orthodontic treatment of the adolescent dentition

D8040 Limited orthodontic treatment of the adult dentition

INTERCEPTIVE ORTHODONTIC TREATMENT

D8050 Interceptive orthodontic treatment of the primary dentition

D8060 Interceptive orthodontic treatment of the transitional dentition

COMPREHENSIVE ORTHODONTIC TREATMENT

D8070 Comprehensive orthodontic treatment of the transitional dentition

D8080 Comprehensive orthodontic treatment of the adolescent dentition

D8090 Comprehensive orthodontic treatment of the adult dentition

MINOR TREATMENT TO CONTROL HARMFUL HABITS

D8210 Removable appliance therapy

Removable indicates patient can remove; includes appliances for thumb sucking and tongue thrusting.

D8220 Fixed appliance therapy

Fixed indicates patient cannot remove appliance; includes appliances for thumb sucking and tongue thrusting.

OTHER ORTHODONTIC SERVICES

▲ **D8660** Pre-orthodontic treatment examination to monitor growth and development

Periodic observation of patient dentition, at intervals established by the dentist, to determine when orthodontic treatment should begin. Diagnostic procedures are documented separately.

▲ **D8670** Periodic orthodontic treatment visit

D8680 Orthodontic retention (removal of appliances, construction and placement of retainer(s))

D8690 Orthodontic treatment (alternative billing to a contract fee)

Services provided by dentist other than original treating dentist. A method of payment between the provider and responsible party for services that reflect an open-ended fee arrangement.

D8691 Repair of orthodontic appliance

Does not include bracket and standard fixed ortho appliances. It does include functional appliances and palatal expanders.

D8692 Replacement of lost or broken retainer

▲ **D8693** Re-cement or re-bond fixed retainer

D8694 Repair of fixed retainers, includes reattachment

NONE

D8999 Unspecified orthodontic procedure, by report

Used for procedure that is not adequately described by a code. Describe procedure.

▲ Revised Code   ● New code   ~~Strikethrough~~ Deleted Code

ADJUNCTIVE GENERAL SERVICES

UNCLASSIFIED TREATMENT

D9110 Palliative (emergency) treatment of dental pain - minor procedure

This is typically reported on a "per visit" basis for emergency treatment of dental pain.

D9120 Fixed partial denture sectioning

Separation of one or more connections between abutments and/or pontics when some portion of a fixed prosthesis is to remain intact and serviceable following sectioning and extraction or other treatment. Includes all recontouring and polishing of retained portions.

ANESTHESIA

D9210 Local anesthesia not in conjunction with operative or surgical procedures

D9211 Regional block anesthesia

D9212 Trigeminal division block anesthesia

D9215 Local anesthesia in conjunction with operative or surgical procedures

● **D9219** Evaluation for deep sedation or general anesthesia

D9220 Deep sedation/general anesthesia - first 30 minutes

Anesthesia time begins when the doctor administering the anesthetic agent initiates the appropriate anesthesia and non-invasive monitoring protocol and remains in continuous attendance of the patient. Anesthesia services are considered completed when the patient may be safely left under the observation of trained personnel and the doctor may safely leave the room to attend to other patients or duties. The level of anesthesia is determined by the anesthesia provider's documentation of the anesthetic's effects upon the central nervous system and not dependent upon the route of administration.

▲ **D9221** Deep sedation/general anesthesia – each additional 15 minutes

D9230 Inhalation of nitrous oxide/analgesia, anxiolysis

▲ **D9241** Intravenous moderate (conscious) sedation/analgesia – first 30 minutes

Anesthesia time begins when the doctor administering the anesthetic agent initiates the appropriate anesthesia and non-invasive monitoring protocol and remains in continuous attendance of the patient. Anesthesia services are considered completed when the patient may be safely left under the observation of trained personnel and the doctor may safely leave the room to attend to other patients or duties. The level of anesthesia is determined by the anesthesia provider's documentation of the anesthetic's effects upon the central nervous system and not dependent upon the route of administration. The level of anesthesia is determined by the anesthesia provider's documentation of the anesthetic's effects upon

the central nervous system and not dependent upon the route of administration.

▲ **D9242** Intravenous moderate (conscious) sedation/analgesia – each additional 15 minutes

▲ **D9248** Non-intravenous moderate (conscious) sedation

A medically controlled state of depressed consciousness while maintaining the patient's airway, protective reflexes and the ability to respond to stimulation or verbal commands. It includes non-intravenous administration of sedative and/or analgesic agent(s) and appropriate monitoring. The level of anesthesia is determined by the anesthesia provider's documentation of the anesthetic's effects upon the central nervous system and not dependent upon the route of administration. The level of anesthesia is determined by the anesthesia provider's documentation of the anesthetic's effects upon the central nervous system and not dependent upon the route of administration.

PROFESSIONAL CONSULTATION

D9310 Consultation - diagnostic service provided by dentist or physician other than requesting dentist or physician

A patient encounter with a practitioner whose opinion or advice regarding evaluation and/or management of a specific problem; may be requested by another practitioner or appropriate source. The consultation includes an oral evaluation. The consulted practitioner may initiate diagnostic and/or therapeutic services.

PROFESSIONAL VISITS

D9410 House/extended care facility call

Includes visits to nursing homes, long-term care facilities, hospice sites, institutions, etc. Report in addition to reporting appropriate code numbers for actual services performed.

D9420 Hospital or ambulatory surgical center call

Care provided outside the dentist's office to a patient who is in a hospital or ambulatory surgical center. Services delivered to the patient on the date of service are documented separately using the applicable procedure codes.

D9430 Office visit for observation (during regularly scheduled hours) - no other services performed

D9440 Office visit - after regularly scheduled hours

D9450 Case presentation, detailed and extensive treatment planning

Established patient. Not performed on same day as evaluation.

DRUGS

D9610 Therapeutic parenteral drug, single administration

Includes single administration of antibiotics, steroids, anti-inflammatory drugs, or other

▲ Revised Code　　● New code　　~~Strikethrough~~ Deleted Code

therapeutic medications. This code should not be used to report administration of sedative, anesthetic or reversal agents.

D9612 Therapeutic parenteral drugs, two or more administrations, different medications

Includes multiple administrations of antibiotics, steroids, anti-inflammatory drugs or other therapeutic medications. This code should not be used to report administration of sedatives, anesthetic or reversal agents. This code should be reported when two or more different medications are necessary and should not be reported in addition to code D9610 on the same date.

D9630 Other drugs and/or medicaments, by report

Includes, but is not limited to oral antibiotics, oral analgesics, and topical fluoride dispensed in the office for home use; does not include writing prescriptions.

MISCELLANEOUS SERVICES

D9910 Application of desensitizing medicament

Includes in-office treatment for root sensitivity. Typically reported on a "per visit" basis for application of topical fluoride. This code is not to be used for bases, liners or adhesives used under restorations.

D9911 Application of desensitizing resin for cervical and/or root surface, per tooth

Typically reported on a "per tooth" basis for application of adhesive resins. This code is not to be used for bases, liners, or adhesives used under restorations.

D9920 Behavior management, by report

May be reported in addition to treatment provided. Should be reported in 15-minute increments.

D9930 Treatment of complications (post-surgical) - unusual circumstances, by report

For example, treatment of a dry socket following extraction or removal of bony sequestrum.

● **D9931** Cleaning and inspection of a removable appliance

This procedure does not include any required adjustments.

D9940 Occlusal guard, by report

Removable dental appliances, which are designed to minimize the effects of bruxism (grinding) and other occlusal factors.

D9941 Fabrication of athletic mouthguard

D9942 Repair and/or reline of occlusal guard

D9950 Occlusion analysis - mounted case

Includes, but is not limited to, facebow, interocclusal records tracings, and diagnostic wax-up; for diagnostic casts, *see* D0470.

D9951 Occlusal adjustment - limited

May also be known as equilibration; reshaping the occlusal surfaces of teeth to create harmonious contact relationships between the maxillary and mandibular teeth. Presently includes discing/odontoplasty/enameloplasty. Typically reported on a "per visit" basis. This should not be reported when the procedure only involves bite adjustment in the routine post-delivery care for a direct/indirect restoration or fixed/removable prosthodontics.

D9952 Occlusal adjustment - complete

Occlusal adjustment may require several appointments of varying length, and sedation may be necessary to attain adequate relaxation of the musculature. Study casts mounted on an articulating instrument may be utilized for analysis of occlusal disharmony. It is designed to achieve functional relationships and masticatory efficiency in conjunction with restorative treatment, orthodontics, orthognathic surgery, or jaw trauma when indicated. Occlusal adjustment enhances the healing potential of tissues affected by the lesions of occlusal trauma.

D9970 Enamel microabrasion

The removal of discolored surface enamel defects resulting from altered mineralization or decalcification of the superficial enamel layer. Submit per treatment visit.

D9971 Odontoplasty 1 - 2 teeth; includes removal of enamel projections

D9972 External bleaching - per arch - performed in office

D9973 External bleaching - per tooth

D9974 Internal bleaching - per tooth

D9975 External bleaching for home application, per arch; includes materials and fabrication of custom trays

NON-CLINICAL PROCEDURES

D9985 Sales tax

NON-CLINICAL PROCEDURES

● **D9986** Missed appointment

● **D9987** Cancelled appointment

NONE

D9999 Unspecified adjunctive procedure, by report

Used for procedure that is not adequately described by a code. Describe procedure.

▲ Revised Code   ● New code   ~~Strikethrough~~ Deleted Code

Appendix A: Table of Drugs and Biologicals

IA - Intra-arterial administration
IV - Intravenous administration
IM - Intramuscular administration
IT - Intrathecal administration
SC - Subcutaneous administration
INH - Administration by inhaled solution
VAR - Various routes of administration
OTH - Other routes of administration
ORAL - Administered orally

Intravenous administration includes all methods, such as gravity infusion, injections, and timed pushes. The 'VAR' posting denotes various routes of administration and is used for drugs that are commonly administered into joints, cavities, tissues, or topical applications, in addition to other parenteral administrations. Listings posted with 'OTH' indicate other administration methods, such as suppositories or catheter injections.

DRUG NAME	UNIT PER	ROUTE	CODE

A

DRUG NAME	UNIT PER	ROUTE	CODE
ABATACEPT	10 MG	IV	J0129
ABBOKINASE, SEE UROKINASE			
ABBOKINASE, OPEN CATH, SEE UROKINASE			
ABCIXIMAB	10 MG	IV	J0130
ABELCET, SEE AMPHOTERICIN B LIPID COMPLEX			
ABLC, SEE AMPHOTERICIN B			
ABOBOTULINUMTOXIN TYPE A	5 UNITS	IM	J0586
ACETAMINOPHEN	10 MG	IV	J0131
ACETAZOLAMIDE SODIUM	UP TO 500 MG	IM, IV	J1120
ACETYLCYSTEINE, INJECTION	100 MG	IV	J0132
ACETYLCYSTEINE, UNIT DOSE FORM	PER GRAM	INH	J7604, J7608
ACHROMYCIN, SEE TETRACYCLINE			
ACTEMRA, SEE TOCILIZUMAB			
ACTH, SEE CORTICOTROPIN			
ACTHAR, SEE CORTICOTROPIN			
ACTIMMUNE, SEE INTERFERON GAMMA 1-B			
ACTIVASE, SEE ALTEPLASE RECOMBINANT			
ACYCLOVIR	5 MG		J0133
ADALIMUMAB	20 MG	SC	J0135
ADCETIS, SEE BRENTUXIMAB VEDOTIN			
ADENOCARD, SEE ADENOSINE			
ADENOSCAN, SEE ADENOSINE			
ADENOSINE	1 MG	IV	J0153
ADO-TRASTUZUMAB EMTANSINE	1 MG	IV	J9354

DRUG NAME	UNIT PER	ROUTE	CODE
ADRENALIN CHLORIDE, SEE ADRENALIN, EPINEPHRINE			
ADRENALIN, EPINEPHRINE	0.1 MG	SC, IM	J0171
ADRIAMYCIN PFS, SEE DOXORUBICIN HCL			
ADRIAMYCIN RDF, SEE DOXORUBICIN HCL			
ADRUCIL, SEE FLUOROURACIL			
AFLIBERCEPT	1 MG	OTH	J0178
AGALSIDASE BETA	1 MG	IV	J0180
AGGRASTAT, SEE TIROFIBAN HYDROCHLORIDE			
A-HYDROCORT, SEE HYDROCORTISONE SODIUM PHOSPHATE			
AKINETON, SEE BIPERIDEN			
ALATROFLOXACIN MESYLATE, INJECTION	100 MG	IV	J0200
ALBUTEROL	0.5 MG	INH	J7620
ALBUTEROL, CONCENTRATED FORM	1 MG	INH	J7610, J7611
ALBUTEROL, UNIT DOSE FORM	1 MG	INH	J7609, J7613
ALDESLEUKIN	PER SINGLE USE VIAL	IM, IV	J9015
ALDOMET, SEE METHYLDOPATE HCL			
ALEFACEPT	0.5 MG	IM, IV	J0215
ALEMTUZUMAB	10 MG	IV	J9010
ALFERON N, SEE INTERFERON ALFA-N3			
ALGLUCERASE	PER 10 UNITS	IV	J0205
ALGLUCOSIDASE ALFA	10 MG	IV	J0220, J0221
ALKABAN-AQ, SEE VINBLASTINE SULFATE			
ALKERAN, SEE MELPHALAN, ORAL			
ALPHA 1-PROTEINASE INHIBITOR, HUMAN	10 MG	IV	J0256, J0257
ALPHANATE			J7186
ALPROSTADIL, INJECTION	1.25 MCG	OTH	J0270
ALPROSTADIL, URETHRAL SUPPOSITORY		OTH	J0275
ALTEPLASE RECOMBINANT	1 MG	IV	J2997
ALUPENT, SEE METAPROTERENOL SULFATE OR METAPROTERENOL, COMPOUNDED			

DRUG NAME	UNIT PER	ROUTE	CODE
AMCORT, *SEE* TRIAMCINOLONE DIACETATE			
A-METHAPRED, *SEE* METHYLPREDNISOLONE SODIUM SUCCINATE			
AMGEN, *SEE* INTERFERON ALPHACON-1			
AMIFOSTINE	500 MG	IV	J0207
AMIKACIN SULFATE	100 MG		J0278
AMINOLEVULINIC ACID HCL	UNIT DOSE (354 MG)	OTH	J7308
AMINOLEVULINATE	1 GM	OTH	J7309
AMINOPHYLLINE/AMINOPHYLLIN	UP TO 250 MG	IV	J0280
AMIODARONE HCL	30 MG	IV	J0282
AMITRIPTYLINE HCL	UP TO 20 MG	IM	J1320
AMOBARBITAL	UP TO 125 MG	IM, IV	J0300
AMPHOCIN, *SEE* AMPHOTERICIN B			
AMPHOTERICIN B	50 MG	IV	J0285
AMPHOTERICIN B, LIPID COMPLEX	10 MG	IV	J0287-J0289
AMPICILLIN SODIUM	UP TO 500 MG	IM, IV	J0290
AMPICILLIN SODIUM/SULBACTAM SODIUM	PER 1.5 GM	IM, IV	J0295
AMYGDALIN, *SEE* LAETRILE, AMYGDALIN, VITAMIN B-17			
AMYTAL, *SEE* AMOBARBITAL			
ANABOLIN LA 100, *SEE* NANDROLONE DECANOATE			
ANIDULAFUNGIN	1 MG	IV	J0348
ANASCORP, *SEE* CENTRUROIDES IMMUNE F(AB)			
ANCEF, *SEE* CEFAZOLIN SODIUM			
ANDREST 90-4, *SEE* TESTOSTERONE ENANTHATE AND ESTRADIOL VALERATE			
ANDRO-CYP, *SEE* TESTOSTERONE CYPIONATE			
ANDRO-CYP 200, *SEE* TESTOSTERONE CYPIONATE			
ANDRO L.A. 200, *SEE* TESTOSTERONE ENANTHATE			
ANDRO-ESTRO 90-4, *SEE* TESTOSTERONE ENANTHATE AND ESTRADIOL VALERATE			
ANDRO/FEM, *SEE* TESTOSTERONE CYPIONATE AND ESTRADIOL CYPIONATE			
ANDROGYN L.A., *SEE* TESTOSTERONE ENANTHATE AND ESTRADIOL VALERATE			
ANDROLONE-50, *SEE* NANDROLONE PHENPROPIONATE			

DRUG NAME	UNIT PER	ROUTE	CODE
ANDROLONE-D 100, *SEE* NANDROLONE DECANOATE			
ANDRONAQ-50, *SEE* TESTOSTERONE SUSPENSION			
ANDRONAQ-LA, *SEE* TESTOSTERONE CYPIONATE			
ANDRONATE-200, *SEE* TESTOSTERONE CYPIONATE			
ANDRONATE-100, *SEE* TESTOSTERONE CYPIONATE			
ANDROPOSITORY 100, *SEE* TESTOSTERONE ENANTHATE			
ANDRYL 200, *SEE* TESTOSTERONE ENANTHATE			
ANECTINE, *SEE* SUCCINYLCHOLINE CHLORIDE			
ANERGAN 25, *SEE* PROMETHAZINE HCL			
ANERGAN 50, *SEE* PROMETHAZINE HCL			
ANISTREPLASE	30 UNITS	IV	J0350
ANTI-INHIBITOR	PER IU	IV	J7198
ANTISPAS, *SEE* DICYCLOMINE HCL			
ANTITHROMBIN III (HUMAN)	PER IU	IV	J7197
ANTITHROMBIN RECOMBINANT	50 IU	IV	J7196
ANZEMET, *SEE* DOLASETRON MESYLATE INJECTION			
A.P.L., *SEE* CHORIONIC GONADOTROPIN			
APOMORPHINE HYDROCHLORIDE	1 MG	SC	J0364
APRESOLINE, *SEE* HYDRALAZINE HCL			
APROTININ	10, 000 KIU		J0365
AQUAMEPHYTON, *SEE* VITAMIN K			
ARALEN, *SEE* CHLOROQUINE HCL			
ARAMINE, *SEE* METARAMINOL			
ARANESP, *SEE* DARBEPOETIN ALFA			
ARBUTAMINE	1 MG	IV	J0395
ARCALYST, *SEE* RILONACEPT			
AREDIA, *SEE* PAMIDRONATE DISODIUM			
ARFONAD, *SEE* TRIMETHAPHAN CAMSYLATE			
ARFORMOTEROL TARTRATE	15 MCG	INH	J7605
ARIDOL, *SEE* MANNITOL			
ARIPIPRAZOLE	0.25 MG	IM	J0400
ARIPIPRAZOLE, EXTENDED RELEASE	1 MG	INJ	J0401
ARISTOCORT FORTE, *SEE* TRIAMCINOLONE DIACETATE			
ARISTOCORT INTRALESIONAL, *SEE* TRIAMCINOLONE DIACETATE			
ARISTOSPAN INTRA-ARTICULAR, *SEE* TRIAMCINOLONE HEXACETONIDE			

DRUG NAME	UNIT PER	ROUTE	CODE
ARISTOSPAN INTRALESIONAL, *SEE* TRIAMCINOLONE HEXACETONIDE			
ARRESTIN, *SEE* TRIMETHOBENZAMIDE HCL			
ARSENIC TRIOXIDE	1 MG	IV	J9017
ARZERRA, *SEE* OFATUMUMAB			
ASPARAGINASE	1, 000 UNITS	IV, IM	J9019
	10, 000 UNITS	IV, IM	J9020
ASTRAMORPH PF, *SEE* MORPHINE SULFATE			
ATGAM, *SEE* LYMPHOCYTE IMMUNE GLOBULIN			
ATIVAN, *SEE* LORAZEPAM			
ATROPINE, CONCENTRATED FORM	PER MG	INH	J7635
ATROPINE, UNIT DOSE FORM	PER MG	INH	J7636
ATROPINE SULFATE	0.01 MG	IV, IM, SC	J0461
ATROVENT, *SEE* IPRATROPIUM BROMIDE			
ATRYN, *SEE* ANTITHROMBIN RECOMBINANT			
AUROTHIOGLUCOSE	UP TO 50 MG	IM	J2910
AUTOLOGOUS CULTURED CHONDROCYTES IMPLANT		OTH	J7330
AUTOPLEX T, *SEE* HEMOPHILIA CLOTTING FACTORS			
AVONEX, *SEE* INTERFERON BETA-1A			
AZACITIDINE	1 MG	SC	J9025
AZATHIOPRINE	50 MG	ORAL	J7500
AZATHIOPRINE, PARENTERAL	100 MG	IV	J7501
AZITHROMYCIN, DIHYDRATE	1 GM	ORAL	Q0144
AZITHROMYCIN, INJECTION	500 MG	IV	J0456

B

DRUG NAME	UNIT PER	ROUTE	CODE
BACLOFEN	10 MG	IT	J0475
BACLOFEN FOR INTRATHECAL TRIAL	50 MCG	OTH	J0476
BACTOCILL, *SEE* OXACILLIN SODIUM			
BAL IN OIL, *SEE* DIMERCAPROL			
BANFLEX, *SEE* ORPHENADRINE CITRATE			
BASILIXIMAB	20 MG		J0480
BCG (BACILLUS CALMETTE AND GUÉRIN), LIVE	PER VIAL INSTILLA-TION	IV	J9031
BECLOMETHASONE INHALATION SOLUTION, UNIT DOSE FORM	PER MG	INH	J7622
BELATACEPT	1 MG	IV	J0485
BELIMUMAB	10 MG	IV	J0490

DRUG NAME	UNIT PER	ROUTE	CODE
BENA-D 10, *SEE* DIPHENHYDRAMINE HCL			
BENA-D 50, *SEE* DIPHENHYDRAMINE HCL			
BENADRYL, *SEE* DIPHENHYDRAMINE HCL			
BENAHIST 10, *SEE* DIPHENHYDRAMINE HCL			
BENAHIST 50, *SEE* DIPHENHYDRAMINE HCL			
BEN-ALLERGIN-50, *SEE* DIPHENHYDRAMINE HCL			
BENDAMUSTINE HCL	1 MG	IV	J9033
BENEFIX, *SEE* FACTOR IX, RECOMBINANT			
BENLYSTA, *SEE* BELIMUMAB			
BENOJECT-10, *SEE* DIPHENHYDRAMINE HCL			
BENOJECT-50, *SEE* DIPHENHYDRAMINE HCL			
BENTYL, *SEE* DICYCLOMINE			
BENZTROPINE MESYLATE	PER 1 MG	IM, IV	J0515
BERINERT, *SEE* C-1 ESTERASE INHIBITOR			
BERUBIGEN, *SEE* VITAMIN B-12 CYANOCOBALAMIN			
BETA AMYLOID	PER STUDY DOSE	OTH	A9599
BETALIN 12, *SEE* VITAMIN B-12 CYANOCOBALAMIN			
BETAMETH, *SEE* BETAMETHASONE SODIUM PHOSPHATE			
BETAMETHASONE ACETATE & BETAMETHASONE SODIUM PHOSPHATE	PER 3 MG	IM	J0702
BETAMETHASONE INHALATION SOLUTION, UNIT DOSE FORM	PER MG	INH	J7624
BETASERON, *SEE* INTERFERON BETA-1B			
BETHANECHOL CHLORIDE	UP TO 5 MG	SC	J0520
BEVACIZUMAB	10 MG	IV	J9035
BICILLIN L-A, *SEE* PENICILLIN G BENZATHINE			
BICILLIN C-R 900/300, *SEE* PENICILLIN G PROCAINE AND PENICILLIN G BENZATHINE			
BICILLIN C-R, *SEE* PENICILLIN G BENZATHINE AND PENICILLIN G PROCAINE			
BICNU, *SEE* CARMUSTINE			
BIPERIDEN LACTATE	PER 5 MG	IM, IV	J0190

DRUG NAME	UNIT PER	ROUTE	CODE
BITOLTEROL MESYLATE, CONCENTRATED FORM	PER MG	INH	J7628
BITOLTEROL MESYLATE, UNIT DOSE FORM	PER MG	INH	J7629
BIVALIRUDIN	1 MG	IV	J0583
BLENOXANE, SEE BLEOMYCIN SULFATE			
BLEOMYCIN SULFATE	15 UNITS	IM, IV, SC	J9040
BORTEZOMIB	0.1 MG	IV	J9041
BOTOX, SEE ONABOTULINUMTOXINA			
BRENTUXIMAB VEDOTIN	1 MG	IV	J9042
BRETHINE, SEE TERBUTALINE SULFATE OR TERBUTALINE, COMPOUNDED			
BRICANYL SUBCUTANEOUS, SEE TERBUTALINE SULFATE			
BROMPHENIRAMINE MALEATE	PER 10 MG	IM, SC, IV	J0945
BRONKEPHRINE, SEE ETHYLNOREPINEPHRINE HCL			
BRONKOSOL, SEE ISOETHARINE HCL			
BUDESONIDE INHALATION SOLUTION, CONCENTRATED FORM	0.25 MG	INH	J7633, J7634
BUDESONIDE INHALATION SOLUTION, UNIT DOSE FORM	0.5 MG	INH	J7626, J7627
BUPRENORPHINE HYDROCHLORIDE	0.1 MG	IM	J0592
BUPRENORPHINE/NALOXONE	1 MG	ORAL	J0571
	<=3 MG	ORAL	J0572
	>3 MG BUT <=6 MG	ORAL	J0573
	>6 MG BUT <=10 MG	ORAL	J0574
	>10 MG	ORAL	J0575
BUSULFAN	1 MG	IV	J0594
BUSULFAN	2 MG	ORAL	J8510
BUTORPHANOL TARTRATE	1 MG		J0595

C

DRUG NAME	UNIT PER	ROUTE	CODE
C1 ESTERASE INHIBITOR	10 UNITS	IV	J0597, J0598
CABAZITAXEL	1 MG	IV	J9043
CABERGOLINE	.25 MG	ORAL	J8515
CAFCIT, SEE CAFFEINE CITRATE			
CAFFEINE CITRATE	5 MG	IV	J0706
CAINE-1, SEE LIDOCAINE HCL			
CAINE-2, SEE LIDOCAINE HCL			
CALCIJEX, SEE CALCITRIOL			
CALCIMAR, SEE CALCITONIN-SALMON			

DRUG NAME	UNIT PER	ROUTE	CODE
CALCITONIN-SALMON	UP TO 400 UNITS	SC, IM	J0630
CALCITRIOL	0.1 MCG	IM	J0636
CALCIUM DISODIUM VERSENATE, SEE EDETATE CALCIUM DISODIUM			
CALCIUM GLUCONATE	PER 10 ML	IV	J0610
CALCIUM GLYCEROPHOSPHATE & CALCIUM LACTATE	PER 10 ML	IM, SC	J0620
CALDOLOR, SEE IBUPROFEN			
CALPHOSAN, SEE CALCIUM GLYCEROPHOSPHATE AND CALCIUM LACTATE			
CAMPTOSAR, SEE IRINOTECAN			
CANAKINUMAB	1 MG	SC	J0638
CAPECITABINE	150 MG	ORAL	J8520
	500 MG	ORAL	J8521
CAPSAICIN PATCH	PER SQ CM	OTH	J7336
CARBOCAINE WITH NEO-COBEFRIN, SEE MEPIVACAINE			
CARBOCAINE, SEE MEPIVACAINE			
CARBOPLATIN	50 MG	IV	J9045
CARFILZOMIB	1 MG	IV	J9047
CARMUSTINE	100 MG	IV	J9050
CARNITOR, SEE LEVOCARNITINE			
CARTICEL, SEE AUTOLOGOUS CULTURED CHONDROCYTES			
CASPOFUNGIN ACETATE	5 MG	IV	J0637
CAYSTON, SEE AZTREONAM			
CEFADYL, SEE CEPHAPIRIN SODIUM			
CEFAZOLIN SODIUM	500 MG	IV, IM	J0690
CEFEPIME HYDROCHLORIDE	500 MG	IV	J0692
CEFIZOX, SEE CEFTIZOXIME SODIUM			
CEFOTAXIME SODIUM	PER 1 G	IV, IM	J0698
CEFOXITIN SODIUM	1 G	IV, IM	J0694
CEFTAROLINE FOSAMIL	1 MG		J0712
CEFTAZIDIME	PER 500 MG	IM, IV	J0713
CEFTIZOXIME SODIUM	PER 500 MG	IV, IM	J0715
CEFTRIAXONE SODIUM	PER 250 MG	IV, IM	J0696
CEFUROXIME SODIUM, STERILE	PER 750 MG	IM, IV	J0697
CELESTONE SOLUSPAN, SEE BETAMETHASONE ACETATE AND BETAMETHASONE SODIUM PHOSPHATE			
CELLCEPT, SEE MYCOPHENOLATE MOFETIL			

DRUG NAME	UNIT PER	ROUTE	CODE
CEL-U-JEC, SEE BETAMETHASONE SODIUM PHOSPHATE			
CENACORT FORTE, SEE TRIAMCINOLONE DIACETATE			
CENACORT A-40, SEE TRIAMCINOLONE ACETONIDE			
CENTRUROIDES IMMUNE F(AB)	UP TO 120 MG	IV	J0716
CEPHALOTHIN SODIUM	UP TO 1 G	IM, IV	J1890
CEPHAPIRIN SODIUM	UP TO 1 G	IV, IM	J0710
CEREDASE, SEE ALGLUCERASE			
CERTOLIZUMAB PEGOL	1 MG	SC	J0717
CERUBIDINE, SEE DAUNORUBICIN HCL			
CETUXIMAB	10 MG	IV	J9055
CHEALAMIDE, SEE ENDRATE ETHYLENEDIAMINE-TETRA-ACETIC ACID			
CHLORAMPHENICOL SODIUM SUCCINATE	UP TO 1 G	IV	J0720
CHLORDIAZEPOXIDE HCL	UP TO 100 MG	IM, IV	J1990
CHLOROMYCETIN SODIUM SUCCINATE, SEE CHLORAMPHENICOL SODIUM SUCCINATE			
CHLOROPROCAINE HCL	PER 30 ML	VAR	J2400
CHLORPROMAZINE	5 MG	ORAL	Q0161
CHLOROQUINE HCL	UP TO 250 MG	IM	J0390
CHLOROTHIAZIDE SODIUM	PER 500 MG	IV	J1205
CHLORPROMAZINE HCL	UP TO 50 MG	IM, IV	J3230
CHOREX-5, SEE CHORIONIC GONADOTROPIN			
CHOREX-10, SEE CHORIONIC GONADOTROPIN			
CHORIGNON, SEE CHORIONIC GONADOTROPIN			
CHORIONIC GONADOTROPIN	PER 1,000 USP UNITS	IM	J0725
CHORON 10, SEE CHORIONIC GONADOTROPIN			
CIDOFOVIR	375 MG	IV	J0740
CILASTATIN SODIUM, IMIPENEM	PER 250 MG	IV, IM	J0743
CIMZIA, SEE CERTOLIZUMAB PEGOL			
CINRYZE, SEE C1 ESTERASE INHIBITOR			
CIPRO IV, SEE CIPROFLOXACIN			
CIPROFLOXACIN	200 MG	IV	J0706

DRUG NAME	UNIT PER	ROUTE	CODE
CISPLATIN, POWDER OR SOLUTION	PER 10 MG	IV	J9060
CLADRIBINE	PER MG	IV	J9065
CLAFORAN, SEE CEFOTAXIME SODIUM			
CLOFARABINE	1 MG	IV	J9027
CLONIDINE HYDROCHLORIDE	1 MG	EPI-DURAL	J0735
COBEX, SEE VITAMIN B-12 CYANOCOBALAMIN			
CODEINE PHOSPHATE	PER 30 MG	IM, IV, SC	J0745
CODIMAL-A, SEE BROMPHENIRAMINE MALEATE			
COGENTIN, SEE BENZTROPINE MESYLATE			
COLLAGENASE, CLOSTRIDIUM HISTOLYTICUM	0.01 MG	OTH	J0775
COLCHICINE	PER 1 MG	IV	J0760
COLISTIMETHATE SODIUM	UP TO 150 MG	IM, IV	J0770
COLY-MYCIN M, SEE COLISTIMETHATE SODIUM			
COMPA-Z, SEE PROCHLORPERAZINE			
COMPAZINE, SEE PROCHLORPERAZINE			
COPHENE-B, SEE BROMPHENIRAMINE MALEATE			
COPPER CONTRACEPTIVE, INTRAUTERINE		OTH	J7300
CORDARONE, SEE AMIODARONE HCL			
CORGONJECT-5, SEE CHORIONIC GONADOTROPIN			
CORTICORELIN OVINE TRIFLUTATE	1 MCG		J0795
CORTICOTROPIN	UP TO 40 UNITS	IV, IM, SC	J0800
CORTROSYN, SEE COSYNTROPIN			
COSMEGEN, SEE DACTINOMYCIN			
COSYNTROPIN	PER 0.25 MG	IM, IV	J0833, J0834
COTRANZINE, SEE PROCHLORPERAZINE			
CROFAB, SEE CROTALIDAE POLYVALENT IMMUNE FAB			
CROMOLYN SODIUM, UNIT DOSE FORM	PER 10 MG	INH	J7631, J7632
CROTALIDAE POLYVALENT IMMUNE FAB	UP TO 1 GRAM	IV	J0840
CRYSTICILLIN 300 A.S., SEE PENICILLIN G PROCAINE			
CRYSTICILLIN 600 A.S., SEE PENICILLIN G PROCAINE			
CYCLOPHOSPHAMIDE	100 MG	IV	J9070

5

DRUG NAME	UNIT PER	ROUTE	CODE
CYCLOPHOSPHAMIDE, ORAL	25 MG	ORAL	J8530
CYCLOSPORINE, ORAL	25 MG	ORAL	J7515
	100 MG	ORAL	J7502
CYCLOSPORINE, PARENTERAL	250 MG	IV	J7516
CYTARABINE	100 MG	SC, IV	J9100
CYTARABINE LIPOSOME	10 MG	IT	J9098
CYTOMEGALOVIRUS IMMUNE GLOBULIN INTRAVENOUS(HUMAN)	PER VIAL	IV	J0850
CYTOSAR-U, SEE CYTARABINE			
CYTOVENE, SEE GANCICLOVIR SODIUM			
CYTOXAN, SEE CYCLOPHOSPHAMIDE; CYCLOPHOSPHAMIDE, LYOPHILIZED; AND CYCLOPHOSPHAMIDE, ORAL			

D

DRUG NAME	UNIT PER	ROUTE	CODE
D-5-W, INFUSION	1000 CC	IV	J7070
DACARBAZINE	100 MG	IV	J9130
DACLIZUMAB	25 MG	IV	J7513
DACTINOMYCIN	0.5 MG	IV	J9120
DALALONE, SEE DEXAMETHASONE SODIUM PHOSPHATE			
DALALONE L.A., SEE DEXAMETHASONE ACETATE			
DALTEPARIN SODIUM	PER 2500 IU	SC	J1645
DAPTOMYCIN	1 MG	IV	J0878
DARBEPOETIN ALFA	1 MCG	IV, SC	J0881, J0882
DAUNORUBICIN CITRATE, LIPOSOMAL FORMULATION	10 MG	IV	J9151
DAUNORUBICIN HCL	10 MG	IV	J9150
DAUNOXOME, SEE DAUNORUBICIN CITRATE			
DDAVP, SEE DESMOPRESSIN ACETATE			
DECADRON PHOSPHATE, SEE DEXAMETHASONE SODIUM PHOSPHATE			
DECADRON, SEE DEXAMETHASONE SODIUM PHOSPHATE			
DECADRON-LA, SEE DEXAMETHASONE ACETATE			
DECA-DURABOLIN, SEE NANDROLONE DECANOATE			
DECAJECT, SEE DEXAMETHASONE SODIUM PHOSPHATE			
DECAJECT-L.A., SEE DEXAMETHASONE ACETATE			
DECITABINE	1 MG	IV	J0894
DECOLONE-50, SEE NANDROLONE DECANOATE			

DRUG NAME	UNIT PER	ROUTE	CODE
DECOLONE-100, SEE NANDROLONE DECANOATE			
DE-COMBEROL, SEE TESTOSTERONE CYPIONATE AND ESTRADIOL CYPIONATE			
DEFEROXAMINE MESYLATE	500 MG	IM, SC, IV	J0895
DEGARELIX	1 MG	SC	J9155
DEHIST, SEE BROMPHENIRAMINE MALEATE			
DELADUMONE OB, SEE TESTOSTERONE ENANTHATE AND ESTRADIOL VALERATE			
DELADUMONE, SEE TESTOSTERONE ENANTHATE AND ESTRADIOL VALERATE			
DELATEST, SEE TESTOSTERONE ENANTHATE			
DELATESTADIOL, SEE TESTOSTERONE ENANTHATE AND ESTRADIOL VALERATE			
DELATESTRYL, SEE TESTOSTERONE ENANTHATE			
DELTA-CORTEF, SEE PREDNISOLONE, ORAL			
DELESTROGEN, SEE ESTRADIOL VALERATE			
DEMADEX, SEE TORSEMIDE			
DEMEROL HCL, SEE MEPERIDINE HCL			
DENILEUKIN DIFTITOX	300 MCG	IV	J9160
DENOSUMAB	1 MG	SC	J0897
DEPANDRO 100, SEE TESTOSTERONE CYPIONATE			
DEPANDRO 200, SEE TESTOSTERONE CYPIONATE			
DEPANDROGYN, SEE TESTOSTERONE CYPIONATE AND ESTRADIOL CYPIONATE			
DEPGYNOGEN, SEE DEPO-ESTRADIOL CYPIONATE			
DEPMEDALONE 40, SEE METHYLPREDNISOLONE ACETATE			
DEPMEDALONE 80, SEE METHYLPREDNISOLONE ACETATE			
DEPO-ESTRADIOL CYPIONATE	UP TO 5 MG	IM	J1000
DEPOGEN, SEE DEPO-ESTRADIOL CYPIONATE			
DEPOJECT, SEE METHYPREDNISOLONE ACETATE			
DEPO-MEDROL, SEE METHYLPREDNISOLONE ACETATE			
DEPOPRED-40, SEE METHYLPREDNISOLONE ACETATE			

DRUG NAME	UNIT PER	ROUTE	CODE
DEPOPRED-80, *SEE* METHYLPREDNISOLONE ACETATE			
DEPO-PROVERA, *SEE* MEDROXYPROGESTERONE ACETATE			
DEPOTEST, *SEE* TESTOSTERONE CYPIONATE			
DEPO-TESTADIOL, *SEE* TESTOSTERONE CYPIONATE AND ESTRADIOL CYPIONATE			
DEPOTESTOGEN, *SEE* TESTOSTERONE CYPIONATE AND ESTRADIOL CYPIONATE			
DEPO-TESTOSTERONE, *SEE* TESTOSTERONE CYPIONATE			
DESFERAL MESYLATE, *SEE* DEFEROXAMINE MESYLATE			
DESMOPRESSIN ACETATE	1 MCG	IV, SC	J2597
DEXACEN LA-8, *SEE* DEXAMETHASONE ACETATE			
DEXACEN-4, *SEE* DEXAMETHASONE SODIUM PHOSPHATE			
DEXAMETHASONE, CONCENTRATED FORM	PER MG	INH	J7637
DEXAMETHASONE, UNIT FORM	PER MG	INH	J7638
DEXAMETHASONE, INTRAVITREAL IMPLANT	0.1 MG	OTH	J7312
DEXAMETHASONE, ORAL	0.25 MG	ORAL	J8540
DEXAMETHASONE ACETATE	1 MG	IM	J1094
DEXAMETHASONE SODIUM PHOSPHATE	1 MG	IM, IV, OTH	J1100
DEXASONE, *SEE* DEXAMETHASONE SODIUM PHOSPHATE			
DEXASONE L.A., *SEE* DEXAMETHASONE ACETATE			
DEXFERRUM, *SEE* IRON DEXTRAN			
DEXONE, *SEE* DEXAMETHASONE SODIUM PHOSPHATE			
DEXONE LA, *SEE* DEXAMETHASONE ACETATE			
DEXRAZOXANE HYDROCHLORIDE	250 MG	IV	J1190
DEXTRAN 40	500 ML	IV	J7100
DEXTRAN 75	500 ML	IV	J7110
DEXTROSE 5%/NORMAL SALINE SOLUTION,	500 ML = 1 UNIT	IV	J7042
DEXTROSE/WATER (5%)	500 ML = 1 UNIT	IV	J7060
D.H.E. 45, *SEE* DIHYDROERGOTAMINE			
DIAMOX, *SEE* ACETAZOLAMIDE SODIUM			
DIAZEPAM	UP TO 5 MG	IM, IV	J3360
DIAZOXIDE	UP TO 300 MG	IV	J1730
DIBENT, *SEE* DICYCLOMINE HCL			

DRUG NAME	UNIT PER	ROUTE	CODE
DICYCLOMINE HCL	UP TO 20 MG	IM	J0500
DIDRONEL, *SEE* ETIDRONATE DISODIUM			
DIETHYLSTILBESTROL DIPHOSPHATE	250 MG	IV	J9165
DIFLUCAN, *SEE* FLUCONAZOLE			
DIGOXIN	UP TO 0.5 MG	IM, IV	J1160
DIGOXIN IMMUNE FAB (OVINE)	PER VIAL		J1162
DIHYDREX, *SEE* DIPHENHYDRAMINE HCL			
DIHYDROERGOTAMINE MESYLATE	PER 1 MG	IM, IV	J1110
DILANTIN, *SEE* PHENYTOIN SODIUM			
DILAUDID, *SEE* HYDROMORPHONE HCL			
DILOCAINE, *SEE* LIDOCAINE HCL			
DILOMINE, *SEE* DICYCLOMINE HCL			
DILOR, *SEE* DYPHYLLINE			
DIMENHYDRINATE	UP TO 50 MG	IM, IV	J1240
DIMERCAPROL	PER 100 MG	IM	J0470
DIMETHYL SULFOXIDE, *SEE* DMSO, DIMETHYLSULFOXIDE			
DINATE, *SEE* DIMENHYDRINATE			
DIOVAL, *SEE* ESTRADIOL VALERATE			
DIOVAL 40, *SEE* ESTRADIOL VALERATE			
DIOVAL XX, *SEE* ESTRADIOL VALERATE			
DIPHENACEN-50, *SEE* DIPHENHYDRAMINE HCL			
DIPHENHYDRAMINE HCL, INJECTION	UP TO 50 MG	IV, IM	J1200
DIPHENHYDRAMINE HCL, ORAL	50 MG	ORAL	Q0163
DIPYRIDAMOLE	PER 10 MG	IV	J1245
DISOTATE, *SEE* ENDRATE ETHYLENEDIAMINE-TETRA-ACETIC ACID			
DI-SPAZ, *SEE* DICYCLOMINE HCL			
DITATE-DS, *SEE* TESTOSTERONE ENANTHATE AND ESTRADIOL VALERATE			
DIURIL SODIUM, *SEE* CHLOROTHIAZIDE SODIUM			
D-MED 80, *SEE* METHYLPREDNISOLONE ACETATE			
DMSO, DIMETHYL SULFOXIDE	50%, 50 ML	OTH	J1212
DOBUTAMINE HCL	PER 250 MG	IV	J1250
DOBUTREX, *SEE* DOBUTAMINE HCL			

DRUG NAME	UNIT PER	ROUTE	CODE
DOCETAXEL	20 MG	IV	J9170
DOLASETRON MESYLATE, INJECTION	10 MG	IV	J1260
DOLASETRON MESYLATE, TABLETS	100 MG	ORAL	Q0180
DOLOPHINE HCL, *SEE* METHADONE HCL			
DOMMANATE, *SEE* DIMENHYDRINATE			
DONBAX, *SEE* DORIPENEM			
DOPAMINE HCL	40 MG		J1265
DORIBAX, *SEE* DORIPENEM			
DORIPENEM	10 MG	IV	J1267
DORNASE ALPHA, UNIT DOSE FORM	PER MG	INH	J7639
DOXERCALCIFEROL	1 MCG	IV	J1270
DOXIL, *SEE* DOXORUBICIN HCL, LIPID			
DOXORUBICIN HCL	10 MG	IV	J9000
DRAMAMINE, *SEE* DIMENHYDRINATE			
DRAMANATE, *SEE* DIMENHYDRINATE			
DRAMILIN, *SEE* DIMENHYDRINATE			
DRAMOCEN, *SEE* DIMENHYDRINATE			
DRAMOJECT, *SEE* DIMENHYDRINATE			
DRONABINOL, ORAL	2.5 MG	ORAL	Q0167
DROPERIDOL	UP TO 5 MG	IM, IV	J1790
DRUG ADMINISTERED THROUGH A METERED DOSE INHALER		INH	J3535
DROPERIDOL AND FENTANYL CITRATE	UP TO 2 ML AMPULE	IM, IV	J1810
DTIC-DOME, *SEE* DACARBAZINE			
DUA-GEN L.A., *SEE* TESTOSTERONE ENANTHATE AND ESTRADIOL VALERATE CYPIONATE			
DUOVAL P.A., *SEE* TESTOSTERONE ENANTHATE AND ESTRADIOL VALERATE			
DURABOLIN, *SEE* NANDROLONE PHENPROPIONATE			
DURACLON, *SEE* CLONIDINE HYDROCHLORIDE			
DURA-ESTRIN, *SEE* DEPO-ESTRADIOL CYPIONATE			
DURACILLIN A.S., *SEE* PENICILLIN G PROCAINE			
DURAGEN-10, *SEE* ESTRADIOL VALERATE			
DURAGEN-20, *SEE* ESTRADIOL VALERATE			
DURAGEN-40, *SEE* ESTRADIOL VALERATE			
DURALONE-40, *SEE* METHYLPREDNISOLONE ACETATE			
DURALONE-80, *SEE* METHYLPREDNISOLONE ACETATE			

DRUG NAME	UNIT PER	ROUTE	CODE
DURALUTIN, *SEE* HYDROXYPROGESTERONE CAPROATE			
DURAMORPH, *SEE* MORPHINE SULFATE			
DURATEST-100, *SEE* TESTOSTERONE CYPIONATE			
DURATEST-200, *SEE* TESTOSTERONE CYPIONATE			
DURATESTRIN, *SEE* TESTOSTERONE CYPIONATE AND ESTRADIOL CYPIONATE			
DURATHATE-200, *SEE* TESTOSTERONE ENANTHATE			
DYMENATE, *SEE* DIMENHYDRINATE			
DYPHYLLINE	UP TO 500 MG	IM	J1180
DYSPORT, *SEE* ABOBOTULINUMTOXINTYPEA			

E

DRUG NAME	UNIT PER	ROUTE	CODE
ECALLANTIDE	1 MG	SC	J1290
ECULIZUMAB	10 MG	IV	J1300
EDETATE CALCIUM DISODIUM	UP TO 1000 MG	IV, SC, IM	J0600
EDETATE DISODIUM	PER 150 MG	IV	J3520
ELAVIL, *SEE* AMITRIPTYLINE HCL			
ELLENCE, *SEE* EPIRUBICIN HCL			
ELLIOTTS B SOLUTION	1 ML	OTH	J9175
ELOSULFASE ALFA	1 MG	IV	J1322
ELSPAR, *SEE* ASPARAGINASE			
EMEND, *SEE* FOSAPREPITANT			
EMETE-CON, *SEE* BENZQUINAMIDE			
EMINASE, *SEE* ANISTREPLASE			
ENBREL, *SEE* ETANERCEPT			
ENDRATE ETHYLENEDIAMINE-TETRA-ACETIC ACID, *SEE* EDETATE DISODIUM			
ENFUVIRTIDE	1 MG	SC	J1324
ENOVIL, *SEE* AMITRIPTYLINE HCL			
ENOXAPARIN SODIUM	10 MG	SC	J1650
EOVIST, *SEE* GADOXETATE DISODIUM			
EPINEPHRINE, ADRENALIN	0.1 MG	SC, IM	J0171
EPIRUBICIN HYDROCHLORIDE	2 MG		J9178
EPOETIN ALFA	1000 UNITS	IV, SC	Q4081
EPOETIN BETA, ESRD USE	1 MCG	IV	J0887
EPOETIN BETA, NON-ESRD USE	1 MCG	IV	J0888
EPOPROSTENOL	0.5 MG	IV	J1325
EPTIFIBATIDE, INJECTION	5 MG	IM, IV	J1327
ERGONOVINE MALEATE	UP TO 0.2 MG	IM, IV	J1330

DRUG NAME	UNIT PER	ROUTE	CODE
ERIBULIN MESYLATE	0.1 MG	IV	J9179
ERTAPENEM SODIUM	500 MG	IM, IV	J1335
ERWINASE, *SEE* ASPARAGINASE			
ERYTHROMYCIN LACTOBIONATE	500 MG	IV	J1364
ESTRA-D, *SEE* DEPO-ESTRADIOL CYPIONATE			
ESTRA-L 20, *SEE* ESTRADIOL VALERATE			
ESTRA-L 40, *SEE* ESTRADIOL VALERATE			
ESTRA-TESTRIN, *SEE* TESTOSTERONE ENANTHATE AND ESTRADIOL VALERATE			
ESTRADIOL CYPIONATE, *SEE* DEPO-ESTRADIOL CYPIONATE			
ESTRADIOL L.A., *SEE* ESTRADIOL VALERATE			
ESTRADIOL L.A. 20, *SEE* ESTRADIOL VALERATE			
ESTRADIOL L.A. 40, *SEE* ESTRADIOL VALERATE			
ESTRADIOL VALERATE	UP TO 10 MG	IM	J1380
ESTRO-CYP, *SEE* DEPO-ESTRADIOL CYPIONATE			
ESTROGEN, CONJUGATED	PER 25 MG	IV, IM	J1410
ESTROJECT L.A., *SEE* DEPO-ESTRADIOL CYPIONATE			
ESTRONE	PER 1 MG	IM	J1435
ESTRONE 5, *SEE* ESTRONE			
ESTRONE AQUEOUS, *SEE* ESTRONE			
ESTRONOL, *SEE* ESTRONE			
ESTRONOL-L.A., *SEE* DEPO-ESTRADIOL CYPIONATE			
ETANERCEPT, INJECTION	25 MG	IM, IV	J1438
ETHANOLAMINE	100 MG		J1430
ETHYOL, *SEE* AMIFOSTINE			
ETIDRONATE DISODIUM	PER 300 MG	IV	J1436
ETONOGESTREL IMPLANT			J7307
ETOPOPHOS, *SEE* ETOPOSIDE			
ETOPOSIDE	10 MG	IV	J9181
ETOPOSIDE, ORAL	50 MG	ORAL	J8560
EUFLEXXA	PER DOSE	OTH	J7323
EVEROLIMUS, ORAL	0.25 MG	ORAL	J7527
EVERONE, *SEE* TESTOSTERONE ENANTHATE			
EYLEA, *SEE* AFLIBERCEPT			

DRUG NAME	UNIT PER	ROUTE	CODE
F			
FACTOR VIIA (COAGULATION FACTOR, RECOMBINANT)	1 MCG	IV	J7189
FACTOR VIII (ANTI-HEMOPHILIC FACTOR, HUMAN)	PER IU	IV	J7190
FACTOR VIII (ANTI-HEMOPHILIC FACTOR, PORCINE)	PER IU	IV	J7191
FACTOR VIII (ANTI-HEMOPHILIC FACTOR, RECOMBINANT)	PER IU	IV	J7182, J7185, J7192
FACTOR IX (ANTI-HEMOPHILIC FACTOR, PURIFIED, NON-RECOMBINANT)	PER IU	IV	J7193
FACTOR IX (ANTI-HEMOPHILIC FACTOR, RECOMBINANT)	PER IU	IV	J7195, J7200-J7201
FACTOR IX, COMPLEX	PER IU	IV	J7194
FACTOR XIII A-SUBUNIT (RECOMBINANT)	PER IU	IV	J7181
FACTORS, OTHER HEMOPHILIA CLOTTING	PER IU	IV	J7196
FACTREL, *SEE* GONADORELIN HCL			
FEIBA VH IMMUNO, *SEE* FACTORS, OTHER HEMOPHILIA CLOTTING			
FENTANYL CITRATE	0.1 MG	IM, IV	J3010
FERAHEME, *SEE* FERUMOXYTOL			
FERRIC CARBOXYMALTOSE	1 MG	IV	J1439
FERRLECIT, *SEE* SODIUM FERRICGLUCONATE COMPLEX IN SUCROSE INJECTION			
FERUMOXYTOL	1 MG		Q0138, Q0139
FILGRASTIM (G-CSF)	1 MCG	SC, IV	J1442
FILGRASTIM (TBO)	5 MCG	SC, IV	J1446
FIRAZYR, *SEE* ICATIBANT			
FIRMAGON, *SEE* DEGARELIX			
FLEBOGAMMA	500 MG	IV	J1572
FLEXOJECT, *SEE* ORPHENADRINE CITRATE			
FLEXON, *SEE* ORPHENADRINE CITRATE			
FLOLAN, *SEE* EPOPROSTENOL			
FLOXURIDINE	500 MG	IV	J9200
FLUCONAZOLE	200 MG	IV	J1450
FLUDARA, *SEE* FLUDARABINE PHOSPHATE			
FLUDARABINE PHOSPHATE	1 MG	ORAL	J8562
	50 MG	IV	J9185
FLUNISOLIDE INHALATION SOLUTION, UNIT DOSE FORM	PER MG	INH	J7641
FLUOCINOLONE		OTH	J7311
FLUOROURACIL	500 MG	IV	J9190
FOLEX, *SEE* METHOTREXATE SODIUM			

DRUG NAME	UNIT PER	ROUTE	CODE
FOLEX PFS, *SEE* METHOTREXATE SODIUM			
FOLLUTEIN, *SEE* CHORIONIC GONADOTROPIN			
FOLOTYN, *SEE* PRALATREXATE			
FOMEPIZOLE	15 MG		J1451
FOMIVIRSEN SODIUM	1.65 MG	IN-TRAOC-ULAR	J1452
FONDAPARINUX SODIUM	0.5 MG	SC	J1652
FORMOTEROL	12 MCG	INH	J7640
FORMOTEROL FUMARATE	20 MCG	INH	J7606
FORTAZ, *SEE* CEFTAZIDIME			
FOSAPREPITANT	1 MG	IV	J1453
FOSCARNET SODIUM	PER 1,000 MG	IV	J1455
FOSCAVIR, *SEE* FOSCARNET SODIUM			
FOSPHENYTOIN	50 MG	IV	Q2009
FUDR, *SEE* FLOXURIDINE			
FULVESTRANT	25 MG	IM	J9395
FUNGIZONE INTRAVENOUS, *SEE* AMPHOTERICIN B			
FUROMIDE M.D., *SEE* FUROSEMIDE			
FUROSEMIDE	UP TO 20 MG	IM, IV	J1940

G

DRUG NAME	UNIT PER	ROUTE	CODE
GADOXETATE DISODIUM	1 ML	IV	A9581
GALLIUM NITRATE	1 MG	IV	J1457
GALSULFASE	1 MG	IV	J1458
GAMASTAN, *SEE* GAMMA GLOBULIN AND IMMUNE GLOBULIN			
GAMMAGARD LIQUID	500 MG	IV	J1569
GAMMA GLOBULIN	1 CC	IM	J1460
	OVER 10 CC	IM	J1560
GAMMAPLEX	500 MG	IV	J1557
GAMMAR, *SEE* GAMMA GLOBULIN AND IMMUNE GLOBULIN			
GAMMAR-IV, *SEE* IMMUNE GLOBULIN INTRAVENOUS (HUMAN)			
GAMULIN RH, *SEE* RHO(D) IMMUNE GLOBULIN			
GAMUNEX	500 MG	IV	J1561
GANCICLOVIR, IMPLANT	4.5 MG	OTH	J7310
GANCICLOVIR SODIUM	500 MG	IV	J1570
GARAMYCIN, GENTAMICIN	UP TO 80 MG	IM, IV	J1580
GATIFLOXACIN	10 MG	IV	J1590
GEFITINIB	250 MG	ORAL	J8565

DRUG NAME	UNIT PER	ROUTE	CODE
GEL-ONE	PER DOSE	OTH	J7326
GEMCITABINE HCL	200 MG	IV	J9201
GEMSAR, *SEE* GEMCITABINE HCL			
GEMTUZUMAB OZOGAMICIN	5 MG	IV	J9300
GENTAMICIN SULFATE, *SEE* GARAMYCIN, GENTAMICIN			
GENTRAN, *SEE* DEXTRAN 40			
GENTRAN 75, *SEE* DEXTRAN 75			
GESTEROL 50, *SEE* PROGESTERONE			
GLASSIA	10 MG	IV	J0257
GLATIRAMER ACETATE	20 MG	SC	J1595
GLUCAGON HCL	PER 1 MG	SC, IM, IV	J1610
GLUKOR, *SEE* CHORIONIC GONADOTROPIN			
GLYCOPYRROLATE, CONCENTRATED FORM	PER 1 MG	INH	J7642
GLYCOPYRROLATE, UNIT DOSE FORM	PER 1 MG	INH	J7643
GOLD SODIUM THIOMALATE	UP TO 50 MG	IM	J1600
GOLIMUMAB	1 MG	IV	J1602
GONADORELIN HCL	PER 100 MCG	SC, IV	J1620
GONIC, *SEE* CHORIONIC GONADOTROPIN			
GOSERELIN ACETATE IMPLANT	PER 3.6 MG	SC	J9202
GRANISETRON HCL, INJECTION	100 MCG	IV	J1626
GRANISETRON HCL, ORAL	1 MG	ORAL	Q0166
GYNOGEN L.A. A10, @ *SEE* ESTRADIOL VALERATE			
GYNOGEN L.A. A20, @ *SEE* ESTRADIOL VALERATE			
GYNOGEN L.A. A40, @ *SEE* ESTRADIOL VALERATE			

H

DRUG NAME	UNIT PER	ROUTE	CODE
HALAVEN, *SEE* ERIBULIN MESYLATE			
HALDOL, *SEE* HALOPERIDOL			
HALOPERIDOL	UP TO 5 MG	IM, IV	J1630
HALOPERIDOL DECANOATE	PER 50 MG	IM	J1631
HECTORAL, *SEE* DOXERCALCIFEROL			
HEMIN	1 MG		J1640
HEMOFIL M, *SEE* FACTOR VIII			
HEMOPHILIA CLOTTING FACTORS(E.G., ANTI-INHIBITORS)	PER IU	IV	J7198
HEMOPHILIA CLOTTING FACTORS, NOC	PER IU	IV	J7199

DRUG NAME	UNIT PER	ROUTE	CODE
HEPAGAM B	0.5 ML	IM	J1571
	0.5 ML	IV	J1573
HEP-LOCK, *SEE* HEPARIN SODIUM (HEPARIN LOCK FLUSH)			
HEP-LOCK U/P, *SEE* HEPARIN SODIUM (HEPARIN LOCK FLUSH)			
HEPARIN SODIUM	1, 000 UNITS	IV, SC	J1644
HEPARIN SODIUM (HEPARIN LOCK FLUSH)	10 UNITS	IV	J1642
HERCEPTIN, *SEE* TRASTUZUMAB			
HEXADROL PHOSPHATE, *SEE* DEXAMETHASONE SODIUM PHOSPHATE			
HISTAJECT, *SEE* BROMPHENIRAMINE MALEATE			
HISTERONE 50, *SEE* TESTOSTERONE SUSPENSION			
HISTERONE 100, *SEE* TESTOSTERONE SUSPENSION			
HISTRELIN ACETATE	10 MCG		J1675
HISTRELIN IMPLANT	50 MG	OTH	J9225
HIZENTRA, *SEE* IMMUNE GLOBULIN			
HUMAN FIBRINOGEN CONCENTRATE	100 MG	IV	J7178
HYALGAN		OTH	J7321
HYALURONAN OR DERIVATIVE	PER DOSE	IV	J7327
HYALURONIDASE	UP TO 150 UNITS	SC, IV	J3470
HYALURONIDASE, OVINE	UP TO 999 UNITS	VAR	J3471
HYALURONIDASE, OVINE	PER 1000 UNITS	VAR	J3472
HYALURONIDASE RECOMBINANT	1 USP	SC	J3473
HYATE:C, *SEE* FACTOR VIII (ANTI-HEMOPHILIC FACTOR (PORCINE))			
HYBOLIN IMPROVED, *SEE* NANDROLONE PHENPROPIONATE			
HYBOLIN DECANOATE, *SEE* NANDROLONE DECANOATE			
HYCAMTIN, *SEE* TOPOTECAN			
HYDRALAZINE HCL	UP TO 20 MG	IV, IM	J0360
HYDRATE, *SEE* DIMENHYDRINATE			
HYDROCORTISONE ACETATE	UP TO 25 MG	IV, IM, SC	J1700
HYDROCORTISONE SODIUM PHOSPHATE	UP TO 50 MG	IV, IM, SC	J1710
HYDROCORTISONE SUCCINATE SODIUM	UP TO 100 MG	IV, IM, SC	J1720

DRUG NAME	UNIT PER	ROUTE	CODE
HYDROCORTONE ACETATE, *SEE* HYDROCORTISONE ACETATE			
HYDROCORTONE PHOSPHATE, *SEE* HYDROCORTISONE SODIUM PHOSPHATE			
HYDROMORPHONE HCL	UP TO 4 MG	SC, IM, IV	J1170
HYDROXYPROGESTERONE CAPROATE	1 MG	IM	J1725
HYDROXYZINE HCL	UP TO 25 MG	IM	J3410
HYDROXYZINE PAMOATE	25 MG	ORAL	Q0177
HYLAN G-F 20		OTH	J7322
HYOSCYAMINE SULFATE	UP TO 0.25 MG	SC, IM, IV	J1980
HYPERSTAT IV, *SEE* DIAZOXIDE			
HYPER-TET, *SEE* TETANUS IMMUNE GLOBULIN, HUMAN			
HYPRHO-D, *SEE* RHO(D) IMMUNE GLOBULIN			
HYREXIN-50, *SEE* DIPHENHYDRAMINE HCL			
HYZINE-50, *SEE* HYDROXYZINE HCL			

I

DRUG NAME	UNIT PER	ROUTE	CODE
IBANDRONATE SODIUM	1 MG	IV	J1740
IBUPROFEN	100 MG	IV	J1741
IBUTILIDE FUMARATE	1 MG	IV	J1742
ICATIBANT	1 MG	SC	J1744
IDAMYCIN, *SEE* IDARUBICIN HCL			
IDARUBICIN HCL	5 MG	IV	J9211
IDURSULFASE	1 MG	IV	J1743
IFEX, *SEE* IFOSFAMIDE			
IFOSFAMIDE	1 G	IV	J9208
ILARIS, *SEE* CANAKINUMAB			
ILOPROST	20 MCG	INH	Q4074
ILOTYCIN, *SEE* ERYTHROMYCIN GLUCEPTATE			
IMFERON, *SEE* IRON DEXTRAN			
IMIGLUCERASE	10 UNITS	IV	J1786
IMITREX, *SEE* SUMATRIPTAN SUCCINATE			
IMMUNE GLOBULIN			
BIVIGAM	500 MG	IV	J1556
FLEBOGAMMA	500 MG	IV	J1572
GAMMAGARD LIQUID	500 MG	IV	J1569
GAMMAPLEX	500 MG	IV	J1557
GAMUNEX	500 MG	IV	J1561
HEPAGAM B	0.5 ML	IM	J1571
HEPAGAM B	0.5 ML	IV	J1573
HIZENTRA	100 MG	SC	J1559

DRUG NAME	UNIT PER	ROUTE	CODE
NOS	500 MG	IV	J1566, J1599
OCTAGAM	500 MG	IV	J1568
PRIVIGEN	500 MG	IV	J1459
RHOPHYLAC	100 IU	IM	J2791
SUBCUTANEOUS	100 MG	SC	J1562
IMMUNOSUPPRESSIVE DRUG, NOT OTHERWISE CLASSIFIED			J7599
IMURAN, *SEE* AZATHIOPRINE			
INAPSINE, *SEE* DROPERIDOL			
INCOBOTULINUMTOXIN TYPE A	1 UNIT	IM	J0588
INDERAL, *SEE* PROPRANOLOL HCL			
INFED, *SEE* IRON DEXTRAN			
INFERGEN, *SEE* INTERFERON ALFA-1			
INFLIXIMAB, INJECTION	10 MG	IM, IV	J1745
INNOHEP, *SEE* TINZARPARIN			
INNOVAR, *SEE* DROPERIDOL WITH FENTANYL CITRATE			
INSULIN	5 UNITS	SC	J1815
INSULIN LISPRO	50 UNITS	SC	J1817
INTAL, *SEE* CROMOLYN SODIUM OR CROMOLYN SODIUM, COMPOUNDED			
INTEGRILIN, INJECTION, *SEE* EPTIFIBATIDE			
INTERFERON ALPHACON-1, RECOMBINANT	1 MCG	SC	J9212
INTERFERON ALFA-2A, RECOMBINANT	3 MILLION UNITS	SC, IM	J9213
INTERFERON ALFA-2B, RECOMBINANT	1 MILLION UNITS	SC, IM	J9214
INTERFERON ALFA-N3 (HUMAN LEUKOCYTE DERIVED)	250, 000 IU	IM	J9215
INTERFERON BETA-1A	30 MCG	IM	J1826
INTERFERON BETA-1A	1 MCG	IM	Q3027
INTERFERON BETA-1A	1 MCG	SC	Q3028
INTERFERON BETA-1B	0.25 MG	SC	J1830
INTERFERON GAMMA-1B	3 MILLION UNITS	SC	J9216
INTRAUTERINE COPPER CONTRACEPTIVE, *SEE* COPPER CONTRACEPTIVE, INTRAUTERINE			
INVEGA SUSTENNA, *SEE* PALIPERIDONE PALMITATE			
IPILIMUMAB	1 MG	IV	J9228
IPRATROPIUM BROMIDE, UNIT DOSE FORM	PER MG	INH	J7644, J7645
IRINOTECAN	20 MG	IV	J9206
IRON DEXTRAN	50 MG	IV	J1750
IRON SUCROSE	1 MG	IV	J1756
IRRIGATION SOLUTION FOR TX OF BLADDER CALCULI	PER 50 ML	OTH	Q2004

DRUG NAME	UNIT PER	ROUTE	CODE
ISOCAINE HCL, *SEE* MEPIVACAINE			
ISOETHARINE HCL, CONCENTRATED FORM	PER MG	INH	J7647, J7648
ISOETHARINE HCL, UNIT DOSE FORM	PER MG	INH	J7649, J7650
ISOPROTERENOL HCL, CONCENTRATED FORM	PER MG	INH	J7657, J7658
ISOPROTERENOL HCL, UNIT DOSE FORM	PER MG	INH	J7659, J7660
ISTODAX, *SEE* ROMIDEPSIN			
ISUPREL, *SEE* ISOPROTERENOL HCL			
ITRACONAZOLE	50 MG	IV	J1835
IXABEPILONE	1 MG	IV	J9207
IXEMPRA, *SEE* IXABEPILONE			

J

DRUG NAME	UNIT PER	ROUTE	CODE
JENAMICIN, *SEE* GARAMYCIN, GENTAMICIN			
JEVTANA, *SEE* CABAZITAXEL			

K

DRUG NAME	UNIT PER	ROUTE	CODE
KABIKINASE, *SEE* STREPTOKINASE			
KALBITOR, *SEE* ECALLANTIDE			
KALEINATE, *SEE* CALCIUM GLUCONATE			
KANAMYCIN SULFATE	UP TO 75 MG	IM, IV	J1850
KANAMYCIN SULFATE	UP TO 500 MG	IM, IV	J1840
KANTREX, *SEE* KANAMYCIN SULFATE			
KEFLIN, *SEE* CEPHALOTHIN SODIUM			
KEFUROX, *SEE* CUFUROXIME SODIUM			
KEFZOL, *SEE* CEFAZOLIN SODIUM			
KENAJECT-40, *SEE* TRIAMCINOLONE ACETONIDE			
KENALOG-10, *SEE* TRIAMCINOLONE ACETONIDE			
KENALOG-40, *SEE* TRIAMCINOLONE ACETONIDE			
KEPPRA, *SEE* LEVETIRACETAM			
KESTRONE 5, *SEE* ESTRONE			
KETOROLAC TROMETHAMINE	PER 15 MG	IM, IV	J1885
KEY-PRED 25, *SEE* PREDNISOLONE ACETATE			
KEY-PRED 50, *SEE* PREDNISOLONE ACETATE			
KEY-PRED-SP, *SEE* PREDNISOLONE SODIUM PHOSPHATE			
K-FLEX, *SEE* ORPHENADRINE CITRATE			
KLEBCIL, *SEE* KANAMYCIN SULFATE			

DRUG NAME	UNIT PER	ROUTE	CODE
KOATE-HP, *SEE* FACTOR VIII			
KOGENATE, *SEE* FACTOR VIII			
KONAKION, *SEE* VITAMIN K, PHYTONADIONE, ETC.			
KONYNE-80, *SEE* FACTOR IX, COMPLEX			
KRYSTEXXA, *SEE* PEGLOTICASE			
KYTRIL, *SEE* GRANISETRON HCL			

L

DRUG NAME	UNIT PER	ROUTE	CODE
L.A.E. 20, *SEE* ESTRADIOL VALERATE			
LAETRILE, AMYGDALIN, VITAMIN B-17			J3570
LANOXIN, *SEE* DIGOXIN			
LANREOTIDE	1 MG	SC	J1930
LARGON, *SEE* PROPIOMAZINE HCL			
LARONIDASE	0.1 MG	IV	J1931
LASIX, *SEE* FUROSEMIDE			
L-CAINE, *SEE* LIDOCAINE HCL			
LEPIRUDIN	50 MG		J1945
LEUCOVORIN CALCIUM	PER 50 MG	IM, IV	J0640
LEUKINE, *SEE* SARGRAMOSTIM (GM-CSF)			
LEUPROLIDE ACETATE (FOR DEPOT SUSPENSION)	PER 3.75 MG	IM	J1950
	7.5 MG	IM	J9217
LEUPROLIDE ACETATE	PER 1 MG	IM	J9218
LEUPROLIDE ACETATE IMPLANT	65 MG	OTH	J9219
LEUSTATIN, *SEE* CLADRIBINE			
LEVALBUTEROL HCL, CONCENTRATED FORM	0.5 MG	INH	J7607, J7612
LEVALBUTEROL HCL, UNIT DOSE FORM	0.5 MG	INH	J7614, J7615
LEVAQUIN I.U., *SEE* LEVOFLOXACIN			
LEVETIRACETAM	10 MG	IV	J1953
LEVOCARNITINE	PER 1 GM	IV	J1955
LEVO-DROMORAN, *SEE* LEVORPHANOL TARTRATE			
LEVOFLOXACIN	250 MG	IV	J1956
LEVOLEUCOVORIN CALCIUM	0.5 MG	IV	J0641
LEVONORGESTREL IMPLANT		OTH	J7306
LEVONORGESTREL RELEASING INTRAUTERIN CONTRACEPTIVE	52 MG	OTH	J7302
LEVORPHANOL TARTRATE	UP TO 2 MG	SC, IV	J1960
LEVSIN, *SEE* HYOSCYAMINE SULFATE			
LEVULAN KERASTICK, *SEE* AMINOLEVULINIC ACID HCL			
LEXISCAN, *SEE* REGADENOSON			
LIBRIUM, *SEE* CHLORDIAZEPOXIDE HCL			

DRUG NAME	UNIT PER	ROUTE	CODE
LIDOCAINE HCL	10 MG	IV	J2001
LIDOJECT-1, *SEE* LIDOCAINE HCL			
LIDOJECT-2, *SEE* LIDOCAINE HCL			
LINCOCIN, *SEE* LINCOMYCIN HCL			
LINCOMYCIN HCL	UP TO 300 MG	IV	J2010
LINEZOLID	200 MG	IV	J2020
LIQUAEMIN SODIUM, *SEE* HEPARIN SODIUM			
LIORESAL, *SEE* BACLOFEN			
LMD (10%), *SEE* DEXTRAN 40			
LOVENOX, *SEE* ENOXAPARIN SODIUM			
LORAZEPAM	2 MG	IM, IV	J2060
LUFYLLIN, *SEE* DYPHYLLINE			
LUMINAL SODIUM, *SEE* PHENOBARBITOL SODIUM			
LUMIZYME, *SEE* ALGLUCOSIDASE ALFA			
LUNELLE, *SEE* MEDROXYPROGESTERONE ACETATE/ ESTRADIOL CYPIONATE			
LUPRON, *SEE* LEUPROLIDE ACETATE			
LYMPHOCYTE IMMUNE GLOBULIN,			
ANTI-THYMOCYTE GLOBULIN, EQUINE	250 MG	IV	J7504
ANTI-THYMOCYTE GLOBULIN, RABBIT	25 MG	IV	J7511
LYOPHILIZED, *SEE* CYCLOPHOSPHAMIDE, LYOPHILIZED			

M

DRUG NAME	UNIT PER	ROUTE	CODE
MAGNESIUM SULFATE	500 MG		J3475
MAKENA, *SEE* HYDROXYPROGESTERONE CAPROATE	25% IN 50 ML	IV	J2150
MANNITOL	5 MG	INH	J7665
MARMINE, *SEE* DIMENHYDRINATE			
MAXIPIME, *SEE* CEFEPIME HYDROCHLORIDE			
MECASERMIN	1 MG	SC	J2170
MECHLORETHAMINE HCL (NITROGEN MUSTARD), HN2	10 MG	IV	J9230
MEDRALONE 40, *SEE* METHYLPREDNISOLONE ACETATE			
MEDRALONE 80, *SEE* METHYLPREDNISOLONE ACETATE			
MEDROL, *SEE* METHYLPREDNISOLONE			
MEDROXYPROGESTERONE ACETATE	1 MG	IM	J1050
MEFOXIN, *SEE* CEFOXITIN SODIUM			
MELPHALAN HCL	50 MG	IV	J9245
MELPHALAN, ORAL	2 MG	ORAL	J8600

DRUG NAME	UNIT PER	ROUTE	CODE
MENOJECT LA, *SEE* TESTOSTERONE CYPIONATE AND ESTRADIOL CYPIONATE			
MEPERGAN INJECTION, *SEE* MEPERDINE AND PROMETHAZINE HCL			
MEPERIDINE HCL	PER 100 MG	IM, IV, SC	J2175
MEPERIDINE AND PROMETHAZINE HCL	UP TO 50 MG	IM, IV	J2180
MEPIVACAINE HCL	PER 10 ML	VAR	J0670
MEROPENEM	100 MG	IV	J2185
MESNA	200 MG	IV	J9209
MESNEX, *SEE* MESNA			
METAPREL, *SEE* METAPROTERENOL SULFATE			
METAPROTERENOL SULFATE, CONCENTRATED FORM	PER 10 MG	INH	J7667, J7668
METAPROTERENOL SULFATE, UNIT DOSE FORM	PER 10 MG	INH	J7669, J7670
METARAMINOL BITARTRATE	PER 10 MG	IV, IM, SC	J0380
METASTRON, *SEE* STRONTIUM-89 CHLORIDE			
METHACHOLINE CHLORIDE	1 MG	INH	J7674
METHADONE HCL	UP TO 10 MG	IM, SC	J1230
METHERGINE, *SEE* METHYLERGONOVINE MALEATE			
METHOCARBAMOL	UP TO 10 ML	IV, IM	J2800
METHOTREXATE, ORAL	2.5 MG	ORAL	J8610
METHOTREXATE SODIUM	5 MG	IV, IM, IT, IA	J9250
	50 MG	IV, IM, IT, IA	J9260
METHOTREXATE LPF, *SEE* METHOTREXATE SODIUM			
METHYLDOPATE HCL	UP TO 250 MG	IV	J0210
METHYLNALTREXONE	0.1 MG	SC	J2212
METHYLPREDNISOLONE, ORAL	PER 4 MG	ORAL	J7509
METHYLPREDNISOLONE ACETATE	20 MG	IM	J1020
	40 MG	IM	J1030
	80 MG	IM	J1040
METHYLPREDNISOLONE SODIUM SUCCINATE	UP TO 40 MG	IM, IV	J2920
	UP TO 125 MG	IM, IV	J2930
METOCLOPRAMIDE HCL	UP TO 10 MG	IV	J2765
METVIXIA, *SEE* AMINOLEVULINATE			

DRUG NAME	UNIT PER	ROUTE	CODE
MIACALCIN, *SEE* CALCITONIN-SALMON			
MICAFUNGIN SODIUM	1 MG		J2248
MIDAZOLAM HCL	PER 1 MG	IM, IV	J2250
MILRINONE LACTATE	5 MG	IV	J2260
MINOCINE, *SEE* MINOCYCLINE HYDROCHLORIDE			
MINOCYCLINE HYDROCHLORIDE	1 MG	IV	J2265
MIRENA, *SEE* LEVONORGESTREL RELEASING INTRAUTERINE CONTRACEPTIVE			
MITHRACIN, *SEE* PLICAMYCIN			
MITOMYCIN	0.2 MG	OPTHAL-MIC	J7315
	5 MG	IV	J9280
MITOSOL, *SEE* MITOMYCIN			
MITOXANTRONE HCL	PER 5 MG	IV	J9293
MONOCID, *SEE* CEFONICIC SODIUM			
MONOCLATE-P, *SEE* FACTOR VIII			
MONOCLONAL ANTIBODIES, PARENTERAL	5 MG	IV	J7505
MONONINE, *SEE* FACTOR IX, PURIFIED, NON-RECOMBINANT			
MORPHINE SULFATE	UP TO 10 MG	IM, IV, SC	J2270
MORPHINE SULFATE, PRESERVATIVE-FREE	10 MG	SC, IM, IV	J2274
MOXIFLOXACIN	100 MG	IV	J2280
MOZOBIL, *SEE* PLERIXAFOR			
M-PREDNISOL-40, *SEE* METHYLPREDNISOLONE ACETATE			
M-PREDNISOL-80, *SEE* METHYLPREDNISOLONE ACETATE			
MUCOMYST, *SEE* ACETYLCYSTEINE OR ACETYLCYSTEINE, COMPOUNDED			
MUCOSOL, *SEE* ACETYLCYSTEINE			
MUROMONAB-CD3	5 MG	IV	J7505
MUSE, *SEE* ALPROSTADIL			
MUSTARGEN, *SEE* MECHLORETHAMINE HCL			
MUTAMYCIN, *SEE* MITOMYCIN			
MYCOPHENOLIC ACID	180 MG	ORAL	J7518
MYCOPHENOLATE MOFETIL	250 MG	ORAL	J7517
MYLERAN, *SEE* BUSULFAN			
MYLOTARG, *SEE* GEMTUZUMAB OZOGAMICIN			
MYOBLOC, *SEE* RIMABOTULINUMTOXINB			
MYOCHRYSINE, *SEE* GOLD SODIUM THIOMALATE			

DRUG NAME	UNIT PER	ROUTE	CODE
MYOLIN, *SEE* ORPHENADRINE CITRATE			

N

DRUG NAME	UNIT PER	ROUTE	CODE
NABILONE	1 MG	ORAL	J8650
NALBUPHINE HCL	PER 10 MG	IM, IV, SC	J2300
NALOXONE HCL	PER 1 MG	IM, IV, SC	J2310
NALTREXONE, DEPOT FORM	1 MG	IM	J2315
NANDROBOLIC L.A., *SEE* NANDROLONE DECANOATE			
NANDROLONE DECANOATE	UP TO 50 MG	IM	J2320
NARCAN, *SEE* NALOXONE HCL			
NAROPIN, *SEE* ROPIVACAINE HCL			
NASAHIST B, *SEE* BROMPHENIRAMINE MALEATE			
NASAL VACCINE INHALATION		INH	J3530
NATALIZUMAB	1 MG	IV	J2323
NAVANE, *SEE* THIOTHIXENE			
NAVELBINE, *SEE* VINORELBINE TARTRATE			
ND STAT, *SEE* BROMPHENIRAMINE MALEATE			
NEBCIN, *SEE* TOBRAMYCIN SULFATE			
NEBUPENT, *SEE* PENTAMIDINE ISETHIONATE			
NELARABINE	50 MG	IV	J9261
NEMBUTAL SODIUM SOLUTION, *SEE* PENTOBARBITAL SODIUM			
NEOCYTEN, *SEE* ORPHENADRINE CITRATE			
NEO-DURABOLIC, *SEE* NANDROLONE DECANOATE			
NEOQUESS, *SEE* DICYCLOMINE HCL			
NEOSAR, *SEE* CYCLOPHOSPHAMIDE			
NEOSTIGMINE METHYLSULFATE	UP TO 0.5 MG	IM, IV, SC	J2710
NEO-SYNEPHRINE, *SEE* PHENYLEPHRINE HCL			
NERVOCAINE 1%, *SEE* LIDOCAINE HCL			
NERVOCAINE 2%, *SEE* LIDOCAINE HCL			
NESACAINE, *SEE* CHLOROPROCAINE HCL			
NESACAINE-MPF, *SEE* CHLOROPROCAINE HCL			
NESIRITIDE	0.1 MG	IV	J2325
NEUMEGA, *SEE* OPRELVEKIN			
NEUPOGEN, *SEE* FILGRASTIM (G-CSF)			
NEUTREXIN, *SEE* TRIMETREXATE GLUCURONATE			

DRUG NAME	UNIT PER	ROUTE	CODE
NIPENT, *SEE* PENTOSTATIN			
NORDRYL, *SEE* DIPHENHYDRAMINE HCL			
NORFLEX, *SEE* ORPHENADRINE CITRATE			
NORZINE, *SEE* THIETHYLPERAZINE MALEATE			
NOT OTHERWISE CLASSIFIED DRUGS		INH	J3490
NOT OTHERWISE CLASSIFIED DRUGS		OTHER THAN INH	J7799
		ADMIN-ISTERED THRU DME	
NOT OTHERWISE CLASSIFIED DRUGS		INH	J7699
		ADMIN-ISTERED THRU DME	
NOT OTHERWISE CLASSIFIED DRUGS, ANTI-NEOPLASTIC			J9999
NOT OTHERWISE CLASSIFIED DRUGS, CHEMOTHERAPEUTIC		ORAL	J8999
NOT OTHERWISE CLASSIFIED DRUGS, IMMUNOSUPPRESSIVE			J7599
NOT OTHERWISE CLASSIFIED DRUGS, NONCHEMOTHERAPEUTIC		ORAL	J8499
NOVANTRONE, *SEE* MITOXANTRONE HCL			
NOVO SEVEN, *SEE* FACTOR VIIA			
NPH, *SEE* INSULIN			
NPLATE, *SEE* ROMIPLOSTIM			
NUBAIN, *SEE* NALBUPHINE HCL			
NULICAINE, *SEE* LIDOCAINE HCL			
NULOJIX, *SEE* BELATACEPT			
NUMORPHAN, *SEE* OXYMORPHONE HCL			
NUMORPHAN H.P., *SEE* OXYMORPHONE HCL			

O

DRUG NAME	UNIT PER	ROUTE	CODE
OCRIPLASMIN	0.125 MG	IV	J7316
OCTAGAM	500 MG	IV	J1568
OCTREOTIDE ACETATE, INJECTION	1 MG	IM	J2353
	25 MCG	IV, SQ	J2354
OCULINUM, *SEE* BOTULINUM TOXIN TYPE A			
OFATUMUMAB	10 MG	IV	J9302
OFIRMEV, *SEE* ACETAMINOPHEN			
O-FLEX, *SEE* ORPHENADRINE CITRATE			

DRUG NAME	UNIT PER	ROUTE	CODE
OFORTA, *SEE* FLUDARABINE PHOSPHATE			
OLANZAPINE	1 MG	IM	J2358
OMACETAXINE MEPESUCCINATE	0.01 MG	IV	J9262
OMALIZUMAB	5 MG	SC	J2357
OMNIPEN-N, *SEE* AMPICILLIN			
OMONTYS, *SEE* PEGINESATIDE			
ONABOTULINUMTOXINA	1 UNIT	IM	J0585
ONCASPAR, *SEE* PEGASPARGASE			
ONCOVIN, *SEE* VINCRISTINE SULFATE			
ONDANSETRON HCl	1 MG	IV	J2405
ONDANSETRON HCL, ORAL	1 MG	ORAL	Q0162
OPRELVEKIN	5 MG	SC	J2355
ORAMINIC II, *SEE* BROMPHENIRAMINE MALEATE			
ORMAZINE, *SEE* CHLORPROMAZINE HCL			
ORPHENADRINE CITRATE	UP TO 60 MG	IV, IM	J2360
ORPHENATE, *SEE* ORPHENADRINE CITRATE			
ORTHOVISC		OTH	J7324
OR-TYL, *SEE* DICYCLOMINE			
OXACILLIN SODIUM	UP TO 250 MG	IM, IV	J2700
OXALIPLATIN	0.5 MG	IV	J9263
OXYMORPHONE HCL	UP TO 1 MG	IV, SC, IM	J2410
OXYTETRACYCLINE HCL	UP TO 50 MG	IM	J2460
OXYTOCIN	UP TO 10 UNITS	IV, IM	J2590
OZURDEX, *SEE* DEXAMETHASONE, INTRAVITREAL IMPLANT			

P

DRUG NAME	UNIT PER	ROUTE	CODE
PACLITAXEL	1 MG	IV	J9267
PACLITAXEL PROTEIN-BOUND PARTICLES	1 MG	IV	J9264
PALIFERMIN	50 MCG	IV	J2425
PALIPERIDONE PALMITATE	1 MG	IM	J2426
PALONOSETRON HCL	25 MCG	IV	J2469
PAMIDRONATE DISODIUM	PER 30 MG	IV	J2430
PANITUMUMAB	10 MG	IV	J9303
PAPAVERINE HCL	UP TO 60 MG	IV, IM	J2440
PARAGARD T 380 A, *SEE* COPPER CONTRACEPTIVE, INTRAUTERINE			
PARAPLATIN, *SEE* CARBOPLATIN			
PARICALCITOL, INJECTION	1 MCG	IV, IM	J2501

DRUG NAME	UNIT PER	ROUTE	CODE
PEGADEMASE BOVINE	25 IU		J2504
PEGAPTINIB	0.3 MG	OTH	J2503
PEGASPARGASE	PER SINGLE DOSE VIAL	IM, IV	J9266
PEGFILGRASTIM	6 MG	SC	J2505
PEGINESATIDE	0.1 MG	IV, SC	J0890
PEGLOTICASE	1 MG	IV	J2507
PEMETREXED	10 MG	IV	J9305
PENICILLIN G BENZATHINE	100, 000 UNITS	IM	J0561
PENICILLIN G BENZATHINE AND PENICILLIN G PROCAINE	100, 000 UNITS	IM	J0558
PENICILLIN G POTASSIUM	UP TO 600, 000 UNITS	IM, IV	J2540
PENICILLIN G PROCAINE, AQUEOUS	UP TO 600, 000 UNITS	IM, IV	J2510
PENTAMIDINE ISETHIONATE	PER 300 MG	INH	J2545, J7676
PENTASTARCH, 10%	100 ML		J2513
PENTAZOCINE HCL	30 MG	IM, SC, IV	J3070
PENTOBARBITAL SODIUM	PER 50 MG	IM, IV, OTH	J2515
PENTOSTATIN	PER 10 MG	IV	J9268
PEFOROMIST, *SEE* FORMOTEROL FUMARATE			
PERMAPEN, *SEE* PENICILLIN G BENZATHINE			
PERPHENAZINE, INJECTION	UP TO 5 MG	IM, IV	J3310
PERPHENAZINE, TABLETS	4 MG	ORAL	Q0175
PERSANTINE IV, *SEE* DIPYRIDAMOLE			
PERTUZUMAB	1 MG	IV	J9306
PFIZERPEN, *SEE* PENICILLIN G POTASSIUM			
PFIZERPEN A.S., *SEE* PENICILLIN G PROCAINE			
PHENAZINE 25, *SEE* PROMETHAZINE HCL			
PHENAZINE 50, *SEE* PROMETHAZINE HCL			
PHENERGAN, *SEE* PROMETHAZINE HCL			
PHENOBARBITAL SODIUM	UP TO 120 MG	IM, IV	J2560
PHENTOLAMINE MESYLATE	UP TO 5 MG	IM, IV	J2760

DRUG NAME	UNIT PER	ROUTE	CODE
PHENYLEPHRINE HCL	UP TO 1 ML	SC, IM, IV	J2370
PHENYTOIN SODIUM	PER 50 MG	IM, IV	J1165
PHOTOFRIN, SEE PORFIMER SODIUM			
PHYTONADIONE (VITAMIN K)	PER 1 MG	IM, SC, IV	J3430
PIPERACILLIN/TAZOBACTAM SODIUM, INJECTION	1.125 G	IV	J2543
PITOCIN, SEE OXYTOCIN			
PLANTINOL AQ, SEE CISPLATIN			
PLAS+SD, SEE PLASMA, POOLED MULTIPLE DONOR			
PLASMA, CRYOPRECIPITATE REDUCED	EACH UNIT	IV	P9044
PLASMA, POOLED MULTIPLE DONOR, FROZEN, EACH UNIT		IV	P9023
PLATINOL, SEE CISPLATIN			
PLERIXAFOR	1 MG	SC	J2562
PLICAMYCIN	2, 500 MCG	IV	J9270
POLOCAINE, SEE MEPIVACAINE			
POLYCILLIN-N, SEE AMPICILLIN			
PORFIMER SODIUM	75 MG	IV	J9600
POTASSIUM CHLORIDE	PER 2 MEQ	IV	J3480
PRALATREXATE	1 MG	IV	J9307
PRALIDOXIME CHLORIDE	UP TO 1 G	IV, IM, SC	J2730
PREDALONE-50, SEE PREDNISOLONE ACETATE			
PREDCOR-25, SEE PREDNISOLONE ACETATE			
PREDCOR-50, SEE PREDNISOLONE ACETATE			
PREDICORT-50, SEE PREDNISOLONE ACETATE			
PREDNISONE	PER 5 MG	ORAL	J7506
PREDNISOLONE, ORAL	5 MG	ORAL	J7510
PREDNISOLONE ACETATE	UP TO 1 ML	IM	J2650
PREDOJECT-50, SEE PREDNISOLONE ACETATE			
PREGNYL, SEE CHORIONIC GONADOTROPIN			
PREMARIN INTRAVENOUS, SEE ESTROGEN, CONJUGATED			
PRESCRIPTION, CHEMOTHERAPEUTIC, NOT OTHERWISE SPECIFIED		ORAL	J8999
PRESCRIPTION, NONCHEMOTHERAPEUTIC, NOT OTHERWISE SPECIFIED		ORAL	J8499
PRIMACOR, SEE MILRINONE LACTATE			

DRUG NAME	UNIT PER	ROUTE	CODE
PRIMAXIN I.M., SEE CILASTATIN SODIUM, IMIPENEM			
PRIMAXIN I.V., SEE CILASTATIN SODIUM, IMIPENEM			
PRISCOLINE HCL, SEE TOLAZOLINE HCL			
PRIVIGEN	500 MG	IV	J1459
PRO-DEPO, SEE HYDROXYPROGESTERONE CAPROATE			
PROCAINAMIDE HCL	UP TO 1 G	IM, IV	J2690
PROCHLORPERAZINE	UP TO 10 MG	IM, IV	J0780
PROCHLORPERAZINE MALEATE, ORAL	5 MG	ORAL	Q0164
PROFASI HP, SEE CHORIONIC GONADOTROPIN			
PROFILNINE HEAT-TREATED, SEE FACTOR IX			
PROGESTAJECT, SEE PROGESTERONE			
PROGESTERONE	PER 50 MG	IM	J2675
PROGRAF, SEE TACROLIMUS, ORAL OR PARENTERAL			
PROKINE, SEE SARGRAMOSTIM (GM-CSF)			
PROLASTIN, SEE ALPHA 1-PROTEINASE INHIBITOR, HUMAN			
PROLEUKIN, SEE ALDESLEUKIN			
PROLIXIN DECANOATE, SEE FLUPHENAZINE DECANOATE			
PROMAZINE HCL	UP TO 25 MG	IM	J2950
PROMETHAZINE HCL, INJECTION	UP TO 50 MG	IM, IV	J2550
PROMETHAZINE HCL, ORAL	12.5 MG	ORAL	Q0169
PRONESTYL, SEE PROCAINAMIDE HCL			
PROPLEX T, SEE FACTOR IX			
PROPLEX SX-T, SEE FACTOR IX			
PROPOFOL	10 MG	IV	J2704
PROPRANOLOL HCL	UP TO 1 MG	IV	J1800
PROREX-25, SEE PROMETHAZINE HCL			
PROREX-50, SEE PROMETHAZINE HCL			
PROSTAPHLIN, SEE PROCAINAMIDE HCL			
PROSTIGMIN, SEE NEOSTIGMINE METHYLSULFATE			
PROTAMINE SULFATE	PER 10 MG	IV	J2720
PROTEIN C CONCENTRATE	10 IU	IV	J2724
PROTIRELIN	PER 250 MCG	IV	J2725

DRUG NAME	UNIT PER	ROUTE	CODE
PROTHAZINE, *SEE* PROMETHAZINE HCL			
PROTOPAM CHLORIDE, *SEE* PRALIDOXIME CHLORIDE			
PROVENTIL, *SEE* ALBUTEROL SULFATE, COMPOUNDED			
PROZINE-50, *SEE* PROMAZINE HCL			
PULMICORT RESPULES, *SEE* BUDESONIDE			
PYRIDOXINE HCL	100 MG		J3415

Q

DRUG NAME	UNIT PER	ROUTE	CODE
QUELICIN, *SEE* SUCCINYLCHOLINE CHLORIDE			
QUINUPRISTIN/DALFOPRISTIN	500 MG (150/350)	IV	J2770
QUTENZA, *SEE* CAPSAICIN PATCH			

R

DRUG NAME	UNIT PER	ROUTE	CODE
RANIBIZUMAB	0.1 MG	OTH	J2778
RANITIDINE HCL, INJECTION	25 MG	IV, IM	J2780
RAPAMUNE, *SEE* SIROLIMUS			
RASBURICASE	0.5 MG	IV	J2783
RECOMBINATE, *SEE* FACTOR VIII			
REDISOL, *SEE* VITAMIN B-12 CYANOCOBALAMIN			
REGADENOSON	0.1 MG	IV	J2785
REGITINE, *SEE* PHENTOLAMINE MESYLATE			
REGLAN, *SEE* METOCLOPRAMIDE HCL			
REGULAR, *SEE* INSULIN			
RELEFACT TRH, *SEE* PROTIRELIN			
RELISTOR, *SEE* METHYLNALTREXONE			
REMICADE, *SEE* INFLIXIMAB, INJECTION			
REO PRO, *SEE* ABCIXIMAB			
REP-PRED 40, *SEE* METHYLPREDNISOLONE ACETATE			
REP-PRED 80, *SEE* METHYLPREDNISOLONE ACETATE			
RESPIGAM, *SEE* RESPIRATORY SYNCYTIAL VIRUS			
RETAVASE, *SEE* RETEPLASE			
RETEPLASE	18.8 MG	IV	J2993
RETROVIR, *SEE* ZIDOVUDINE			
RHEOMACRODEX, *SEE* DEXTRAN 40			
RHESONATIV, *SEE* RHO(D) IMMUNE GLOBULIN, HUMAN			
RHEUMATREX DOSE PACK, *SEE* METHOTREXATE, ORAL			
RHO(D) IMMUNE GLOBULIN		IM, IV	J2791

DRUG NAME	UNIT PER	ROUTE	CODE
RHO(D) IMMUNE GLOBULIN, HUMAN	1 DOSE PACKAGE, 300 MCG	IM	J2790
	50 MG	IM	J2788
RHO(D)IMMUNE GLOBULIN, HUMAN, SOLVENT DETERGENT	100 IU	IV	J2792
RHOGAM, *SEE* RHO(D) IMMUNE GLOBULIN, HUMAN			
RHOPHYLAC	100 IU	IM, IV	J2791
RIASTAP, *SEE* HUMAN FIBRINOGEN CONCENTRATE			
RILONACEPT	1 MG	SC	J2793
RIMABOTULINUMTOXINB	100 UNITS	IM	J0587
RINGERS LACTATE INFUSION	UP TO 1,000 CC	IV	J7120
RISPERIDONE	0.5 MG	IM	J2794
RITUXAN, *SEE* RITUXIMAB			
RITUXIMAB	100 MG	IV	J9310
ROBAXIN, *SEE* METHOCARBAMOL			
ROCEPHIN, *SEE* CEFTRIAXONE SODIUM			
ROFERON-A, *SEE* INTERFERON ALFA-2A, RECOMBINANT			
ROMIDEPSIN	1 MG	IV	J9315
ROMIPLOSTIM	10 MCG	SC	J2796
ROPIVACAINE HYDROCHLORIDE	1 MG	OTH	J2795
RUBEX, *SEE* DOXORUBICIN HCL			
RUBRAMIN PC, *SEE* VITAMIN B-12 CYANOCOBALAMIN			

S

DRUG NAME	UNIT PER	ROUTE	CODE
SALINE SOLUTION	5% DEXTROSE, 500 ML	IV	J7042
	INFUSION, 250 CC	IV	J7050
	INFUSION, 1,000 CC	IV	J7030
SALINE SOLUTION, STERILE	500 ML = 1 UNIT	IV, OTH	J7040
SANDIMMUNE, *SEE* CYCLOSPORINE			
SANDOGLOBULIN, *SEE* IMMUNE GLOBULIN INTRAVENOUS (HUMAN)			
SANDOSTATIN LAR DEPOT, *SEE* OCTREOTIDE			
SARGRAMOSTIM (GM-CSF)	50 MCG	IV	J2820
SCULPTRA	0.5 MG	IV	Q2028
SELESTOJECT, *SEE* BETAMETHASONE SODIUM PHOSPHATE			

DRUG NAME	UNIT PER	ROUTE	CODE
SERMORELIN ACETATE	1 MCG	SC	Q0515
SINCALIDE	5 MCG	IV	J2805
SINUSOL-B, *SEE* BROMPHENIRAMINE MALEATE			
SIROLIMUS	1 MG	ORAL	J7520
SKYLA	13.5 MG	OTH	J7301
SODIUM FERRICGLUCONATE IN SUCROSE	12.5 MG		J2916
SODIUM HYALURONATE			
EUFLEXXA			J7323
HYALGAN			J7321
ORTHOVISC			J7324
SUPARTZ			J7321
SOLGANAL, *SEE* AUROTHIOGLUCOSE			
SOLU-CORTEF, *SEE* HYDROCORTISONE SODIUM PHOSPHATE (J1710)			
SOLU-MEDROL, *SEE* METHYLPREDNISOLONE SODIUM SUCCINATE			
SOLUREX, *SEE* DEXAMETHASONE SODIUM PHOSPHATE			
SOLUREX LA, *SEE* DEXAMETHASONE ACETATE			
SOMATREM	1 MG	SC	J2940
SOMATROPIN	1 MG	SC	J2941
SOMATULIN DEPOT, *SEE* LANREOTIDE			
SPARINE, *SEE* PROMAZINE HCL			
SPASMOJECT, *SEE* DICYCLOMINE HCL			
SPECTINOMYCIN HCL	UP TO 2 G	IM	J3320
SPORANOX, *SEE* ITRACONAZOLE			
STAPHCILLIN, *SEE* METHICILLIN SODIUM			
STELARA, *SEE* USTEKINUMAB			
STILPHOSTROL, *SEE* DIETHYLSTILBESTROL DIPHOSPHATE			
STREPTASE, *SEE* STREPTOKINASE			
STREPTOKINASE	PER 250,000 IU	IV	J2995
STREPTOMYCIN SULFATE, *SEE* STREPTOMYCIN			
STREPTOMYCIN	UP TO 1 G	IM	J3000
STREPTOZOCIN	1 GM	IV	J9320
STRONTIUM-89 CHLORIDE	PER MILLICURIE		A9600
SUBLIMAZE, *SEE* FENTANYL CITRATE			
SUCCINYLCHOLINE CHLORIDE	UP TO 20 MG	IV, IM	J0330
SUMATRIPTAN SUCCINATE	6 MG	SC	J3030
SUPARTZ		OTH	J7321

DRUG NAME	UNIT PER	ROUTE	CODE
SUROSTRIN, *SEE* SUCCINYCHOLINE CHLORIDE			
SUS-PHRINE, *SEE* ADRENALIN, EPINEPHRINE			
SYNERCID, *SEE* QUINUPRISTIN/ DALFOPRISTIN			
SYNKAVITE, *SEE* VITAMIN K, PHYTONADIONE, ETC.			
SYNTOCIONON, *SEE* OXYTOCIN			
SYNVISC AND SYNVISC-ONE	1 MG	OTH	J7325
SYTOBEX, *SEE* VITAMIN B-12 CYANOCOBALAMIN			

T

DRUG NAME	UNIT PER	ROUTE	CODE
TACROLIMUS, ORAL, EXTENDED RELEASE	0.1 MG	ORAL	J7508
TACROLIMUS, ORAL, IMMEDIATE RELEASE	PER 1 MG	ORAL	J7507
TACROLIMUS, PARENTERAL	5 MG	IV	J7525
TALIGLUCERACE ALFA	10 UNITS	IV	J3060
TALWIN, *SEE* PENTAZOCINE HCL			
TARACTAN, *SEE* CHLORPROTHIXENE			
TAXOL, *SEE* PACLITAXEL			
TAXOTERE, *SEE* DOCETAXEL			
TAZIDIME, *SEE* CEFTAZIDIME TECHNETIUM TC SESTAMBI	PER DOSE		A9500
TEEV, *SEE* TESTOSTERONE ENANTHATE AND ESTRADIOL VALERATE			
TEFLARO, *SEE* CEFTAROLINE FOSAMIL			
TELAVANCIN	10 MG	IV	J3095
TEMOZOLOMIDE	1 MG	IV	J9328
	5 MG	ORAL	J8700
TEMSIROLIMUS	1 MG	IV	J9330
TENECTEPLASE	1 MG	IV	J3101
TENIPOSIDE	50 MG		Q2017
TEQUIN, *SEE* GATIFLOXACIN			
TERBUTALINE SULFATE	UP TO 1 MG	SC, IV	J3105
TERBUTALINE SULFATE, CONCENTRATED FORM	PER 1 MG	INH	J7680
TERBUTALINE SULFATE, UNIT DOSE FORM	PER 1 MG	INH	J7681
TERIPARATIDE	10 MCG	SC	J3110
TERRAMYCIN IM, *SEE* OXYTETRACYCLINE HCL			
TESTA-C, *SEE* TESTOSTERONE CYPIONATE			
TESTADIATE, *SEE* TESTOSTERONE ENANTHATE AND ESTRADIOL VALERATE			

DRUG NAME	UNIT PER	ROUTE	CODE
TESTADIATE-DEPO, *SEE* TESTOSTERONE CYPIONATE			
TESTAJECT-LA, *SEE* TESTOSTERONE CYPIONATE			
TESTAQUA, *SEE* TESTOSTERONE SUSPENSION			
TEST-ESTRO CYPIONATES, *SEE* TESTOSTERONE CYPIONATE AND ESTRADIOL CYPIONATE			
TEST-ESTRO-C, *SEE* TESTOSTERONE CYPIONATE AND ESTRADIOL CYPIONATE			
TESTEX, *SEE* TESTOSTERONE PROPIONATE			
TESTOJECT-50, *SEE* TESTOSTERONE SUSPENSION			
TESTOJECT-LA, *SEE* TESTOSTERONE CYPIONATE			
TESTONE LA 200, *SEE* TESTOSTERONE ENANTHATE			
TESTONE LA 100, *SEE* TESTOSTERONE ENANTHATE			
TESTOSTERONE AQUEOUS, *SEE* TESTOSTERONE SUSPENSION			
TESTOSTERONE ENANTHATE	1 MG	IM	J3121
TESTOSTERONE CYPIONATE	1 MG	IM	J1071
TESTOSTERONE UNDECANOATE	1 MG	IM	J3145
TESTRADIOL 90/4, *SEE* TESTOSTERONE ENANTHATE AND ESTRADIOL VALERATE			
TESTRIN PA, *SEE* TESTOSTERONE ENANTHATE			
TETANUS IMMUNE GLOBULIN, HUMAN	UP TO 250 UNITS	IM	J1670
TETRACYCLINE	UP TO 250 MG	IM, IV	J0120
THALLOUS CHLORIDE TL 201	PER MCI		A9505
THEELIN AQUEOUS, *SEE* ESTRONE			
THEOPHYLLINE	PER 40 MG	IV	J2810
THERACYS, *SEE* BCG LIVE			
THIAMINE HCL	100 MG		J3411
THIETHYLPERAZINE MALEATE, INJECTION	UP TO 10 MG	IM	J3280
THIETHYLPERAZINE MALEATE, ORAL	10 MG	ORAL	Q0174
THIOTEPA	15 MG	IV	J9340
THORAZINE, *SEE* CHLORPROMAZINE HCL			
THYMOGLOBULIN, *SEE* IMMUNE GLOBULIN, ANTI-THYMOCYTE			
THYPINONE, *SEE* PROTIRELIN			
THYROGEN, *SEE* THYROTROPIN ALFA			
THYROTROPIN ALFA, INJECTION	0.9 MG	IM, SC	J3240
TICE BCG, *SEE* BCG LIVE			

DRUG NAME	UNIT PER	ROUTE	CODE
TICON, *SEE* TRIMETHOBENZAMIDE HCL			
TIGAN, *SEE* TRIMETHOBENZAMIDE HCL			
TIGECYCLINE	1 MG	IV	J3243
TIJECT-20, *SEE* TRIMETHOBENZAMIDE HCL			
TINZAPARIN	1000 IU	SC	J1655
TIROFIBAN HYDROCHLORIDE, INJECTION	0.25 MG	IM, IV	J3246
TNKASE, *SEE* TENECTEPLASE			
TOBI, *SEE* TOBRAMYCIN, INHALATION SOLUTION			
TOBRAMYCIN, INHALATION SOLUTION	300 MG	INH	J7682, J7685
TOBRAMYCIN SULFATE	UP TO 80 MG	IM, IV	J3260
TOCILIZUMAB	1 MG	IV	J3262
TOFRANIL, *SEE* IMIPRAMINE HCL			
TOLAZOLINE HCL	UP TO 25 MG	IV	J2670
TOPOTECAN	0.25 MG	ORAL	J8705
	0.1 MG	IV	J9351
TORADOL, *SEE* KETOROLAC TROMETHAMINE			
TORECAN, *SEE* THIETHYLPERAZINE MALEATE			
TORISEL, *SEE* TEMSIROLIMUS			
TORNALATE, *SEE* BITOLTEROL MESYLATE			
TORSEMIDE	10 MG/ML	IV	J3265
TOTACILLIN-N, *SEE* AMPICILLIN			
TRASTUZUMAB	10 MG	IV	J9355
TREANDA, *SEE* BENDAMUSTINE HCL			
TREPROSTINIL	1 MG		J3285
TRI-KORT, *SEE* TRIAMCINOLONE ACETONIDE			
TRIAM-A, *SEE* TRIAMCINOLONE ACETONIDE			
TRIAMCINOLONE, CONCENTRATED FORM	PER 1 MG	INH	J7683
TRIAMCINOLONE, UNIT DOSE	PER 1 MG	INH	J7684
TRIAMCINOLONE ACETONIDE	1 MG		J3300
	PER 10 MG	IM	J3301
TRIAMCINOLONE DIACETATE	PER 5 MG	IM	J3302
TRIAMCINOLONE HEXACETONIDE	PER 5 MG	VAR	J3303
TRIESENCE, *SEE* TRIAMCINOLONE ACETONIDE			

DRUG NAME	UNIT PER	ROUTE	CODE
TRIFLUPROMAZINE HCL	UP TO 20 MG	IM, IV	J3400
TRILAFON, *SEE* PERPHENAZINE			
TRILOG, *SEE* TRIAMCINOLONE ACETONIDE			
TRILONE, *SEE* TRIAMCINOLONE DIACETATE			
TRIMETHOBENZAMIDE HCL, INJECTION	UP TO 200 MG	IM	J3250
TRIMETHOBENZAMIDE HCL, ORAL	250 MG	ORAL	Q0173
TRIMETREXATE GLUCURONATE	PER 25 MG	IV	J3305
TRIPTORELIN PAMOATE	3.75 MG	SC	J3315
TRISENOX, *SEE* ARSENIC TRIOXIDE			
TROBICIN, *SEE* SPECTINOMYCIN HCL			
TROVAN, *SEE* ALATROFLOXACIN MESYLATE			
TYSABRI, *SEE* NATALIZUMAB			

U

DRUG NAME	UNIT PER	ROUTE	CODE
ULTRAZINE-10, *SEE* PROCHLORPERAZINE			
UNASYN, *SEE* AMPICILLIN SODIUM/ SULBACTAM SODIUM			
UNCLASSIFIED DRUGS (*SEE ALSO* NOT ELSEWHERE CLASSIFIED)			J3490
UNSPECIFIED ORAL ANTIEMETIC			Q0181
UREA	UP TO 40 G	IV	J3350
UREAPHIL, *SEE* UREA			
URECHOLINE, *SEE* BETHANECHOL CHLORIDE			
UROFOLLITROPIN	75 IU		J3355
UROKINASE	5, 000 IU VIAL	IV	J3364
	250, 000 IU VIAL	IV	J3365
USTEKINUMAB	1 MG	SC	J3357

V

DRUG NAME	UNIT PER	ROUTE	CODE
V-GAN 25, *SEE* PROMETHAZINE HCL			
V-GAN 50, *SEE* PROMETHAZINE HCL			
VALERGEN 10, *SEE* ESTRADIOL VALERATE			
VALERGEN 20, *SEE* ESTRADIOL VALERATE			
VALERGEN 40, *SEE* ESTRADIOL VALERATE			
VALERTEST NO. 1, *SEE* TESTOSTERONE ENANTHATE AND ESTRADIOL VALERATE			

DRUG NAME	UNIT PER	ROUTE	CODE
VALERTEST NO. 2, *SEE* TESTOSTERONE ENANTHATE AND ESTRADIOL VALERATE			
VALIUM, *SEE* DIAZEPAM			
VALRUBICIN, INTRAVESICAL	200 MG	OTH	J9357
VALSTAR, *SEE* VALRUBICIN			
VANCOCIN, *SEE* VANCOMYCIN HCL			
VANCOLED, *SEE* VANCOMYCIN HCL			
VANCOMYCIN HCL	500 MG	IV, IM	J3370
VASOXYL, *SEE* METHOXAMINE HCL			
VELAGLUCERASE ALFA	100 UNITS	IV	J3385
VELBAN, *SEE* VINBLASTINE SULFATE			
VELSAR, *SEE* VINBLASTINE SULFATE			
VENOFER, *SEE* IRON SUCROSE			
VENTOLIN, *SEE* ALBUTEROL SULFATE			
VEPESID, *SEE* ETOPOSIDE AND ETOPOSIDE, ORAL			
VERSED, *SEE* MIDAZOLAM HCL			
VERTEPORFIN	0.1 MG	IV	J3396
VESPRIN, *SEE* TRIFLUPROMAZINE HCL			
VIADUR, *SEE* LEUPROLIDE ACETATE IMPLANT			
VIBATIV, *SEE* TELAVANCIN			
VINBLASTINE SULFATE	1 MG	IV	J9360
VINCASAR PFS, *SEE* VINCRISTINE SULFATE			
VINCRISTINE SULFATE	1 MG	IV	J9370
VINCRISTINE SULFATE LIPOSOME	1 MG	IV	J9371
VINORELBINE TARTRATE	PER 10 MG	IV	J9390
VISTAJECT-25, *SEE* HYDROXYZINE HCL			
VISTARIL, *SEE* HYDROXYZINE HCL			
VISTIDE, *SEE* CIDOFOVIR			
VISUDYNE, *SEE* VERTEPORFIN			
VITAMIN K, PHYTONADIONE, MENADIONE, MENADIOL SODIUM DIPHOSPHATE	PER 1 MG	IM, SC, IV	J3430
VITAMIN B-12 CYANOCOBALAMIN	UP TO 1, 000 MCG	IM, SC	J3420
VON WILLEBRAND FACTOR COMPLEX, HUMAN	PER IU VWF:R-CO	IV	J7187
	PER IU VWF:R-CO	IV	J7183
VORICONAZOLE	10 MG	IV	J3465
VPRIV, *SEE* VELAGLUCERASE ALFA			

DRUG NAME	UNIT PER	ROUTE	CODE
W			
WEHAMINE, *SEE* DIMENHYDRINATE			
WEHDRYL, *SEE* DIPHENHYDRAMINE HCL			
WELLCOVORIN, *SEE* LEUCOVORIN CALCIUM			
WILATE, *SEE* VON WILLEBRAND FACTOR COMPLEX (HUMAN)			
WIN RHO SD, *SEE* RHO(D) IMMUGLOBULIN, HUMAN, SOLVENT DETERGENT			
WYAMINE SULFATE, *SEE* MEPHENTERMINE SULFATE			
WYCILLIN, *SEE* PENICILLIN G PROCAINE			
WYDASE, *SEE* HYALURONIDASE			

DRUG NAME	UNIT PER	ROUTE	CODE
X			
XELODA, *SEE* CAPECITABINE			
XEOMIN, *SEE* INCOBOTULINUMTOXIN TYPE A			
XGEVA, *SEE* DENOSUMAB			
XIAFLEX, *SEE* COLLAGENASE			
XOPENEX, *SEE* ALBUTEROL			
XYLOCAINE HCL, *SEE* LIDOCAINE HCL			
XYNTHA, *SEE* FACTOR VIII (ANTI-HEMOPHILIC FACTOR, RECOMBINANT)			

DRUG NAME	UNIT PER	ROUTE	CODE
Y			
YERVOY, *SEE* IPILIMUMAB			

DRUG NAME	UNIT PER	ROUTE	CODE
Z			
ZANOSAR, *SEE* STREPTOZOCIN			
ZANTAC, *SEE* RANITIDINE HCL			
ZEMPLAR, *SEE* PARICALCITOL			
ZENAPAX, *SEE* DACLIZUMAB			
ZETRAN, *SEE* DIAZEPAM			
ZICONOTIDE	1 MCG	OTH	J2278
ZIDOVUDINE	10 MG	IV	J3485
ZINACEF, *SEE* CEFUROXIME SODIUM			
ZIPRASIDONE MESYLATE	10 MG	IM	J3486
ZITHROMAX, *SEE* AZITHROMYCIN DIHYDRATE			
ZITHROMAX I.V., *SEE* AZITHROMYCIN, INJECTION			
ZIV-AFLIBERCEPT	1 MG	IV	J9400
ZOFRAN, *SEE* ONDANSETRON HCL			
ZOLADEX, *SEE* GOSERELIN ACETATE IMPLANT			
ZOLEDRONIC ACID	1 MG	IV	J3489

DRUG NAME	UNIT PER	ROUTE	CODE
ZOLICEF, *SEE* CEFAZOLIN SODIUM			
ZORTRESS, *SEE* EVEROLIMUS			
ZOSYN, *SEE* PIPERACILLIN			
ZYPREXA RELPREVV, *SEE* OLANZAPINE			
ZYVOX, *SEE* LINEZOLID			

Appendix B: HCPCS Modifiers

A1	Dressing for one wound
A2	Dressing for two wounds
A3	Dressing for three wounds
A4	Dressing for four wounds
A5	Dressing for five wounds
A6	Dressing for six wounds
A7	Dressing for seven wounds
A8	Dressing for eight wounds
A9	Dressing for nine or more wounds
AA	Anesthesia services performed personally by anesthesiologist
AD	Medical supervision by a physician: more than four concurrent anesthesia procedures
AE	Registered dietician
AF	Specialty physician
AG	Primary physician
AH	Clinical psychologist
AI	Principal physician of record
AJ	Clinical social worker
AK	Non participating physician
AM	Physician, team member service
AO	Alternate payment method declined by provider of service
AP	Determination of refractive state was not performed in the course of diagnostic ophthalmological examination
AQ	Physician providing a service in an unlisted health professional shortage area (HPSA)
AR	Physician provider services in a physician scarcity area
AS	Physician assistant, nurse practitioner, or clinical nurse specialist services for assistant at surgery
AT	Acute treatment (this modifier should be used when reporting service 98940, 98941, 98942)
AU	Item furnished in conjunction with a urological, ostomy, or tracheostomy supply
AV	Item furnished in conjunction with a prosthetic device, prosthetic or orthotic
AW	Item furnished in conjunction with a surgical dressing
AX	Item furnished in conjunction with dialysis services
AY	Item or service furnished to an ESRD patient that is not for the treatment of ESRD
AZ	Physician providing a service in a dental health professional shortage area for the purpose of an electronic health record incentive payment
BA	Item furnished in conjunction with parenteral enteral nutrition (PEN) services
BL	Special acquisition of blood and blood products
BO	Orally administered nutrition, not by feeding tube
BP	The beneficiary has been informed of the purchase and rental options and has elected to purchase the item
BR	The beneficiary has been informed of the purchase and rental options and has elected to rent the item

BU	The beneficiary has been informed of the purchase and rental options and after 30 days has not informed the supplier of his/her decision
CA	Procedure payable only in the inpatient setting when performed emergently on an outpatient who expires prior to admission
CB	Service ordered by a renal dialysis facility (RDF) physician as part of the esrd beneficiary's dialysis benefit, is not part of the composite rate, and is separately reimbursable
CC	Procedure code change (use 'CC' when the procedure code submitted was changed either for administrative reasons or because an incorrect code was filed)
CD	AMCC test has been ordered by an ESRD facility or MCP physician that is part of the composite rate and is not separately billable
CE	AMCC test has been ordered by an ESRD facility or MCP physician that is a composite rate test but is beyond the normal frequency covered under the rate and is separately reimbursable based on medical necessity
CF	AMCC test has been ordered by an ESRD facility or MCP physician that is not part of the composite rate and is separately billable
CG	Policy criteria applied
CH	0 percent impaired, limited or restricted
CI	At least 1 percent but less than 20 percent impaired, limited or restricted
CJ	At least 20 percent but less than 40 percent impaired, limited or restricted
CK	At least 40 percent but less than 60 percent impaired, limited or restricted
CL	At least 60 percent but less than 80 percent impaired, limited or restricted
CM	At least 80 percent but less than 100 percent impaired, limited or restricted
CN	100 percent impaired, limited or restricted
CR	Catastrophe/disaster related
CS	Item or service related, in whole or in part, to an illness, injury, or condition that was caused by or exacerbated by the effects, direct or indirect, of the 2010 oil spill in the gulf of mexico, including but not limited to subsequent clean-up activities
DA	Oral health assessment by a licensed health professional other than a dentist
E1	Upper left, eyelid
E2	Lower left, eyelid
E3	Upper right, eyelid
E4	Lower right, eyelid
EA	Erythropoetic stimulating agent (ESA) administered to treat anemia due to anti-cancer chemotherapy
EB	Erythropoetic stimulating agent (ESA) administered to treat anemia due to anti-cancer radiotherapy
EC	Erythropoetic stimulating agent (ESA) administered to treat anemia not due to anti-cancer radiotherapy or anti-cancer chemotherapy

ED Hematocrit level has exceeded 39% (or hemoglobin level has exceeded 13.0 G/dl) for 3 or more consecutive billing cycles immediately prior to and including the current cycle

EE Hematocrit level has not exceeded 39% (or hemoglobin level has not exceeded 13.0 G/dl) for 3 or more consecutive billing cycles immediately prior to and including the current cycle

EJ Subsequent claims for a defined course of therapy, e.g., EPO, sodium hyaluronate, infliximab

EM Emergency reserve supply (for ESRD benefit only)

EP Service provided as part of medicaid early periodic screening diagnosis and treatment (EPSDT) program

ET Emergency services

EY No physician or other licensed health care provider order for this item or service

F1 Left hand, second digit

F2 Left hand, third digit

F3 Left hand, fourth digit

F4 Left hand, fifth digit

F5 Right hand, thumb

F6 Right hand, second digit

F7 Right hand, third digit

F8 Right hand, fourth digit

F9 Right hand, fifth digit

FA Left hand, thumb

FB Item provided without cost to provider, supplier or practitioner, or full credit received for replaced device (examples, but not limited to, covered under warranty, replaced due to defect, free samples)

FC Partial credit received for replaced device

FP Service provided as part of family planning program

G1 Most recent URR reading of less than 60

G2 Most recent URR reading of 60 to 64.9

G3 Most recent URR reading of 65 to 69.9

G4 Most recent URR reading of 70 to 74.9

G5 Most recent URR reading of 75 or greater

G6 ESRD patient for whom less than six dialysis sessions have been provided in a month

G7 Pregnancy resulted from rape or incest or pregnancy certified by physician as life threatening

G8 Monitored anesthesia care (MAC) for deep complex, complicated, or markedly invasive surgical procedure

G9 Monitored anesthesia care for patient who has history of severe cardio-pulmonary condition

GA Waiver of liability statement issued as required by payer policy, individual case

GB Claim being re-submitted for payment because it is no longer covered under a global payment demonstration

GC This service has been performed in part by a resident under the direction of a teaching physician

GD Units of service exceeds medically unlikely edit value and represents reasonable and necessary services

GE This service has been performed by a resident without the presence of a teaching physician under the primary care exception

GF Non-physician (e.g. nurse practitioner (NP), certified registered nurse anesthetist (CRNA), certified registered nurse (CRN), clinical nurse specialist (CNS), physician assistant (PA) services in a critical access hospital

GG Performance and payment of a screening mammogram and diagnostic mammogram on the same patient, same day

GH Diagnostic mammogram converted from screening mammogram on same day

GJ "Opt out" physician or practitioner emergency or urgent service

GK Reasonable and necessary item/service associated with a GA or GZ modifier

GL Medically unnecessary upgrade provided instead of non-upgraded item, no charge, no advance beneficiary notice (ABN)

GM Multiple patients on one ambulance trip

GN Services delivered under an outpatient speech language pathology plan of care

GO Services delivered under an outpatient occupational therapy plan of care

GP Services delivered under an outpatient physical therapy plan of care

GQ Via asynchronous telecommunications system

GR This service was performed in whole or in part by a resident in a department of veterans affairs medical center or clinic, supervised in accordance with VA policy

GS Dosage of erythropoietin stimulating agent has been reduced and maintained in response to hematocrit or hemoglobin level

GT Via interactive audio and video telecommunication systems

GU Waiver of liability statement issued as required by payer policy, routine notice

GV Attending physician not employed or paid under arrangement by the patient's hospice provider

GW Service not related to the hospice patient's terminal condition

GX Notice of liability issued, voluntary under payer policy

GY Item or service statutorily excluded, does not meet the definition of any Medicare benefit or, for non-Medicare insurers, is not a contract benefit

GZ Item or service expected to be denied as not reasonable and necessary

H9 Court-ordered

HA Child/adolescent program

HB Adult program, non geriatric

HC Adult program, geriatric

HD Pregnant/parenting women's program

HE Mental health program

HF Substance abuse program

HG Opioid addiction treatment program

HH Integrated mental health/substance abuse program

HI Integrated mental health and intellectual disability/developmental disabilities program

HJ Employee assistance program

HK Specialized mental health programs for high-risk populations

HL	Intern
HM	Less than bachelor degree level
HN	Bachelors degree level
HO	Masters degree level
HP	Doctoral level
HQ	Group setting
HR	Family/couple with client present
HS	Family/couple without client present
HT	Multi-disciplinary team
HU	Funded by child welfare agency
HV	Funded state addictions agency
HW	Funded by state mental health agency
HX	Funded by county/local agency
HY	Funded by juvenile justice agency
HZ	Funded by criminal justice agency
J1	Competitive acquisition program no-pay submission for a prescription number
J2	Competitive acquisition program, restocking of emergency drugs after emergency administration
J3	Competitive acquisition program (CAP), drug not available through CAP as written, reimbursed under average sales price methodology
J4	DMEPOS item subject to DMEPOS competitive bidding program that is furnished by a hospital upon discharge
JA	Administered intravenously
JB	Administered subcutaneously
JC	Skin substitute used as a graft
JD	Skin substitute not used as a graft
JE	Administered via dialysate
JW	Drug amount discarded/not administered to any patient
K0	Lower extremity prosthesis functional level 0 - does not have the ability or potential to ambulate or transfer safely with or without assistance and a prosthesis does not enhance their quality of life or mobility.
K1	Lower extremity prosthesis functional level 1 - has the ability or potential to use a prosthesis for transfers or ambulation on level surfaces at fixed cadence. typical of the limited and unlimited household ambulator.
K2	Lower extremity prosthesis functional level 2 - has the ability or potential for ambulation with the ability to traverse low level environmental barriers such as curbs, stairs or uneven surfaces. typical of the limited community ambulator.
K3	Lower extremity prosthesis functional level 3 - has the ability or potential for ambulation with variable cadence. typical of the community ambulator who has the ability to transverse most environmental barriers and may have vocational, therapeutic, or exercise activity that demands prosthetic utilization beyond simple locomotion.
K4	Lower extremity prosthesis functional level 4 - has the ability or potential for prosthetic ambulation that exceeds the basic ambulation skills, exhibiting high impact, stress, or energy levels, typical of the prosthetic demands of the child, active adult, or athlete.
KA	Add on option/accessory for wheelchair
KB	Beneficiary requested upgrade for ABN, more than 4 modifiers identified on claim
KC	Replacement of special power wheelchair interface
KD	Drug or biological infused through DME
KE	Bid under round one of the DMEPOS competitive bidding program for use with non-competitive bid base equipment
KF	Item designated by FDA as class III device
KG	DMEPOS item subject to DMEPOS competitive bidding program number 1
KH	DMEPOS item, initial claim, purchase or first month rental
KI	DMEPOS item, second or third month rental
KJ	DMEPOS item, parenteral enteral nutrition (PEN) pump or capped rental, months four to fifteen
KK	DMEPOS item subject to DMEPOS competitive bidding program number 2
KL	DMEPOS item delivered via mail
KM	Replacement of facial prosthesis including new impression/moulage
KN	Replacement of facial prosthesis using previous master model
KO	Single drug unit dose formulation
KP	First drug of a multiple drug unit dose formulation
KQ	Second or subsequent drug of a multiple drug unit dose formulation
KR	Rental item, billing for partial month
KS	Glucose monitor supply for diabetic beneficiary not treated with insulin
KT	Beneficiary resides in a competitive bidding area and travels outside that competitive bidding area and receives a competitive bid item
KU	DMEPOS item subject to DMEPOS competitive bidding program number 3
KV	DMEPOS item subject to DMEPOS competitive bidding program that is furnished as part of a professional service
KW	DMEPOS item subject to DMEPOS competitive bidding program number 4
KX	Requirements specified in the medical policy have been met
KY	DMEPOS item subject to DMEPOS competitive bidding program number 5
KZ	New coverage not implemented by managed care
L1	Provider attestation that the hospital laboratory test(s) is not packaged under the hospital OPPS
LC	Left circumflex coronary artery
LD	Left anterior descending coronary artery
LL	Lease/rental (use the 'LL' modifier when DME equipment rental is to be applied against the purchase price)
LM	Left main coronary artery
LR	Laboratory round trip
LS	FDA-monitored intraocular lens implant
LT	Left side (used to identify procedures performed on the left side of the body)
M2	Medicare secondary payer (MSP)
MS	Six month maintenance and servicing fee for reasonable and necessary parts and labor which are not covered under any manufacturer or supplier warranty

NB	Nebulizer system, any type, FDA-cleared for use with specific drug
NR	New when rented (use the 'NR' modifier when DME which was new at the time of rental is subsequently purchased)
NU	New equipment
P1	A normal healthy patient
P2	A patient with mild systemic disease
P3	A patient with severe systemic disease
P4	A patient with severe systemic disease that is a constant threat to life
P5	A moribund patient who is not expected to survive without the operation
P6	A declared brain-dead patient whose organs are being removed for donor purposes
PA	Surgical or other invasive procedure on wrong body part
PB	Surgical or other invasive procedure on wrong patient
PC	Wrong surgery or other invasive procedure on patient
PD	Diagnostic or related non diagnostic item or service provided in a wholly owned or operated entity to a patient who is admitted as an inpatient within 3 days
PI	Positron emission tomography (PET) or PET/computed tomography (CT) to inform the initial treatment strategy of tumors that are biopsy proven or strongly suspected of being cancerous based on other diagnostic testing
PL	Progressive addition lenses
PM	Post mortem
PO	Services, procedures and/or surgeries provided at off-campus provider-based outpatient departments
PS	Positron emission tomography (PET) or PET/computed tomography (CT) to inform the subsequent treatment strategy of cancerous tumors when the beneficiary's treating physician determines that the pet study is needed to inform subsequent anti-tumor strategy
PT	Colorectal cancer screening test; converted to diagnostic test or other procedure
Q0	Investigational clinical service provided in a clinical research study that is in an approved clinical research study
Q1	Routine clinical service provided in a clinical research study that is in an approved clinical research study
Q2	HCFA/ORD demonstration project procedure/service
Q3	Live kidney donor surgery and related services
Q4	Service for ordering/referring physician qualifies as a service exemption
Q5	Service furnished by a substitute physician under a reciprocal billing arrangement
Q6	Service furnished by a locum tenens physician
Q7	One class A finding
Q8	Two class B findings
Q9	One class C and two class C findings
QC	Single channel monitoring
QD	Recording and storage in solid state memory by a digital recorder
QE	Prescribed amount of oxygen is less than 1 liter per minute (LPM)
QF	Prescribed amount of oxygen exceeds 4 liters per minute (LPM) and portable oxygen is prescribed

QG	Prescribed amount of oxygen is greater than 4 liters per minute (LPM)
QH	Oxygen conserving device is being used with an oxygen delivery system
QJ	Services/items provided to a prisoner or patient in state or local custody, however the state or local government, as applicable, meets the requirements in 42 CFR 411.4 (B)
QK	Medical direction of two, three, or four concurrent anesthesia procedures involving qualified individuals
QL	Patient pronounced dead after ambulance called
QM	Ambulance service provided under arrangement by a provider of services
QN	Ambulance service furnished directly by a provider of services
QP	Documentation is on file showing that the laboratory test(s) was ordered individually or ordered as a CPT®-recognized panel other than automated profile codes 80002-80019, G0058, G0059, and G0060.
QS	Monitored anesthesia care service
QT	Recording and storage on tape by an analog tape recorder
QW	CLIA waived test
QX	CRNA service: with medical direction by a physician
QY	Medical direction of one certified registered nurse anesthetist (CRNA) by an anesthesiologist
QZ	CRNA service: without medical direction by a physician
RA	Replacement of a DME, orthotic or prosthetic item
RB	Replacement of a part of a DME, orthotic or prosthetic item furnished as part of a repair
RC	Right coronary artery
RD	Drug provided to beneficiary, but not administered "incident-to"
RE	Furnished in full compliance with FDA-mandated risk evaluation and mitigation strategy (REMS)
RI	Ramus intermedius coronary artery
RR	Rental (use the 'RR' modifier when DME is to be rented)
RT	Right side (used to identify procedures performed on the right side of the body)
SA	Nurse practitioner rendering service in collaboration with a physician
SB	Nurse midwife
SC	Medically necessary service or supply
SD	Services provided by registered nurse with specialized, highly technical home infusion training
SE	State and/or federally-funded programs/services
SF	Second opinion ordered by a professional review organization (PRO) per section 9401, p.l. 99-272 (100% reimbursement - no medicare deductible or coinsurance)
SG	Ambulatory surgical center (ASC) facility service
SH	Second concurrently administered infusion therapy
SJ	Third or more concurrently administered infusion therapy
SK	Member of high risk population (use only with codes for immunization)
SL	State supplied vaccine
SM	Second surgical opinion
SN	Third surgical opinion

SQ	Item ordered by home health	**U2**	Medicaid level of care 2, as defined by each state
SS	Home infusion services provided in the infusion suite of the IV therapy provider	**U3**	Medicaid level of care 3, as defined by each state
ST	Related to trauma or injury	**U4**	Medicaid level of care 4, as defined by each state
SU	Procedure performed in physician's office (to denote use of facility and equipment)	**U5**	Medicaid level of care 5, as defined by each state
		U6	Medicaid level of care 6, as defined by each state
SV	Pharmaceuticals delivered to patient's home but not utilized	**U7**	Medicaid level of care 7, as defined by each state
		U8	Medicaid level of care 8, as defined by each state
SW	Services provided by a certified diabetic educator	**U9**	Medicaid level of care 9, as defined by each state
SY	Persons who are in close contact with member of high-risk population (use only with codes for immunization)	**UA**	Medicaid level of care 10, as defined by each state
		UB	Medicaid level of care 11, as defined by each state
SZ	Habilitative services	**UC**	Medicaid level of care 12, as defined by each state
T1	Left foot, second digit	**UD**	Medicaid level of care 13, as defined by each state
T2	Left foot, third digit	**UE**	Used durable medical equipment
T3	Left foot, fourth digit	**UF**	Services provided in the morning
T4	Left foot, fifth digit	**UG**	Services provided in the afternoon
T5	Right foot, great toe	**UH**	Services provided in the evening
T6	Right foot, second digit	**UJ**	Services provided at night
T7	Right foot, third digit	**UK**	Services provided on behalf of the client to someone other than the client (collateral relationship)
T8	Right foot, fourth digit		
T9	Right foot, fifth digit	**UN**	Two patients served
TA	Left foot, great toe	**UP**	Three patients served
TD	RN	**UQ**	Four patients served
TC	Technical component; under certain circumstances, a charge may be made for the technical component alone; under those circumstances the technical component charge is identified by adding modifier 'TC' to the usual procedure number; technical component charges are institutional charges and not billed separately by physicians; however, portable x-ray suppliers only bill for technical component and should utilize modifier TC; the charge data from portable x-ray suppliers will then be used to build customary and prevailing profiles	**UR**	Five patients served
		US	Six or more patients served
		V5	Vascular catheter (alone or with any other vascular access)
		V6	Arteriovenous graft (or other vascular access not including a vascular catheter)
		V7	Arteriovenous fistula only (in use with two needles)
		V8	Infection present
		V9	No infection present
		VP	Aphakic patient
TE	LPN/LVN	**XE**	Separate encounter, a service that is distinct because it occurred during a separate encounter
TF	Intermediate level of care		
TG	Complex/high tech level of care	**XP**	Separate practitioner, a service that is distinct because it was performed by a different practitioner
TH	Obstetrical treatment/services, prenatal or postpartum		
TJ	Program group, child and/or adolescent	**XS**	Separate structure, a service that is distinct because it was performed on a separate organ/structure
TK	Extra patient or passenger, non-ambulance		
TL	Early intervention/individualized family service plan (IFSP)	**XU**	Unusual non-overlapping service, the use of a service that is distinct because it does not overlap usual components of the main service
TM	Individualized education program (IEP)		
TN	Rural/outside providers' customary service area		
TP	Medical transport, unloaded vehicle		
TQ	Basic life support transport by a volunteer ambulance provider		
TR	School-based individualized education program (IEP) services provided outside the public school district responsible for the student		
TS	Follow-up service		
TT	Individualized service provided to more than one patient in same setting		
TU	Special payment rate, overtime		
TV	Special payment rates, holidays/weekends		
TW	Back-up equipment		
U1	Medicaid level of care 1, as defined by each state		

Appendix C: List of Abbreviations

Abbreviation	Description
/	Or
<	Less than
<=	Less than equal to
>	Greater than
>=	Greater than equal to
AAA	Abdominal arotic aneurysm
AC	Alternating current
ACE	Angiotensin converting enzyme
AFO	Ankle-foot orthosis
AICC	Anti-inhibitor coagulant complex
AK	Above the knee
AKA	above knee amputation
ALS	advanced life support
AMP	ampule
ARB	Angiotensin receptor blocker
ART	arterial
ASC	ambulatory surgery center
ATT	attaced
A-V	Arteriovenous
AVF	arteriovenous fistula
BICROS	bilateral routing of signals
BK	below the knee
BLS	basic life suppot
BMI	body mass index
BP	blood pressure
BTE	behind the ear (hearing aid)
CAD	coronary artery disease
CAPD	continuous ambulatory perioneal dialysis
Carb	carbohydrate
CBC	complete blood count
cc	cubic centimeter
CCPD	continuous cycling peritoneal analysis
CGH	comparative genomic hybridization
CHF	congestive heart failure
CIC	completely in the canal (hearing aid)
CIM	Coverage Issue Manual
Cisd	closed
cm	centimeter
CMN	certificate of medical necessity
CMS	Centers for Medicare and Medicaid Services
CMV	Cytomegalovirus
Conc	concentrate
Conc	concentrated
Cont	continuous
CP	clinical psychologist

Abbreviation	Description
CPAP	continuous positive airway pressure
CPT®	Current Procedural Terminology
CRF	chronic renal failure
CRNA	certified registered nurse anesthetist
CROS	contralateral routing of signals
CSW	clinical social worker
CT	computed tomography
CTLSO	cervical-thoracic-lumbar-sacral orthosis
cu	cubic centimeter
DC	direct current
DI	diurnal rhythm
DLI	donor leukocyte infusion
DME	durable medical equipment
DME MAC	durable medical equipment Medicare administrative contractor
DMEPOS	Durable Medical Equipment , Prosthestics , Orthotics and Other Supplies
DMERC	durable medical equipment regional carrier
DR	diagnostic radiology
Dx	diagnosis
DX	diagnostic
DXA	dual-energy x-ray absorptiometry
e.g.	for example
Ea	each
ECF	extended care facility
EEG	eletroencephalogram
EKG	electrocardiogram
EMG	electromyography
EO	elbow orthosis
EP	electrophysiologic
EPO	epoetin alfa
EPSDT	early periodic screening , diagnosis and treatment
ESRD	end-stage renal disease
Ex	extended
EXPER	experimental
Ext	external
F	french
FDA	Food and Drug Administration
FDG-PET	positron emission with tomography with 18 fluoro-deoxyglucose
Fem	female
FO	finger orthosis
FPD	fixed partial denture
Fr	french
ft	foot
G-CSF	filgrastim (granulocyte colony- stimulating factor)

Abbreviation	Description
gm	gram (g)
H2O	water
HCL	hydrochloric acid, hydrochloride
HCPCS	Healthcare Common Procedural Coding System
HCT	hematocrit
HCV	Hepatitis C virus
HDL-C	High - density lipoprotein- cholesterol
HF	Heart Failure
HFO	hand-finger orthosis
HHA	home health agency
HI	high
HI-LO	high-low
HIT	home infusion therapy
HKAFO	hip-knee-ankle foot orthosis
HLA	human luukocyte antigen
HMES	heat and moisture exchange system
HNPCC	hereditary non-polyposis colorectal cancer
HO	hip orthosis
HPSA	health professional shortage area
HST	home sleep test
I-131	Iodine 131
IA	intra- arterial administration
lbs	pounds
ICF	intermediate care facility
ICU	intensive care unit
IM	intramuscular
in	inch
INF	infusion
INH	inhalation solution
INJ	injection
IOL	intraocular lens
ip	interphalangeal
IPD	intermittent peritoneal dialysis
IPPB	intermittent positive pressure breathing
IT	intrathecal administration
ITC	in the canal (hearing aid)
ITE	in the ear (hearing aid)
IU	international units
IV	intravenous
IVF	in vito fertillization
IVP	Intrauterine pregnancy
KAFO	knee-ankle-foot orthosis
KO	knee orthosis
KOH	potassium hydroxide
L	left
LASIK	laser in situ keratomileusis
LAUP	laser assisted uvulopalatoplasty
LDL	low density lipoprotein

Abbreviation	Description
lbs	pounds
LDS	lipodystrophy syndrome
Lo	low
LOPS	loss of protective sensation
LPM	liters per minute
LPN/LVN	Licensed Practical Nurse/Licensed Vocational Nurse
LSO	lumbar-sacral orthosis
LTC	long term care facility
LVEF	left ventricular enjection fraction
MAC	Medicare administrative contractor
mcg	microgram
mCi	millicurie
MCM	Medicare Carriers Manual
MCP	metacarparpophalangeal joint
mEq	milliequivalent
MESA	microsurgical epididymal sperm aspiration
mg	milligram
mgs	milligrams
MHT	megahertz
ml	milliliter
mm	millimeter
mmHg	millimeters of Mercury
mp	metacarpophalangeal
MRA	magnetic resonance angiography
MRI	magnetic resonance imaging
NA	sodium
NCI	National Cancer Institute
NEC	not elsewhere classified
NG	nasogastric
NH	nursing home
NMES	neuromuscular electrical stimulation
NOC	not otherwise classified
NOS	not otherwise specified
O2	oxygen
OBRA	Omnibus Budget Reconcilliation Act
OMT	osteopathic manipulation therapy
OPPS	outpatient prospective payment system
ORAL	oral administration
OSA	obstrutive sleep apnea
Ost	ostomy
OTH	other routes of administration
oz	ounce
PA	physician's assistant
PAR	parenteral
PCA	patient controlled analgesia
PCH	pouch
PEN	parenteral and enteral nutrition
PENS	percutaneous electrical nerve stimulation

Abbreviation	Description
PET	positron emission tomography
PHP	pre-paid health plan
PHP	physician hospital plan
PI	paramedic intercept
PICC	peripherally insertedcentral venous catheter
PKR	photorefractive keratotomy
PNB	peripheral nerve block
Pow	powder
PPPS	personalized prevention plan of service
PQRS	physician quality reporting system
PRK	photoreactive keratectomy
PRO	peer reviwe organization
PSA	prostate specific antigen
PSA	prostate specific antigen test
PTB	patellar tendon bearing
PTK	phototherapeutic keratectomy
PVC	polyvinyl chloride
R	right
Repl	replace
RN	registered nurse
RP	retrograde pyelogram
Rx	prescription
SACH	solid ankle, cushion heel
SC	subcutaneous
SCT	specialty care transport
SEO	shoulder-elbow orthosis
SEWHO	shoulder-elbow-wrist-hand orthosis
SEXA	single energy x- ray absorptiometry
SGD	speech generating device
SGD	sinus rhythm
SM	samarium
SNCT	sensory nerve condution test
SNF	skillied nursing facillity
SO	sacroilliac othrosis
SO	shoulder orthosis
Sol	solution
SQ	square
SR	screen
ST	standard
ST	sustained release
Syr	syrup
TABS	tablets
Tc	Technetium
Tc 99m	technetium isotope
TD	diphtheria toxoids vaccine
TDAP	diphtheria toxoids and acellular pertussis vaccine
TEE	Transesophageal echocardiography
TENS	transcutaneous electrival nerve stimulator

Abbreviation	Description
THKAO	thoracic-hip-knee-ankle orthosis
TLSO	thoracic-lumbar-sacral-orthosis
TM	temporomandibular
TMJ	temporomandibular joint
TPN	total parenteral nutrition
U	unit
uCi	microcurie
VAR	various routes of administration
w	with
w/	with
w/o	without
WAK	wearable artificial kidney
wc	wheelchair
WHFO	wrist-hand-finger orthotic
wk	week
Xe	xenon (isotope mass of xenon 133)

Appendix D: Place of Service

Code	Place of Service	Place of Service Description
01	Pharmacy	A facility or location where drugs and other medically related items and services are sold, dispensed, or otherwise provided directly to patients. (Effective October 1, 2005)
02	Unassigned	N/A
03	School	A facility whose primary purpose is education. (Effective January 1, 2003)
04	Homeless Shelter	A facility or location whose primary purpose is to provide temporary housing to homeless individuals (e.g., emergency shelters, individual or family shelters). (Effective January 1, 2003)
05	Indian Health Service Free-standing Facility	A facility or location, owned and operated by the Indian Health Service, which provides diagnostic, therapeutic (surgical and non-surgical), and rehabilitation services to American Indians and Alaska Natives who do not require hospitalization. (Effective January 1, 2003)
06	Indian Health Service Provider-based Facility	A facility or location, owned and operated by the Indian Health Service, which provides diagnostic, therapeutic (surgical and non-surgical), and rehabilitation services rendered by, or under the supervision of, physicians to American Indians and Alaska Natives admitted as inpatients or outpatients. (Effective January 1, 2003)
07	Tribal 638 Free-standing Facility	A facility or location owned and operated by a federally recognized American Indian or Alaska Native tribe or tribal organization under a 638 agreement, which provides diagnostic, therapeutic (surgical and non-surgical), and rehabilitation services to tribal members who do not require hospitalization. (Effective January 1, 2003)
08	Tribal 638 Provider-based Facility	A facility or location owned and operated by a federally recognized American Indian or Alaska Native tribe or tribal organization under a 638 agreement, which provides diagnostic, therapeutic (surgical and non-surgical), and rehabilitation services to tribal members admitted as inpatients or outpatients. (Effective January 1, 2003)
09	Prison/Correctional Facility	A prison, jail, reformatory, work farm, detention center, or any other similar facility maintained by either Federal, State or local authorities for the purpose of confinement or rehabilitation of adult or juvenile criminal offenders. (Effective July 1, 2006)
10	Unassigned	N/A
11	Office	Location, other than a hospital, skilled nursing facility (SNF), military treatment facility, community health center, State or local public health clinic, or intermediate care facility (ICF), where the health professional routinely provides health examinations, diagnosis, and treatment of illness or injury on an ambulatory basis.
12	Home	Location, other than a hospital or other facility, where the patient receives care in a private residence.
13	Assisted Living Facility	Congregate residential facility with self-contained living units providing assessment of each resident's needs and on-site support 24 hours a day, 7 days a week, with the capacity to deliver or arrange for services including some health care and other services. (Effective October 1, 2003)
14	Group Home *	A residence, with shared living areas, where clients receive supervision and other services such as social and/or behavioral services, custodial service, and minimal services (e.g., medication administration). (Effective October 1, 2003)
15	Mobile Unit	A facility/unit that moves from place-to-place equipped to provide preventive, screening, diagnostic, and/or treatment services. (Effective January 1, 2003)
16	Temporary Lodging	A short term accommodation such as a hotel, camp ground, hostel, cruise ship or resort where the patient receives care, and which is not identified by any other POS code. (Effective April 1, 2008)
17	Walk-in Retail Health Clinic	A walk-in health clinic, other than an office, urgent care facility, pharmacy or independent clinic and not described by any other Place of Service code, that is located within a retail operation and provides, on an ambulatory basis, preventive and primary care services. (Effective May 1, 2010)
18	Place of Employment-Worksite	A location, not described by any other POS code, owned or operated by a public or private entity where the patient is employed, and where a health professional provides on-going or episodic occupational medical, therapeutic or rehabilitative services to the individual. (This code is available for use effective January 1, 2013 but no later than May 1, 2013)
19	Unassigned	N/A
20	Urgent Care Facility	Location, distinct from a hospital emergency room, an office, or a clinic, whose purpose is to diagnose and treat illness or injury for unscheduled, ambulatory patients seeking immediate medical attention. (Effective January 1, 2003)
21	Inpatient Hospital	A facility, other than psychiatric, which primarily provides diagnostic, therapeutic (both surgical and nonsurgical), and rehabilitation services by, or under, the supervision of physicians to patients admitted for a variety of medical conditions.
22	Outpatient Hospital	A portion of a hospital which provides diagnostic, therapeutic (both surgical and nonsurgical), and rehabilitation services to sick or injured persons who do not require hospitalization or institutionalization.
23	Emergency Room – Hospital	A portion of a hospital where emergency diagnosis and treatment of illness or injury is provided.
24	Ambulatory Surgical Center	A freestanding facility, other than a physician's office, where surgical and diagnostic services are provided on an ambulatory basis.
25	Birthing Center	A facility, other than a hospital's maternity facilities or a physician's office, which provides a setting for labor, delivery, and immediate post-partum care as well as immediate care of new born infants.
26	Military Treatment Facility	A medical facility operated by one or more of the Uniformed Services. Military Treatment Facility (MTF) also refers to certain former U.S. Public Health Service (USPHS) facilities now designated as Uniformed Service Treatment Facilities (USTF).
27-30	Unassigned	N/A

Code	Place of Service	Place of Service Description
31	Skilled Nursing Facility	A facility which primarily provides inpatient skilled nursing care and related services to patients who require medical, nursing, or rehabilitative services but does not provide the level of care or treatment available in a hospital.
32	Nursing Facility	A facility which primarily provides to residents skilled nursing care and related services for the rehabilitation of injured, disabled, or sick persons, or, on a regular basis, health-related care services above the level of custodial care to other than mentally retarded individuals.
33	Custodial Care Facility	A facility which provides room, board and other personal assistance services, generally on a long-term basis, and which does not include a medical component.
34	Hospice	A facility, other than a patient's home, in which palliative and supportive care for terminally ill patients and their families are provided.
35-40	Unassigned	N/A
41	Ambulance - Land	A land vehicle specifically designed, equipped and staffed for lifesaving and transporting the sick or injured.
42	Ambulance – Air or Water	An air or water vehicle specifically designed, equipped and staffed for lifesaving and transporting the sick or injured.
43-48	Unassigned	N/A
49	Independent Clinic	A location, not part of a hospital and not described by any other Place of Service code, that is organized and operated to provide preventive, diagnostic, therapeutic, rehabilitative, or palliative services to outpatients only. (Effective October 1, 2003)
50	Federally Qualified Health Center	A facility located in a medically underserved area that provides Medicare beneficiaries preventive primary medical care under the general direction of a physician.
51	Inpatient Psychiatric Facility	A facility that provides inpatient psychiatric services for the diagnosis and treatment of mental illness on a 24-hour basis, by or under the supervision of a physician.
52	Psychiatric Facility-Partial Hospitalization	A facility for the diagnosis and treatment of mental illness that provides a planned therapeutic program for patients who do not require full time hospitalization, but who need broader programs than are possible from outpatient visits to a hospital-based or hospital-affiliated facility.
53	Community Mental Health Center	A facility that provides the following services: outpatient services, including specialized outpatient services for children, the elderly, individuals who are chronically ill, and residents of the CMHC's mental health services area who have been discharged from inpatient treatment at a mental health facility; 24 hour a day emergency care services; day treatment, other partial hospitalization services, or psychosocial rehabilitation services; screening for patients being considered for admission to State mental health facilities to determine the appropriateness of such admission; and consultation and education services.
54	Intermediate Care Facility/ Mentally Retarded	A facility which primarily provides health-related care and services above the level of custodial care to mentally retarded individuals but does not provide the level of care or treatment available in a hospital or SNF.
55	Residential Substance Abuse Treatment Facility	A facility which provides treatment for substance (alcohol and drug) abuse to live-in residents who do not require acute medical care. Services include individual and group therapy and counseling, family counseling, laboratory tests, drugs and supplies, psychological testing, and room and board.
56	Psychiatric Residential Treatment Center	A facility or distinct part of a facility for psychiatric care which provides a total 24-hour therapeutically planned and professionally staffed group living and learning environment.
57	Non-residential Substance Abuse Treatment Facility	A location which provides treatment for substance (alcohol and drug) abuse on an ambulatory basis. Services include individual and group therapy and counseling, family counseling, laboratory tests, drugs and supplies, and psychological testing. (Effective October 1, 2003)
58-59	Unassigned	N/A
60	Mass Immunization Center	A location where providers administer pneumococcal pneumonia and influenza virus vaccinations and submit these services as electronic media claims, paper claims, or using the roster billing method. This generally takes place in a mass immunization setting, such as, a public health center, pharmacy, or mall but may include a physician office setting.
61	Comprehensive Inpatient Rehabilitation Facility	A facility that provides comprehensive rehabilitation services under the supervision of a physician to inpatients with physical disabilities. Services include physical therapy, occupational therapy, speech pathology, social or psychological services, and orthotics and prosthetics services.
62	Comprehensive Outpatient Rehabilitation Facility	A facility that provides comprehensive rehabilitation services under the supervision of a physician to outpatients with physical disabilities. Services include physical therapy, occupational therapy, and speech pathology services.
63-64	Unassigned	N/A
65	End-Stage Renal Disease Treatment Facility	A facility other than a hospital, which provides dialysis treatment, maintenance, and/or training to patients or caregivers on an ambulatory or home-care basis.
66-70	Unassigned	N/A
71	Public Health Clinic	A facility maintained by either State or local health departments that provides ambulatory primary medical care under the general direction of a physician.
72	Rural Health Clinic	A certified facility which is located in a rural medically underserved area that provides ambulatory primary medical care under the general direction of a physician.
73-80	Unassigned	N/A
81	Independent Laboratory	A laboratory certified to perform diagnostic and/or clinical tests independent of an institution or a physician's office.
82-98	Unassigned	N/A
99	Other Place of Service	Other place of service not identified above.

Appendix E: Type of Service

Code	Type of Service
1	Medical care
2	Surgery
3	Consultation
4	Diagnostic radiology
5	Diagnostic laboratory
6	Therapeutic radiology
7	Anesthesia
8	Assistant at surgery
9	Other medical items or services
0	Whole blood only eff 01/96, whole blood or packed red cells before 01/96
A	Used durable medical equipment (DME)
B	High risk screening mammography (obsolete 1/1/98)
C	Low risk screening mammography (obsolete 1/1/98)
D	Ambulance (eff 04/95)
E	Enteral/parenteral nutrients/supplies (eff 04/95)
F	Ambulatory surgical center (facility usage for surgical services)
G	Immunosuppressive drugs
H	Hospice services (discontinued 01/95)
I	Purchase of DME (installment basis) (discontinued 04/95)
J	Diabetic shoes (eff 04/95)
K	Hearing items and services (eff 04/95)
L	ESRD supplies (eff 04/95) (renal supplier in the home before 04/95)
M	Monthly capitation payment for dialysis
N	Kidney donor
P	Lump sum purchase of DME, prosthetics orthotics
Q	Vision items or services
R	Rental of DME
S	Surgical dressings or other medical supplies (eff 04/95)
T	Psychological therapy (term. 12/31/97) outpatient mental health limitation (eff. 1/1/98)
U	Occupational therapy
V	Pneumococcal/flu vaccine (eff 01/96), Pneumococcal/flu/hepatitis B vaccine (eff 04/95-12/95), Pneumococcal only before 04/95
W	Physical therapy
Y	Second opinion on elective surgery (obsoleted 1/97)
Z	Third opinion on elective surgery (obsoleted 1/97)

Appendix F: Medically Unlikely Edits (MUEs) Including Hospital Outpatient Services

Practitioner Services

Code	MUE Values	Code	MUE Values	Code	MUE Values	Code	MUE Values	Code	MUE Values
A0382	0	A4638	0	A7020	0	A9541	1	B4189	0
A0384	0	A4640	0	A7025	0	A9542	1	B4199	0
A0392	0	A4642	1	A7026	0	A9543	1	B5200	0
A0394	0	A4648	5	A7027	0	A9544	1	C1722	1
A0396	0	A4650	3	A7028	0	A9545	1	C1749	1
A0398	0	A5056	90	A7029	0	A9546	1	C1767	2
A0420	0	A5057	90	A7032	0	A9547	2	C1772	1
A0422	0	A5120	150	A7035	0	A9550	1	C1785	1
A0424	0	A5500	0	A7036	0	A9551	1	C1813	1
A0426	2	A5501	0	A7037	0	A9552	1	C1820	2
A0427	2	A5503	0	A7039	0	A9553	1	C1830	2
A0428	4	A5504	0	A7040	2	A9554	1	C1840	1
A0429	2	A5505	0	A7041	2	A9555	3	C1841	1
A0430	1	A5506	0	A7042	2	A9556	10	C1886	1
A0431	1	A5507	0	A7043	10	A9557	2	C2616	1
A0432	1	A5508	0	A7044	0	A9559	1	C5271	1
A0433	1	A5510	0	A7047	0	A9560	2	C5272	3
A0434	2	A5512	0	A7501	0	A9561	1	C5273	1
A0435	999	A5513	0	A7504	0	A9562	2	C5274	35
A0436	300	A6501	2	A7507	0	A9566	1	C5275	1
A4221	1	A6502	2	A7520	0	A9567	2	C5276	3
A4235	2	A6503	2	A7524	0	A9569	1	C5277	1
A4253	0	A6504	4	A7527	0	A9570	1	C5278	15
A4255	0	A6505	4	A9272	0	A9571	1	C9254	0
A4257	0	A6506	4	A9284	0	A9579	100	C9275	1
A4258	0	A6507	4	A9500	3	A9580	1	C9285	2
A4259	0	A6508	4	A9501	3	A9582	1	C9290	266
A4301	1	A6509	2	A9502	3	A9583	18	C9293	700
A4356	1	A6510	2	A9503	1	A9584	1	C9352	3
A4470	1	A6511	2	A9504	1	A9585	300	C9353	4
A4480	1	A6513	0	A9507	1	A9586	1	C9354	300
A4555	0	A6531	0	A9508	2	A9599	1	C9355	3
A4557	2	A6532	0	A9510	1	A9600	7	C9356	125
A4561	1	A6545	0	A9512	30	A9604	1	C9358	800
A4562	1	A7000	0	A9520	1	A9700	2	C9359	30
A4565	2	A7003	0	A9521	2	B4083	0	C9360	300
A4606	1	A7005	0	A9526	2	B4149	0	C9361	10
A4611	0	A7006	0	A9536	1	B4153	0	C9362	60
A4614	1	A7013	0	A9537	1	B4157	0	C9363	500
A4625	30	A7014	0	A9538	1	B4160	0	C9364	600
A4633	0	A7016	0	A9539	2	B4164	0	C9600	3
A4635	0	A7017	0	A9540	2	B4176	0	C9601	2

Code	MUE Values	Code	MUE Values	Code	MUE Values	Code	MUE Values	Code	MUE Values
C9602	3	E0172	0	E0261	0	E0442	0	E0616	1
C9603	2	E0175	0	E0265	0	E0443	0	E0617	0
C9604	3	E0181	0	E0266	0	E0444	0	E0618	0
C9605	3	E0182	0	E0270	0	E0445	0	E0619	0
C9606	2	E0184	0	E0271	0	E0446	0	E0620	0
C9607	1	E0185	0	E0272	0	E0450	0	E0621	0
C9608	2	E0186	0	E0273	0	E0455	0	E0625	0
C9733	1	E0187	0	E0274	0	E0457	0	E0627	0
C9734	1	E0188	0	E0275	0	E0459	0	E0628	0
C9735	1	E0189	0	E0276	0	E0460	0	E0629	0
C9737	1	E0190	0	E0277	0	E0461	0	E0630	0
C9739	1	E0191	0	E0280	0	E0462	0	E0635	0
C9740	1	E0193	0	E0290	0	E0463	0	E0636	0
E0100	0	E0194	0	E0291	0	E0464	0	E0637	0
E0105	0	E0196	0	E0292	0	E0470	0	E0638	0
E0110	0	E0197	0	E0293	0	E0471	0	E0639	0
E0111	0	E0198	0	E0294	0	E0472	0	E0640	0
E0112	0	E0199	0	E0295	0	E0480	0	E0641	0
E0113	0	E0200	0	E0296	0	E0481	0	E0642	0
E0114	0	E0202	0	E0297	0	E0482	0	E0650	0
E0116	0	E0203	0	E0300	0	E0483	0	E0651	0
E0117	0	E0205	0	E0301	0	E0484	0	E0652	0
E0118	0	E0210	0	E0302	0	E0485	0	E0655	0
E0130	0	E0215	0	E0303	0	E0486	0	E0656	0
E0135	0	E0217	0	E0304	0	E0487	0	E0657	0
E0140	0	E0218	0	E0305	0	E0500	0	E0660	0
E0141	0	E0221	0	E0310	0	E0550	0	E0665	0
E0143	0	E0225	0	E0315	0	E0555	0	E0666	0
E0144	0	E0231	0	E0316	0	E0560	0	E0667	0
E0147	0	E0232	0	E0325	0	E0561	0	E0668	0
E0148	0	E0235	0	E0326	0	E0562	0	E0669	MUE Values
E0149	0	E0236	0	E0328	0	E0565	0	E0670	0
E0153	0	E0239	0	E0329	0	E0570	0	E0671	0
E0154	0	E0240	0	E0350	0	E0572	0	E0672	0
E0155	0	E0241	0	E0352	0	E0574	0	E0673	0
E0156	0	E0242	0	E0370	0	E0575	0	E0675	0
E0157	0	E0243	0	E0371	0	E0580	0	E0676	1
E0158	0	E0244	0	E0372	0	E0585	0	E0691	0
E0159	2	E0245	0	E0373	0	E0600	0	E0692	0
E0160	0	E0246	0	E0424	0	E0601	0	E0693	0
E0161	0	E0247	0	E0425	0	E0602	0	E0694	0
E0162	0	E0248	0	E0430	0	E0603	0	E0700	0
E0163	0	E0249	0	E0431	0	E0604	0	E0705	0
E0165	0	E0250	0	E0434	0	E0605	0	E0710	0
E0167	0	E0251	0	E0435	0	E0606	0	E0720	0
E0168	0	E0255	0	E0439	0	E0607	0	E0730	0
E0170	0	E0256	0	E0440	0	E0610	0	E0731	0
E0171	0	E0260	0	E0441	0	E0615	0	E0740	0

Code	MUE Values	Code	MUE Values	Code	MUE Values	Code	MUE Values	Code	MUE Values
E0744	0	E0946	0	E1028	0	E1234	0	E1634	0
E0745	0	E0947	0	E1029	0	E1235	0	E1635	0
E0746	1	E0948	0	E1030	0	E1236	0	E1636	0
E0747	0	E0950	0	E1031	0	E1237	0	E1637	0
E0748	0	E0951	0	E1035	0	E1238	0	E1639	0
E0749	1	E0952	0	E1037	0	E1240	0	E1700	0
E0755	0	E0955	0	E1038	0	E1250	0	E1701	0
E0760	0	E0956	0	E1039	0	E1260	0	E1702	0
E0761	0	E0957	0	E1050	0	E1270	0	E1800	0
E0762	0	E0958	0	E1060	0	E1280	0	E1801	0
E0764	0	E0959	0	E1070	0	E1285	0	E1802	0
E0765	0	E0960	0	E1083	0	E1290	0	E1805	0
E0766	0	E0961	0	E1084	0	E1295	0	E1806	0
E0769	0	E0966	0	E1085	0	E1300	0	E1810	0
E0770	1	E0967	0	E1086	0	E1310	0	E1811	0
E0776	0	E0968	0	E1087	0	E1352	0	E1812	0
E0779	0	E0970	0	E1088	0	E1353	0	E1815	0
E0780	0	E0971	0	E1089	0	E1354	0	E1816	0
E0781	1	E0973	0	E1090	0	E1355	0	E1818	0
E0782	1	E0974	0	E1092	0	E1356	0	E1820	0
E0783	1	E0978	0	E1093	0	E1357	0	E1821	0
E0784	0	E0981	0	E1100	0	E1358	0	E1825	0
E0785	1	E0982	0	E1110	0	E1372	0	E1830	0
E0786	1	E0983	0	E1130	0	E1390	0	E1831	0
E0791	0	E0984	0	E1140	0	E1391	0	E1840	0
E0830	0	E0985	0	E1150	0	E1392	0	E1841	0
E0840	0	E0986	0	E1160	0	E1405	0	E1902	0
E0849	0	E0988	0	E1161	0	E1406	0	E2000	0
E0850	0	E0990	0	E1170	0	E1500	0	E2100	0
E0855	0	E0992	0	E1171	0	E1510	0	E2101	0
E0856	0	E0994	0	E1172	0	E1520	0	E2120	0
E0860	0	E0995	0	E1180	0	E1530	0	E2201	0
E0870	0	E1002	0	E1190	0	E1540	0	E2202	0
E0880	0	E1003	0	E1195	0	E1550	0	E2203	0
E0890	0	E1004	0	E1200	0	E1560	0	E2204	0
E0900	0	E1005	0	E1220	0	E1570	0	E2205	0
E0910	0	E1006	0	E1221	0	E1575	0	E2206	0
E0911	0	E1007	0	E1222	0	E1580	0	E2207	0
E0912	0	E1008	0	E1223	0	E1590	0	E2208	0
E0920	0	E1009	0	E1224	0	E1592	0	E2209	0
E0930	0	E1010	0	E1225	0	E1594	0	E2210	0
E0935	0	E1011	0	E1226	0	E1600	0	E2211	0
E0936	0	E1014	0	E1228	0	E1610	0	E2212	0
E0940	0	E1015	0	E1229	0	E1615	0	E2213	0
E0941	0	E1016	0	E1230	0	E1620	0	E2214	0
E0942	0	E1017	0	E1231	0	E1625	0	E2215	0
E0944	0	E1018	0	E1232	0	E1630	0	E2216	0
E0945	0	E1020	0	E1233	0	E1632	0	E2217	0

Code	MUE Values	Code	MUE Values	Code	MUE Values	Code	MUE Values	Code	MUE Values
E2218	0	E2371	0	E2619	0	G0182	1	G0402	1
E2219	0	E2373	0	E2620	0	G0186	1	G0403	1
E2220	0	E2374	0	E2621	0	G0202	1	G0404	1
E2221	0	E2375	0	E2622	0	G0204	2	G0405	1
E2222	0	E2376	0	E2623	0	G0206	2	G0406	1
E2224	0	E2377	0	E2624	0	G0235	1	G0407	1
E2225	0	E2378	0	E2625	0	G0239	1	G0408	1
E2226	0	E2381	0	E2626	0	G0245	1	G0412	1
E2227	0	E2382	0	E2627	0	G0246	1	G0413	1
E2228	0	E2383	0	E2628	0	G0247	1	G0414	1
E2231	0	E2384	0	E2629	0	G0248	1	G0415	1
E2291	1	E2385	0	E2630	0	G0249	1	G0416	1
E2292	1	E2386	0	E2631	0	G0250	1	G0417	1
E2293	1	E2387	0	E2632	0	G0251	2	G0418	1
E2294	1	E2388	0	E2633	0	G0259	2	G0419	1
E2295	0	E2389	0	G0008	1	G0260	2	G0420	2
E2300	0	E2390	0	G0009	1	G0268	1	G0424	2
E2301	0	E2391	0	G0010	2	G0278	1	G0425	1
E2310	0	E2392	0	G0027	1	G0281	1	G0426	1
E2311	0	E2394	0	G0101	1	G0283	1	G0427	1
E2312	0	E2395	0	G0102	1	G0288	1	G0429	1
E2313	0	E2396	0	G0103	1	G0289	1	G0431	1
E2321	0	E2397	0	G0104	1	G0293	1	G0432	1
E2322	0	E2402	0	G0105	1	G0294	1	G0433	1
E2323	0	E2500	0	G0106	1	G0302	1	G0434	1
E2324	0	E2502	0	G0117	1	G0303	1	G0435	1
E2325	0	E2504	0	G0118	1	G0304	1	G0436	1
E2326	0	E2506	0	G0120	1	G0305	1	G0437	1
E2327	0	E2508	0	G0121	1	G0306	2	G0438	1
E2328	0	E2510	0	G0123	1	G0307	2	G0439	1
E2329	0	E2511	0	G0124	1	G0328	1	G0442	1
E2330	0	E2512	0	G0127	1	G0329	1	G0443	1
E2331	0	E2601	0	G0128	1	G0333	0	G0444	1
E2340	0	E2602	0	G0130	1	G0337	1	G0445	1
E2341	0	E2603	0	G0141	1	G0339	1	G0448	1
E2342	0	E2604	0	G0143	1	G0340	2	G0452	1
E2343	0	E2605	0	G0144	1	G0341	1	G0454	1
E2351	0	E2606	0	G0145	1	G0342	1	G0455	1
E2358	0	E2607	0	G0147	1	G0343	1	G0456	1
E2359	0	E2608	0	G0148	1	G0364	2	G0457	1
E2361	0	E2609	0	G0166	2	G0365	2	G0458	1
E2363	0	E2611	0	G0168	2	G0372	1	G0459	1
E2365	0	E2612	0	G0173	1	G0389	1	G0460	1
E2366	0	E2613	0	G0175	1	G0396	1	G0461	9
E2367	0	E2614	0	G0177	0	G0397	1	G0462	60
E2368	0	E2615	0	G0179	1	G0398	1	G0463	0
E2369	0	E2616	0	G0180	1	G0399	1	G3001	1
E2370	0	E2617	0	G0181	1	G0400	1	G9143	1

Code	MUE Values	Code	MUE Values	Code	MUE Values	Code	MUE Values	Code	MUE Values
G9156	1	J1557	300	J7667	0	K0065	0	K0835	0
G9157	1	J1561	300	J7670	0	K0069	0	K0836	0
G9187	1	J1568	300	J7676	0	K0070	0	K0837	0
J0130	6	J1569	300	J7680	0	K0071	0	K0838	0
J0131	400	J1572	300	J7681	0	K0072	0	K0839	0
J0133	1200	J1725	250	J7683	0	K0073	0	K0840	0
J0135	8	J1744	30	J7684	0	K0077	0	K0841	0
J0151	180	J2212	240	J7685	0	K0105	0	K0842	0
J0178	4	J2265	400	J8510	0	K0195	0	K0843	0
J0210	4	J2507	8	J9019	60	K0455	0	K0848	0
J0215	30	J2995	0	J9042	200	K0462	0	K0849	0
J0220	1	J3010	100	J9047	120	K0602	0	K0850	0
J0221	300	J3060	900	J9179	50	K0605	0	K0851	0
J0256	3500	J3285	1	J9228	450	K0606	0	K0852	0
J0257	1400	J3465	40	J9262	700	K0607	0	K0853	0
J0275	1	J3489	5	J9306	840	K0608	0	K0854	0
J0278	15	J7196	175	J9354	600	K0609	0	K0855	0
J0280	7	J7301	0	J9355	100	K0672	0	K0856	0
J0289	50	J7310	2	J9400	600	K0730	0	K0857	0
J0300	8	J7316	4	K0001	0	K0733	0	K0858	0
J0348	200	J7326	2	K0002	0	K0738	0	K0859	0
J0350	0	J7527	0	K0003	0	K0743	0	K0860	0
J0360	2	J7604	0	K0004	0	K0744	0	K0861	0
J0364	6	J7607	0	K0005	0	K0745	0	K0862	0
J0456	4	J7609	0	K0006	0	K0746	0	K0863	0
J0475	8	J7610	0	K0007	0	K0800	0	K0864	0
J0485	1500	J7615	0	K0009	0	K0801	0	K0868	0
J0490	160	J7622	0	K0015	0	K0802	0	K0869	0
J0597	250	J7624	0	K0017	0	K0806	0	K0870	0
J0638	150	J7627	0	K0018	0	K0807	0	K0871	0
J0697	4	J7628	0	K0019	0	K0808	0	K0877	0
J0712	120	J7629	0	K0020	0	K0812	0	K0878	0
J0717	400	J7632	0	K0037	0	K0813	0	K0879	0
J0745	2	J7634	0	K0038	0	K0814	0	K0880	0
J0760	4	J7635	0	K0039	0	K0815	0	K0884	0
J0770	5	J7636	0	K0040	0	K0816	0	K0885	0
J0780	4	J7637	0	K0041	0	K0820	0	K0886	0
J0800	3	J7638	0	K0042	0	K0821	0	K0890	0
J0833	3	J7640	0	K0043	0	K0822	0	K0891	0
J0890	0	J7641	0	K0044	0	K0823	0	K0898	1
J0897	120	J7642	0	K0045	0	K0824	0	K0900	0
J0900	1	J7643	0	K0046	0	K0825	0	L0112	0
J0945	4	J7645	0	K0047	0	K0826	0	L0113	0
J1050	1000	J7647	0	K0050	0	K0827	0	L0120	0
J1162	1	J7650	0	K0051	0	K0828	0	L0130	0
J1442	3360	J7657	0	K0052	0	K0829	0	L0140	0
J1446	192	J7660	0	K0053	0	K0830	0	L0150	0
J1556	300	J7665	127	K0056	0	K0831	0	L0160	0

Code	MUE Values	Code	MUE Values	Code	MUE Values	Code	MUE Values	Code	MUE Values
L0170	0	L0638	0	L1260	0	L1920	0	L2230	0
L0172	0	L0639	0	L1270	0	L1930	0	L2232	0
L0174	0	L0640	0	L1280	0	L1932	0	L2240	0
L0180	0	L0641	0	L1290	0	L1940	0	L2250	0
L0190	0	L0642	0	L1300	0	L1945	0	L2260	0
L0200	0	L0643	0	L1310	0	L1950	0	L2265	0
L0220	0	L0648	0	L1499	1	L1951	0	L2270	0
L0450	0	L0649	0	L1600	0	L1960	0	L2275	0
L0452	0	L0650	0	L1610	0	L1970	0	L2280	0
L0454	0	L0651	0	L1620	0	L1971	0	L2300	0
L0455	0	L0700	0	L1630	0	L1980	0	L2310	0
L0456	0	L0710	0	L1640	0	L1990	0	L2320	0
L0457	0	L0810	0	L1650	0	L2000	0	L2330	0
L0458	0	L0820	0	L1652	0	L2005	0	L2335	0
L0460	0	L0830	0	L1660	0	L2010	0	L2340	0
L0462	0	L0859	0	L1680	0	L2020	0	L2350	0
L0464	0	L0861	0	L1685	0	L2030	0	L2360	0
L0466	0	L0970	0	L1686	0	L2034	0	L2370	0
L0467	0	L0972	0	L1690	0	L2035	0	L2375	0
L0468	0	L0974	0	L1700	0	L2036	0	L2380	0
L0469	0	L0976	0	L1710	0	L2037	0	L2385	0
L0470	0	L0978	0	L1720	0	L2038	0	L2387	0
L0472	0	L0980	0	L1730	0	L2040	0	L2390	0
L0480	0	L0982	0	L1755	0	L2050	0	L2395	0
L0482	0	L0984	0	L1810	0	L2060	0	L2397	0
L0484	0	L1000	0	L1812	0	L2070	0	L2405	0
L0486	0	L1001	0	L1820	0	L2080	0	L2415	0
L0488	0	L1005	0	L1830	0	L2090	0	L2425	0
L0490	0	L1010	0	L1831	0	L2106	0	L2430	0
L0491	0	L1020	0	L1832	0	L2108	0	L2492	0
L0492	0	L1025	0	L1833	0	L2112	0	L2500	0
L0621	0	L1030	0	L1834	0	L2114	0	L2510	0
L0622	0	L1040	0	L1836	0	L2116	0	L2520	0
L0623	0	L1050	0	L1840	0	L2126	0	L2525	0
L0624	0	L1060	0	L1843	0	L2128	0	L2526	0
L0625	0	L1070	0	L1844	0	L2132	0	L2530	0
L0626	0	L1080	0	L1845	0	L2134	0	L2540	0
L0627	0	L1085	0	L1846	1	L2136	0	L2550	0
L0628	0	L1090	0	L1847	0	L2180	0	L2570	0
L0629	0	L1100	0	L1848	0	L2182	0	L2580	0
L0630	0	L1110	0	L1850	0	L2184	0	L2600	0
L0631	0	L1120	0	L1860	0	L2186	0	L2610	0
L0632	0	L1200	0	L1900	0	L2188	0	L2620	0
L0633	0	L1210	0	L1902	0	L2190	0	L2622	0
L0634	0	L1220	0	L1904	0	L2192	0	L2624	0
L0635	0	L1230	0	L1906	0	L2200	0	L2627	0
L0636	0	L1240	0	L1907	0	L2210	0	L2628	0
L0637	0	L1250	0	L1910	0	L2220	0	L2630	0

Code	MUE Values	Code	MUE Values	Code	MUE Values	Code	MUE Values	Code	MUE Values
L2640	0	L3300	0	L3710	0	L3980	0	L5280	0
L2650	0	L3310	0	L3720	0	L3982	0	L5301	0
L2660	0	L3330	0	L3730	0	L3984	0	L5312	0
L2670	0	L3332	0	L3740	0	L4000	0	L5321	0
L2680	0	L3334	0	L3760	0	L4002	0	L5331	0
L2750	0	L3340	0	L3762	0	L4010	0	L5341	0
L2755	0	L3350	0	L3763	0	L4020	0	L5400	0
L2760	0	L3360	0	L3764	0	L4030	0	L5410	0
L2768	0	L3370	0	L3765	0	L4040	0	L5420	0
L2780	0	L3380	0	L3766	0	L4045	0	L5430	0
L2785	0	L3390	0	L3806	0	L4050	0	L5450	0
L2795	0	L3400	0	L3807	0	L4055	0	L5460	0
L2800	0	L3410	0	L3808	0	L4060	0	L5500	0
L2810	0	L3420	0	L3809	0	L4070	0	L5505	0
L2820	0	L3430	0	L3900	0	L4080	0	L5510	0
L2830	0	L3440	0	L3901	0	L4090	0	L5520	0
L3000	0	L3450	0	L3904	0	L4100	0	L5530	0
L3001	0	L3455	0	L3905	0	L4110	0	L5535	0
L3002	0	L3460	0	L3906	0	L4130	0	L5540	0
L3003	0	L3465	0	L3908	0	L4205	0	L5560	0
L3010	0	L3470	0	L3912	0	L4210	0	L5570	0
L3020	0	L3480	0	L3913	0	L4350	0	L5580	0
L3030	0	L3485	0	L3915	0	L4360	0	L5585	0
L3031	0	L3500	0	L3916	0	L4361	0	L5590	0
L3040	0	L3510	0	L3917	0	L4370	0	L5595	0
L3050	0	L3520	0	L3918	0	L4386	0	L5600	0
L3060	0	L3530	0	L3919	0	L4387	0	L5610	0
L3070	0	L3540	0	L3921	0	L4392	0	L5611	0
L3080	0	L3550	0	L3923	0	L4394	0	L5613	0
L3090	0	L3560	0	L3924	0	L4396	0	L5614	0
L3100	0	L3570	0	L3925	0	L4397	0	L5616	0
L3140	0	L3580	0	L3927	0	L4398	0	L5617	0
L3150	0	L3590	0	L3929	0	L4631	0	L5618	0
L3160	0	L3595	0	L3930	0	L5000	0	L5620	0
L3170	0	L3600	0	L3931	0	L5010	0	L5622	0
L3215	0	L3610	0	L3933	0	L5020	0	L5624	0
L3216	0	L3620	0	L3935	0	L5050	0	L5626	0
L3217	0	L3630	0	L3956	0	L5060	0	L5628	0
L3219	0	L3640	0	L3960	0	L5100	0	L5629	0
L3221	0	L3650	0	L3961	0	L5105	0	L5630	0
L3222	0	L3660	0	L3962	0	L5150	0	L5631	0
L3224	0	L3670	0	L3967	0	L5160	0	L5632	0
L3225	0	L3671	0	L3971	0	L5200	0	L5634	0
L3230	0	L3674	0	L3973	0	L5210	0	L5636	0
L3250	0	L3675	0	L3975	0	L5220	0	L5637	0
L3251	0	L3677	0	L3976	0	L5230	0	L5638	0
L3252	0	L3678	0	L3977	0	L5250	0	L5639	0
L3253	0	L3702	0	L3978	0	L5270	0	L5640	0

Code	MUE Values	Code	MUE Values	Code	MUE Values	Code	MUE Values	Code	MUE Values
L5642	0	L5704	0	L5962	0	L6500	0	L6688	0
L5643	0	L5705	0	L5964	0	L6550	0	L6689	0
L5644	0	L5706	0	L5966	0	L6570	0	L6690	0
L5645	0	L5707	0	L5968	0	L6580	0	L6691	0
L5646	0	L5710	0	L5969	0	L6582	0	L6692	0
L5647	0	L5711	0	L5970	0	L6584	0	L6693	0
L5648	0	L5712	0	L5971	0	L6586	0	L6694	0
L5649	0	L5714	0	L5972	0	L6588	0	L6695	0
L5650	0	L5716	0	L5974	0	L6590	0	L6696	0
L5651	0	L5718	0	L5975	0	L6600	0	L6697	0
L5652	0	L5722	0	L5976	0	L6605	0	L6698	0
L5653	0	L5724	0	L5978	0	L6610	0	L6703	0
L5654	0	L5726	0	L5979	0	L6611	0	L6704	0
L5655	0	L5728	0	L5980	0	L6615	0	L6706	0
L5656	0	L5780	0	L5981	0	L6616	0	L6707	0
L5658	0	L5781	0	L5982	0	L6620	0	L6708	0
L5661	0	L5782	0	L5984	0	L6621	0	L6709	0
L5665	0	L5785	0	L5985	0	L6623	0	L6711	0
L5666	0	L5790	0	L5986	0	L6624	0	L6712	0
L5668	0	L5795	0	L5987	0	L6625	0	L6713	0
L5670	0	L5810	0	L5988	0	L6628	0	L6714	0
L5671	0	L5811	0	L5990	0	L6629	0	L6715	0
L5672	0	L5812	0	L6000	0	L6630	0	L6721	0
L5673	0	L5814	0	L6010	0	L6632	0	L6722	0
L5676	0	L5816	0	L6020	0	L6635	0	L6805	0
L5677	0	L5818	0	L6025	0	L6637	0	L6810	0
L5678	0	L5822	0	L6050	0	L6638	0	L6880	0
L5679	0	L5824	0	L6055	0	L6640	0	L6881	0
L5680	0	L5826	0	L6100	0	L6641	0	L6882	0
L5681	0	L5828	0	L6110	0	L6642	0	L6883	0
L5682	0	L5830	0	L6120	0	L6645	0	L6884	0
L5683	0	L5840	0	L6130	0	L6646	0	L6885	0
L5684	0	L5845	0	L6200	0	L6647	0	L6890	0
L5685	0	L5848	0	L6205	0	L6648	0	L6895	0
L5686	0	L5850	0	L6250	0	L6650	0	L6900	0
L5688	0	L5855	0	L6300	0	L6655	0	L6905	0
L5690	0	L5856	0	L6310	0	L6660	0	L6910	0
L5692	0	L5857	0	L6320	0	L6665	0	L6915	0
L5694	0	L5858	0	L6350	0	L6670	0	L6920	0
L5695	0	L5859	0	L6360	0	L6672	0	L6925	0
L5696	0	L5910	0	L6370	0	L6675	0	L6930	0
L5697	0	L5920	0	L6380	0	L6676	0	L6935	0
L5698	0	L5925	0	L6382	0	L6677	0	L6940	0
L5699	0	L5930	0	L6384	0	L6680	0	L6945	0
L5700	0	L5940	0	L6386	0	L6682	0	L6950	0
L5701	0	L5950	0	L6388	0	L6684	0	L6955	0
L5702	0	L5960	0	L6400	0	L6686	0	L6960	0
L5703	0	L5961	0	L6450	0	L6687	0	L6965	0

Code	MUE Values	Code	MUE Values	Code	MUE Values	Code	MUE Values	Code	MUE Values
L6970	0	L8048	1	L8642	2	Q0483	1	Q4025	1
L6975	0	L8049	0	L8658	4	Q0484	1	Q4026	1
L7007	0	L8300	0	L8659	4	Q0485	1	Q4027	1
L7008	0	L8310	0	L8670	4	Q0486	1	Q4028	1
L7009	0	L8320	0	L8679	3	Q0487	1	Q4074	3
L7040	0	L8330	0	L8681	1	Q0488	1	Q4101	88
L7045	0	L8400	0	L8682	2	Q0489	1	Q4102	21
L7170	0	L8410	0	L8683	1	Q0490	1	Q4103	0
L7180	0	L8415	0	L8684	1	Q0491	1	Q4104	50
L7181	0	L8417	0	L8685	1	Q0492	1	Q4105	250
L7185	0	L8420	0	L8686	2	Q0493	1	Q4106	76
L7186	0	L8430	0	L8687	1	Q0494	1	Q4107	50
L7190	0	L8435	0	L8688	1	Q0495	1	Q4108	250
L7191	0	L8440	0	L8689	1	Q0497	2	Q4110	250
L7260	0	L8460	0	L8690	2	Q0498	1	Q4111	56
L7261	0	L8465	0	L8691	1	Q0499	1	Q4112	2
L7360	0	L8470	0	L8692	0	Q0501	1	Q4113	4
L7362	0	L8480	0	L8693	1	Q0502	1	Q4114	6
L7364	0	L8485	0	L8695	1	Q0503	3	Q4115	240
L7366	0	L8500	0	M0064	1	Q0504	1	Q4116	192
L7367	0	L8501	0	P2028	1	Q0507	1	Q4117	0
L7368	0	L8507	0	P2029	1	Q0508	1	Q4118	1000
L7400	0	L8509	1	P2033	1	Q0509	1	Q4119	150
L7401	0	L8510	0	P2038	1	Q0510	0	Q4120	0
L7402	0	L8511	1	P3000	1	Q0511	0	Q4121	78
L7403	0	L8514	1	P3001	1	Q0512	0	Q4122	96
L7404	0	L8515	1	P9041	5	Q0513	0	Q4123	160
L7405	0	L8600	2	P9043	5	Q0514	0	Q4124	140
L7900	0	L8604	3	P9045	20	Q1004	2	Q4125	28
L7902	0	L8605	4	P9046	25	Q1005	2	Q4126	32
L8000	0	L8606	5	P9047	20	Q2004	1	Q4127	100
L8001	0	L8609	1	P9048	1	Q2028	1470	Q4128	128
L8002	0	L8610	2	P9612	1	Q2034	1	Q4129	81
L8015	0	L8612	2	P9615	1	Q2035	1	Q4130	100
L8020	0	L8613	2	Q0035	1	Q2036	1	Q4131	49
L8030	0	L8614	2	Q0091	1	Q2037	1	Q4132	50
L8031	0	L8615	2	Q0111	2	Q2038	1	Q4133	113
L8032	0	L8616	2	Q0112	3	Q2039	1	Q4134	160
L8035	0	L8617	2	Q0113	2	Q2043	1	Q4135	900
L8039	0	L8618	2	Q0114	1	Q2050	14	Q4136	900
L8040	0	L8619	2	Q0115	1	Q2052	1	Q9955	10
L8041	0	L8621	600	Q0144	0	Q3014	1	R0070	2
L8042	0	L8622	2	Q0161	0	Q3027	30	R0075	2
L8043	0	L8627	2	Q0478	1	Q3028	0	V2020	0
L8044	0	L8628	2	Q0479	1	Q4001	1	V2100	0
L8045	0	L8629	2	Q0480	1	Q4002	1	V2101	0
L8046	0	L8631	4	Q0481	1	Q4003	2	V2102	0
L8047	0	L8641	4	Q0482	1	Q4004	2	V2103	0

Code	MUE Values	Code	MUE Values	Code	MUE Values	Code	MUE Values	Code	MUE Values
V2104	0	V2209	0	V2312	0	V2530	0	V2755	0
V2105	0	V2210	0	V2313	0	V2531	0	V2761	0
V2106	0	V2211	0	V2314	0	V2599	2	V2770	0
V2107	0	V2212	0	V2315	0	V2600	0	V2780	0
V2108	0	V2213	0	V2318	0	V2610	0	V2781	0
V2109	0	V2214	0	V2319	0	V2615	0	V2782	0
V2110	0	V2215	0	V2320	0	V2623	0	V2783	0
V2111	0	V2218	0	V2321	0	V2624	0	V2784	0
V2112	0	V2219	0	V2399	0	V2625	0	V2785	2
V2113	0	V2220	0	V2410	0	V2626	0	V2790	1
V2114	0	V2221	0	V2430	0	V2627	0	V2797	0
V2115	0	V2299	0	V2499	2	V2628	0	V5008	0
V2118	0	V2300	0	V2500	0	V2629	0	V5010	0
V2121	0	V2301	0	V2501	0	V2630	2	V5011	0
V2199	2	V2302	0	V2502	0	V2631	2	V5274	0
V2200	0	V2303	0	V2503	0	V2632	2	V5281	0
V2201	0	V2304	0	V2510	0	V2700	0	V5282	0
V2202	0	V2305	0	V2511	0	V2710	0	V5284	0
V2203	0	V2306	0	V2512	0	V2715	0	V5285	0
V2204	0	V2307	0	V2513	0	V2718	0	V5286	0
V2205	0	V2308	0	V2520	2	V2730	0	V5287	0
V2206	0	V2309	0	V2521	2	V2744	0	V5288	0
V2207	0	V2310	0	V2522	2	V2745	0	V5289	0
V2208	0	V2311	0	V2523	2	V2750	0		

Outpatient Hospital Services

Code	MUE Values	Code	MUE Values	Code	MUE Values	Code	MUE Values	Code	MUE Values
A0382	0	A4595	0	A6508	4	A7047	0	A9560	2
A0384	0	A4604	0	A6509	2	A7502	3	A9561	1
A0392	0	A4605	0	A6510	2	A7503	3	A9562	2
A0394	0	A4606	1	A6511	2	A7504	180	A9566	1
A0396	0	A4611	0	A6513	2	A7506	90	A9567	2
A0398	0	A4612	0	A6545	2	A7507	200	A9569	1
A0420	0	A4613	0	A6550	0	A7508	200	A9570	1
A0422	0	A4614	0	A7000	0	A7509	300	A9571	1
A0424	0	A4618	0	A7001	0	A7522	1	A9579	100
A0426	2	A4623	90	A7002	0	A7524	2	A9580	1
A0427	2	A4624	0	A7003	0	A7526	36	A9582	1
A0428	4	A4625	30	A7004	0	A9272	0	A9583	18
A0429	2	A4628	0	A7005	0	A9284	1	A9584	1
A0430	1	A4633	0	A7006	0	A9500	3	A9585	300
A0431	1	A4635	0	A7007	0	A9501	3	A9586	1
A0432	1	A4636	0	A7010	0	A9502	3	A9599	1
A0433	1	A4637	0	A7012	0	A9503	1	A9600	7
A0434	2	A4638	0	A7013	0	A9504	1	A9604	1
A0435	999	A4640	0	A7014	0	A9507	1	A9700	2
A0436	300	A4642	1	A7015	0	A9508	2	B4034	0
A4221	0	A4648	3	A7016	0	A9510	1	B4035	0
A4222	0	A4650	3	A7017	0	A9512	30	B4036	0
A4233	0	A4670	0	A7018	0	A9520	1	B4081	0
A4234	0	A4932	0	A7020	0	A9521	2	B4082	0
A4235	0	A5056	90	A7025	0	A9526	2	B4083	0
A4236	0	A5057	90	A7026	0	A9536	1	B4087	1
A4253	0	A5102	1	A7027	0	A9537	1	B4149	0
A4255	0	A5120	150	A7028	0	A9538	1	B4150	0
A4256	0	A5500	0	A7029	0	A9539	2	B4152	0
A4257	0	A5501	0	A7030	0	A9540	2	B4153	0
A4258	0	A5503	0	A7031	0	A9541	1	B4154	0
A4259	0	A5504	0	A7032	0	A9542	1	B4155	0
A4262	4	A5505	0	A7033	0	A9543	1	B4157	0
A4263	4	A5506	0	A7034	0	A9544	1	B4158	0
A4301	1	A5507	0	A7035	0	A9545	1	B4159	0
A4356	1	A5508	0	A7036	0	A9546	1	B4160	0
A4396	3	A5510	0	A7037	0	A9547	2	B4161	0
A4399	2	A5512	0	A7038	0	A9550	1	B4162	0
A4463	3	A5513	0	A7039	0	A9551	1	B4164	0
A4470	1	A6501	2	A7040	2	A9552	1	B4168	0
A4480	1	A6502	2	A7041	2	A9553	1	B4172	0
A4555	0	A6503	2	A7042	2	A9554	1	B4176	0
A4557	0	A6504	4	A7043	10	A9555	3	B4178	0
A4561	1	A6505	4	A7044	0	A9556	10	B4180	0
A4562	1	A6506	4	A7045	0	A9557	2	B4189	0
A4565	2	A6507	4	A7046	0	A9559	1	B4193	0

Code	MUE Values	Code	MUE Values	Code	MUE Values	Code	MUE Values	Code	MUE Values
B4197	0	C1815	1	C8909	1	C9605	3	E0167	0
B4199	0	C1816	2	C8910	1	C9606	2	E0168	0
B4216	0	C1817	1	C8911	1	C9607	1	E0170	0
B4220	0	C1818	2	C8912	1	C9608	2	E0171	0
B4222	0	C1820	2	C8913	1	C9724	1	E0172	0
B4224	0	C1830	2	C8914	1	C9725	1	E0175	0
B5000	0	C1840	1	C8918	1	C9726	2	E0181	0
B5100	0	C1841	1	C8919	1	C9727	1	E0182	0
B5200	0	C1878	2	C8920	1	C9728	1	E0184	0
B9000	0	C1880	2	C8921	1	C9733	1	E0185	0
B9002	0	C1881	2	C8922	1	C9734	1	E0186	0
B9004	0	C1882	1	C8923	1	C9735	1	E0187	0
B9006	0	C1886	1	C8924	1	C9737	1	E0188	0
C1721	1	C1888	2	C8925	1	C9739	1	E0189	0
C1722	1	C1891	1	C8926	1	C9740	1	E0190	0
C1731	2	C1895	2	C8927	1	C9800	1	E0191	0
C1732	3	C1896	2	C8928	1	C9898	1	E0193	0
C1733	3	C1897	2	C8929	1	E0100	0	E0194	0
C1749	1	C1898	2	C8930	1	E0105	0	E0196	0
C1750	2	C1899	2	C8931	1	E0110	0	E0197	0
C1751	3	C1900	1	C8932	1	E0111	0	E0198	0
C1752	2	C2614	3	C8933	1	E0112	0	E0199	0
C1753	2	C2615	2	C8934	2	E0113	0	E0200	0
C1754	2	C2616	1	C8935	2	E0114	0	E0202	0
C1755	2	C2619	1	C8936	2	E0116	0	E0203	0
C1756	2	C2620	1	C8957	2	E0117	0	E0205	0
C1758	2	C2621	1	C9254	400	E0118	0	E0210	0
C1759	2	C2622	1	C9275	1	E0130	0	E0215	0
C1764	1	C2626	1	C9285	2	E0135	0	E0217	0
C1767	2	C2627	2	C9290	266	E0140	0	E0218	0
C1768	3	C2631	1	C9293	700	E0141	0	E0221	0
C1770	3	C5271	1	C9352	3	E0143	0	E0225	0
C1771	1	C5272	3	C9353	4	E0144	0	E0231	0
C1772	1	C5273	1	C9354	300	E0147	0	E0232	0
C1773	3	C5274	35	C9355	3	E0148	0	E0235	0
C1777	2	C5275	1	C9356	125	E0149	0	E0236	0
C1779	2	C5276	3	C9358	800	E0153	0	E0239	0
C1780	2	C5277	1	C9359	30	E0154	0	E0240	0
C1782	1	C5278	15	C9360	300	E0155	0	E0241	0
C1783	2	C8900	1	C9361	10	E0156	0	E0242	0
C1784	2	C8901	1	C9362	60	E0157	0	E0243	0
C1785	1	C8902	1	C9363	500	E0158	0	E0244	0
C1786	1	C8903	1	C9364	600	E0159	0	E0245	0
C1787	2	C8904	1	C9600	3	E0160	0	E0246	0
C1788	2	C8905	1	C9601	2	E0161	0	E0247	0
C1789	2	C8906	1	C9602	3	E0162	0	E0248	0
C1813	1	C8907	1	C9603	2	E0163	0	E0249	0
C1814	2	C8908	1	C9604	3	E0165	0	E0250	0

Code	MUE Values	Code	MUE Values	Code	MUE Values	Code	MUE Values	Code	MUE Values
E0251	0	E0434	0	E0605	0	E0710	0	E0940	0
E0255	0	E0435	0	E0606	0	E0720	0	E0941	0
E0256	0	E0439	0	E0607	0	E0730	0	E0942	0
E0260	0	E0440	0	E0610	0	E0731	0	E0944	0
E0261	0	E0441	0	E0615	0	E0740	0	E0945	0
E0265	0	E0442	0	E0616	1	E0744	0	E0946	0
E0266	0	E0443	0	E0617	0	E0745	0	E0947	0
E0270	0	E0444	0	E0618	0	E0746	1	E0948	0
E0271	0	E0445	0	E0619	0	E0747	0	E0950	0
E0272	0	E0446	0	E0620	0	E0748	0	E0951	0
E0273	0	E0450	0	E0621	0	E0749	1	E0952	0
E0274	0	E0455	0	E0625	0	E0755	0	E0955	0
E0275	0	E0457	0	E0627	0	E0760	0	E0956	0
E0276	0	E0459	0	E0628	0	E0761	0	E0957	0
E0277	0	E0460	0	E0629	0	E0762	1	E0958	0
E0280	0	E0461	0	E0630	0	E0764	0	E0959	2
E0290	0	E0462	0	E0635	0	E0765	0	E0960	0
E0291	0	E0463	0	E0636	0	E0766	0	E0961	2
E0292	0	E0464	0	E0637	0	E0769	0	E0966	1
E0293	0	E0470	0	E0638	0	E0770	1	E0967	0
E0294	0	E0471	0	E0639	0	E0776	0	E0968	0
E0295	0	E0472	0	E0640	0	E0779	0	E0970	0
E0296	0	E0480	0	E0641	0	E0780	0	E0971	2
E0297	0	E0481	0	E0642	0	E0781	0	E0973	2
E0300	0	E0482	0	E0650	0	E0782	1	E0974	2
E0301	0	E0483	0	E0651	0	E0783	1	E0978	1
E0302	0	E0484	0	E0652	0	E0784	0	E0981	0
E0303	0	E0485	0	E0655	0	E0785	1	E0982	0
E0304	0	E0486	0	E0656	0	E0786	1	E0983	0
E0305	0	E0487	0	E0657	0	E0791	0	E0984	0
E0310	0	E0500	0	E0660	0	E0830	0	E0985	0
E0315	0	E0550	0	E0665	0	E0840	0	E0986	0
E0316	0	E0555	0	E0666	0	E0849	0	E0988	0
E0325	0	E0560	0	E0667	0	E0850	0	E0990	2
E0326	0	E0561	0	E0668	0	E0855	0	E0992	1
E0328	0	E0562	0	E0669	0	E0856	0	E0994	0
E0329	0	E0565	0	E0670	0	E0860	0	E0995	2
E0350	0	E0570	0	E0671	0	E0870	0	E1002	0
E0352	0	E0572	0	E0672	0	E0880	0	E1003	0
E0370	0	E0574	0	E0673	0	E0890	0	E1004	0
E0371	0	E0575	0	E0675	0	E0900	0	E1005	0
E0372	0	E0580	0	E0676	1	E0910	0	E1006	0
E0373	0	E0585	0	E0691	0	E0911	0	E1007	0
E0424	0	E0600	0	E0692	0	E0912	0	E1008	0
E0425	0	E0601	0	E0693	0	E0920	0	E1009	0
E0430	0	E0602	0	E0694	0	E0930	0	E1010	0
E0431	0	E0603	0	E0700	0	E0935	0	E1011	0
E0433	0	E0604	0	E0705	1	E0936	0	E1014	0

Code	MUE Values	Code	MUE Values	Code	MUE Values	Code	MUE Values	Code	MUE Values
E1015	0	E1228	0	E1600	0	E2211	0	E2363	0
E1016	0	E1229	0	E1610	0	E2212	0	E2365	0
E1017	0	E1230	0	E1615	0	E2213	0	E2366	0
E1018	0	E1231	0	E1620	0	E2214	0	E2367	0
E1020	0	E1232	0	E1625	0	E2215	0	E2368	0
E1028	0	E1233	0	E1630	0	E2216	0	E2369	0
E1029	0	E1234	0	E1632	0	E2217	0	E2370	0
E1030	0	E1235	0	E1634	0	E2218	0	E2371	0
E1031	0	E1236	0	E1635	0	E2219	0	E2373	0
E1035	0	E1237	0	E1636	0	E2220	0	E2374	0
E1036	0	E1238	0	E1637	0	E2221	0	E2375	0
E1037	0	E1239	0	E1639	0	E2222	0	E2376	0
E1038	0	E1240	0	E1700	0	E2224	0	E2377	0
E1039	0	E1250	0	E1701	0	E2225	0	E2378	0
E1050	0	E1260	0	E1702	0	E2226	0	E2381	0
E1060	0	E1270	0	E1800	0	E2227	0	E2382	0
E1070	0	E1280	0	E1801	0	E2228	0	E2383	0
E1083	0	E1285	0	E1802	0	E2231	0	E2384	0
E1084	0	E1290	0	E1805	0	E2291	1	E2385	0
E1085	0	E1295	0	E1806	0	E2292	1	E2386	0
E1086	0	E1300	0	E1810	0	E2293	1	E2387	0
E1087	0	E1310	0	E1811	0	E2294	1	E2388	0
E1088	0	E1352	0	E1812	0	E2295	0	E2389	0
E1089	0	E1353	0	E1815	0	E2300	0	E2390	0
E1090	0	E1354	0	E1816	0	E2301	0	E2391	0
E1092	0	E1355	0	E1818	0	E2310	0	E2392	0
E1093	0	E1356	0	E1820	0	E2311	0	E2394	0
E1100	0	E1357	0	E1821	0	E2312	0	E2395	0
E1110	0	E1358	0	E1825	0	E2313	0	E2396	0
E1130	0	E1372	0	E1830	0	E2321	0	E2397	0
E1140	0	E1390	0	E1831	0	E2322	0	E2402	0
E1150	0	E1391	0	E1840	0	E2323	0	E2500	0
E1160	0	E1392	0	E1841	0	E2324	0	E2502	0
E1161	0	E1405	0	E1902	0	E2325	0	E2504	0
E1170	0	E1406	0	E2000	0	E2326	0	E2506	0
E1171	0	E1500	0	E2100	0	E2327	0	E2508	0
E1172	0	E1510	0	E2101	0	E2328	0	E2510	0
E1180	0	E1520	0	E2120	0	E2329	0	E2511	0
E1190	0	E1530	0	E2201	0	E2330	0	E2512	0
E1195	0	E1540	0	E2202	0	E2331	0	E2601	0
E1200	0	E1550	0	E2203	0	E2340	0	E2602	0
E1220	0	E1560	0	E2204	0	E2341	0	E2603	0
E1221	0	E1570	0	E2205	0	E2342	0	E2604	0
E1222	0	E1575	0	E2206	0	E2343	0	E2605	0
E1223	0	E1580	0	E2207	0	E2351	0	E2606	0
E1224	0	E1590	0	E2208	0	E2358	0	E2607	0
E1225	0	E1592	0	E2209	0	E2359	0	E2608	0
E1226	1	E1594	0	E2210	0	E2361	0	E2609	0

Code	MUE Values	Code	MUE Values	Code	MUE Values	Code	MUE Values	Code	MUE Values
E2611	0	G0166	2	G0343	1	G0455	1	J0800	3
E2612	0	G0168	2	G0364	2	G0456	1	J0833	3
E2613	0	G0173	1	G0365	2	G0457	1	J0890	0
E2614	0	G0175	1	G0372	1	G0458	1	J0897	120
E2615	0	G0176	5	G0379	1	G0459	0	J0900	1
E2616	0	G0177	3	G0380	2	G0460	1	J0945	4
E2617	0	G0179	1	G0381	2	G0461	9	J1050	1000
E2619	0	G0180	1	G0382	2	G0462	60	J1162	10
E2620	0	G0181	1	G0383	2	G0463	6	J1442	3360
E2621	0	G0182	1	G0384	2	G3001	1	J1446	192
E2622	0	G0186	1	G0389	1	G9143	1	J1556	300
E2623	0	G0202	1	G0390	1	G9156	1	J1557	300
E2624	0	G0204	2	G0396	1	G9157	1	J1561	300
E2625	0	G0206	2	G0397	1	G9187	0	J1568	300
E2626	0	G0235	1	G0398	1	J0130	6	J1569	300
E2627	0	G0239	2	G0399	1	J0131	400	J1572	300
E2628	0	G0245	1	G0400	1	J0133	1200	J1725	250
E2629	0	G0246	1	G0402	1	J0135	8	J1744	90
E2630	0	G0247	1	G0403	1	J0151	180	J2212	240
E2631	0	G0248	1	G0404	1	J0178	4	J2265	400
E2632	0	G0249	3	G0405	1	J0210	16	J2507	8
E2633	0	G0250	1	G0412	1	J0215	30	J2995	0
G0008	1	G0251	2	G0413	1	J0220	20	J3010	100
G0009	1	G0257	2	G0414	1	J0221	300	J3060	900
G0010	2	G0259	2	G0415	1	J0256	3500	J3285	9
G0027	1	G0260	2	G0416	1	J0257	1400	J3465	120
G0101	1	G0268	1	G0417	1	J0275	1	J3489	5
G0102	1	G0278	1	G0418	1	J0278	15	J7196	175
G0103	1	G0281	1	G0419	1	J0280	10	J7301	0
G0104	1	G0283	1	G0420	2	J0289	115	J7310	2
G0105	1	G0288	1	G0424	2	J0300	8	J7316	4
G0106	1	G0289	1	G0429	1	J0348	200	J7326	2
G0117	1	G0293	1	G0431	1	J0350	0	J7527	20
G0118	1	G0294	1	G0432	1	J0360	6	J7604	0
G0120	1	G0302	1	G0433	1	J0364	6	J7607	0
G0121	1	G0303	1	G0434	1	J0456	4	J7609	0
G0123	1	G0304	1	G0435	1	J0475	8	J7610	0
G0124	1	G0305	1	G0436	1	J0485	1500	J7615	0
G0127	1	G0306	2	G0437	1	J0490	160	J7622	0
G0128	1	G0307	2	G0438	1	J0597	250	J7624	0
G0129	3	G0328	1	G0439	1	J0638	150	J7627	0
G0130	1	G0329	1	G0442	1	J0697	12	J7628	0
G0141	1	G0333	0	G0443	1	J0712	180	J7629	0
G0143	1	G0337	1	G0444	1	J0717	400	J7632	0
G0144	1	G0339	1	G0445	1	J0745	8	J7634	0
G0145	1	G0340	2	G0448	1	J0760	4	J7635	0
G0147	1	G0341	1	G0452	1	J0770	5	J7636	0
G0148	1	G0342	1	G0454	1	J0780	10	J7637	0

Code	MUE Values	Code	MUE Values	Code	MUE Values	Code	MUE Values	Code	MUE Values
J7638	0	K0040	0	K0816	0	K0885	0	L0625	1
J7640	0	K0041	0	K0820	0	K0886	0	L0626	1
J7641	0	K0042	0	K0821	0	K0890	0	L0627	1
J7642	0	K0043	0	K0822	0	K0891	0	L0628	1
J7643	0	K0044	0	K0823	0	K0898	1	L0629	1
J7645	0	K0045	0	K0824	0	K0900	0	L0630	1
J7647	0	K0046	0	K0825	0	L0112	1	L0631	1
J7650	0	K0047	0	K0826	0	L0113	1	L0632	1
J7657	0	K0050	0	K0827	0	L0120	1	L0633	1
J7660	0	K0051	0	K0828	0	L0130	1	L0634	1
J7665	127	K0052	0	K0829	0	L0140	1	L0635	1
J7667	0	K0053	0	K0830	0	L0150	1	L0636	1
J7670	0	K0056	0	K0831	0	L0160	1	L0637	1
J7676	0	K0065	0	K0835	0	L0170	1	L0638	1
J7680	0	K0069	0	K0836	0	L0172	1	L0639	1
J7681	0	K0070	0	K0837	0	L0174	1	L0640	1
J7683	0	K0071	0	K0838	0	L0180	1	L0641	1
J7684	0	K0072	0	K0839	0	L0190	1	L0642	1
J7685	0	K0073	0	K0840	0	L0200	1	L0643	1
J8510	5	K0077	0	K0841	0	L0220	1	L0648	1
J9019	60	K0105	0	K0842	0	L0450	1	L0649	1
J9042	200	K0195	0	K0843	0	L0452	1	L0650	1
J9047	120	K0455	0	K0848	0	L0454	1	L0651	1
J9179	50	K0462	0	K0849	0	L0455	1	L0700	1
J9228	450	K0552	0	K0850	0	L0456	1	L0710	1
J9262	700	K0601	0	K0851	0	L0457	1	L0810	1
J9306	840	K0602	0	K0852	0	L0458	1	L0820	1
J9354	600	K0603	0	K0853	0	L0460	1	L0830	1
J9355	100	K0604	0	K0854	0	L0462	1	L0859	1
J9400	600	K0605	0	K0855	0	L0464	1	L0861	1
K0001	0	K0606	0	K0856	0	L0466	1	L0970	1
K0002	0	K0607	0	K0857	0	L0467	1	L0972	1
K0003	0	K0608	0	K0858	0	L0468	1	L0974	1
K0004	0	K0609	0	K0859	0	L0469	1	L0976	1
K0005	0	K0730	0	K0860	0	L0470	1	L0978	2
K0006	0	K0733	0	K0861	0	L0472	1	L0980	1
K0007	0	K0738	0	K0862	0	L0480	1	L0982	1
K0008	0	K0743	0	K0863	0	L0482	1	L0984	3
K0009	0	K0800	0	K0864	0	L0484	1	L1000	1
K0013	0	K0801	0	K0868	0	L0486	1	L1001	1
K0015	0	K0802	0	K0869	0	L0488	1	L1005	1
K0017	0	K0806	0	K0870	0	L0490	1	L1010	2
K0018	0	K0807	0	K0871	0	L0491	1	L1020	2
K0019	0	K0808	0	K0877	0	L0492	1	L1025	1
K0020	0	K0812	0	K0878	0	L0621	1	L1030	1
K0037	0	K0813	0	K0879	0	L0622	1	L1040	1
K0038	0	K0814	0	K0880	0	L0623	1	L1050	1
K0039	0	K0815	0	K0884	0	L0624	1	L1060	1

Code	MUE Values	Code	MUE Values	Code	MUE Values	Code	MUE Values	Code	MUE Values
L1070	2	L1844	2	L2132	2	L2627	1	L3360	2
L1080	2	L1845	2	L2134	2	L2628	1	L3370	2
L1085	1	L1846	2	L2136	2	L2630	1	L3380	2
L1090	1	L1847	2	L2180	2	L2640	1	L3390	2
L1100	2	L1848	2	L2182	4	L2650	2	L3400	2
L1110	2	L1850	2	L2184	4	L2660	1	L3410	2
L1120	3	L1860	2	L2186	4	L2670	2	L3420	2
L1200	1	L1900	2	L2188	2	L2680	2	L3430	2
L1210	2	L1902	2	L2190	2	L2795	2	L3440	2
L1220	1	L1904	2	L2192	2	L2800	2	L3450	2
L1230	1	L1906	2	L2200	4	L2820	2	L3455	2
L1240	1	L1907	2	L2210	4	L2830	2	L3460	2
L1250	2	L1910	2	L2220	4	L3000	2	L3465	2
L1260	1	L1920	2	L2230	2	L3001	2	L3470	2
L1270	3	L1930	2	L2232	2	L3002	2	L3480	2
L1280	2	L1932	2	L2240	2	L3003	2	L3485	2
L1290	2	L1940	2	L2250	2	L3010	2	L3500	2
L1300	1	L1945	2	L2260	2	L3020	2	L3510	2
L1310	1	L1950	2	L2265	2	L3030	2	L3520	2
L1499	1	L1951	2	L2270	2	L3031	2	L3530	2
L1600	1	L1960	2	L2275	2	L3040	2	L3540	2
L1610	1	L1970	2	L2280	2	L3050	2	L3550	2
L1620	1	L1971	2	L2300	1	L3060	2	L3560	2
L1630	1	L1980	2	L2310	1	L3070	2	L3570	2
L1640	1	L1990	2	L2320	2	L3080	2	L3580	2
L1650	1	L2000	2	L2330	2	L3090	2	L3590	2
L1652	1	L2005	2	L2335	2	L3100	2	L3595	2
L1660	1	L2010	2	L2340	2	L3140	1	L3600	2
L1680	1	L2020	2	L2350	2	L3150	1	L3610	2
L1685	1	L2030	2	L2360	2	L3160	2	L3620	2
L1686	1	L2034	2	L2370	2	L3170	2	L3630	2
L1690	1	L2035	2	L2375	2	L3215	0	L3640	1
L1700	1	L2036	2	L2380	2	L3216	0	L3650	1
L1710	1	L2037	2	L2500	2	L3217	0	L3660	1
L1720	2	L2038	2	L2510	2	L3219	0	L3670	1
L1730	1	L2040	1	L2520	2	L3221	0	L3671	1
L1755	2	L2050	1	L2525	2	L3222	0	L3674	1
L1810	2	L2060	1	L2526	2	L3224	2	L3675	1
L1812	2	L2070	1	L2530	2	L3225	2	L3677	1
L1820	2	L2080	1	L2540	2	L3230	2	L3678	1
L1830	2	L2090	1	L2550	2	L3250	2	L3702	2
L1831	2	L2106	2	L2570	2	L3251	2	L3710	2
L1832	2	L2108	2	L2580	2	L3252	2	L3720	2
L1833	2	L2112	2	L2600	2	L3253	2	L3730	2
L1834	2	L2114	2	L2610	2	L3330	2	L3740	2
L1836	2	L2116	2	L2620	2	L3332	2	L3760	2
L1840	2	L2126	2	L2622	2	L3340	2	L3762	2
L1843	2	L2128	2	L2624	2	L3350	2	L3763	2

Code	MUE Values	Code	MUE Values	Code	MUE Values	Code	MUE Values	Code	MUE Values
L3764	2	L4045	2	L5505	2	L5666	2	L5811	2
L3765	2	L4050	2	L5510	2	L5668	2	L5812	2
L3766	2	L4055	2	L5520	2	L5670	2	L5814	2
L3806	2	L4060	2	L5530	2	L5671	2	L5816	2
L3807	2	L4070	2	L5535	2	L5672	2	L5818	2
L3808	2	L4080	2	L5540	2	L5676	2	L5822	2
L3809	2	L4100	2	L5560	2	L5677	2	L5824	2
L3900	2	L4130	2	L5570	2	L5678	2	L5826	2
L3901	2	L4350	2	L5580	2	L5680	2	L5828	2
L3904	2	L4360	2	L5585	2	L5681	2	L5830	2
L3905	2	L4361	2	L5590	2	L5682	2	L5840	2
L3906	2	L4370	2	L5595	2	L5683	2	L5845	2
L3908	2	L4386	2	L5600	2	L5684	2	L5848	2
L3912	2	L4387	2	L5610	2	L5686	2	L5850	2
L3913	2	L4392	2	L5611	2	L5688	2	L5855	2
L3915	2	L4394	2	L5613	2	L5690	2	L5856	2
L3916	2	L4396	2	L5614	2	L5692	2	L5857	2
L3917	2	L4397	2	L5616	2	L5694	2	L5858	2
L3918	2	L4398	2	L5617	2	L5695	2	L5859	2
L3919	2	L4631	2	L5628	2	L5696	2	L5910	2
L3921	2	L5000	2	L5629	2	L5697	2	L5920	2
L3923	2	L5010	2	L5630	2	L5698	2	L5925	2
L3924	2	L5020	2	L5631	2	L5699	2	L5930	2
L3925	4	L5050	2	L5632	2	L5700	2	L5940	2
L3927	4	L5060	2	L5634	2	L5701	2	L5950	2
L3929	2	L5100	2	L5636	2	L5702	2	L5960	2
L3930	2	L5105	2	L5637	2	L5703	2	L5961	1
L3931	2	L5150	2	L5638	2	L5704	2	L5962	2
L3933	3	L5160	2	L5639	2	L5705	2	L5964	2
L3935	3	L5200	2	L5640	2	L5706	2	L5966	2
L3960	1	L5210	2	L5642	2	L5707	2	L5968	2
L3961	1	L5220	2	L5643	2	L5710	2	L5969	0
L3962	1	L5230	2	L5644	2	L5711	2	L5970	2
L3967	1	L5250	2	L5645	2	L5712	2	L5971	2
L3971	1	L5270	2	L5646	2	L5714	2	L5972	2
L3973	1	L5280	2	L5647	2	L5716	2	L5973	2
L3975	1	L5301	2	L5648	2	L5718	2	L5974	2
L3976	1	L5312	2	L5649	2	L5722	2	L5975	2
L3977	1	L5321	2	L5650	2	L5724	2	L5976	2
L3978	1	L5331	2	L5651	2	L5726	2	L5978	2
L3980	2	L5341	2	L5652	2	L5728	2	L5979	2
L3982	2	L5400	2	L5653	2	L5780	2	L5980	2
L3984	2	L5410	2	L5654	2	L5781	2	L5981	2
L4000	1	L5420	2	L5655	2	L5782	2	L5982	2
L4010	2	L5430	2	L5656	2	L5785	2	L5984	2
L4020	2	L5450	2	L5658	2	L5790	2	L5985	2
L4030	2	L5460	2	L5661	2	L5795	2	L5986	2
L4040	2	L5500	2	L5665	2	L5810	2	L5987	2

Code	MUE Values	Code	MUE Values	Code	MUE Values	Code	MUE Values	Code	MUE Values
L5988	2	L6628	2	L6883	2	L8032	2	L8670	4
L5990	2	L6629	2	L6884	2	L8035	2	L8679	3
L6000	2	L6630	2	L6885	2	L8039	2	L8681	1
L6010	2	L6635	2	L6890	2	L8040	1	L8682	2
L6020	2	L6637	2	L6895	2	L8041	1	L8683	1
L6025	2	L6638	2	L6900	2	L8042	2	L8684	1
L6050	2	L6640	2	L6905	2	L8043	1	L8685	1
L6055	2	L6641	2	L6910	2	L8044	1	L8686	2
L6100	2	L6642	2	L6915	2	L8045	2	L8687	1
L6110	2	L6645	2	L6920	2	L8046	1	L8688	1
L6120	2	L6646	2	L6925	2	L8047	1	L8689	1
L6130	2	L6647	2	L6930	2	L8048	1	L8690	2
L6200	2	L6648	2	L6935	2	L8300	1	L8691	1
L6205	2	L6650	2	L6940	2	L8310	1	L8692	0
L6250	2	L6670	2	L6945	2	L8320	2	L8693	1
L6300	2	L6672	2	L6950	2	L8330	2	L8695	1
L6310	2	L6675	2	L6955	2	L8500	1	M0064	1
L6320	2	L6676	2	L6960	2	L8501	2	P2028	1
L6350	2	L6677	2	L6965	2	L8507	3	P2029	1
L6360	2	L6686	2	L6970	2	L8509	1	P2033	1
L6370	2	L6687	2	L6975	2	L8510	1	P2038	1
L6380	2	L6688	2	L7007	2	L8511	1	P3000	1
L6382	2	L6689	2	L7008	2	L8514	1	P3001	1
L6384	2	L6690	2	L7009	2	L8515	1	P9041	100
L6386	2	L6693	2	L7040	2	L8600	2	P9043	10
L6388	2	L6694	2	L7045	2	L8604	3	P9045	20
L6400	2	L6695	2	L7170	2	L8605	4	P9046	40
L6450	2	L6696	2	L7180	2	L8606	5	P9047	20
L6500	2	L6697	2	L7181	2	L8609	1	P9048	2
L6550	2	L6698	2	L7185	2	L8610	2	P9612	1
L6570	2	L6703	2	L7186	2	L8612	2	P9615	1
L6580	2	L6704	2	L7190	2	L8613	2	Q0035	1
L6582	2	L6706	2	L7191	2	L8614	2	Q0085	2
L6584	2	L6707	2	L7260	2	L8615	2	Q0091	1
L6586	2	L6708	2	L7261	2	L8616	2	Q0111	2
L6588	2	L6709	2	L7362	1	L8617	2	Q0112	3
L6590	2	L6711	2	L7366	1	L8618	2	Q0113	2
L6600	2	L6712	2	L7368	1	L8619	2	Q0114	1
L6605	2	L6713	2	L7400	2	L8621	600	Q0115	1
L6610	2	L6714	2	L7401	2	L8622	2	Q0144	0
L6611	2	L6715	4	L7402	2	L8627	2	Q0161	30
L6615	2	L6721	2	L7403	2	L8628	2	Q0478	1
L6616	2	L6722	2	L7404	2	L8629	2	Q0479	1
L6620	2	L6805	2	L7405	2	L8631	4	Q0480	1
L6621	2	L6810	2	L7900	1	L8641	4	Q0481	1
L6623	2	L6880	2	L7902	1	L8642	2	Q0482	1
L6624	2	L6881	2	L8030	2	L8658	4	Q0483	1
L6625	2	L6882	2	L8031	2	L8659	4	Q0484	1

Code	MUE Values	Code	MUE Values	Code	MUE Values	Code	MUE Values	Code	MUE Values
Q0485	1	Q4026	1	V2106	2	V2314	2	V2785	2
Q0486	1	Q4027	1	V2107	2	V2315	2	V2790	1
Q0487	1	Q4028	1	V2108	2	V2318	2	V2797	1
Q0488	1	Q4074	0	V2109	2	V2319	2	V5008	0
Q0489	1	Q4101	176	V2110	2	V2320	2	V5010	0
Q0490	1	Q4102	140	V2111	2	V2321	2	V5011	0
Q0491	1	Q4103	0	V2112	2	V2399	2	V5274	0
Q0492	1	Q4104	250	V2113	2	V2410	2	V5281	0
Q0493	1	Q4105	250	V2114	2	V2430	2	V5282	0
Q0494	1	Q4106	152	V2115	2	V2499	2	V5284	0
Q0495	1	Q4107	128	V2118	2	V2500	2	V5285	0
Q0497	2	Q4108	250	V2121	2	V2501	2	V5286	0
Q0498	1	Q4110	250	V2199	2	V2502	2	V5287	0
Q0499	1	Q4111	112	V2200	2	V2503	2	V5288	0
Q0501	1	Q4112	2	V2201	2	V2510	2	V5289	0
Q0502	1	Q4113	4	V2202	2	V2511	2		
Q0503	3	Q4114	6	V2203	2	V2512	2		
Q0504	1	Q4115	240	V2204	2	V2513	2		
Q0507	1	Q4116	320	V2205	2	V2520	2		
Q0508	1	Q4117	0	V2206	2	V2521	2		
Q0509	1	Q4118	1000	V2207	2	V2522	2		
Q0510	1	Q4119	300	V2208	2	V2523	2		
Q0511	1	Q4120	0	V2209	2	V2530	2		
Q0512	4	Q4121	156	V2210	2	V2531	2		
Q0513	1	Q4122	96	V2211	2	V2599	2		
Q0514	1	Q4123	160	V2212	2	V2600	1		
Q1004	2	Q4124	280	V2213	2	V2610	1		
Q1005	2	Q4125	28	V2214	2	V2615	2		
Q2004	1	Q4126	0	V2215	2	V2623	2		
Q2028	1470	Q4127	100	V2218	2	V2624	2		
Q2034	1	Q4128	128	V2219	2	V2625	2		
Q2035	1	Q4129	81	V2220	2	V2626	2		
Q2036	1	Q4130	100	V2221	2	V2627	2		
Q2037	1	Q4131	49	V2299	2	V2628	2		
Q2038	1	Q4132	50	V2300	2	V2629	2		
Q2039	1	Q4133	113	V2301	2	V2630	2		
Q2043	1	Q4134	160	V2302	2	V2631	2		
Q2050	20	Q4135	900	V2303	2	V2632	2		
Q2052	1	Q4136	900	V2304	2	V2700	2		
Q3014	2	Q9955	10	V2305	2	V2710	2		
Q3027	30	R0070	2	V2306	2	V2718	2		
Q3028	0	R0075	2	V2307	2	V2730	2		
Q3031	1	R0076	1	V2308	2	V2761	2		
Q4001	1	V2020	1	V2309	2	V2770	2		
Q4002	1	V2101	2	V2310	2	V2780	2		
Q4003	2	V2102	2	V2311	2	V2781	2		
Q4004	2	V2104	2	V2312	2	V2782	2		
Q4025	1	V2105	2	V2313	2	V2783	2		

Appendix G: PQRS Table with HCPCS Code Numerator and Corresponding Denominator

Numerator	Diagnostic Denominator	CPT® Procedure Denominator
G0101, G0108	N/A	99201-99215, 99324-99337, 99341-99350, 90801-90809, 90957-90960, 90962, 90965-90966, 92002-92014, 92506-92507, 92526, 92541-92545, 92547-92548, 92552-92555, 92557, 92561-92582, 92584-92588, 92601-92604, 92610-92612, 92620-92627, 92640, 95920, 96116, 96150-96152, 97001-97004, 97750, 97802-97804, 98940-98942, 98960-98962
G0105	V12.72	44388-44389, 44392-44394, 45355-45378, 45380-45381, 45383-45385
G0106, G0120, G0275, G0278	N/A	25606, 25651, 26608, 26650, 26676, 26706, 26727, 27235, 27244-27245, 27509, 27756, 27759, 28406, 28436, 28456, 28476, 36147, 36598, 37182-37184, 37187-37188, 37210, 37225, 37227, 37229, 37231, 43260-43272, 43752, 44500, 49440-49465, 50382-50389, 50590, 61623, 62263-62264, 62280-62282, 63610, 64610, 64620, 70010-70015, 70170, 70332, 70370-70373, 70390, 71023, 71034, 71040-71090, 72240-72291, 72295, 73040, 73085, 73115, 73525, 73542, 73580, 73615, 74190-74260, 74270-74300, 74305-74363, 74425-74485, 74740-74742, 75600-75630, 75650-75756, 75791-75810, 75825-75940, 75952-75962, 75966, 75970-75984, 76000-76001, 76080, 76120, 76496, 77001-77003, 92611, 93565-93568, 0075T, 0080T, 0234T-0235T, 0238T
G0109	N/A	99201-99215, 90801-90809, 92002-92014, 92506-92507, 92526, 92541-92544, 92548, 92552-92555, 92557, 92561-92582, 92584-92588, 92601-92604, 92610-92612, 92620-92627, 92640, 95920, 96150-96152, 97001-97004, 97750, 97802-97804, 98940-98942
G0270	250.00-250.03, 250.10-250.13, 250.20-250.23, 250.30-250.33, 250.40-250.43, 250.50-250.53, 250.60-250.63, 250.70-250.73, 250.80-250.83, 250.90-250.93, 357.2, 362.01-362.07, 366.41, 648.04	99201-99215, 99304-99310, 99324-99337, 99341-99350, 90801-90815, 90845, 90862, 90957-90960, 90962, 90965-90966, 92002-92014, 92506-92507, 92526, 92541-92545, 92547-92548, 92552-92555, 92557, 92561-92582, 92584-92588, 92601-92604, 92610-92612, 92620-92627, 92640, 95920, 96116, 96150-96152, 97001-97004, 97750, 97802-97804, 98940-98942, 98960-98962
G0271	250.00-250.03, 250.10-250.13, 250.20-250.23, 250.30-250.33, 250.40-250.43, 250.50-250.53, 250.60-250.63, 250.70-250.73, 250.80-250.83, 250.90-250.93, 357.2, 362.01-362.07, 366.41, 648.04	99201-99215, 99304-99310, 99324-99337, 99341-99350, 90801-90815, 90845, 90862, 92002-92014, 92506-92507, 92526, 92541-92544, 92548, 92552-92555, 92557, 92561-92582, 92584-92588, 92601-92604, 92610-92612, 92620-92627, 92640, 95920, 96150-96152, 97001-97004, 97750, 97802-97804, 98940-98942, 98960-98962
G8126, G8127, G8128	296.20-296.25, 296.30-296.35, 298.0, 300.4, 309.0-309.1, 311	99201-99205, 99212-99215, 99341-99350, 90801-90815, 90821-90824, 90829-90845, 90849-90862, 99078
G8395, G8396, G8450, G8451, G8452	402.01, 402.11, 402.91, 404.01, 404.03, 404.11, 404.13, 404.91, 404.93, 428.0-428.1, 428.20-428.23, 428.30-428.33, 428.9	99201-99205, 99212-99215, 99304-99310, 99324-99337, 99341-99350
G8397, G8398	362.06	99201-99205, 99212-99215, 99304-99310, 99324-99337, 92002-92014
G8399, G8400, G8401	N/A	99201-99205, 99212-99215
G8404, G8405, G8406, G8410, G8415, G8416	250.00-250.03, 250.10-250.13, 250.20-250.23, 250.30-50.33, 250.40-250.43, 250.50-250.53, 250.60-250.63, 250.70-250.73, 250.80-250.83, 250.93	99201-99205, 99212-99215, 99304-99310, 99324-99337, 99341-99350, 11042, 11043, 11044, 11055-11057, 11719-11730, 11740, 97001-97002, 97597-97598, 97802-97803
G8417, G8418, G8419, G8420, G8421, G8422	N/A	99201-99215, 99324-99337, 99341-99350, 90801-90809, 97001, 97003, 97802-97803, 98960
G8427, G8428, G8430	N/A	99201-99215, 90801-90802, 90957-90960, 90962, 90965-90966, 92002-92014, 92541-92545, 92547-92548, 92557, 92567-92570, 92585, 92588, 92626, 96116, 96150, 96152, 97001-97004, 97802-97804, 98960-98962
G8431, G8432, G8433, G8510, G8511	N/A	90801-90809, 92557, 92567-92568, 92590, 92625-92626, 96150-96151, 97003
G8442, G8508, G8509	N/A	90801-90802, 96116, 96150, 97001, 97003, 98940-98942
G8464, G8465	185	77427

Numerator	Diagnostic Denominator	CPT® Procedure Denominator
G8473, G8474, G8475	250.00-250.03, 250.10-250.13, 250.20-250.23, 250.30-250.33, 250.40-250.43, 250.50-250.53, 250.60-250.63, 250.70-250.73, 250.80-250.83, 250.90-250.93, 410.00-410.02, 410.10-410.12, 410.20-410.22, 410.30-410.32, 410.40-410.42, 410.50-410.52, 410.60-410.62, 410.70-410.72, 410.80-410.82, 410.90-410.92, 411.0-411.1, 411.81-412, 413.0-413.9, 414.00-414.07, 414.8-414.9, V45.82	99201-99205, 99212-99215, 99304-99310, 99324-99337, 99341-99350
G8482, G8483, G8484	N/A	99201-99205, 99212-99215, 99304-99316, 99324-99337, 99341-99350
G8530, G8531, G8532	585.4-585.6, 996.73	36818-36821, 36825-36830
G8535, G8536	N/A	90801-90802, 96116, 96150, 97003, 97802-97803
G8539, G8540, G8541, G8542, G8543	N/A	98940-98942
G8556, G8557, G8558	380.00-380.03, 380.10, 380.30-380.39, 380.51, 380.81-380.9, 744.01-744.03, 744.09	92557, 92567-92568, 92575
G8559, G8560, G8561, G8562, G8563	381.01, 382.00-382.9, 388.69	92557, 92567-92568, 92575
G8564, G8565, G8566, G8567, G8568	389.00-389.08, 389.10-389.18, 389.20-389.22, 389.9	92550, 92557, 92567-92570, 92575
G8569, G8570, G8571, G8572, G8573, G8574, G8575, G8576, G8577, G8578, G8579, G8580, G8581, G8582, G8583, G8584, G8585, G8586, G8587	N/A	33510-33523, 33533-33536
G8588, G8589, G8590, G8591, G8592, G8593, G8594, G8595, G8596, G8597, G8598, G8599	410.11, 410.21, 410.31, 410.41, 410.51, 410.61, 410.71, 410.81, 410.91, 411.0-411.1, 411.81-411.89, 413.0-413.9, 414.00-414.07, 414.8-414.9, 429.2, 433.00-433.01, 433.10-433.11, 433.20-433.21, 433.30-433.31, 433.80-433.81, 433.90-433.91, 434.00-434.01, 434.10-434.11, 434.90-434.91, 440.1, 440.20-440.29, 440.4, 444.0, 444.1, 444.21-444.22, 444.81-444.9, 445.01-445.02, 445.89	99201-99220, 99341-99350, 99455-99456, 33140, 33510-33523, 33533-33536, 92980, 92982, 92995
G8600, G8601, G8602	433.01, 433.10-433.11, 433.21, 433.31, 433.81, 433.91, 434.00-434.01, 434.11, 434.91, 436	99221-99223, 99291
G8603, G8604, G8605, G8612, G8613, G8614, G8615, G8616, G8617, G8618, G8619, G8620, G8621, G8622, G8623	438.10-438.19, 438.20-438.22, 438.30-438.32, 438.40-438.42, 438.50-438.7, 438.81-438.9, 784.3	92507-92508
G8606, G8607, G8608, G8609, G8610, G8611	438.0, 438.10-438.19, 438.20-438.22, 438.30-438.32, 438.40-438.42, 438.50-438.7, 438.9	97532
G8624, G8625, G8626	438.82, 784.51, 787.29	92526

Numerator	Diagnostic Denominator	CPT® Procedure Denominator
G8627, G8628	360.11-360.12, 360.20-360.21, 360.30-360.34, 362.21, 364.00-364.05, 364.10-364.11, 364.21-364.3, 364.42, 364.60-364.64, 364.70-364.77, 364.81-364.89, 365.10-365.15, 365.20-365.24, 365.31-365.32, 365.51-365.59, 365.60-365.65, 365.81-365.89, 366.11, 366.20-366.23, 366.32-366.33, 366.9, 367.0, 370.03, 371.00-371.04, 371.20-371.23, 371.43-371.44, 371.50-371.58, 376.50-376.52, 379.32-379.34, 379.42, 743.30-743.31, 743.36, 871.0-871.9, 921.3, 940.0-940.9, 950.9	66840-66984, 67036-67039, 67041-67043
G8629, G8630, G8631, G8632	N/A	15734, 15738, 19260-19272, 19301-19307, 19361-19369, 21346-21348, 21422-21423, 21432-21436, 21454-21470, 21627, 21632, 21740, 21750, 21805, 21825, 22325, 22524, 22554, 22558, 22600, 22612, 22630, 22800-22804, 27125-27138, 27235-27236, 27244-27245, 27269, 27440-27447, 27702-27704, 27758-27759, 27766, 27769, 27792, 27814, 28192-28193, 28293, 28415-28420, 28445, 28465, 28485, 28505, 28525, 28531, 28555, 28585, 28615, 28645, 28675-28737, 31360-31395, 31760-31775, 31786, 31805, 32095, 32100-32150, 32215-32320, 32402, 32440-32501, 32800-32815, 32900-32940, 33020-33208, 33212-33220, 33222-33226, 33233-33256, 33261, 33300-33322, 33332-33411, 33413, 33416, 33422-33465, 33475, 33496, 33510-33572, 33877-33883, 33886, 33891, 34051, 34800-34805, 34825, 34830-34832, 34900, 35021, 35081, 35091, 35102, 35131, 35141, 35151, 35211-35216, 35241-35246, 35271-35276, 35301, 35311, 35526, 35601-35671, 36830, 37616, 38115, 38381, 38746, 39000-39220, 39545, 39561, 41130-41155, 43045-43135, 43300-43313, 43320, 43325, 43327-43337, 43340-43425, 43496, 43500-43520, 43605-43634, 43640-43641, 43653, 43800-43840, 43843-43880, 44005-44010, 44020-44120, 44125-44127, 44130-44136, 44140-44160, 44202, 44204-44212, 44300-44346, 44602-44661, 44700, 44950, 45108-45190, 45500-45825, 47135-47142, 47420-47480, 47560-47561, 47570, 47600-47620, 47700-47800, 47802-47900, 48020-48100, 48120-48155, 48500-48548, 48554-48556, 49215, 49568, 50320, 50340-50380, 51550-51597, 51920-51925, 52450, 52601-52630, 52647-52649, 54401-54410, 54415-54416, 55801-55845, 58150-58210, 58260-58294, 60521-60522, 61154, 61312-61313, 61315, 61510-61512, 61518, 61520, 61526-61530, 61548, 61591, 61595-61596, 61598, 61606, 61616-61619, 61697, 61700, 61750-61751, 61867, 62223, 62230, 63015, 63020-63030, 63042, 63045, 63047, 63056, 63075, 63081, 63267, 63276, 64746, 69720, 69930, 69955-69970, 0236T
G8633, G8634, G8635	733.00-733.09, 805.00-805.08, 805.2, 805.4, 805.6, 805.8, 813.40-813.42, 813.44-813.45, 813.47, 813.50-813.52, 813.54, 820.00-820.09, 820.20-820.22, 820.8	99201-99205, 99212-99215, 22305-22327, 22520-22521, 22523-22524, 25600-25609, 27230-27248
G8647, G8648, G8649, G8650, G8651, G8652, G8653, G8654, G8655, G8656, G8657, G8658, G8659, G8660, G8661, G8662, G8663, G8664, G8665, G8666, G8667, G8668, G8669, G8670, G8671, G8672, G8673, G8674	N/A	97001-97004

Appendix H: Column 1 and Column 2 Correct Coding Edits

Column 1	Column 2	Modifier
A9500	A9512	1
A9501	A9512	0
A9502	A9512	0
A9503	A9512	0
A9504	A9512	0
A9510	A9512	0
A9521	A9512	0
A9536	A9512	0
A9537	A9512	0
A9538	A9512	0
A9539	A9512	0
A9540	A9512	1
A9541	A9512	1
A9550	A9512	0
A9551	A9512	0
A9557	A9512	0
A9560	A9512	0
A9561	A9512	0
A9562	A9512	0
A9566	A9512	0
A9567	A9512	0
A9568	A9512	0
A9569	A9512	0
C5271	G0168	1
C5271	G0456	1
C5271	G0457	1
C5271	J0670	1
C5271	J2001	1
C5272	G0168	1
C5272	G0456	1
C5272	G0457	1
C5272	J0670	1
C5272	J2001	1
C5273	G0168	1
C5273	G0456	1
C5273	G0457	1
C5273	J0670	1
C5273	J2001	1
C5274	G0168	1
C5274	G0456	1
C5274	G0457	1
C5274	J0670	1
C5274	J2001	1

Column 1	Column 2	Modifier
C5275	G0168	1
C5275	G0456	1
C5275	G0457	1
C5275	J0670	1
C5275	J2001	1
C5276	G0168	1
C5276	G0456	1
C5276	G0457	1
C5276	J0670	1
C5276	J2001	1
C5277	G0168	1
C5277	G0456	1
C5277	G0457	1
C5277	J0670	1
C5277	J2001	1
C5278	G0168	1
C5278	G0456	1
C5278	G0457	1
C5278	J0670	1
C5278	J2001	1
C8906	C8903	1
C8906	C8904	1
C8906	C8905	1
C8907	C8903	1
C8907	C8904	1
C8907	C8905	1
C8908	C8903	1
C8908	C8904	1
C8908	C8905	1
C8921	C8922	1
C8923	C8924	1
C8923	C8929	0
C8928	C8923	1
C8928	C8924	1
C8928	C8925	1
C8928	C8927	0
C8928	C8929	1
C8928	C8930	0
C8929	C8924	1
C8930	C8929	1
C8931	C8932	0
C8931	J1642	1
C8932	J1642	1

Column 1	Column 2	Modifier
C8933	C8931	0
C8933	C8932	0
C8933	J1642	1
C8934	C8935	0
C8934	J1642	1
C8935	J1642	1
C8936	C8934	0
C8936	C8935	0
C8936	J1642	1
C8957	G0463	1
C9600	G0269	1
C9601	G0269	1
C9602	G0269	1
C9603	G0269	1
C9604	G0269	1
C9605	G0269	1
C9606	G0269	1
C9607	G0269	1
C9608	G0269	1
C9725	C9735	0
C9735	J0670	1
C9735	J2001	1
C9739	G0463	1
C9739	J2001	1
C9739	P9612	0
C9740	C9739	0
C9740	G0463	1
C9740	J2001	1
C9740	P9612	0
C9800	G0429	0
C9800	J2001	1
C9800	Q2026	0
E0781	E0782	1
G0101	G0181	1
G0101	G0182	1
G0101	G0380	1
G0101	G0381	1
G0101	G0382	1
G0101	G0383	1
G0101	G0384	1
G0101	G0406	1
G0101	G0407	1
G0101	G0408	1

Column 1	Column 2	Modifier
G0101	G0425	1
G0101	G0426	1
G0101	G0427	1
G0101	G0463	1
G0104	C9735	0
G0104	G0105	0
G0104	G0106	1
G0104	G0120	1
G0104	G0121	0
G0104	G0181	1
G0104	G0182	1
G0104	G0380	1
G0104	G0381	1
G0104	G0382	1
G0104	G0383	1
G0104	G0384	1
G0104	G0406	1
G0104	G0407	1
G0104	G0408	1
G0104	G0425	1
G0104	G0426	1
G0104	G0427	1
G0104	G0463	1
G0105	G0181	1
G0105	G0182	1
G0105	G0380	1
G0105	G0381	1
G0105	G0382	1
G0105	G0383	1
G0105	G0384	1
G0105	G0406	1
G0105	G0407	1
G0105	G0408	1
G0105	G0425	1
G0105	G0426	1
G0105	G0427	1
G0105	G0463	1
G0106	G0105	0
G0106	G0121	0
G0106	G0181	1
G0106	G0182	1
G0106	G0380	1
G0106	G0381	1

Column 1	Column 2	Modifier
G0106	G0382	1
G0106	G0383	1
G0106	G0384	1
G0106	G0406	1
G0106	G0407	1
G0106	G0408	1
G0106	G0425	1
G0106	G0426	1
G0106	G0427	1
G0106	G0463	1
G0108	G0270	0
G0108	G0271	0
G0109	G0270	0
G0109	G0271	0
G0117	G0118	0
G0120	G0105	0
G0120	G0106	0
G0120	G0121	0
G0120	G0181	1
G0120	G0182	1
G0120	G0380	1
G0120	G0381	1
G0120	G0382	1
G0120	G0383	1
G0120	G0384	1
G0120	G0406	1
G0120	G0407	1
G0120	G0408	1
G0120	G0425	1
G0120	G0426	1
G0120	G0427	1
G0120	G0463	1
G0121	G0105	0
G0121	G0380	1
G0121	G0381	1
G0121	G0382	1
G0121	G0383	1
G0121	G0384	1
G0121	G0406	1
G0121	G0407	1
G0121	G0408	1
G0121	G0425	1
G0121	G0426	1
G0121	G0427	1
G0121	G0463	1
G0123	P3000	0
G0124	G0141	0
G0124	G0147	0

Column 1	Column 2	Modifier
G0124	G0148	0
G0124	P3000	0
G0124	P3001	0
G0127	G0380	1
G0127	G0381	1
G0127	G0382	1
G0127	G0383	1
G0127	G0384	1
G0127	G0406	1
G0127	G0407	1
G0127	G0408	1
G0127	G0425	1
G0127	G0426	1
G0127	G0427	1
G0127	G0456	1
G0127	G0457	1
G0127	G0463	1
G0141	G0123	0
G0141	G0143	0
G0141	G0144	0
G0141	P3000	0
G0145	G0147	0
G0145	G0148	0
G0148	G0147	0
G0151	G0281	1
G0151	G0283	1
G0151	G0329	1
G0154	G0008	1
G0154	G0009	1
G0154	G0010	1
G0154	G0128	1
G0154	P9612	1
G0154	P9615	1
G0157	G0281	1
G0157	G0283	1
G0157	G0329	1
G0159	G0281	1
G0159	G0283	1
G0159	G0329	1
G0162	G0008	1
G0162	G0009	1
G0162	G0010	1
G0162	G0128	1
G0162	P9612	1
G0162	P9615	1
G0163	G0008	1
G0163	G0009	1
G0163	G0010	1

Column 1	Column 2	Modifier
G0163	G0128	1
G0163	P9612	1
G0163	P9615	1
G0164	G0008	1
G0164	G0009	1
G0164	G0010	1
G0164	G0128	1
G0164	P9612	1
G0164	P9615	1
G0168	G0463	1
G0168	J0670	1
G0168	J2001	1
G0173	G0251	1
G0173	G0339	0
G0173	G0340	0
G0173	G0459	0
G0173	G0463	0
G0173	M0064	0
G0179	G0180	0
G0181	G0102	1
G0181	G0182	1
G0182	G0102	1
G0204	G0206	0
G0239	G0237	1
G0239	G0238	1
G0245	G0127	0
G0245	G0246	0
G0245	G0456	0
G0245	G0457	0
G0246	G0127	0
G0246	G0456	0
G0246	G0457	0
G0247	G0127	0
G0247	G0456	0
G0247	G0457	0
G0251	G0339	0
G0251	G0340	0
G0251	G0459	0
G0251	G0463	0
G0251	M0064	0
G0268	G0463	1
G0270	G0271	0
G0281	G0283	1
G0281	G0329	0
G0302	G0303	0
G0302	G0304	0
G0302	G0380	1
G0302	G0381	1

Column 1	Column 2	Modifier
G0302	G0382	1
G0302	G0383	1
G0302	G0384	1
G0302	G0406	1
G0302	G0407	1
G0302	G0408	1
G0302	G0425	1
G0302	G0426	1
G0302	G0427	1
G0302	G0463	1
G0303	G0304	0
G0303	G0380	1
G0303	G0381	1
G0303	G0382	1
G0303	G0383	1
G0303	G0384	1
G0303	G0406	1
G0303	G0407	1
G0303	G0408	1
G0303	G0425	1
G0303	G0426	1
G0303	G0427	1
G0303	G0463	1
G0304	G0380	1
G0304	G0381	1
G0304	G0382	1
G0304	G0383	1
G0304	G0384	1
G0304	G0406	1
G0304	G0407	1
G0304	G0408	1
G0304	G0425	1
G0304	G0426	1
G0304	G0427	1
G0304	G0463	1
G0305	G0380	1
G0305	G0381	1
G0305	G0382	1
G0305	G0383	1
G0305	G0384	1
G0305	G0406	1
G0305	G0407	1
G0305	G0408	1
G0305	G0425	1
G0305	G0426	1
G0305	G0427	1
G0305	G0463	1
G0306	G0307	0

Column 1	Column 2	Modifier
G0329	G0283	1
G0337	G0101	0
G0337	G0102	0
G0337	G0104	0
G0337	G0105	0
G0337	G0106	0
G0337	G0117	0
G0337	G0118	0
G0337	G0120	0
G0337	G0121	0
G0337	G0245	0
G0337	G0246	0
G0337	G0248	0
G0337	G0250	1
G0337	G0270	0
G0337	G0271	0
G0337	G0410	1
G0337	G0411	1
G0337	G0459	0
G0337	G0463	0
G0337	M0064	0
G0337	P3000	0
G0337	P3001	0
G0337	Q0091	0
G0339	G0340	1
G0339	G0459	0
G0339	G0463	0
G0339	M0064	0
G0340	G0459	0
G0340	G0463	0
G0340	M0064	0
G0341	G0463	1
G0341	J0670	1
G0341	J1644	1
G0341	J2001	1
G0342	G0341	0
G0342	G0463	1
G0343	G0341	0
G0343	G0342	0
G0343	G0463	1
G0380	G0102	1
G0380	G0245	1
G0380	G0246	1
G0380	G0270	1
G0380	G0271	1
G0380	G0459	1
G0380	M0064	1
G0381	G0102	1

Column 1	Column 2	Modifier
G0381	G0245	1
G0381	G0246	1
G0381	G0270	1
G0381	G0271	1
G0381	G0380	1
G0381	G0459	1
G0381	M0064	1
G0382	G0102	1
G0382	G0245	1
G0382	G0246	1
G0382	G0270	1
G0382	G0271	1
G0382	G0380	1
G0382	G0381	1
G0382	G0459	1
G0382	M0064	1
G0383	G0102	1
G0383	G0245	1
G0383	G0246	1
G0383	G0270	1
G0383	G0271	1
G0383	G0380	1
G0383	G0381	1
G0383	G0382	1
G0383	G0459	1
G0383	M0064	1
G0384	G0102	1
G0384	G0245	1
G0384	G0246	1
G0384	G0270	1
G0384	G0271	1
G0384	G0380	1
G0384	G0381	1
G0384	G0382	1
G0384	G0383	1
G0384	G0459	1
G0384	M0064	1
G0396	G0442	0
G0397	G0396	0
G0397	G0442	0
G0398	G0399	0
G0398	G0400	0
G0399	G0400	0
G0402	G0250	1
G0402	G0270	0
G0402	G0271	0
G0402	G0380	1
G0402	G0381	1

Column 1	Column 2	Modifier
G0402	G0382	1
G0402	G0383	1
G0402	G0384	1
G0402	G0438	0
G0402	G0439	0
G0402	G0444	0
G0402	G0459	1
G0402	G0463	1
G0402	M0064	1
G0403	G0404	0
G0403	G0405	0
G0406	G0102	0
G0406	G0245	0
G0406	G0246	0
G0406	G0270	0
G0406	G0271	0
G0406	G0459	0
G0406	M0064	0
G0407	G0102	0
G0407	G0245	0
G0407	G0246	0
G0407	G0270	0
G0407	G0271	0
G0407	G0406	0
G0407	G0459	0
G0407	M0064	0
G0408	G0102	0
G0408	G0245	0
G0408	G0246	0
G0408	G0270	0
G0408	G0271	0
G0408	G0406	0
G0408	G0407	0
G0408	G0459	0
G0408	M0064	0
G0409	G0155	1
G0409	G0176	1
G0409	G0177	1
G0409	G0459	1
G0410	G0176	1
G0410	G0177	1
G0410	G0270	0
G0410	G0271	0
G0410	G0380	1
G0410	G0381	1
G0410	G0382	1
G0410	G0383	1
G0410	G0384	1

Column 1	Column 2	Modifier
G0410	G0459	0
G0410	G0463	1
G0410	M0064	0
G0411	G0176	1
G0411	G0177	1
G0411	G0270	0
G0411	G0271	0
G0411	G0380	1
G0411	G0381	1
G0411	G0382	1
G0411	G0383	1
G0411	G0384	1
G0411	G0410	1
G0411	G0459	0
G0411	G0463	1
G0411	M0064	0
G0412	G0456	1
G0412	G0457	1
G0412	G0463	1
G0413	G0456	1
G0413	G0457	1
G0413	G0463	1
G0414	G0456	1
G0414	G0457	1
G0414	G0463	1
G0415	G0413	1
G0415	G0456	1
G0415	G0457	1
G0415	G0463	1
G0417	G0416	0
G0418	G0416	0
G0418	G0417	0
G0419	G0416	0
G0419	G0417	0
G0419	G0418	0
G0420	G0421	1
G0422	G0423	1
G0424	G0237	0
G0424	G0238	0
G0424	G0239	0
G0424	G0406	1
G0424	G0407	1
G0424	G0408	1
G0424	G0422	1
G0424	G0423	1
G0425	G0102	0
G0425	G0245	0
G0425	G0246	0

Column 1	Column 2	Modifier
G0425	G0270	0
G0425	G0271	0
G0425	G0406	0
G0425	G0407	0
G0425	G0408	0
G0425	G0424	1
G0425	G0459	0
G0425	M0064	0
G0426	G0102	0
G0426	G0245	0
G0426	G0246	0
G0426	G0270	0
G0426	G0271	0
G0426	G0406	0
G0426	G0407	0
G0426	G0408	0
G0426	G0424	1
G0426	G0425	0
G0426	G0459	0
G0426	M0064	0
G0427	G0102	0
G0427	G0245	0
G0427	G0246	0
G0427	G0270	0
G0427	G0271	0
G0427	G0406	0
G0427	G0407	0
G0427	G0408	0
G0427	G0424	1
G0427	G0425	0
G0427	G0426	0
G0427	G0459	0
G0427	M0064	0
G0429	G0463	1
G0429	J2001	1
G0431	G0434	0
G0436	G0396	1
G0436	G0397	1
G0437	G0396	1
G0437	G0397	1
G0437	G0436	0
G0438	G0250	1
G0438	G0270	0
G0438	G0271	0
G0438	G0380	1
G0438	G0381	1
G0438	G0382	1
G0438	G0383	1

Column 1	Column 2	Modifier
G0438	G0384	1
G0438	G0439	0
G0438	G0444	0
G0438	G0459	1
G0438	G0463	1
G0438	M0064	1
G0439	G0250	1
G0439	G0270	0
G0439	G0271	0
G0439	G0380	1
G0439	G0381	1
G0439	G0382	1
G0439	G0383	1
G0439	G0384	1
G0439	G0459	1
G0439	G0463	1
G0439	M0064	1
G0443	G0396	0
G0443	G0397	0
G0455	G0463	1
G0458	M0064	0
G0458	P9612	0
G0459	G0270	0
G0459	G0271	0
G0459	G0444	1
G0459	G0445	1
G0459	G0446	1
G0459	G0447	1
G0460	P9020	1
G0463	G0102	0
G0463	G0117	0
G0463	G0118	0
G0463	G0245	0
G0463	G0246	0
G0463	G0248	1
G0463	G0250	1
G0463	G0270	0
G0463	G0271	0
G0463	G0396	1
G0463	G0397	1
G0463	G0442	1
G0463	G0443	1
G0463	G0444	1
G0463	G0445	1
G0463	G0446	1
G0463	G0447	1
G0463	G0459	0
G0463	M0064	0

Column 1	Column 2	Modifier
G3001	C8957	1
J1560	J1460	0
J2790	J2792	1
M0064	G0459	0
P3000	G0380	1
P3000	G0381	1
P3000	G0382	1
P3000	G0383	1
P3000	G0384	1
P3000	G0406	1
P3000	G0407	1
P3000	G0408	1
P3000	G0425	1
P3000	G0426	1
P3000	G0427	1
P3000	G0463	1
P3001	G0123	0
P3001	G0141	0
P3001	G0143	0
P3001	G0144	0
P3001	G0145	0
P3001	G0147	0
P3001	G0148	0
P3001	G0380	1
P3001	G0381	1
P3001	G0382	1
P3001	G0383	1
P3001	G0384	1
P3001	G0406	1
P3001	G0407	1
P3001	G0408	1
P3001	G0425	1
P3001	G0426	1
P3001	G0427	1
P3001	G0463	1
P9011	P9010	1
P9011	P9021	0
P9011	P9022	0
P9011	P9039	0
P9022	P9010	1
P9022	P9016	1
P9022	P9021	1
P9022	P9039	1
P9032	P9010	1
P9032	P9011	1
P9032	P9016	1
P9032	P9019	1
P9032	P9020	1

Column 1	Column 2	Modifier
P9032	P9021	1
P9032	P9022	1
P9032	P9031	1
P9032	P9034	1
P9032	P9035	1
P9032	P9039	1
P9033	P9010	1
P9033	P9011	1
P9033	P9016	1
P9033	P9019	1
P9033	P9020	1
P9033	P9021	1
P9033	P9022	1
P9033	P9031	1
P9033	P9034	1
P9033	P9035	1
P9033	P9039	1
P9036	P9010	1
P9036	P9011	1
P9036	P9016	1
P9036	P9019	1
P9036	P9020	1
P9036	P9021	1
P9036	P9022	1
P9036	P9031	1
P9036	P9034	1
P9036	P9035	1
P9036	P9039	1
P9037	P9010	1
P9037	P9011	1
P9037	P9016	1
P9037	P9019	1
P9037	P9020	1
P9037	P9021	1
P9037	P9022	1
P9037	P9031	1
P9037	P9034	1
P9037	P9035	1
P9037	P9039	1
P9038	P9010	1
P9038	P9011	1
P9038	P9016	1
P9038	P9019	1
P9038	P9020	1
P9038	P9021	1
P9038	P9022	1
P9038	P9031	1
P9038	P9034	1

Column 1	Column 2	Modifier
P9038	P9035	1
P9038	P9039	1
P9039	P9010	1
P9039	P9016	1
P9039	P9021	1
P9040	P9010	1
P9040	P9011	1
P9040	P9016	1
P9040	P9019	1
P9040	P9020	1
P9040	P9021	1
P9040	P9022	1
P9040	P9031	1
P9040	P9034	1
P9040	P9035	1
P9040	P9039	1
P9603	P9604	1
P9612	P9615	0
Q0091	G0181	1
Q0091	G0182	1
Q0091	G0380	1
Q0091	G0381	1
Q0091	G0382	1
Q0091	G0383	1
Q0091	G0384	1
Q0091	G0406	1
Q0091	G0407	1
Q0091	G0408	1
Q0091	G0425	1
Q0091	G0426	1
Q0091	G0427	1
Q0091	G0463	1
Q1004	Q1005	1
Q2035	Q2034	0
Q2035	Q2036	0
Q2035	Q2037	0
Q2035	Q2038	0
Q2035	Q2039	0
Q2036	Q2034	0
Q2036	Q2037	0
Q2036	Q2038	0
Q2036	Q2039	0
Q2037	Q2034	0
Q2037	Q2038	0
Q2037	Q2039	0
Q2038	Q2034	0
Q2038	Q2039	0
Q2039	Q2034	0

Column 1	Column 2	Modifier
Q2043	G0380	1
Q2043	G0381	1
Q2043	G0382	1
Q2043	G0383	1
Q2043	G0384	1
Q2043	G0463	1
R0075	R0070	1

Appendix I: General Correct Coding Policies

CHAPTER XII SUPPLEMENTAL SERVICES

HCPCS LEVEL II CODES A0000 - V9999 FOR

NATIONAL CORRECT CODING INITIATIVE POLICY MANUAL FOR MEDICARE SERVICES

Current Procedural Terminology (CPT®) codes, descriptions and other data only are copyright 2014 American Medical Association. All rights reserved.

CPT® is a registered trademark of the American Medical Association.

Applicable FARS\DFARS Restrictions Apply to Government Use.

Fee schedules, relative value units, conversion factors and/or related components are not assigned by the AMA, are not part of CPT®, and the AMA is not recommending their use. The AMA does not directly or indirectly practice medicine or dispense medical services. The AMA assumes no liability for the data contained or not contained herein.

TABLE OF CONTENTS

Chapter XII Supplemental Services
HCPCS Level II Codes A0000 - V9999

A. Introduction

The principles of correct coding discussed in Chapter I apply to HCPCS codes in the range A0000-V9999. Several general guidelines are repeated in this chapter. However, those general guidelines from Chapter I not discussed in this chapter are nonetheless applicable.

Physicians should report the HCPCS/CPT® code that describes the procedure performed to the greatest specificity possible. A HCPCS/CPT® code should be reported only if all services described by the code are performed. A physician should not report multiple HCPCS/CPT® codes if a single HCPCS/CPT® code exists that describes the services. This type of unbundling is incorrect coding.

HCPCS/CPT® codes include all services usually performed as part of the procedure as a standard of medical/surgical practice. A physician should not separately report these services simply because HCPCS/CPT® codes exist for them.

Specific issues unique to HCPCS Level II codes are clarified in this chapter.

The HCPCS Level II codes are alpha-numeric codes developed by the Centers for Medicare & Medicaid Services (CMS) as a complementary coding system to the CPT® Manual. These codes describe physician and non-physician services not included in the CPT® Manual, supplies, drugs, durable medical equipment, ambulance services, etc. The correct coding edits and policy statements that follow address those HCPCS Level II codes that are reported to Medicare carriers, Fiscal Intermediaries, and A/B MACs for Part B services.

B. Evaluation and Management (E&M) Services

Medicare Global Surgery Rules define the rules for reporting evaluation and management (E&M) services with procedures covered by these rules. This section summarizes some of the rules.

All procedures on the Medicare Physician Fee Schedule are assigned a global period of 000, 010, 090, XXX, YYY, ZZZ, or MMM.

The global concept does not apply to XXX procedures. The global period for YYY procedures is defined by the Carrier (A/B MAC processing practitioner service claims). All procedures with a global period of ZZZ are related to another procedure, and the applicable global period for the ZZZ code is determined by the related procedure. Procedures with a global period of MMM are maternity procedures.

Since NCCI PTP edits are applied to same day services by the same provider to the same beneficiary, certain Global Surgery Rules are applicable to NCCI. An E&M service is separately reportable on the same date of service as a procedure with a global period of 000, 010, or 090 under limited circumstances.

If a procedure has a global period of 090 days, it is defined as a major surgical procedure. If an E&M is performed on the same date of service as a major surgical procedure for the purpose of deciding whether to perform this surgical procedure, the E&M service is separately reportable with modifier 57. Other preoperative E&M services on the same date of service as a major surgical procedure are included in the global payment for the procedure and are not separately reportable. NCCI does not contain edits based on this rule because Medicare Carriers (A/B MACs processing practitioner service claims) have separate edits.

If a procedure has a global period of 000 or 010 days, it is defined as a minor surgical procedure. In general E&M services on the same date of service as the minor surgical procedure are included in the payment for the procedure. The decision to perform a minor surgical procedure is included in the payment for the minor surgical procedure and should not be reported separately as an E&M service. However, a significant and separately identifiable E&M service unrelated to the decision to perform the minor surgical procedure is separately reportable with modifier 25. The E&M service and minor surgical procedure do not require different diagnoses. If a minor surgical procedure is performed on a new patient, the same rules for reporting E&M services apply. The fact that the patient is "new" to the provider is not sufficient alone to justify reporting an E&M service on the same date of service as a minor surgical procedure. NCCI contains many, but not all, possible edits based on these principles.

Example: If a physician determines that a new patient with head trauma requires sutures, confirms the allergy and immunization status, obtains informed consent, and performs the repair, an E&M service is not separately reportable. However, if the physician also performs a medically reasonable and necessary full neurological examination, an E&M service may be separately reportable.

For major and minor surgical procedures, postoperative E&M services related to recovery from the surgical procedure during the postoperative period are included in the global surgical package as are E&M services related to complications of the surgery. Postoperative visits unrelated to the diagnosis for which the surgical procedure was performed unless related to a complication of surgery may be reported separately on the same day as a surgical procedure with modifier 24 ("Unrelated Evaluation and Management Service by the Same Physician or Other Qualified Health Care Professional During a Postoperative Period").

Procedures with a global surgery indicator of "XXX" are not covered by these rules. Many of these "XXX" procedures are performed by physicians and have inherent pre-procedure, intra-procedure, and post-procedure work usually performed each time the procedure is completed. This work should never be reported as a separate E&M code. Other "XXX" procedures are not usually performed by a physician and have no physician work relative value units associated with them. A physician should never report a separate E&M code with these procedures for the supervision of others performing the procedure or for the interpretation of the procedure. With most "XXX" procedures, the physician may, however, perform a significant and separately identifiable E&M service on the same date of service which may be reported by appending modifier 25 to the E&M code. This E&M service may be related to the same diagnosis necessitating performance of the "XXX" procedure but cannot include any work inherent in the "XXX" procedure, supervision of others performing the "XXX" procedure, or time for interpreting the result of the "XXX" procedure. Appending modifier 25 to a significant, separately identifiable E&M service when performed on the same date of service as an "XXX" procedure is correct coding.

C. NCCI Procedure to Procedure (PTP) Edit Specific Issues

1. HCPCS code M0064 describes a brief face-to-face office visit with a practitioner licensed to perform the service for the sole purpose of monitoring or changing drug prescriptions used in the treatment of psychiatric disorders. HCPCS code M0064 is not separately reportable with CPT® codes 90785-90853 (psychiatric services). (HCPCS code M0064 was deleted January 1, 2015.)

2. HCPCS code Q0091 (Screening Papanicolaou smear; obtaining, preparing and conveyance of cervical or vaginal smear to laboratory) describes the services necessary to procure and transport a pap smear specimen to the laboratory. If an evaluation and management (E&M) service is performed at the same patient encounter solely for the purpose of performing a screening pap smear, the E&M service is not separately reportable. However, if a significant, separately identifiable E&M service is performed to evaluate other medical problems, both the screening pap smear and the E&M service may be reported separately. Modifier 25 should be appended to the E&M CPT® code indicating that a significant, separately identifiable E&M service was rendered.

3. HCPCS code G0101 (cervical or vaginal cancer screening; pelvic and clinical breast examination) may be reported with evaluation and management (E&M) services under certain circumstances. If a Medicare covered reasonable and medically necessary E&M service requires breast and pelvic examination, HCPCS code G0101 should not be additionally reported. However, if the Medicare covered reasonable and medically necessary E&M service and the screening service, G0101, are unrelated to one another, both HCPCS code G0101 and the E&M service may be reported appending modifier 25 to the E&M service CPT® code. Use of modifier 25 indicates that the E&M service is significant and separately identifiable from the screening service, G0101.

4. HCPCS code G0102 (Prostate cancer screening; digital rectal examination) is not separately payable with an evaluation and management code (CPT® codes 99201-99499). CMS published this policy in the *Federal Register*, November 2, 1999, Page 59414 as follows:

   "As stated in the July 1999 proposed rule, a digital rectal exam (DRE) is a very quick and simple examination taking only a few seconds. We believe it is rarely the sole reason for a physician encounter and is usually part of an E/M encounter. In those instances when it is the only service furnished or it is furnished as part of an otherwise non- covered service, we will pay separately for code G0102. In those instances when it is furnished on the same day as a covered E/M service, we believe it is appropriate to bundle it into the payment for the covered E/M encounter."

5. Positron emission tomography (PET) imaging requires use of a radiopharmaceutical diagnostic imaging agent. HCPCS codes A9555 (Rubidium Rb-82...) and A9526 (Nitrogen N-13 Ammonia...) may only be reported with PET scan CPT® codes 78491 and 78492. HCPCS code A9552 (Fluorodeoxyglucose F-18, FDG,...) may only be reported with PET scan CPT® codes 78459, 78608, and 78811-78816.

6. HCPCS code A9512 (Technetium Tc-99m pertechnetate, diagnostic...) describes a radiopharmaceutical utilized for nuclear medicine studies. Technetium Tc-99m pertechnetate is also a component of other Technetium Tc-99m radiopharmaceuticals with separate AXXXX codes. Code A9512 should not be reported with other AXXXX radiopharmaceuticals containing Technetium Tc-99m for a single nuclear medicine study. However, if two separate nuclear medicine studies are performed on the same date of service, one with the radiopharmaceutical described by HCPCS code A9512 and one with another AXXXX radiopharmaceutical labeled with Technetium Tc-99m, both codes may be reported utilizing an NCCI-associated modifier. HCPCS codes A9500, A9540, and A9541 describe radiopharmaceuticals labeled with Technetium Tc-99m that may be utilized for separate nuclear medicine studies on the same date of service as a nuclear medicine study utilizing the radiopharmaceutical described by HCPCS code A9512.

7. HCPCS code A4220 describes a refill kit for an implantable pump. It should not be reported separately with CPT® codes 95990 (refilling and maintenance of implantable pump..., spinal... or brain...) or 95991 (refilling and maintenance of implantable pump,... spinal... or brain... requiring skill of physician or other qualified health care professional) since Medicare payment for these two CPT® codes includes the refill kit.

   Similarly, HCPCS code A4220 should not be reported separately with CPT® codes 62369 (Electronic analysis of programmable, implanted pump for intrathecal or epidural drug infusion (includes evaluation of reservoir status, alarm status, drug prescription status); with reprogramming and refill) or 62370 (Electronic analysis of programmable, implanted pump for intrathecal or epidural drug infusion (includes evaluation of reservoir status, alarm status, drug prescription status); with reprogramming and refill (requiring skill of a physician or other qualified health care professional)) since Medicare payment for these two CPT® codes includes the refill kit.

8. HCPCS code E0781 describes an ambulatory infusion pump utilized by a patient for infusions outside the physician office or clinic. It is a misuse of this code to report the infusion pump typically utilized in the physician office or clinic.

9. HCPCS codes G0422 and G0423 (intensive cardiac rehabilitation;...per session) include the same services as the cardiac rehabilitation CPT® codes 93797 and 93798 but at a greater frequency. Intensive cardiac rehabilitation may be reported with as many as six hourly sessions on a single date of service. Cardiac rehabilitation services include medical nutrition services to reduce cardiac disease risk factors. Medical nutrition therapy (CPT® codes 97802-97804) should not be reported separately for the same patient encounter. However, medical nutrition therapy services provided under the Medicare benefit for patients with diabetes or chronic renal failure performed at a separate patient encounter on the same date of service may be reported separately. The Medicare covered medical nutrition service cannot be provided at the same patient encounter as the cardiac rehabilitation service.

   Physical or occupational therapy services performed at the same patient encounter as cardiac rehabilitation services are included in the cardiac rehabilitation benefit and are not separately reportable. (CMS Final Rule (*Federal Register*, Vol. 74, No. 226, November 25, 2009, pages 61884-61885)). If physical therapy or occupational therapy services are performed at a separate, medically reasonable and necessary patient encounter on the same date of service as cardiac rehabilitation services, both types of services may be reported utilizing an NCCI-associated modifier.

10. Pulmonary rehabilitation (HCPCS code G0424) includes therapeutic services and all related monitoring services to improve respiratory function. It requires measurement of patient outcome which includes, but is not limited to, pulmonary function testing (e.g., pulmonary stress testing (CPT® codes 94620 and 94621)). Pulmonary rehabilitation should not be reported with HCPCS

codes G0237 (therapeutic procedures to increase strength or endurance of respiratory muscles... (includes monitoring)), G0238 (therapeutic procedures to improve respiratory function... (includes monitoring)), or G0239 (therapeutic procedures to improve respiratory function or increase strength... (includes monitoring)). The services are mutually exclusive. The procedures described by HCPCS codes G0237-G0239 include therapeutic procedures as well as all related monitoring services, the latter including, but not limited to, pulmonary function testing (e.g., pulmonary stress testing (CPT® codes 94620 and 94621)).

Physical or occupational therapy services performed at the same patient encounter as pulmonary rehabilitation services are included in the pulmonary rehabilitation benefit and are not separately reportable. (CMS Final Rule (*Federal Register*, Vol. 74, No. 226, November 25, 2009, Pages 61884-61885)). If physical therapy or occupational therapy services are performed at a separate, medically reasonable and necessary patient encounter on the same date of service as pulmonary rehabilitation services, both types of services may be reported utilizing an NCCI-associated modifier. Similarly physical and occupational therapy services are not separately reportable with therapeutic pulmonary procedures for the same patient encounter.

Medical nutrition therapy services (CPT® codes 97802-97804) performed at the same patient encounter as a pulmonary rehabilitation or pulmonary therapeutic service are included in the pulmonary rehabilitation or pulmonary therapeutic service and are not separately reportable. The Medicare program provides a medical nutrition therapy benefit to beneficiaries for medical nutrition therapy related to diabetes mellitus or renal disease. If a physician provides a Medicare covered medical nutrition service to a beneficiary with diabetes mellitus or renal disease on the same date of service as a pulmonary rehabilitation or pulmonary therapeutic service but at a separate patient encounter, the medical nutrition therapy service may be separately reportable with an NCCI-associated modifier. The Medicare covered medical nutrition service cannot be provided at the same patient encounter as the pulmonary rehabilitation or pulmonary therapeutic service.

11. This paragraph was revised and moved to Section D (Medically Unlikely Edits (MUEs)), Paragraph 13.

12. HCPCS code G0434 (drug screen..., by CLIA waived test or moderate complexity test, per patient encounter) is utilized to report urine drug screening performed by a test that is CLIA waived or CLIA moderate complex. The code is reported with only one (1) unit of service regardless of the number of drugs screened. HCPCS code G0431 (drug screen... by high complexity test method..., per patient encounter) is utilized to report drug urine screening performed by a CLIA high complexity test method. This code is also reported with only one (1) unit of service regardless of the number of drugs screened. If a provider performs urine drug screening, it is generally not necessary for that provider to send an additional specimen from the patient to another laboratory for urine drug screening for the same drugs.

For a single patient encounter only G0431 or G0434 may be reported. The testing described by G0431 includes all CLIA high complexity urine drug screen testing as well as any less complex urine drug screen testing performed at the same patient encounter. HCPCS code G0431 describes a more extensive procedure than HCPCS

code G0434. Physicians should not unbundle urine drug screen testing and report HCPCS codes G0431 and G0434 for the same patient encounter.

13. HCPCS codes G0416-G0419 describe surgical pathology, including gross and microscopic examination, of separately identified and submitted prostate needle biopsy specimens from a saturation biopsy sampling procedure. CMS requires that these codes rather than CPT® code 88305 be utilized to report surgical pathology on prostate needle biopsy specimens only if the number of separately identified and submitted needle biopsy specimens is ten or more. Surgical pathology on nine or fewer separately identified and submitted prostate needle biopsy specimens should be reported with CPT® code 88305 with the unit of service corresponding to the number of separately identified and submitted biopsy specimens.

14. Blood products are described by HCPCS Level II P codes. If a P code describes an irradiated blood product, CPT® code 86945 (irradiation of blood product, each unit) should not be reported separately since the P code includes irradiation of the blood product. If a P code describes a CMV negative blood product, CPT® codes 86644 and/or 86645 (CMV antibody) should not be reported separately for that blood product since the P code includes the CMV antibody testing. If a P code describes a deglycerolized blood product, CPT® codes 86930 (frozen blood, each unit; freezing...), 86931 (frozen blood, each unit; thawing), and/or 86932 (frozen blood, each unit; freezing (includes preparation) and thawing) should not be reported separately since the P code includes the freezing and thawing processes. If a P code describes a pooled blood product, CPT® code 86965 (pooling of platelets or other blood products) should not be reported separately since the P code includes the pooling of the blood products. If the P code describes a "frozen" plasma product, CPT® code 86927 (fresh frozen plasma, thawing, each unit) should not be reported separately since the P code includes the thawing process.

15. HCPCS codes G0396 and G0397 describe alcohol and/or substance (other than tobacco) abuse structured assessment and intervention services. These codes should not be reported separately with an evaluation and management (E&M), psychiatric diagnostic, or psychotherapy service code for the same work/time. If the E&M, psychiatric diagnostic, or psychotherapy service would normally include assessment and/or intervention of alcohol or substance abuse based on the patient's clinical presentation, HCPCS G0396 or G0397 should not be additionally reported. If a physician reports either of these G codes with an E&M, psychiatric diagnostic, or psychotherapy code utilizing an NCCI- associated modifier, the physician is certifying that the G code service is a distinct and separate service performed during a separate time period (not necessarily a separate patient encounter) than the E&M, psychiatric diagnostic, or psychotherapy service and is a service that is not included in the E&M, psychiatric diagnostic, or psychotherapy service based on the clinical reason for the E&M, psychiatric diagnostic, or psychotherapy service.

CPT® codes 99408 and 99409 describe services which are similar to those described by HCPCS codes G0396 and G0397, but are "screening" services which are not covered under the Medicare program. Where CPT® codes 99408 and 99409 are covered by State Medicaid programs, the policies explained in the previous paragraph for G0396/G0397 also apply to 99408/99409.

The same principles apply to separate reporting of E&M services with other screening, intervention, or counseling service HCPCS codes (e.g., G0442 (annual alcohol misuse screening, 15 minutes), G0443 (brief face-to-face behavioral counseling for alcohol misuse, 15 minutes), and G0444 (annual depression screening, 15 minutes). If an E&M, psychiatric diagnostic, or psychotherapy service is related to a problem which would normally require evaluation and management duplicative of the HCPCS code, the HCPCS code is not separately reportable. For example, if a patient presents with symptoms suggestive of depression, the provider should not report G0444 in addition to the E&M, psychiatric diagnostic, or psychotherapy service code. The time and work effort devoted to the HCPCS code screening, intervention, or counseling service must be distinct and separate from the time and work of the E&M, psychiatric diagnostic, or psychotherapy service. Both services may occur at the same patient encounter.

16. HCPCS code G0269 describes placement of an occlusive device into a venous or arterial access site after an open or percutaneous vascular procedure. Since this code is status "B" on the Medicare Physician Fee Schedule Database, payment for this service is included in the payment for the vascular procedure. For OPPS, HCPCS code G0269 has payment status indicator "N" indicating that payment is packaged into the payment for other services paid. Providers reporting services under Medicare's hospital outpatient prospective payment system (OPPS) should report all services in accordance with appropriate Medicare *Internet-Only Manual* (*IOM*) instructions.

17. HCPCS code V2790 (amniotic membrane for surgical reconstruction, per procedure) should not be reported separately with CPT® codes 65778 (Placement of amniotic membrane on the ocular surface; without sutures) or 65779 (Placement of amniotic membrane on the ocular surface; single layer, sutured) since Medicare payment for these two CPT® codes includes the amniotic membrane.

D. Medically Unlikely Edits (MUEs)

1. MUEs are described in Chapter I, Section V.

2. Providers/suppliers should be cautious about reporting services on multiple lines of a claim utilizing modifiers to bypass MUEs. MUEs were set so that such occurrences should be uncommon. If a provider/supplier does this frequently for any HCPCS/CPT® code, the provider/supplier may be coding units of service incorrectly. The provider/supplier should consider contacting his/her national healthcare organization or the national medical/surgical society whose members commonly perform the procedure to clarify the correct reporting of units of service. A national healthcare organization, provider/supplier, or other interested third party may request a reconsideration of the MUE value of a HCPCS/CPT® code by CMS by writing the MUE contractor, Correct Coding Solutions, LLC, at the address indicated in Chapter I, Section V.

3. MUE values of HCPCS codes for discontinued drugs are zero (0).

4. The MUE value of HCPCS codes describing compounded inhalation drugs is zero (0) because compounded drugs are not FDA approved. The CMS *Internet-Only Manual, Medicare Benefit Policy Manual,* Chapter 15, Section 50.4.1 requires that claims processing contractors only pay for FDA approved drugs unless CMS issues other instructions.

5. In 2011 new HCPCS code J0171 (injection, adrenalin, epinephrine, 0.1 mg) replaced deleted HCPCS code J0170 (injection, adrenalin, epinephrine, up to 1 ml ampule). HCPCS code J0170 was often reported incorrectly. A 1 ml ampule of adrenalin/epinephrine contains 1.0 mg of adrenalin/epinephrine in a 1:1,000 solution. However, a 10 ml prefilled syringe with a 1:10,000 solution of adrenalin/epinephrine also contains only 1.0 mg of adrenalin/epinephrine. Thus a physician must recognize that ten (10) units of service for HCPCS code J0171 correspond to a 1 ml ampule or 10 ml of a prefilled syringe (1:10,000 (0.1 mg/ml) solution).

6. There are two HCPCS codes describing injectable dexamethasone. HCPCS code J1094 (injection, dexamethasone acetate, 1 mg) is no longer manufactured and has an MUE value of zero(0). HCPCS code J1100 (injection, dexamethasone sodium phosphate, 1 mg) is currently available. When billing for dexamethasone, physicians should be careful to report the correct formulation with the correct HCPCS code.

7. Based on the code descriptor, HCPCS code J3471 (injection, hyaluronidase, ovine, preservative free, per 1 USP unit (up to 999 units)) should not be reported with more than 999 units of service. Per the CMS ASP (Average Sale Price) NDC (National Drug Code) HCPCS Crosswalk table, HCPCS code J3472 (injection, hyaluronidase, ovine, preservative free, per 1000 USP units) should be reported for a product that is no longer available. Therefore, if a physician utilizes more than 999 USP units of the product described by J3471, the physician may report HCPCS code J3471 on more than one line of a claim appending modifier 59 to additional claim lines and should report no more than 999 units of service on any one claim line.

8. The Medically Unlikely Edit (MUE) values for practitioner services for oral immunosuppressive, oral anti-cancer, and oral anti-emetic drugs are set at zero (0). Practitioners providing these medications to patients must bill the Durable Medical Equipment Medicare Administrative Contractors (DME MACs), rather than the Part A/Part B Medicare Administrative Contractors (A/B MACs), using the National Drug Codes(NDC). A/B MACs do not pay codes for these oral medications when submitted on practitioner claims. The MUE values for outpatient hospital services are based on the amount of drug that might be administered to a patient on a single date of service. Facilities may not report to the A/B MAC more than a one day supply of any of these drugs for a single date of service. Outpatient hospital facilities may submit claims to DME MACs for a multiple day supply of these drugs provided on a single date of service.

9. The MUE values for HCPCS codes G0431 (Drug screen, qualitative; multiple drug classes by high complexity test method (e.g., immunoassay, enzyme assay), per patient encounter) and G0434 (Drug screen, other than chromatographic; any number of drug classes, by CLIA waived test or moderate complexity test, per patient encounter) are one (1) since the UOS for each code is defined as "per patient encounter" and the likelihood that a patient needs this type of testing at more than one encounter on a single date of service is very small. These codes include all drug screening at the patient encounter and should not be reported with multiple UOS at the same patient encounter.

10. HCPCS codes Q9951 and Q9965-Q9967 describe low osmolar contrast material with different iodine concentrations. The appropriate code to report is based on the iodine concentration in the contrast material administered. The MUE value for HCPCS code Q9951 (Low osmolar contrast material, 400 or greater mg/ml iodine concentration, per ml) is zero (0). When this MUE value was established, no low osmolar contrast material products with iodine concentration of 400 mg iodine or greater per ml were identified. HCPCS code Q9951 is often incorrectly reported for low osmolar contrast material products with lower iodine concentrations. Similarly HCPCS codes Q9958-Q9964 describe high osmolar contrast material with different iodine concentrations. The appropriate code to report is based on the iodine concentration in the contrast material administered.

11. Generally only one unit of service for an item of durable medical equipment (DME) (e.g., oxygen concentrator, wheelchair base) may be paid on a single date of service. Medicare does not allow payment for backup or duplicate durable medical equipment. More than one unit of service may be paid on a single date of service for accessories and supplies related to DME when appropriate. Prosthetics and orthotics may also be paid with more than one unit of service on a single date of service when appropriate.

12. *The CMS Internet-Only Manual* (Publication 100-04 *Medicare Claims Processing Manual*, Chapter 12 (Physicians/Nonphysician Practitioners), Section 40.7.B. and Chapter 4 (Part B Hospital (Including Inpatient Hospital Part B and OPPS)), Section 20.6.2 requires that practitioners and outpatient hospitals report bilateral surgical procedures with modifier 50 and one (1) UOS on a single claim line. MUE values for surgical procedures that may be performed bilaterally are based on this reporting requirement. Since this reporting requirement does not apply to an ambulatory surgical center (ASC), an ASC should report a bilateral surgical procedure on two claim lines, each with one (1) UOS using modifiers LT and RT on different claim lines. This reporting requirement does not apply to non-surgical diagnostic procedures.

13. HCPCS codes G0406-G0408 describe follow-up inpatient consultation services via telehealth and HCPCS codes G0425-G0427 describe emergency or initial inpatient telehealth consultation services via telehealth. These codes should not be reported by a practitioner on the same date of service that the practitioner reports a face-to-face evaluation and management code. These codes are utilized to report telehealth services that, if performed with the patient physically present, would be reported with corresponding CPT® codes.

Since follow-up inpatient consultation services with a patient present are reported utilizing per diem CPT® codes 99231-99233, HCPCS codes G0406-G0408 may only be reported with a single unit of service per day.

Since initial inpatient consultation services with a patient present are reported utilizing per diem CPT® codes 99231-99233, HCPCS codes G0425-G0427 may only be reported with a single unit of service per day when reporting inpatient telehealth consultation services. However, if HCPCS codes G0425-G0427 are utilized to report emergency department services, reporting rules are comparable to CPT® codes 99281-99285.

E. General Policy Statements

1. In this Manual many policies are described utilizing the term "physician". Unless indicated differently the usage of this term does not restrict the policies to physicians only but applies to all practitioners, hospitals, providers, or suppliers eligible to bill the relevant HCPCS/CPT® codes pursuant to applicable portions of the Social Security Act (SSA) of 1965, the Code of Federal Regulations (CFR), and Medicare rules. In some sections of this Manual, the term "physician" would not include some of these entities because specific rules do not apply to them. For example, Anesthesia Rules [e.g., CMS Internet-Only Manual, Publication 100-04 (Medicare Claims Processing Manual), Chapter 12 (Physician/Nonphysician Practitioners), Section 50(Payment for Anesthesiology Services)] and Global Surgery Rules [e.g., CMS Internet-Only Manual, Publication 100-04 (Medicare Claims Processing Manual), Chapter 12 (Physician/Nonphysician Practitioners), Section 40 (Surgeons and Global Surgery)] do not apply to hospitals.

2. Providers reporting services under Medicare's hospital outpatient prospective payment system (OPPS) should report all services in accordance with appropriate Medicare *Internet-Only Manual* (*IOM*) instructions.

3. In 2010 the *CPT® Manual* modified the numbering of codes so that the sequence of codes as they appear in the *CPT® Manual* does not necessarily correspond to a sequential numbering of codes. In the *National Correct Coding Initiative Policy Manual for Medicare Services,* use of a numerical range of codes reflects all codes that numerically fall within the range regardless of their sequential order in the *CPT® Manual.*

4. With few exceptions the payment for a surgical procedure includes payment for dressings, supplies, and local anesthesia. These items are not separately reportable under their own HCPCS/CPT® codes. Wound closures utilizing adhesive strips or tape alone are not separately reportable. In the absence of an operative procedure, these types of wound closures are included in an E&M service. Under limited circumstances wound closure utilizing tissue adhesive may be reported separately. If a practitioner utilizes a tissue adhesive alone for a wound closure, it may be reported separately with HCPCS code G0168 (wound closure utilizing tissue adhesive(s) only). If a practitioner utilizes tissue adhesive in addition to staples or sutures to close a wound, HCPCS code G0168 is not separately reportable but is included in the tissue repair. Under OPPS HCPCS code G0168 is not recognized and paid. Facilities may report wound closure utilizing sutures, staples, or tissue adhesives, either singly or in combination with each other, with the appropriate CPT® code in the "Repair (Closure)" section of the *CPT® Manual.*

5. With limited exceptions Medicare Anesthesia Rules prevent separate payment for anesthesia for a medical or surgical procedure when provided by the physician performing the procedure. The physician should not report CPT® codes 00100-01999, 62310-62319, or 64400-64530 for anesthesia for a procedure. Additionally, the physician should not unbundle the anesthesia procedure and report component codes individually. For example, introduction of a needle or intracatheter into a vein (CPT® code 36000), venipuncture (CPT® code 36410), drug administration (CPT® codes 96360-96376) or cardiac assessment (e.g., CPT® codes 93000-93010, 93040-93042) should not be reported when these procedures are related to the delivery of an anesthetic agent.

Medicare allows separate reporting for moderate conscious sedation services (CPT® codes 99143-99145) when provided by the same physician performing a medical or surgical procedure except for those procedures listed in Appendix G of the *CPT® Manual*.

Under Medicare Global Surgery Rules, drug administration services (CPT® codes 96360-96376) are not separately reportable by the physician performing a procedure for drug administration services related to the procedure.

Under the OPPS drug administration services related to operative procedures are included in the associated procedural HCPCS/CPT® codes. Examples of such drug administration services include, but are not limited to, anesthesia (local or other), hydration, and medications such as anxiolytics or antibiotics. Providers should not report CPT® codes 96360-96376 for these services.

Medicare Global Surgery Rules prevent separate payment for postoperative pain management when provided by the physician performing an operative procedure. CPT® codes 36000, 36410, 37202, 62310-62319, 64400-64489, and 96360-96376 describe some services that may be utilized for postoperative pain management. The services described by these codes may be reported by the physician performing the operative procedure only if provided for purposes unrelated to the postoperative pain management, the operative procedure, or anesthesia for the procedure.

If a physician performing an operative procedure provides a drug administration service (CPT® codes 96360-96375) for a purpose unrelated to anesthesia, intra-operative care, or post-procedure pain management, the drug administration service (CPT® codes 96360-96375) may be reported with an NCCI-associated modifier if performed in a non-facility site of service.

6. The Medicare global surgery package includes insertion of urinary catheters. CPT® codes 51701-51703 (insertion of bladder catheters) should not be reported with any procedure with a global period of 000, 010, or 090 days nor with some procedures with a global period of MMM.

7. Closure/repair of a surgical incision is included in the global surgical package except as noted below. Wound repair CPT® codes 12001-13153 should not be reported separately to describe closure of surgical incisions for procedures with global surgery indicators of 000, 010, 090, or MMM. Simple, intermediate, and complex wound repair codes may be reported with Mohs surgery (CPT® codes 17311-17315). Intermediate and complex repair codes may be reported with excision of benign lesions (CPT® codes 11401-11406, 11421-11426, 11441-11471) and excision of malignant lesions (CPT® codes 11600-11646). Wound repair codes (CPT® codes 12001-13153) should not be reported with excisions of benign lesions with an excised diameter of 0.5 cm or less (CPT® codes 11400, 11420, 11440).

8. Control of bleeding during an operative procedure is an integral component of a surgical procedure and is not separately reportable. Postoperative control of bleeding not requiring return to the operating room is included in the global surgical package and is not separately reportable. However, control of bleeding requiring return to the operating room in the postoperative period is separately reportable utilizing modifier 78.

9. A biopsy performed at the time of another more extensive procedure (e.g., excision, destruction, removal) is separately reportable under specific circumstances.

If the biopsy is performed on a separate lesion, it is separately reportable. This situation may be reported with anatomic modifiers or modifier 59.

If the biopsy is performed on the same lesion on which a more extensive procedure is performed, it is separately reportable only if the biopsy is utilized for immediate pathologic diagnosis prior to the more extensive procedure, and the decision to proceed with the more extensive procedure is based on the diagnosis established by the pathologic examination. The biopsy is not separately reportable if the pathologic examination at the time of surgery is for the purpose of assessing margins of resection or verifying resectability. When separately reportable modifier 58 may be reported to indicate that the biopsy and the more extensive procedure were planned or staged procedures.

If a biopsy is performed and submitted for pathologic evaluation that will be completed after the more extensive procedure is performed, the biopsy is not separately reportable with the more extensive procedure.

10. Most NCCI PTP edits for codes describing procedures that may be performed on bilateral organs or structures (e.g., arms, eyes, kidneys, lungs) allow use of NCCI-associated modifiers (modifier indicator of "1") because the two codes of the code pair edit may be reported if the two procedures are performed on contralateral organs or structures. Most of these code pairs should not be reported with NCCI-associated modifiers when the corresponding procedures are performed on the ipsilateral organ or structure unless there is a specific coding rationale to bypass the edit. The existence of the NCCI PTP edit indicates that the two codes generally should not be reported together unless the two corresponding procedures are performed at two separate patient encounters or two separate anatomic sites. However, if the corresponding procedures are performed at the same patient encounter and in contiguous structures, NCCI-associated modifiers should generally not be utilized.

11. If fluoroscopy is performed during an endoscopic procedure, it is integral to the procedure. This principle applies to all endoscopic procedures including, but not limited to, laparoscopy, hysteroscopy, thoracoscopy, arthroscopy, esophagoscopy, colonoscopy, other GI endoscopy, laryngoscopy, bronchoscopy, and cystourethroscopy.

Appendix J: Publication 100 References

100-1, Chapter-1, 10.1

Hospital Insurance (Part A) for Inpatient Hospital, Hospice, Home Health and Skilled Nursing Facility (SNF) Services - A Brief Description

Hospital insurance is designed to help patients defray the expenses incurred by hospitalization and related care. In addition to inpatient hospital benefits, hospital insurance covers post hospital extended care in SNFs and post hospital care furnished by a home health agency in the patient's home. Blood clotting factors, for hemophilia patients competent to use such factors to control bleeding without medical or other supervision, and items related to the administration of such factors, are also a Part A benefit for beneficiaries in a covered Part A stay. The purpose of these additional benefits is to provide continued treatment after hospitalization and to encourage the appropriate use of more economical alternatives to inpatient hospital care. Program payments for services rendered to beneficiaries by providers (i.e., hospitals, SNFs, and home health agencies) are generally made to the provider. In each benefit period, payment may be made for up to 90 inpatient hospital days, and 100 days of post hospital extended care services.

Hospices also provide Part A hospital insurance services such as short-term inpatient care. In order to be eligible to elect hospice care under Medicare, an individual must be entitled to Part A of Medicare and be certified as being terminally ill. An individual is considered to be terminally ill if the individual has a medical prognosis that his or her life expectancy is 6 months or less if the illness runs its normal course.

The various Part A benefit categories (inpatient hospital services, SNF services, home health services, etc.) are subject to separate and mutually exclusive day limits, so that the use of benefit days under one of these benefits does not affect the number of benefit days that remain available under any of the other benefits. For example, the 90 days of inpatient hospital benefits (plus 60 non-renewable lifetime reserve days-- see Pub. 100-02, Medicare Benefit Policy Manual, chapter 5) that are available to a beneficiary in a hospital do not count against the 100 days of post hospital extended care benefits that are available in a SNF, and vice-versa.

100-1, Chapter-3, 20.5

Blood Deductibles (Part A and Part B)

Program payment may not be made for the first 3 pints of whole blood or equivalent units of packed red cells received under Part A and Part B combined in a calendar year. However, blood processing (e.g., administration, storage) is not subject to the deductible.

The blood deductibles are in addition to any other applicable deductible and coinsurance amounts for which the patient is responsible.

The deductible applies only to the first 3 pints of blood furnished in a calendar year, even if more than one provider furnished blood.

100-1, Chapter-3, 20.5.2

Part B Blood Deductible

Blood is furnished on an outpatient basis or is subject to the Part B blood deductible and is counted toward the combined limit. It should be noted that payment for blood may be made to the hospital under Part B only for blood furnished in an outpatient setting. Blood is not covered for inpatient Part B services.

100-1, Chapter-3, 20.5.3

Items Subject to Blood Deductibles

The blood deductibles apply only to whole blood and packed red cells. The term whole blood means human blood from which none of the liquid or cellular components have been removed. Where packed red cells are furnished, a unit of packed red cells is considered equivalent to a pint of whole blood. Other components of blood such as platelets, fibrinogen, plasma, gamma globulin, and serum albumin are not subject to the blood deductible. However, these components of blood are covered as biological.

Refer to Pub. 100-04, Medicare Claims Processing Manual, chapter 4, §231 regarding billing for blood and blood products under the Hospital Outpatient Prospective Payment System (OPPS).

100-1, Chapter-3, 30

Outpatient Mental Health Treatment Limitation

Regardless of the actual expenses a beneficiary incurs in connection with the treatment of mental, psychoneurotic, and personality disorders while the beneficiary is not an inpatient of a hospital at the time such expenses are incurred, the amount of those expenses that may be recognized for Part B deductible and payment purposes is limited to 62.5 percent of the Medicare approved amount for those services. The limitation is called the outpatient mental health treatment limitation (the limitation). The 62.5 percent limitation has been in place since the inception of the Medicare Part B program and it will remain effective at this percentage amount until January 1, 2010. However, effective January 1, 2010, through January 1, 2014, the limitation will be phased out as follows:

- January 1, 2010 –December 31, 2011, the limitation percentage is 68.75%.
  (Medicare pays 55% and the patient pays 45%).
- January 1, 2012 –December 31, 2012, the limitation percentage is 75%
  (Medicare pays 60% and the patient pays 40%).
- January 1, 2013 –December 31, 2013, the limitation percentage is 81.25%.
  (Medicare pays 65% and the patient pays 35%).
- January 1, 2014 –onward, the limitation percentage is 100%
  (Medicare pays 65% and the patient pays 35%).
- January 1, 2014 –onward, the limitation percentage is 100%
  (Medicare pays 80% and the patient pays 20%).

For additional details concerning the outpatient mental health treatment limitation, please see the Medicare Claims Processing Manual, Publication 100-04, chapter 9, section 60 and chapter 12, section 210.

100-1, Chapter-5, 90.2

Laboratory Defined

Laboratory means a facility for the biological, microbiological, serological, chemical, immuno-hematological, hematological, biophysical, cytological, pathological, or other examination of materials derived from the human body for the purpose of providing information for the diagnosis, prevention, or treatment of any disease or impairment of, or the assessment of the health of, human beings. These examinations also include procedures to determine, measure, or otherwise describe the presence or absence of various substances or organisms in the body. Facilities only collecting or preparing specimens (or both) or only serving as a mailing service and not performing testing are not considered laboratories.

100-2, Chapter-1, 10

Covered Inpatient Hospital Services Covered Under Part A

Patients covered under hospital insurance are entitled to have payment made on their behalf for inpatient hospital services. (Inpatient hospital services do not include extended care services provided by hospitals pursuant to swing bed approvals. See Pub. 100-1, Chapter 8, §10.1,"Hospital Providers of Extended Care Services."). However, both inpatient hospital and inpatient SNF benefits are provided under Part A -Hospital Insurance Benefits for the Aged and Disabled, of Title XVIII).

Additional information concerning the following topics can be found in the following manual chapters:

- Benefit periods is found in Chapter 3, "Duration of Covered Inpatient Services";
- Copayment days is found in Chapter 2, "Duration of Covered Inpatient Services";
- Lifetime reserve days is found in Chapter 5, "Lifetime Reserve Days";
- Related payment information is housed in the Provider Reimbursement Manual.

Blood must be furnished on a day which counts as a day of inpatient hospital services to be covered as a Part A service and to count toward the blood deductible. Thus, blood is not covered under Part A and does not count toward the Part A blood deductible when furnished to an inpatient after the inpatient has exhausted all benefit days in a benefit period, or where the individual has elected not to use lifetime reserve days. However, where the patient is discharged on their first day of entitlement or on the hospital's first day of participation, the hospital is permitted to submit a billing form with no accommodation charge, but with ancillary charges including blood.

The records for all Medicare hospital inpatient discharges are maintained in CMS for statistical analysis and use in determining future PPS DRG classifications and rates.

Non-PPS hospitals do not pay for non covered services generally excluded from cover age in the Medicare Program. This may result in denial of a part of the billed charges or in denial of the entire admission, depending upon circumstance. In PPS hospitals, the following are also possible:

1. In appropriately admitted cases where a non covered procedure was performed, denied services may result in payment of a different DRG (i.e., one which excludes payment for the non covered procedure); or

2. In appropriately admitted cases that become cost outlier cases, denied services may lead to denial of some or all of an outlier payment.

The following examples illustrate this principle. If care is non covered because a patient does not need to be hospitalized, the intermediary denies the admission and makes no Part A (i.e., PPS) payment unless paid under limitation on liability. Under limitation on liability, Medicare payment may be made when the provider and the beneficiary were not aware the services were not necessary and could not reasonably be expected to know that he services were not necessary. For detailed instructions, see the Medicare Claims Processing Manual, Chapter 30,"Limitation on Liability." If a patient is appropriately hospitalized but receives (beyond routine services) only non covered care, the admission is denied.

NOTE: The intermediary does not deny an admission that includes covered care, even if non covered care was also rendered. Under PPS, Medicare assumes that it is paying for only the covered care rendered whenever covered services needed to treat and/or diagnose the illness were in fact provided.

If a non covered procedure is provided along with covered non routine care, a DRG change rather than an admission denial might occur. If non covered procedures are elevating costs into the cost outlier category, outlier payment is denied in whole or in part.

When the hospital is included in PPS, most of the subsequent discussion regarding coverage of inpatient hospital services is relevant only in the context of determining the appropriateness of admissions, which DRG, if any, to pay, and the appropriateness of payment for any outlier cases.

If a patient receives items or services in excess of, or more expensive than, those for which payment can be made, payment is made only for the covered items or services or for only the appropriate prospective payment amount. This provision applies not only to inpatient services, but also to all hospital services under Parts A and B of the program. If the items or services were requested by the patient, the hospital may charge him the difference between the amount customarily charged for the services requested and the amount customarily charged for covered services.

An inpatient is a person who has been admitted to a hospital for bed occupancy for purposes of receiving inpatient hospital services. Generally, a patient is considered an inpatient if formally admitted as inpatient with the expectation that he or she will remain at least overnight and occupy a bed even though it later develops that the patient can be discharged or transferred to another hospital and not actually use a hospital bed overnight.

The physician or other practitioner responsible for a patient's care at the hospital is also responsible for deciding whether the patient should be admitted as an inpatient. Physicians should use a 24-hour period as a benchmark, i.e., they should order admission for patients who are expected to need hospital care for 24 hours or more, and treat other patients on an outpatient basis. However, the decision to admit a patient is a complex medical judgment which can be made only after the physician has considered a number of factors, including the patient's medical history and current medical needs, the types of facilities available to inpatients and to outpatients, the hospital's by-laws and admissions policies, and the relative appropriateness of treatment in each setting. Factors to be considered when making the decision to admit include such things as:

- The severity of the signs and symptoms exhibited by the patient;
- The medical predictability of something adverse happening to the patient;
- The need for diagnostic studies that appropriately are outpatient services (i.e., their performance does not ordinarily require the patient to remain at the hospital for 24 hours or more) to assist in assessing whether the patient should be admitted; and
- The availability of diagnostic procedures at the time when and at the location where the patient presents

Admissions of particular patients are not covered or non covered solely on the basis of the length of time the patient actually spends in the hospital. In certain specific situations coverage of services on an inpatient or outpatient basis is determined by the following rules:

Minor Surgery or Other Treatment - When patients with known diagnoses enter a hospital for a specific minor surgical procedure or other treatment that is expected to keep them in the hospital for only a few hours (less than 24), they are considered outpatients for coverage purposes regardless of: the hour they came to the hospital, whether they used a bed, and whether they remained in the hospital past midnight.

Renal Dialysis - Renal dialysis treatments are usually covered only as outpatient services but may under certain circumstances be covered as inpatient services depending on the patient's condition. Patients staying at home, who are ambulatory, whose conditions are stable and who come to the hospital for routine chronic dialysis treatments, and not for a diagnostic workup or a change in therapy, are considered outpatients. On the other hand, patients undergoing short-term dialysis until their kidneys recover from an acute illness (acute dialysis), or persons with borderline renal failure who develop acute renal failure every time they have an illness and require dialysis (episodic dialysis) are usually inpatients. A patient may begin dialysis as an inpatient and then progress to an outpatient status.

Under original Medicare, the Quality Improvement Organization (QIO), for each hospital is responsible for deciding, during review of inpatient admissions on a case-by-case basis, whether the admission was medically necessary. Medicare law authorizes the QIO to make these judgments, and the judgments are binding for purposes of Medicare coverage. In making these judgments, however, QIOs consider only the medical evidence which was available to the physician at the time an admission decision had to be made. They do not take into account other information (e.g., test results) which became available only after admission, except in cases where considering the post-admission information would support a finding that an admission was medically necessary.

Refer to Parts 4 and 7 of the QIO Manual with regard to initial determinations for these services. The QIO will review the swing bed services in these PPS hospitals as well.

NOTE: When patients requiring extended care services are admitted to beds in a hospital, they are considered inpatients of the hospital. In such cases, the services furnished in the hospital will not be considered extended care services, and payment may not be made under the program for such services unless the services are extended care services furnished pursuant to a swing bed agreement granted to the hospital by the Secretary of Health and Human Services.

100-2, Chapter-1, 10.1.4

Charges for Deluxe Private Room

Beneficiaries found to need a private room (either because they need isolation for medical reasons or because they need immediate admission when no other accommodations are available) may be assigned to any of the provider's private rooms. They do not have the right to insist on the private room of their choice, but their preferences should be given the same consideration as if they were paying all provider charges themselves. The program does not, under any circumstances, pay for personal comfort items. Thus, the program does not pay for deluxe accommodations and/or services. These would include a suite, or a room substantially more spacious than is required for treatment, or specially equipped or decorated, or serviced for the comfort and convenience of persons willing to pay a differential for such amenities. If the beneficiary (or representative) requests such deluxe accommodations, the provider should advise that there will be a charge, not covered by Medicare, of a specified amount per day (not exceeding the differential defined in the next sentence); and may charge the beneficiary that amount for each day he/she occupies the deluxe accommodations. The maximum amount the provider may charge the beneficiary for such accommodations is the differential between the most prevalent private room rate at the time of admission and the customary charge for the room occupied. Beneficiaries may not be charged this differential if they (or their representative) do not request the deluxe accommodations.

The beneficiary may not be charged such a differential in private room rates if that differential is based on factors other than personal comfort items. Such factors might include differences between older and newer wings, proximity to lounge, elevators or nursing stations, desirable view, etc. Such rooms are standard 1-bed units and not deluxe rooms for purposes of these instructions, even though the provider may call them deluxe and have a higher customary charge for them. No additional charge may be imposed upon the beneficiary who is assigned to a room that may be somewhat more desirable because of these factors.

100-2, Chapter-1, 40

Supplies, Appliances, and Equipment

Supplies, appliances, and equipment, which are ordinarily furnished by the hospital for the care and treatment of the beneficiary solely during the inpatient hospital stay, are covered inpatient hospital services.

Under certain circumstances, supplies, appliances, and equipment used during the beneficiary's inpatient stay are covered under Part A even though the supplies, appliances and equipment leave the hospital with the patient upon discharge. These are circumstances in which it would be unreasonable or impossible from a medical standpoint to limit the patient's use of the item to the periods during which the individual is an inpatient. Examples of items covered under this rule are:

- Items permanently installed in or attached to the patient's body while an inpatient, such as cardiac valves, cardiac pacemakers, and artificial limbs; and
- Items which are temporarily installed in or attached to the patient's body while an inpatient, and which are also necessary to permit or facilitate the patient's release from the hospital, such as tracheotomy or drainage tubes.

Hospital "admission packs" containing primarily toilet articles, such as soap, toothbrushes, toothpaste, and combs, are covered under Part A if routinely furnished by the hospital to all its inpatients. If not routinely furnished to all patients, the packs are not covered. In that situation, the hospital may charge beneficiaries for the pack, but only if they request it with knowledge of what they are requesting and what the charge to them will be.

Supplies, appliances, and equipment furnished to an inpatient for use Only outside the hospital are not, in general, covered as inpatient hospital services. However, a temporary or disposable item, which is medically necessary to permit or facilitate the patient's departure from the hospital and is required until the patient can obtain a continuing supply, is covered as an inpatient hospital service.

Oxygen furnished to hospital inpatients is covered under Part A as an inpatient supply.

100-2, Chapter-1, 70

Inpatient Services in Connection With Dental Services

When a patient is hospitalized for a dental procedure and the dentist's service is covered under Part B, the inpatient hospital services furnished are covered under Part A. For example, both the professional services of the dentist and the inpatient hospital expenses are covered when the Dentist reduces a jaw fracture of an inpatient at a participating hospital. In addition, hospital inpatient services, which are necessary because of the patient's underlying medical condition and clinical status or the severity of a non covered dental procedure, are covered.

When the hospital services are covered, all ancillary services such as x-rays, administration of anaesthesia, use of the operating room, etc., are covered.

Regardless of whether the inpatient hospital services are covered, the medical services of physicians furnished in connection with non covered dental services are not covered. The services of an anaesthesiologist, radiologist, or pathologist whose services are performed in connection with the care, treatment, filling, removal, or replacement of teeth or structures directly supporting teeth are not covered.

100-2, Chapter-6, 10

Medical and Other Health Services Furnished to Inpatients of Participating Hospitals

Payment may be made under Part B for physician services and for the nonphysician medical and other health services as provided in this section when furnished by a participating hospital (either directly or under arrangements) to an inpatient of the hospital, but only if payment for these services cannot be made under Part A. This policy applies to all hospitals and critical access hospitals (CAHs) participating in Medicare, including those paid under a prospective payment system or alternative payment methodology such as State cost control systems, and to emergency hospital services furnished by nonparticipating hospitals. In this section, the term "hospital" includes all hospitals and CAHs, regardless of payment methodology, unless otherwise specified.

For services to be covered under Part A or Part B, a hospital must furnish nonphysician services to its inpatients directly or under arrangements (see chapter 16, §170 of this manual, "Inpatient Hospital or SNF Services Not Delivered Directly or Under Arrangement by the Provider"). A nonphysician service is one which does not meet the criteria defining physicians' services specifically provided for in regulation at 42 CFR 415.102. Services "incident to" physicians' services

(except for the services of nurse anesthetists employed by anesthesiologists) are nonphysician services for purposes of this provision.

100-2, Chapter 6, 20.6

Outpatient Observation Services

A. Outpatient Observation Services Defined

Observation care is a well-defined set of specific, clinically appropriate services, which include ongoing short term treatment, assessment, and reassessment before a decision can be made regarding whether patients will require further treatment as hospital inpatients or if they are able to be discharged from the hospital. Observation services are commonly ordered for patients who present to the emergency department and who then require a significant period of treatment or monitoring in order to make a decision concerning their admission or discharge.

Observation services are covered only when provided by the order of a physician or another individual authorized by State licensure law and hospital staff bylaws to admit patients to the hospital or to order outpatient tests. In the majority of cases, the decision whether to discharge a patient from the hospital following resolution of the reason for the observation care or to admit the patient as an inpatient can be made in less than 48 hours, usually in less than 24 hours. In only rare and exceptional cases do reasonable and necessary outpatient observation services span more than 48 hours.

Hospitals may bill for patients who are directly referred to the hospital for outpatient observation services. A direct referral occurs when a physician in the community refers a patient to the hospital for outpatient observation, bypassing the clinic or emergency department (ED) visit. Effective for services furnished on or after January 1, 2003, hospitals may bill for patients directly referred for observation services.

See, Pub. 100-04, Medicare Claims Processing Manual, chapter 4, section 290, at http://www.cms.hhs.gov/manuals/downloads/clm104c04.pdf for billing and payment instructions for outpatient observation services.

Future updates will be issued in a Recurring Update Notification.

B. Coverage of Outpatient Observation Services

When a physician orders that a patient receive observation care, the patient's status is that of an outpatient. The purpose of observation is to determine the need for further treatment or for inpatient admission. Thus, a patient receiving observation services may improve and be released, or be admitted as an inpatient (see Pub. 100-02, Medicare Benefit Policy Manual, Chapter 1, Section 10 "Covered Inpatient Hospital Services Covered Under Part A" at http://www.cms.hhs.gov/manuals/Downloads/bp102c01.pdf). For more information on correct reporting of observation services, see Pub. 100-04, Medicare Claims Processing Manual, chapter 4, section 290.2.2.)

All hospital observation services, regardless of the duration of the observation care, that are medically reasonable and necessary are covered by Medicare. Observation services are reported using HCPCS code G0378 (Hospital observation service, per hour). Beginning January 1, 2008, HCPCS code G0378 for hourly observation services is assigned status indicator N, signifying that its payment is always packaged. No separate payment is made for observation services reported with HCPCS code G0378. In most circumstances, observation services are supportive and ancillary to the other separately payable services provided to a patient. In certain circumstances when observation care is billed in conjunction with a high level clinic visit (Level 5), high level Type A emergency department visit (Level 4 or 5), high level Type B emergency department visit (Level5), critical care services, or direct referral for observation services as an integral part of a patient's extended encounter of care, payment may be made for the entire extended care encounter through one of two composite APCs when certain criteria are met. For information about billing and payment methodology for observation services in years prior to CY 2008, see Pub. 100-04, Medicare Claims Processing Manual, Chapter 4,§§290.3-290.4. For information about payment for extended assessment and management under composite APCs, see §290.5.

Payment for all reasonable and necessary observation services is packaged into the payments for other separately payable services provided to the patient in the same encounter. Observation services packaged through assignment of status indicator N are covered OPPS services. Since the payment for these services is included in the APC payment for other separately payable services on the claim, hospitals must not bill Medicare beneficiaries directly for the packaged services.

C. Services Not Covered by Medicare and Notification to the Beneficiary

In making the determination whether an ABN can be used to shift liability to a beneficiary for the cost of non-covered items or services related to an encounter that includes observation care, the provider should follow a two step process. First, the provider must decide whether the item or service meets either the definition of observation care or would be otherwise covered. If the item or service does not meet the definitional requirements of any Medicare-covered benefit under Part B, then the item or service is not covered by Medicare and an ABN is not required to shift the liability to the beneficiary. However, the provider may choose to provide voluntary notification for these items or services.

Second, if the item or service meets the definition of observation services or would be otherwise covered, then the provider must decide whether the item or service is "reasonable and necessary" for the beneficiary on the occasion in question, or if the item or service exceeds any frequency limitation for the particular benefit or falls outside of a timeframe for receipt of a particular benefit. In these cases, the ABN would be used to shift the liability to the beneficiary (see Pub. 100-04, Medicare Claims Processing Manual; Chapter 30, "Financial Liability Protections," Section 20, at http://www.cms.hhs.gov/manuals/downloads/clm104c30.pdf for information regarding Limitation On Liability (LOL) Under §1879 Where Medicare Claims Are Disallowed).

If an ABN is not issued to the beneficiary, the provider may be held liable for the cost of the item or service unless the provider/supplier is able to demonstrate that they did not know and could not have reasonably been expected to know that Medicare would not pay for the item or service.

100-2, Chapter 10, 10.2.2

Reasonableness of the Ambulance Trip

Under the FS payment is made according to the level of medically necessary services actually furnished. That is, payment is based on the level of service furnished (provided they were medically necessary), not simply on the vehicle used. Even if a local government requires an ALS response for all calls, payment under the FS is made only for the level of

service furnished, and then only when the service is medically necessary.

100-2, Chapter 10,10.3.3

Separately Payable Ambulance Transport Under Part B versus Patient Transportation that is Covered Under a Packaged Hospital Service

Transportation of a beneficiary from his or her home, an accident scene, or any other point of origin is covered under Part B as an ambulance service only to the nearest hospital, critical access hospital (CAH), or skilled nursing facility (SNF) that is capable of furnishing the required level and type of care for the beneficiary's illness or injury and only if medical necessity and other program coverage criteria are met.

Medicare-covered ambulance services are paid either as separately billed services, in which case the entity furnishing the ambulance service bills Part B of the program, or as a packaged service, in which case the entity furnishing the ambulance service must seek payment from the provider who is responsible for the beneficiary's care. If either the origin or the destination of the ambulance transport is the beneficiary's home, then the ambulance transport is paid separately by Medicare Part B, and the entity that furnishes the ambulance transport may bill its Medicare carrier or intermediary directly. If both the origin and destination of the ambulance transport are providers, e.g., a hospital, critical access hospital (CAH), skilled nursing facility (SNF), then responsibility for payment for the ambulance transport is determined in accordance with the following sequential criteria.

NOTE: These criteria must be applied in sequence as a flow chart and not independently of one another.

1. Provider Numbers:

   If the Medicare-assigned provider numbers of the two providers are different, then the ambulance service is separately billable to the program. If the provider number of both providers is the same, then consider criterion 2, "campus".

2. Campus:

   Following criterion 1, if the campuses of the two providers (sharing the same provider numbers) are the same, then the transport is not separately billable to the program. In this case the provider is responsible for payment. If the campuses of the two providers are different, then consider criterion 3, "patient status." "Campus" means the physical area immediately adjacent to the provider's main buildings, other areas and structures that are not strictly contiguous to the main buildings, but are located within 250 yards of the main buildings, and any of the other areas determined on an individual case basis by the CMS regional office to be part of the provider's campus.

3. Patient Status: Inpatient vs. Outpatient

   Following criteria 1 and 2, if the patient is an inpatient at both providers (i.e., inpatient status both at the origin and at the destination, providers sharing the same provider number but located on different campuses), then the transport is not separately billable. In this case the provider is responsible for payment. All other combinations (i.e., outpatient-to inpatient, inpatient-to-outpatient, outpatient-to-outpatient) are separately billable to the program.

In the case where the point of origin is not a provider, Part A coverage is not available because, at the time the beneficiary is being transported, the beneficiary is not an inpatient of any provider paid under Part A of the program and ambulance services are excluded from the 3-day preadmission payment window.

The transfer, i.e., the discharge of a beneficiary from one provider with a subsequent admission to another provider, is also payable as a Part B ambulance transport, provided all program coverage criteria are met, because, at the time that the beneficiary is in transit, the beneficiary is not a patient of either provider and not subject to either the inpatient preadmission payment window or outpatient payment packaging requirements. This includes an outpatient transfer from a remote, off- campus emergency department (ER) to becoming an inpatient or outpatient at the main campus hospital, even if the ER is owned and operated by the hospital.

Once a beneficiary is admitted to a hospital, CAH, or SNF, it may be necessary to transport the beneficiary to another hospital or other site temporarily for specialized care while the beneficiary maintains inpatient status with the original provider. This movement of the patient is considered "patient transportation" and is covered as an inpatient hospital or CAH service and as a SNF service when the SNF is furnishing it as a covered SNF service and payment is made under Part

A for that service. (If the beneficiary is a resident of a SNF and must be transported by ambulance to receive dialysis or certain other high-end outpatient hospital services, the ambulance transport may be separately payable under Part B.) Because the service is covered and payable as a beneficiary transportation service under Part A, the service cannot be classified and paid for as an ambulance service under Part B. This includes intra-campus transfers between different departments of the same hospital, even where the departments are located in separate buildings. Such intra-campus transfers are not separately payable under the Part B ambulance benefit. Such costs are accounted for in the same manner as the costs of such a transfer within a single building.

100-2, Chapter 10, 20

Coverage Guidelines for Ambulance Service Claims

Payment may be made for expenses incurred by a patient for ambulance service provided conditions l, 2, and 3 in the left-hand column have been met. The right-hand column indicates the documentation needed to establish that the condition has been met.

Conditions	Review Action
1. Patient was transported by an approved supplier of ambulance services.	1. Ambulance suppliers are explained in greater detail in §10.1.3
2. The patient was suffering from an illness or injury, which contraindicated transportation by other means. (§10.2)	2. (a) The contractor presumes the requirement was met if the submitted documentation indicates that the patient: • Was transported in an emergency situation, e.g., as a result of an accident, injury or acute illness, or • Needed to be restrained to prevent injury to the beneficiary or others; or • Was unconscious or in shock; or • Required oxygen or other emergency treatment during transport to the nearest appropriate facility; or • Exhibits signs and symptoms that indicate the possibility of acute stroke; or • Had to remain immobile because of a fracture that had not been set or the possibility of a fracture; or • Was experiencing severe hemorrhage; or • Could be moved only by stretcher; or • Was bed-confined before and after the ambulance trip.
	b. In the absence of any of the conditions listed in (a) above additional documentation should be obtained to establish medical need where the evidence indicates the existence of the circumstances listed below: i. Patient's condition would not ordinarily require movement by stretcher, or ii. The individual was not admitted as a hospital inpatient (except in accident cases), or iii. The ambulance was used solely because other means of transportation were unavailable, or iv. (iv) The individual merely needed assistance in getting from his room or home to a vehicle. c. Where the information indicates a situation not listed in 2(a) or 2(b) above, refer the case to your supervisor.

3. The patient was transported from and to points listed below.
 	
  a. From patient's residence (or other place where need arose) to hospital or skilled nursing facility.
	3. Claims should show the ZIP Code of the point of pickup.
	
	  a.
	  i. Condition met if trip began within the institution's service area as shown in the carrier's locality guide.
	  ii. Condition met where the trip began outside the institution's service area if the institution was the nearest one with appropriate facilities.

NOTE: A patient's residence is the place where he or she makes his/her home and dwells permanently, or for an extended period of time. A skilled nursing facility is one, which is listed in the Directory of Medical Facilities as a participating SNF or as an institution which meets §1861(j)(1) of the Act.

NOTE: A claim for ambulance service to a participating hospital or skilled nursing facility should not be denied on the grounds that there is a nearer nonparticipation institution having appropriate facilities.

b. Skilled nursing facility to a hospital or hospital to a skilled nursing facility.	b. i. Condition met if the ZIP Code of the pickup point is within the service area of the destination as shown in the carrier's locality guide. ii. Condition met where the ZIP Code of the pickup point is outside the service area of the destination if the destination institution was the nearest appropriate facility.
c. Hospital to hospital or skilled nursing facility to skilled nursing facility.	c. Condition met if the discharging institution was not an appropriate facility and the admitting institution was the nearest appropriate facility.
d. From a hospital or skilled nursing facility to patient's residence.	d. i. Condition met if patient's residence is within the institution's service area as shown in the carrier's locality guide. ii. Condition met where the patient's residence is outside the institution's service area if the institution was the nearest appropriate facility.
e. Round trip for hospital or participating skilled nursing facility inpatients to the nearest hospital or nonhospital treatment facility.	e. Condition met if the reasonable and necessary diagnostic or therapeutic service required by patient's condition is not available at the institution where the beneficiary is an inpatient.

NOTE: Ambulance service to a physician's office or a physician-directed clinic is not covered. See §10.3.8 above, where a stop is made at a physician's office en route to a hospital and §10.3.3 for additional exceptions.)

4. Ambulance services involving hospital admissions in Canada or Mexico are covered (Medicare Claims Processing Manual, Chapter 1, "General Billing Requirements," §10.1.3.) if the following conditions are met :	4. (a) The foreign hospitalization has been determined to be covered; and b. The ambulance service meets the coverage requirements set forth in §§10-10.3. If the foreign hospitalization has been determined to be covered on the basis of emergency services (See the Medicare Claims Processing Manual, Chapter 1, "General Billing Requirements," §10.1.3), the necessity requirement (§10.2) and the destination requirement (§10.3) are considered met.
5. The carrier will make partial payment for otherwise covered ambulance service, which exceeded limits defined in item	5 & 6 (a) From the pickup point to the nearest appropriate facility, or 5 & 6 (b) From the nearest appropriate facility to the beneficiary's residence where he or she is being returned home from a distant institution.
6. The carrier will base the payment on the amount payable had the patient been transported:	

100-2, Chapter 10, 30.1.1

Ground Ambulance Services

Basic Life Support (BLS)

Definition: Basic life support (BLS) is transportation by ground ambulance vehicle and the provision of medically necessary supplies and services, including BLS ambulance services as defined by the State. The ambulance must be staffed by an individual who is qualified in accordance with State and local laws as an emergency medical technician-basic (EMT-Basic). These laws may vary from State to State or within a State. For example, only in some jurisdictions is an EMT-Basic permitted to operate limited equipment onboard the vehicle, assist more qualified personnel in performing assessments and interventions, and establish a peripheral intravenous (iv) line.

Basic Life Support (BLS) –Emergency

Definition: When medically necessary, the provision of BLS services, as specified above, in the context of an emergency response. An emergency response is one that, at the time the ambulance provider or supplier is called, it responds immediately. An immediate response is one in which the ambulance provider/supplier begins as quickly as possible to take the steps necessary to respond to the call.

Application: The determination to respond emergently with a BLS ambulance must be in accord with the local 911 or equivalent service dispatch protocol. If the call came in directly to the ambulance provider/supplier, then the provider's/supplier's dispatch protocol must meet, at a minimum, the standards of the dispatch protocol of the local 911 or equivalent service. In areas that do not have a local 911 or equivalent service, then the protocol must meet, at a minimum, the standards of a dispatch protocol in another similar jurisdiction within the State or, if there is no similar jurisdiction within the State, then the standards of any other dispatch protocol within the State. Where the dispatch was inconsistent with this standard of protocol, including where no protocol was used, the beneficiary's condition (for example, symptoms) at the scene determines the appropriate level of payment.

Advanced Life Support, Level 1 (ALS1)

Definition: Advanced life support, level 1 (ALS1) is the transportation by ground ambulance vehicle and the provision of medically necessary supplies and services including the provision of an ALS assessment or at least one ALS intervention.

Advanced Life Support Assessment

Definition: An advanced life support (ALS) assessment is an assessment performed by an ALS crew as part of an emergency response that was necessary because the patient's reported condition at the time of dispatch was such that only an ALS crew was qualified to perform the assessment. An ALS assessment does not necessarily result in a determination that the patient requires an ALS level of service.

Application: The determination to respond emergently with an ALS ambulance must be in accord with the local 911 or equivalent service dispatch protocol. If the call came in directly to the ambulance provider/supplier, then the provider's/supplier's dispatch protocol must meet, at a minimum, the standards of the dispatch protocol of the local 911 or equivalent service. In areas that do not have a local 911 or equivalent service, then the protocol must meet, at a minimum, the standards of a dispatch protocol in another similar jurisdiction within the State or, if there is no similar jurisdiction within the State, then the standards of any other dispatch protocol within the State. Where the dispatch was inconsistent with this standard of protocol, including where no protocol was used, the beneficiary's condition (for example, symptoms) at the scene determines the appropriate level of payment.

Advanced Life Support Intervention

Definition: An advanced life support (ALS) intervention is a procedure that is in accordance with State and local laws, required to be done by an emergency medical technician-intermediate (EMT-Intermediate) or EMT-Paramedic.

Application: An ALS intervention must be medically necessary to qualify as an intervention for payment for an ALS level of service. An ALS intervention applies only to ground transports.

Advanced Life Support, Level 1 (ALS1) –Emergency

Definition: When medically necessary, the provision of ALS1 services, as specified above, in the context of an emergency response. An emergency response is one that, at the time the ambulance provider or supplier is called, it responds immediately. An immediate response is one in which the ambulance provider/supplier begins as quickly as possible to take the steps necessary to respond to the call.

Application: The determination to respond emergently with an ALS ambulance must be in accord with the local 911 or equivalent service dispatch protocol. If the call came in directly to the ambulance provider/supplier, then the provider's/supplier's dispatch protocol must meet, at a minimum, the standards of the dispatch protocol of the local 911 or equivalent service. In areas that do not have a local 911 or equivalent service, then the protocol must meet, at a minimum, the standards of a dispatch protocol in another similar jurisdiction within the State or, if there is no similar jurisdiction within the State, then the standards of any other dispatch protocol within the State. Where the dispatch was inconsistent with this standard of protocol, including where no protocol was used, the beneficiary's condition (for example, symptoms) at the scene determines the appropriate level of payment.

Advanced Life Support, Level 2 (ALS2)

Definition: Advanced life support, level 2 (ALS2) is the transportation by ground ambulance vehicle and the provision of medically necessary supplies and services including (1) at least three separate administrations of one or more medications by intravenous push/bolus or by continuous infusion (excluding crystalloid fluids) or (2) ground ambulance transport, medically necessary supplies and services, and the provision of at least one of theALS2 procedures listed below:

 a. Manual defibrillation/cardioversion;

 b. Endo tracheal intubation;

 c. Central venous line;

 d. Cardiac pacing;

 e. Chest decompression;

 f. Surgical airway; or

 g. Intraosseous line.

Application: Crystalloid fluids include fluids such as 5 percent Dextrose in water, Saline and Lactated Ringer's. Medications that are administered by other means, for example: intramuscular/subcutaneous injection, oral, sublingually or nebulized, do not qualify to determine whether theALS2 level rate is payable. However, this is not an all-inclusive list. Likewise, a single dose of medication administered fractionally (i.e., one-third of a single dose quantity) on three separate occasions does not qualify for the ALS2 payment rate. The criterion of multiple administrations of the same drug requires a suitable quantity and amount of time between administrations that is in accordance with standard medical practice guidelines. The fractional administration of a single dose (for this purpose meaning a standard or protocol dose) on three separate occasions does not qualify for ALS2 payment.

In other words, the administration of 1/3of a qualifying dose 3 times does not equate to three qualifying doses for purposes of indicating ALS2 care. One-third of X given 3 times might = X (where X is a standard/protocol drug amount), but the same sequence does not equal 3 times X. Thus, if 3 administrations of the same drug are required to show that ALS2 care was given, each of those administrations must be in accord with local protocols. The run will not qualify on the basis of drug administration if that administration was not according to protocol.

An example of a single dose of medication administered fractionally on three separate occasions that would not qualify for the ALS2 payment rate would be the use of Intravenous (IV) Epinephrine in the treatment of pulse less Ventricular Tachycardia/Ventricular Fibrillation (VF/VT) in the adult patient. Administering this medication in increments of 0.25 mg, 0.25 mg, and 0.50 mg would not qualify for the ALS2 level of payment. This medication, according to the American Heart Association (AHA), Advanced Cardiac Life Support (ACLS) protocol, calls for Epinephrine to be administered in 1 mg increments every 3 to 5minutes. Therefore, in order to receive payment for an ALS2 level of service, based in part on the administration of Epinephrine, three separate administrations of Epinephrine in 1 mg increments must be administered for the treatment of pulse less VF/VT.

A second example that would not qualify for the ALS2 payment level is the use of Adenosine in increments of 2 mg, 2 mg, and 2 mg for a total of 6 mg in the treatment of an adult patient with Paroxysmal Supra ventricular Tachycardia (PSVT). According to ACLS guidelines, 6 mg of Adenosine should be given by rapid intravenous push (IVP) over 1 to 2 seconds. If the first dose does not result in the elimination of the supra ventricular tachycardia within 1 to 2 minutes, 12 mg of Adenosine should be administered IVP. If the supra ventricular tachycardia persists, a second 12 mg dose of Adenosine can be administered for a total of 30 mg of Adenosine. Three separate Administrations of the drug Adenosine in the dosage amounts outlined in the later case would qualify forALS2 payment.

Endotracheal intubation is one of the services that qualifies for the ALS2 level of payment; therefore, it is not necessary to consider medications administered by Endo tracheal intubation for the purpose of determining whether the ALS2 rate is payable. The monitoring and maintenance of an end tracheal tube that was previously inserted prior to transport also qualifies as an ALS2 procedure.

Advanced Life Support (ALS) Personnel

Definition: ALS personnel are individuals trained to the level of the emergency medical technician-intermediate (EMT-Intermediate) or paramedic.

Specialty Care Transport (SCT)

Definition: Specialty care transport (SCT) is the inter facility transportation of a critically injured or ill beneficiary by a ground ambulance vehicle, including the provision of medically necessary supplies and services, at a level of service beyond the scope of the EMT-Paramedic. SCT is necessary when a beneficiary's condition requires ongoing care that must be furnished by one or more health professionals in an appropriate specialty area, for example, emergency or critical care nursing, emergency medicine, respiratory care, cardiovascular care, or a paramedic with additional training.

Application: The EMT-Paramedic level of care is set by each State. SCT is necessary when a beneficiary's condition requires ongoing care that must be furnished by one or more health professionals in an appropriate specialty area. Care above that level that is medically necessary and that is furnished at a level of service above the EMT-Paramedic level of care is considered SCT. That is to say, if EMT-Paramedics -without specialty care certification or qualification -are permitted to furnish a given service in a State, then that service does not qualify for SCT. The phrase "EMT-Paramedic with additional training" recognizes that a State may permit a person who is not only certified as an EMT-Paramedic, but who also has successfully completed additional education as determined by the State in furnishing higher level medical services required by critically ill or critically injured patients, to furnish a level of service that otherwise would require a health professional in an appropriate specialty care area (for example, a nurse) to provide. "Additional training" means the specific additional training that a State requires a paramedic to complete in order to qualify to furnish specialty care to a critically ill or injured patient during an SCT.

Paramedic Intercept (PI)

Definition: Paramedic Intercept services are ALS services provided by an entity that does not provide the ambulance transport. This type of service is most often provided for an emergency ambulance transport in which a local volunteer ambulance that can provide only basic life support (BLS) level of service is dispatched to transport a patient. If the patient needs ALS services such as EKG monitoring, chest decompression, or I.V. therapy, another entity dispatches a paramedic to meet the BLS ambulance at the scene or once the ambulance is on the way to the hospital. The ALS paramedics then provide services to the patient.

This tiered approach to life saving is cost effective in many areas because most volunteer ambulances do not charge for their services and one paramedic service can cover many communities. Prior to March 1, 1999, Medicare payment could be made for these services, but only when the claim was submitted by the entity that actually furnished the ambulance transport. Payment could not be made directly to the intercept service provider. In those areas where State laws prohibit volunteer ambulances from billing Medicare and other health insurance, the intercept service could not receive payment for treating a Medicare beneficiary and was forced to bill the beneficiary for the entire service.

Paramedic intercept services furnished on or after March 1, 1999, may be payable separate from the ambulance transport, subject to the requirements specified below.

The intercept service(s) is:

- Furnished in a rural area;
- Furnished under a contract with one or more volunteer ambulance services; and,
- Medically necessary based on the condition of the beneficiary receiving the ambulance service.
- In addition, the volunteer ambulance service involved must:
- Meet the program's certification requirements for furnishing ambulance services;
- Furnish services only at the BLS level at the time of the intercept; and,
- Be prohibited by State law from billing anyone for any service. Finally, the entity furnishing the ALS paramedic intercept service must:
- Meet the program's certification requirements for furnishing ALS services, and,
- Bill all recipients who receive ALS paramedic intercept services from the entity, regardless of whether or not those recipients are Medicare beneficiaries.

For purposes of the paramedic intercept benefit, a rural area is an area that is designated as rural by a State law or regulation or any area outside of a Metropolitan Statistical Area or in New England, outside a New England County Metropolitan Area as defined by the Office of Management and Budget. The current list of these areas is periodically published in the Federal Register.

See the Medicare Claims Processing Manual, Chapter 15, "Ambulance," §20.1.4 for payment of paramedic intercept services.

Services in a Rural Area

Definition: Services in a rural area are services that are furnished (1) in an area outside a Metropolitan Statistical Area (MSA); or, (2) in New England, outside a New England County Metropolitan Area (NECMA); or, (3) an area identified as rural using the Goldsmith modification even though the area is within an MSA.

Emergency Response

Definition: Emergency response is a BLS or ALS1 level of service that has been provided in immediate response to a 911 call or the equivalent. An immediate response is one in which the ambulance provider/supplier begins as quickly as possible to take the steps necessary to respond to the call.

Application: The phrase "911 call or equivalent" is intended to establish the standard that the nature of the call at the time of dispatch is the determining factor. Regardless of the medium by which the call is made (e.g., a radio call could be appropriate) the call is of an emergent nature when, based on the information available to the dispatcher at the time of the call, it is reasonable for the dispatcher to issue an emergency dispatch in light of accepted, standard dispatch protocol. An emergency call need not come through 911 even in areas where a 911 call system exists. However, the determination to respond emergently must be in accord with the local 911 or equivalent service dispatch protocol. If the call came in directly to the ambulance provider/supplier, then the provider's/supplier's dispatch protocol and the dispatcher's actions must meet, at a minimum, the standards of the dispatch protocol of the local 911 or equivalent service. In areas that do not have a local 911 or equivalent service, then both the protocol and the dispatcher's actions must meet, at a minimum, the standards of the dispatch protocol in another similar jurisdiction within the State, or if there is no similar jurisdiction, then the standards of any other dispatch protocol within the State. Where the dispatch was inconsistent with this standard of protocol, including where no protocol was used, the beneficiary's condition (for example, symptoms) at the scene determines the appropriate level of payment.

EMT-Intermediate

Definition: EMT-Intermediate is an individual who is qualified, in accordance with State and local laws, as an EMT-Basic and who is also certified in accordance with State and local laws to perform essential advanced techniques and to administer a limited number of medications.

EMT-Paramedic

Definition: EMT-Paramedic possesses the qualifications of the EMT-Intermediate and, in accordance with State and local laws, has enhanced skills that include being able to administer additional interventions and medications.

Relative Value Units

Definition: Relative value units (RVUs) measure the value of ambulance services relative to the value of a base level ambulance service.

Application: The RVUs for the ambulance fee schedule are as follows:

Service Level RVUs
BLS 1.00
BLS –Emergency 1.60
ALS1 1.20
ALS1 –Emergency 1.90
ALS2 2.75
SCT 3.25
PI 1.75
RVUs are not applicable to FW and RW services.

100-2, Chapter 12, 30.1

Rules for Payment of CORF Services

The payment basis for CORF services is 80 percent of the lesser of: (1) the actual charge for the service or (2) the physician fee schedule amount for the service when the physician fee schedule establishes a payment amount for such service. Payment for CORF services under the phnysician fee schedule is made for physical therapy, occupational therapy, speech-language pathology and respiratory therapy services, as well as the nursing and social and/or psychological services, which are a part of, or directly relate to, the rehabilitation plan of treatment.

Payment for covered durable medical equipment, orthotic and prosthetic (DMEPOS) devices and supplies provided by a CORF is based upon: the lesser of 80 percent of actual charges or the payment amount established under the DMEPOS fee schedule; or, the single payment amount established under the DMEPOS competitive bidding program, provided that payment for such an item is not included in the payment amount for other CORF services.

If there is no fee schedule amount for a covered CORF item or service, payment should be based on the lesser of 80 percent of the actual charge for the service provided or an amount determined by the local Medicare contractor.

The following conditions apply to CORF physical therapy, occupational therapy, and speech-language pathology services;

- Claims must contain the required functional reporting. (Reference: Sections 42 CFR 410.105.) Refer to Pub. 100-04, Medicare Claims Processing Manual, chapter 5, section 10.6.
- The functional reporting on claims must be consistent with the functional limitations identified as part of the patient's therapy plan of care and expressed as part of the patient's therapy goals; effective for claims with dates of service on and after January, 1, 2013. (Reference: 42 CFR 410.105.) See Pub. 100-04, Medicare Claims Processing Manual, chapter 5, section 10.6.
- The National Provider Identifier (NPI) of the certifying physician identified for a CORF physical therapy, occupational therapy, and speech-language pathology plan of treatment must be included on the therapy claim. This requirement is effective for claims with dates of service on or after October 1, 2012. (See Pub. 100-04, Medicare Claims Processing Manual, chapter 5, section 10.3.)

Payment for CORF social and/or psychological services is made under the physician fee schedule only for HCPCS code G0409, as appropriate, and only when billed using revenue codes 0560, 0569, 0910, 0911, 0914 and 0919.

Payment for CORF respiratory therapy services is made under the physician fee schedule when provided by a respiratory therapist as defined at 42CFR485.70(j) and, only to the extent that these services support or are an adjunct to the rehabilitation plan of treatment, when billed using revenue codes 0410, 0412 and 0419. Separate payment is not made for diagnostic tests or for services related to physiologic monitoring services which are bundled into other respiratory therapy services appropriately performed by a respiratory therapist, such as HCPCS codes G0237, G0238 and G0239.

Payment for CORF nursing services is made under the physician fee schedule only when provided by a registered nurse as defined at 42CFR485.70 (h) for nursing services only to the extent that these services support or are an adjunct to the rehabilitation plan of treatment. In addition, payment for CORF nursing services is made only when provided by a registered nurse. HCPCS code G0128 is used to bill for these services and only with revenue codes 0550 and 0559.

For specific payment requirements for CORF items and services see Pub. 100-04, Medicare Claims Processing Manual, Chapter 5, Part B Outpatient Rehabilitation and CORF/OPT Services.

100-2, Chapter 12, 40.5

Respiratory Therapy Services

A respiratory therapy plan of treatment is wholly established and signed by the referring physician before the respiratory therapist initiates the actual treatment.

A. Definition

Respiratory therapy services include only those services that can be appropriately provided to CORF patients by a qualified respiratory therapist, as defined at 42CFR485.70 (j), under a physician-established respiratory therapy plan of treatment. The facility physician must be present in the facility for a sufficient time to provide, in accordance with accepted principles of medical practice, medical direction, medical care services and consultation. Respiratory therapy services include the physiological monitoring necessary to furnish these services. Payment for these services is bundled into the payment for respiratory therapy services and is not payable separately. Diagnostic and other medical services provided in the CORF setting are not considered CORF services, and therefore may not be included in a respiratory therapy plan of treatment because these are covered under separate benefit categories.

The respiratory therapist assesses the patient to determine the appropriateness of pursed lip breathing activity and may check the patient's oxygen saturation level (via pulse oximetry). If appropriate, the respiratory therapist then provides the initial training in order to ensure that the patient can accurately perform the activity. The respiratory therapist may again check the patient's oxygen saturation level, or perform peak respiratory flow, or check other respiratory parameters. These types of services are considered "physiological monitoring" and are bundled into the payment for HCPCS codes G0237, G0238 and G0239. Physiological monitoring also includes the provision of a 6-minute walk test that is typically conducted before the start of the patient's respiratory therapy activities. The time to provide this walk "test" assessment is included as part of the HCPCS code G0238. When provided as part of a CORF respiratory therapy plan of treatment, payment for these monitoring activities is bundled into the payment for other services provided by the respiratory therapist, such as the three respiratory therapy specific G-codes.

B. Guidelines for Applying Coverage Criteria

There are some conditions for which respiratory therapy services may be indicated. However, respiratory therapy performed as part of a standard protocol without regard to the individual patient's actual condition, capacity for improving, and the need for such services as established, is not reasonable and medically necessary. All respiratory therapy services must meet the test of being "reasonable and medically necessary" pursuant to §1862(a)(1)(A) of the Act. Determinations of medical necessity are made based on local contractor decisions on a claim-by-claim basis.

The three HCPCS codes G0237, G0238, and G0239 are specific to services provided under the respiratory therapy plan of treatment and, as such, are not designated as subject to the therapy caps.

C. Patient Education Programs

Instructing a patient in the use of equipment, breathing exercises, etc. may be considered reasonable and necessary to the patient's respiratory therapy plan of treatment and can usually be given to a patient during the course of treatment by the respiratory therapist.

These educational instructions are bundled into the covered service and separate payment is not made.

100-2, Chapter 12, 40.8

Nursing Services

CORF nursing services may only be provided by an individual meeting the qualifications of a registered nurse, as defined at 42CFR485.70 (h). They must relate to, or be a part of, the rehabilitation plan of treatment.

CORF nursing services must be reasonable and medically necessary and are provided as an adjunct to the rehabilitation plan of treatment. For example, a registered nurse may perform or instruct a patient, as appropriate, in the proper procedure of "in and out" urethral catheterization,

tracheostomy tube suctioning, or the cleaning for ileostomy or colostomy bags.

Nursing services may not substitute for or supplant the services of physical therapists, occupational therapists, speech-language pathologists and respiratory therapists, but instead must support or further the services and goals provided in the rehabilitation plan of treatment.

CORF nursing services must be provided by a registered nurse and may only be coded as HCPCS code G0128 indicating that CORF "nursing services" were provided.

100-2, Chapter 12, 40.11

Vaccines

A CORF may provide pneumococcal pneumonia, influenza virus, and hepatitis B vaccines to its patients. While not included as a service under the CORF benefit, Medicare will make payment to the CORF for certain vaccines and their administration provided to CORF patients (CY 2008 PFS Rule 72 FR 66293).

The following three vaccinations are covered in a CORF if a physician who is a doctor of medicine or osteopathy orders it for a CORF patient:

- Pneumococcal pneumonia vaccine and its administration;
- Hepatitis B vaccine and its administration furnished to a beneficiary who is at high or intermediate risk of contracting hepatitis B; and
- Influenza virus vaccine and its administration

Payment for covered pneumococcal pneumonia, influenza virus, and hepatitis B vaccines provided in the CORF setting is based on 95 percent of the average wholesale price. The CORF registered nurse provides administration of any of these vaccines using HCPCS codes G0008, G0009 or G0010 with payment based on CPT® code 90471.

100-2, Chapter 15, 50

Drugs and Biologicals

The Medicare program provides limited benefits for outpatient drugs. The program covers drugs that are furnished "incident to" a physician's service provided that the drugs are not usually self-administered by the patients who take them.

Generally, drugs and biologicals are covered only if all of the following requirements are met:

- They meet the definition of drugs or biologicals (see §50.1);
- They are of the type that are not usually self-administered. (see §50.2);
- They meet all the general requirements for coverage of items as incident to a physician's services (see §§50.1 and 50.3);
- They are reasonable and necessary for the diagnosis or treatment of the illness or injury for which they are administered according to accepted standards of medical practice (see §50.4);
- They are not excluded as non covered immunizations (see §50.4.4.2); and
- They have not been determined by the FDA to be less than effective. (See §§50.4.4)

Medicare Part B does generally not cover drugs that can be self-administered, such as those in pill form, or are used for self-injection. However, the statute provides for the coverage of some self-administered drugs. Examples of self-administered drugs that are covered include blood-clotting factors, drugs used in immunosuppressive therapy, erythropoietin for dialysis patients, osteoporosis drugs for certain homebound patients, and certain oral cancer drugs. (See §110.3 for coverage of drugs, which are necessary to the effective use of Durable Medical Equipment (DME) or prosthetic devices.)

100-2, Chapter 15, 50.2

Determining Self-Administration of Drug or Biological

The Medicare program provides limited benefits for outpatient prescription drugs. The program covers drugs that are furnished "incident to" a physician's service provided that the drugs are not usually self-administered by the patients who take them. Section 112 of the Benefits, Improvements & Protection Act of 2000 (BIPA) amended sections 1861(s)(2)(A) and 1861(s)(2)(B) of the Act to redefine this exclusion. The prior statutory language referred to those drugs "which cannot be self-administered." Implementation of the BIPA provision requires interpretation of the phrase "not usually self-administered by the patient"

A. Policy

Fiscal intermediaries, carriers and Medicare Administrative Contractors (MACs) are instructed to follow the instructions below when applying the exclusion for drugs that are usually self administered by the patient. Each individual contractor must make its own individual determination on each drug. Contractors must continue to apply the policy that not only the drug is medically reasonable and necessary for any individual claim, but also that the route of administration is medically reasonable and necessary. That is, if a drug is available in both oral and injectable forms, the injectable form of the drug must be medically reasonable and necessary as compared to using the oral form.

For certain injectable drugs, it will be apparent due to the nature of the condition(s) for which they are administered or the usual course of treatment for those conditions, they are, or are not, usually self-administered. For example, an injectable drug used to treat migraine headaches is usually self-administered. On the other hand, an injectable drug, administered at the same time as chemotherapy, used to treat anemia secondary to chemotherapy is not usually self-administered.

B. Administered

The term "administered" refers only to the physical process by which the drug enters the patient's body. It does not refer to whether the process is supervised by a medical professional (for example, to observe proper technique or side-effects of the drug). Injectable drugs, including intravenously administered drugs, are typically eligible for inclusion under the "incident to" benefit. With limited exceptions, other routes of administration including, but not limited to, oral drugs, suppositories, topical medications are considered to be usually self-administered by the patient.

C. Usually

For the purposes of applying this exclusion, the term "usually" means more than 50 percent of the time for all Medicare beneficiaries who use the drug. Therefore, if a drug is self-administered by more than 50 percent of Medicare beneficiaries, the drug is excluded from coverage and the contractor may not make any Medicare payment for it. In arriving at a single

determination as to whether a drug is usually self-administered, contractors should make a separate determination for each indication for a drug as to whether that drug is usually self-administered.

After determining whether a drug is usually self-administered for each indication, contractors should determine the relative contribution of each indication to total use of the drug (i.e., weighted average) in order to make an overall determination as to whether the drug is usually self-administered. For example, if a drug has three indications, is not self-administered for the first indication, but is self administered for the second and third indications, and the first indication makes up 40 percent of total usage, the second indication makes up 30 percent of total usage, and the third indication makes up 30 percent of total usage, then the drug would be considered usually self-administered.

Reliable statistical information on the extent of self-administration by the patient may not always be available. Consequently, CMS offers the following guidance for each contractor's consideration in making this determination in the absence of such data:

1. Absent evidence to the contrary, presume that drugs delivered intravenously are not usually self- administered by the patient.

2. Absent evidence to the contrary, presume that drugs delivered by intramuscular injection are not usually self-administered by the patient. (Avonex, for example, is delivered by intramuscular injection, not usually self-administered by the patient.) The contractor may consider the depth and nature of the particular intramuscular injection in applying this presumption. In applying this presumption, contractors should examine the use of the particular drug and consider the following factors:

3. Absent evidence to the contrary, presume that drugs delivered by subcutaneous injection are self-administered by the patient. However, contractors should examine the use of the particular drug and consider the following factors:

   A. **Acute Condition** -Is the condition for which the drug is used an acute condition? If so, it is less likely that a patient would self-administer the drug. If the condition were longer term, it would be more likely that the patient would self-administer the drug.

   B. **Frequency of Administration** -How often is the injection given? For example, if the drug is administered once per month, it is less likely to be self-administered by the patient. However, if it is administered once or more per week, it is likely that the drug is self-administered by the patient.

In some instances, carriers may have provided payment for one or perhaps several doses of a drug that would otherwise not be paid for because the drug is usually self-administered. Carriers may have exercised this discretion for limited coverage, for example, during a brief time when the patient is being trained under the supervision of a physician in the proper technique for self-administration. Medicare will no longer pay for such doses. In addition, contractors may no longer pay for any drug when it is administered on an outpatient emergency basis, if the drug is excluded because it is usually self-administered by the patient.

D. Definition of Acute Condition

For the purposes of determining whether a drug is usually self-administered, an acute condition means a condition that begins over a short time period, is likely to be of short duration and/or the expected course of treatment is for a short, finite interval. A course of treatment consisting of scheduled injections lasting less than 2 weeks, regardless of frequency or route of administration, is considered acute. Evidence to support this may include Food and Drug Administration (FDA) approval language, package inserts, drug compendia, and other information.

E. By the Patient

The term "by the patient" means Medicare beneficiaries as a collective whole. The carrier includes only the patients themselves and not other individuals (that is, spouses, friends, or other care- givers are not considered the patient). The determination is based on whether the drug is self-administered by the patient a majority of the time that the drug is used on an outpatient basis by Medicare beneficiaries for medically necessary indications. The carrier ignores all instances when the drug is administered on an inpatient basis.

The carrier makes this determination on a drug-by-drug basis, not on a beneficiary-by-beneficiary basis. In evaluating whether beneficiaries as a collective whole self-administer, individual beneficiaries who do not have the capacity to self-administer any drug due to a condition other than the condition for which they are taking the drug in question are not considered. For example, an individual afflicted with paraplegia or advanced dementia would not have the capacity to self-administer any injectable drug, so such individuals would not be included in the population upon which the determination for self-administration by the patient was based. Note that some individuals afflicted with a less severe stage of an otherwise debilitating condition would be included in the population upon which the determination for "self-administered by the patient" was based; for example, an early onset of dementia.

F. Evidentiary Criteria

Contractors are only required to consider the following types of evidence: peer reviewed medical literature, standards of medical practice, evidence-based practice guidelines, FDA approved label, and package inserts. Contractors may also consider other evidence submitted by interested individuals or groups subject to their judgment.

Contractors should also use these evidentiary criteria when reviewing requests for making a determination as to whether a drug is usually self-administered, and requests for reconsideration of a pending or published determination.

Note that prior to August 1, 2002, one of the principal factors used to determine whether a drug was subject to the self-administered exclusion was whether the FDA label contained instructions for self-administration. However, CMS notes that under the new standard, the fact that the FDA label includes instructions for self-administration is not, by itself, a determining factor that a drug is subject to this exclusion.

G. Provider Notice of Noncovered Drugs

Contractors must describe on their Web site the process they will use to determine whether a drug is usually self-administered and thus does not meet the "incident to" benefit category. Contractors must publish a list of the injectable drugs that are subject to the self-administered exclusion on their Web site, including the data and rationale that led to the determination. Contractors will report the workload associated with developing new coverage statements in CAFM 21208.

Contractors must provide notice 45 days prior to the date that these drugs will not be covered. During the 45-day time period, contractors will maintain existing medical review and payment procedures. After the 45-day notice, contractors may deny payment for the drugs subject to the notice.

Contractors must not develop local coverage determinations (LCDs) for this purpose because further elaboration to describe drugs that do not meet the 'incident to' and the 'not usually self-administered' provisions of the statute are unnecessary. Current LCDs based solely on these provisions must be withdrawn. LCDs that address the self-administered exclusion and other information may be reissued absent the self-administered drug exclusion material. Contractors will report this workload in CAFM 21206. However, contractors may continue to use and write LCDs to describe reasonable and necessary uses of drugs that are not usually self-administered.

H. Conferences Between Contractor

Contractors' Medical Directors may meet and discuss whether a drug is usually self-administered without reaching a formal consensus. Each contractor uses its discretion as to whether or not it will participate in such discussions. Each contractor must make its own individual determinations, except that fiscal intermediaries may, at their discretion, follow the determinations of the local carrier with respect to the self-administered exclusion.

I. Beneficiary Appeals

If a beneficiary's claim for a particular drug is denied because the drug is subject to the "Self-administered drug" exclusion, the beneficiary may appeal the denial. Because it is a "benefit category" denial and not a denial based on medical necessity, an Advance Beneficiary Notice (ABN) is not required. A "benefit category" denial (i.e., a denial based on the fact that there is no benefit category under which the drug may be covered) does not trigger the financial liability protection provisions of Limitation On Liability (under §1879 of the Act). Therefore, physicians or providers may charge the beneficiary for an excluded drug.

J. Provider and Physician Appeals

A physician accepting assignment may appeal a denial under the provisions found in Pub. 100-04, Medicare Claims Processing Manual, chapter 29.

K. Reasonable and Necessary

Contractors will make the determination of reasonable and necessary with respect to the medical appropriateness of a drug to treat the patient's condition. Contractors will continue to make the determination of whether the intravenous or injection form of a drug is appropriate as opposed to the oral form. Contractors will also continue to make the determination as to whether a physician's office visit was reasonable and necessary. However, contractors should not make a determination of whether it was reasonable and necessary for the patient to choose to have his or her drug administered in the physician's office or outpatient hospital setting. That is, while a physician's office visit may not be reasonable and necessary in a specific situation, in such a case an injection service would be payable.

L. Reporting Requirements

Each carrier, intermediary and Medicare Administrative Contractor (MAC) must report to CMS its complete list of injectable drugs that the contractor has determined are excluded when furnished incident to a physician's service on the basis that the drug is usually self-administered. The CMS expects that contractors will review injectable drugs on a rolling basis and update their list of excluded drugs as it is developed and no less frequently than annually. For example, contractors should not wait to publish this list until every drug has been reviewed. Contractors must enter their self-administered drug exclusion list to the Medicare Coverage Database (MCD). This database can be accessed at www.cms.hhs.gov/mcd. See Pub.100-08, Medicare Program Integrity Manual, Chapter 3, Section 3.3, "Policies and Guidelines Applied During Review", for instructions on submitting these lists to the MCD.

M. Drugs Treated as Hospital Outpatient Supplies

In certain circumstances, Medicare pays for drugs that may be considered usually self-administered by the patient when such drugs function as supplies. This is the case when the drugs provided are an integral component of a procedure or are directly related to it, i.e., when they facilitate the performance of or recovery from a particular procedure. Except for the applicable copayment, hospitals may not bill beneficiaries for these types of drugs because their costs, as supplies, are packaged into the payment for the procedure with which they are used. Listed below are examples of when drugs are treated as supplies and hospitals should bill Medicare for the drug as a supply and should not separately bill the beneficiary.

- Sedatives administered to a patient while he or she is in the preoperative area being prepared for a procedure.
- Mydriatic drops instilled into the eye to dilate the pupils, anti-inflammatory drops, antibiotic drops/ointments, and ocular hypotensives that are administered to a patient immediately before, during, or immediately following an ophthalmic procedure. This does not refer to the patient's eye drops that the patient uses pre-and postoperatively.
- Barium or low osmolar contrast media provided integral to a diagnostic imaging procedure.
- Topical solution used with photodynamic therapy furnished at the hospital to treat nonhyperkeratotic actinic keratosis lesions of the face or scalp.
- Antibiotic ointments such as bacitracin, placed on a wound or surgical incision at the completion of a procedure.

The following are examples of when a drug is not directly related or integral to a procedure, and does not facilitate the performance of or recovery from a procedure. Therefore the drug is not considered a packaged supply. In many of these cases the drug itself is the treatment instead of being integral or directly related to the procedure, or facilitating the performance of or recovery from a particular procedure.

- Drugs given to a patient for his or her continued use at home after leaving the hospital.
- Oral pain medication given to an outpatient who develops a headache while receiving chemotherapy administration treatment.
- Daily routine insulin or hypertension medication given preoperatively to a patient.
- A fentanyl patch or oral pain medication such as hydrocodone, given to an outpatient presenting with pain.
- A laxative suppository for constipation while the patient waits to receive an unrelated X-ray.

These two lists of examples may serve to guide hospitals in deciding which drugs are supplies packaged as a part of a procedure, and thus may be billed under Part B. Hospitals should follow CMS' guidance for billing drugs that are packaged and paid as supplies, reporting coded and uncoded drugs with their charges under the revenue code associated with the cost center under which the hospital accumulates the costs for the drugs.

100-2, Chapter 15, 50.4.2

Unlabeled Use of Drug

An unlabeled use of a drug is a use that is not included as an indication on the drugs label as approved by the FDA. FDA approved drugs used for indications other than what is indicated on the official label may be covered under Medicare if the carrier determines the use to be medically accepted, taking into consideration the major drug compendia, authoritative medical literature and/or accepted standards of medical practice. In the case of drugs used in an anti-cancer chemotherapeutic regimen, unlabeled uses are covered for a medically accepted indication as defined in §50.5.

These decisions are made by the contractor on a case-by-case basis.

100-2, Chapter 15, 50.4.4.2

Immunizations

Vaccinations or inoculations are excluded as immunizations unless they are directly related to the treatment of an injury or direct exposure to a disease or condition, such as anti-rabies treatment, tetanus antitoxin or booster vaccine, botulin antitoxin, antivenin sera, or immune globulin. In the absence of injury or direct exposure, preventive immunization (vaccination or inoculation) against such diseases as smallpox, polio, diphtheria, etc., is not covered. However, pneumococcal, hepatitis B, and influenza virus vaccines are exceptions to this rule. (See items A, B, and C below.) In cases where a vaccination or inoculation is excluded from coverage, related charges are also not covered.

A. Pneumococcal Pneumonia Vaccinations

Effective for services furnished on or after May 1, 1981, the Medicare Part B program covers pneumococcal pneumonia vaccine and its administration when furnished in compliance with any applicable State law by any provider of services or any entity or individual with a supplier number. This includes revaccination of patients at highest risk of pneumococcal infection. Typically, these vaccines are administered once in a lifetime except for persons at highest risk. Effective July 1, 2000, Medicare does not require for coverage purposes that a doctor of medicine or osteopathy order the vaccine. Therefore, the beneficiary may receive the vaccine upon request without a physician's order and without physician supervision.

An initial vaccine may be administered only to persons at high risk (see below) of pneumococcal disease. Revaccination may be administered only to persons at highest risk of serious pneumococcal infection and those likely to have a rapid decline in pneumococcal antibody levels, provided that at least 5 years have [passed since the previous dose of pneumococcal vaccine.

Persons at high risk for whom an initial vaccine may be administered include all people age 65 and older; immunocompetent adults who are at increased risk of pneumococcal disease or its complications because of chronic illness (e.g., cardiovascular disease, pulmonary disease, diabetes mellitus, alcoholism, cirrhosis, or cerebrospinal fluid leaks); and individuals with compromised immune systems (e.g., splenic dysfunction or anatomic asplenia, Hodgkin's disease, lymphoma, multiple myeloma, chronic renal failure, HIV infection, nephrotic syndrome, sickle cell disease, or organ transplantation).

Persons at highest risk and those most likely to have rapid declines in antibody levels are those for whom revaccination may be appropriate. This group includes persons with functional or anatomicasplenia (e.g., sickle cell disease, splenectomy), HIV infection, leukemia, lymphoma, Hodgkin's disease, multiple myeloma, generalized malignancy, chronic renal failure, nephrotic syndrome, or other conditions associated with immunosuppression such as organ or bone marrow transplantation, and those receiving immunosuppressive chemotherapy. It is not appropriate for routine revaccination of people age 65 or older that are not at highest risk.

Those administering the vaccine should not require the patient to present an immunization record prior to administering the pneumococcal vaccine, nor should they feel compelled to review the patient's complete medical record if it is not available. Instead, provided that the patient is competent, it is acceptable to rely on the patient's verbal history to determine prior vaccination status. If the patient is uncertain about his or her vaccination history in the past 5 years, the vaccine should be given. However, if the patient is certain he/she was were vaccinated in the last 5 years, the vaccine should not be given. If the patient is certain that the vaccine was given more than 5 years ago, revaccination is covered only if the patient is at high risk.

B. Hepatitis B Vaccine

Effective for services furnished on or after September 1, 1984, P.L. 98-369 provides coverage under Part B for hepatitis B vaccine and its administration, furnished to a Medicare beneficiary who is at high or intermediate risk of contracting hepatitis B. This coverage is effective for services furnished on or after September 1, 1984. High-risk groups currently identified include (see exception below):

- ESRD patients;
- Hemophiliacs who receive Factor VIII or IX concentrates;
- Clients of institutions for the mentally retarded;
- Persons who live in the same household as a Hepatitis B Virus (HBV) carrier;
- Homosexual men;
- Illicit injectable drug abusers; and
- Persons diagnosed with diabetes mellitus.

Intermediate risk groups currently identified include:

- Staff in institutions for the mentally retarded; and
- Workers in health care professions who have frequent contact with blood or blood-derived body fluids during routine work.

EXCEPTION: Persons in both of the above-listed groups in paragraph B, would not be considered at high or intermediate risk of contracting hepatitis B, however, if there were laboratory evidence positive for antibodies to hepatitis B. (ESRD patients are routinely tested for hepatitis B antibodies as part of their continuing monitoring and therapy.)

For Medicare program purposes, the vaccine may be administered upon the order of a doctor of medicine or osteopathy, by a doctor of medicine or osteopathy, or by home health agencies, skilled nursing facilities, ESRD facilities, hospital outpatient departments, and persons recognized under the incident to physicians' services provision of law.

A charge separate from the ESRD composite rate will be recognized and paid for administration of the vaccine to ESRD patients.

C. Influenza Virus Vaccine

Effective for services furnished on or after May 1, 1993, the Medicare Part B program covers influenza virus vaccine and its administration when furnished in compliance with any applicable State law by any provider of services or any entity or individual with a supplier number. Typically, these vaccines are administered once a flu season. Medicare does not require, for coverage purposes, that a doctor of medicine or osteopathy order the vaccine. Therefore, the beneficiary may receive the vaccine upon request without a physician's order and without physician supervision.

100-2, Chapter 15, 100

Surgical Dressings, Splints, Casts, and Other Devices Used for Reductions of Fractures and Dislocations

Surgical dressings are limited to primary and secondary dressings required for the treatment of a wound caused by, or treated by, a surgical procedure that has been performed by a physician or other health care professional to the extent permissible under State law. In addition, surgical dressings required after debridement of a wound are also covered, irrespective of the type of debridement, as long as the debridement was reasonable and necessary and was performed by a health care professional acting within the scope of his/her legal authority when performing this function. Surgical dressings are covered for as long as they are medically necessary.

Primary dressings are therapeutic or protective coverings applied directly to wounds or lesions either on the skin or caused by an opening to the skin. Secondary dressing materials that serve a therapeutic or protective function and that are needed to secure a primary dressing are also covered. Items such as adhesive tape, roll gauze, bandages, and disposable compression material are examples of secondary dressings. Elastic stockings, support hose, foot coverings, leotards, knee supports, surgical leggings, gauntlets, and pressure garments for the arms and hands are examples of items that are not ordinarily covered as surgical dressings. Some items, such as transparent film, may be used as a primary or secondary dressing.

If a physician, certified nurse midwife, physician assistant, nurse practitioner, or clinical nurse specialist applies surgical dressings as part of a professional service that is billed to Medicare, the surgical dressings are considered incident to the professional services of the health care practitioner. (See §§60.1, 180, 190, 200, and 210.) When surgical dressings are not covered incident to the services of a health care practitioner and are obtained by the patient from a supplier (e.g., a drugstore, physician, or other health care practitioner that qualifies as a supplier) on an order from a physician or other health care professional authorized under State law or regulation to make such an order, the surgical dressings are covered separately under Part B.

Splints and casts, and other devices used for reductions of fractures and dislocations are covered under Part B of Medicare. This includes dental splints.

100-2, Chapter 15, 110

Durable Medical Equipment -General

Expenses incurred by a beneficiary for the rental or purchases of durable medical equipment (DME) are reimbursable if the following three requirements are met:

- The equipment meets the definition of DME (§110.1);
- The equipment is necessary and reasonable for the treatment of the patient's illness or injury or to improve the functioning of his or her malformed body member (§110.1); and
- The equipment is used in the patient's home.

The decision whether to rent or purchase an item of equipment generally resides with the beneficiary, but the decision on how to pay rests with CMS. For some DME, program payment policy calls for lump sum payments and in others for periodic payment. Where covered DME is furnished to a beneficiary by a supplier of services other than a provider of services, the DMERC makes the reimbursement. If a provider of services furnishes the equipment, the intermediary makes the reimbursement. The payment method is identified in the annual fee schedule update furnished by CMS.

The CMS issues quarterly updates to a fee schedule file that contains rates by HCPCS code and also identifies the classification of the HCPCS code within the following categories.

Category Code	Definition
IN	Inexpensive and Other Routinely Purchased Items
FS	Frequently Serviced Items
CR	Capped Rental Items
OX	Oxygen and Oxygen Equipment
OS	Ostomy, Tracheostomy & Urological Items
SD	Surgical Dressings
PO	Prosthetics & Orthotics
SU	Supplies
TE	Transcutaneous Electrical Nerve Stimulators

The DMERCs, carriers, and intermediaries, where appropriate, use the CMS files to determine payment rules. See the Medicare Claims Processing Manual, Chapter 20, "Durable Medical Equipment, Surgical Dressings and Casts, Orthotics and Artificial Limbs, and Prosthetic Devices," for a detailed description of payment rules for each classification.

Payment may also be made for repairs, maintenance, and delivery of equipment and for expendable and nonreusable items essential to the effective use of the equipment subject to the conditions in §110.2 .

See the Medicare Benefit Policy Manual, Chapter 11, "End Stage Renal Disease," for hemodialysis equipment and supplies.

100-2, Chapter 15, 110.1

Definition of Durable Medical Equipment

Durable medical equipment is equipment which:

- Can withstand repeated use;
- Is primarily and customarily used to serve a medical purpose;
- Generally is not useful to a person in the absence of an illness or injury; and
- Is appropriate for use in the home.

All requirements of the definition must be met before an item can be considered to be durable medical equipment.

The following describes the underlying policies for determining whether an item meets the definition of DME and may be covered.

A. Durability

An item is considered durable if it can withstand repeated use, i.e., the type of item that could normally be rented. Medical supplies of an expendable nature, such as incontinent pads, lambs wool pads, catheters, ace bandages, elastic stockings, surgical facemasks, irrigating kits, sheets, and bags are not considered "durable" within the meaning of the definition. There are other items that, although durable in nature, may fall into other coverage categories such as supplies, braces, prosthetic devices, artificial arms, legs, and eyes.

B. Medical Equipment

Medical equipment is equipment primarily and customarily used for medical purposes and is not generally useful in the absence of illness or injury. In most instances, no development will be needed to determine whether a specific item of equipment is medical in nature. However, some cases will require development to determine whether the item constitutes medical equipment. This development would include the advice of local medical organizations (hospitals, medical schools, medical societies) and specialists in the field of physical medicine and rehabilitation. If the equipment is new on the market, it may be necessary, prior to seeking professional advice, to obtain information from the supplier or manufacturer explaining the design, purpose, effectiveness and method of using the equipment in the home as well as the results of any tests or clinical studies that have been conducted.

1. Equipment Presumptively Medical

Items such as hospital beds, wheelchairs, hemodialysis equipment, iron lungs, respirators, intermittent positive pressure breathing machines, medical regulators, oxygen tents, crutches, canes, trapeze bars, walkers, inhalators, nebulizers, commodes, suction machines, and traction equipment presumptively constitute medical equipment. (Although hemodialysis equipment is covered as a prosthetic device (§120), it also meets the definition of DME, and reimbursement for the rental or purchase of such equipment for use in the beneficiary's home will be made only under the provisions for payment applicable to DME. See the Medicare Benefit Policy Manual, Chapter 11, "End Stage Renal Disease" §30.1, for coverage of home use of hemodialysis.) *NOTE:* There is a wide variety in types of respirators and suction machines. The DMERC's medical staff should determine whether the apparatus specified in the claim is appropriate for home use.

2. Equipment Presumptively Nonmedical

Equipment which is primarily and customarily used for a nonmedical purpose may not be considered "medical" equipment for which payment can be made under the medical insurance program. This is true even though the item has some remote medically related use. For example, in the case of a cardiac patient, an air conditioner might possibly be used to lower room temperature to reduce fluid loss in the patient and to restore an environment conducive to maintenance of the proper fluid balance. Nevertheless, because the primary and customary use of an air conditioner is a nonmedical one, the air conditioner cannot be deemed to be medical equipment for which payment can be made.

Other devices and equipment used for environmental control or to enhance the environmental setting in which the beneficiary is placed are not considered covered DME. These include, for example, room heaters, humidifiers, dehumidifiers, and electric air cleaners. Equipment which basically serves comfort or convenience functions or is primarily for the convenience of a person caring for the patient, such as elevators, stairway elevators, and posture chairs, do not constitute medical equipment. Similarly, physical fitness equipment (such as an exercycle), first-aid or precautionary-type equipment (such as preset portable oxygen units), self-help devices (such as safety grab bars), and training equipment (such as Braille training texts) are considered nonmedical in nature.

3. Special Exception Items

Specified items of equipment may be covered under certain conditions even though they do not meet the definition of DME because they are not primarily and customarily used to serve a medical purpose and/or are generally useful in the absence of illness or injury. These items would be covered when it is clearly established that they serve a therapeutic purpose in an individual case and would include:

a. Gel pads and pressure and water mattresses (which generally serve a preventive purpose) when prescribed for a patient who had bed sores or there is medical evidence indicating that they are highly susceptible to such ulceration; and

b. Heat lamps for a medical rather than a soothing or cosmetic purpose, e.g., where the need for heat therapy has been established.

In establishing medical necessity for the above items, the evidence must show that the item is included in the physician's course of treatment and a physician is supervising its use.

NOTE: The above items represent special exceptions and no extension of coverage to other items should be inferred

C. Necessary and Reasonable

Although an item may be classified as DME, it may not be covered in every instance. Coverage in a particular case is subject to the requirement that the equipment be necessary and reasonable for treatment of an illness or injury, or to improve the functioning of a malformed body member. These considerations will bar payment for equipment which cannot reasonably be expected to perform a therapeutic function in an individual case or will permit only partial therapeutic function in an individual case or will permit only partial payment when the type of equipment furnished substantially exceeds that required for the treatment of the illness or injury involved.

See the Medicare Claims Processing Manual, Chapter 1, "General Billing Requirements;" §60, regarding the rules for providing advance beneficiary notices (ABNs) that advise beneficiaries, before items or services actually are furnished, when Medicare is likely to deny payment for them. ABNs allow beneficiaries to make an informed consumer decision about receiving items or services for which they may have to pay out-of-pocket and to be more active participants in their own health care treatment decisions.

1. Necessity for the Equipment

Equipment is necessary when it can be expected to make a meaningful contribution to the treatment of the patient's illness or injury or to the improvement of his or her malformed body member. In most cases the physician's prescription for the equipment and other medical information available to the DMERC will be sufficient to establish that the equipment serves this purpose.

2. Reasonableness of the Equipment

Even though an item of DME may serve a useful medical purpose, the DMERC or intermediary must also consider to what extent, if any, it would be reasonable for the Medicare program to pay for the item prescribed. The following considerations should enter into the determination of reasonableness:

1. Would the expense of the item to the program be clearly disproportionate to the therapeutic benefits which could ordinarily be derived from use of the equipment?

2. Is the item substantially more costly than a medically appropriate and realistically feasible alternative pattern of care?

3. Does the item serve essentially the same purpose as equipment already available to the beneficiary?

3. Payment Consistent With What is Necessary and Reasonable

Where a claim is filed for equipment containing features of an aesthetic nature or features of a medical nature which are not required by the patient's condition or where there exists a reasonably feasible and medically appropriate alternative pattern of care which is less costly than the equipment furnished, the amount payable is based on the rate for the equipment or alternative treatment which meets the patient's medical needs.

The acceptance of an assignment binds the supplier-assignee to accept the payment for the medically required equipment or service as the full charge and the supplier-assignee cannot charge the beneficiary the differential attributable to the equipment actually furnished.

4. Establishing the Period of Medical Necessity

Generally, the period of time an item of durable medical equipment will be considered to be medically necessary is based on the physician's estimate of the time that his or her patient will need the equipment. See the Medicare Program Integrity Manual, Chapters 5 and 6, for medical review guidelines.

D. Definition of a Beneficiary's Home

For purposes of rental and purchase of DME a beneficiary's home may be his/her own dwelling, an apartment, a relative's home, a home for the aged, or some other type of institution (such as an assisted living facility, or an intermediate care facility for the mentally retarded (ICF/MR)). However, an institution may not be considered a beneficiary's home if it:

• Meets at least the basic requirement in the definition of a hospital, i.e., it is primarily engaged in providing by or under the supervision of physicians, to inpatients, diagnostic and therapeutic services for medical diagnosis, treatment, and care of injured, disabled, and sick persons, or rehabilitation services for the rehabilitation of injured, disabled, or sick persons; or

• Meets at least the basic requirement in the definition of a skilled nursing facility, i.e., it is primarily engaged in providing to inpatients skilled nursing care and related services for patients who require medical or nursing care, or rehabilitation services for the rehabilitation of injured, disabled, or sick persons.

Thus, if an individual is a patient in an institution or distinct part of an institution which provides the services described in the bullets above, the individual is not entitled to have separate Part B payment made for rental or purchase of DME. This is because such an institution may not be considered the individual's home. The same concept applies even if the patient resides in a bed or portion of the institution not certified for Medicare.

If the patient is at home for part of a month and, for part of the same month is in an institution that cannot qualify as his or her home, or is outside the U.S., monthly payments may be made for the entire month. Similarly, if DME is returned to the provider before the end of a payment month because the beneficiary died in that month or because the equipment became unnecessary in that month, payment may be made for the entire month.

100-2, Chapter 15, 110.2

Repairs, Maintenance, Replacement, and Delivery

Under the circumstances specified below, payment may be made for repair, maintenance, and replacement of medically required DME, including equipment which had been in use before the user enrolled in Part B of the program. However, do not pay for repair, maintenance, or replacement of equipment in the frequent and substantial servicing or oxygen equipment payment categories. In addition, payments for repair and maintenance may not include payment for parts and labor covered under a manufacturer's or supplier's warranty.

A. Repairs

To repair means to fix or mend and to put the equipment back in good condition after damage or wear. Repairs to equipment which a beneficiary owns are covered when necessary to make the equipment serviceable. However, do not pay for repair of previously denied equipment or equipment in the frequent and substantial servicing or oxygen equipment payment categories. If the expense for repairs exceeds the estimated expense of purchasing or renting another item of equipment for the remaining period of medical need, no payment can be made for the amount of the excess. (See subsection C where claims for repairs suggest malicious damage or culpable neglect.)

Since renters of equipment recover from the rental charge the expenses they incur in maintaining in working order the equipment they rent out, separately itemized charges for repair of rented equipment are not covered. This includes items in the frequent and substantial servicing, oxygen equipment, capped rental, and inexpensive or routinely purchased payment categories which are being rented.

A new Certificate of Medical Necessity (CMN) and/or physician's order is not needed for repairs.

B. Maintenance

Routine periodic servicing, such as testing, cleaning, regulating, and checking of the beneficiary's equipment, is not covered. The owner is expected to perform such routine maintenance rather than a retailer or some other person who charges the beneficiary. Normally, purchasers of DME are given operating manuals which describe the type of servicing an owner may perform to properly maintain the equipment. It is reasonable to expect that beneficiaries will perform this maintenance. Thus, hiring a third party to do such work is for the convenience of the beneficiary and is not covered. However, more extensive maintenance which, based on the manufacturers' recommendations, is to be performed by authorized technicians, is covered as repairs for medically necessary equipment which a beneficiary owns. This might include, for example, breaking down sealed components and performing tests which require specialized testing equipment not available to the beneficiary. Do not pay for maintenance of purchased items that require frequent and substantial servicing or oxygen equipment.

Since renters of equipment recover from the rental charge the expenses they incur in maintaining in working order the equipment they rent out, separately itemized charges for maintenance of rented equipment are generally not covered. Payment may not be made for maintenance of rented equipment other than the maintenance and servicing fee established for capped rental items. For capped rental items which have reached the 15-month rental cap, contractors pay claims for maintenance and servicing fees after 6 months have passed from the end of the final paid rental month or from the end of the period the item is no longer covered under the supplier's or manufacturer's warranty, whichever is later. See

the Medicare Claims Processing Manual, Chapter 20, "Durable Medical Equipment, Prosthetics and Orthotics, and Supplies (DMEPOS)," for additional instruction and an example.

A new CMN and/or physician's order is not needed for covered maintenance.

C. Replacement

Replacement refers to the provision of an identical or nearly identical item. Situations involving the provision of a different item because of a change in medical condition are not addressed in this section.

Equipment which the beneficiary owns or is a capped rental item may be replaced in cases of loss or irreparable damage. Irreparable damage refers to a specific accident or to a natural disaster (e.g., fire, flood). A physician's order and/or new Certificate of Medical Necessity (CMN), when required, is needed to reaffirm the medical necessity of the item.

Irreparable wear refers to deterioration sustained from day-to-day usage over time and a specific event cannot be identified. Replacement of equipment due to irreparable wear takes into consideration the reasonable useful lifetime of the equipment. If the item of equipment has been in continuous use by the patient on either a rental or purchase basis for the equipment's useful lifetime, the beneficiary may elect to obtain a new piece of equipment. Replacement may be reimbursed when a new physician order and/or new CMN, when required, is needed to reaffirm the medical necessity of the item.

The reasonable useful lifetime of durable medical equipment is determined through program instructions. In the absence of program instructions, carriers may determine the reasonable useful lifetime of equipment, but in no case can it be less than 5 years. Computation of the useful lifetime is based on when the equipment is delivered to the beneficiary, not the age of the equipment. Replacement due to wear is not covered during the reasonable useful lifetime of the equipment. During the reasonable useful lifetime, Medicare does cover repair up to the cost of replacement (but not actual replacement) for medically necessary equipment owned by the beneficiary. (See subsection A.)

Charges for the replacement of oxygen equipment, items that require frequent and substantial servicing or inexpensive or routinely purchased items which are being rented are not covered.

Cases suggesting malicious damage, culpable neglect, or wrongful disposition of equipment should be investigated and denied where the DMERC determines that it is unreasonable to make program payment under the circumstances. DMERCs refer such cases to the program integrity specialist in the RO.

D. Delivery

Payment for delivery of DME whether rented or purchased is generally included in the fee schedule allowance for the item. See Pub. 100-04, Medicare Claims Processing Manual, Chapter 20, "Durable Medical Equipment, Prosthetics and Orthotics, and Supplies (DMEPOS)," for the rules that apply to making reimbursement for exceptional cases.

100-2, Chapter 15, 110.3

Coverage of Supplies and Accessories

Payment may be made for supplies, e.g., oxygen, that are necessary for the effective use of durable medical equipment. Such supplies include those drugs and biologicals which must be put directly into the equipment in order to achieve the therapeutic benefit of the durable medical equipment or to assure the proper functioning of the equipment, e.g., tumor chemotherapy agents used with an infusion pump or heparin used with a home dialysis system. However, the coverage of such drugs or biologicals does not preclude the need for a determination that the drug or biological itself is reasonable and necessary for treatment of the illness or injury or to improve the functioning of a malformed body member.

In the case of prescription drugs, other than oxygen, used in conjunction with durable medical equipment, prosthetic, orthotics, and supplies (DMEPOS) or prosthetic devices, the entity that dispenses the drug must furnish it directly to the patient for whom a prescription is written. The entity that dispenses the drugs must have a Medicare supplier number, must possess a current license to dispense prescription drugs in the State in which the drug is dispensed, and must bill and receive payment in its own name. A supplier that is not the entity that dispenses the drugs cannot purchase the drugs used in conjunction with DME for resale to the beneficiary. Reimbursement may be made for replacement of essential accessories such as hoses, tubes, mouthpieces, etc., for necessary DME, only if the beneficiary owns or is purchasing the equipment.

100-2, Chapter 15, 120

Prosthetic Devices

A. General

Prosthetic devices (other than dental) which replace all or part of an internal body organ (including contiguous tissue), or replace all or part of the function of a permanently inoperative or malfunctioning internal body organ are covered when furnished on a physician's order. This does not require a determination that there is no possibility that the patient's condition may improve sometime in the future. If the medical record, including the judgment of the attending physician, indicates the condition is of long and indefinite duration, the test of permanence is considered met. (Such a device may also be covered under §60.1 as a supply when furnished incident to a physician's service.)

Examples of prosthetic devices include artificial limbs, parenteral and enteral (PEN) nutrition, cardiac pacemakers, prosthetic lenses (see subsection B), breast prostheses (including a surgical brassiere) for post mastectomy patients, maxillofacial devices, and devices which replace all or part of the ear or nose. A urinary collection and retention system with or without a tube is a prosthetic device replacing bladder function in case of permanent urinary incontinence. The foley catheter is also considered a prosthetic device when ordered for a patient with permanent urinary incontinence. However, chucks, diapers, rubber sheets, etc., are supplies that are not covered under this provision. Although hemodialysis equipment is a prosthetic device, payment for the rental or purchase of such equipment in the home is made only for use under the provisions for payment applicable to durable medical equipment.

An exception is that if payment cannot be made on an inpatient's behalf under Part A, hemodialysis equipment, supplies, and services required by such patient could be covered under Part B as a prosthetic device, which replaces the function of a kidney. See the Medicare Benefit Policy Manual, Chapter 11, "End Stage Renal Disease," for payment for hemodialysis equipment used in the home. See the Medicare Benefit Policy Manual, Chapter 1, "Inpatient Hospital Services," §10, for additional instructions on hospitalization for renal dialysis.

NOTE: Medicare does not cover a prosthetic device dispensed to a patient prior to the time at which the patient undergoes the procedure that makes necessary the use of the device. For example, the carrier does not make a separate Part B payment for an intraocular lens (IOL) or pacemaker that a physician, during an office visit prior to the actual surgery, dispenses to the patient for his or her use. Dispensing a prosthetic device in this manner raises health and safety issues. Moreover, the need for the device cannot be clearly established until the procedure that makes its use possible is successfully performed. Therefore, dispensing a prosthetic device in this manner is not considered reasonable and necessary for the treatment of the patient's condition.

Colostomy (and other ostomy) bags and necessary accouterments required for attachment are covered as prosthetic devices. This coverage also includes irrigation and flushing equipment and other items and supplies directly related to ostomy care, whether the attachment of a bag is required.

Accessories and/or supplies which are used directly with an enteral or parenteral device to achieve the therapeutic benefit of the prosthesis or to assure the proper functioning of the device may also be covered under the prosthetic device benefit subject to the additional guidelines in the Medicare National Coverage Determinations Manual.

Covered items include catheters, filters, extension tubing, infusion bottles, pumps (either food or infusion), intravenous (I.V.) pole, needles, syringes, dressings, tape, Heparin Sodium (parenteral only), volumetric monitors (parenteral only), and parenteral and enteral nutrient solutions. Baby food and other regular grocery products that can be blenderized and used with the enteral system are not covered. Note that some of these items, e.g., a food pump and an I.V. pole, qualify as DME. Although coverage of the enteral and parenteral nutritional therapy systems is provided on the basis of the prosthetic device benefit, the payment rules relating to lump sum or monthly payment for DME apply to such items.

The coverage of prosthetic devices includes replacement of and repairs to such devices as explained in subsection D.

Finally, the Benefits Improvement and Protection Act of 2000 amended §1834(h)(1) of the Act by adding a provision (1834(h)(1)(G)(i)) that requires Medicare payment to be made for the replacement of prosthetic devices which are artificial limbs, or for the replacement of any part of such devices, without regard to continuous use or useful lifetime restrictions if an ordering physician determines that the replacement device, or replacement part of such a device, is necessary.

Payment may be made for the replacement of a prosthetic device that is an artificial limb, or replacement part of a device if the ordering physician determines that the replacement device or part is necessary because of any of the following:

1. A change in the physiological condition of the patient;

2. An irreparable change in the condition of the device, or in a part of the device; or

3. The condition of the device, or the part of the device, requires repairs and the cost of such repairs would be more than 60 percent of the cost of a replacement device, or, as the case may be, of the part being replaced.

This provision is effective for items replaced on or after April 1, 2001. It supersedes any rule that that provided a 5-year or other replacement rule with regard to prosthetic devices.

B. Prosthetic Lenses

The term "internal body organ" includes the lens of an eye. Prostheses replacing the lens of an eye include post-surgical lenses customarily used during convalescence from eye surgery in which the lens of the eye was removed. In addition, permanent lenses are also covered when required by an individual lacking the organic lens of the eye because of surgical removal or congenital absence. Prosthetic lenses obtained on or after the beneficiary's date of entitlement to supplementary medical insurance benefits may be covered even though the surgical removal of the crystalline lens occurred before entitlement.

1. Prosthetic Cataract Lenses

One of the following prosthetic lenses or combinations of prosthetic lenses furnished by a physician (see §30.4 for coverage of prosthetic lenses prescribed by a doctor of optometry) may be covered when determined to be reasonable and necessary to restore essentially the vision provided by the crystalline lens of the eye:

- Prosthetic bifocal lenses in frames;
- Prosthetic lenses in frames for far vision, and prosthetic lenses in frames for near vision; or
- When a prosthetic contact lens(es) for far vision is prescribed (including cases of binocular and monocular aphakia), make payment for the contact lens(es) and prosthetic lenses in frames for near vision to be worn at the same time as the contact lens(es), and prosthetic lenses in frames to be worn when the contacts have been removed.

Lenses which have ultraviolet absorbing or reflecting properties may be covered, in lieu of payment for regular (untinted) lenses, if it has been determined that such lenses are medically reasonable and necessary for the individual patient.

Medicare does not cover cataract sunglasses obtained in addition to the regular (untinted) prosthetic lenses since the sunglasses duplicate the restoration of vision function performed by the regular prosthetic lenses.

2. Payment for Intraocular Lenses (IOLs) Furnished in Ambulatory Surgical Centers (ASCs)

Effective for services furnished on or after March 12, 1990, payment for intraocular lenses (IOLs) inserted during or subsequent to cataract surgery in a Medicare certified ASC is included with the payment for facility services that are furnished in connection with the covered surgery.

Refer to the Medicare Claims Processing Manual, Chapter 14, "Ambulatory Surgical Centers," for more information.

3. Limitation on Coverage of Conventional Lenses

One pair of conventional eyeglasses or conventional contact lenses furnished after each cataract surgery with insertion of an IOL is covered.

C. Dentures

Dentures are excluded from coverage. However, when a denture or a portion of the denture is an integral part (built-in) of a covered prosthesis (e.g., an obturatorto fill an opening in the palate), it is covered as part of that prosthesis.

D. Supplies, Repairs, Adjustments, and Replacement

Supplies are covered that are necessary for the effective use of a prosthetic device (e.g., the batteries needed to operate an artificial larynx). Adjustment of prosthetic devices required by wear or by a change in the patient's condition is covered when ordered by a physician. General provisions relating to the repair and replacement of durable medical equipment in §110.2 for the repair and replacement of prosthetic devices are applicable. (See the Medicare Benefit Policy Manual, Chapter 16, "General Exclusions from Coverage," §40.4, for payment for devices replaced under a warranty.) Replacement of conventional eyeglasses or contact lenses furnished in accordance with §120.B.3 is not covered.

Necessary supplies, adjustments, repairs, and replacements are covered even when the device had been in use before the user enrolled in Part B ofthe program, so long as the device continues to be medically required.

100-2, Chapter 15, 130

Leg, Arm, Back, and Neck Braces, Trusses, and Artificial Legs, Arms, and Eyes

These appliances are covered under Part B when furnished incident to physicians' services or on a physician's order. A brace includes rigid and semi-rigid devices which are used for the purpose of supporting a weak or deformed body member or restricting or eliminating motion in a diseased or injured part of the body. Elastic stockings, garter belts, and similar devices do not come within the scope of the definition of a brace. Back braces include, but are not limited to, special corsets, e.g., sacroiliac, sacrolumbar, dorsolumbar corsets, and belts. A terminal device (e.g., hand or hook) is covered under this provision whether an artificial limb is required by the patient. Stump stockings and harnesses (including replacements) are also covered when these appliances are essential to the effective use of the artificial limb.

Adjustments to an artificial limb or other appliance required by wear or by a change in the patient's condition are covered when ordered by a physician.

Adjustments, repairs and replacements are covered even when the item had been in use before the user enrolled in Part B of the program so long as the device continues to be medically required.

100-2, Chapter 15, 140

Therapeutic Shoes for Individuals with Diabetes

Coverage of therapeutic shoes (depth or custom-molded) along with inserts for individuals with diabetes is available as of May 1, 1993. These diabetic shoes are covered if the requirements as specified in this section concerning certification and prescription are fulfilled. In addition, this benefit provides for a pair of diabetic shoes even if only one foot suffers from diabetic foot disease. Each shoe is equally equipped so that the affected limb, as well as the remaining limb, is protected. Claims for therapeutic shoes for diabetics are processed by the Durable Medical Equipment Regional Carriers (DMERCs).

Therapeutic shoes for diabetics are not DME and are not considered DME nor orthotics, but a separate category of coverage under Medicare Part B. (See §1861(s)(12)and §1833(o) of the Act.)

A. Definitions

The following items may be covered under the diabetic shoe benefit:

1. Custom-Molded Shoes

Custom-molded shoes are shoes that:

- Are constructed over a positive model of the patient's foot;
- Are made from leather or other suitable material of equal quality;
- Have removable inserts that can be altered or replaced as the patient's condition warrants; and
- Have some form of shoe closure.

2. Depth Shoes

Depth shoes are shoes that:

- Have a full length, heel-to-toe filler that, when removed, provides a minimum of 3/16 inch of additional depth used to accommodate custom-molded or customized inserts;
- Are made from leather or other suitable material of equal quality;
- Have some form of shoe closure; and
- Are available in full and half sizes with a minimum of three widths so that the sole is graded to the size and width of the upper portions of the shoes according to the American standard last sizing schedule or its equivalent. (The American standard last sizing schedule is the numerical shoe sizing system used for shoes sold in the United States.)

3. Inserts

Inserts are total contact, multiple density, removable inlays that are directly molded to the patient's foot or a model of the patient's foot and that are made of a suitable material with regard to the patient's condition.

B. Coverage

1. Limitations

For each individual, coverage of the footwear and inserts is limited to one of the following within one calendar year:

- No more than one pair of custom-molded shoes (including inserts provided with such shoes) and two additional pairs of inserts; or
- No more than one pair of depth shoes and three pairs of inserts (not including the non customized removable inserts provided with such shoes).

2. Coverage of Diabetic Shoes and Brace

Orthopedic shoes, as stated in the Medicare Claims Processing Manual, Chapter 20, "Durable Medical Equipment, Surgical Dressings and Casts, Orthotics and Artificial Limbs, and Prosthetic Devices," generally are not covered. This exclusion does not apply to orthopedic shoes that are an integral part of a leg brace. In situations in which an individual qualifies for both diabetic shoes and a leg brace, these items are covered separately. Thus, the diabetic shoes may be covered if the requirements for this section are met, while the brace may be covered if the requirements of §130 are met.

3. Substitution of Modifications for Inserts

An individual may substitute modification(s) of custom-molded or depth shoes instead of obtaining a pair(s) of inserts in any combination. Payment for the modification(s) may not exceed the limit set for the inserts for which the individual is entitled. The following is a list of the most common shoe modifications available, but it is not meant as an exhaustive list of the modifications available for diabetic shoes:

- **Rigid Rocker Bottoms** - These are exterior elevations with apex positions for 51 percent to 75 percent distance measured from the back end of the heel. The apex is a

narrowed or pointed end of an anatomical structure. The apex must be positioned behind the metatarsal heads and tapered off sharply to the front tip of the sole. Apex height helps to eliminate pressure at the metatarsal heads. Rigidity is ensured by the steel in the shoe. The heel of the shoe tapers off in the back in order to cause the heel to strike in the middle of the heel;

- **Roller Bottoms (Sole or Bar)**-These are the same as rocker bottoms, but the heel is tapered from the apex to the front tip of the sole;
- **Metatarsal Bars**-An exterior bar is placed behind the metatarsal heads in order to remove pressure from the metatarsal heads. The bars are of various shapes, heights, and construction depending on the exact purpose;
- **Wedges (Posting)**-Wedges are either of hind foot, fore foot, or both and may be in the middle or to the side. The function is to shift or transfer weight bearing upon standing or during ambulation to the opposite side for added support, stabilization, equalized weight distribution, or balance; and
- **Offset Heels**-This is a heel flanged at its base either in the middle, to the side, or a combination, that is then extended upward to the shoe in order to stabilize extreme positions of the hind foot.

Other modifications to diabetic shoes include, but are not limited to flared heels, Velcro closures, and inserts for missing toes.

4. Separate Inserts

Inserts may be covered and dispensed independently of diabetic shoes if the supplier of the shoes verifies in writing that the patient has appropriate footwear into which the insert can be placed. This footwear must meet the definitions found above for depth shoes and custom-molded shoes.

C. Certification

The need for diabetic shoes must be certified by a physician who is a doctor of medicine or a doctor of osteopathy and who is responsible for diagnosing and treating the patient's diabetic systemic condition through a comprehensive plan of care. This managing physician must:

- Document in the patient's medical record that the patient has diabetes;
- Certify that the patient is being treated under a comprehensive plan of care for diabetes, and that the patient needs diabetic shoes; and
- Document in the patient's record that the patient has one or more of the following conditions
  - Peripheral neuropathy with evidence of callus formation;
  - History of pre-ulcerative calluses;
  - History of previous ulceration;
  - Foot deformity;
  - Previous amputation of the foot or part of the foot; or
  - Poor circulation.

D. Prescription

Following certification by the physician managing the patient's systemic diabetic condition, a podiatrist or other qualified physician who is knowledgeable in the fitting of diabetic shoes and inserts may prescribe the particular type of footwear necessary.

E. Furnishing Footwear

The footwear must be fitted and furnished by a podiatrist or other qualified individual such as a pedorthist, an orthotist, or a prosthetist. The certifying physician may not furnish the diabetic shoes unless the certifying physician is the only qualified individual in the area. It is left to the discretion of each carrier to determine the meaning of "in the area."

100-2, Chapter 15, 150

Dental Services

As indicated under the general exclusions from coverage, items and services in connection with the care, treatment, filling, removal, or replacement of teeth or structures directly supporting the teeth are not covered. "Structures directly supporting the teeth" means the periodontium, which includes the gingivae, dentogingival junction, periodontal membrane, cementum of the teeth, and alveolar process.

In addition to the following, see Pub 100-01, the Medicare General Information, Eligibility, and Entitlement Manual, Chapter 5, Definitions and Pub 3, the Medicare National Coverage Determinations Manual for specific services which may be covered when furnished by a dentist. If an otherwise non covered procedure or service is performed by a dentist as incident to and as an integral part of a covered procedure or service performed by the dentist, the total service performed by the dentist on such an occasion is covered.

EXAMPLE 1:

The reconstruction of a ridge performed primarily to prepare the mouth for dentures is a noncovered procedure. However, when the reconstruction of a ridge is performed as a result of and at the same time as the surgical removal of a tumor (for other than dental purposes), the totality of surgical procedures is a covered service.

EXAMPLE 2:

Medicare makes payment for the wiring of teeth when this is done in connection with the reduction of a jaw fracture.

The extraction of teeth to prepare the jaw for radiation treatment of neoplastic disease is also covered. This is an exception to the requirement that to be covered, a noncovered procedure or service performed by a dentist must be an incident to and an integral part of a covered procedure or service performed by the dentist. Ordinarily, the dentist extracts the patient's teeth, but another physician, e.g., a radiologist, administers the radiation treatments.

When an excluded service is the primary procedure involved, it is not covered, regardless of its complexity or difficulty. For example, the extraction of an impacted tooth is not covered. Similarly, an alveoplasty (the surgical improvement of the shape and condition of the alveolar process) and a frenectomy are excluded from coverage when either of these procedures is performed in connection with an excluded service, e.g., the preparation of the mouth for dentures. In a like manner, the removal of a torus palatinus (a bony protuberance of the hard palate) may be a covered service. However, with rare exception, this surgery is performed in connection with an excluded service, i.e., the preparation of the mouth for dentures. Under such circumstances, Medicare does not pay for this procedure.

Dental splints used to treat a dental condition are excluded from coverage under 1862(a)(12) of the Act. On the other hand, if the treatment is determined to be a covered medical condition (i.e., dislocated upper/lower jaw joints), then the splint can be covered. Whether such services as the administration of anesthesia, diagnostic x-rays, and other related procedures are covered depends upon whether the primary procedure being performed by the dentist is itself covered. Thus, an x-ray taken in connection with the reduction of a fracture of the jaw or facial bone is covered. However, a single x-ray or x-ray survey taken in connection with the care or treatment of teeth or the periodontium is not covered.

Medicare makes payment for a covered dental procedure no matter where the service is performed. The hospitalization or non hospitalization of a patient has no direct bearing on the coverage or exclusion of a given dental procedure.

Payment may also be made for services and supplies furnished incident to covered dental services. For example, the services of a dental technician or nurse who is under the direct supervision of the dentist or physician are covered if the services are included in the dentist's or physician's bill.

100-2, Chapter 15, 150.1

Treatment of Temporomandibular Joint (TMJ) Syndrome

There are a wide variety of conditions that can be characterized as TMJ, and an equally wide variety of methods for treating these conditions. Many of the procedures fall within the Medicare program's statutory exclusion that prohibits payment for items and services that have not been demonstrated to be reasonable and necessary for the diagnosis and treatment of illness or injury (§1862(a)(1) of the Act). Other services and appliances used to treat TMJ fall within the Medicare program's statutory exclusion at 1862(a)(12), which prohibits payment "for services in connection with the care, treatment, filling, removal, or replacement of teeth or structures directly supporting teeth...." For these reasons, a diagnosis of TMJ on a claim is insufficient. The actual condition or symptom must be determined.

100-2, Chapter 15, 230

Practice of Physical Therapy, Occupational Therapy, and Speech-Language Pathology

A. Group Therapy Services. Contractors pay for outpatient physical therapy services (which includes outpatient speech-language pathology services) and outpatient occupational therapy services provided simultaneously to two or more individuals by a practitioner as group therapy services (97150). The individuals can be, but need not be performing the same activity. The physician or therapist involved in group therapy services must be in constant attendance, but one-on-one patient contact is not required.

B. Therapy Students

1. General

Only the services of the therapist can be billed and paid under Medicare Part B. The services performed by a student are not reimbursed even if provided under "line of sight" supervision of the therapist; however, the presence of the student "in the room" does not make the service unbillable. Pay for the direct (one-to-one) patient contact services of the physician or therapist provided to Medicare Part B patients. Group therapy services performed by a therapist or physician may be billed when a student is also present "in the room".

EXAMPLES

Therapists may bill and be paid for the provision of services in the following scenarios:

- The qualified practitioner is present and in the room for the entire session. The student participates in the delivery of services when the qualified practitioner is directing the service, making the skilled judgment, and is responsible for the assessment and treatment.
- The qualified practitioner is present in the room guiding the student in service delivery when the therapy student and the therapy assistant student are participating in the provision of services, and the practitioner is not engaged in treating another patient or doing other tasks at the same time.
- The qualified practitioner is responsible for the services and as such, signs all documentation. (A student may, of course, also sign but it is not necessary since the Part B payment is for the clinician's service, not for the student's services).

2. Therapy Assistants as Clinical Instructors

Physical therapist assistants and occupational therapy assistants are not precluded from serving as clinical instructors for therapy students, while providing services within their scope of work and performed under the direction and supervision of a licensed physical or occupational therapist to a Medicare beneficiary.

3. Services Provided Under Part A and Part B

The payment methodologies for Part A and B therapy services rendered by a student are different. Under the MPFS (Medicare Part B), Medicare pays for services provided by physicians and practitioners that are specifically authorized by statute. Students do not meet the definition of practitioners under Medicare Part B. Under SNF PPS, payments are based upon the case mix or Resource Utilization Group (RUG) category that describes the patient. In the rehabilitation groups, the number of therapy minutes delivered to the patient determines the RUG category. Payment levels for each category are based upon the costs of caring for patients in each group rather than providing specific payment for each therapy service as is done in Medicare Part B.

100-2, Chapter 15, 231

Pulmonary Rehabilitation (PR) Program Services Furnished On or After January 1, 2010

A pulmonary rehabilitation (PR) program is typically a physician-supervised, multidisciplinary program individually tailored and designed to optimize physical and social performance and autonomy of care for patients with chronic respiratory impairment. The main goal is to empower the individuals' ability to exercise independently. Exercise is combined with other training and support mechanisms to encourage long-term adherence to the treatment plan. Effective January 1, 2010, Medicare Part B pays for PR programs and related items and services if specific criteria is met by the Medicare beneficiary, the PR program itself, the setting in which it is administered, and the physician administering the program, as outlined below:

PR Program Beneficiary Requirements:

As specified in 42 CFR 410.47, Medicare covers PR items and services for patients with moderate to very severe chronic obstructive pulmonary disease (COPD) (defined as GOLD classification II, III, and IV), when referred by the physician treating the chronic respiratory disease. Additional medical indications for coverage for PR program services may be established through the national coverage determination process.

PR Program Component Requirements:

- Physician-prescribed exercise. This physical activity includes techniques such as exercise conditioning, breathing retraining, and step and strengthening exercises. Some aerobic exercise must be included in each PR session. Both low-and high-intensity exercise is recommended to produce clinical benefits and a combination of endurance and strength training should be conducted at least twice per week.
- Education or training. This should be closely and clearly related to the individual's care and treatment and tailored to the individual's needs, including information on respiratory problem management and, if appropriate, brief smoking cessation counseling. Any education or training must assist in achievement of individual goals towards independence in activities of daily living, adaptation to limitations, and improved quality of life (QoL).
- Psychosocial assessment. This assessment means a written evaluation of an individual's mental and emotional functioning as it relates to the individual's rehabilitation or respiratory condition. It should include: (1) an assessment of those aspects of the individual's family and home situation that affects the individual's rehabilitation treatment, and, (2) a psychological evaluation of the individual's response to, and rate of progress under, the treatment plan. Periodic re-evaluations are necessary to ensure the individual's psychosocial needs are being met.
- Outcomes assessment. These should include: (1) beginning and end evaluations based on patient-centered outcomes, which are conducted by the physician at the start and end of the program, and, (2) objective clinical measures of the effectiveness of the PR program for the individual patient, including exercise performance and self-reported measures of shortness of breath, and behavior. The assessments should include clinical measures such as the 6-minute walk, weight, exercise performance, self-reported dyspnea, behavioral measures(supplemental oxygen use, smoking status,) and a QoL assessment.
- An individualized treatment plan describing the individual's diagnosis and detailing how components are utilized for each patient. The plan must be established, reviewed, and signed by a physician every 30 days. The plan may initially be developed by the referring physician or the PR physician. If the plan is developed by the referring physician who is not the PR physician, the PR physician must also review and sign the plan prior to imitation of the PR program. It is expected that the supervising physician would have initial, direct contact with the individual prior to subsequent treatment by ancillary personnel, and also have at least one direct contact in each 30-day period. The plan must have written specificity with regards to the type, amount, frequency, and duration of PR items and services furnished to the individual, and specify the appropriate mix of services for the patient's needs. It must include measurable and expected outcomes and estimated timetables to achieve these outcomes.

As specified at 42 CFR 410.47(f), PR program sessions are limited to a maximum of 2 1-hour sessions per day for up to 36 sessions, with the option for an additional 36 sessions if medically necessary.

PR Program Setting Requirements:

PR items and services must be furnished in a physician's office or a hospital outpatient setting. The setting must have the necessary cardio-pulmonary, emergency, diagnostic, and therapeutic life-saving equipment accepted by the medical community as medically necessary (for example, oxygen, cardiopulmonary resuscitation equipment, and a defibrillator) to treat chronic respiratory disease. All settings must have a physician immediately available and accessible for medical consultations and emergencies at all times that the PR items and services are being furnished under the program. This provision is satisfied if the physician meets the requirements for direct supervision of physician office services as specified at 42 CFR 410.26, and for hospital outpatient therapeutic services as specified at 42 CFR 410.27.

PR Program Physician Requirements:

Medicare Part B pays for PR services supervised by a physician only if the physician meets all of the following requirements: (1) expertise in the management of individuals with respiratory pathophysiology, (2) licensed to practice medicine in the state in which the PR program is offered, (3) responsible and accountable for the PR program, and, (4) involved substantially, in consultation with staff, in directing the progress of the individual in the PR program.

(See Publication 100-04, Claims Processing Manual, chapter 32, section 140.4, for specific claims processing, coding, and billing requirements for PR program services.)

100-2, Chapter 15, 232

Cardiac Rehabilitation (CR) and Intensive Cardiac Rehabilitation (ICR) Services Furnished On or After January 1, 2010

Cardiac rehabilitation (CR) services mean a physician-supervised program that furnishes physician prescribed exercise, cardiac risk factor modification, including education, counseling, and behavioral intervention; psychosocial assessment, outcomes assessment, and other items/services as determined by the Secretary under certain conditions. Intensive cardiac rehabilitation (ICR) services mean a physician-supervised program that furnishes the same items/services under the same conditions as a CR program but must also demonstrate, as shown in peer-reviewed published research, that it improves patients' cardiovascular disease through specific outcome measurements described in 42 CFR 410.49(c). Effective January 1, 2010, Medicare Part B pays for CR/ICR programs and related items/services if specific criteria is met by the Medicare beneficiary, the CR/ICR program itself, the setting in which is it administered, and the physician administering the program, as outlined below:

CR/ICR Program Beneficiary Requirements:

Medicare covers CR/ICR program services for beneficiaries who have experienced one or more of the following:

- Acute myocardial infarction within the preceding 12 months;
- Coronary artery bypass surgery;
- Current stable angina pectoris;
- Heart valve repair or replacement;
- Percutaneous transluminal coronary angioplasty (PTCA) or coronary stenting;
- Heart or heart-lung transplant;

For cardiac rehabilitation only: Stable, chronic heart failure defined as patients with left ventricular ejection fraction of 35% or less and New York Heart Association (NYHA) class II to IV symptoms despite being on optimal heart failure therapy for at least 6 weeks. (Effective February 18, 2014.)

CR/ICR Program Component Requirements:

Physician-prescribed exercise. This physical activity includes aerobic exercise combined with other types of exercise (i.e., strengthening, stretching) as determined to be appropriate for individual patients by a physician each day CR/ICR items/services are furnished.

Cardiac risk factor modification. This includes education, counseling, and behavioral intervention, tailored to the patients' individual needs.

Psychosocial assessment. This assessment means an evaluation of an individual's mental and emotional functioning as it relates to the individual's rehabilitation. It should include: (1) an assessment of those aspects of the individual's family and home situation that affects the individual's rehabilitation treatment, and, (2) a psychosocial evaluation of the individual's response to, and rate of progress under, the treatment plan.

Outcomes assessment. These should include: (i) minimally, assessments from the commencement and conclusion of CR/ICR, based on patient-centered outcomes which must be measured by the physician immediately at the beginning and end of the program, and, (ii) objective clinical measures of the effectiveness of the CR/ICR program for the individual patient, including exercise performance and self-reported measures of exertion and behavior.

Individualized treatment plan. This plan should be written and tailored to each individual patient and include (i) a description of the individual's diagnosis; (ii) the type, amount, frequency, and duration of the CR/ICR items/services furnished; and (iii) the goals set for the individual under the plan. The individualized treatment plan must be established, reviewed, and signed by a physician every 30 days.

As specified at 42 CFR 410.49(f)(1), CR sessions are limited to a maximum of 2 1-hour sessions per day for up to 36 sessions over up to 36 weeks with the option for an additional 36 sessions over an extended period of time if approved by the contractor under section 1862(a)(1)(A) of the Act. ICR sessions are limited to 72 1-hour sessions (as defined in section 1848(b)(5) of the Act), up to 6 sessions per day, over a period of up to 18 weeks.

CR/ICR Program Setting Requirements:

CR/ICR services must be furnished in a physician's office or a hospital outpatient setting (for ICR, the hospital outpatient setting must provide ICR using an approved ICR program). All settings must have a physician immediately available and accessible for medical consultations and emergencies at all times when items/services are being furnished under the program. This provision is satisfied if the physician meets the requirements for direct supervision of physician office services as specified at 42 CFR 410.26, and for hospital outpatient services as specified at 42 CFR 410.27.

ICR Program Approval Requirements:

All prospective ICR programs must be approved through the national coverage determination (NCD) process. To be approved as an ICR program, it must demonstrate through peer-reviewed, published research that it has accomplished one or more of the following for its patients: (i) positively affected the progression of coronary heart disease, (ii) reduced the need for coronary bypass surgery, or, (iii) reduced the need for percutaneous coronary interventions.

An ICR program must also demonstrate through peer-reviewed, published research that it accomplished a statistically significant reduction in five or more of the following measures for patients from their levels before CR services to after CR services: (i) low density lipoprotein, (ii) triglycerides, (iii) body mass index, (iv) systolic blood pressure, (v) diastolic blood pressure, and (vi) the need for cholesterol, blood pressure, and diabetes medications.

A list of approved ICR programs, identified through the NCD process, will be posted to the CMS Web site and listed in the Federal Register.

Once an ICR program is approved through the NCD process, all prospective ICR sites wishing to furnish ICR items/services via an approved ICR program may enroll with their local contractor to become an ICR program supplier using the designated forms as specified at 42 CFR 424.510, and report specialty code 31 to be identified as an enrolled ICR supplier. For purposes of appealing an adverse determination concerning site approval, an ICR site is considered a supplier (or prospective supplier) as defined in 42 CFR 498.2.

CR/ICR Program Physician Requirements:

Physicians responsible for CR/ICR programs are identified as medical directors who oversee or supervise the CR/ICR program at a particular site. The medical director, in consultation with staff, is involved in directing the progress of individuals in the program. The medical director, as well as physicians acting as the supervising physician, must possess all of the following: (1) expertise in the management of individuals with cardiac pathophysiology, (2) cardiopulmonary training in basic life support or advanced cardiac life support, and (3) licensed to practice medicine in the state in which the CR/ICR program is offered. Direct physician supervision may be provided by a supervising physician or the medical director.

(See Pub. 100-03, Medicare National Coverage Determinations Manual, Chapter 1, Part 1, section 20.10.1, Pub. 100-04, Medicare Claims Processing Manual, Chapter 32, section 140, Pub. 100-08, Medicare Program Integrity Manual, Chapter 15, section 15.4.2.8, for specific claims processing, coding, and billing requirements for CR/ICR program services).

100-2, Chapter 15, 270

Telehealth Services

Background

Section 223 of the Medicare, Medicaid and SCHIP Benefits Improvement and Protection Act of 2000 (BIPA) -Revision of Medicare Reimbursement for Telehealth Services amended §1834 of the Act to provide for an expansion of Medicare payment for telehealth services.

Effective October 1, 2001, coverage and payment for Medicare telehealth includes consultation, office visits, individual psychotherapy, and pharmacologic management delivered via a telecommunications system. Eligible geographic areas include rural health professional shortage areas (HPSA) and counties not classified as a metropolitan statistical area (MSA). Additionally, Federal telemedicine demonstration projects as of December 31, 2000, may serve as the originating site regardless of geographic location.

An interactive telecommunications system is required as a condition of payment; however, BIPA does allow the use of asynchronous "store and forward" technology in delivering these services when the originating site is a Federal telemedicine demonstration program in Alaska or Hawaii. BIPA does not require that a practitioner present the patient for interactive telehealth services.

With regard to payment amount, BIPA specified that payment for the professional service performed by the distant site practitioner (i.e., where the expert physician or practitioner is physically located at time of telemedicine encounter) is equal to what would have been paid without the use of telemedicine. Distant site practitioners include only a physician as described in §1861(r) of the Act and a medical practitioner as described in §1842(b)(18)(C) of the Act. BIPA also expanded payment under Medicare to include a $20 originating site facility fee (location of beneficiary).

Previously, the Balanced Budget Act of 1997 (BBA) limited the scope of Medicare telehealth coverage to consultation services and the implementing regulation prohibited the use of an asynchronous 'store and forward' telecommunications system. The BBA of 1997 also required the professional fee to be shared between the referring and consulting practitioners, and prohibited Medicare payment for facility fees and line charges associated with the telemedicine encounter.

The BIPA required that Medicare Part B (Supplementary Medical Insurance) pay for this expansion of telehealth services beginning with services furnished on October 1, 2001.

Section 149 of the Medicare Improvements for Patients and Providers Act of 2008 (MIPPA) amended §1834(m) of the Act to add certain entities as originating sites for payment of telehealth services. Effective for services furnished on or after January 1, 2009, eligible originating sites include a hospital-based or critical access hospital-based renal dialysis center (including satellites); a skilled nursing facility (as defined in §1819(a) of the Act); and a community mental health center (as defined in §1861(ff)(3)(B) of the Act). MIPPA also amended §1888(e)(2)(A)(ii) of the Act to exclude telehealth services furnished under §1834(m)(4)(C)(ii)(VII) from the consolidated billing provisions of the skilled nursing facility prospective payment system (SNF PPS).

NOTE: MIPPA did not add independent renal dialysis facilities as originating sites for payment of telehealth services.

The telehealth provisions authorized by §1834(m) of the Act are implemented in 42 CFR 410.78 and 414.65.

100-2, Chapter 15, 270.2

List of Medicare Telehealth Services

The use of a telecommunications system may substitute for an in-person encounter for professional consultations, office visits, office psychiatry services, and a limited number of other physician fee schedule (PFS) services. These services are listed below.

Consultations (Effective October 1, 2001-December 31, 2009)

Telehealth consultations, emergency department or initial inpatient (Effective January 1, 2010)

Follow-up inpatient telehealth consultations (Effective January 1, 2009)

Office or other outpatient visits

Subsequent hospital care services (with the limitation of one telehealth visit every 3 days) (Effective January 1, 2011)

Subsequent nursing facility care services (with the limitation of one telehealth visit every 30 days) (Effective January 1, 2011)

Individual psychotherapy

Pharmacologic management (Effective March 1, 2003)

Psychiatric diagnostic interview examination (Effective March 1, 2003)

End stage renal disease related services (Effective January 1, 2005)

Individual and group medical nutrition therapy (Individual effective January 1, 2006; group effective January 1, 2011)

Neurobehavioral status exam (Effective January 1, 2008)

Individual and group health and behavior assessment and intervention (Individual effective January 1, 2010; group effective January 1, 2011)

Individual and group kidney disease education (KDE) services (Effective January 1, 2011)

Individual and group diabetes self-management training (DSMT) services (with a minimum of 1 hour of in-person instruction to be furnished in the initial year training period to ensure effective injection training) (Effective January 1, 2011).

Smoking Cessation Services (Effective January 1, 2012)

Alcohol and/or substance (other than tobacco) abuse structured assessment and intervention services (Effective January 1, 2013)

Annual alcohol misuse screening (Effective January 1, 2013)

Brief face-to-face behavioral counseling for alcohol misuse (Effective January 1, 2013)

Annual Depression Screening (Effective January 1, 2013)

High-intensity behavioral counseling to prevent sexually transmitted infections (Effective January 1, 2013)

Annual, face-to-face Intensive behavioral therapy for cardiovascular disease (Effective January 1, 2013)

Face-to-face behavioral counseling for obesity (Effective January 1, 2013)

Transitional Care Management Services (Effective January 1, 2014)

NOTE: Beginning January 1, 2010, CMS eliminated the use of all consultation codes, except for inpatient telehealth consultation G-codes. CMS no longer recognizes office/outpatient or inpatient consultation CPT® codes for payment of office/outpatient or inpatient visits. Instead, physicians and practitioners are instructed to bill a new or established patient office/outpatient visit CPT® code or appropriate hospital or nursing facility care code, as appropriate to the particular patient, for all office/outpatient or inpatient visits. For detailed instructions regarding reporting these and other telehealth services, see Pub. 100-04, Medicare Claims Processing Manual, chapter 12, section 190.3.

The conditions of payment for Medicare telehealth services, including qualifying originating sites and the types of telecommunications systems recognized by Medicare, are subject to the provisions of 42 CFR 410.78. Payment for these services is subject to the provisions of 42 CFR 414.65.

100-2, Chapter 15, 270.4.3

Payment for Diabetes Self-Management Training (DSMT) as a Telehealth Service

Individual and group DSMT services may be paid as a Medicare telehealth service; however, at least 1 hour of the 10 hour benefit in the year following the initial DSMT service must be furnished in-person to allow for effective injection training. The injection training may be furnished through either individual or group DSMT services. By reporting the –GT or –GQ modifier with HCPCS code GO108 (Diabetes outpatient self-management

training services, individual, per 30 minutes) or G0109 Diabetes outpatient self-management training services, group session (2 or more), per 30 minutes), the distant site practitioner certifies that the beneficiary has received or will receive 1 hour of in-person DSMT services for purposes of injection training during the year following the initial DSMT service.

As specified in 42 CFR 410.141(e) and stated in section 300.2 of this chapter, individual DSMT services may be furnished by a physician, individual, or entity that furnishes other services for which direct Medicare payment may be made and that submits necessary documentation to, and is accredited by, an accreditation organization approved by CMS. However, consistent with the statutory requirements of section 1834(m)(1) of the Act, as provided in 42 CFR 410.78(b)(1) and (b)(2) and stated in section 270.4 of this chapter, Medicare telehealth services, including individual DSMT services furnished as a telehealth service, could only be furnished by a licensed physician assistant (PA), nurse practitioner (NP), clinical nurse specialist (CNS), certified nurse-midwife (CNM), clinical psychologist, clinical social worker, or registered die titian or nutrition professional.

100-2, Chapter 15, 280.1

Glaucoma Screening

A. Conditions of Coverage

The regulations implementing the Benefits Improvements and Protection Act of 2000, §102, provide for annual coverage for glaucoma screening for beneficiaries in the following high risk categories:

- Individuals with diabetes mellitus;
- Individuals with a family history of glaucoma; or
- African-Americans age 50 and over.

In addition, beginning with dates of service on or after January 1, 2006, 42 CFR 410.23(a)(2), revised, the definition of an eligible beneficiary in a high-risk category is expanded to include:

- Hispanic-Americans age 65 and over.

Medicare will pay for glaucoma screening examinations where they are furnished by or under the direct supervision in the office setting of an ophthalmologist or optometrist, who is legally authorized to perform the services under State law.

Screening for glaucoma is defined to include:

- A dilated eye examination with an intraocular pressure measurement; and
- A direct ophthalmoscopy examination, or a slit-lamp biomicroscopic examination.

Payment may be made for a glaucoma screening examination that is performed on an eligible beneficiary after at least 11 months have passed following the month in which the last covered glaucoma screening examination was performed.

The following HCPCS codes apply for glaucoma screening:

G0117-Glaucoma screening for high-risk patients furnished by an optometrist or ophthalmologist; and

G0118 -Glaucoma screening for high-risk patients furnished under the direct supervision of an optometrist or ophthalmologist.

The type of service for the above G codes is: TOS Q.

For providers who bill A/B MACs, applicable types of bill for screening glaucoma services are 13X, 22X, 23X, 71X, 73X, 75X, and 85X. The following revenue codes should be reported when billing for screening glaucoma services:

- Comprehensive outpatient rehabilitation facilities (CORFs), critical access hospitals (CAHs), skilled nursing facilities (SNFs), independent and provider-based RHCs and free standing and provider-based FQHCs bill for this service under revenue code 770. CAHs electing the optional method of payment for outpatient services report this service under revenue codes 96X, 97X,or 98X.

- Hospital outpatient departments bill for this service under any valid/appropriate revenue code. They are not required to report revenue code 770.

Calculating the Frequency

- Once a beneficiary has received a covered glaucoma screening procedure, the beneficiary may receive another procedure after 11 full months have passed. To determine the 11-month period, start the count beginning with the month after the month in which the previous covered screening procedure was performed.

Diagnosis Coding Requirements

- Providers bill glaucoma screening using diagnosis codes for screening services. Claims submitted without a screening diagnosis code may be returned to the provider as unprocessable.

Payment Methodology

A/B MACs (B)

- Contractors pay for glaucoma screening based on the Medicare physician fee schedule. Deductible and coinsurance apply. Claims from physicians or other providers where assignment was not taken are subject to the Medicare limiting charge (refer to the Medicare Claims Processing Manual, Chapter 12, "Physician/Non-physician Practitioners," for more information about the Medicare limiting charge).

A/B MACs (A)

- Payment is made for the facility expense as follows:
- Independent and provider-based RHC/free standing and provider-based FQHC -payment is made under the all inclusive rate for the screening glaucoma service based on the visit furnished to the RHC/FQHC patient;
- CAH -payment is made on a reasonable cost basis unless the CAH has elected the optional method of payment for outpatient services in which case, procedures outlined in the Medicare Claims Processing Manual, Chapter 3, §30.1.1, should be followed;
- CORF -payment is made under the Medicare physician fee schedule;
- Hospital outpatient department -payment is made under outpatient prospective payment system (OPPS);
- Hospital inpatient Part B -payment is made under OPPS;
- SNF outpatient -payment is made under the Medicare physician fee schedule (MPFS); and
- SNF inpatient Part B -payment is made under MPFS

Deductible and coinsurance apply.

E. Special Billing Instructions for RHCs and FQHCs

Screening glaucoma services are considered RHC/FQHC services. RHCs and FQHCs bill the contractor under bill type 71X or 73X along with revenue code 770 and HCPCS codes G0117 or G0118 and RHC/FQHC revenue code 520 or 521 to report the related visit. Reporting of revenue code 770 and HCPCS codes G0117 and G0118 in addition to revenue code 520 or 521 is required for this service in order for CWF to perform frequency editing.

Payment should not be made for a screening glaucoma service unless the claim also contains a visit code for the service. Therefore, the contractor installs an edit in its system to assure payment is not made for revenue code 770 unless the claim also contains a visit revenue code (520 or 521).

100-2, Chapter 15, 280.5

Annual Wellness Visit (AWV) Providing Personalized Prevention Plan Services (PPPS)

A. General

Pursuant to section 4103 of the Affordable Care Act of 2010 (the ACA), the; Centers for Medicare & Medicaid Services (CMS) amended section 42 CFR 411.15(a)(1) and 42 CFR 411.15(k)(15) (list of examples of routine physical examinations excluded from coverage), effective for services furnished on or after January 1, 2011. This expanded coverage, as established at 42 CFR 410.15, is subject to certain eligibility and other limitations that allow payment for an annual wellness visit (AWV) providing personalized prevention plan services (PPPS), when performed by a health professional (as defined in this section), for an individual who is no longer within 12 months after the effective date of his/her first Medicare Part B coverage period, and has not received either an initial preventive physical examination (IPPE) or an AWV within the past 12 months. Medicare coinsurance and Part B deductibles do not apply.

The AWV will include the establishment of, or update to, the individual's medical/family history, measurement of his/her height, weight, body-mass index (BMI) or waist circumference, and blood pressure (BP), with the goal of health promotion and disease detection and encouraging patients to obtain the screening and preventive services that may already be covered and paid for under Medicare Part B. Definitions relative to the AWV are included below.

Coverage is available for an AWV that meets the following requirements:

1. It is performed by a health professional; and,
2. It is furnished to an eligible beneficiary who is no longer within 12 months after the effective date of his/her first Medicare Part B coverage period, and he/she has not received either an IPPE or an AWV providing PPPS within the past 12 months.

Sections 4103 and 4104 of the ACA also provide for a waiver of the Medicare coinsurance and Part B deductible requirements for an AWV effective for services furnished on or after January 1, 2011.

B. Definitions Relative to the AWV:

Detection of any cognitive impairment: The assessment of an individual's cognitive function by direct observation, with due consideration of information obtained by way of patient reorts, concerns raised by family members, friends, caretakers, or others.

Eligible beneficiary: An individual who is no longer within 12 months after the effective date of his/her first Medicare Part B coverage period and who has not received either an IPPE or an AWV providing PPPS within the past 12 months.

Establishment of, or an update to, the individual's medical/family history:

At a minimum, the collection and documentation of the following:

a. Past medical and surgical history, including experiences with illnesses, hospital stays, operations, allergies, injuries, and treatments.

b. Use or exposure to medications and supplements, including calcium and vitamins.

c. Medical events in the beneficiary's parents and any siblings and children, including diseases that may be hereditary or place the individual at increased risk.

First AWV providing PPPS: The provision of the following services to an eligible beneficiary by a health professional that include, and take into account the results of, a health risk assessment as those terms are defined in this section:

a. Review (and administration if needed) of a health risk assessment (as defined in this section).

b. Establishment of an individual's medical/family history.

c. Establishment of a list of current providers and suppliers that are regularly involved in providing medical care to the individual.

d. Measurement of an individual's height, weight, BMI (or waist circumference, if appropriate), BP, and other routine measurements as deemed appropriate, based on the beneficiary's medical/family history.

e. Detection of any cognitive impairment that the individual may have as defined in this section.

f. Review of the individual's potential (risk factors) for depression, including current or past experiences with depression or other mood disorders, based on the use of an appropriate screening instrument for persons without a current diagnosis of depression, which the health professional may select from various available standardized screening tests designed for this purpose and recognized by national medical professional organizations.

g. Review of the individual's functional ability and level of safety based on direct observation, or the use of appropriate screening questions or a screening questionnaire, which the health professional may select from various available screening questions or standardized questionnaires designed for this purpose and recognized by national professional medical organizations.

h. Establishment of the following:

1. A written screening schedule for the individual, such as a checklist for the next 5 to 10 years, as appropriate, based on recommendations of the United States Preventive Services Task Force (USPSTF) and the Advisory Committee on Immunization Practices (ACIP), and the individual's health risk assessment (as that term is defined in this section), the individual's health status, screening history, and age-appropriate preventive services covered by Medicare.

2. A list of risk factors and conditions for which primary, secondary, or tertiary interventions are recommended or are underway for the individual, including any mental health conditions or any such risk factors or conditions that have been identified through an IPPE, and a list of treatment options and their associated risks and benefits.

i. Furnishing of personalized health advice to the individual and a referral, as appropriate, to health education or preventive counseling services or programs aimed at reducing identified risk factors and improving self-management, or community-based lifestyle interventions to reduce health risks and promote self-management and wellness, including weight loss, physical activity, smoking cessation, fall prevention, and nutrition.

j. Any other element determined appropriate through the National Coverage Determination (NCD) process.

Health professional:

a. A physician who is a doctor of medicine or osteopathy (as defined in section 1861(r)(1) of the Social Security Act (the Act); or,

b. A physician assistant, nurse practitioner, or clinical nurse specialist (as defined in section 1861(aa)(5) of the Act); or,

c. A medical professional (including a health educator, registered dietitian, or nutrition professional or other licensed practitioner) or a team of such medical professionals, working under the direct supervision (as defined in 42CFR 410.32(b)(3)(ii)) of a physician as defined in this section.

Health Risk Assessment means, for the purposes of the annual wellness visit, an evaluation tool that meets the following criteria:

a. collects self-reported information about the beneficiary.

b. can be administered independently by the beneficiary or administered by a health professional prior to or as part of the AWV encounter.

c. is appropriately tailored to and takes into account the communication needs of underserved populations, persons with limited English proficiency, and persons with health literacy needs.

d. takes no more than 20 minutes to complete.

e. addresses, at a minimum, the following topics:

1. demographic data, including but not limited to age, gender, race, and ethnicity.

2. self assessment of health status, frailty, and physical functioning.

3. psychosocial risks, including but not limited to, depression/life satisfaction, stress, anger, loneliness/social isolation, pain, and fatigue.

4. Behavioral risks, including but not limited to, tobacco use, physical activity, nutrition and oral health, alcohol consumption, sexual health, motor vehicle safety (seat belt use), and home safety.

5. Activities of daily living (ADLs), including but not limited to, dressing, feeding, toileting, grooming, physical ambulation (including balance/risk of falls), and bathing.

6. Instrumental activities of daily living (IADLs), including but not limited to, shopping, food preparation, using the telephone, housekeeping, laundry, mode of transportation, responsibility for own medications, and ability to handle finances.

Review of the individual's functional ability and level of safety: At a minimum, includes assessment of the following topics:

a. Hearing impairment,

b. Ability to successfully perform activities of daily living,

c. Fall risk, and,

d. Home safety.

Subsequent AWV providing PPPS: The provision of the following services to an eligible beneficiary by a health professional that include, and take into account the results of an updated health risk assessment, as those terms are defined in this section:

a. Review (and administration if needed) of an updated health risk assessment (as defined in this section).

b. An update of the individual's medical/family history.

c. An update of the list of current providers and suppliers that are regularly involved in providing medical care to the individual, as that list was developed for the first AWV providing PPPS or the previous subsequent AWV providing PPPS.

d. Measurement of an individual's weight (or waist circumference), BP, and other routine measurements as deemed appropriate, based on the individual's medical/family history.

e. Detection of any cognitive impairment that the individual may have as defined in this section.

f. An update to the following:

1. The written screening schedule for the individual as that schedule is defined in this section, that was developed at the first AWV providing PPPS, and,

2. The list of risk factors and conditions for which primary, secondary, or tertiary interventions are recommended or are under way for the individual, as that list was developed at the first AWV providing PPPS or the previous subsequent AWV providing PPPS.

g. Furnishing of personalized health advice to the individual and a referral, as appropriate, to health education or preventive counseling services or programs as that advice and related services are defined for the first AWV providing PPPS.

h. Any other element determined appropriate by the Secretary through the NCD process.

See Pub. 100-04, Medicare Claims Processing Manual, chapter 18, section 140, for detailed claims processing and billing instructions.

100-2, Chapter 15, 290

Foot Care

A. Treatment of Subluxation of Foot

Subluxations of the foot are defined as partial dislocations or displacements of joint surfaces, tendons ligaments, or muscles of the foot. Surgical or nonsurgical treatments undertaken for the sole purpose of correcting a subluxated structure in the foot as an isolated entity are not covered.

However, medical or surgical treatment of subluxation of the ankle joint (talo-crural joint) is covered. In addition, reasonable and necessary medical or surgical services, diagnosis, or treatment for medical conditions that have resulted from or are associated with partial displacement of structures is covered. For example, if a patient has osteoarthritis that has resulted in a partial displacement of joints in the foot, and the primary treatment is for the osteoarthritis, coverage is provided.

B. Exclusions from Coverage

The following foot care services are generally excluded from coverage under both Part A and Part B. (See §290.Fand §290. Gfor instructions on applying foot care exclusions.)

1. Treatment of Flat Foot

The term "flat foot" is defined as a condition in which one or more arches of the foot have flattened out. Services or devices directed toward the care or correction of such conditions, including the prescription of supportive devices, are not covered.

2. Routine Foot Care

Except as provided above, routine foot care is excluded from coverage. Services that normally are considered routine and not covered by Medicare include the following:

- The cutting or removal of corns and calluses;
- The trimming, cutting, clipping, or debriding of nails; and
- Other hygienic and preventive maintenance care, such as cleaning and soaking the feet, the use of skin creams to maintain skin tone of either ambulatory or bedfast patients, and any other service performed in the absence of localized illness, injury, or symptoms involving the foot.

3. Supportive Devices for Feet

Orthopedic shoes and other supportive devices for the feet generally are not covered. However, this exclusion does not apply to such a shoe if it is an integral part of a leg brace, and its expense is included as part of the cost of the brace. Also, this exclusion does not apply to therapeutic shoes furnished to diabetics.

C. Exceptions to Routine Foot Care Exclusion

1. Necessary and Integral Part of Otherwise Covered Services

In certain circumstances, services ordinarily considered to be routine may be covered if they are performed as a necessary and integral part of otherwise covered services, such as diagnosis and treatment of ulcers, wounds, or infections.

2. Treatment of Warts on Foot

The treatment of warts (including plantar warts) on the foot is covered to the same extent as services provided for the treatment of warts located elsewhere on the body.

3. Presence of Systemic Condition

The presence of a systemic condition such as metabolic, neurologic, or peripheral vascular disease may require scrupulous foot care by a professional that in the absence of such condition(s) would be considered routine (and, therefore, excluded from coverage). Accordingly, foot care that would otherwise be considered routine may be covered when systemic condition(s) result in severe circulatory embarrassment or areas of diminished sensation in the individual's legs or feet. (See subsection A.)

In these instances, certain foot care procedures that otherwise are considered routine (e.g., cutting or removing corns and calluses, or trimming, cutting, clipping, or debriding nails) may pose a hazard when performed by a nonprofessional person on patients with such systemic conditions. (See§290.G for procedural instructions.)

4. Mycotic Nails

In the absence of a systemic condition, treatment of mycotic nails may be covered.

The treatment of mycotic nails for an ambulatory patient is covered only when the physician attending the patient's mycotic condition documents that (1) there is clinical evidence of mycosis of the toenail, and (2) the patient has marked limitation of ambulation, pain, or secondary infection resulting from the thickening and dystrophy of the infected toenail plate.

The treatment of mycotic nails for a nonambulatory patient is covered only when the physician attending the patient's mycotic condition documents that (1) there is clinical evidence of mycosis of the toenail, and (2) the patient suffers from pain or secondary infection resulting from the thickening and dystrophy of the infected toenail plate.

For the purpose of these requirements, documentation means any written information that is required by the carrier in order for services to be covered. Thus, the information submitted with claims must be substantiated by information found in the patient's medical record. Any information, including that contained in a form letter, used for documentation purposes is subject to carrier verification in order to ensure that the information adequately justifies coverage of the treatment of mycotic nails.

D. Systemic Conditions That Might Justify Coverage

Although not intended as a comprehensive list, the following metabolic, neurologic, and peripheral vascular diseases (with synonyms in parentheses) most commonly represent the underlying conditions that might justify coverage for routine foot care.

Diabetes mellitus *

Arteriosclerosis obliterans (A.S.O., arteriosclerosis of the extremities, occlusive peripheral arteriosclerosis)

Buerger's disease (thromboangiitis obliterans)

Chronic thrombophlebitis *

Peripheral neuropathies involving the feet-

    Associated with malnutrition and vitamin deficiency *

- Malnutrition (general, pellagra)
- Alcoholism
- Malabsorption (celiac disease, tropical sprue)
- Pernicious anemia

Associated with carcinoma *

Associated with diabetes mellitus *

Associated with drugs and toxins *

Associated with multiple sclerosis *

Associated with uremia (chronic renal disease) *

Associated with traumatic injury

Associated with leprosy or neurosyphilis

Associated with hereditary disorders

- Hereditary sensory radicular neuropathy
- Angiokeratoma corporis diffusum (Fabry's)
- Amyloid neuropathy

When the patient's condition is one of those designated by an asterisk (*), routine procedure s are covered only if the patient is under the active care of a doctor of medicine or osteopathy who documents the condition.

E. Supportive Devices for Feet

Orthopedic shoes and other supportive devices for the feet generally are not covered. However, this exclusion does not apply to such a shoe if it is an integral part of a leg brace, and its expense is included as part of the cost of the brace. Also, this exclusion does not apply to therapeutic shoes furnished to diabetics.

F. Presumption of Coverage

In evaluating whether the routine services can be reimbursed, a presumption of coverage may be made where the evidence available discloses certain physical and/or clinical findings consistent with the diagnosis and indicative of severe peripheral involvement. For purposes of applying this presumption the following findings are pertinent:

Class A Findings

Nontraumatic amputation of foot or integral skeletal portion thereof.

Class B Findings

Absent posterior tibial pulse;

Advanced trophic changes as: hair growth (decrease or absence) nail changes (thickening) pigmentary changes (discoloration) skin texture (thin, shiny) skin color (rubor or redness) (Three required); and

Absent dorsalis pedis pulse.

Class C Findings

    Claudication;

    Temperature changes (e.g., cold feet);

    Edema;

    Paresthesias (abnormal spontaneous sensations in the feet); and

    Burning.

The presumption of coverage may be applied when the physician rendering the routine foot care has identified:

1. A Class A finding;
2. Two of the Class B findings; or
3. One Class B and two Class C findings

Cases evidencing findings falling short of these alternatives may involve podiatric treatment that may constitute covered care and should be reviewed by the intermediary's medical staff and developed as necessary.

For purposes of applying the coverage presumption where the routine services have been rendered by a podiatrist, the contractor may deem the active care requirement met if the claim or other evidence available discloses that the patient has seen an M.D. or D.O. for treatment and/or evaluation of the complicating disease process during the 6-month period prior to the rendition of the routine-type services. The intermediary may also accept the podiatrist's statement that the diagnosing and treating M.D. or D.O. also concurs with the podiatrist's findings as to the severity of the peripheral involvement indicated.

Services ordinarily considered routine might also be covered if they are performed as a necessary and integral part of otherwise covered services, such as diagnosis and treatment of diabetic ulcers, wounds, and infections.

G. Application of Foot Care Exclusions to Physician's Services

The exclusion of foot care is determined by the nature of the service. Thus, payment for an excluded service should be denied whether performed by a podiatrist, osteopath, or a doctor of medicine, and without regard to the difficulty or complexity of the procedure.

When an itemized bill shows both covered services and noncovered services not integrally related to the covered service, the portion of charges attributable to the noncovered services should be denied. (For example, if an itemized bill shows surgery for an ingrown toenail and also removal of calluses not necessary for the performance of toe surgery, any additional charge attributable to removal of the calluses should be denied.)

In reviewing claims involving foot care, the carrier should be alert to the following exceptional situations:

1. Payment may be made for incidental noncovered services performed as a necessary and integral part of, and secondary to, a covered procedure. For example, if trimming of toenails is required for application of a cast to a fractured foot, the carrier need not allocate and deny a portion of the charge for the trimming of the nails. However, a separately itemized charge for such excluded service should be disallowed. When the primary procedure is covered the administration of anesthesia necessary for the performance of such procedure is also covered.

2. Payment may be made for initial diagnostic services performed in connection with a specific symptom or complaint if it seems likely that its treatment would be covered even though the resulting diagnosis may be one requiring only noncovered care.

The name of the M.D. or D.O. who diagnosed the complicating condition must be submitted with the claim. In those cases, where active care is required, the approximate date the beneficiary was last seen by such physician must also be indicated.

NOTE: Section 939 of P.L. 96-499 removed "warts" from the routine foot care exclusion effective July 1, 1981.

Relatively few claims for routine-type care are anticipated considering the severity of conditions contemplated as the basis for this exception. Claims for this type of foot care should not be paid in the absence of convincing evidence that nonprofessional performance of the service would have been hazardous for the beneficiary because of an underlying systemic disease. The mere statement of a diagnosis such as those mentioned in §D above does not of itself indicate the severity of the condition. Where development is indicated to verify diagnosis and/or severity the carrier should follow existing claims processing practices, which may include review of carrier's history and medical consultation as well as physician contacts.

The rules in §290.F concerning presumption of coverage also apply.

Codes and policies for routine foot care and supportive devices for the feet are not exclusively for the use of podiatrists. These codes must be used to report foot care services regardless of the specialty of the physician who furnishes the services. Carriers must instruct physicians to use the most appropriate code available when billing for routine foot care.

100-2, Chapter 15, 300

Diabetes Self-Management Training Services

Section 4105 of the Balanced Budget Act of 1997 permits Medicare coverage of diabetes self- management training (DSMT) services when these services are furnished by a certified provider who meets certain quality standards. This program is intended to educate beneficiaries in the successful self-management of diabetes. The program includes instructions in self-monitoring of blood glucose; education about diet and exercise; an insulin treatment plan developed specifically for the patient who is insulin-dependent; and motivation for patients to use the skills for self-management.

Diabetes self-management training services may be covered by Medicare only if the treating physician or treating qualified non-physician practitioner who is managing the beneficiary's diabetic condition certifies that such services are needed. The referring physician or qualified non-physician practitioner must maintain the plan of care in the beneficiary's medical record and documentation substantiating the need for training on an individual basis when group training is typically covered, if so ordered. The order must also include a statement signed by the physician that the service is needed as well as the following:

- The number of initial or follow-up hours ordered (the physician can order less than 10 hours of training);
- The topics to be covered in training (initial training hours can be used for the full initial training program or specific areas such as nutrition or insulin training); and
- A determination that the beneficiary should receive individual or group training.

The provider of the service must maintain documentation in a file that includes the original order from the physician and any special conditions noted by the physician.

When the training under the order is changed, the training order/referral must be signed by the physician or qualified non-physician practitioner treating the beneficiary and maintained in the beneficiary's file in the DSMT's program records.

NOTE: All entities billing for DSMT under the fee-for-service payment system or other payment systems must meet all national coverage requirements.

100-2, Chapter 15, 300.2

Certified Providers

A designated certified provider bills for DSMT provided by an accredited DSMT program. Certified providers must submit a copy of their accreditation certificate to the contractor. The statute states that a "certified provider" is a physician or other individual or entity designated by the Secretary that, in addition to providing outpatient self management training services, provides other items and services for which payment may be made under title XVIII, and meets certain quality standards. The CMS is designating all providers and suppliers that bill Medicare for other individual services such as hospital outpatient departments, renal dialysis facilities, physicians and durable medical equipment suppliers as certified. All suppliers/providers who may bill for other Medicare services or items and who represent a DSMT program that is accredited as meeting quality standards can bill and receive payment for the entire DSMT program. Registered dietitians are eligible to bill on behalf of an entire DSMT program on or after January 1, 2002, as long as the provider has obtained a Medicare provider number. A dietitian may not be the sole provider of the

DSMT service. There is an exception for rural areas. In a rural area, an individual who is qualified as a registered dietitian and as a certified diabetic educator who is currently certified by an organization approved by CMS may furnish training and is deemed to meet the multidisciplinary team requirement.

The CMS will not reimburse services on a fee-for-service basis rendered to a beneficiary under Part A.

NOTE: While separate payment is not made for this service to Rural Health Clinics (RHCs), the service is covered but is considered included in the all-inclusive encounter rate. Effective January 1, 2006, payment for DSMT provided in a Federally Qualified Health Clinic (FQHC) that meets all of the requirements identified in Pub. 100-04, chapter 18, section 120 may be made in addition to one other visit the beneficiary had during the same day.

All DSMT programs must be accredited as meeting quality standards by a CMS approved national accreditation organization. Currently, CMS recognizes the American Diabetes Association, American Association of Diabetes Educators and the Indian Health Service as approved national accreditation organizations. Programs without accreditation by a CMS-approved national accreditation organization are not covered. Certified providers may be asked to submit updated accreditation documents at any time or to submit outcome data to an organization designated by CMS.

Enrollment of DMEPOS Suppliers

The DMEPOS suppliers are reimbursed for diabetes training through local carriers. In order to file claims for DSMT, a DMEPOS supplier must be enrolled in the Medicare program with the National Supplier Clearinghouse (NSC). The supplier must also meet the quality standards of a CMS-approved national accreditation organization as stated above. DMEPOS suppliers must obtain a provider number from the local carrier in order to bill for DSMT.

The carrier requires a completed Form CMS-855, along with an accreditation certificate as part of the provider application process. After it has been determined that the quality standards are met, a billing number is assigned to the supplier. Once a supplier has received a National Provider Identification (NPI) number, the supplier can begin receiving reimbursement for this service.

Carriers should contact the National Supplier Clearinghouse (NSC) according to the instruction in Pub 100-08, the Medicare Program Integrity Manual, Chapter 10, "Healthcare Provider/Supplier Enrollment," to verify an applicant is currently enrolled and eligible to receive direct payment from the Medicare program.

The applicant is assigned specialty 87.

Any DMEPOS supplier that has its billing privileges deactivated or revoked by the NSC will also have the billing number deactivated by the carrier.

100-2, Chapter 15, 300.3

Frequency of Training

A -Initial Training

The initial year for DSMT is the 12 month period following the initial date.

Medicare will cover initial training that meets the following conditions:

- Is furnished to a beneficiary who has not previously received initial or follow-up training under HCPCS codes G0108 or G0109;
- Is furnished within a continuous 12-month period;
- Does not exceed a total of 10 hours* (the 10 hours of training can be done in any combination of 1/2 hour increments);
- With the exception of 1 hour of individual training, training is usually furnished in a group setting, which can contain other patients besides Medicare beneficiaries, and;
- One hour of individual training may be used for any part of the training including insulin training.

* When a claim contains a DSMT HCPCS code and the associated units cause the total time for the DSMT initial year to exceed '10' hours, a CWF error will set.

B -Follow-Up Training

Medicare covers follow-up training under the following conditions:

- No more than 2 hours individual or group training per beneficiary per year;
- Group training consists of 2 to 20 individuals who need not all be Medicare beneficiaries;
- Follow-up training for subsequent years is based on a 12 month calendar after completion of the full 10 hours of initial training;
- Follow-up training is furnished in increments of no less than one-half hour*; and
- The physician (or qualified non-physician practitioner) treating the beneficiary must document in the beneficiary's medical record that the beneficiary is a diabetic.

*When a claim contains a DSMT HCPCS code and the associated units cause the total time for any follow-up year to exceed 2 hours, a CWF error will set.

100-2, Chapter 15, 300.4

Coverage Requirements for Individual Training

Medicare covers training on an individual basis for a Medicare beneficiary under any of the following conditions.

- No group session is available within 2 months of the date the training is ordered;
- The beneficiary's physician (or qualified non-physician practitioner) documents in the beneficiary's medical record that the beneficiary has special needs resulting from conditions, such as severe vision, hearing or language limitations or other such special conditions as identified by the treating physician or non-physician practitioner, that will hinder effective participation in a group training session; or
- The physician orders additional insulin training.
- The need for individual training must be identified by the physician or non-physician practitioner in the referral.

NOTE: If individual training has been provided to a Medicare beneficiary and subsequently the carrier or intermediary determines that training should have been provided in a group, carriers and intermediaries down-code the reimbursement from individual to the group level and provider education would be the appropriate actions instead of denying the service as billed.

100-2, Chapter 15, 310

Kidney Disease Patient Education Services

By definition, chronic kidney disease (CKD) is kidney damage for 3 months or longer, regardless of the cause of kidney damage. CKD typically evolves over a long period of time and patients may not have symptoms until significant, possibly irreversible, damage has been done. Complications can develop from kidneys that do not function properly, such as high blood pressure, anemia, and weak bones. When CKD progresses, it may lead to kidney failure, which requires artificial means to perform kidney functions (dialysis) or a kidney transplant to maintain life.

Patients can be classified into 5 stages based on their glomerular filtration rate (GFR, how quickly blood is filtered through the kidneys), with stage I having kidney damage with normal or increased GFR to stage V with kidney failure, also called end-stage renal disease (ESRD). Once patients with CKD are identified, treatment is available to help prevent complications of decreased kidney function, slow the progression of kidney disease, and reduce the risk of other diseases such as heart disease.

Beneficiaries with CKD may benefit from kidney disease education (KDE) interventions due to the large amount of medical information that could affect patient outcomes, including the increasing emphasis on self-care and patients' desire for informed, autonomous decision-making. Pre-dialysis education can help patients achieve better understanding of their illness, dialysis modality options, and may help delay the need for dialysis. Education interventions should be patient-centered, encourage collaboration, offer support to the patient, and be delivered consistently.

Effective for claims with dates of service on and after January 1, 2010, Section 152(b) of the Medicare Improvements for Patients and Providers Act of 2008 (MIPPA) covers KDE services under Medicare Part B. KDE services are designed to provide beneficiaries with Stage IV CKD comprehensive information regarding: the management of comorbidities, including delaying the need for dialysis; prevention of uremic complications; all therapeutic options (each option for renal replacement therapy, dialysis access options, and transplantation); ensuring that the beneficiary has opportunities to actively participate in his/her choice of therapy; and that the services be tailored to meet the beneficiary's needs.

Regulations for KDE services were established at 42 CFR 410.48. Claims processing instructions and billing requirements can be found in Pub. 100-04, Medicare Claims Processing Manual, Chapter 32 –Billing Requirements for Special Services, Section 20.

100-2, Chapter 15, 310.1

Beneficiaries Eligible for Coverage

Medicare Part B covers outpatient, face-to-face KDE services for a beneficiary that:

- is diagnosed with Stage IV CKD, using the Modification of Diet in Renal Disease (MDRD) Study formula (severe decrease in GFR, GFR value of 15-29 mL/min/1.73 m2), and
- obtains a referral from the physician managing the beneficiary's kidney condition. The referral should be documented in the beneficiary's medical records.

100-2, Chapter 15, 310.2

Qualified Person

Medicare Part B covers KDE services provided by a 'qualified person,' meaning a:

- physician (as defined in section 30 of this chapter),
- physician assistant, nurse practitioner, or clinical nurse specialist (as defined in sections 190, 200, and 210 of this chapter),
- hospital, critical access hospital (CAH), skilled nursing facility (SNF), comprehensive outpatient rehabilitation facility (CORF), home health agency (HHA), or hospice,if the KDE services are provided in a rural area (using the actual geographic location core based statistical area (CBSA) to identify facilities located in rural areas), or
- hospital or CAH that is treated as being rural (was reclassified from urban to rural status per 42 CFR 412.103).

NOTE: The "incident to" requirements at section 1861(s)(2)(A) of the Social Security Act (the Act) do not apply to KDE services.

The following providers are not 'qualified persons' and are excluded from furnishing KDE services:

- A hospital, CAH, SNF, CORF, HHA, or hospice located outside of a rural area (using the actual geographic location CBSA to identify facilities located outside of a rural area), unless the services are furnished by a hospital or CAH that is treated as being in a rural area; and
- Renal dialysis facilities.

100-2, Chapter 15, 310.3

Limitations for Coverage

Medicare Part B covers KDE services:

- Up to six (6) sessions as a beneficiary lifetime maximum. A session is 1 hour. In order to bill for a session, a session must be at least 31 minutes in duration. A session that lasts at least 31 minutes, but less than 1 hour still constitutes 1 session.
- On an individual basis or in group settings; if the services are provided in a group setting, a group consists of 2 to 20 individuals who need not all be Medicare beneficiaries.

NOTE: Two HCPCS codes were created for this benefit and one or the other must be present, along with ICD-9-CM code 585.4 (chronic kidney disease, Stage IV (severe)), in order for a claim to be processed and paid correctly. They are:

- G0420: Face-to-face educational services related to the care of chronic kidney disease; individual, per session, per one hour
- G0421:Face-to-face educational services related to the care of chronic kidney disease; group, per session, per one hour

100-2, Chapter 15, 310.4

Standards for Content

Medicare Part B covers KDE services, provided by a qualified person, which provide comprehensive information regarding:

A. The management of comorbidities, including delaying the need for dialysis, which includes, but is not limited to, the following topics:

- Prevention and treatment of cardiovascular disease,
- Prevention and treatment of diabetes,
- Hypertension management,
- Anemia management,
- Bone disease and disorders of calcium and phosphorus metabolism management,
- Symptomatic neuropathy management, and
- Impairments in functioning and well-being.

B. Prevention of uremic complications, which includes, but is not limited to, the following topics

- Information on how the kidneys work and what happens when the kidneys fail,
- Understanding if remaining kidney function can be protected, preventing disease progression, and realistic chances of survival,
- Diet and fluid restrictions, and
- Medication review, including how each medication works, possible side effects and minimization of side effects, the importance of compliance, and informed decision making if the patient decides not to take a specific drug.

C. Therapeutic options, treatment modalities and settings, advantages and disadvantages of each treatment option, and how the treatments replace the kidney, including, but not limited to, the following topics:

- Hemodialysis, both at home and in-facility;
- Peritoneal dialysis (PD), including intermittent PD, continuous ambulatory PD, and continuous cycling PD, both at home and in-facility;
- All dialysis access options for hemodialysis and peritoneal dialysis; and
- Transplantation.

D. Opportunities for beneficiaries to actively participate in the choice of therapy and be tailored to meet the needs of the individual beneficiary involved, which includes, but is not limited to, the following topics:

- Physical symptoms,
- Impact on family and social life,
- Exercise,
- The right to refuse treatment,
- Impact on work and finances,
- The meaning of test results, and
- Psychological impact.

100-2, Chapter 15, 310.5

Outcomes Assessment

Qualified persons that provide KDE services must develop outcomes assessments that are designed to measure beneficiary knowledge about CKD and its treatment. The assessment must be administered to the beneficiary during a KDE session, and be made available to the Centers for Medicare & Medicaid Services (CMS) upon request. The outcomes assessments serve to assist KDE educators and CMS in improving subsequent KDE programs, patient understanding, and assess program effectiveness of:

- Preparing the beneficiary to make informed decisions about their healthcare options related to CKD, and

- Meeting the communication needs of underserved populations, including persons with disabilities, persons with limited English proficiency, and persons with health literacy needs.

100-2, Chapter 16, 10

General Exclusions From Coverage

No payment can be made under either the hospital insurance or supplementary medical insurance program for certain items and services, when the following conditions exist:

- Not reasonable and necessary (§20);
- No legal obligation to pay for or provide (§40);
- Paid for by a governmental entity (§50);
- Not provided within United States (§60);
- Resulting from war (§70);
- Personal comfort (§80);
- Routine services and appliances (§90);
- Custodial care (§110);
- Cosmetic surgery (§120);
- Charges by immediate relatives or members of household (§130);
- Dental services (§140);
- Paid or expected to be paid under workers' compensation (§150);
- Nonphysician services provided to a hospital inpatient that were not provided directly or arranged for by the hospital (§170);
- Services Related to and Required as a Result of Services Which are not Covered Under Medicare (§180);
- Excluded foot care services and supportive devices for feet (§30); or
- Excluded investigational devices (See Chapter 14, §30)

100-2, Chapter 16, 20

Services Not Reasonable and Necessary

Items and services which are not reasonable and necessary for the diagnosis or treatment of illness or injury or to improve the functioning of a malformed body member are not covered, e.g., payment cannot be made for the rental of a special hospital bed to be used by the patient in their home unless it was a reasonable and necessary part of the patient's treatment. See also §80.

A health care item or service for the purpose of causing, or assisting to cause, the death of any individual (assisted suicide) is not covered. This prohibition does not apply to the provision of an item or service for the purpose of alleviating pain or discomfort, even if such use may increase the risk of death, so long as the item or service is not furnished for the specific purpose of causing death.

100-2, Chapter 16, 90

Routine Services and Appliances

Routine physical checkups; eyeglasses, contact lenses, and eye examinations for the purpose of prescribing, fitting, or changing eyeglasses; eye refractions by whatever practitioner and for whatever purpose performed; hearing aids and examinations for hearing aids; and immunizations are not covered.

The routine physical checkup exclusion applies to (a) examinations performed without relationship to treatment or diagnosis for a specific illness, symptom, complaint, or injury; and (b) examinations required by third parties such as insurance companies, business establishments, or Government agencies.

The routine physical checkup exclusion does not apply to the following services (as noted in section 42 CFR 411.15(a)(1)):

- Screening mammography,
- Colorectal cancer screening tests,
- Screening pelvic exams,
- Prostate cancer screening tests,
- Glaucoma screening exams,
- Ultrasound screening for abdominal aortic aneurysms (AAA),
- cardiovascular disease screening tests,
- diabetes screening tests,
- screening electrocardiogram,
- Initial preventive physical examinations,
- Annual wellness visits providing personalized prevention plan services, and
- Additional preventive services that meet the criteria specified in 42 CFR 410.64.

If the claim is for a diagnostic test or examination performed solely for the purpose of establishing a claim under title IV of Public Law 91-173, "Black Lung Benefits," the service is not covered under Medicare and the claimant should be advised to contact their Social Security office regarding the filing of a claim for reimbursement under the "Black Lung" program.

The exclusions apply to eyeglasses or contact lenses, and eye examinations for the purpose of prescribing, fitting, or changing eyeglasses or contact lenses for refractive errors. The exclusions do not apply to physicians' services (and services incident to a physicians' service) performed in conjunction with an eye disease, as for example, glaucoma or cataracts, or to post-surgical prosthetic lenses which are customarily used during convalescence from eye surgery in which the lens of the eye was removed, or to permanent prosthetic lenses required by an individual lacking the organic lens of the eye, whether by surgical removal or congenital disease. Such prosthetic lens is a replacement for an internal body organ -the lens of the eye. (See the Medicare Benefit Policy Manual, Chapter 15, "Covered Medical and Other Health Services," §120).

Expenses for all refractive procedures, whether performed by an ophthalmologist (or any other physician) or an optometrist and without regard to the reason for performance of the refraction, are excluded from coverage.

A. Immunizations

Vaccinations or inoculations are excluded as immunizations unless they are either:

- Directly related to the treatment of an injury or direct exposure to a disease or condition, such as antirabies treatment, tetanus antitoxin or booster vaccine, botulin antitoxin, antivenin sera, or immune globulin. (In the absence of injury or direct exposure, preventive immunization (vaccination or inoculation) against such diseases as smallpox, polio, diphtheria, etc., is not covered.); or
- Specifically covered by statute, as described in the Medicare Benefit Policy Manual, Chapter 15, "Covered Medical and Other Health Services," §50.4.4.2.

B. Antigens

Prior to the Omnibus Reconciliation Act of 1980, a physician who prepared an antigen for a patient could not be reimbursed for that service unless the physician also administered the antigen to the patient. Effective January 1, 1981, payment may be made for a reasonable supply of antigens that have been prepared for a particular patient even though they have not been administered to the patient by the same physician who prepared them if:

- The antigens are prepared by a physician who is a doctor of medicine or osteopathy, and
- The physician who prepared the antigens has examined the patient and has determined a plan of treatment and a dosage regimen.

A reasonable supply of antigens is considered to be not more than a 12-month supply of antigens that has been prepared for a particular patient at any one time. The purpose of the reasonable supply limitation is to assure that the antigens retain their potency and effectiveness over the period in which they are to be administered to the patient. (See the Medicare Benefit Policy Manual, Chapter 15, "Covered Medical and Other Health Services," §50.4.4.1)

100-2, Chapter 16, 140

Dental Services Exclusion

Items and services in connection with the care, treatment, filling, removal, or replacement of teeth, or structures directly supporting the teeth are not covered. Structures directly supporting the teeth mean the periodontium, which includes the gingivae, dentogingival junction, periodontal membrane, cementum, and alveolar process. However, payment may be made for certain other services of a dentist. (See the Medicare Benefit Policy Manual, Chapter 15, "Covered Medical and Other Health Services," §150.)

The hospitalization or nonhospitalization of a patient has no direct bearing on the coverage or exclusion of a given dental procedure.

When an excluded service is the primary procedure involved, it is not covered regardless of its complexity or difficulty. For example, the extraction of an impacted tooth is not covered. Similarly, an alveoplasty (the surgical improvement of the shape and condition of the alveolar process) and a frenectomy are excluded from coverage when either of these procedures is performed in connection with an excluded service, e.g., the preparation of the mouth for dentures. In like manner , the removal of the torus palatinus (a bony protuberance of the hard palate) could be a covered service. However, with rare exception, this surgery is performed in connection with an excluded service, i.e., the preparation of the mouth for dentures. Under such circumstances, reimbursement is not made for this purpose.

The extraction of teeth to prepare the jaw for radiation treatments of neoplastic disease is also covered. This is an exception to the requirement that to be covered, a noncovered procedure or service performed by a dentist must be an incident to and an integral part of a covered procedure or service performed by the dentist. Ordinarily, the dentist extracts the patient's teeth, but another physician, e.g., a radiologist, administers the radiation treatments.

Whether such services as the administration of anesthesia, diagnostic x-rays, and other related procedures are covered depends upon whether the primary procedure being performed by the dentist is covered. Thus, an x-ray taken in connection with the reduction of a fracture of the jaw or facial bone is covered. However, a single x-ray or x-ray survey taken in connection with the care or treatment of teeth or the periodontium is not covered.

See also the Medicare Benefit Policy Manual, Chapter 1, "Inpatient Hospital Services," §70, and Chapter 15, "Covered Medical and Other Health Services," §150 for additional information on dental services

100-3, Chapter 1, Part 1, 10.2

Transcutaneous Electrical Nerve Stimulation (TENS) for Acute Post-Operative Pain

The use of transcutaneous electrical nerve stimulation (TENS) for the relief of acute post-operative pain is covered under Medicare. TENS may be covered whether used as an adjunct to the use of drugs, or as an alternative to drugs, in the treatment of acute pain resulting from surgery.

The TENS devices, whether durable or disposable, may be used in furnishing this service. When used for the purpose of treating acute post-operative pain, TENS devices are considered supplies. As such they may be hospital supplies furnished inpatients covered under Part A, or supplies incident to a physician's service when furnished in connection with surgery done on an outpatient basis, and covered under Part B.

It is expected that TENS, when used for acute post-operative pain, will be necessary for relatively short periods of time, usually 30 days or less. In cases when TENS is used for longer periods, contractors should attempt to ascertain whether TENS is no longer being used for acute pain but rather for chronic pain, in which case the TENS device may be covered as durable medical equipment as described in §160.27.

Cross-references:

Medicare Benefit Policy Manual, Chapter 1, "Inpatient Hospital Services," §40;

Medicare Benefit Policy Manual, Chapter 2, "Hospital Services Covered Under Part B," §§20, 20.4, and 80; Medicare Benefit Policy Manual, Chapter 15, "Covered Medical and other Health Services, §110."

100-3, Chapter 1, Part 1, 20.21

Chelation Therapy for Treatment of Atherosclerosis

Chelation therapy is the application of chelation techniques for the therapeutic or preventive effects of removing unwanted metal ions from the body. The application of chelation therapy using ethylenediamine-tetra-acetic acid (EDTA) for the treatment and prevention of atherosclerosis is controversial. There is no widely accepted rationale to explain the beneficial effects attributed to this therapy. Its safety is questioned and its clinical effectiveness has never been established by well-designed, controlled clinical trials. It is not widely accepted and practiced by American physicians. EDTA chelation therapy for atherosclerosis is considered experimental. For these reasons, EDTA chelation therapy for the treatment or prevention of atherosclerosis is not covered. Some practitioners refer to this therapy as chemoendarterectomy and may also show a diagnosis other than atherosclerosis, such as arteriosclerosis or calcinosis. Claims employing such variant terms should also be denied under this section.

Cross-reference: §20.22

100-3, Chapter 1, Part 1, 20.22

Ethylenediamine-Tetra-Acetic (EDTA) Chelation Therapy for Treatment of Atherosclerosis

The use of EDTA as a chelating agent to treat atherosclerosis, arteriosclerosis, calcinosis, or similar generalized condition not listed by the FDA as an approved use is not covered. Any such use of EDTA is considered experimental. See §20.21 for an explanation of this conclusion.

100-3, Chapter 1, Part 1, 40.7

Outpatient Intravenous Insulin Treatment (Effective December 23, 2009)

A. General

The term outpatient intravenous (IV) insulin therapy (OIVIT) refers to an outpatient regimen that integrates pulsatile or continuous intravenous infusion of insulin via any means, guided by the results of measurement of:

- respiratory quotient; and/or
- urine urea nitrogen (UUN); and/or
- arterial, venous, or capillary glucose; and/or
- potassium concentration; and

performed in scheduled recurring periodic intermittent episodes.

This regimen is also sometimes termed Cellular Activation Therapy (CAT), Chronic Intermittent Intravenous Insulin Therapy (CIIT), Hepatic Activation Therapy (HAT), Intercellular Activation Therapy (iCAT), Metabolic Activation Therapy (MAT), Pulsatile Intravenous Insulin Treatment (PIVIT), Pulse Insulin Therapy (PIT), and Pulsatile Therapy (PT).

In OIVIT, insulin is intravenously administered in the outpatient setting for a variety of indications. Most commonly, it is delivered in pulses, but it may be delivered as a more conventional drip solution. The insulin administration is adjunctive to the patient's routine diabetic management regimen (oral agent or insulin-based) or other disease management regimen, typically performed on an intermittent basis (often weekly), and frequently performed chronically without duration limits. Glucose or other carbohydrate is available ad libitum (in accordance with patient desire).

B. Nationally Covered Indications

N/A

C. Nationally Non-Covered Indications

Effective for claims with dates of service on and after December 23, 2009, the Centers for Medicare and Medicaid Services (CMS) determines that the evidence does not support a conclusion that OIVIT improves health outcomes in Medicare beneficiaries. Therefore, CMS has determined that OIVIT is not reasonable and necessary for any indication under section 1862(a)(1)(A) of the Social Security Act. Services comprising an OIVIT regimen are nationally non-covered under Medicare when furnished pursuant to an OIVIT regimen (see subsection A. above).

D. Other

Individual components of OIVIT may have medical uses in conventional treatment regimens for diabetes and other conditions. Coverage for such other uses may be determined by other local or national Medicare determinations, and do not pertain to OIVIT. For example, see Pub. 100-03, NCD Manual, Section 40.2, Home Blood Glucose Monitors, Section 40.3,

Closed-loop Blood Glucose Control Devices (CBGCD), Section 190.20, Blood Glucose Testing, and Section 280.14, Infusion Pumps, as well as Pub. 100-04, Claims Processing Manual, Chapter 18, Section 90, Diabetics Screening.

100-3, Chapter 1, Part 1, 80.2

Photodynamic Therapy

Photodynamic therapy is a medical procedure which involves the infusion of a photosensitive (light-activated) drug with a very specific absorption peak. This drug is chemically designed to have a unique affinity for the diseased tissue intended for treatment. Once introduced to the body, the drug accumulates and is retained in diseased tissue to a greater degree than in normal tissue. Infusion is followed by the targeted irradiation of this tissue with a non-thermal laser, calibrated to emit light at a wavelength that corresponds to the drug's absorption peak. The drug then becomes active and locally treats the diseased tissue.

Ocular Photodynamic Therapy (OPT)

Ocular Photodynamic Therapy (OPT) is used in the treatment of ophthalmologic diseases. OPT is only covered when used in conjunction with verteporfin (see section 80.3, "Photosensitive Drugs").

- Classic Subfoveal Choroidal Neovascular (CNV) Lesions -OPT is covered with a diagnosis of neovascular age-related macular degeneration (AMD) with predominately classic subfoveal choroidal neovascular (CNV) lesions (where the area of classic CNV occupies ≥ 50 percent of the area of the entire lesion) at the initial visit as determined by a fluorescein angiogram. Subsequent follow-up visits will require either an optical coherence tomography (OCT) or a fluorescein angiogram (FA) to access treatment response. There are no requirements regarding visual acuity, lesion size, and number of re-treatments.
- Occult Subfoveal Choroidal Neovascular (CNV) Lesions -OPT is noncovered for patients with a diagnosis of age-related macular degeneration (AMD) with occult and no classic CNV lesions.

Other Conditions -Use of OPT with verteporfin for other types of AMD (e.g.,patients with minimally classic CNV lesions, atrophic, or dry AMD) is noncovered. OPT with verteporfin for other ocular indications such as pathologic myopia or presumed ocular histoplasmosis syndrome, is eligible for coverage through individual contractor discretion.

100-3, Chapter 1, Part 1, 80.2.1

A. General

Ocular Photodynamic Therapy (OPT) is used in the treatment of ophthalmologic diseases; specifically, for age-related macular degeneration (AMD), a common eye disease among the elderly. OPT involves the infusion of an intravenous photosensitizing drug called verteporfin followed by exposure to a laser. OPT is only covered when used in conjunction with verteporfin.

Effective July 1, 2001, OPT with verteporfin was approved for a diagnosis of neovascular AMD with predominately classic subfoveal choroidal neovascularization (CNV) lesions (where the area of classic CNV occupies ≥ 50% of the area of the entire lesion) at the initial visit as determined by a fluorescein angiogram (FA).

On October 17, 2001, the Centers for Medicare & Medicaid Services (CMS) announced its "intent to cover" OPT with verteporfin for AMD patients with occult and no classic subfoveal CNV as determined by an FA. The October 17, 2001, decision was never implemented.

On March 28, 2002, after thorough review and reconsideration of the October 17, 2001, intent to cover policy, CMS determined that the current non-coverage policy for OPT for verteporfin for AMD patients with occult and no classic subfoveal CNV as determined by an FA should remain in effect.

Effective August 20, 2002, CMS issued a non-covered instruction for OPT with verteporfin for AMD patients with occult and no classic subfoveal CNVas determined by an FA.

B. Nationally Covered Indications

Effective April 1, 2004, OPT with verteporfin continues to be approved for a diagnosis of neovascular AMD with predominately classic subfoveal CNV lesions (where the area of classic CNV occupies ≥ 50% of the area of the entire lesion) at the initial visit as determined by an FA. (CNV lesions are comprised of classic and/or occult components.) Subsequent follow-up visits require either an optical coherence tomography (OCT) (effective April 3. 2013) or an FA (effective April 1, 2004) to access treatment response. There are no requirements regarding visual acuity, lesion size, and number of re-treatments when treating predominantly classic lesions.

In addition, after thorough review and reconsideration of the August 20, 2002, non-coverage policy, CMS determines that the evidence is adequate to conclude that OPT with verteporfin is reasonable and necessary for treating:

1. Subfoveal occult with no classic CNV associated with AMD; and,
2. Subfoveal minimally classic CNV (where the area of classic CNV occupies <50% of the area of the entire lesion) associated with AMD.

The above 2 indications are considered reasonable and necessary only when:

1. The lesions are small (4 disk areas or less in size)at the time of initial treatment or within the 3 months prior to initial treatment; and,
2. The lesions have shown evidence of progression within the 3 months prior to initial treatment. Evidence of progression must be documented by deterioration of visual acuity (at least 5 letters on a standard eye examination chart), lesion growth (an increase in at least 1 disk area), or the appearance of blood associated with the lesion.

C. Nationally Non-Covered Indications

Other uses of OPT with verteporfin to treat AMD not already addressed by CMS will continue to be non-covered. These include, but are not limited to, the following AMD indications:

- Juxtafoveal or extrafoveal CNV lesions (lesions outside the fovea),
- Inability to obtain a fluorescein angiogram,
- Atrophic or "dry" AMD.

D. Other

The OPT with verteporfin for other ocular indications, such as pathologic myopia or presumed ocular histoplasmosis syndrome, continue to be eligible for local coverage determinations through individual contractor discretion.

100-3, Chapter 1, Part 1, 80.3

Photosensitive Drugs

Photosensitive drugs are the light-sensitive agents used in photodynamic therapy. Once introduced into the body, these drugs selectively identify and adhere to diseased tissue. The drugs remain inactive until they are exposed to a specific wavelength of light, by means of a laser, that corresponds to their absorption peak. The activation of a photosensitive drug results in a photochemical reaction which treats the diseased tissue without affecting surrounding normal tissue.

Verteporfin

Verteporfin, a benzoporphyrin derivative, is an intravenous lipophilic photosensitive drug with an absorption peak of 690 nm. This drug was first approved by the Food and Drug Administration (FDA) on April 12, 2000, and subsequently, approved for inclusion in the United States Pharmacopoeia on July 18, 2000, meeting Medicare's definition of a drug when used in conjunction with ocular photodynamic therapy (OPT) (see section 80.2, "Photodynamic Therapy") when furnished intravenously incident to a physician's service. For patients with age-related macular degeneration (AMD), Verteporfin is only covered with a diagnosis of neovascular age-related macular degeneration with predominately classic subfoveal choroidal neovascular (CNV) lesions (where the area of classic CNV occupies ≥ 50 percent of the area of the entire lesion) at the initial visit as determined by a fluorescein angiogram (FA). Subsequent follow-up visits will require either an optical coherence tomography (OCT) or an FA to access treatment response. OPT with verteporfin is covered for the above indication and will remain non-covered for all other indications related to AMD (see section 80.2). OPT with Verteporfin for use in non-AMD conditions is eligible for coverage through individual contractor discretion.

100-3, Chapter 1, Part 1, 80.3.1

Verteporfin -Effective April 3, 2013

A. General

Verteporfin, a benzoporphyrin derivative, is an intravenous lipophilic photosensitive drug with an absorption peak of 690 nm. Verteporfin was first approved by the Food and Drug Administration on April 12, 2000, and subsequently approved for inclusion in the United States Pharmacopoeia on July 18, 2000, meeting Medicare's definition of a drug as defined under §1861(t)(1) of the Social Security Act. Verteporfin is only covered when used in conjunction with ocular photodynamic therapy OPT) when furnished intravenously incident to a physician's service.

B. Nationally Covered Indications

Effective April 1, 2004, OPT with verteporfin is covered for patients with a diagnosis of neovascular age-related macular degeneration (AMD) with:

- Predominately classic subfoveal choroidal neovascularization (CNV) lesions (where the area of classic CNV occupies ≥ 50% of the area of the entire lesion) at the initial visit as determined by a fluorescein angiogram. (CNV lesions are comprised of classic and/or occult components.) Subsequent follow-up visits require either an optical coherence tomography (OCT) (effective April 3, 2013) or a fluorescein angiogram (FA) (effective April 1, 2004) to access treatment response.

  There are no requirements regarding visual acuity, lesion size,and number of retreatments when treating predominantly classic lesions.

- Subfoveal occult with no classic associated with AMD.
- Subfoveal minimally classic CNV CNV (where the area of classic CNV occupies <50% of the area of the entire lesion) associated with AMD.
- The above 2 indications are considered reasonable and necessary only when:

1. The lesions are small (4 disk areas or less in size) at the time of initial treatment or within the 3 months prior to initial treatment; and,

2. The lesions have shown evidence of progression within the 3 months prior to initial treatment. Evidence of progression must be documented by deterioration of visual acuity (at least 5 letters on a standard eye examination chart), lesion growth (an increase in at least 1 disk area), or the appearance of blood associated with the lesion.

C. Nationally Non-Covered Indications

Other uses of OPT with verteporfin to treat AMD not already addressed by the Centers for Medicare & Medicaid Services will continue to be non-covered. These include, but are not limited to, the following AMD indications: juxtafoveal or extrafoveal CNV lesions (lesions outside the fovea), inability to obtain an FA, or atrophic or "dry" AMD.

D. Other

The OPT with verteporfin for other ocular indications, such as pathologic myopia or presumed ocular histoplasmosis syndrome, continue to be eligible for local coverage determinations through individual contractor discretion.

100-3, Chapter 1, Part 2, 90.1

Pharmacogenomic Testing to Predict Warfarin Responsiveness (Effective August 3, 2009)

A. General

Warfarin sodium is an orally administered anticoagulant drug that is marketed most commonly as Coumadin®. (The Food and Drug Administration (FDA) approved labeling for Coumadin® includes a Black Box Warning dating back to 2007.) Anticoagulant drugs are sometimes referred to as blood thinners by the lay public. Warfarin affects the vitamin K-dependent clotting factors II, VII, IX, and X. Warfarin is thought to interfere with clotting factor synthesis by inhibition of the C1 subunit of the vitamin K epoxide reductase (VKORC1) enzyme complex, thereby reducing the regeneration of vitamin K1 epoxide. The elimination of warfarin is almost entirely by metabolic conversion to inactive metabolites by cytochrome P450 (CYP) enzymes in liver cells. CYP2C9 is the principal cytochrome P450 enzyme that modulates the anticoagulant activity of warfarin. From results of clinical studies, genetic variation in the CYP2C9 and/or VKORC1 genes can, in concert with clinical factors, predict how each individual responds to warfarin.

Pharmacogenomics denotes the study of how an individual's genetic makeup, or genotype, affects the body's response to drugs. Pharmacogenomics as a science examines associations among variations in genes with individual responses to a drug or medication. In application, pharmacogenomic results (i.e., information on the patient's genetic variations) can contribute to predicting a patient's response to a given drug: good, bad, or none at all. Pharmacogenomic testing of CYP2C9 or VKORC1 alleles to predict a patient's response to warfarin occurs ideally prior to initiation of the drug. This would be an once-in-a-lifetime test, absent any reason to believe that the patient's personal genetic characteristics would change over time. Although such pharmacogenomic testing would be used to attempt to better approximate the best starting dose of warfarin, it would not eliminate the need for periodic PT/INR testing, a standard diagnostic test for coagulation activity and for assessing how a patient is reacting to a warfarin dose.

Nationally Covered Indications

Effective August 3, 2009, the Centers for Medicare & Medicaid Services (CMS) believes that the available evidence supports that coverage with evidence development (CED) under §1862(a)(1)(E) of the Social Security Act (the Act) is appropriate for pharmacogenomic testing of CYP2C9 or VKORC1 alleles to predict warfarin responsiveness by any method, and is therefore covered only when provided to Medicare beneficiaries who are candidates for anticoagulation therapy with warfarin who:

1. Have not been previously tested for CYP2C9 or VKORC1 alleles; and

2. Have received fewer than five days of warfarin in the anticoagulation regimen for which the testing is ordered; and

3. Are enrolled in a prospective, randomized, controlled clinical study when that study meets the following standards.

A clinical study seeking Medicare payment for pharmacogenomic testing of CYP2C9 or VKORC1 alleles to predict warfarin responsiveness provided to the Medicare beneficiary who is a candidate for anticoagulation therapy with warfarin pursuant to CED must address one or more aspects of the following question:

Prospectively, in Medicare-aged subjects whose warfarin therapy management includes pharmacogenomic testing of CYP2C9 or VKORC1 alleles to predict warfarin response, what is the frequency and severity of the following outcomes, compared to subjects whose warfarin therapy management does not include pharmacogenomic testing?

- Major hemorrhage
- Minor hemorrhage
- Thromboembolism related to the primary indication for anticoagulation
- Other thromboembolic event
- Mortality

The study must adhere to the following standards of scientific integrity and relevance to the Medicare population:

a. The principal purpose of the research study is to test whether a particular intervention potentially improves the participants' health outcomes.

b. The research study is well-supported by available scientific and medical information or it is intended to clarify or establish the health outcomes of interventions already in common clinical use.

c. The research study does not unjustifiably duplicate existing studies.

d. The research study design is appropriate to answer the research question being asked in the study.

e. The research study is sponsored by an organization or individual capable of executing the proposed study successfully.

f. The research study is in compliance with all applicable Federal regulations concerning the protection of human subjects found in the Code of Federal Regulations (CFR) at 45 CFR Part 46. If a study is regulated by the FDA, it also must be in compliance with 21 CFR Parts 50 and 56.

g. All aspects of the research study are conducted according to the appropriate standards of scientific integrity.

h. The research study has a written protocol that clearly addresses, or incorporates by reference, the Medicare standards.

i. The clinical research study is not designed to exclusively test toxicity or disease pathophysiology in healthy individuals. Trials of all medical technologies measuring therapeutic outcomes as one of the objectives meet this standard only if the disease or condition being studied is life-threatening as defined in 21 CFR § 312.81(a) and the patient has no other viable treatment options.

j. The clinical research study is registered on the www. ClinicalTrials.gov website by the principal sponsor/ investigator prior to the enrollment of the first study subject.

k. The research study protocol specifies the method and timing of public release of all pre-specified outcomes to be measured including release of outcomes if outcomes are negative or study is terminated early. The results must be made public within 24 months of the end of data collection. If a report is planned to be published in a peer-reviewed journal, then that initial release may be an abstract that meets the requirements of the International Committee of Medical Journal Editors. However, a full report of the outcomes must be made public no later than 3 years after the end of data collection.

l. The research study protocol must explicitly discuss subpopulations affected by the treatment under investigation, particularly traditionally underrepresented groups in clinical studies, how the inclusion and exclusion criteria affect enrollment of these populations, and a plan for the retention and reporting of said populations on the trial. If the inclusion and exclusion criteria are expected to have a negative effect on the recruitment or retention of underrepresented populations, the protocol must discuss why these criteria are necessary.

m. The research study protocol explicitly discusses how the results are or are not expected to be generalizable to the Medicare population to infer whether Medicare patients may benefit from the intervention. Separate discussions in the protocol may be necessary for populations eligible for Medicare due to age, disability or Medicaid eligibility.

B. Nationally Non-Covered Indications

The CMS believes that the available evidence does not demonstrate that pharmacogenomic testing of CYP2C9 or VKORC1 alleles to predict warfarin responsiveness improves health outcomes in Medicare beneficiaries outside the context of CED, and is therefore not reasonable and necessary under §1862(a)(1)(A) of the Act.

C. Other

This NCD does not determine coverage to identify CYP2C9 or VKORC1 alleles for other purposes, nor does it determine national coverage to identify other alleles to predict warfarin responsiveness.

100-3, Chapter 1, Part 2, 110.22

Autologous Cellular Immunotherapy Treatment (Effective June 30, 2011)

A. General

Prostate cancer is the most common non-cutaneous cancer in men in the United States. In 2009, an estimated 192,280 new cases of prostate cancer were diagnosed and an estimated 27,360 deaths were reported. The National Cancer Institute states that prostate cancer is predominantly a cancer of older men; the median age at diagnosis is 72 years. Once the patient has castration-resistant, metastatic prostate cancer the median survival is generally less than two years.

In 2010 the Food and Drug Administration (FDA) approved sipuleucel-T (PROVENGE®; APC8015), for patients with castration-resistant, metastatic prostate cancer. The posited mechanism of action, immunotherapy, is different from that of anti-cancer chemotherapy such as docetaxel. This is the first immunotherapy for prostate cancer to receive FDA approval.

The goal of immunotherapy is to stimulate the body's natural defenses (such as the white blood cells called dendritic cells, T-lymphocytes and mononuclear cells) in a specific manner so that they attack and destroy, or at least prevent, the proliferation of cancer cells. Specificity is attained by intentionally exposing a patient's white blood cells to a particular protein (called an antigen) associated with the prostate cancer. This exposure "trains" the white blood cells to target and attack the prostate cancer cells. Clinically, this is expected to result in a decrease in the size and/or number of cancer sites, an increase in the time to cancer progression, and/or an increase in survival of the patient.

Sipuleucel-T differs from other infused anti-cancer therapies. Most such anti-cancer therapies are manufactured and sold by a biopharmaceutical company and then purchased by and dispensed from a pharmacy. In contrast, once the decision is made to treat with sipuleucel-T, a multi-step process is used to produce sipuleucel-T. Sipuleucel-T is made individually for each patient with his own white blood cells. The patient's white blood cells are removed via a procedure called leukapheresis. In a laboratory the white blood cells are exposed to PA2024, which is a molecule created by linking prostatic acid phosphatase (PAP) with granulocyte/macrophage-colony stimulating factor (GM-CSF). PAP is an antigen specifically associated with prostate cancer cells; GM-CSF is a protein that targets a receptor on the surface of white blood cells. Hence, PAP serves to externally manipulate the immunological functioning of the patient's white blood cells while GM-CSF serves to stimulate the white blood cells into action. As noted in the FDA's clinical review, each dose of sipuleucel-T contains a minimum of 40 million treated white blood cells, however there is "high inherent variability" in the yield of sipuleucel-T from leukapheresis to leukapheresis in the same patient as well as from patient to patient. The treated white blood cells are then infused back into the same patient. The FDA-approved dosing regimen is three doses with each dose administered two weeks apart.

Indications and Limitations of Coverage

B. Nationally Covered Indications

Effective for services performed on or after June 30, 2011, The Centers for Medicare and Medicaid Services (CMS) proposes that the evidence is adequate to conclude that the use of autologous cellular immunotherapy treatment -sipuleucel-T; PROVENGE® improves health outcomes for Medicare beneficiaries with asymptomatic or minimally symptomatic metastatic castrate-resistant (hormone refractory) prostate cancer, and thus is reasonable and necessary for this on-label indication under 1862(a)(1)(A) of the Social Security Act.

C. Nationally Non-Covered Indications

N/A

D. Other

Effective for services performed on or after June 30, 2011, coverage of all off-label uses of autologous cellular immunotherapy treatment –sipuleucel-T; PROVENGE® for the treatment of pro state cancer is left to the discretion of the local Medicare Administrative Contractors.

(NCD last reviewed June 2011.)

100-3, Chapter 1, Part 2, 150.11

Thermal Intradiscal Procedures (TIPs) (Effective September 29, 2008)

A. General

Percutaneous thermal intradiscal procedures (TIPs) involve the insertion of a catheter(s)/probe(s) in the spinal disc under fluoroscopic guidance for the purpose of producing or applying heat and/or disruption within the disc to relieve low back pain.

The scope of this national coverage determination on TIPs includes percutaneous intradiscal techniques that employ the use of a radiofrequency energy source or electrothermal energy to apply or create heat and/or disruption within the disc for coagulation and/or decompression of disc material to treat symptomatic patients with annular disruption of a contained herniated disc, to seal annular tears or fissures, or destroy nociceptors for the purpose of relieving pain. This includes techniques that use single or multiple probe(s)/catheter(s), which utilize a resistance coil or other delivery system technology, are flexible or rigid, and are placed within the nucleus, the nuclear-annular junction, or the annulus.

Although not intended to be an all inclusive list, TIPs are commonly identified as intradiscal electrothermal therapy (IDET), intradiscal thermal annuloplasty (IDTA), percutaneous intradiscal radiofrequency thermocoagulation (PIRFT), radiofrequency annuloplasty (RA), intradiscal biacuplasty (IDB), percutaneous (or plasma) disc decompression (PDD) or coblation, or targeted disc decompression (TDD). At times, TIPs are identified or labeled based on the name of the catheter/probe that is used (e.g., SpineCath, discTRODE, SpineWand, Accutherm, or TransDiscal electrodes). Each technique or device has it own protocol for application of the therapy. Percutaneous disc decompression or nucleoplasty procedures that do not utilize a radiofrequency energy procedure) are not within the scope of this NCD.

B. Nationally Covered Indications

N/A

C. Nationally Non-Covered Indications

Effective for services performed on or after September 29, 2008, the Centers for Medicare and Medicaid Services has determined that TIPs are not reasonable and necessary for the treatment of low back pain. Therefore, TIPs, which include procedures that employ the use of a radiofrequency energy source or electrothermal energy to apply or create heat and/or disruption within the disc for the treatment of low back pain, are noncovered.

D. Other

N/A

(This NCD last reviewed September 2008.)

100-3, Chapter 1, Part 2, 150.12

Collagen Meniscus Implant (Effective May 25, 2010)

A. General

The knee menisci are wedge-shaped, semi-lunar discs of fibrous tissue located in the knee joint between the ends of the femur and the tibia and fibula. There is a lateral and medial meniscus in each knee. It is known now that the menisci provide mechanical support, localized pressure distribution, and lubrication of the knee joint. Initially, meniscal tears were treated with total meniscectomy; however, as knowledge of the function of the menisci and the potential long term effects of total meniscectomy on the knee joint evolved, treatment of symptomatic meniscal tears gravitated to repair of the tear, when possible, or partial meniscectomy.

The collagen meniscus implant (also referred to as collagen scaffold (CS), CMI or Menaflex ™ meniscus implant throughout the published literature) is used to fill meniscal defects that result from partial meniscectomy. The collagenmeniscus implant is not intended to replace the entire meniscus at it requires a meniscal rim for attachment. The literature describes the placement of the collagen meniscus implant through an arthroscopic procedure with an additional incision for capture of the repair needles and tying of the sutures. After debridement of the damaged meniscus, the implant is trimmed to the size of meniscal defect and sutured into place. The collagen meniscus implant is described as a tissue engineered scaffold to support the generation of new meniscus-like tissue. The collagen meniscus implant is manufactured from bovine collagen and should not be confused with the meniscus transplant which involves the replacement of the meniscus with a transplant meniscus from a cadaver donor. The meniscus transplant is not addressed under this national coverage determination.

B. Nationally Covered Indications

N/A

C. Nationally Non-Covered Indications

Effective for claims with dates of service performed on or after May 25, 2010, the Centers for Medicare & Medicaid Services has determined that the evidence is adequate to conclude that the collagen meniscus implant does not improve health outcomes and, therefore, is not reasonable and necessary for the treatment of meniscal injury/tear under section 1862(a)(1)(A) of the Social Security Act. Thus, the collagen meniscus implant is non-covered by Medicare.

D. Other

N/A

(This NCD last reviewed May 2010.)

100-3, Chapter 1, Part 2, 160.13

Supplies Used in the Delivery of Transcutaneous Electrical Nerve Stimulation (TENS) and Neuromuscular Electrical Stimulation (NMES)

Transcutaneous Electrical Nerve Stimulation (TENS) and/or Neuromuscular Electrical Stimulation (NMES) can ordinarily be delivered to patients through the use of conventional electrodes, adhesive tapes and lead wires. There may be times, however, where it might be medically necessary for certain patients receiving TENS or NMES treatment to use, as an alternative to conventional electrodes, adhesive tapes and lead wires, a form-fitting conductive garment (i.e., a garment with conductive fibers which are separated from the patients' skin by layers of fabric).

A form-fitting conductive garment (and medically necessary related supplies) may be covered under the program only when:

1. It has received permission or approval for marketing by the Food and Drug Administration;

2. It has been prescribed by a physician for use in delivering covered TENS or NMES treatment; and

3. One of the medical indications outlined below is met:

   - The patient cannot manage without the conductive garment because there is such a large area or so many sites to be stimulated and the stimulation would have to be delivered so frequently that it is not feasible to use conventional electrodes, adhesive tapes and lead wires;

   - The patient cannot manage without the conductive garment for the treatment of chronic intractable pain because the areas or sites to be stimulated are inaccessible with the use of conventional electrodes, adhesive tapes and lead wires;

   - The patient has a documented medical condition such as skin problems that preclude the application of conventional electrodes, adhesive tapes and lead wires;

   - The patient requires electrical stimulation beneath a cast either to treat disuse atrophy, where the nerve supply to the muscle is intact, or to treat chronic intractable pain; or

   - The patient has a medical need for rehabilitation strengthening (pursuant to a written plan of rehabilitation) following an injury where the nerve supply to the muscle is intact.

A conductive garment is not covered for use with a TENS device during the trial period specified in §160.3 unless:

4. The patient has a documented skin problem prior to the start of the trial period; and

5. The A/B MAC (B)'s medical consultants are satisfied that use of such an item is medically necessary for the patient.

(See conditions for coverage of the use of TENS in the diagnosis and treatment of chronic intractable pain in §§160.3, 160.13, and 160.27, and the use of NMES in the treatment of disuse atrophy in §150.4.)

100-3, Chapter 1, Part 2, 160.27

Transcutaneous Electrical Nerve Stimulation (TENS) for Chronic Low Back Pain (CLBP)

The TENS is a type of electrical nerve stimulator that is employed to treat chronic intractable pain. This stimulator is attached to the surface of the patient's skin over the peripheral nerve to be stimulated. It may be applied in a variety of settings (in the patient's home, a physician's office, or in an outpatient clinic). Payment for TENS may be made under the durable medical equipment benefit.

A. General

For the purposes of this decision chronic low back pain (CLBP) is defined as:

1. an episode of low back pain that has persisted for three months or longer; and

2. is not a manifestation of a clearly defined and generally recognizable primary disease entity. For example, there

are cancers that, through metastatic spread to the spine or pelvis, may elicit pain in the lower back as a symptom; and certain systemic diseases such as rheumatoid arthritis and multiple sclerosis manifest many debilitating symptoms of which low back pain is not the primary focus.

B. Nationally Covered Indications

Effective June 8, 2012, the Centers for Medicare & Medicaid Services (CMS) will allow coverage for Transcutaneous Electrical Nerve Stimulation (TENS) for CLBP only when all of the following conditions are met.

In order to support additional research on the use of TENS for CLBP, we will cover this item under section 1862(a)(1)(E) of the Social Security Act (the Act) subject to all of the following conditions:

1. Coverage under this section expires three years after the publication of this decision on the CMS website.

2. The beneficiary is enrolled in an approved clinical study meeting all of the requirements below. The study must address one or more aspects of the following questions in a randomized, controlled design using validated and reliable instruments. This can include randomized crossover designs when the impact of prior TENS use is appropriately accounted for in the study protocol.

    i. Does the use of TENS provide clinically meaningful reduction in pain in Medicare beneficiaries with CLBP?

    ii. Does the use of TENS provide a clinically meaningful improvement of function in Medicare beneficiaries with CLBP?

    iii. Does the use of TENS impact the utilization of other medical treatments or services used in the medical management of CLBP?

These studies must be designed so that the patients in the control and comparison groups receive the same concurrent treatments and either sham (placebo) TENS or active TENS intervention.

The study must adhere to the following standards of scientific integrity and relevance to the Medicare population:

a. The principal purpose of the research study is to test whether a particular intervention potentially improves the participants' health outcomes.

b. The research study is well supported by available scientific and medical information or it is intended to clarify or establish the health outcomes of interventions already in common clinical use.

c. The research study does not unjustifiably duplicate existing studies.

d. The research study design is appropriate to answer the research question being asked in the study.

e. The research study is sponsored by an organization or individual capable of executing the proposed study successfully.

f. The research study is in compliance with all applicable Federal regulations concerning the protection of human subjects found at 45 CFR Part 46. If a study is regulated by the Food and Drug Administration (FDA), it must be in compliance with 21 CFR parts 50 and 56.

g. All aspects of the research study are conducted according to appropriate standards of scientific integrity (see http://www.icmje.org).

h. The research study has a written protocol that clearly addresses, or incorporates by reference, the standards listed here as Medicare requirements for CED coverage.

i. The clinical research study is not designed to exclusively test toxicity or disease pathophysiology in healthy individuals. Trials of all medical technologies measuring therapeutic outcomes as one of the objectives meet this standard only if the disease or condition being studied is life threatening as defined in 21 CFR §312.81(a) and the patient has no other viable treatment options.

j. The clinical research study is registered on the ClinicalTrials. gov website by the principal sponsor/investigator prior to the enrollment of the first study subject.

k. The research study protocol specifies the method and timing of public release of all prespecified outcomes to be measured including release of outcomes if outcomes are negative or study is terminated early. The results must be made public within 24 months of the end of data collection. If a report is planned to be published in a peer reviewed journal, then that initial release may be an abstract that meets the requirements of the International Committee of Medical Journal Editors (http://www.icmje.org).

l. The research study protocol must explicitly discuss subpopulations affected by the treatment under investigation, particularly traditionally underrepresented groups in clinical studies, how the inclusion and exclusion criteria effect enrollment of these populations, and a plan for the retention and reporting of said populations on the trial. If the inclusion and exclusion criteria are expected to have a negative effect on the recruitment or retention of underrepresented populations, the protocol must discuss why these criteria are necessary.

m. The research study protocol explicitly discusses how the results are or are not expected to be generalizable to the Medicare population to infer whether Medicare patients may benefit from the intervention. Separate discussions in the protocol may be necessary for populations eligible for Medicare due to age, disability or Medicaid eligibility.

C. Nationally Non-Covered Indications

TENS is not reasonable and necessary for the treatment of CLBP under section 1862(a)(1)(A) of the Act.

D. Other

See §160.13 for an explanation of coverage of medically necessary supplies for the effective use of TENS. See §160.7.1 for an explanation of coverage for assessing patients suitability for electrical nerve stimulation therapy. See §10.2 for an explanation of coverage of transcutaneous electrical nerve stimulation (TENS) for acute post-operative pain. Please note, §280.13 Transcutaneous Electrical Nerve Stimulators (TENS) NCD has been removed from the NCD manual and incorporated into NCD 160.27

(This NCD last reviewed June 2012.)

100-3, Chapter 1, Part 2, 160.7.1

Assessing Patients Suitability for Electrical Nerve Stimulation Therapy

Electrical nerve stimulation is an accepted modality for assessing a patient's suitability for ongoing treatment with a transcutaneous or an implanted nerve stimulator.

Accordingly, program payment may be made for the following techniques when used to determine the potential therapeutic usefulness of an electrical nerve stimulator:

A. Transcutaneous Electrical Nerve Stimulation (TENS)

This technique involves attachment of a transcutaneous nerve stimulator to the surface of the skin over the peripheral nerve to be stimulated. It is used by the patient on a trial basis and its effectiveness in modulating pain is monitored by the physician, or physical therapist. Generally, the physician or physical therapist is able to determine whether the patient is likely to derive a significant therapeutic benefit from continuous use of a transcutaneous stimulator within a trial period of one month; in a few cases this determination may take longer to make. Document the medical necessity for such services which are furnished beyond the first month.(See §160.13 for an explanation of coverage of medically necessary supplies for the effective use of TENS.)

If TENS significantly alleviates pain, it may be considered as primary treatment; if it produces no relief or greater discomfort than the original pain electrical nerve stimulation therapy is ruled out. However, where TENS produces incomplete relief, further evaluation with percutaneous electrical nerve stimulation may be considered to determine whether an implanted peripheral nerve stimulator would provide significant relief from pain.

Usually, the physician or physical therapist providing the services will furnish the equipment necessary for assessment. Where the physician or physical therapist advises the patient to rent the TENS from a supplier during the trial period rather than supplying it himself/herself, program payment may be made for rental of the TENS as well as for the services of the physician or physical therapist who is evaluating its use. However, the combined program payment which is made for the physician's or physical therapist's services and the rental of the stimulator from a supplier should not exceed the amount which would be payable for the total service, including the stimulator, furnished by the physician or physical therapist alone.

B. Percutaneous Electrical Nerve Stimulation (PENS)

This diagnostic procedure which involves stimulation of peripheral nerves by a needle electrode inserted through the skin is performed only in a physician's office, clinic, or hospital outpatient department. Therefore, it is covered only when performed by a physician or incident to physician's service. If pain is effectively controlled by percutaneous stimulation, implantation of electrodes is warranted.

As in the case of TENS (described in subsection A), generally the physician should be able to determine whether the patient is likely to derive a significant therapeutic benefit from continuing use of an implanted nerve stimulator within a trial period of 1 month. In a few cases, this determination may take longer to make. The medical necessity for such diagnostic services which are furnished beyond the first month must be documented.

NOTE: Electrical nerve stimulators do not prevent pain but only alleviate pain as it occurs. A patient can be taught how to employ the stimulator, and once this is done, can use it safely and effectively without direct physician supervision. Consequently, it is inappropriate for a patient to visit his/her physician, physical therapist, or an outpatient clinic on a continuing basis for treatment of pain with electrical nerve stimulation. Once it is determined that electrical nerve stimulation should be continued as therapy and the patient has been trained to use the stimulator, it is expected that a stimulator will be implanted or the patient will employ the TENS on a continual basis in his/her home. Electrical nerve stimulation treatments furnished by a physician in his/her office, by a physical therapist or outpatient clinic are excluded from coverage by §1862(a)(1) of the Act. (See §160.7 for an explanation of coverage of the therapeutic use of implanted peripheral nerve stimulators under the prosthetic devices benefit.) See §160.27 for an explanation of coverage of the therapeutic use of TENS under the durable medical equipment benefit.

100-3, Chapter 1, Part 3, 190.11

Home Prothrombin Time/International Normalized Ratio (PT/INR) Monitoring for Anticoagulation Management –Effective March 19, 2008

A. General

Use of the International Normalized Ratio (INR) or prothrombin time (PT) -standard measurement for reporting the blood's clotting time) -allows physicians to determine the level of anticoagulation in a patient independent of the laboratory reagents used. The INR is the ratio of the patient's PT (extrinsic or tissue-factor dependent coagulation pathway) compared to the mean PT for a group of normal individuals. Maintaining patients within his/her prescribed therapeutic range minimizes adverse events associated with inadequate or excessive anticoagulation such as serious bleeding or thromboembolic events. Patient self-testing and self-management through the use of a home INR monitor may be used to improve the time in therapeutic rate (TTR) for select groups of patients. increased TTR leads to improved clinical outcomes and reductions in thromboembolic and hemorrhagic events.

Warfarin (also prescribed under other trade names, e.g., Coumadin®) is a self-administered, oral anticoagulant (blood thinner) medication that affects the vitamin K-dependent clotting factors II, VII, IX and X. It is widely used for various medical conditions, and has a narrow therapeutic index, meaning it is a drug with less than a 2-fold difference between median lethal dose and median effective dose. For this reason, since October 4, 2006, it falls under the category of a Food and Drug Administration (FDA) "black-box" drug whose dosage must be closely monitored to avoid serious complications. A PT/INR monitoring system is a portable testing device that includes a finger-stick and an FDA-cleared meter that measures the time it takes for a person's blood plasma to clot

B. Nationally Covered Indications

For services furnished on or after March 19, 2008, Medicare will cover the use of home PT/INR monitoring for chronic, oral anticoagulation management for patients with mechanical heart valves, chronic atrial fibrillation, or venous thromboembolism (inclusive of deep venous thrombosis and pulmonary embolism) on warfarin. The monitor and the home testing must be prescribed by a treating physician as provided at 42 CFR 410.32(a), and all of the following requirements must be met:

1. The patient must have been anticoagulated for at least 3 months prior to use of the home INR device; and,

2. The patient must undergo a face-to-face educational program on anticoagulation management and must have demonstrated the correct use of the device prior to its use in the home; and,

3. The patient continues to correctly use the device in the context of the management of the anticoagulation therapy following the initiation of home monitoring; and,

4. Self-testing with the device should not occur more frequently than once a week.

C. Nationally Non-Covered Indications

N/A

D. Other

1. All other indications for home PT/INR monitoring not indicated as nationally covered above remain at local Medicare contractor discretion.

2. This national coverage determination (NCD) is distinct from, and makes no changes to, the PT clinical laboratory NCD at section 190.17 of Publication 100-03 of the NCD Manual.

(This NCD last reviewed March 2008.)

100-3, Chapter 1, Part 3, 190.14

Human Immunodeficiency Virus (HIV) Testing (Diagnosis)

Diagnosis of HIV infection is primarily made through the use of serologic assays. These assays take one of two forms: antibody detection assays and specific HIV antigen (p24) procedures. The antibody assays are usually enzyme immunoassays (EIA), which are used to confirm exposure of an individual's immune system to specific viral antigens. These assays may be formatted to detect HIV-1, HIV-2, or HIV-1 and 2 simultaneously, and to detect both IgM and IgG. When the initial EIA test is repeatedly positive or indeterminant, an alternative test is used to confirm the specificity of the antibodies to individual viral components. The most commonly used method is the Western Blot.

The HIV-1 core antigen (p24) test detects circulating viral antigen which may be found prior to the development of antibodies and may also be present in later stages of illness in the form of recurrent or persistent antigenemia. Its prognostic utility in HIV infection has been diminished as a result of development of sensitive viral RNA assays, and its primary use today is as a routine screening tool in potential blood donors.

In several unique situations, serologic testing alone may not reliably establish an HIV infection. This may occur because the antibody response (particularly the IgG response detected by Western Blot) has not yet developed (that is, acute retroviral syndrome) or is persistently equivocal because of inherent viral antigen variability. It is also an issue in perinatal HIV infection due to transplacental passage of maternal HIV antibody. In these situations, laboratory evidence of HIV in blood by culture, antigen assays, or proviral DNA or viral RNA assays, is required to establish a definitive determination of HIV infection.

Indications

Diagnostic testing to establish HIV infection may be indicated when there is a strong clinical suspicion supported by one or more of the following clinical findings:

1. The patient has a documented, otherwise unexplained, AIDS-defining or AIDS-associated opportunistic infection.

2. The patient has another documented sexually transmitted disease, which identifies significant risk of exposure to HIV and the potential for an early or subclinical infection.

3. The patient has documented acute or chronic hepatitis B or C infection that identifies a significant risk of exposure to HIV and the potential for an early or subclinical infection.

4. The patient has a documented AIDS-defining or AIDS-associated neoplasm.

5. The patient has a documented AIDS-associated neurologic disorder or otherwise unexplained dementia.

6. The patient has another documented AIDS-defining clinical condition, or a history of other severe, recurrent, or persistent conditions which suggest an underlying immune deficiency (for example, cutaneous or mucosal disorders).

7. The patient has otherwise unexplained generalized signs and symptoms suggestive of a chronic process with an underlying immune deficiency (for example, fever, weight loss, malaise, fatigue, chronic diarrhea, failure to thrive, chronic cough, hemoptysis, shortness of breath, or lymphadenopathy).

8. The patient has otherwise unexplained laboratory evidence of a chronic disease process with an underlying immune deficiency (for example, anemia, leukopenia, pancytopenia, lymphopenia, or low CD4+ lymphocyte count).

9. The patient has signs and symptoms of acute retroviral syndrome with fever, malaise, lymphadenopathy, and skin rash.

10. The patient has documented exposure to blood or body fluids known to be capable of transmitting HIV (for example, needle sticks and other significant blood exposures) and antiviral therapy is initiated or anticipated to be initiated.

11. The patient is undergoing treatment for rape. (HIV testing is part of the rape treatment protocol.)

Limitations

1. 1.HIV antibody testing in the United States is usually performed using HIV-1 or HIV-1/2 combination tests. HIV-2 testing is indicated if clinical circumstances suggest HIV-2 is likely (that is, compatible clinical finding and HIV-1 test negative). HIV-2 testing may also be indicated in areas of the country where there is greater prevalence of HIV-2 infections.

2. The Western Blot test should be performed only after documentation that the initial EIA tests are repeatedly positive or equivocal on a single sample.

3. The HIV antigen tests currently have no defined diagnostic usage.

4. Direct viral RNA detection may be performed in those situations where serologic testing does not establish a diagnosis but strong clinical suspicion persists (for example, acute retroviral syndrome, nonspecific serologic evidence of HIV, or perinatal HIV infection).

5. If initial serologic tests confirm an HIV infection, repeat testing is not indicated.

6. If initial serologic tests are HIV EIA negative and there is no indication for confirmation of infection by viral RNA detection, the interval prior to retesting is 3-6 months.

7. Testing for evidence of HIV infection using serologic methods may be medically appropriate in situations where there is a risk of exposure to HIV.

8. The CPT® Editorial Panel has issued a number of codes for infectious agent detection by direct antigen or nucleic acid probe techniques that have not yet been developed or are only being used on an investigational basis. Laboratory providers are advised to remain current on FDA-approved status for these tests.

100-3, Chapter 1, Part 4, 210.3

Colorectal Cancer Screening Tests

A. General

Section 4104 of the Balanced Budget Act of 1997 provides for coverage of screening colorectal cancer procedures under Medicare Part B. Medicare currently covers: (1) annual fecal occult blood tests (FOBTs); (2) flexible sigmoidoscopy over 4 years; (3) screening colonoscopy for persons at average risk for colorectal cancer every 10 years, or for persons at high risk for colorectal cancer every 2 years; (4) barium enema every 4 years as an alternative to flexible sigmoidoscopy, or every 2 years as an alternative to colonoscopy for persons at high risk for colorectal cancer; and, (5) other procedures the Secretary finds appropriate based on consultation with appropriate experts and organizations.

Coverage of the above screening examinations was implemented in regulations through a final rule that was published on October 31, 1997 (62 FR 59079), and was effective January 1, 1998. At that time, based on consultation with appropriate experts and organizations, the definition of the term "FOBT" was defined in 42 CFR §410.37(a)(2) of the regulation to mean a "guaiac-based test for peroxidase activity, testing two samples from each of three consecutive stools."

In the 2003 Physician Fee Schedule Final Rule (67 FR 79966) effective March 1, 2003, the Centers for Medicare & Medicaid Services (CMS) amended the FOBT screening test regulation definition to provide that it could include either: (1) a guaiac-based FOBT, or, (2) other tests determined by the Secretary through a national coverage determination.

B. Nationally Covered Indications

Fecal Occult Blood Tests (FOBT) (effective for services performed on or after January 1, 2004)

1. History

The FOBTs are generally divided into two types: immunoassay and guaiac types. Immunoassay (or immunochemical) fecal occult blood tests (iFOBT) use "antibodies directed against human globin epitopes. While most iFOBTs use spatulas to collect stool samples, some use a brush to collect toilet water surrounding the stool. Most iFOBTs require laboratory processing.

Guaiac fecal occult blood tests (gFOBT) use a peroxidase reaction to indicate presence of the heme portion of hemoglobin. Guaiac turns blue after oxidation by oxidants or peroxidases in the presence of an oxygen donor such as hydrogen peroxide. Most FOBTs use sticks to collect stool samples and may be developed in a physician's office or a laboratory. In 1998, Medicare began reimbursement for guaiac FOBTs, but not immunoassay type tests for colorectal cancer screening. Since the fundamental process is similar for other iFOBTs, CMS evaluated colorectal cancer screening using immunoassay FOBTs in general.

2. Expanded Coverage

Medicare covers one screening FOBT per annum for the early detection of colorectal cancer. This means that Medicare will cover one guaiac-based (gFOBT) or one immunoassay-based (iFOBT) at a frequency of every 12 months; i.e., at least 11 months have passed following the month in which the last covered screening FOBT was performed, for beneficiaries aged 50 years and older. The beneficiary completes the existing gFOBT by taking samples from two different sites of three consecutive stools; the beneficiary completes the iFOBT by taking the appropriate number of stool samples

according to the specific manufacturer's instructions. This screening requires a written order from the beneficiary's attending physician, or for claims with dates of service on or after January 27, 2014, by a beneficiary's attending physician assistant, nurse practitioner, or clinical nurse specialist. ("Attending physician means a doctor of medicine or osteopathy (as defined in §1861(r)(1) of the Social Security Act) who is fully knowledgeable about the beneficiary's medical condition, and who would be responsible for using the results of any examination performed in the overall management of the beneficiary's specific medical problem.)

C. Nationally Non-Covered Indications

All other indications for colorectal cancer screening not otherwise specified above remain non-covered. Non-coverage specifically includes:

1. Screening DNA (Deoxyribonucleic acid) stool tests, effective April 28, 2008, and,

2. Screening computed tomographic colonography (CTC), effective May 12, 2009.

D. Other

N/A

(This NCD last reviewed May 2009.)

100-3, Chapter 1, Part 4, 210.4

Smoking and Tobacco-Use Cessation Counseling (Effective March 22, 2005)

A. General

Tobacco use continues to be the leading cause of preventable death in the United States. In 1964, the Surgeon General of the U.S. Public Health Service (PHS) issued the report of his Advisory Committee on Smoking and Health, officially recognizing that cigarette smoking is a cause of cancer and other serious diseases. Though smoking rates have significantly declined, 9.3% of the population age 65 and older smokes cigarettes. Approximately 440,000 people die annually from smoking related disease, with 68% (300,000) age 65 or older. Many more people of all ages suffer from serious illness caused from smoking, leading to disability and decreased quality of life. Reduction in smoking prevalence is a national objective in Healthy People 2010.

B. Nationally Covered Indications

Effective March 22, 2005, the Centers for Medicare and Medicaid Services (CMS) has determined that the evidence is adequate to conclude that smoking and tobacco use cessation counseling, based on the current PHS Guideline, is reasonable and necessary for a patient with a disease or an adverse health effect that has been found by the U.S. Surgeon General to be linked to tobacco use, or who is taking a therapeutic agent whose metabolism or dosing is affected by tobacco use as based on FDA-approved information.

Patients must be competent and alert at the time that services are provided. Minimal counseling is already covered at each evaluation and management (E&M) visit. Beyond that, Medicare will cover 2 cessation attempts per year. Each attempt may include a maximum of 4 intermediate or intensive sessions, with the total annual benefit covering up to 8 sessions in a 12-month period. The practitioner and patient have flexibility to choose between intermediate or intensive cessation strategies for each attempt.

Intermediate and intensive smoking cessation counseling services will be covered for outpatient and hospitalized beneficiaries who are smokers and who qualify as above, as long as those services are furnished by qualified physicians and other Medicare-recognized practitioners.

C. Nationally Non-Covered Indications

Inpatient hospital stays with the principal diagnosis of Tobacco Use Disorder are not reasonable and necessary for the effective delivery of tobacco cessation counseling services. Therefore, we will not cover tobacco cessation services if tobacco cessation is the primary reason for the patient's hospital stay.

D. Other

N/A

(This NCD last reviewed May 2005.)

100-3, Chapter-1, Part-4, 210.7

Screening for the Human Immunodeficiency Virus (HIV)

A. General

Infection with the human immunodeficiency virus (HIV) is a continuing, worldwide pandemic described by the World Health Organization as "the most serious infectious disease challenge to global public health". Acquired immunodeficiency syndrome (AIDS) is diagnosed when a HIV-infected person's immune system becomes severely compromised and/or a person becomes ill with a HIV-related opportunistic infection. Without treatment, AIDS usually develops within 8-10 years after a person's initial HIV infection. While there is presently no cure for HIV, an infected individual can be recognized by screening, and subsequent access to skilled care plus vigilant monitoring and adherence to continuous antiretroviral therapy may delay the onset of AIDS and increase quality of life for many years.

Significantly, more than half of new HIV infections are estimated to be sexually transmitted from infected individuals who are unaware of their HIV status. Consequently, improved secondary disease prevention and wider availability of screening linked to HIV care and treatment would not only delay disease progression and complications in untested or unaware older individuals, but could also decrease the spread of disease to those living with or partnered with HIV-infected individuals.

HIV antibody testing first became available in 1985. These commonly used, Food and Drug Administration (FDA)-approved HIV antibody screening tests –using serum or plasma from a venipuncture or blood draw –are known as EIA (enzyme immunoassay) or ELISA (enzyme-linked immunosorbent assay) tests.

Developed for point-of-care testing using alternative samples, six rapid HIV-1 and/or HIV-2 antibody tests –using fluid obtained from the oral cavity or using whole blood, serum, or plasma from a blood draw or fingerstick –were approved by the FDA from 2002-2006.

Effective January 1, 2009, the Centers for Medicare & Medicaid Services (CMS) is allowed to add coverage of "additional preventive services" through the national coverage determination (NCD) process if certain statutory requirements are met, as provided under section 101(a) of the Medicare Improvements for Patients and Providers Act. One of those requirements is that the service(s) be categorized as a grade A (strongly recommends) or grade B (recommends) rating by the US Preventive Services Task Force (USPSTF). The USPSTF

strongly recommends screening for all adolescents and adults at risk for HIV infection, as well as all pregnant women.

B. Nationally Covered Indications

Effective for claims with dates of service on and after December 8, 2009, CMS determines that the evidence is adequate to conclude that screening for HIV infection is reasonable and necessary for early detection of HIV and is appropriate for individuals entitled to benefits under Part A or enrolled under Part B. Therefore, CMS proposes to cover both standard and FDA-approved HIV rapid screening tests for:

1. A maximum of one, annual voluntary HIV screening of Medicare beneficiaries at increased risk for HIV infection per USPSTF guidelines as follows:

   - Men who have had sex with men after 1975
   - Men and women having unprotected sex with multiple [more than one] partners
   - Past or present injection drug users
   - Men and women who exchange sex for money or drugs, or have sex partners who do
   - Individuals whose past or present sex partners were HIV-infected, bisexual or injection drug users
   - Persons being treated for sexually transmitted diseases
   - Persons with a history of blood transfusion between 1978 and 1985
   - Persons who request an HIV test despite reporting no individual risk factors, since this group is likely to include individuals not willing to disclose high-risk behaviors; and,

2. A maximum of three, voluntary HIV screenings of pregnant Medicare beneficiaries: (1) when the diagnosis of pregnancy is known, (2) during the third trimester, and (3) at labor, if ordered by the woman's clinician.

C. Nationally Non-Covered Indications

Effective for claims with dates of service on and after December 8, 2009, Medicare beneficiaries with any known diagnosis of a HIV-related illness are not eligible for this screening test.

Medicare beneficiaries (other than those who are pregnant) who have had a prior HIV screening test within one year are not eligible (11 full months must have elapsed following the month in which the previous test was performed in order for the subsequent test to be covered).

Pregnant Medicare beneficiaries who have had three screening tests within their respective term of pregnancy are not eligible (beginning with the date of the first test).

D. Other

N/A

(This NCD last reviewed November 2009.)

100-3, Chapter-1, Part-4, 210.8

Screening and Behavioral Counseling Interventions in Primary Care to Reduce Alcohol Misuse(Effective October 14, 2011)

A. General

Based upon authority to cover "additional preventive services" for Medicare beneficiaries if certain statutory requirements are met, the Centers for Medicare & Medicaid Services

(CMS) initiated a new national coverage analysis on annual screening and brief behavioral counseling in primary care to reduce alcohol misuse in adults, including pregnant women. Annual screening and behavioural counseling for alcohol misuse in adults is recommended with a grade of B by the U.S. Preventive Services Task Force (USPSTF) and is appropriate for individuals entitled to benefits under Part A and Part B.

CMS will cover annual alcohol screening and up to four, brief face-to-face behavioral counseling in primary care settings to reduce alcohol misuse. CMS does not identify specific alcohol misuse screening tools. Rather, the decision to use a specific tool is at the discretion of the clinician in the primary care setting. Various screening tools are available for screening for alcohol misuse.

B. Nationally Covered Indications

Effective for claims with dates of service on or after October 14, 2011, CMS will cover annual alcohol screening, and for those that screen positive, up to four brief, face-to-face, behavioral counseling interventions per year for Medicare beneficiaries, including pregnant women:

- Who misuse alcohol, but whose levels or patterns of alcohol consumption do not meet criteria for alcohol dependence (defined as at least three of the following: tolerance, withdrawal symptoms, impaired control, preoccupation with acquisition and/or use, persistent desire or unsuccessful efforts to quit, sustains social, occupational, or recreational disability, use continues despite adverse consequences); and
- Who are competent and alert at the time that counseling is provided; and,
- Whose counseling is furnished by qualified primary care physicians or other primary care practitioners in a primary care setting.

Each of the behavioral counseling interventions should be consistent with the 5A's approach that has been adopted by the USPSTF to describe such services. They are:

1. Assess: Ask about/assess behavioral health risk(s) and factors affecting choice of behavior change goals/methods.

2. Advise: Give clear, specific, and personalized behavior change advice, including information about personal health harms and benefits.

3. Agree: Collaboratively select appropriate treatment goals and methods based on the patient's interest in and willingness to change the behavior.

4. Assist: Using behavior change techniques (self-help and/or counseling), aid the patient in achieving agreed upon goals by acquiring the skills, confidence, and social/environmental supports for behavior change, supplemented with adjunctive medical treatments when appropriate.

5. Arrange: Schedule follow-up contacts (in person or by telephone) to provide ongoing assistance/support and to adjust the treatment plan as needed, including referral to more intensive or specialized treatment.

For the purposes of this policy, a primary care setting is defined as one in which there is provision of integrated, accessible health care services by clinicians who are accountable for addressing a large majority of personal health care needs, developing a sustained partnership with patients, and practicing in the context of family and community. Emergency departments, inpatient hospital settings, ambulatory surgical centers, independent diagnostic testing facilities, skilled nursing facilities, inpatient rehabilitation facilities and hospices are not considered primary care settings under this definition.

For the purposes of this policy a "primary care physician" and "primary care practitioner" are to be defined based on two existing sections of the Social Security Act, §1833(u)(6), §1833(x)(2)(A)(i)(I) and §1833(x)(2)(A)(i)(II):

§1833(u)

6. Physician Defined.—For purposes of this paragraph, the term "physician" means a physician described in section 1861(r)(1) and the term "primary care physician" means a physician who is identified in the available data as a general practitioner, family practice practitioner, general internist, or obstetrician or gynecologist.

§1833(x)(2)(A)(i)

i. is a physician (as described in section 1861(r)(1)) who has a primary specialty designation of family medicine, internal medicine, geriatric medicine, or pediatric medicine; or

ii. is a nurse practitioner, clinical nurse specialist, or physician assistant (as those terms are defined in section 1861(aa)(5)).

C. Nationally Non-Covered Indications

1. Alcohol screening is non-covered when performed more than one time in a 12-month period.

2. Brief face-to-face behavioral counseling interventions are non-covered when performed more than once a day; that is, two counseling interventions on the same day are non-covered.

3. Brief face-to-face behavioral counseling interventions are non-covered when performed more than four times in a 12-month period

D. Other

Medicare coinsurance and Part B deductible are waived for this preventive service

(This NCD last reviewed October 2011.)

100-3, Chapter-1, Part-4, 210.10

Screening for Sexually Transmitted Infections (STIs) and High Intensity Behavioral Counseling (HIBC) to Prevent STIs

A. General

Sexually transmitted infections (STIs) are infections that are passed from one person to another through sexual contact. STIs remain an important cause of morbidity in the United States and have both health and economic consequences. Many of the complications of STIs are borne by women and children Often, STIs do not present any symptoms so can go untreated for long periods of time The presence of an STI during pregnancy may result in significant health complications for the woman and infant. In fact, any person who has an STI may develop health complications. Screening tests for the STIs in this national coverage determination (NCD) are laboratory tests.

Under §1861(ddd) of the Social Security Act (the Act), the Centers for Medicare & Medicaid Services (CMS) has the authority to add coverage of additional preventive services if certain statutory requirements are met. The regulations provide:

§410.64 Additional preventive services

a. Medicare Part B pays for additional preventive services not described in paragraph (1) or (3) of the definition of "preventive services" under §410.2, that identify medical conditions or risk factors for individuals if the Secretary determines through the national coverage determination process (as defined in section 1869(f)(1)(B) of the Act) that these services are all of the following: (1) reasonable and necessary for the prevention or early detection of illness or disability.(2)recommended with a grade of A or B by the United States Preventive Services Task Force, (3) appropriate for individuals entitled to benefits under Part A or enrolled under Part B.

b. In making determinations under paragraph (a) of this section regarding the coverage of a new preventive service, the Secretary may conduct an assessment of the relation between predicted outcomes and the expenditures for such services and may take into account the results of such an assessment in making such national coverage determinations.

The scope of the national coverage analysis for this NCD evaluated the evidence for the following STIs and high intensity behavioral counseling (HIBC) to prevent STIs for which the United States Preventive Services Task Force (USPSTF) has issued either an A or B recommendation:

- Screening for chlamydial infection for all sexually active non-pregnant young women aged 24 and younger and for older non-pregnant women who are at increased risk,
- Screening for chlamydial infection for all pregnant women aged 24 and younger and for older pregnant women who are at increased risk,
- Screening for gonorrhea infection in all sexually active women, including those who are pregnant, if they are at increased risk,
- Screening for syphilis infection for all pregnant women and for all persons at increased risk,
- Screening for hepatitis B virus (HBV) infection in pregnant women at their first prenatal visit,
- HIBC for the prevention of STIs for all sexually active adolescents, and for adults at increased risk for STIs

B. Nationally Covered Indications

CMS has determined that the evidence is adequate to conclude that screening for chlamydia, gonorrhea, syphilis, and hepatitis B, as well as HIBC to prevent STIs, consistent with the grade A and B recommendations by the USPSTF, is reasonable and necessary for the early detection or prevention of an illness or disability and is appropriate for individuals entitled to benefits under Part A or enrolled under Part B.

Therefore, effective for claims with dates of services on or after November 8, 2011, CMS will cover screening for these USPSTF-indicated STIs with the appropriate Food and Drug Administration (FDA) -approved/cleared laboratory tests, used consistent with FDA-approved labeling, and in compliance with the Clinical Laboratory Improvement Act (CLIA) regulations, when ordered by the primary care physician or practitioner, and performed by an eligible Medicare provider for these services.

Screening for chlamydia and gonorrhea:

- Pregnant women who are 24 years old or younger when the diagnosis of pregnancy is known, and then repeat screening during the third trimester if high-risk sexual behavior has occurred since the initial screening test.

- Pregnant women who are at increased risk for STIs when the diagnosis of pregnancy is known, and then repeat screening during the third trimester if high-risk sexual behavior has occurred since the initial screening test.
- Women at increased risk for STIs annually.

Screening for syphilis:

- Pregnant women when the diagnosis of pregnancy is known, and then repeat screening during the third trimester and at delivery if high-risk sexual behaviour has occurred since the previous screening test.
- Men and women at increased risk for STIs annually.

Screening for hepatitis B:

- Pregnant women at the first prenatal visit when the diagnosis of pregnancy is known, and then rescreening at time of delivery for those with new or continuing risk factors.

In addition, effective for claims with dates of service on or after November 8, 2011, CMS will cover up to two individual 20-to 30-minute, face-to-face counseling sessions annually for Medicare beneficiaries for HIBC to prevent STIs, for all sexually active adolescents, and for adults at increased risk for STIs, if referred for this service by a primary care physician or practitioner, and provided by a Medicare eligible primary care provider in a primary care setting. Coverage of HIBC to prevent STIs is consistent with the USPSTF recommendation. HIBC is defined as a program intended to promote sexual risk reduction or risk avoidance, which includes each of these broad topics, allowing flexibility for appropriate patient-focused elements:

- education,
- skills training,
- guidance on how to change sexual behavior.

The high/increased risk individual sexual behaviors, based on the USPSTF guidelines, include any of the following:

- Multiple sex partners
- Using barrier protection inconsistently
- Having sex under the influence of alcohol or drugs
- Having sex in exchange for money or drugs
- Age (24 years of age or younger and sexually active for women for chlamydia and gonorrhea)
- Having an STI within the past year
- IV drug use (for hepatitis B only)
- In addition for men - men having sex with men (MSM) and engaged in high risk sexual behavior, but no regard to age

In addition to individual risk factors, in concurrence with the USPSTF recommendations, community social factors such as high prevalence of STIs in the community populations should be considered in determining high/increased risk for chlamydia, gonorrhea, syphilis, and for recommending HIBC.

High/increased risk sexual behavior for STIs is determined by the primary care provider by assessing the patient's sexual history which is part of any complete medical history, typically part of an annual wellness visit or prenatal visit and considered in the development of a comprehensive prevention plan. The medical record should be a reflection of the service provided.

For the purposes of this NCD, a primary care setting defined as the provision of integrated, accessible health care services by clinicians who are accountable for addressing a large majority of personal health care needs, developing a sustained partnership with patients, and practicing in the context of family and community. Emergency departments, inpatient hospital settings, ambulatory surgical centers, independent diagnostic testing facilities, skilled nursing facilities, inpatient rehabilitation facilities, clinics providing a limited focus of health care services, and hospice are examples of settings not considered primary care settings under this definition.

For the purposes of this NCD, a "primary care physician" and "primary care practitioner" will be defined based on existing sections of the Social Security Act (§1833(u)(6), §1833(x)(2)(A)(i)(I) and §1833(x)(2)(A)(i)(II)).

§1833(u)

(6) Physician Defined.—For purposes of this paragraph, the term "physician" means a

physician described in section 1861(r)(1)and the term "primary care physician" means a physician who is identified in the available data as a general practitioner, family practice practitioner, general internist, or obstetrician or gynecologist.

§1833(x)(2)(A)(i)

i.   is a physician (as described in section 1861(r)(1)) who has a primary specialty designation of family medicine, internal medicine, geriatric medicine, or pediatric medicine; or

ii. is a nurse practitioner, clinical nurse specialist, or physician assistant (as those terms are defined in section 1861(aa)(5));

C. Nationally Non-Covered Indications

Unless specifically covered in this NCD, any other NCD, or in statute, preventive services are non-covered by Medicare.

D. Other

Medicare coinsurance and Part B deductible are waived for these preventive services.

HIBC to prevent STIs may be provided on the same date of services as an annual wellness visit, evaluation and management (E&M) service, or during the global billing period for obstetrical car, but only one HIBC may be provided on any one date of service. See the claims processing manual for further instructions on claims processing.

For services provided on an annual basis, this is defined as a 12-Month period.

(This NCD last reviewed November 2011.)

100-3, Chapter-1, Part-4, 210.11

Intensive Behavioral Therapy for Cardiovascular Disease (CVD) (Effective November 8, 2011)

A. General

Cardiovascular disease (CVD) is the leading cause of mortality in the United States. CVD, which is comprised of hypertension, coronary heart disease (such as myocardial infarction and angina pectoris), heart failure and stroke, is also the leading cause of hospitalizations. Although the overall adjusted mortality rate from heart disease has declined over the past decade, opportunities for improvement still exist. Risk factors for CVD include being overweight, obesity, physical inactivity, diabetes, cigarette smoking, high blood pressure, high blood cholesterol, family history of myocardial infarction, and older age.

Under §1861(ddd) of the Social Security Act (the Act), the Centers for Medicare & Medicaid Services (CMS) has the authority to add coverage of additional preventive services through the National Coverage Determination (NCD) process if certain statutory requirements are met. Following its review, CMS has determined that the evidence is adequate to conclude that intensive behavioral therapy for CVD is reasonable and necessary for the prevention or early detection of illness or disability, is appropriate for individuals entitled to benefits under Part A or enrolled under Part B,and is comprised of components that are recommended with a grade of A or B by the U.S. Preventive Services Task Force (USPSTF).

B. Nationally Covered Indications

Effective for claims with dates of service on or after November 8, 2011, CMS covers intensive behavioral therapy for CVD (referred to below as a CVD risk reduction visit), which consists of the following three components:

- encouraging aspirin use for the primary prevention of CVD when the benefits outweigh the risks for men age 45-79 years and women 55-79 years;
- screening for high blood pressure in adults age 18 years and older; and
- intensive behavioral counseling to promote a healthy diet for adults with hyperlipidemia, hypertension, advancing age, and other known risk factors for cardiovascular-and diet-related chronic disease.

We note that only a small proportion (about 4%) of the Medicare population is under 45 years (men) or 55 years (women), therefore the vast majority of beneficiaries should receive all three components. Intensive behavioral counseling to promote a healthy diet is broadly recommended to cover close to 100% of the population due to the prevalence of known risk factors.

Therefore, CMS covers one, face-to-face CVD risk reduction visit per year for Medicare beneficiaries who are competent and alert at the time that counseling is provided, and whose counseling is furnished by a qualified primary care physician or other primary care practitioner in a primary care setting.

The behavioral counseling intervention for aspirin use and healthy diet should be consistent with the Five As approach that has been adopted by the USPSTF to describe such services:

- **Assess:** Ask about/assess behavioral health risk(s) and factors affecting choice of behavior change goals/methods.
- **Advise:** Give clear, specific, and personalized behavior change advice, including information about personal health harms and benefits.
- **Agree:** Collaboratively select appropriate treatment goals and methods based on the patient's interest in and willingness to change the behavior.
- **Assist:** Using behavior change techniques (self-help and/or counseling), aid the patient in achieving agreed-upon goals by acquiring the skills, confidence, and social/environmental supports for behavior change, supplemented with adjunctive medical treatments when appropriate.
- **Arrange:** Schedule follow-up contacts (in person or by telephone) to provide ongoing assistance/support and to adjust the treatment plan as needed, including referral to more intensive or specialized treatment.

For the purpose of this NCD, a primary care setting is defined as the provision of integrated, accessible health care services by clinicians who are accountable for addressing a large majority of personal health care needs, developing a sustained partnership with patients, and practicing in the context of family and community. Emergency departments, inpatient hospital settings, ambulatory surgical centers, independent diagnostic testing facilities, skilled nursing facilities, inpatient rehabilitation facilities, and hospices are not considered primary care settings under this definition.

For the purpose of this NCD, a "primary care physician" and "primary care practitioner" are defined consistent with existing sections of the Act (§1833(u)(6), §1833(x)(2)(A)(i)(I) and §1833(x)(2)(A)(i)(II)).

§1833(u)

(6) Physician Defined.—For purposes of this paragraph, the term "physician" means a physician described in section 1861(r)(1)and the term "primary care physician" means a physician who is identified in the available data as a general practitioner, family practice practitioner, general internist, or obstetrician or gynecologist.

physician who is identified in the available data as a general practitioner, family practice practitioner, general internist, or obstetrician or gynecologist.

§1833(x)(2) (A) Primary care practitioner.—The term "primary care practitioner" means an individual—

(i) who—

    I. is a physician (as described in section 1861(r)(1)) who has a primary specialty designation of family medicine, internal medicine, geriatric medicine, or pediatric medicine; or

    II. is a nurse practitioner, clinical nurse specialist, or physician assistant (as those terms are defined in section 1861(aa)(5)).

C. Nationally Non-Covered Indications

Unless specifically covered in this NCD, any other NCD, or in statute, preventive services are non-covered by Medicare.

D. Other

Medicare coinsurance and Part B deductible are waived for this preventive service.

(This NCD last reviewed November 2011.)

100-3, Chapter-1, Part-4, 210.12

Intensive Behavioral Therapy for Obesity (Effective November 29, 2011)

A. General

Based upon authority to cover "additional preventive services" for Medicare beneficiaries if certain statutory requirements are met, the Centers for Medicare & Medicaid Services (CMS) initiated a new national coverage analysis on intensive behavioral therapy for obesity. Screening for obesity in adults is recommended with a grade of B by the U.S. Preventive Services Task Force (USPSTF) and is appropriate for individuals entitled to benefits under Part A and Part B.

The Centers for Disease Control (CDC) reported that "obesity rates in the U.S. have increased dramatically over the last 30 years, and obesity is now epidemic in the United States." In the Medicare population over 30% of men and women are obese. Obesity is directly or indirectly associated with many chronic diseases including cardiovascular disease, musculoskeletal conditions and diabetes.

B. Nationally Covered Indications

Effective for claims with dates of service on or after November 29, 2011, CMS covers intensive behavioral therapy for obesity, defined as a body mass index (BMI) ≥ 30 kg/m2, for the prevention or early detection of illness or disability.

Intensive behavioral therapy for obesity consists of the following:

1. Screening for obesity in adults using measurement of BMI calculated by dividing weight in kilograms by the square of height in meters (expressed kg/m2);

2. Dietary (nutritional) assessment; and Intensive behavioral counseling and behavioral therapy to promote sustained

3. weight loss through high intensity interventions on diet and exercise.

The intensive behavioral intervention for obesity should be consistent with the 5-A

framework that has been highlighted by the USPSTF:

1. **Assess:** Ask about/assess behavioral health risk(s) and factors affecting choice of behavior change goals/methods.

2. **Advise:** Give clear, specific, and personalized behavior change advice, including information about personal health harms and benefits.

3. **Agree:** Collaboratively select appropriate treatment goals and methods based on the patient's interest in and willingness to change the behavior.

4. **Assist:** Using behavior change techniques (self-help and/or counseling), aid the patient in achieving agreed-upon goals by acquiring the skills, confidence, and social/environmental supports for behavior change, supplemented with adjunctive medical treatments when appropriate.

5. **Arrange:** Schedule follow-up contacts (in person or by telephone) to provide ongoing assistance/support and to adjust the treatment plan as needed, including referral to more intensive or specialized treatment.

For Medicare beneficiaries with obesity, who are competent and alert at the time that counseling is provided and whose counseling is furnished by a qualified primary care physician or other primary care practitioner and in a primary care setting, CMS covers:

- One face-to-face visit every week for the first month;
- One face-to-face visit every other week for months 2-6;
- One face-to-face visit every month for months 7-12, if the beneficiary meets the 3kg weight loss requirement during the first six months as discussed below.

At the six month visit, a reassessment of obesity and a determination of the amount of weight loss must be performed. To be eligible for additional face-to-face visits occurring once a month for an additional six months, beneficiaries must have achieved a reduction in weight of at least 3kg over the course of the first six months of intensive therapy. This determination must be documented in the physician office records for applicable beneficiaries consistent with usual practice. For beneficiaries who do not achieve a weight loss of at least 3kg during the first six months of intensive therapy, a reassessment of their readiness to change and BMI is appropriate after an additional six month period.

For the purposes of this decision memorandum, a primary care setting is defined as one in which there is provision of integrated, accessible health care services by clinicians who are accountable for addressing a large majority of personal health care needs, developing a sustained partnership with patients, and practicing in the context of family and community. Emergency departments, inpatient hospital settings, ambulatory surgical centers, independent diagnostic testing facilities, skilled nursing facilities, inpatient rehabilitation facilities and hospices are not considered primary care settings under this definition.

For the purposes of this decision memorandum a "primary care physician" and "primary care practitioner" will be defined consistent with existing sections of the Social Security Act (§1833(u)(6), §1833(x)(2)(A)(i)(I) and §1833(x)(2)(A)(i)(II)).

§1833(u)

(6) Physician Defined.—For purposes of this paragraph, the term "physician" means a physician described in section 1861(r)(1) and the term "primary care physician" means a physician who is identified in the available data as a general practitioner, family practice practitioner, general internist, or obstetrician or gynecologist.

§1833(x)(2)(A)

Primary care practitioner—The term "primary care practitioner" means an individual—

(i) who—

   I. is a physician (as described in section 1861(r)(1)) who has a primary specialty designation of family medicine, internal medicine, geriatric medicine, or pediatric medicine; or

   II. is a nurse practitioner, clinical nurse specialist, or physician assistant (as those terms are defined in section 1861(aa)(5))

C. Nationally Non-Covered Indications

All other indications remain non-covered.

D. Other

Medicare coinsurance and Part B deductible are waived for this service

(This NCD last reviewed November 2011)

100-3, Chapter-1, Part-4, 220.6

Positron Emission Tomography (PET) Scans

Positron Emission Tomography (PET) is a minimally invasive diagnostic imaging procedure used to evaluate metabolism in normal tissues as well as in diseased tissues in conditions such as cancer, ischemic heart disease, and some neurologic disorders. A radiopharmaceutical is injected into the patient that gives off sub-atomic particles, known as positrons, as it decays. PET uses a positron camera (tomograph) to measure the decay of the radiopharmaceutical. The rate of decay provides biochemical information to on the metabolism of the tissue being studied.

NOTE: This manual section, 220.6 lists all Medicare–covered uses of PET scans. Except as set forth below in cancer indications listed as "Coverage with Evidence Development," a particular use of PET scans is not covered unless this manual specifically provides that such use is covered. Although this section, 220.6 lists some non-covered uses of PET scans, it does not non-covered uses of PET scans, it does not constitute an exhaustive list of all non- covered uses.

Effective for dates of service on or after March 7, 2013, local Medicare Administrative Contractors (MACs) may determine coverage within their respective jurisdictions for positron emission tomography (PET) using radiopharmaceuticals for their Food and Drug Administration (FDA) approved labeled indications for oncologic imaging.

We emphasize each of the following points:

1. Changing the 'restrictive' language of prior PET decisions will not by itself suffice to expand Medicare coverage to new PET radiopharmaceuticals.

2. The scope of this change extends only to FDA-approved indications for oncologic uses of PET tracers.

3. This change does not include screening uses of PET scanning.

The Centers for Medicare & Medicaid Services (CMS) acknowledges the advances relating to the assessment of diagnostic performance and patient safety, as pioneered by the FDA in its regulatory policies and guidelines for diagnostic PET imaging agents and systems during the past decade. We note for completeness that local coverage cannot be in conflict with NCDs or other national policies. Finally, we note that future CMS NCDs, if any, regarding diagnostic PET imaging would not be precluded by this NCD.

100-3, Chapter-1, Part-4, 220.6.1

PET for Perfusion of the Heart (220.6.1) (Various Effective Dates)

1. Rubidium 82 (Effective March 14, 1995)

Effective for services performed on or after March 14, 1995, PET scans performed at rest or with pharmacological stress used for noninvasive imaging of the perfusion of the heart for the diagnosis and management of patients with known or suspected coronary artery disease using the FDA approved radiopharmaceutical Rubidium 82 (Rb 82) are covered, provided the requirements below are met:

- The PET scan, whether at rest alone, or rest with stress, is performed in place of, but not in addition to, a single photon emission computed tomography (SPECT); or

- The PET scan, whether at rest alone or rest with stress, is used following a SPECT that was found to be inconclusive. In these cases, the PET scan must have been considered necessary in order to determine what medical or surgical intervention is required to treat the patient. (For purposes of this requirement, an inconclusive test is a test(s) whose results are equivocal, technically uninterpretable, or discordant with a patient's other clinical data and must be documented in the beneficiary's file.)

- For any PET scan for which Medicare payment is claimed for dates of services prior to July 1, 2001, the claimant must submit additional specified information on the claim form (including proper codes and/or modifiers), to indicate the results of the PET scan. The claimant must also include information on whether the PET scan was performed after an inconclusive non-invasive cardiac test. The information submitted with respect to the previous noninvasive cardiac test must specify the type of test performed prior to the PET scan and whether it was inconclusive or unsatisfactory. These explanations are in the form of special G codes used for billing PET scans using Rb 82. Beginning July 1, 2001, claims should be submitted with the appropriate codes.

2. Ammonia N-13 (Effective October 1, 2003)

Effective for services performed on or after October 1, 2003, PET scans performed at rest or with pharmacological stress used for noninvasive imaging of the perfusion of the heart for the diagnosis and management of patients with known or suspected coronary artery disease using the FDA approved radiopharmaceutical ammonia N-13 are covered, provided the requirements below are met:

- The PET scan, whether at rest alone, or rest with stress, is performed in place of, but not in addition to, a SPECT; or

- The PET scan, whether at rest alone or rest with stress, is used following a SPECT that was found to be inconclusive. In these cases, the PET scan must have been considered necessary in order to determine what medical or surgical intervention is required to treat the patient. (For purposes of this requirement, an inconclusive test is a test whose results are equivocal, technically uninterpretable, or discordant with a patient's other clinical data and must be documented in the beneficiary's file.)

(This NCD last reviewed March 2005.)

100-3, Chapter-1, Part-4, 220.6.17

Positron Emission Tomography (FDG PET) for Oncologic Conditions (Effective June 11, 2013)

A. General

FDG (2-[F18] fluoro-2-deoxy-D-glucose) Positron Emission Tomography (PET) is a minimally-invasive diagnostic imaging procedure used to evaluate glucose metabolism in normal tissue as well as in diseased tissues in conditions such as cancer, ischemic heart disease, and some neurologic disorders. FDG is an injected radionuclide (orradiopharmaceutical) that emits sub-atomic particles, known as positrons, as it decays. FDG PET uses a positron camera (tomograph) to measure the decay of FDG. The rate of FDG decay provides biochemical information on glucose metabolism in the tissue being studied. As malignancies can cause abnormalities of metabolism and blood flow, FDG PET evaluation may indicate the probable presence or absence of a malignancy based upon observed differences in biologic activity compared to adjacent tissues.

The Centers for Medicare and Medicaid Services (CMS) was asked by the National Oncologic PET Registry (NOPR) to reconsider section 220.6 of the National Coverage Determinations (NCD) Manual to end the prospective data collection requirements under Coverage with Evidence Development (CED) across all oncologic indications ofFDG PET imaging. The CMS received public input indicating that the current coverage framework of prospective data collection under CED be ended for all oncologic uses of FDG PET imaging.

1. Framework

Effective for claims with dates of service on and after June 11, 2013, CMS is adopting a coverage framework that ends the prospective data collection requirements by NOPR under CED for all oncologic uses of FDG PET imaging. CMS is making this change for all NCDs that address coverage of FDG PET for oncologic uses addressed in this decision. This decision does not change coverage for any use of PET imaging using radiopharmaceuticals NaF-18 (fluorine-18 labeled sodium fluoride), ammonia N-13, or rubidium-82 (Rb-82).

4. Initial Anti-Tumor Treatment Strategy

CMS continues to believe that the evidence is adequate to determine that the results of FDG PET imaging are useful in determining the appropriate initial anti-tumor treatment strategy for beneficiaries with suspected cancer and improve health outcomes and thus are reasonable and necessary under §1862(a)(1)(A) of the Social Security Act (the Act).

Therefore, CMS continues to nationally cover one FDG PET study for beneficiaries who have cancers that are biopsy proven or strongly suspected based on other diagnostic testing when the beneficiary's treating physician determines that the FDG PET study is needed to determine the location and/or extent of the tumor for the following therapeutic purposes related to the initial anti-tumor treatment strategy:

- To determine whether or not the beneficiary is an appropriate candidate for an invasive diagnostic or therapeutic procedure; or

- To determine the optimal anatomic location for an invasive procedure; or

- To determine the anatomic extent of tumor when the recommended anti-tumor treatment reasonably depends on the extent of the tumor.

See the table at the end of this section for a synopsis of all nationally covered and non-covered oncologic uses of FDG PET imaging.

B.1. Initial Anti-Tumor Treatment Strategy Nationally Covered Indications

a. CMS continues to nationally cover FDG PET imaging for the initial anti-tumor treatment strategy for male and female breast cancer only when used in staging distant metastasis.

b. CMS continues to nationally cover FDG PET to determine initial anti-tumor treatment strategy for melanoma other than for the evaluation of regional lymph Nodes

c. CMS continues to nationally cover FDG PET to determine initial anti-tumor treatment strategy for melanoma other than for the evaluation of regional lymph nodes

d. C.1 Initial Anti-Tumor Treatment Strategy Nationally Non-Covered Indications

a. CMS continues to nationally non-cover initial anti-tumor treatment strategy in Medicare beneficiaries who have adenocarcinoma of the prostate.

b. CMS continues to nationally non-cover FDG PET imaging for diagnosis of breast cancer and initial staging of axillary nodes.

c. CMS continues to nationally non-cover FDG PET imaging for initial anti-tumor treatment strategy for the evaluation of regional lymph nodes in melanoma.

d. CMS continues to nationally non-cover FDG PET imaging for the diagnosis of cervical cancer related to initial anti-tumor treatment strategy.

3. Subsequent Anti-Tumor Treatment Strategy

B.2. Subsequent Anti-Tumor Treatment Strategy Nationally Covered Indications

Three FDG PET scans are nationally covered when used to guide subsequent management of anti-tumor treatment strategy after completion of initial anti-cancer therapy. Coverage of more than three FDG PET scans to guide subsequent management of anti-tumor treatment strategy after completion of initial anti-cancer therapy shall be determined by the local Medicare Administrative Contractors.

4. Synopsis of Coverage of FDG PET for Oncologic Conditions

Effective for claims with dates of service on and after June 11, 2013, the chart below summarizes national FDG PET coverage for oncologic conditions:

FDG PET for Cancers Tumor Type	Initial Treatment Strategy (formerly "diagnosis" & "staging"	Subsequent Treatment Strategy (formerly "restaging" & "monitoring response to treatment"
Colorectal	Cover	Cover
Esophagus	Cover	Cover
Head and Neck (not thyroid, CNS)	Cover	Cover
Lymphoma	Cover	Cover
Non-small cell lung	Cover	Cover
Ovary	Cover	Cover
Brain	Cover	Cover
Cervix	Cover with exceptions *	Cover
Small cell lung	Cover	Cover
Soft tissue sarcoma	Cover	Cover
Pancreas	Cover	Cover
Testes	Cover	Cover
Prostate	Non-cover	Cover
Thyroid	Cover	Cover
Breast (male and female)	Cover with exceptions *	Cover
Melanoma	Cover with exceptions *	Cover
All other solid tumors	Cover	Cover
Myeloma	Cover	Cover
All other cancers not listed	Cover	Cover

*Cervix: Nationally non-covered for the initial diagnosis of cervical cancer related to initial anti-tumor treatment strategy. All other indications for initial anti-tumor treatment strategy for cervical cancer are nationally covered.

*Breast: Nationally non-covered for initial diagnosis and/or staging of axillary lymph nodes. Nationally covered for initial staging of metastatic disease. All other indications for initial anti-tumor treatment strategy for breast cancer are nationally covered.

*Melanoma: Nationally non-covered for initial staging of regional lymph nodes. All other indications for initial anti-tumor treatment strategy for melanoma are nationally covered.

D. Other

N/A

100-3, Chapter-1, Part-4, 220.6.19

Positron Emission Tomography NaF-18 (NaF-18 PET) to Identify Bone Metastasis of Cancer (Effective February 26, 2010)

A. General

Positron Emission Tomography (PET) is a non-invasive, diagnostic imaging procedure that assesses the level of metabolic activity and perfusion in various organ systems of the body. A positron camera (tomograph) is used to produce cross-sectional tomographic images, which are obtained from positron-emitting radioactive tracer substances (radiopharmaceuticals) such as F-18 sodium fluoride. NaF-18 PET has been recognized as an excellent technique for imaging areas of altered osteogenic activity in bone. The clinical value of detecting and assessing the initial extent of metastatic cancer in bone is attested by a number of professional guidelines for oncology. Imaging to detect bone metastases is also recommended when a patient, following completion of initial treatment, is symptomatic with bone pain suspicious for metastases from a known primary tumor.

B. Nationally Covered Indications

Effective February 26, 2010, the Centers for Medicare & Medicaid Services (CMS) will cover NaF-18 PET imaging when the beneficiary's treating physician determines that the NaF-18 PET study is needed to inform to inform the initial antitumor treatment strategy or to guide subsequent antitumor treatment strategy after the completion of initial treatment, and when the beneficiary is enrolled in, and the NaF-18 PET provider is participating in, the following type of prospective clinical study:

A NaF-18 PET clinical study that is designed to collect additional information at the time of the scan to assist in initial antitumor treatment planning or to guide subsequent treatment strategy by the identification, location and quantification of bone metastases in beneficiaries in whom bone metastases are strongly suspected based on clinical symptoms or the results of other diagnostic studies. Qualifying clinical studies must ensure that specific hypotheses are addressed; appropriate data elements are collected; hospitals and providers are qualified to provide the PET scan and interpret the results; participating hospitals and providers accurately report data on all enrolled patients not included in other qualifying trials through adequate auditing mechanisms; and all patient confidentiality, privacy, and other Federal laws must be followed.

The clinical studies for which Medicare will provide coverage must answer one or more of the following questions:

Prospectively, in Medicare beneficiaries whose treating physician determines that the NaF-18 PET study results are needed to inform the initial antitumor treatment strategy or to guide subsequent antitumor treatment strategy after the completion of initial treatment, does the addition of NaF-18 PET imaging lead to:

- A change in patient management to more appropriate palliative care; or
- A change in patient management to more appropriate curative care; or
- Improved quality of life; or
- Improved survival?

The study must adhere to the following standards of scientific integrity and relevance to the Medicare population:

a. The principal purpose of the research study is to test whether a particular intervention potentially improves the participants' health outcomes.

b. The research study is well-supported by available scientific and medical information or it is intended to

121

clarify or establish the health outcomes of interventions already in common clinical use.

c. The research study does not unjustifiably duplicate existing studies.

d. The research study design is appropriate to answer the research question being asked in the study

e. The research study is sponsored by an organization or individual capable of executing the proposed study successfully.

f. The research study is in compliance with all applicable Federal regulations concerning the protection of human subjects found in the Code of Federal Regulations (CFR) at 45 CFR Part 46. If a study is regulated by the Food and Drug Administration (FDA), it also must be in compliance with 21 CFR Parts 50 and 56.

g. All aspects of the research study are conducted according to the appropriate standards of scientific integrity.

h. The research study has a written protocol that clearly addresses, or incorporates by reference, the Medicare standards.

i. The clinical research study is not designed to exclusively test toxicity or disease pathophysiology in healthy individuals. Trials of all medical technologies measuring therapeutic outcomes as one of the objectives meet this standard only if the disease or condition being studied is life-threatening as defined in 21 CFR §312.81(a) and the patient has no other viable treatment options.

j. The clinical research study is registered on the www.ClinicalTrials.gov Web site by the principal sponsor/investigator prior to the enrollment of the first study subject.

k. The research study protocol specifies the method and timing of public release of all pre-specified outcomes to be measured including release of outcomes if outcomes are negative or study is terminated early. The results must be made public within 24 months of the end of data collection. If a report is planned to be published in a peer-reviewed journal, then that initial release may be an abstract that meets the requirements of the International Committee of Medical Journal Editors. However, a full report of the outcomes must be made public no later than three (3) years after the end of data collection.

l. The research study protocol must explicitly discuss subpopulations affected by the treatment under investigation, particularly traditionally underrepresented groups in clinical studies, how the inclusion and exclusion criteria affect enrollment of these populations, and a plan for the retention and reporting of said populations on the trial. If the inclusion an exclusion criteria are expected to have a negative effect on the recruitment or retention of underrepresented populations, the protocol must discuss why these criteria are necessary.

m. The research study protocol explicitly discusses how the results are or are not expected to be generalizable to the Medicare population to infer whether Medicare patients may benefit from the intervention. Separate discussions in the protocol may be necessary for populations eligible for Medicare due to age, disability or Medicaid eligibility.

Consistent with section 1142 of the Social Security Act (the Act), the Agency for Healthcare Research and Quality (AHRQ) supports clinical research studies that the Centers for Medicare and Medicaid Services (CMS) determines meet the above-listed standards and address the above-listed research questions.

C. Nationally Non-Covered Indications

Effective February 26, 2010, CMS determines that the evidence is not sufficient to determine that the results of NaF-18 PET imaging to identify bone metastases improve health outcomes of beneficiaries with cancer and is not reasonable and necessary under §1862(a)(1)(A) of the Act unless it is to inform initial antitumor treatment strategy or to guide subsequent antitumor treatment strategy after completion of initial treatment, and then only under CED. All other uses and clinical indications of NaF-18 PET are nationally non-covered.

D. Other

The only radiopharmaceutical diagnostic imaging agents covered by Medicare for PET cancer imaging are 2-[F-18] Fluoro-D-Glucose (FDG) and NaF-18 (sodium fluoride-18). All other PET radiopharmaceutical diagnostic imaging agents are non-covered for this indication.

(This NCD was last reviewed in February 2010.)

100-3, Chapter-1, Part-4, 240.4

Continuous Positive Airway Pressure (CPAP) Therapy For Obstructive Sleep Apnea (OSA) (Effective April 4, 2005) (Effective March 13, 2008)

A. General

Continuous Positive Airway Pressure (CPAP) is a non-invasive technique for providing single levels of air pressure from a flow generator, via a nose mask, through the nares. The purpose is to prevent the collapse of the oropharyngeal walls and the obstruction of airflow during sleep, which occurs in obstructive sleep apnea (OSA).

The apnea hypopnea index (AHI) is equal to the average number of episodes of apnea and hypopnea per hour. The respiratory disturbance index (RDI) is equal to the average number of respiratory disturbances per hour.

Apnea is defined as a cessation of airflow for at least 10 seconds. Hypopnea is defined as an abnormal respiratory event lasting at least 10 seconds with at least a 30% reduction in thoracoabdominal movement or airflow as compared to baseline, and with at least a 4% oxygen desaturation.

The AHI and/or RDI may be measured by polysomnography (PSG) in a facility-based sleep study laboratory, or by a Type II home sleep test (HST) monitor, a Type III HST monitor, or a Type IV HST monitor measuring at least 3 channels.

B. Nationally Covered Indications

Effective for claims with dates of service on and after March 13, 2008, the Centers for Medicare & Medicaid Services (CMS) determines that CPAP therapy when used in adult patients with OSA is considered reasonable and necessary under the following situations:

1. The use of CPAP is covered under Medicare when used in adult patients with OSA. Coverage of CPAP is initially limited to a 12-week period to identify beneficiaries diagnosed with OSA as subsequently described who benefit from CPAP. CPAP is subsequently covered only for those beneficiaries diagnosed with OSA who benefit from CPAP during this 12-week period.

2. The provider of CPAP must conduct education of the beneficiary prior to the use of the CPAP device to ensure that the beneficiary has been educated in the proper use of the device. A caregiver, for example a family member, may be compensatory, if consistently available in the

beneficiary's home and willing and able to safely operate the CPAP device.

3. A positive diagnosis of OSA for the coverage of CPAP must include a clinical evaluation and a positive:

   a. attended PSG performed in a sleep laboratory; or

   b. unattended HST with a Type II home sleep monitoring device; or

   c. unattended HST with a Type III home sleep monitoring device; or

   d. unattended HST with a Type IV home sleep monitoring device that measures at least 3 channels.

4. The sleep test must have been previously ordered by the beneficiary's treating physician and furnished under appropriate physician supervision.

5. An initial 12-week period of CPAP is covered in adult patients with OSA if either of the following criterion using the AHI or RDI are met:

   a. AHI or RDI greater than or equal to 15 events per hour, or

   b. AHI or RDI greater than or equal to 5 events and less than or equal to 14 events per hour with documented symptoms of excessive daytime sleepiness, impaired cognition, mood disorders or insomnia, or documented hypertension, ischemic heart disease, or history of stroke.

6. The AHI or RDI is calculated on the average number of events of per hour. If the AHI or RDI is calculated based on less than 2 hours of continuous recorded sleep, the total number of recorded events to calculate the AHI or RDI during sleep testing must be at a minimum the number of events that would have been required in a 2-hour period.

7. Apnea is defined as a cessation of airflow for at least 10 seconds. Hypopnea is defined as an abnormal respiratory event lasting at least 10 seconds with at least a 30% reduction in thoracoabdominal movement or airflow as compared to baseline, and with at least a 4% oxygen desaturation.

8. Coverage with Evidence Development (CED): Medicare provides the following limited coverage for CPAP in adult beneficiaries who do not qualify for CPAP coverage based on criteria 1-7 above. A clinical study seeking Medicare payment for CPAP provided to a beneficiary who is an enrolled subject in that study must address one or more of the following questions:

   a. In Medicare-aged subjects with clinically identified risk factors for OSA, how does the diagnostic accuracy of a clinical trial of CPAP compare with PSG and Type II, III & IV HST in identifying subjects with OSA who will respond to CPAP?

   b. In Medicare-aged subjects with clinically identified risk factors for OSA who have not undergone confirmatory testing with PSG or Type II, III & IV HST, does CPAP cause clinically meaningful harm?

   c. The study must meet the following additional standards:

   d. The principal purpose of the research study is to test whether a particular intervention potentially improves the participants' health outcomes.

   e. The research study is well-supported by available scientific and medical information or it is intended to clarify or establish the health outcomes of interventions already in common clinical use.

   f. The research study does not unjustifiably duplicate existing studies.

   g. The research study design is appropriate to answer the research question being asked in the study.

   h. The research study is sponsored by an organization or individual capable of executing the proposed study successfully.

   i. The research study is in compliance with all applicable Federal regulations concerning the protection of human subjects found at 45 CFR Part 46. If a study is Food and Drug Administration-regulated, it also must be in compliance with 21 CFR Parts 50 and 56.

   j. All aspects of the research study are conducted according to the appropriate standards of scientific integrity.

   k. The research study has a written protocol that clearly addresses, or incorporates by reference, the Medicare standards.

   l. The clinical research study is not designed to exclusively test toxicity or disease pathophysiology in healthy individuals. Trials of all medical technologies measuring therapeutic outcomes as one of the objectives meet this standard only if the disease or condition being studied is life-threatening as defined in 21 CFR §312.81(a) and the patient has no other viable treatment options.

   m. The clinical research study is registered on the ClinicalTrials.gov Web site by the principal sponsor/investigator prior to the enrollment of the first study subject.

   n. The research study protocol specifies the method and timing of public release of all pre-specified outcomes to be measured, including release of outcomes if outcomes are negative or study is terminated early. The results must be made public within 24 months of the end of data collection. If a report is planned for publication in a peer-reviewed journal, then that initial release may be an abstract that meets the requirements of the International Committee of Medical Journal Editors. However, a full report of the outcomes must be made public no later than 3 years after the end of data collection.

   o. The research study protocol must explicitly discuss subpopulations affected by the treatment under investigation, particularly traditionally underrepresented groups in clinical studies, how the inclusion and exclusion criteria affect enrollment of these populations, and a plan for the retention and reporting of said populations in the trial. If the inclusion and exclusion criteria are expected to have a negative effect on the recruitment or retention of underrepresented populations, the protocol must discuss why these criteria are necessary.

   p. The research study protocol explicitly discusses how the results are or are not expected to be generalizable to the Medicare population to infer whether Medicare patients may benefit from the intervention. Separate discussions in the protocol may be necessary for populations eligible for Medicare due to age, disability, or Medicaid eligibility.

C. Nationally Non-covered Indications

Effective for claims with dates of services on and after March 13, 2008, other diagnostic tests for the diagnosis of OSA, other than those noted above for prescribing CPAP, are not sufficient for the coverage of CPAP.

D. Other

N/A

(This NCD last reviewed March 2008.)

100-3, Chapter-1, Part-4, 240.4.1

Sleep Testing for Obstructive Sleep Apnea (OSA) (Effective March 3, 2009)

A. General

Obstructive sleep apnea (OSA) is the collapse of the oropharyngeal walls and the obstruction of airflow occurring during sleep. Diagnostic tests for OSA have historically been classified into four types. The most comprehensive is designated Type I attended facility based polysomnography (PSG), which is considered the reference standard for diagnosing OSA. Attended facility based polysomnogram is a comprehensive diagnostic sleep test including at least electroencephalography (EEG), electro-oculography (EOG), electromyography (EMG), heart rate or electrocardiography (ECG), airflow, breathing/respiratory effort, and arterial oxygen saturation (SaO2) furnished in a sleep laboratory facility in which a technologist supervises the recording during sleep time and has the ability to intervene if needed. Overnight PSG is the conventional diagnostic test for OSA. The American Thoracic Society and the American Academy of Sleep Medicine have recommended supervised PSG in the sleep laboratory over 2 nights for the diagnosis of OSA and the initiation of continuous positive airway pressure (CPAP).

Three categories of portable monitors (used both in attended and unattended settings) have been developed for the diagnosis of OSA. Type II monitors have a minimum of 7 channels (e.g., EEG, EOG, EMG, ECG-heart rate, airflow, breathing/respiratory effort, SaO2)-this type of device monitors sleep staging, so AHI can be calculated). Type III monitors have a minimum of 4 monitored channels including ventilation or airflow (at least two channels of respiratory movement or respiratory movement and airflow), heart rate or ECG, and oxygen saturation. Type IV devices may measure one, two, three or more parameters but do not meet all the criteria of a higher category device. Some monitors use an actigraphy algorithm to identify periods of sleep and wakefulness.

B. Nationally Covered Indications

Effective for claims with dates of service on and after March 3, 2009, the Centers for Medicare & Medicaid Services finds that the evidence is sufficient to determine that the results of the sleep tests identified below can be used by a beneficiary's treating physician to diagnose OSA, that the use of such sleep testing technologies demonstrates improved health outcomes in Medicare beneficiaries who have OSA and receive the appropriate treatment, and that these tests are thus reasonable and necessary under section 1862(a)(1)(A) of the Social Security Act.

1. Type I PSG is covered when used to aid the diagnosis of OSA in beneficiaries who have clinical signs and symptoms indicative of OSA if performed attended in a sleep lab facility.

2. Type II or Type III sleep testing devices are covered when used to aid the diagnosis of OSA in beneficiaries who have clinical signs and symptoms indicative of OSA if performed unattended in or out of a sleep lab facility or attended in a sleep lab facility.

3. Type IV sleep testing devices measuring three or more channels, one of which is airflow, are covered when used to aid the diagnosis of OSA in beneficiaries who have signs and symptoms indicative of OSA if performed unattended in or out of a sleep lab facility or attended in a sleep lab facility.

4. Sleep testing devices measuring three or more channels that include actigraphy, oximetry, and peripheral arterial tone, are covered when used to aid the diagnosis of OSA in beneficiaries who have signs and symptoms indicative of OSA if performed unattended in or out of a sleep lab facility or attended in a sleep lab facility.

C. Nationally Non-Covered Indications

Effective for claims with dates of services on and after March 3, 2009, other diagnostic sleep tests for the diagnosis of OSA, other than those noted above for prescribing CPAP, are not sufficient for the coverage of CPAP and are not covered.

D. Other

N/A

(This NCD last reviewed March 2009.)

100-3, Chapter-1, Part-4, 250.5

Dermal Injections for the Treatment of Facial Lipodystrophy Syndrome (LDS) - Effective March 23, 2010

A. General

Treatment of persons infected with the human immunodeficiency virus (HIV) or persons who have Acquired Immune Deficiency Syndrome (AIDS) may include highly active antiretroviral therapy (HAART). Drug reactions commonly associated with long-term use of HAART include metabolic complications such as, lipid abnormalities, e.g., hyperlipidemia, hyperglycemia, diabetes, lipodystrophy, and heart disease. Lipodystrophy is characterized by abnormal fat distribution in the body.

The LDS is often characterized by a loss of fat that results in a facial abnormality such as severely sunken cheeks. The patient's physical appearance may contribute to psychological conditions (e.g., depression) or adversely impact a patient's adherence to antiretroviral regimens (therefore jeopardizing their health) and both of these are important health-related outcomes of interest in this population. Therefore, improving a patient's physical appearance through the use of dermal injections could improve these health-related outcomes.

B. Nationally Covered Indications

Effective for claims with dates of service on and after March 23, 2010, dermal injections for LDS are only reasonable and necessary using dermal fillers approved by the Food and Drug Administration (FDA) for this purpose, and then only in HIV-infected beneficiaries when LDS caused by antiretroviral HIV treatment is a significant contributor to their depression.

C. Nationally Non-Covered Indications

1. Dermal fillers that are not approved by the FDA for the treatment of LDS.

2. Dermal fillers that are used for any indication other than LDS in HIV-infected individuals who manifest depression as a result of their antiretroviral HIV treatments.

D. Other

N/A

(This NCD last reviewed March 2010.)

100-3, Chapter-1, Part-4, 260.6

Dental Examination Prior to Kidney Transplantation

Despite the "dental services exclusion" in §1862(a)(12) of the Act (see the Medicare Benefit Policy Manual, Chapter 16, "General Exclusions From Coverage," §140;), an oral or dental examination performed on an inpatient basis as part of a comprehensive workup prior to renal transplant surgery is a covered service. This is because the purpose of the examination is not for the care of the teeth or structures directly supporting the teeth. Rather, the examination is for the identification, prior to a complex surgical procedure, of existing medical problems where the increased possibility of infection would not only reduce the chances for successful surgery but would also expose the patient to additional risks in undergoing such surgery.

Such a dental or oral examination would be covered under Part A of the program if performed by a dentist on the hospital's staff, or under Part B if performed by a physician. (When performing a dental or oral examination, a dentist is not recognized as a physician under §1861(r) of the Act.) (See the Medicare General Information, Eligibility, and Entitlement Manual, Chapter 5, "Definitions," §70.2, and the Medicare Benefit Policy Manual, Chapter 15, "Covered Medical and Other Health Services," §150.)

100-3, Chapter-1, Part-4, 270.3

Blood-Derived Products for Chronic Non-Healing Wounds

A. General

Wound healing is a dynamic, interactive process that involves multiple cells and proteins. There are three progressive stages of normal wound healing, and the typical wound healing duration is about 4 weeks. While cutaneous wounds are a disruption of the normal, anatomic structure and function of the skin, subcutaneous wounds involve tissue below the skin's surface. Wounds are categorized as either acute, in where the normal wound healing stages are not yet completed but it is presumed they will be, resulting in orderly and timely wound repair, or chronic, in where a wound has failed to progress through the normal wound healing stages and repair itself within a sufficient time period.

Platelet-rich plasma (PRP) is produced in an autologous or homologous manner. Autologous PRP is comprised of blood from the patient who will ultimately receive the PRP. Alternatively, homologous PRP is derived from blood from multiple donors.

Blood is donated by the patient and centrifuged to produce an autologous gel for treatment of chronic, non-healing cutaneous wounds that persists for 30 days or longer and fail to properly complete the healing process. Autologous blood derived products for chronic, non-healing wounds includes both: (1) platelet derived growth factor (PDGF) products (such as Procuren), and (2) PRP (such as AutoloGel).

The PRP is different from previous products in that it contains whole cells including white cells, red cells, plasma, platelets, fibrinogen, stem cells, macrophages, and fibroblasts.

The PRP is used by physicians in clinical settings in treating chronic, non-healing wounds, open, cutaneous wounds, soft tissue, and bone. Alternatively, PDGF does not contain cells and was previously marketed as a product to be used by patients at home.

B. Nationally Covered Indications

Effective August 2, 2012, upon reconsideration, The Centers for Medicare and Medicaid Services (CMS) has determined that platelet-rich plasma (PRP) – an autologous blood-derived product, will be covered only for the treatment of chronic non-healing diabetic, venous and/or pressure wounds and only when the following conditions are met:

The patient is enrolled in a clinical trial that addresses the following questions using validated and reliable methods of evaluation. Clinical study applications for coverage pursuant to this National coverage Determination (NCD) must be received by August 2, 2014.

The clinical research study must meet the requirements specified below to assess the effect of PRP for the treatment of chronic non-healing diabetic, venous and/or pressure wounds. The clinical study must address:

Prospectively, do Medicare beneficiaries that have chronic non-healing diabetic, venous and/or pressure wounds who receive well-defined optimal usual care along with PRP therapy, experience clinically significant health outcomes compared to patients who receive well-defined optimal usual care for chronic non-healing diabetic, venous and/or pressure wounds as indicated by addressing at least one of the following:

a. Complete wound healing?

b. Ability to return to previous function and resumption of normal activities?

c. Reduction of wound size or healing trajectory which results in the patient's ability to return to previous function and resumption of normal activities?

The required clinical trial of PRP must adhere to the following standards of scientific integrity and relevance to the Medicare population:

a. The principal purpose of the CLINICAL STUDY is to test whether PRP improves the participants' health outcomes.

b. The CLINICAL STUDY is well supported by available scientific and medical information or it is intended to clarify or establish the health outcomes of interventions already in common clinical use.

c. The CLINICAL STUDY does not unjustifiably duplicate existing studies.

d. The CLINICAL STUDY design is appropriate to answer the research question being asked in the study.

e. The CLINICAL STUDY is sponsored by an organization or individual capable of executing the proposed study successfully.

f. The CLINICAL STUDY is in compliance with all applicable Federal regulations concerning the protection of human subjects found at 45 CFR Part 46.

g. All aspects of the CLINICAL STUDY are conducted according to appropriate standards of scientific integrity set by the International Committee of Medical Journal Editors (http://www.icmje.org).

h. The CLINICAL STUDY has a written protocol that clearly addresses, or incorporates by reference, the standards listed here as Medicare requirements for coverage with evidence development (CED).

i. The CLINICAL STUDY is not designed to exclusively test toxicity or disease pathophysiology in healthy individuals. Trials of all medical technologies measuring therapeutic outcomes as one of the objectives meet this standard only if the disease or condition being studied is life threatening as defined in 21 CFR §312.81(a) and the patient has no other viable treatment options.

j. The CLINICAL STUDY is registered on the ClinicalTrials. gov website by the principal sponsor/investigator prior to the enrollment of the first study subject.

k. The CLINICAL STUDY protocol specifies the method and timing of public release of all pre-specified outcomes to be measured including release of outcomes if outcomes are negative or study is terminated early. The results must be made public within 24 months of the end of data collection. If a report is planned to be published in a peer reviewed journal, then that initial release may be an abstract that meets the requirements of the International Committee of Medical Journal Editors (http://www.icmje. org). However a full report of the outcomes must be made public no later than three (3) years after the end of data collection.

l. The CLINICAL STUDY protocol must explicitly discuss subpopulations affected by the treatment under investigation, particularly traditionally underrepresented groups in clinical studies, how the inclusion and exclusion criteria effect enrollment of these populations, and a plan for the retention and reporting of said populations on the trial. If the inclusion and exclusion criteria are expected to have a negative effect on the recruitment or retention of underrepresented populations, the protocol must discuss why these criteria are necessary.

m. The CLINICAL STUDY protocol explicitly discusses how the results are or are not expected to be generalizable to the Medicare population to infer whether Medicare patients may benefit from the intervention. Separate discussions in the protocol may be necessary for populations eligible for Medicare due to age, disability or Medicaid eligibility.

Consistent with §1142 of the Social Security Act (the Act), the Agency for Healthcare Research and Quality (AHRQ) supports clinical research studies that CMS determines meet the above-listed standards and address the above-listed research questions.

Any clinical study undertaken pursuant to this NCD must be approved no later than August 2, 2014. If there are no approved clinical studies on or before August 2, 2014, this CED will expire. Any clinical study approved will adhere to the timeframe designated in the approved clinical study protocol.

C. Nationally Non-Covered Indications

1. Effective December 28, 1992, the Centers for Medicare & Medicaid Services (CMS) issued a national non-coverage determination for platelet-derived wound-healing formulas intended to treat patients with chronic, non-healing wounds. This decision was based on a lack of sufficient published data to determine safety and efficacy, and a public health service technology assessment.

2. Effective July 23, 2004, upon reconsideration, the clinical effectiveness of autologous PDGF products continues to not be adequately proven in scientific literature. As the evidence is insufficient to conclude that autologous PDGF in a platelet-poor plasma is reasonable and necessary, it remains non-covered for treatment of chronic, non-healing cutaneous wounds. Also, the clinical

evidence does not support a benefit in the application of autologous PRP for the treatment of chronic, non-healing, cutaneous wounds. Therefore, CMS determines it is not reasonable and necessary and is nationally non-covered.

3. Effective April 27, 2006, coverage for treatments utilizing coverage for treatments utilizing becaplermin, a non-autologous growth factor for chronic, non-healing subcutaneous wounds, remains nationally non-covered under Part B based on section 1861(s)(2)(A) and (B) of the Social Security Act because this product is usually administered by the patient.

4. Effective March 19, 2008, upon reconsideration, the evidence is not adequate to conclude that autologous PRP is reasonable and necessary and remains non-covered for the treatment of chronic non-healing, cutaneous wounds. Additionally, upon reconsideration, the evidence is not adequate to conclude that autologous PRP is reasonable and necessary for the treatment of acute surgical wounds when the autologous PRP is applied directly to the closed incision, or for dehiscent wounds.

D. Other

In accordance with section 310.1 of the National Coverage Determinations Manual, the routine costs in Federally sponsored or approved clinical trials assessing the efficacy of autologous PRP in treating chronic, non-healing cutaneous wounds are covered by Medicare.

100-4, Chapter-1, 10.1.4.1

Physician and Ambulance Services Furnished in Connection With Covered Foreign Inpatient Hospital Services

Payment is made for necessary physician and ambulance services that meet the other coverage requirements of the Medicare program, and are furnished in connection with a covered foreign hospitalization.

A. Coverage of Physician and Ambulance Services Furnished Outside the U.S.

Where inpatient services in a foreign hospital are covered, payment may also be made for:

- Physicians' services furnished to the beneficiary while he/she is an inpatient,

- Physicians' services furnished to the beneficiary outside the hospital on the day of his/her admission as an inpatient, provided the services were for the same condition for which the beneficiary was hospitalized (including the services of a physician who furnishes emergency services in Canadian waters on the day the patient is admitted to a Canadian hospital for a covered emergency stay) and,

- Ambulance services, where necessary, for the trip to the hospital in conjunction with the beneficiary's admission as an inpatient. Return trips from a foreign hospital are not covered.

In cases involving foreign ambulance services, the general requirements in chapter 15 are also applicable, subject to the following special rules:

- If the foreign hospitalization was determined to be covered on the basis of emergency services, the medical necessity requirements outlined in chapter 15 are considered met.

- The definition of "physician," for purposes of coverage of services furnished outside the U.S., is expanded to include a foreign practitioner, provided the practitioner is legally licensed to practice in the country in which the services are furnished.
- Only the enrollee can file for Part B benefits; the assignment method may not be used.
- Where the enrollee is deceased, the rules for settling Part B underpayments are applicable. Payment is made to the foreign physician or foreign ambulance company on an unpaid bill provided the physician or ambulance company accepts the payment as the full charge for the service, or payment can be made to a person who has agreed to assume legal liability to pay the physician or supplier. Where the bill is paid, payment may be made in accordance with Medicare regulations. The regular deductible and coinsurance requirements apply to physicians' and ambulance services furnished outside the U.S.

100-4, Chapter-1, 30.3.1

Mandatory Assignment on Carrier Claims

The following practitioners who provide services under the Medicare program are required to accept assignment for all Medicare claims for their services. This means that they must accept the Medicare allowed amount as payment in full for their practitioner services. The beneficiary's liability is limited to any applicable deductible plus the 20 percent coinsurance.

Assignment is mandated for the following claims:

- Clinical diagnostic laboratory services and physician lab services;
- Physician services to individuals dually entitled to Medicare and Medicaid;

Services of physician assistants, nurse practitioners, clinical nurse specialists, nurse midwives, certified registered nurse anesthetists, clinical psychologists, clinical social workers, registered dietitians/nutritionists, anesthesiologist assistants, and mass immunization roster billers.

NOTE: The provider type Mass Immunization Roster Biller can only bill for influenza and pneumococcal vaccinations and administrations. These services are not subject to the deductible or the 20 percent coinsurance.

- Ambulatory surgical center services; (No deductible and 25% coinsurance for colorectal cancer screening colonoscopies {G0105 and G0121} and effective for dates of service on or after January 1, 2008 G0104 also applies);
- Home dialysis supplies and equipment paid under Method II for dates of service prior to January 1, 2011. Refer to Section 30.3.8 for information regarding the elimination of Method II home dialysis for dates of service on and after January 1, 2011;
- Drugs and biologicals; and,
- Ambulance services

When these claims are inadvertently submitted as unassigned, carriers process them as assigned.

Note that, unlike physicians, practitioners, or suppliers bound by a participation agreement, practitioners/entities providing the services/supplies identified above are required to accept assignment only with respect to these services/supplies

(unless they have signed participation agreements which blanket the full range of their services).

The carrier system must be able to identify (and update) the codes for those services subject to the assignment mandate.

For the practitioner services of physicians and independently practicing physical and occupational therapists, the acceptance of assignment is not mandatory. Nor is the acceptance of assignment mandatory for the suppliers of radiology services or diagnostic tests. However, these practitioners and suppliers may nevertheless voluntarily agree to participate to take advantage of the higher payment rate, in which case the participation status makes assignment mandatory for the term of the agreement. Such an agreement is known as the Medicare Participating Physician or Supplier Agreement. (See §30.3.12.2 Carrier Participation Agreement.) Physicians, practitioners, and suppliers who sign this agreement to participate are agreeing to accept assignment on all Medicare claims. The Medicare Participation Agreement and general instructions are on the CMS Web site.

Future updates to this section will be communicated in a Recurring Update Notification.

100-4, Chapter-1, 30.3.5

Effect of Assignment Upon Purchase of Cataract Glasses From Participating Physician or Supplier on Claims Submitted to Carriers

A pair of cataract glasses is comprised of two distinct products: a professional product (the prescribed lenses) and a retail commercial product (the frames). The frames serve not only as a holder of lenses but also as an article of personal apparel. As such, they are usually selected on the basis of personal taste and style. Although Medicare will pay only for standard frames, most patients want deluxe frames. Participating physicians and suppliers cannot profitably furnish such deluxe frames unless they can make an extra (noncovered) charge for the frames even though they accept assignment.

Therefore, a participating physician or supplier (whether an ophthalmologist, optometrist, or optician) who accepts assignment on cataract glasses with deluxe frames may charge the Medicare patient the difference between his/her usual charge to private pay patients for glasses with standard frames and his/her usual charge to such patients for glasses with deluxe frames, in addition to the applicable deductible and coinsurance on glasses with standard frames, if all of the following requirements are met:

A. The participating physician or supplier has standard frames available, offers them for sale to the patient, and issues and ABN to the patient that explains the price and other differences between standard and deluxe frames. Refer to Chapter 30.

B. The participating physician or supplier obtains from the patient (or his/her representative) and keeps on file the following signed and dated statement:

Name of Patient   Medicare Claim Number

Having been informed that an extra charge is being made by the physician or supplier for deluxe frames, that this extra charge is not covered by Medicare, and that standard frames are available for purchase from the physician or supplier at no extra charge, I have chosen to purchase deluxe frames.

Signature Date

C. The participating physician or supplier itemizes on his/her claim his/her actual charge for the lenses, his/her actual charge for the standard frames, and his/her actual extra charge for the deluxe frames (charge differential).

Once the assigned claim for deluxe frames has been processed, the carrier will follow the ABN instructions as described in §60.

100-4, Chapter-1, 50.3.2

Policy and Billing Instructions for Condition Code 44

In cases where a hospital or a CAH's UR committee determines that an inpatient admission does not meet the hospital's inpatient criteria, the hospital or CAH may change the beneficiary's status from inpatient to outpatient and submit an outpatient claim (bill type 13x or 85x) for medically necessary Medicare Part B services that were furnished to the beneficiary, provided all of the following conditions are met:

1. The change in patient status from inpatient to outpatient is made prior to discharge or release, while the beneficiary is still a patient of the hospital;

2. The hospital has not submitted a claim to Medicare for the inpatient admission;

3. The practitioner responsible for the care of the patient and the UR committee concur with the decision; and

4. The concurrence of the practitioner responsible for the care of the patient and the UR committee is documented in the patient's medical record.

While typically the full UR committee makes the decision for the committee that a change in patient status under Condition Code 44 is warranted, in accordance with §482.30(d)(1) one physician member of the UR committee may make the decision for the committee, provided he or she is a different person from the concurring practitioner who is responsible for the care of the patient.

When the hospital has determined that it may submit an outpatient claim according to the conditions described above, the entire episode of care should be billed as an outpatient episode of care on a 13x or 85x bill type and outpatient services that were ordered and furnished should be billed as appropriate.

Refer to Pub. 100-04, Medicare Claims Processing Manual; Chapter 30, Financial Liability Protections; Section 20, Limitation On Liability (LOL) Under §1879 Where Medicare Claims Are Disallowed, for information regarding financial liability protections.

When the hospital submits a 13x or 85x bill for services furnished to a beneficiary whose status was changed from inpatient to outpatient, the hospital is required to report Condition Code 44 on the outpatient claim in one of Form Locators 24-30, or in the ASC X12N 837 institutional claim in loop 2300, HI segment, with qualifier BG, on the outpatient claim. Additional information may be found in Chapter 25 of this manual, (Completing and Processing the Form CMS-1450 Data Set). Condition Code 44 is used by CMS and QIOs to track and monitor these occurrences. The reporting of Condition Code 44 on a claim does not affect the amount of hospital outpatient payment that would otherwise be made for a hospital outpatient claim that did not require the reporting Condition Code 44.

One of the requirements for the use of Condition Code 44 is concurrence by the practitioner who is responsible for the care of the patient with the determination that an inpatient admission does not meet the hospital's admission criteria and that the patient should have been registered as an outpatient. This prerequisite for use of Condition Code 44 is consistent with the requirements in the CoP in §482.30 (d) of the regulations. This paragraph provides that the practitioner or practitioners responsible for the care of the patient must be consulted and allowed to present their views before the UR committee or QIO makes its determination that an admission is not medically necessary. It may also be appropriate to include the practitioner who admitted the patient if this is a different person than the practitioner responsible for the care of the patient.

If the conditions for use of Condition Code 44 are not met, the hospital may submit a 12x bill type for covered "Part B Only" services that were furnished to the inpatient. Medicare may still make payment for certain Part B services furnished to an inpatient of a hospital when payment cannot be made under Part A because an inpatient admission is determined not to be medically necessary. Information about "Part B Only" services is located in Pub. 100-02, Medicare Benefit Policy Manual, chapter 6, section 10. Examples of such services include, but are not limited to, diagnostic x-ray tests, diagnostic laboratory tests, surgical dressings and splints, prosthetic devices, and certain other services. The Medicare Benefit Policy Manual includes a complete list of the payable "Part B Only" services. See Pub. 100-04, Medicare Claims Processing Manual, chapter 4, section 10.12 for a discussion of the billing and payment rules regarding services furnished within the payment window for outpatient services treated as inpatient services.

Entries in the medical record cannot be expunged or deleted and must be retained in their original form. Therefore, all orders and all entries related to the inpatient admission must be retained in the record in their original form. If a patient's status changes in accordance with the requirements for use of Condition Code 44, the change must be fully documented in the medical record, complete with orders and notes that indicate why the change was made, the care that was furnished to the beneficiary, and the participants in making the decision to change the patient's status.

When Condition Code 44 is appropriately used, the hospital reports on the outpatient bill the services that were ordered and provided to the patient for the entire patient encounter. However, in accordance with the general Medicare requirements for services furnished to beneficiaries and billed to Medicare, even in Condition Code 44 situations, hospitals may not report observation services using HCPCS code G0378 (Hospital observation service, per hour) for observation services furnished during a hospital encounter prior to a physician's order for observation services. Medicare does not permit retroactive orders or the inference of physician orders. Like all hospital outpatient services, observation services must be ordered by a physician. The clock time begins at the time that observation services are initiated in accordance with a physician's order.

While hospitals may not report observation services under HCPCS code G0378 for the time period during the hospital encounter prior to a physician's order for observation services, in Condition Code 44 situations, as for all other hospital outpatient encounters, hospitals may include charges on the outpatient claim for the costs of all hospital resources utilized in the care of the patient during the entire encounter. For example, a beneficiary is admitted as an inpatient and receives 12 hours of monitoring and nursing care, at which point the hospital changes the status of the beneficiary from inpatient to outpatient and the physician orders observation services, with all criteria for billing under Condition Code 44 being met.

On the outpatient claim on an uncoded line with revenue code 0762, the hospital could bill for the 12 hours of monitoring and nursing care that were provided prior to the change in status and the physician order for observation services, in addition to billing HCPCS code G0378 for the observation services that followed the change in status and physician order for observation services. For other rules related to billing and payment of observation services, see chapter 4, section 290 of this manual, and Pub.100-02, Medicare Benefit Policy Manual, chapter 6, Section 20.6.

100-4, Chapter-3, 10.4

Payment of Nonphysician Services for Inpatients

All items and nonphysician services furnished to inpatients must be furnished directly by the hospital or billed through the hospital under arrangements. This provision applies to all hospitals, regardless of whether they are subject to PPS.

A. Other Medical Items, Supplies, and Services

The following medical items, supplies, and services furnished to inpatients are covered under Part A. Consequently, they are covered by the prospective payment rate or reimbursed as reasonable costs under Part A to hospitals excluded from PPS.

- Laboratory services (excluding anatomic pathology services and certain clinical pathology services);
- Pacemakers and other prosthetic devices including lenses, and artificial limbs,knees, and hips;
- Radiology services including computed tomography (CT) scans furnished to inpatients by a physician's office, other hospital, or radiology clinic;
- Total parenteral nutrition (TPN) services; and
- Transportation, including transportation by ambulance, to and from another hospital or freestanding facility to receive specialized diagnostic or therapeutic services not available at the facility where the patient is an inpatient.

The hospital must include the cost of these services in the appropriate ancillary service cost center, i.e., in the cost of the diagnostic or therapeutic service. It must not show them separately under revenue code 0540.

EXCEPTIONS:

- **Pneumococcal Vaccine** - is payable under Part B only and is billed by the hospital on the Form CMS-1450.
- **Ambulance Service** - For purposes of this section "hospital inpatient" means a beneficiary who has been formally admitted it does not include a beneficiary who is in the process of being transferred from one hospital to another. Where the patient is transferred from one hospital to another, and is admitted as an inpatient to the second, the ambulance service is payable under only Part B. If transportation is by a hospital owned and operated ambulance, the hospital bills separately on Form CMS-1450 as appropriate. Similarly, if the hospital arranges for the ambulance transportation with an ambulance operator, including paying the ambulance operator, it bills separately. However, if the hospital does not assume any financial responsibility, the billing is to the carrier by the ambulance operator or beneficiary, as appropriate, if an ambulance is used for the transportation of a hospital inpatient to another facility for diagnostic tests or special treatment the ambulance trip is considered part of the DRG, and not separately billable, if the resident hospital is under PPS.

- **Part B Inpatient Services** - Where Part A benefits are not payable, payment may be made to the hospital under Part B for certain medical and other health services. See Chapter 4 for a description of Part B inpatient services.
- **Anesthetist Services "Incident to" Physician Services** - If a physician's practice was to employ anesthetists and to bill on a reasonable charge basis for these services and that practice was in effect as of the last day of the hospital's most recent 12-month cost reporting period ending before September 30, 1983, the physician may continue that practice through cost reporting periods beginning October 1, 1984. However, if the physician chooses to continue this practice, the hospital may not add costs of the anesthetist's service to its base period costs for purposes of its transition payment rates. If it is the existing or new practice of the physician to employ certified registered nurse anesthetists (CRNAs) and other qualified anesthetists and include charges for their services in the physician bills for anesthesiology services for the hospital's cost report periods beginning on or after October 1, 1984, and before October 1, 1987, the physician may continue to do so.

B. Exceptions/Waivers

These provisions were waived before cost reporting periods beginning on or after October 1, 1986, under certain circumstances. The basic criteria for waiver was that services furnished by outside suppliers are so extensive that a sudden change in billing practices would threaten the stability of patient care. Specific criteria for waiver and processing procedures are in §2804 of the Provider Reimbursement Manual (CMS Pub. 15-1).

100-4, Chapter-3, 20.7.3

Payment for Blood Clotting Factor Administered to Hemophilia Inpatients

Section 6011 of Public Law (P.L.) 101-239 amended §1886(a)(4) of the Social Security Act (the Act) to provide that prospective payment system (PPS) hospitals receive an additional payment for the costs of administering blood clotting factor to Medicare hemophiliacs who are hospital inpatients. Section 6011(b) of P.L. 101.239 specified that the payment be based on a predetermined price per unit of clotting factor multiplied by the number of units provided. This add-on payment originally was effective for blood clotting factors furnished on or after June 19, 1990, and before December 19, 1991. Section 13505 of P. L. 103-66 amended §6011 (d) of P.L. 101-239 to extend the period covered by the add-on payment for blood clotting factors administered to Medicare inpatients with hemophilia through September 30, 1994 Section 4452 of P.L. 105-33 amended §6011(d) of P.L. 101-239 to reinstate the add-on payment for the costs of administering blood-clotting factor to Medicare beneficiaries who have hemophilia and who are hospital inpatients for discharges occurring on or after October 1, 1998.

A/B MACs (B) shall process non-institutional blood clotting factor claims.

The A/B MACs (A) shall process institutional blood clotting factor claims payable under either Part A or Part B.

A. Inpatient Bills

Under the Inpatient Prospective Payment System (IPPS), hospitals receive a special add-on payment for the costs of furnishing blood clotting factors to Medicare beneficiaries with hemophilia, admitted as inpatients of PPS hospitals. The clotting factor add-on payment is calculated using the number of units (as defined in the HCPCS code long descriptor) billed by the provider under special instructions for units of service.

The PPS Pricer software does not calculate the payment amount. The Fiscal Intermediary Shared System (FISS) calculates the payment amount and subtracts the charges from those submitted to Pricer so that the clotting factor charges are not included in cost outlier computations.

Blood clotting factors not paid on a cost or PPS basis are priced as a drug/biological under the Medicare Part B Drug Pricing File effective for the specific date of service. As of January 1, 2005, the average sales price (ASP) plus 6 percent shall be used.

If a beneficiary is in a covered Part A stay in a PPS hospital, the clotting factors are paid in addition to the DRG/HIPPS payment (For FY 2004, this payment is based on 95 percent of average wholesale price.) For a SNF subject to SNF/PPS, the payment is bundled into the SNF/PPS rate.

For SNF inpatient Part A, there is no add-on payment for blood clotting factors.

The codes for blood-clotting factors are found on the Medicare Part B Drug Pricing File. This file is distributed on a quarterly basis.

For discharges occurring on or after October 1, 2000, and before December 31, 2005, report HCPCS Q0187 based on 1 billing unit per 1.2 mg. Effective January 1, 2006, HCPCS code J7189 replaces Q0187 and is defined as 1 billing unit per 1 microgram (mcg).

The examples below include the HCPCS code and indicate the dosage amount specified in the descriptor of that code. Facilities use the units field as a multiplier to arrive at the dosage amount.

EXAMPLE 1

HCPCS	Drug	Dosage
J7189	Factor VIIa	1 mcg

Actual dosage: 13,365 mcg

On the bill, the facility shows J7189 and 13,365 in the units field (13,365 mcg divided by 1 mcg = 13,365 units).

NOTE: The process for dealing with one international unit (IU) is the same as the process of dealing with one microgram.

EXAMPLE 2

HCPCS	Drug	Dosage
J9355	Trastuzumab	10 mg

Actual dosage: 140 mg

On the bill, the facility shows J9355 and 14 in the units field (140 mg divided by 10mg = 14 units).

When the dosage amount is greater than the amount indicated for the HCPCS code, the facility rounds up to determine units. When the dosage amount is less than the amount indicated for the HCPCS code, use 1 as the unit of measure.

EXAMPLE 3

HCPCS	Drug	Dosage
J9355	Tenecteplase	50 mg

Actual Dosage: 40 mg

The provider would bill for 1 unit, even though less than 1 full unit was furnished. At times, the facility provides less than the amount provided in a single use vial and there is waste, i.e.; some drugs may be available only in packaged amounts that exceed the needs of an individual patient. Once the drug is reconstituted in the hospital's pharmacy, it may have a limited shelf life. Since an individual patient may receive less than the fully reconstituted amount, we encourage hospitals to schedule patients in such a way that the hospital can use the drug most efficiently. However, if the hospital must discard the remainder of a vial after administering part of it to a Medicare patient, the provider may bill for the amount of drug discarded plus the amount administered.

Example 1:

Drug X is available only in a 100-unit size. A hospital schedules three Medicare patients to receive drug X on the same day within the designated shelf life of the product. An appropriate hospital staff member administers 30 units to each patient. The remaining 10 units are billed to Medicare on the account of the last patient. Therefore, 30 units are billed on behalf of the first patient seen and 30 units are billed on behalf of the second patient seen. Forty units are billed on behalf of the last patient seen because the hospital had to discard 10 units at that point.

Example 2:

An appropriate hospital staff member must administer 30 units of drug X to a Medicare patient, and it is not practical to schedule another patient who requires the same drug. For example, the hospital has only one patient who requires drug X, or the hospital sees the patient for the first time and did not know the patient's condition. The hospital bills for 100 units on behalf of the patient, and Medicare pays for 100 units.

When the number of units of blood clotting factor administered to hemophiliac inpatients exceeds 99,999, the hospital reports the excess as a second line for revenue code 0636 and repeats the HCPCS code. One hundred thousand fifty (100,050) units are reported on one line as 99,999, and another line shows 1,051.

Revenue Code 0636 is used. It requires HCPCS. Some other inpatient drugs continue to be billed without HCPCS codes under pharmacy.

No changes in beneficiary notices are required. Coverage is applicable to hospital Part A claims only. Coverage is also applicable to inpatient Part B services in SNFs and all types of hospitals, including CAHs. Separate payment is not made to SNFs for beneficiaries in an inpatient Part A stay.

B. -A/B MAC (A) Action

The contractor is responsible for the following:

- It accepts HCPCS codes for inpatient services;
- It edits to require HCPCS codes with Revenue Code 0636. Multiple iterations of the revenue code are possible with the same or different HCPCS codes. It does not edit units except to ensure a numeric value;
- It reduces charges forwarded to Pricer by the charges for hemophilia clotting factors in revenue code 0636. It retains the charges and revenue and HCPCS codes for CWF; and
- It modifies data entry screens to accept HCPCS codes for hospital (including CAH) swing bed, and SNF inpatient claims (bill types 11X, 12X, 18x, 21x and, 22x).

The September 1, 1993, IPPS final rule (58 FR 46304) states that payment will be made for the blood clotting factor only if an ICD-9-CM diagnosis code for hemophilia is included on the bill.

Inpatient blood-clotting factors are covered only for beneficiaries with hemophilia. One of the following hemophilia diagnosis codes must be reported on the claim for payment to be made for blood clotting factors.

Table 1 - Effective for discharges September 1 1993 through the implementation of ICD-10

Icd-9-cm	Description code
286.0	Congenital factor VIII disorder
286.1	Congenital factor IX disorder
286.2	Congenital factor XI deficiency
286.3	Congenital deficiency of other clotting factors
286.4	von Willebrands' disease

Table 2 - Effective for discharges August 1, 2001 through the implementation of ICD-10, payment may be made if a diagnosis codes from either Table 1 or Table 2 is reported is reported:

Icd-9-cm	Description code
286.5	Hemorrhagic disorder due to intrinsic circulating anticoagulants (terminate effective September 30, 2011)
286.7	Acquired coagulation factor deficiency

Table 3 - Effective for discharges on October 1, 2011, through the implementation of ICD-10 payment may be made if a diagnosis code from any of Table 1, Table 2 or Table 3 is reported:

Icd-9-cm	Description code
286.52	Acquired haemophilia
286.53	Antiphospholipid antibody with hemorrhagic disorder
286.59	Other hemorrhagic disorder due to intrinsic circulating anticoagulants, antibodies, or inhibitors

Effective for discharges on or after the implementation of ICD-10-CM, the following codes are applicable, and payment may be made for blood clotting factors only if a hemophilia code from the range D66 - D68.4 is reported.

A crosswalk of ICD 9 to ICD10 hemophilia diagnosis codes follows:

Insert Table here from CMS mentioned on page number 99,100

C. Part A Remittance Advice

For remittance reporting PIP and/or non-PIP payments, the Hemophilia Add On is included in the overall claim payment (Provider Reimbursement, CLP04).

If an inpatient claim has a Hemophilia Add On payment, the payment to the provider is increased in the PLB segment with a PLB adjustment HM. The Hemophilia Add On amount will always be included in the CLP04 Claim Payment Amount.

For remittance reporting PIP payments, the Hemophilia Add On will also be reported in the provider level adjustment (element identifier PLB) segment with the provider level adjustment reason code HM. For remittances reporting PIP payments, the sum of inpatient claims, CLP04, is backed out at PLB with PI/PA. If an inpatient claim has a Hemophilia Add On payment, the payment to the provider is increased in the PLB segment with a PLB adjustment HM.

D. Standard Hard Copy Remittance Advice

For paper remittances reporting non-PIP payments involving Hemophilia Add On, add a "Hemophilia Add On" category to the end of the "Pass Thru Amounts" listings in the "Summary" section of the paper remittance. Enter the total of the Hemophilia Add On amounts due for the claims covered by this remittance next to the Hemophilia Add On heading.

Contractors add the Remark Code "MA103" (Hemophilia Add On) to the remittance advice under the REM column for those claims that qualify for Hemophilia Add On payments.

This will be the full extent of Hemophilia Add On reporting on paper remittance notices; providers wishing more detailed information must subscribe to the Medicare Part A specifications for the ANSI ASC X12N 835, where additional information is available.

100-4, Chapter-3, 40.2.2

Charges to Beneficiaries for Part A Services

The hospital submits a bill even where the patient is responsible for a deductible which covers the entire amount of the charges for non-PPS hospitals, or in PPS hospitals, where the DRG payment amount will be less than the deductible.

A hospital receiving payment for a covered hospital stay (or PPS hospital that includes at least one covered day, or one treated as covered under guarantee of payment or limitation on liability) may charge the beneficiary, or other person, for items and services furnished during the stay only as described in subsections A through H. If limitation of liability applies, a beneficiary's liability for payment is governed by the limitation on liability notification rules in Chapter 30 of this manual. For related notices for inpatient hospitals, see CMS Transmittal 594, Change Request 3903, dated June 24, 2005.

A. Deductible and Coinsurance

The hospital may charge the beneficiary or other person for applicable deductible and coinsurance amounts. The deductible is satisfied only by charges for covered services. The FI deducts the deductible and coinsurance first from the PPS payment. Where the deductible exceeds the PPS amount, the excess will be applied to a subsequent payment to the hospital. (See Chapter 3 of the Medicare General Information, Eligibility, and Entitlement Manual for specific policies.)

B. Blood Deductible

The Part A blood deductible provision applies to whole blood and red blood cells, and reporting of the number of pints is applicable to both PPS and non-PPS hospitals. (See Chapter 3 of the Medicare General Information, Eligibility, and Entitlement Manual for specific policies.) Hospitals shall report charges for red blood cells using revenue code 381, and charges for whole blood using revenue code 382.

C. Inpatient Care No Longer Required

The hospital may charge for services that are not reasonable and necessary or that constitute custodial care. Notification may be required under limitation of liability. See CMS Transmittal 594, Change Request 3903, dated June 24, 2005, section V. of the attachment, for specific notification requirements. Note this transmittal will be placed in Chapter 30 of this manual at a future point. Chapter 1, section 150 of this manual also contains related billing information in addition to that provided below.

In general, after proper notification has occurred, and assuming an expedited decision is received from a Quality Improvement Organization (QIO), the following entries are required on the bill the hospital prepares:

- Occurrence code 3I (and date) to indicate the date the hospital notified the patient in accordance with the first bullet above;
- Occurrence span code 76 (and dates) to indicate the period of noncovered care for which it is charging the beneficiary;
- Occurrence span code 77 (and dates) to indicate the period of noncovered care for which the provider is liable, when it is aware of this prior to billing; and
- Value code 3I (and amount) to indicate the amount of charges it may bill the beneficiary for days for which inpatient care was no longer required. They are included as noncovered charges on the bill.

D. Change in the Beneficiary's Condition

If the beneficiary remains in the hospital after receiving notice as described in subsection C, and the hospital, the physician who concurred in the hospital's determination, or the QIO, subsequently determines that the beneficiary again requires inpatient hospital care, the hospital may not charge the beneficiary or other person for services furnished after the beneficiary again required inpatient hospital care until proper notification occurs (see subsection C).

If a patient who needs only a SNF level of care remains in the hospital after the SNF bed becomes available, and the bed ceases to be available, the hospital may continue to charge the beneficiary. It need not provide the beneficiary with another notice when the patient chose not to be discharged to the SNF bed.

E. Admission Denied

If the entire hospital admission is determined to be not reasonable or necessary, limitation of liability may apply. See 2005 CMS transmittal 594, section V. of the attachment, for specific notification requirements.

NOTE: This transmittal will be placed in Chapter 30 of this manual at a future point.

In such cases the following entries are required on the bill:

- Occurrence code 3I (and date) to indicate the date the hospital notified the beneficiary.
- Occurrence span code 76 (and dates) to indicate the period of noncovered care for which the hospital is charging the beneficiary.
- Occurrence span code 77 (and dates) to indicate any period of noncovered care for which the provider is liable (e.g., the period between issuing the notice and the time it may charge the beneficiary) when the provider is aware of this prior to billing.
- Value code 3I (and amount) to indicate the amount of charges the hospital may bill the beneficiary for hospitalization that was not necessary or reasonable. They are included as noncovered charges on the bill.

F. Procedures, Studies and Courses of Treatment That Are Not Reasonable or Necessary

If diagnostic procedures, studies, therapeutic studies and courses of treatment are excluded from coverage as not reasonable and necessary (even though the beneficiary requires inpatient hospital care) the hospital may charge the beneficiary or other person for the services or care according

the procedures given in CMS Transmittal 594, Change Request 3903, dated June 24, 2005.

The following bill entries apply to these circumstances:

- Occurrence code 32 (and date) to indicate the date the hospital provided the notice to the beneficiary.
- Value code 3I (and amount) to indicate the amount of such charges to be billed to the beneficiary. They are included as noncovered charges on the bill.

G. Nonentitlement Days and Days after Benefits Exhausted

If a hospital stay exceeds the day outlier threshold, the hospital may charge for some, or all, of the days on which the patient is not entitled to Medicare Part A, or after the Part A benefits are exhausted (i.e., the hospital may charge its customary charges for services furnished on those days). It may charge the beneficiary for the lesser of:

- The number of days on which the patient was not entitled to benefits or after the benefits were exhausted; or
- The number of outlier days. (Day outliers were discontinued at the end of FY 1997.)

If the number of outlier days exceeds the number of days on which the patient was not entitled to benefits, or after benefits were exhausted, the hospital may charge for all days on which the patient was not entitled to benefits or after benefits were exhausted. If the number of days on which the beneficiary was not entitled to benefits, or after benefits were exhausted, exceeds the number of outlier days, the hospital determines the days for which it may charge by starting with the last day of the stay (i.e., the day before the day of discharge) and identifying and counting off in reverse order, days on which the patient was not entitled to benefits or after the benefits were exhausted, until the number of days counted off equals the number of outlier days. The days counted off are the days for which the hospital may charge.

H. Contractual Exclusions

In addition to receiving the basic prospective payment, the hospital may charge the beneficiary for any services that are excluded from coverage for reasons other than, or in addition to, absence of medical necessity, provision of custodial care, non-entitlement to Part A, or exhaustion of benefits. For example, it may charge for most cosmetic and dental surgery.

I. Private Room Care

Payment for medically necessary private room care is included in the prospective payment. Where the beneficiary requests private room accommodations, the hospital must inform the beneficiary of the additional charge. (See the Medicare Benefit Policy Manual, Chapter 1.) When the beneficiary accepts the liability, the hospital will supply the service, and bill the beneficiary directly. If the beneficiary believes the private room was medically necessary, the beneficiary has a right to a determination and may initiate a Part A appeal.

J. Deluxe Item or Service

Where a beneficiary requests a deluxe item or service, i.e., an item or service which is more expensive than is medically required for the beneficiary's condition, the hospital may collect the additional charge if it informs the beneficiary of the additional charge. That charge is the difference between the customary charge for the item or service most commonly furnished by the hospital to private pay patients with the beneficiary's condition, and the charge for the more expensive item or service requested. If the beneficiary believes that the more expensive item or service was medically necessary, the beneficiary has a right to a determination and may initiate a Part A appeal.

K – Inpatient Acute Care Hospital Admission Followed By a Death or Discharge Prior To Room Assignment

A patient of an acute care hospital is considered an inpatient upon issuance of written doctor's orders to that effect. If a patient either dies or is discharged prior to being assigned and/or occupying a room, a hospital may enter an appropriate room and board charge on the claim. If a patient leaves of their own volition prior to being assigned and/or occupying a room, a hospital may enter an appropriate room and board charge on the claim as well as a patient status code 07 which indicates they left against medical advice. A hospital is not required to enter a room and board charge, but failure to do so may have a minimal impact on future DRG weight calculations.

100-4, Chapter-4, 10.4

Packaging

Under the OPPS, packaged services are items and services that are considered to be an integral part of another service that is paid under the OPPS. No separate payment is made for packaged services, because the cost of these items and services is included in the APC payment for the service of which they are an integral part. For example, routine supplies, anesthesia, recovery room use, and most drugs are considered to be an integral part of a surgical procedure so payment for these items is packaged into the APC payment for the surgical procedure.

A. Packaging for Claims Resulting in APC Payments

If a claim contains services that result in an APC payment but also contains packaged services, separate payment for the packaged services is not made since payment is included in the APC. However, charges related to the packaged services are used for outlier and Transitional Corridor Payments (TOPs) as well as for future rate setting.

Therefore, it is extremely important that hospitals report all HCPCS codes consistent with their descriptors; CPT® and/or CMS instructions and correct coding principles, and all charges for all services they furnish, whether payment for the services is made separately paid or is packaged.

B. Packaging for Claims Resulting in No APC Payments

If the claim contains only services payable under cost reimbursement, such as corneal tissue, and services that would be packaged services if an APC were payable, then the packaged services are not separately payable. In addition, these charges for the packaged services are not used to calculate TOPs.

If the claim contains only services payable under a fee schedule, such as clinical diagnostic laboratory tests, and also contains services that would be packaged services if an APC were payable, the packaged services are not separately payable. In addition, the charges are not used to calculate TOPs.

If a claim contains services payable under cost reimbursement, services payable under a fee schedule, and services that would be packaged services if an APC were payable, the packaged services are not separately payable. In addition, the charges are not used to calculate TOPs payments.

C. Packaging Types Under the OPPS

1. Unconditionally packaged services are services for which separate payment is never made because the payment for the service is always packaged into the payment for other services. Unconditionally packaged services are identified in the OPPS Addendum B with status indictor of N. See the OPPS Web site at http://www.cms.hhs.gov/HospitalOutpatientPPS/ for the most recent Addendum B (HCPCS codes with status indicators). In general, the charges for unconditionally packaged services are used to calculate outlier and TOPS payments when they appear on a claim with a service that is separately paid under the OPPS because the packaged service is considered to be part of the package of services for which payment is being made through the APC payment for the separately paid service.

2. STVX-packaged services are services for which separate payment is made only if there is no service with status indicator S, T, V or X reported with the same date of service on the same claim. If a claim includes a service that is assigned status indicator S, T, V, or X reported on the same date of service as the STVX-packaged service, the payment for the STVX-packaged service is packaged into the payment for the service(s) with status indicator S, T, V or X and no separate payment is made for the STVX-packaged service. STVX-packaged services are assigned status indicator Q1. See the OPPS Webpage at http://www.cms.hhs.gov/HospitalOutpatientPPS/ for identification of STVX-packaged codes.

3. T-packaged services are services for which separate payment is made only if there is no service with status indicator T reported with the same date of service on the same claim. When there is a claim that includes a service that is assigned status indicator T reported on the same date of service as the T-packaged service, the payment for the T-packaged service is packaged into the payment for the service(s) with status indicator T and no separate payment is made for the T-packaged service. T-packaged services are assigned status indicator Q2. See the OPPS Web site at http://www.cms.hhs.gov/HospitalOutpatientPPS/ for identification of T-packaged codes.

4. A service that is assigned to a composite APC is a major component of a single episode of care. The hospital receives one payment through a composite APC for multiple major separately identifiable services. Services mapped to composite APCs are assigned status indicator Q3. See the discussion of composite APCs in section 10.2.1.

100-4, Chapter-4, 160

Clinic and Emergency Visits

CMS has acknowledged from the beginning of the OPPS that CMS believes that CPT® Evaluation and Management (E/M) codes were designed to reflect the activities of physicians and do not describe well the range and mix of services provided by hospitals during visits of clinic and emergency department patients. While awaiting the development of a national set of facility-specific codes and guidelines, providers should continue to apply their current internal guidelines to the existing CPT® codes. Each hospital's internal guidelines should follow the intent of the CPT® code descriptors, in that the guidelines should be designed to reasonably relate the intensity of hospital resources to the different levels of effort represented by the codes. Hospitals should ensure that their guidelines accurately reflect resource distinctions between the five levels of codes.

Effective January 1, 2007, CMS is distinguishing between two types of emergency departments: Type A emergency departments and Type B emergency departments.

A Type A emergency department is defined as an emergency department that is available 24 hours a day, 7 days a week and is either licensed by the State in which it is located under applicable State law as an emergency room or emergency department or it is held out to the public (by name, posted signs, advertising, or other means) as a place that provides care for emergency medical conditions on an urgent basis without requiring a previously scheduled appointment.

A Type B emergency department is defined as an emergency department that meets the definition of a "dedicated emergency department" as defined in 42 CFR 489.24 under the EMTALA regulations. It must meet at least one of the following requirements:

(1) It is licensed by the State in which it is located under applicable State law as an emergency room or emergency department;

(2) It is held out to the public (by name, posted signs, advertising, or other means) as a place that provides care for emergency medical conditions on an urgent basis without requiring a previously scheduled appointment; or

(3) During the calendar year immediately preceding the calendar year in which a determination under 42 CFR 489.24 is being made, based on a representative sample of patient visits that occurred during that calendar year, it provides at least one-third of all of its outpatient visits for the treatment of emergency medical conditions on an urgent basis without requiring a previously scheduled appointment.

Hospitals must bill for visits provided in Type A emergency departments using CPT® emergency department E/M codes. Hospitals must bill for visits provided in Type B emergency departments using the G-codes that describe visits provided in Type B emergency departments.

Hospitals that will be billing the new Type B ED visit codes may need to update their internal guidelines to report these codes.

Emergency department and clinic visits are paid in some cases separately and in other cases as part of a composite APC payment.

100-4, Chapter-4, 160.1

Critical Care Services

Hospitals should separately report all HCPCS codes in accordance with correct coding principles, CPT® code descriptions, and any additional CMS guidance, when available. Specifically with respect to CPT® code 99291 (Critical care, evaluation and management of the critically ill or critically injured patient; first 30-74 minutes), hospitals must follow the CPT® instructions related to reporting that CPT® code. Prior to January 1, 2011, any services that CPT® indicates are included in the reporting of CPT® code 99291 (including those services that would otherwise be reported by and paid to hospitals using any of the CPT® codes specified by CPT®) should not be billed separately by the hospital. Instead, hospitals should report charges for any services provided as part of the critical care services. In establishing payment rates for critical care services, and other services, CMS packages the costs of certain items and services separately reported by HCPCS codes into payment for critical care services and other

services, according to the standard OPPS methodology for packaging costs.

Beginning January 1, 2011, in accordance with revised CPT® guidance, hospitals that report in accordance with the CPT® guidelines will begin reporting all of the ancillary services and their associated charges separately when they are provided in conjunction with critical care. CMS will continue to recognize the existing CPT® codes for critical care services and will establish payment rates based on historical data, into which the cost of the ancillary services is intrinsically packaged. The I/OCE conditionally packages payment for the ancillary services that are reported on the same date of service as critical care services in order to avoid overpayment. The payment status of the ancillary services does not change when they are not provided in conjunction with critical care services. Hospitals may use HCPCS modifier -59 to indicate when an ancillary procedure or service is distinct or independent from critical care when performed on the same day but in a different encounter.

Beginning January 1, 2007, critical care services will be paid at two levels, depending on the presence or absence of trauma activation. Providers will receive one payment rate for critical care without trauma activation and will receive additional payment when critical care is associated with trauma activation.

To determine whether trauma activation occurs, follow the National Uniform Billing Committee (NUBC) guidelines in the Claims Processing Manual, Pub 100-04, Chapter 25, §75.4 related to the reporting of the trauma revenue codes in the 68x series. The revenue code series 68x can be used only by trauma centers/hospitals as licensed or designated by the state or local government authority authorized to do so, or as verified by the American College of Surgeons. Different subcategory revenue codes are reported by designated Level 1-4 hospital trauma centers. Only patients for whom there has been prehospital notification based on triage information from prehospital caregivers, who meet either local, state or American College of Surgeons field triage criteria, or are delivered by inter-hospital transfers, and are given the appropriate team response can be billed a trauma activation charge.

When critical care services are provided without trauma activation, the hospital may bill CPT® code 99291, Critical care, evaluation and management of the critically ill or critically injured patient; first 30-74 minutes (and 99292, if appropriate). If trauma activation occurs under the circumstances described by the NUBC guidelines that would permit reporting a charge under 68x, the hospital may also bill one unit of code G0390, which describes trauma activation associated with hospital critical care services. Revenue code 68x must be reported on the same date of service. The OCE will edit to ensure that G0390 appears with revenue code 68x on the same date of service and that only one unit of G0390 is billed. CMS believes that trauma activation is a one-time occurrence in association with critical care services, and therefore, CMS will only pay for one unit of G0390 per day.

The CPT® code 99291 is defined by CPT® as the first 30-74 minutes of critical care. This 30 minute minimum has always applied under the OPPS. The CPT® code 99292, Critical care, evaluation and management of the critically ill or critically injured patient; each additional 30 minutes, remains a packaged service under the OPPS, so that hospitals do not have the ongoing administrative burden of reporting precisely the time for each critical service provided. As the CPT® guidelines indicate, hospitals that provide less than 30 minutes of critical care should bill for a visit, typically an emergency department visit, at a level consistent with their own internal guidelines.

Under the OPPS, the time that can be reported as critical care is the time spent by a physician and/or hospital staff engaged in active face-to-face critical care of a critically ill or critically injured patient. If the physician and hospital staff or multiple hospital staff members are simultaneously engaged in this active face-to-face care, the time involved can only be counted once.

- Beginning in CY 2007 hospitals may continue to report a charge with RC 68x without any HCPCS code when trauma team activation occurs. In order to receive additional payment when critical care services are associated with trauma activation, the hospital must report G0390 on the same date of service as RC 68x, in addition to CPT® code 99291 (or 99292, if appropriate.)

- Beginning in CY 2007 hospitals should continue to report 99291 (and 99292 as appropriate) for critical care services furnished without trauma team activation. CPT® 99291 maps to APC 0617 (Critical Care). (CPT® 99292 is packaged and not paid separately, but should be reported if provided.)

Critical care services are paid in some cases separately and in other cases as part of a composite APC payment.

Future updates will be issued in a Recurring Update Notification.

100-4, Chapter-4, 200.1

Billing for Corneal Tissue

Corneal tissue will be paid on a cost basis, not under OPPS. To receive cost based reimbursement hospitals must bill charges for corneal tissue using HCPCS code V2785.

100-4, Chapter-4, 200.2

Hospital Dialysis Services For Patients With and Without End Stage Renal Disease (ESRD)

Effective with claims with dates of service on or after August 1, 2000, hospital-based End Stage Renal Disease (ESRD) facilities must submit services covered under the ESRD benefit in 42 CFR 413.174 (maintenance dialysis and those items and services directly related to dialysis such as drugs, supplies) on a separate claim from services not covered under the ESRD benefit. Items and services not covered under the ESRD benefit must be billed by the hospital using the hospital bill type and be paid under the Outpatient Prospective Payment System (OPPS) (or to a CAH at reasonable cost). Services covered under the ESRD benefit in 42 CFR 413.174 must be billed on the ESRD bill type and must be paid under the ESRD PPS. This requirement is necessary to properly pay only unrelated ESRD services (those not covered under the ESRD benefit) under OPPS (or to a CAH at reasonable cost).

Medicare does not allow payment for routine or related dialysis treatments, which are covered and paid under the ESRD PPS, when furnished to ESRD patients in the outpatient department of a hospital. However, in certain medical situations in which the ESRD outpatient cannot obtain her or his regularly scheduled dialysis treatment at a certified ESRD facility, the OPPS rule for 2003 allows payment for non-routine dialysis treatments (which are not covered under the ESRD benefit) furnished to ESRD outpatients in the outpatient department of a hospital. Payment for unscheduled dialysis furnished to ESRD outpatients and paid under the OPPS is limited to the following circumstances:

- Dialysis performed following or in connection with a dialysis-related procedure such as vascular access procedure or blood transfusions;

- Dialysis performed following treatment for an unrelated medical emergency; e.g., if a patient goes to the emergency room for chest pains and misses a regularly scheduled dialysis treatment that cannot be rescheduled, CMS allows the hospital to provide and bill Medicare for the dialysis treatment; or

- Emergency dialysis for ESRD patients who would otherwise have to be admitted as inpatients in order for the hospital to receive payment.

In these situations, non-ESRD certified hospital outpatient facilities are to bill Medicare using the Healthcare Common Procedure Coding System (HCPCS) code G0257 (Unscheduled or emergency dialysis treatment for an ESRD patient in a hospital outpatient department that is not certified as an ESRD facility).

HCPCS code G0257 may only be reported on type of bill 13X (hospital outpatient service) or type of bill 85X (critical access hospital) because HCPCS code G0257 only reports services for hospital outpatients with ESRD and only these bill types are used to report services to hospital outpatients. Effective for services on and after October 1, 2012, claims containing HCPCS code G0257 will be returned to the provider for correction if G0257 is reported with a type of bill other than 13X or 85X (such as a 12x inpatient claim).

HCPCS code 90935 (Hemodialysis procedure with single physician evaluation) may be reported and paid only if one of the following two conditions is met:

1. The patient is a hospital inpatient with or without ESRD and has no coverage under Part A, but has Part B coverage. The charge for hemodialysis is a charge for the use of a prosthetic device. See Benefits Policy Manual 100-02 Chapter 15 section 120. A. The service must be reported on a type of bill 12X or type of bill 85X. See the Benefits Policy Manual 100-02 Chapter 6 section 10 (Medical and Other Health Services Furnished to Inpatients of Participating Hospitals) for the criteria that must be met for services to be paid when a hospital inpatient has Part B coverage but does not have coverage under Part A; or

2. A hospital outpatient does not have ESRD and is receiving hemodialysis in the hospital outpatient department. The service is reported on a type of bill 13X or type of bill 85X.

CPT® code 90945 (Dialysis procedure other than hemodialysis (e.g. peritoneal dialysis, hemofiltration, or other continuous replacement therapies)), with single physician evaluation, may be reported by a hospital paid under the OPPS or CAH method I or method II on type of bill 12X, 13X or 85X.

100-4, Chapter-4, 200.3.4

Billing for Linear Accelerator (Robotic Image-Guided and Non-Robotic Image-Guided) SRS Planning and Delivery

Effective for services furnished on or after January 1, 2006, hospitals must bill using existing CPT® codes that most accurately describe the service furnished for both robotic and non-robotic image-guided SRS planning. For robotic image-guided SRS delivery, hospitals must bill using HCPCS code

G0339 for the first session and HCPCS code G0340 for the second through the fifth sessions. For non-robotic image-guided SRS delivery, hospitals must bill G0173 for delivery if the delivery occurs in one session, and G0251 for delivery per session (not to exceed five sessions) if delivery occurs during multiple sessions.

Linear Accelerator-Based Robotic Image-Guided SRS	
Planning	Use existing CPT® codes
Delivery	G0339 (complete, 1st session) G0340 (2nd – 5th session)

Linear Accelerator-Based Non-Robotic Image-Guided SRS	
Planning	Use existing CPT® codes
Delivery	G0173 (single session) G0251 (multiple)

HCPCS Code	Long Descriptors
G0173	Linear accelerator based stereotactic radiosurgery, delivery including collimator changes and custom plugging, complete course of treatment in one session, all lesions.
G0251	Linear accelerator based stereotactic radiosurgery, delivery including collimator changes and custom plugging, fractionated treatment, all lesions, per session, maximum 5 sessions per course of treatment.
G0339	Image-guided robotic linear accelerator-based stereotactic radiosurgery, complete course of therapy in one session or first session of fractionated treatment.
G0340	Image-guided robotic linear accelerator-based stereotactic radiosurgery, delivery including collimator changes and custom plugging, fractionated treatment, all lesions, per session, second through fifth sessions, maximum five sessions per course of treatment.

100-4, Chapter-4, 200.4

Billing for Amniotic Membrane

Hospitals should report HCPCS code V2790 (Amniotic membrane for surgical reconstruction, per procedure) to report amniotic membrane tissue when the tissue is used. A specific procedure code associated with use of amniotic membrane tissue is CPT® code 65780 (Ocular surface reconstruction; amniotic membrane transplantation). Payment for the amniotic membrane tissue is packaged into payment for CPT® code 65780 or other procedures with which the amniotic membrane is used.

100-4, Chapter-4, 200.6

Billing and Payment for Alcohol and/or Substance Abuse Assessment and Intervention Services

For CY 2008, the CPT® Editorial Panel has created two new Category I CPT® codes for reporting alcohol and/or substance abuse screening and intervention services. They are CPT® code 99408 (Alcohol and/or substance (other than tobacco) abuse structured screening (e.g., AUDIT, DAST), and brief intervention (SBI) services; 15 to 30 minutes); and CPT® code 99409 (Alcohol and/or substance (other than tobacco) abuse structured screening (e.g., AUDIT, DAST), and brief intervention (SBI) services; greater than 30 minutes). However, screening services are not covered by Medicare without specific statutory authority, such as has been provided for mammography, diabetes, and

colorectal cancer screening. Therefore, beginning January 1, 2008, the OPPS recognizes two parallel G-codes (HCPCS codes G0396 and G0397) to allow for appropriate reporting and payment of alcohol and substance abuse structured assessment and intervention services that are not provided as screening services, but that are performed in the context of the diagnosis or treatment of illness or injury.

Contractors shall make payment under the OPPS for HCPCS code G0396 (Alcohol and/or substance (other than tobacco) abuse structured assessment (e.g., AUDIT, DAST) and brief intervention, 15 to 30 minutes) and HCPCS code G0397, (Alcohol and/or substance (other than tobacco) abuse structured assessment (e.g., AUDIT, DAST) and intervention greater than 30 minutes), only when reasonable and necessary (i.e., when the service is provided to evaluate patients with signs/symptoms of illness or injury) as per section 1862(a)(1)(A) of the Act.

HCPCS codes G0396 and G0397 are to be used for structured alcohol and/or substance (other than tobacco) abuse assessment and intervention services that are distinct from other clinic and emergency department visit services performed during the same encounter. Hospital resources expended performing services described by HCPCS codes G0396 and G0397 may not be counted as resources for determining the level of a visit service and vice versa (i.e., hospitals may not double count the same facility resources in order to reach a higher level clinic or emergency department visit). However, alcohol and/or substance structured assessment or intervention services lasting less than 15 minutes should not be reported using these HCPCS codes, but the hospital resources expended should be included in determining the level of the visit service reported.

100-4, Chapter-4, 200.7.2

Cardiac Echocardiography With Contrast

Hospitals are instructed to bill for echocardiograms with contrast using the applicable HCPCS code(s) included in Table 200.7.2 below. Hospitals should also report the appropriate units of the HCPCS codes for the contrast agents used in the performance of the echocardiograms.

Table 200.7.2 – HCPCS Codes For Echocardiograms With Contrast

HCPCS   Long Descriptor

C8921   Transthoracic echocardiography with contrast, or without contrast followed by with contrast, for congenital cardiac anomalies; complete

C8922   Transthoracic echocardiography with contrast, or without contrast followed by with contrast, for congenital cardiac anomalies; follow-up or limited study

C8923   Transthoracic echocardiography with contrast, or without contrast followed by with contrast, real-Time with image documentation (2D), includes M-mode recording, when performed, complete, without spectral or color Doppler echocardiography

C8924   Transthoracic echocardiography with contrast, or without contrast followed by with contrast, real-time with image documentation (2D), includes M-mode recording, when performed, follow-up or limited study

C8925   Transesophageal echocardiography (TEE) with contrast, or without contrast followed by with contrast, real time with image documentation (2D)

(with or without M-mode recording); including probe placement, image acquisition, interpretation and report

C8926   Transesophageal echocardiography (TEE) with contrast, or without contrast followed by with contrast, for congenital cardiac anomalies; including probe placement, image acquisition, interpretation and report

C8927   Transesophageal echocardiography (TEE) with contrast, or without contrast followed by with contrast, for monitoring purposes, including probe placement, real time 2-dimensional image acquisition and interpretation leading to ongoing (continuous) assessment of (dynamically changing) cardiac pumping function and to therapeutic measures on an immediate time basis

C8928   Transthoracic echocardiography with contrast, or without contrast followed by with contrast, real-time with image documentation (2D), includes M-mode recording, when performed, during rest and cardiovascular stress test using treadmill, bicycle exercise and/or pharmacologically induced stress, with interpretation and report

C8929   Transthoracic echocardiography with contrast, or without contrast followed by with contrast, real-time with image documentation (2D), includes M-mode recording, when performed, complete, with spectral Doppler echocardiography, and with color flow Doppler echocardiography

C8930   Transthoracic echocardiography, with contrast, or without contrast followed by with contrast, real-time with image documentation (2D), includes M-mode recording, when performed, during rest and cardiovascular stress test using treadmill, bicycle exercise and/or pharmacologically induced stress, with interpretation and report; including performance of continuous electrocardiographic monitoring, with physician supervision

100-4, Chapter-4, 230.2

Coding and Payment for Drug Administration

A. Overview

Drug administration services furnished under the Hospital Outpatient Prospective Payment System (OPPS) during CY 2005 were reported using CPT® codes 90780, 90781, and 96400-96459.

Effective January 1, 2006, some of these CPT® codes were replaced with more detailed CPT® codes incorporating specific procedural concepts, as defined and described by the CPT® manual, such as initial, concurrent, and sequential.

Hospitals are instructed to use the full set of CPT® codes, including those codes referencing concepts of initial, concurrent, and sequential, to bill for drug administration services furnished in the hospital outpatient department beginning January 1, 2007. In addition, hospitals are instructed to continue billing the HCPCS codes that most accurately describe the service(s) provided.

Hospitals are reminded to bill a separate Evaluation and Management code (with modifier 25) only if a significant, separately identifiable E/M service is performed in the same encounter with OPPS drug administration services.

B. Billing for Infusions and Injections

Beginning in CY 2007, hospitals were instructed to use the full set of drug administration CPT® codes (90760-90779; 96401-96549), (96413-96523 beginning in CY 2008) (96360-96549 beginning in CY 2009) when billing for drug administration services provided in the hospital outpatient department. In addition, hospitals are to continue to bill HCPCS code C8957 (Intravenous infusion for therapy/diagnosis; initiation of prolonged infusion (more than 8 hours), requiring use of portable or implantable pump) when appropriate. Hospitals are expected to report all drug administration CPT® codes in a manner consistent with their descriptors, CPT® instructions, and correct coding principles. Hospitals should note the conceptual changes between CY 2006 drug administration codes effective under the OPPS and the CPT® codes in effect beginning January 1, 2007, in order to ensure accurate billing under the OPPS. Hospitals should report all HCPCS codes that describe the drug administration services provided, regardless of whether or not those services are separately paid or their payment is packaged.

Medicare's general policy regarding physician supervision within hospital outpatient departments meets the physician supervision requirements for use of CPT® codes 90760-90779, 96401-96549, (96413-96523 beginning in CY 2008). (Reference: Pub.100-02, Medicare Benefit Policy Manual, Chapter 6, §20.4.)

Drug administration services are to be reported with a line item date of service on the day they are provided. In addition, only one initial drug administration service is to be reported per vascular access site per encounter, including during an encounter where observation services span more than 1 calendar day.

C. Payments For Drug Administration Services

For CY 2007, OPPS drug administration APCs were restructured, resulting in a six-level hierarchy where active HCPCS codes have been assigned according to their clinical coherence and resource use. Contrary to the CY 2006 payment structure that bundled payment for several instances of a type of service (non-chemotherapy, chemotherapy by infusion, non-infusion chemotherapy) into a per-encounter APC payment, structure introduced in CY 2007 provides a separate APC payment for each reported unit of a separately payable HCPCS code.

Hospitals should note that the transition to the full set of CPT® drug administration codes provides for conceptual differences when reporting, such as those noted below.

- In CY 2006, hospitals were instructed to bill for the first hour (and any additional hours) by each type of infusion service (non-chemotherapy, chemotherapy by infusion, non-infusion chemotherapy). Beginning in CY 2007, the first hour concept no longer exists. CPT® codes in CY 2007 and beyond allow for only one initial service per encounter, for each vascular access site, no matter how many types of infusion services are provided; however, hospitals will receive an APC payment for the initial service and separate APC payment(s) for additional hours of infusion or other drug administration services provided that are separately payable.

- In CY 2006, hospitals were instructed to bill for the first hour (and any additional hours) by each type of infusion service (non-chemotherapy, chemotherapy by infusion, non-infusion chemotherapy). Beginning in CY 2007, the first hour concept no longer exists. CPT® codes in CY 2007 and beyond allow for only one initial service per encounter, for each vascular access site, no matter how many types of infusion services are provided; however, hospitals will receive an APC payment for the initial service and separate APC payment(s) for additional hours of infusion or other drug administration services provided that are separately payable.

(NOTE: This list above provides a brief overview of a limited number of the conceptual changes between CY 2006 OPPS drug administration codes and CY 2007 OPPS drug administration codes - this list is not comprehensive and does not include all items hospitals will need to consider during this transition)

For APC payment rates, refer to the most current quarterly version of Addendum B on the CMS Web site at http://www. cms.hhs.gov/HospitalOutpatientPPS/.

D. Infusions Started Outside the Hospital

Hospitals may receive Medicare beneficiaries for outpatient services who are in the process of receiving an infusion at their time of arrival at the hospital (e.g., a patient who arrives via ambulance with an ongoing intravenous infusion initiated by paramedics during transport). Hospitals are reminded to bill for all services provided using the HCPCS code(s) that most accurately describe the service(s) they provided. This includes hospitals reporting an initial hour of infusion, even if the hospital did not initiate the infusion, and additional HCPCS codes for additional or sequential infusion services if needed.

1100-4, Chapter-4, 231.4

Billing for Split Unit of Blood

HCPCS code P9011 was created to identify situations where one unit of blood or a blood product is split and some portion of the unit is transfused to one patient and the other portions are transfused to other patients or to the same patient at other times. When a patient receives a transfusion of a split unit of blood or blood product, OPPS providers should bill P9011 for the blood product transfused, as well as CPT® 86985 (Splitting, blood products) for each splitting procedure performed to prepare the blood product for a specific patient.

Providers should bill split units of packed red cells and whole blood using Revenue Code 389 (Other blood), and should not use Revenue Codes 381 (Packed red cells) or 382 (Whole blood). Providers should bill split units of other blood products using the applicable revenue codes for the blood product type, such as 383 (Plasma) or 384 (Platelets), rather than 389. Reporting revenue codes according to these specifications will ensure the Medicare beneficiary's blood deductible is applied correctly

EXAMPLE: OPPS provider splits off a 100cc aliquot from a 250 cc unit of leukocyte-reduced red blood cells for a transfusion to Patient X. The hospital then splits off an 80cc aliquot of the remaining unit for a transfusion to Patient Y. At a later time, the remaining 70cc from the unit is transfused to Patient Z.

In billing for the services for Patient X and Patient Y, the OPPS provider should report the charges by billing P9011 and 86985 in addition to the CPT® code for the transfusion service, because a specific splitting service was required to prepare a split unit for transfusion to each of those patients. However, the OPPS provider should report only P9011 and the CPT® code for the transfusion service for Patient Z because no additional splitting was necessary to prepare the split unit for transfusion to Patient Z. The OPPS provider should bill Revenue Code 0389 for each split unit of the leukocyte-reduced red blood cells that was transfused.

100-4, Chapter-4, 240

Inpatient Part B Hospital Services

Medicare pays for hospital (including CAH) inpatient Part B services in the circumstances provided in Pub. 100-02, Medicare Benefit Policy Manual, Chapter 6, §10 ("Medical and Other Health Services Furnished to Inpatients of Participating Hospitals"). Hospitals must bill Part B inpatient services on a 12x Type of Bill. This Part B inpatient claim is subject to the statutory time limit for filing Part B claims described in chapter 1, §70 of this manual.

Inpatient Part B services include inpatient ancillary services that do not require an outpatient status and are not strictly provided in an outpatient setting. Services that require an outpatient status and are provided only in an outpatient setting are not payable inpatient Part B services, including Clinic Visits, Emergency Department Visits, and Observation Services (this is not a complete listing).

Inpatient routine services in a hospital generally are those services included by the provider in a daily service charge--sometimes referred to as the "Room and Board" charge. They include the regular room, dietary and nursing services, minor medical and surgical supplies, medical social services, psychiatric social services, and the use of certain equipment and facilities for which a separate charge is not customarily made to Medicare Part A. These services are never outpatient services, and therefore are not separately billable Inpatient Part B ancillary services. They include routine nursing services that are captured in the Room and Board rate (such as IV infusions and injections, blood administration, and nebulizer treatments), which are not separately billable Inpatient Part B ancillary services.

100-4, Chapter-4, 290.1

Observation Services Overview

Observation care is a well-defined set of specific, clinically appropriate services, which include ongoing short term treatment, assessment, and reassessment, that are furnished while a decision is being made regarding whether patients will require further treatment as hospital inpatients or if they are able to be discharged from the hospital. Observation services are commonly ordered for patients who present to the emergency department and who then require a significant period of treatment or monitoring in order to make a decision concerning their admission or discharge. Observation services are covered only when provided by the order of a physician or another individual authorized by State licensure law and hospital staff bylaws to admit patients to the hospital or to order outpatient services.

Observation services must also be reasonable and necessary to be covered by Medicare. In only rare and exceptional cases do reasonable and necessary outpatient observation services span more than 48 hours. In the majority of cases, the decision whether to discharge a patient from the hospital following resolution of the reason for the observation care or to admit the patient as an inpatient can be made in less than 48 hours,usually in less than 24 hours.

100-4, Chapter-4, 290.2.2

Reporting Hours of Observation

Observation time begins at the clock time documented in the patient's medical record, which coincides with the time that observation care is initiated in accordance with a physician's order. Hospitals should round to the nearest hour. For example, a patient who began receiving observation services at 3:03 p.m. according to the nurses' notes and was discharged to home at 9:45 p.m. when observation care and other outpatient services were completed, should have a "7" placed in the units field of the reported observation HCPCS code.

General standing orders for observation services following all outpatient surgery are not recognized. Hospitals should not report as observation care, services that are part of another Part B service, such as postoperative monitoring during a standard recovery period (e.g., 4-6 hours), which should be billed as recovery room services. Similarly, in the case of patients who undergo diagnostic testing in a hospital outpatient department, routine preparation services furnished prior to the testing and recovery afterwards are included in the payments for those diagnostic services.

Observation services should not be billed concurrently with diagnostic or therapeutic services for which active monitoring is a part of the procedure (e.g., colonoscopy, chemotherapy). In situations where such a procedure interrupts observation services, hospitals may determine the most appropriate way to account for this time. For example, a hospital may record for each period of observation services the beginning and ending times during the hospital outpatient encounter and add the length of time for the periods of observation services together to reach the total number of units reported on the claim for the hourly observation services HCPCS code G0378 (Hospital observation service, per hour). A hospital may also deduct the average length of time of the interrupting procedure, from the total duration of time that the patient receives observation services.

Observation time ends when all medically necessary services related to observation care are completed. For example, this could be before discharge when the need for observation has ended, but other medically necessary services not meeting the definition of observation care are provided (in which case, the additional medically necessary services would be billed separately or included as part of the emergency department or clinic visit). Alternatively, the end time of observation services may coincide with the time the patient is actually discharged from the hospital or admitted as an inpatient. Observation time may include medically necessary services and follow-up care provided after the time that the physician writes the discharge order, but before the patient is discharged. However, reported observation time would not include the time patients remain in the hospital after treatment is finished for reasons such as waiting for transportation home.

If a period of observation spans more than 1 calendar day, all of the hours for the entire period of observation must be included on a single line and the date of service for that line is the date that observation care begins.

100-4, Chapter-4, 290.4.1

Billing and Payment for All Hospital Observation Services Furnished Between January 1, 2006 and December 31, 2007

Since January 1, 2006, two G-codes have been used to report observation services and direct referral for observation care. For claims for dates of service January 1, 2006 through December 31, 2007, the Integrated Outpatient Code Editor (I/OCE) determines whether the observation care or direct referral services are packaged or separately payable. Thus, hospitals provide consistent coding and billing under all circumstances in which they deliver observation care.

Beginning January 1, 2006, hospitals should not report CPT® codes 99217-99220 or 99234-99236 for observation services. In addition, the following HCPCS codes were discontinued as of January 1, 2006: G0244 (Observation care by facility to patient), G0263 (Direct Admission with congestive heart failure, chest pain or asthma), and G0264 (Assessment other than congestive heart failure, chest pain, or asthma).

The three discontinued G-codes and the CPT® codes that were no longer recognized were replaced by two new G-codes to be used by hospitals to report all observation services, whether separately payable or packaged, and direct referral for observation care, whether separately payable or packaged:

- G0378- Hospital observation service, per hour; and
- G0379- Direct admission of patient for hospital observation care.

The I/OCE determines whether observation services billed as units of G0378 are separately payable under APC 0339 (Observation) or whether payment for observation services will be packaged into the payment for other services provided by the hospital in the same encounter. Therefore, hospitals should bill HCPCS code G0378 when observation services are ordered and provided to any patient regardless of the patient's condition. The units of service should equal the number of hours the patient receives observation services.

Hospitals should report G0379 when observation services are the result of a direct referral for observation care without an associated emergency room visit, hospital outpatient clinic visit, critical care service, or hospital outpatient surgical procedure (status indicator T procedure) on the day of initiation of observation services. Hospitals should only report HCPCS code G0379 when a patient is referred directly for observation care after being seen by a physician in the community (see §290.4.2 below)

Some non-repetitive OPPS services provided on the same day by a hospital may be billed on different claims, provided that all charges associated with each procedure or service being reported are billed on the same claim with the HCPCS code which describes that service. See chapter 1, section 50.2.2 of this manual. It is vitally important that all of the charges that pertain to a non-repetitive, separately paid procedure or service be reported on the same claim with that procedure or service. It should also be emphasized that this relaxation of same day billing requirements for some non-repetitive services does not apply to non-repetitive services provided on the same day as either direct referral to observation care or observation services because the OCE claim-by-claim logic cannot function properly unless all services related to the episode of observation care, including diagnostic tests, lab services, hospital clinic visits, emergency department visits, critical care services, and status indicator T procedures, are reported on the same claim. Additional guidance can be found in chapter 1, section 50.2.2 of this manual.

100-4, Chapter-4, 290.4.2

Separate and Packaged Payment for Direct Referral for Observation Services Furnished Between January 1, 2006 and December 31, 2007

In order to receive separate payment for a direct referral for observation care (APC 0604), the claim must show:

1. Both HCPCS codes G0378 (Hourly Observation) and G0379 (Direct Admit to Observation) with the same date of service;

2. That no services with a status indicator T or V or Critical care (APC 0617) were provided on the same day of service as HCPCS code G0379; and

3. The observation care does not qualify for separate payment under APC 0339.

Only a direct referral for observation services billed on a 13X bill type may be considered for a separate APC payment.

Separate payment is not allowed for HCPCS code G0379, direct admission to observation care, when billed with the same date of service as a hospital clinic visit, emergency room visit, critical care service, or "T" status procedure.

If a bill for the direct referral for observation services does not meet the three requirements listed above, then payment for the direct referral service will be packaged into payments for other separately payable services provided to the beneficiary in the same encounter.

100-4, Chapter-4, 290.4.3

Separate and Packaged Payment for Observation Services Furnished Between January 1, 2006 and December 31, 2007

Separate payment may be made for observation services provided to a patient with congestive heart failure, chest pain, or asthma. The list of ICD-9-CM diagnosis codes eligible for separate payment is reviewed annually. Any changes in applicable ICD-9-CM diagnosis codes are included in the October quarterly update of the OPPS and also published in the annual OPPS Final Rule. The list of qualifying ICD-9-CM diagnosis codes is also published on the OPPS Web page.

All of the following requirements must be met in order for a hospital to receive a separate APC payment for observation services through APC 0339:

1. Diagnosis Requirements
   a. The beneficiary must have one of three medical conditions: congestive heart failure, chest pain, or asthma.
   b. Qualifying ICD-9-CM diagnosis codes must be reported in Form Locator (FL) 76, Patient Reason for Visit, or FL 67, principal diagnosis, or both in order for the hospital to receive separate payment for APC 0339. If a qualifying ICD-9-CM diagnosis code(s) is reported in the secondary diagnosis field, but is not reported in either the Patient Reason for Visit field (FL 76) or in the principal diagnosis field (FL 67), separate payment for APC 0339 is not allowed.

2. Observation Time
   a. Observation time must be documented in the medical record.
   b. Hospital billing for observation services begins at the clock time documented in the patient's medical record, which coincides with the time that observation services are initiated in accordance with a physician's order for observation services.
   c. A beneficiary's time receiving observation services (and hospital billing) ends when all clinical or medical interventions have been completed, including follow-up care furnished by hospital staff and physicians that may take place after a physician has ordered the patient be released or admitted as an inpatient.
   d. The number of units reported with HCPCS code G0378 must equal or exceed 8 hours.

3. Additional Hospital Services
   a. The claim for observation services must include one of the following services in addition to the reported observation services. The additional services listed below must have a line item date of service on the same day or the day before the date reported for observation:
      - An emergency department visit (APC 0609, 0613, 0614, 0615, 0616) or
      - A clinic visit (APC 0604, 0605, 0606, 0607, 0608); or
      - Critical care (APC 0617); or
      - Direct referral for observation care reported with HCPCS code G0379 (APC 0604); must be reported on the same date of service as the date reported for observation services.
   b. No procedure with a T status indicator can be reported on the same day or day before observation care is provided.

4. Physician Evaluation
   a. The beneficiary must be in the care of a physician during the period of observation, as documented in the medical record by outpatient registration, discharge, and other appropriate progress notes that are timed, written, and signed by the physician.
   b. The medical record must include documentation that the physician explicitly assessed patient risk to determine that the beneficiary would benefit from observation care.

Only observation services that are billed on a 13X bill type may be considered for a separate APC payment.

Hospitals should bill all of the other services associated with the observation care, including direct referral for observation, hospital clinic visits, emergency room visits, critical care services, and T status procedures, on the same claim so that the claims processing logic may appropriately determine the payment status (either packaged or separately payable) of HCPCS codes G0378 and G0379.

If a bill for observation care does not meet all of the requirements listed above, then payment for the observation care will be packaged into payments for other separately payable services provided to the beneficiary in the same encounter.

100-4, Chapter-4, 290.5.1

Billing and Payment for Observation Services Beginning January 1, 2008

Observation services are reported using HCPCS code G0378 (Hospital observation service, per hour). Beginning January 1, 2008, HCPCS code G0378 for hourly observation services is assigned status indicator N, signifying that its payment is always packaged. No separate payment is made for observation services reported with HCPCS code G0378, and APC 0339 is deleted as of January 1, 2008. In most circumstances, observation services are supportive and ancillary to the other services provided to a patient. Beginning January 1, 2014, in certain circumstances when observation care is billed in conjunction with a clinic visit, high level Type A emergency department visit (Level 4 or 5), high level Type B emergency department visit (Level 5), critical care services, or a direct referral as an integral part of a patient's extended encounter of care, payment may be made for the entire extended care encounter through APC 8009 (Extended Assessment and Management Composite) when certain criteria are met. Prior to January 1, 2014, in certain circumstances when observation care was billed in conjunction with a high level clinic visit (Level 5), high level Type A emergency department visit (Level 4 or 5), high level Type B emergency department visit (Level 5), critical care services, or a direct referral as an integral part of a patient's extended encounter of care, payment could be made for the entire extended care encounter through one of two composite APCs (APCs 8002 and 8003) when certain criteria were met. APCs 8002 and 8003 are deleted as of January 1, 2014. For information about payment for extended assessment and management composite APC, see §10.2.1 (Composite APCs) of this chapter.

There is no limitation on diagnosis for payment of APC 8009; however, composite APC payment will not be made when observation services are reported in association with a surgical procedure (T status procedure) or the hours of observation care reported are less than 8. The I/OCE evaluates every claim received to determine if payment through a composite APC is appropriate. If payment through a composite APC is inappropriate, the I/OCE, in conjunction with the Pricer, determines the appropriate status indicator, APC, and payment for every code on a claim.

All of the following requirements must be met in order for a hospital to receive an APC payment for an extended assessment and management composite APC:

1. Observation Time
   a. Observation time must be documented in the medical record.
   b. Hospital billing for observation services begins at the clock time documented in the patient's medical record, which coincides with the time that observation services are initiated in accordance with a physician's order for observation services.
   c. A beneficiary's time receiving observation services (and hospital billing) ends when all clinical or medical interventions have been completed, including follow-up care furnished by hospital staff and physicians that may take place after a physician has ordered the patient be released or admitted as an inpatient.
   d. The number of units reported with HCPCS code G0378 must equal or exceed 8 hours.
2. Additional Hospital Services
   a. The claim for observation services must include one of the following services in addition to the reported observation services. The additional services listed below must have a line item date of service on the same day or the day before the date reported for observation:
      - A Type A or B emergency department visit (CPT® codes 99284 or 99285 or HCPCS code G0384); or
      - A clinic visit (HCPCS code G0463 beginning January 1, 2014; CPT® code 99205 or 99215 prior to January 1, 2014); or
      - Critical care (CPT® code 99291); or
      - Direct referral for observation care reported with HCPCS code G0379 (APC 0633) must be reported on the same date of service as the date reported for observation services.
   b. No procedure with a T status indicator can be reported on the same day or day before observation care is provided.

3. Physician Evaluation.
   a. The beneficiary must be in the care of a physician during the period of observation, as documented in the medical record by outpatient registration, discharge, and other appropriate progress notes that are timed, written, and signed by the physician.
   b. The medical record must include documentation that the physician explicitly assessed patient risk to determine that the beneficiary would benefit from observation care.

Criteria 1 and 3 related to observation care beginning and ending time and physician evaluation apply regardless of whether the hospital believes that the criteria will be met for payment of the extended encounter through extended assessment and management composite payment.

Only visits, critical care and observation services that are billed on a 13X bill type may be considered for a composite APC payment.

Non-repetitive services provided on the same day as either direct referral for observation care or observation services must be reported on the same claim because the OCE claim-by-claim logic cannot function properly unless all services related to the episode of observation care, including hospital clinic visits, emergency department visits, critical care services, and T status procedures, are reported on the same claim. Additional guidance can be found in chapter 1, section 50.2.2 of this manual.

If a claim for services provided during an extended assessment and management encounter including observation care does not meet all of the requirements listed above, then the usual APC logic will apply to separately payable items and services on the claim; the special logic for direct admission will apply, and payment for the observation care will be packaged into payments for other separately payable services provided to the beneficiary in the same encounter.

100-4, Chapter-4, 290.5.2

Billing and Payment for Direct Referral for Observation Care Furnished Beginning January 1, 2008

Direct referral for observation is reported using HCPCS code G0379 (Direct referral for hospital observation care). : Prior to January 1, 2010, the code descriptor for HCPCS code G0379 was (Direct admission of patient for hospital observation care). Hospitals should report G0379 when observation services are the result of a direct referral for observation care without an associated emergency room visit, hospital outpatient clinic visit, or critical care service on the day of initiation of observation services. Hospitals should only report HCPCS code G0379 when a patient is referred directly to observation care after being seen by a physician in the community.

Payment for direct referral for observation care will be made either separately as a low level hospital clinic visit under APC 0633 (Level 3 Examinations & Related Services) or packaged into payment for composite APC 8009 (Extended Assessment and Management Composite) or packaged into the payment for other separately payable services provided in the same encounter. For information about payment for extended assessment and management composite APCs, see, §10.2.1 (Composite APCs) of this chapter.

The criteria for payment of HCPCS code G0379 under either APC 0633 or APC 8009 include:

1. Both HCPCS codes G0378 (Hospital observation services, per hr.) and G0379 (Direct referral for hospital observation care) are reported with the same date of service.
2. No service with a status indicator of T or V or Critical Care (APC 0617) is provided on the same day of service as HCPCS code G0379.

If either of the above criteria is not met, HCPCS code G0379 will be assigned status indicator N and will be packaged into payment for other separately payable services provided in the same encounter.

Only a direct referral for observation services billed on a 13X bill type may be considered for a composite APC payment.

100-4, Chapter-4, 300.6

Common Working File (CWF) Edits

The CWF edit will allow 3 hours of therapy for MNT in the initial calendar year. The edit will allow more than 3 hours of therapy if there is a change in the beneficiary's medical condition, diagnosis, or treatment regimen and this change must be documented in the beneficiary's medical record. Two new G codes have been created for use when a beneficiary receives a second referral in a calendar year that allows the beneficiary to receive more than 3 hours of therapy. Another edit will allow 2 hours of follow up MNT with another referral in subsequent years.

Advance Beneficiary Notice (ABN)

The beneficiary is liable for services denied over the limited number of hours with referrals for MNT. An ABN should be issued in these situations. In absence of evidence of a valid ABN, the provider will be held liable.

An ABN should not be issued for Medicare-covered services such as those provided by hospital dietitians or nutrition professionals who are qualified to render the service in their state but who have not obtained Medicare provider numbers.

Duplicate Edits

Although beneficiaries are allowed to receive training and therapy during the same time period Diabetes Self-Management and Training (DSMT) and Medical Nutrition Therapy (MNT) services may not be provided on the same day to the same beneficiary. Effective April 1, 2010 CWF shall implement a new duplicate crossover edit to identify and prevent claims for DSMT/MNT services from being billed with the same dates of services for the same beneficiaries submitted from institutional providers and from a professional provider.

100-4, Chapter-4, 320

Outpatient Intravenous Insulin Treatment (OIVIT)

Effective for claims with dates of service on and after December 23, 2009, the Centers for Medicare and Medicaid Services (CMS) determines that the evidence does not support a conclusion that OIVIT improves health outcomes in Medicare beneficiaries. Therefore, CMS has determined that OIVIT is not reasonable and necessary for any indication under section 1862(a)(1)(A) of the Social Security Act. Services comprising an OIVIT regimen are nationally non-covered under Medicare when furnished pursuant to an OIVIT regimen.

See Pub. 100-03, Medicare National Coverage Determinations Manual, Section 40.7, Outpatient Intravenous Insulin

Treatment (Effective December 23, 2009), for general information and coverage indications.

100-4, Chapter-4, 320.1

HCPCS Coding for OIVIT

HCPCS code G9147, effective with the April IOCE and MPFSDB updates, is to be used on claims with dates of service on and after December 23, 2009, billing for non-covered OIVIT and any services comprising an OIVIT regimen.

NOTE: HCPCS codes 99199 or 94681(with or without diabetes related conditions 250.00-250.93) are not to be used on claims billing for non-covered OIVIT and any services comprising an OIVIT regimen when furnished pursuant to an OIVIT regimen. Claims billing for HCPCS codes 99199 and 94681 for non-covered OIVIT are to be returned to provider/returned as unprocessable.

100-4, Chapter-4, 320.2

Medicare Summary Notices (MSN), Reason Codes, and Remark Codes

When returning non-covered OIVIT claims billed with HCPCS 99199 to provider/returning as unprocessable, contractors shall use:

Claims Adjustment Reason Code (CARC) 189: NOS or unlisted procedure code (CPT®/HCPCS) was billed when there is a specific procedure code for this procedure/service,

Remittance Advice Remark Code (RARC) N56: The procedure code billed is not correct/valid for the services billed or the date of service billed, and,

RARC MA66: Missing/incomplete/invalid principal procedure code.

When returning non-covered OIVIT claims billed with HCPCS 94681 with or without diabetes-related conditions 250-00-250.93 to provider/returning as unprocessable, contractors shall use:

CARC 11: The diagnosis is inconsistent with the procedure,

RARC N56: The procedure code billed is not correct/valid for the services billed or the date of service billed, and,

RARC MA66: Missing/incomplete/invalid principal procedure code.

When denying claims for non-covered OIVIT and any services comprising an OIVIT regimen billed with HCPCS code G9147, contractors shall use:

MSN 16.10 - Medicare does not pay for these item(s) or service(s),

CARC 96: Non-covered charge(s),

CARC M51: Missing/Incomplete /Invalid Procedure Code(s), and,

RARC N386: This decision was based on an NCD. An NCD provides a coverage determination as to whether a particular item or service is covered. A copy of this policy is available at http://www.cms.hhs.gov/mcd/search.asp. If you do not have Web access, you may contact the contractor to request a copy of the NCD.

100-4, Chapter-5, 10.2

The Financial Limitation

A. Legislation on Limitations

The dollar amount of the limitations (caps) on outpatient therapy services is established by statute. The updated amount of the caps is released annually via Recurring Update Notifications and posted on the CMS Website www.cms.gov/TherapyServices, on contractor Websites, and on each beneficiary's Medicare Summary Notice. Medicare contractors shall publish the financial limitation amount in educational articles. It is also available at 1-800-Medicare.

Section 4541(a)(2) of the Balanced Budget Act (BBA) (P.L. 105-33) of 1997, which added §1834(k)(5) to the Act, required payment under a prospective payment system (PPS) for outpatient rehabilitation services (except those furnished by or under arrangements with a hospital). Outpatient rehabilitation services include the following services:

- Physical therapy
- Speech-language pathology; and
- Occupational therapy.

Section 4541(c) of the BBA required application of financial limitations to all outpatient rehabilitation services (except those furnished by or under arrangements with a hospital). In 1999, an annual per beneficiary limit of $1,500 was applied, including all outpatient physical therapy services and speech-language pathology services. A separate limit applied to all occupational therapy services. The limits were based on incurred expenses and included applicable deductible and coinsurance. The BBA provided that the limits be indexed by the Medicare Economic Index (MEI) each year beginning in 2002.

Since the limitations apply to outpatient services, they do not apply to skilled nursing facility (SNF) residents in a covered Part A stay, including patients occupying swing beds. Rehabilitation services are included within the global Part A per diem payment that the SNF receives under the prospective payment system (PPS) for the covered stay. Also, limitations do not apply to any therapy services covered under prospective payment systems for home health or inpatient hospitals, including critical access hospitals.

The limitation is based on therapy services the Medicare beneficiary receives, not the type of practitioner who provides the service. Physical therapists, speech-language pathologists, and occupational therapists, as well as physicians and certain nonphysician practitioners, could render a therapy service.

B. Moratoria and Exceptions for Therapy Claims

Since the creation of therapy caps, Congress has enacted several moratoria. The Deficit Reduction Act of 2005 directed CMS to develop exceptions to therapy caps for calendar year 2006 and the exceptions have been extended periodically. The cap exception for therapy services billed by outpatient hospitals was part of the original legislation and applies as long as caps are in effect. Exceptions to caps based on the medical necessity of the service are in effect only when Congress legislates the exceptions.

100-4, Chapter-5, 10.6

Functional Reporting

A. General

Section 3005(g) of the Middle Class Tax Relief and Jobs Creation Act (MCTRJCA) amended Section 1833(g) of the Act to require a claims-based data collection system for outpatient therapy services, including physical therapy (PT), occupational therapy (OT) and speech-language pathology (SLP) services. 42 CFR 410.59, 410.60, 410.61, 410.62 and 410.105 implement this requirement. The system will collect data on beneficiary function during the course of therapy services in order to better understand beneficiary conditions, outcomes, and expenditures.

Beneficiary unction information is reported using 42 nonpayable functional G-codes and seven severity/complexity modifiers on claims for PT, OT, and SLP services. Functional reporting on one functional limitation at a time is required periodically throughout an entire PT, OT, or SLP therapy episode of care.

The nonpayable G-codes and severity modifiers provide information about the beneficiary's functional status at the outset of the therapy episode of care, including projected goal status, at specified points during treatment, and at the time of discharge. These G-codes, along with the associated modifiers, are required at specified intervals on all claims for outpatient therapy services –not just those over the cap.

B. Application of New Coding Requirements

This functional data reporting and collection system is effective for therapy services with dates of service on and after January 1, 2013. A testing period will be in effect from January 1, 2013, until July 1, 2013, to allow providers and practitioners to use the new coding requirements to assure that systems work. Claims for therapy services furnished on and after July 1,2013, that do not contain the required functional G-code/modifier information will be returned or rejected, as applicable.

C. Services Affected

These requirements apply to all claims for services furnished under the Medicare Part B outpatient therapy benefit and the PT, OT, and SLP services furnished under the CORF benefit. They also apply to the therapy services furnished personally by and incident to the service of a physician or a nonphysician practitioner (NPP), including a nurse practitioner (NP), a certified nurse specialist (CNS), or a physician assistant (PA), as applicable.

D. Providers and Practitioners Affected.

The functional reporting requirements apply to the therapy services furnished by the following providers: hospitals, CAHs, SNFs, CORFs, rehabilitation agencies, and HHAs (when the beneficiary is not under a home health plan of care). It applies to the following practitioners: physical therapists, occupational therapists, and speech-language pathologists in private practice (TPPs), physicians, and NPPs as noted above. The term "clinician" is applied to these practitioners throughout this manual section. (See definition section of Pub. 100-02, Chapter 15, section 220.)

E. Function-related G-codes

There are 42 functional G-codes, 14 sets of three codes each. Six of the G-code sets are generally for PT and OT functional limitations and eight sets of G-codes are for SLP functional limitations.

The following G-codes are for functional limitations typically seen in beneficiaries receiving PT or OT services. The first four of these sets describe categories of functional limitations and the final two sets describe "other" functional limitations, which are to be used for functional limitations not described by one of the four categories.

NONPAYABLE G-CODES FOR FUNCTIONAL LIMITATIONS		
Long Descriptor		**Short Descriptor**
Mobility G-code Set		
G8978	Mobility: walking & moving around functional limitation, current status, at therapy episode outset and at reporting intervals	Mobility current status
G8979	Mobility: walking & moving around functional limitation, projected goal status, at therapy episode outset, at reporting intervals, and at discharge or to end reporting	Mobility goal status
G8980	Mobility: walking & moving around functional limitation, discharge status, at discharge from therapy or to end reporting	Mobility D/C status
Changing & Maintaining Body Position G-code Set		
G8981	Changing & maintaining body position functional limitation, current status, at therapy episode outset and at reporting intervals	Body pos current status end reporting
G8982	Changing & maintaining body position functional limitation, projected goal status, at therapy episode outset, at reporting intervals, and at discharge or to end reporting	Body pos goal status
G8983	Changing & maintaining body position functional limitation, discharge status, at discharge from therapy or to end reporting	Body pos D/C status
Carrying, Moving & Handling Objects G-code Set		
G8984	Carrying, moving & handling objects functional limitation, current status, at therapy episode outset and at reporting intervals	Carry current status
G8985	Carrying, moving & handling objects functional limitation, projected goal status, at therapy episode outset, at reporting intervals, and at discharge or to end reporting	Carry goal status
G8986	Carrying, moving & handling objects functional limitation, discharge status, at discharge from therapy or to end reporting	Carry D/C status
Self Care G-code Set		
G8987	Self care functional limitation, current status, at therapy episode outset and at reporting intervals	Self care current status
G8988	Self care functional limitation, projected goal status, at therapy episode outset, at reporting intervals, and at discharge or to end reporting	Self care goal status
G8989	Self care functional limitation, discharge status, at discharge from therapy or to end reporting	Self care D/C status

The following "other PT/OT" functional G-codes are used to report:

- a beneficiary's functional limitation that is not defined by one of the above four categories;
- a beneficiary whose therapy services are not intended to treat a functional limitation;
- or a beneficiary's functional limitation when an overall, composite or other score from a functional assessment too is used and it does not clearly represent a functional limitation defined by one of the above four code sets.

	Long Descriptor	**Short Descriptor**
Other PT/OT Primary G-code Set		
G8990	Other physical or occupational therapy primary functional limitation, current status, at therapy episode outset and at reporting intervals	Other PT/OT current status
G8991	Other physical or occupational therapy primary functional limitation, projected goal status, at therapy episode outset, at reporting intervals, and at discharge or to end reporting	Other PT/OT goal status
G8992	Other physical or occupational therapy primary functional limitation, discharge status, at discharge from therapy or to end reporting	Other PT/OT D/C status

The following G-codes are for functional limitations typically seen in beneficiaries receiving SLP services. Seven are for specific functional communication measures, which are modeled after the National Outcomes Measurement System (NOMS), and one is for any "other" measure not described by one of the other seven.

	Long Descriptor	**Short Descriptor**
Swallowing G-code Set		
G8996	Swallowing functional limitation, current status, at therapy episode outset and at reporting intervals	Swallow current status
G8997	Swallowing functional limitation, projected goal status, at therapy episode outset, at reporting intervals, and at discharge or to end reporting	Swallow goal status
G8998	Swallowing functional limitation, discharge status, at discharge from therapy or to end reporting	Swallow D/C status
Motor Speech G-code Set **(Note: These codes are not sequentially numbered)**		
G8999	Motor speech functional limitation, current status, at therapy episode outset and at reporting intervals	Motor speech current status
G9186	Motor speech functional limitation, projected goal status at therapy episode outset, at reporting intervals, and at discharge or to end reporting	Motor speech goal status
G9158	Motor speech functional limitation, discharge status, at discharge from therapy or to end reporting	Motor speech D/C status
Spoken Language Comprehension G-code Set		
G9159	Spoken language comprehension functional limitation, current status, at therapy episode outset and at reporting intervals	Lang comp current status
G9160	Spoken language comprehension functional limitation, projected goal status, at therapy episode outset, at reporting intervals, and at discharge or to end reporting	Lang comp goal status
G9161	Spoken language comprehension functional limitation, discharge status, at discharge from therapy or to end reporting	Lang comp D/C status

Spoken Language Expressive G-code Set		
G9162	Spoken language expression functional limitation, current status, at therapy episode outset and at reporting intervals	Lang express current status
G9163	Spoken language expression functional limitation, projected goal status, at therapy episode outset, at reporting intervals, and at discharge or to end reporting	Lang press goal status
G9164	Spoken language expression functional limitation, discharge status, at discharge from therapy or to end reporting	Lang express D/C status
Attention G-code Set		
G9165	Attention functional limitation, current status, at therapy episode outset and at reporting intervals	Atten current status
G9166	Attention functional limitation, projected goal status, at therapy episode outset, at reporting intervals, and at discharge or to end reporting	Atten goal status
G9167	Attention functional limitation, discharge status, at discharge from therapy or to end reporting	Atten D/C status
Memory G-code Set		
G9168	Memory functional limitation, current status, at therapy episode outset and at reporting intervals	Memory current status
G9169	Memory functional limitation, projected goal status, at therapy episode outset, at reporting intervals, and at discharge or to end reporting	Memory goal status
G9170	Memory functional limitation, discharge status, at discharge from therapy or to end reporting	Memory D/C status
Voice G-code Set		
G9171	Voice functional limitation, current status, at therapy episode outset and at reporting intervals	Voice current status
G9172	Voice functional limitation, projected goal status, at therapy episode outset, at reporting intervals, and at discharge or to end reporting	Voice goal status
G9173	Voice functional limitation, discharge status, at discharge from therapy or to end reporting	Voice D/C status
G9162	Spoken language expression functional limitation, current status, at therapy episode outset and at reporting intervals	Lang express current status
G9163	Spoken language expression functional limitation, projected goal status, at therapy episode outset, at reporting intervals, and at discharge or to end reporting	Lang press goal status
G9164	Spoken language expression functional limitation, discharge status, at discharge from therapy or to end reporting	Lang express D/C status
Attention G-code Set		
G9165	Attention functional limitation, current status, at therapy episode outset and at reporting intervals	Atten current status
G9166	Attention functional limitation, projected goal status, at therapy episode outset, at reporting intervals, and at discharge or to end reporting	Atten goal status
G9167	Attention functional limitation, discharge status, at discharge from therapy or to end reporting	Atten D/C status

Memory G-code Set		
G9168	Memory functional limitation, current status, at therapy episode outset and at reporting intervals	Memory current status
G9169	Memory functional limitation, projected goal status, at therapy episode outset, at reporting intervals, and at discharge or to end reporting	Memory goal status
G9170	Memory functional limitation, discharge status, at discharge from therapy or to end reporting	Memory D/C status
Voice G-code Set		
G9171	Voice functional limitation, current status, at therapy episode outset and at reporting intervals	Voice current status
G9172	Voice functional limitation, projected goal status, at therapy episode outset, at reporting intervals, and at discharge or to end reporting	Voice goal status
G9173	Voice functional limitation, discharge status, at discharge from therapy or to end reporting	Voice D/C status

The following "other SLP" G-code set is used to report:

- on one of the other eight NOMS-defined functional measures not described by the above code sets; or
- to report an overall, composite or other score from assessment tool that does not clearly represent one of the above seven categorical SLP functional measures.

	Long Descriptor	Short Descriptor
Other Speech Language Pathology G-code Set		
G9174	Other speech language pathology functional limitation, current status, at therapy episode outset and at reporting intervals	Speech lang current
G9175	Other speech language pathology functional limitation, projected goal status, at therapy episode outset, at reporting intervals, and at discharge or to end reporting	Speech lang goal status
G9176	Other speech language pathology functional limitation, discharge status, at discharge from therapy or to end reporting	Speech lang D/C status

F. Severity/Complexity Modifiers

For each nonpayable functional G-code, one of the modifiers listed below must be used to report the severity/complexity for that functional limitation.

Modifier	Impairment Limitation Restriction
CH	0 percent impaired, limited or restricted
CI	At least 1 percent but less than 20 percent impaired, limited or restricted
CJ	At least 20 percent but less than 40 percent impaired, limited or restricted
CK	At least 40 percent but less than 60 percent impaired, limited or restricted
CL	At least 60 percent but less than 80 percent impaired, limited or restricted
CM	At least 80 percent but less than 100 percent impaired, limited or restricted
CN	100 percent impaired, limited or restricted

The severity modifiers reflect the beneficiary's percentage of functional impairment as determined by the clinician furnishing the therapy services.

G. Required Reporting of Functional G-codes and Severity Modifiers

The functional G-codes and severity modifiers listed above are used in the required reporting on therapy claims at certain specified points during therapy episodes of care. Claims containing these functional G-codes must also contain another billable and separately payable (non-bundled) service. Only one functional limitation shall be reported at a given time for each related therapy plan of care (POC).

Functional reporting using the G-codes and corresponding severity modifiers is required reporting on specified therapy claims. Specifically, they are required on claims:

- At the outset of a therapy episode of care (i.e., on the claim for the date of service (DOS) of the initial therapy service);
- At least once every 10 treatment days, which corresponds with the progress reporting period;
- When an evaluative procedure, including a re-evaluative one, (HCPCS/CPT® codes 92521, 92522, 92523, 92524, 92597, 92607, 92608, 92610, 92611, 92612, 92614, 92616, 96105, 96125, 97001, 97002, 97003, 97004) is furnished and billed;
- At the time of discharge from the therapy episode of care–(i.e., on the date services related to the discharge [progress] report are furnished); and
- At the time reporting of a particular functional limitation is ended in cases where the need for further therapy is necessary.
- At the time reporting is begun for a new or different functional limitation within the same episode of care (i.e., after the reporting of the prior functional limitation is ended)

Functional reporting is required on claims throughout the entire episode of care. When the beneficiary has reached his or her goal or progress has been maximized on the initially selected functional limitation, but the need for treatment continues, reporting is required for a second functional limitation using another set of G-codes. In these situations two or more functional limitations will be reported for a beneficiary during the therapy episode of care. Thus, reporting on more than one functional limitation may be required for some beneficiaries but not simultaneously.

When the beneficiary stops coming to therapy prior to discharge, the clinician should report the functional information on the last claim. If the clinician is unaware that the beneficiary is not returning for therapy until after the last claim is submitted, the clinician cannot report the discharge status.

When functional reporting is required on a claim for therapy services, two G-codes will generally be required.

Two exceptions exist:

1. Therapy services under more than one therapy POC-- Claims may contain more than two nonpayable functional G-codes when in cases where a beneficiary receives therapy services under multiple POCs (PT, OT, and/or SLP) from the same therapy provider.

2. One-Time Therapy Visit--When a beneficiary is seen and future therapy services are either not medically indicated or are going to be furnished by another provider, the clinician reports on the claim for the DOS of the visit, all three G-codes in the appropriate code set (current status, goal status and discharge status), along with corresponding severity modifiers.

Each reported functional G-code must also contain the following line of service information:

- Functional severity modifier

- Therapy modifier indicating the related discipline/ POC -- GP, GO or GN --for PT, OT, and SLP services, respectively
- Date of the related therapy service
- Nominal charge, e.g., a penny, for institutional claims submitted to the FIs and A/MACs. For professional claims, a zero charge is acceptable for the service line. If provider billing software requires an amount for professional claims, a nominal charge, e.g., a penny, may be included.

NOTE: The KX modifier is not required on the claim line for nonpayable G-codes, but would be required with the procedure code for medically necessary therapy services furnished once the beneficiary's annual cap has been reached.

The following example demonstrates how the G-codes and modifiers are used. In this example, the clinician determines that the beneficiary's mobility restriction is the most clinically relevant functional limitation and selects the Mobility G-code set (G8978 – G8980) to represent the beneficiary's functional limitation. The clinician also determines the severity/complexity of the beneficiary's functional limitation and selects the appropriate modifier. In this example, the clinician determines that the beneficiary has a 75 percent mobility restriction for which the CL modifier is applicable. The clinician expects that at the end of therapy the beneficiaries will have only a 15 percent mobility restriction for which the CI modifier is applicable. When the beneficiary attains the mobility goal, therapy continues to be medically necessary to address a functional limitation for hich there is no categorical G-code. The clinician reports this using (G8990 – G8992).

At the outset of therapy -- On the DOS for which the initial evaluative procedure is furnished or the initial treatment day of a therapy POC, the claim for the service will also include two G-codes as shown below.

- G8978-CL to report the functional limitation (Mobility with current mobility limitation of "at least 60 percent but less than 80 percent impaired, limited or restricted")
- G8979-CI to report the projected goal for a mobility restriction of "at least 1 percent but less than 20 percent impaired, limited or restricted."

At the end of each progress reporting period -- On the claim for the DOS when the services related to the progress report (which must be done at least once each 10 treatment days) are furnished, the clinician will report the same two G-codes but the modifier for the current status may be different.

- G8978 with the appropriate modifier are reported to show the beneficiary's current status as of this DOS. So if the beneficiary has made no progress, this claim will include G8978-CL. If the beneficiary made progress and now has a mobility restriction of 65 percent CL would still be the appropriate modifier for 65 percent, and G8978-CL would be reported in this case. If the beneficiary now has a mobility restriction of 45 percent, G8978-CK would be reported.
- G8979-CI would be reported to show the projected goal. This severity modifier would not change unless the clinician adjusts the beneficiary's goal.

This step is repeated as necessary and clinically appropriate, adjusting the current status modifier used as the beneficiary progresses through therapy.

At the time the beneficiary is discharged from the therapy episode. The final claim for therapy episode will include two G-codes.

- G8979-CI would be reported to show the projected goal. G8980-CI would be reported if the beneficiary attained the 15 percent mobility goal. Alternatively, if the beneficiary's mobility restriction only reached 25 percent; G8980-CJ would be reported.

To end reporting of one functional limitation--As noted above, functional reporting is required to continue throughout the entire episode of care. Accordingly, when further therapy is medically necessary after the beneficiary attains the goal for the first reported functional limitation, the clinician would end reporting of the first functional limitation by using the same G-codes and modifiers that would be used at the time of discharge. Using the mobility example, to end reporting of the mobility functional limitation, G8979-CI and G8980-CI would be reported on the same DOS that coincides with end of that progress reporting period.

To begin reporting of a second functional limitation. At the time reporting is begun for a new and different functional limitation, within the same episode of care (i.e., after the reporting of the prior functional limitation is ended). Reporting on the second functional limitation, however, is not begun until the DOS of the next treatment day -- which is day one of the new progress reporting period. When the next functional limitation to be reported is NOT defined by one of the other three PT/OT categorical codes, the G-code set (G8990 - G8992) for the "other PT/OT primary" functional limitation is used, rather than the G-code set for the "other PT/OT subsequent" because it is the first reported "other PT/OT" functional limitation. This reporting begins on the DOS of the first treatment day following the mobility "discharge" reporting, which is counted as the initial service for the "other PT/OT primary" functional limitation and the first treatment day of the new progress reporting period. In this case, G8990 and G8991, along with the corresponding modifiers, are reported on the claim for therapy services.

The table below illustrates when reporting is required using this example and what G-codes would be used.

Example of Required Reporting

Key: Reporting Period (RP)	Begin RP #1 for Mobility at Episode Outset	End RP#1for Mobility at Progress Report	Mobility RP #2 Begins Next Treatment Day	End RP #2 for Mobility at Progress Report	Mobility RP #3 Begins Next Treatment Day	D/C or End Reporting for Mobility	Begin RP #1 for Other PT/OT Primary
Mobility: Walking & Moving Around							
G8978 – Current Status	X	X		X			
G 8979– Goal Status	X	X		X		X	
G8980 – Discharge Status						X	
Other PT/OT Primary							
G8990 – Current Status							X
G8991 – Goal Status							X
G8992 – Discharge Status							
No Functional Reporting Required			X		X		

H. Required Tracking and Documentation of Functional G-codes and Severity Modifiers

The clinician who furnishes the services must not only report the functional information on the therapy claim, but, he/she must track and document the G-codes and severity modifiers used for this reporting in the beneficiary's medical record of therapy services.

For details related to the documentation requirements, refer to, Medicare Benefit Policy Manual, Pub. 100-02, Chapter 15, section 220.4 - Functional Reporting. For coverage rules related to MCTRJCA and therapy goals, refer to Pub. 100-02: a) for outpatient therapy services, see Chapter 15, section 220.1.2 B and b) for instructions specific to PT, OT, and SLP services in the CORF, see Chapter 12, section 10.

100-4, Chapter-5, 20

HCPCS Coding Requirement

A. Uniform Coding

Section 1834(k)(5)of the Act requires that all claims for outpatient rehabilitation therapy services and all comprehensive outpatient rehabilitation facility (CORF) services be reported using a uniform coding system. The current Healthcare Common Procedure Coding System/Current Procedural Terminology is used for the reporting of these services. The uniform coding requirement in the Act is specific to payment for all CORF services and outpatient rehabilitation therapy services -including physical therapy, occupational therapy, and speech-language pathology -that is provided and billed to Medicare contractors. The Medicare physician fee schedule (MPFS) is used to make payment for these therapy services at the non facility rate.

Effective for claims submitted on or after April 1, 1998, providers that had not previously reported HCPCS/CPT® for outpatient rehabilitation and CORF services began using HCPCS to report these services. This requirement does not apply to outpatient rehabilitation services provided by:

- Critical access hospitals, which are paid on a cost basis, not MPFS;
- RHCs, and FQHCs for which therapy is included in the all-inclusive rate; or
- Providers that do not furnish therapy services.

The following "providers of services" must bill the FI for outpatient rehabilitation services using HCPCS codes:

- Hospitals (to outpatients and inpatients who are not in a covered Part A1stay);
- Skilled nursing facilities (SNFs) (to residents not in a covered Part A1stay and to nonresidents who receive outpatient rehabilitation services from the SNF);
- Home health agencies (HHAs) (to individuals who are not homebound or otherwise are not receiving services under a home health plan of care[2] (POC).(See 60.4.1, Definition of Homebound Patient Under the Medicare Home Health (HH) Benefit.)
- Comprehensive outpatient rehabilitation facilities (CORFs); and
- Providers of outpatient physical therapy and speech-language pathology services (OPTs), also known as rehabilitation agencies (previously termed outpatient physical therapy facilities in this instruction).

Note 1. The requirements for hospitals and SNFs apply to inpatient Part B and outpatient services only. Inpatient Part A services are bundled into the respective prospective payment system payment; no separate payment is made.

Note 2. For HHAs, HCPCS/CPT® coding for outpatient rehabilitation services is required only when the HHA provides such service to individuals that are not homebound and, therefore, not under a home health plan of care.

The following practitioners must bill the carrier for outpatient rehabilitation therapy services using HCPCS/CPT® codes:

- Physical therapists in private practice (PTPPs),
- Occupational therapists in private practice (OTPPs),
- Speech-language pathologists in private practice (SLPPs),
- Physicians, including MDs, DOs, podiatrists and optometrists, and
- Certain nonphysician practitioners (NPPs), acting within their State scope of practice, e.g., nurse practitioners and clinical nurse specialists.

Providers billing to intermediaries shall report:

- The date the therapy plan of care was either established or last reviewed (see §220.1.3B) in Occurrence Code 17, 29, or 30.
- The first day of treatment in Occurrence Code 35, 44, or 45.

B. Applicable Outpatient Rehabilitation HCPCS Codes

The CMS identifies the codes listed at: http://www.cms.hhs.gov/TherapyServices/05_Annual_Therapy_Update.asp#TopOfPage as therapy services, regardless of the presence of a financial limitation. Therapy services include only physical therapy, occupational therapy and speech-language pathology services. Therapist means only a physical therapist, occupational therapist or speech-language pathologist. Therapy modifiers are GP for physical therapy, GO for occupational therapy,and GN for speech-language pathology.

When in effect, any financial limitation will also apply to services represented unless otherwise noted on the therapy page on the CMS Web site.

100-4, Chapter-5, 20.4

Coding Guidance for Certain CPT® Codes - All Claims

The following provides guidance about the use of codes 96105, 97026, 97150, 97545, 97546, and G0128.

- CPT® Codes 96105, 97545, and 97546.

Providers report code 96105, assessment of aphasia with interpretation and report in 1-hour units. This code represents formal evaluation of aphasia with an instrument such as the Boston Diagnostic Aphasia Examination. If this formal assessment is performed during treatment, it is typically performed only once during treatment and its medical necessity should be documented. If the test is repeated during treatment, the medical necessity of the repeat administration of the test must also be documented. It is common practice for regular assessment of a patient's progress in therapy to be documented in the chart, and this may be done using test items taken from the formal examinations. This is considered to be part of the treatment and should not be billed as 96105 unless a full, formal assessment is completed.

Other timed physical medicine codes are 97545 and 97546. The interval for code 97545 is 2 hours and for code 97546, 1 hour. These are specialized codes to be used in the context of rehabilitating a worker to return to a job. The expectation is that the entire time period specified in the codes 97545 or 97546 would be the treatment period, since a shorter period of treatment could be coded with another code such as codes 97110, 97112, or 97537. (Codes 97545 and 97546 were developed for reporting services to persons in the worker's compensation program, thus CMS does not expect to see them reported for Medicare patients except under very unusual circumstances. Further, CMS would not expect to see code 97546 without also seeing code 97545 on the same claim. Code 97546, when used, is used in conjunction with 97545.)

- CPT® Code 97026

Effective for services performed on or after October 24, 2006, the Centers for Medicare & Medicaid Services announce a NCD stating the use of infrared and/or near-infrared light and/or heat, including monochromatic infrared energy (MIRE), is non-covered for the treatment, including symptoms such as pain arising from these conditions, of diabetic and/or non-diabetic peripheral sensory neuropathy, wounds and/or ulcers of the skin and/or subcutaneous tissues in Medicare beneficiaries. Further coverage guidelines can be found in the National Coverage Determination Manual (Publication 100-03), section 270.6.

Contractors shall deny claims with CPT® 97026 (infrared therapy incident to or as a PT/OT benefit) and HCPCS E0221 or A4639, if the claim contains any of the following diagnosis codes:

ICD-9-CM

250.60 - 250.63

354.4, 354.5, 354.9

355.1 - 355.4

355.6 - 355.9

356.0, 356.2-356.4, 356.8-356.9

357.0 - 357.7

674.10, 674.12, 674.14, 674.20, 674.22, 674.24

707.00 -707.07, 707.09-707.15, 707.19

870.0 - 879.9

880.00 - 887.7

890.0 - 897.7

998.31 - 998.32

Contractors can use the following messages when denying the service:

- Medicare Summary Notice # 21.11 "This service was not covered by Medicare at the time you received it."
- Reason Claim Adjustment Code #50 "These are noncovered services because this is not deemed a medical necessity by the payer."

Advanced Beneficiary Notice (ABN):

Physicians, physical therapists, occupational therapists, outpatient rehabilitation facilities (ORFs), comprehensive outpatient rehabilitation facilities (CORFs), home health agencies (HHA), and hospital outpatient departments are liable if the service is performed, unless the beneficiary signs an ABN.

Similarly, DME suppliers and HHA are liable for the devices when they are supplied, unless the beneficiary signs an ABN.

100-4, Chapter-5, 100.4

Outpatient Mental Health Treatment Limitation

The Outpatient Mental Health Treatment Limitation (the limitation) is not applicable to CORF services because CORFs do not provide services to treat mental, psychoneurotic and personality disorders that are subject to the limitation in section 1833(c) of the Act. For dates of service on or after October 1, 2012, HCPCS code G0409 is the only code allowed for social work and psychological services furnished in a CORF. This service is not subject to the limitation because it is not a sychiatric mental health treatment service.

For additional information on the limitation, see Publication 100-01, Chapter 3, section 30 and Publication 100-02, Chapter 12, sections 50-50.5.

100-4, Chapter-5, 100.11

Billing for Social Work and Psychological Services in a CORF

The CORF providers shall only bill social work and psychological services with the following HCPCS code:

G0409 –Social work and psychological services, directly relating to and/or the patient's rehabilitation goals, each 15 minutes, face-to-face; individual (services provided by a CORF-qualified social worker or psychologist in a CORF)

In addition, HCPCS code G0409 shall only be billed with revenue code 0569 or 0911.

100-4, Chapter-8, 60.2.1.1

Separately Billable ESRD Drugs

The following categories of drugs (including but not limited to) are separately billable when used to treat the patient's renal condition:

- Antibiotics;
- Analgesics;
- Anabolics;
- Hematinics;
- Muscle relaxants;
- Sedatives;
- Tranquilizers; and
- Thrombolytics: used to declot central venous catheters. Note: Thrombolytics were removed from the separately billable drugs for claims with dates of service on or after January 1, 2013.

For claims with dates of service on or after July 1, 2013, when these drugs are administered through the dialysate the provider must append the modifier JE (Administered via Dialysate).

These separately billable drugs may only be billed by an ESRD facility if they are actually administered in the facility by the facility staff. Staff time used to administer separately billable drugs is covered under the composite rate and may not be billed separately. However, the supplies used to administer these drugs may be billed in addition to the composite rate.

Effective January 1, 2011, section 153b of the MIPPA requires that all ESRD-related drugs and biologicals be billed by the renal dialysis facility. When a drug or biological is billed by providers other than the ESRD facility and the drug or biological furnished is designated as a drug or biological that is included in the ESRD PPS (ESRD-related), the claim will be rejected or denied. In the event that an ESRD-related drug or biological was furnished to an ESRD beneficiary for reasons other than for the treatment of ESRD, the provider may submit a claim for separate payment using modifier AY.

All drugs reported on the renal dialysis facility claim are considered included in the ESRD PPS. The list of drugs and biologicals for consolidated billing are designated as always ESRD-related and therefore not allowing separate payment to be made to ESRD facilities. However, CMS has determined that some of these drugs may warrant separate payment.

Exceptions to "Always ESRD Related" Drugs:

The following drugs have been approved for separate payment consideration when billed with the AY modifier attesting to the drug not being used for the treatment of ESRD. The ESRD facility is required to indicate (in accordance with ICD-coding guidelines) the diagnosis code for which the drug is indicated.

- Vancomycin, effective January 1, 2012
- Daptomycin, effective January 1, 2013

Items and services subject to the consolidated billing requirements for the ESRD PPS can be found on the CMS website at:

http://www.cms.gov/ESRDPayment/50_Consolidated_Billing.asp# TopOfPage.

Other drugs and biologicals may be considered separately payable to the dialysis facility if the drug was not for the treatment of ESRD. The facility must include the modifier AY to indicate it was not for the treatment of ESRD.

Drugs are assigned HCPCS codes. If no HCPCS code is listed for a drug (e.g., a new drug) the facility bills using HCPCS code J3490, "Unclassified Drugs," and submits documentation identifying the drug. To establish a code for the drug, the FI checks HCPCS to verify that there is no acceptable HCPCS code for billing and if a code is not found checks with the local carrier, which may have a code and price that is appropriate.

If no code is found the drug is processed under HCPCS code J3490. See Chapter 17 for a complete description of drug pricing.

100-4, Chapter-8, 60.4

Erythropoietin Stimulating Agents (ESAs)

Coverage rules for ESAs are explained in the Medicare Benefit Policy Manual, Publication 100-02, chapter 11.

Fiscal intermediaries (FIs) pay for ESAs, to end-stage renal disease (ESRD) facilities as separately billable drugs to the composite rate. No additional payment is made to administer an ESA, whether in a facility or a home. Effective January 1, 2005, the cost of supplies to administer EPO may be billed to the FI. HCPCS A4657 and Revenue Code 270 should be used to capture the charges for syringes used in the administration of EPO.

ESAs and their administration supplies are included in the payment for the ESRD Prospective Payment System effective January 1, 2011. Providers must continue to report ESAs on the claim as ESAs are subject to a national claims monitoring program and are entitled to outlier payment consideration. The Medicare allowed payment (MAP) amount for outlier includes the ESA rate provided on the Average Sale Price (ASP) list, subject to reduction based on the ESA monitoring policy.

Medicare has an established national claims monitoring policy for erythropoietin stimulating agents for the in-facility dialysis population as outlined in the sections below.

100-4, Chapter-8, 60.4.1

ESA Claims Monitoring Policy

Effective for services provided on or after April 1, 2006, Medicare has implemented a national claims monitoring policy for ESAs administered in Medicare renal dialysis facilities. This policy does not apply to claims for ESAs for patients who receive their dialysis at home and self-administer their ESA.

While Medicare is not changing its coverage policy on erythropoietin use to maintain a target hematocrit level between 30% and 36%, we believe the variability in response to ESAs warrants postponing requiring monitoring until the hematocrit reaches higher levels. For dates of services April 1, 2006, and later, the Centers for Medicare & Medicaid Services (CMS) claims monitoring policy applies when the hematocrit level exceeds 39.0% or the hemoglobin level exceeds 13.0g/dL. This does not preclude the contractors from performing medical review at lower levels.

Effective for services provided on or after April 1, 2006, for claims reporting hematocrit or hemoglobin levels exceeding the monitoring threshold, the dose shall be reduced by 25% over the preceding month. Providers may report that a dose reduction did occur in response to the reported elevated hematocrit or hemoglobin level by adding a GS modifier on the claim. The definition of the GS modifier is defined as: "Dosage of ESA has been reduced and maintained in response to hematocrit or hemoglobin level." Thus, for claims reporting a hematocrit level or hemoglobin level exceeding the monitoring threshold without the GS modifier, CMS will reduce the covered dosage reported on the claim by 25%. The excess dosage is considered to be not reasonable and necessary. Providers are reminded that the patient's medical records should reflect hematocrit/hemoglobin levels and any dosage reduction reported on the claim during the same time period for which the claim is submitted.

Effective for dates of service provided on and after January 1, 2008, requests for payments or claims for ESAs for ESRD patients receiving dialysis in renal dialysis facilities reporting a hematocrit level exceeding 39.0% (or hemoglobin exceeding 13.0g/dL) shall also include modifier ED or EE. Claims reporting neither modifier or both modifiers will be returned to the provider for correction.

The definition of modifier ED is "The hematocrit level has exceeded 39.0% (or hemoglobin level has exceeded 13.0g/dL) 3 or more consecutive billing cycles immediately prior to and including the current billing cycle." The definition of modifier EE is "The hematocrit level has exceeded 39.0% (or hemoglobin level has exceeded 13.0g/dL) less than 3 consecutive billing cycles immediately prior to and including the current billing cycle." The GS modifier continues to be defined as stated above.

Providers may continue to report the GS modifier when the reported hematocrit or hemoglobin levels exceed the monitoring threshold for less than 3 months and a dose reduction has occurred. When both modifiers GS and EE are included, no reduction in the covered dose will occur. Claims reporting a hematocrit or hemoglobin level exceeding the monitoring threshold and the ED modifier shall have an automatic 50% reduction in the covered dose applied, even if the claim also reports the GS modifier.

Below is a chart illustrating the resultant claim actions under all possible reporting scenarios:

Hct Exceeds 39.0% or Hgb Exceeds 13.0g/dL	ED Modifier? (Hct >39% or Hgb >13g/dL ≥3 cycles)	EE Modifier? (Hct >39% or Hgb >13g/dL <3 cycles)	GS Modifier? (Dosage reduced and maintained)	Claim Action
No	N/A	N/A	N/A	Do not reduce reported dose.
Yes	No	No	No	Return to provider for correction. Claim must report either modifier ED or EE.
Yes	No	No	Yes	Return to provider for correction. Claim must report either modifier ED or EE.
Yes	No	Yes	Yes	Do not reduce reported dose.
Yes	No	Yes	No	Reduce reported dose 25%.
Yes	Yes	No	Yes	Reduce reported dose 50%.
Yes	Yes	No	No	Reduce reported dose 50%.

In some cases, physicians may believe there is medical justification to maintain a hematocrit above 39.0% or hemoglobin above 13.0g/dL. Beneficiaries, physicians, and/or renal facilities may submit additional medical documentation to justify this belief under the routine appeal process. You may reinstate any covered dosage reduction amounts under this first level appeal process when you believe the documentation supports a higher hematocrit/hemoglobin level.

Providers are reminded that, in accordance with FDA labeling, CMS expects that as the hematocrit approaches 36.0% (hemoglobin 12.0g/dL), a dosage reduction occurs. Providers are expected to maintain hematocrit levels between 30.0 to 36.0% (hemoglobin 10.0-12.0g/dL). Hematocrit levels that remain below 30.0% (hemoglobin levels below 10.0g/dL)) despite dosage increases, should have causative factors evaluated. The patient's medical record should reflect the clinical reason for dose changes and hematocrit levels outside the range of 30.0-36.0% (hemoglobin levels 10.0-12.0g/dL). Medicare contractors may review medical records to assure appropriate dose reductions are applied and maintained and hematological target ranges are maintained.

These hematocrit requirements apply only to ESAs furnished as an ESRD benefit under §1881(b) of the Social Security Act.

Medically Unlikely Edits (MUE)

For dates of service on and after January 1, 2008, the MUE for claims billing for Epogen® is reduced to 400,000 units from 500,000. The MUE for claims for Aranesp® is reduced to 1200 mcg from 1500 mcg.

For dates of service on and after April 1, 2013, the MUE for claims billing for peginesatide is applicable when units billed are equal to or greater than 26 mg.

It is likely that claims reporting doses exceeding the threshold reflect typographical errors and will be returned to providers for correction.

100-4, Chapter-8, 60.4.4.1

Payment for Epoetin Alfa (EPO) in Other Settings

With the implementation of the ESRD PPS, ESRD-related EPO is included in ESRD PPS payment amount and is not separately payable on Part B claims with dates of service on or after January 1, 2011 for other providers with the exception of a hospital billing for an emergency or unscheduled dialysis session.

In the hospital inpatient setting, payment under Part A is included in the DRG.

In the hospital inpatient setting, payment under Part B is made on bill type 12x. Hospitals report the drug units based on the units defined in the HCPCS description. Hospitals do not report value code 68 for units of EPO. For dates of service prior to April 1, 2006, report EPO under revenue code 0636. For dates of service from April 1, 2006 report EPO under the respective revenue code 0634 for EPO less than 10,000 units and revenue code 0635 for EPO over 10,000 units. Payment will be based on the ASP Pricing File.

In a skilled nursing facility (SNF), payment for EPO covered under the Part B EPO benefit is not included in the prospective payment rate for the resident's Medicare-covered SNF stay.

In a hospice, payment is included in the hospice per diem rate.

For a service furnished by a physician or incident to a physician's service, payment is made to the physician by the carrier in accordance with the rules for 'incident to" services. When EPO is administered in the renal facility, the service is not an "incident to" service and not under the "incident to" provision.

100-4, Chapter-8, 60.4.4.2

Epoetin Alfa (EPO) Provided in the Hospital Outpatient Departments

When ESRD patients come to the hospital for an unscheduled or emergency dialysis treatment they may also require the administration of EPO. Effective January 1, 2005, EPO will be paid based on the ASP Pricing File.

Hospitals use type of bill 13X (or 85X for Critical Access Hospitals) and report charges under the respective revenue code 0634 for EPO less than 10,000 units and revenue code 0635 for EPO over 10,000 units. Hospitals report the drug units based on the units defined in the HCPCS description. Hospitals do not report value code 68 for units of EPO. Value code 49 must be reported with the hematocrit value for the hospital outpatient visits prior to January 1, 2006, and for all claims with dates of service on or after January 1, 2008.

100-4, Chapter-8, 60.4.5.1

Self Administered ESA Supply

Initially, facilities may bill for up to a 2-month supply of an ESA for Method I beneficiaries who meet the criteria for selection for self-administration. After the initial two months' supply, the facility will bill for one month's supply at a time. Condition code 70 is used to indicate payment requested for a supply of an ESA furnished a beneficiary. Usually, revenue code 0635 would apply to EPO since the supply would be over 10,000 units. Facilities leave FL 46, Units of Service, blank since they are not administering the drug.

For claims with dates of service on or after January 1, 2008, supplies of an ESA for self administration should be billed according to the pre-determined plan of care schedule provided to the beneficiary. Submit a separate line item for each date an administration is expected to be performed with the expected dosage. In the event that the schedule was changed, the provider should note the changes in the medical record and bill according to the revised schedule. For patients beginning to self administer an ESA at home receiving an extra month supply of the drug, bill the one month reserve supply on one claim line and include modifier EM defined as "Emergency Reserve Supply (for ESRD benefit only)".

When billing for drug wastage in accordance with the policy in chapter 17 of this manual, section 40.1 the provider must show the wastage on a separate line item with the modifier JW. The line item date of service should be the date of the last covered administration according to the plan of care or if the patient dies use the date of death.

Condition code 70 should be reported on claims billing for home dialysis patients that self administer anemia management drugs including ESAs.

100-4, Chapter-8, 60.4.6.3

Payment Amount for Darbepoetin Alfa (Aranesp)

For Method I patients, the FI pays the facility per one mcg of Aranesp administered, in accordance with the MMA Drug Payment Limits Pricing File rounded up to the next highest whole mcg. Effective January 1, 2005, Aranesp will be paid based on the ASP Pricing File. Effective January 1, 2005, the cost of supplies to administer Aranesp may be billed to the FI. HCPCS A4657 and Revenue Code 270 should be used to capture the charges for syringes used in the administration of Aranesp.

Physician payment is calculated through the drug payment methodology described in Chapter 17, of the Claims Processing Manual.

The coinsurance and deductible are based on the Medicare allowance payable, not on the provider's charges. The provider may not charge the beneficiary more than 20 percent of the Medicare Aranesp allowance. This rule applies to independent and hospital based renal facilities.

Payment for ESRD-related Aranesp is included in the ESRD PPS for claims with dates of service on or after January 1, 2011.

100-4, Chapter-8, 60.4.6.4

Payment for Darbepoetin Alfa (Aranesp) in Other Settings

In the hospital inpatient setting, payment under Part A for Aranesp is included in the DRG.

In the hospital inpatient setting, payment under Part B is made on bill type 12x when billed with revenue code 0636. The total number of units as a multiple of 1mcg is placed in the unit field. Reimbursement is based on the payment allowance limit for Medicare Part B drugs as found in the ASP pricing file.

In a skilled nursing facility (SNF), payment for Aranesp covered under the Part B EPO benefit is not included in the prospective payment rate for the resident's Medicare-covered SNF stay.

In a hospice, payment is included in the hospice per diem rate.

For a service furnished by a physician or incident to a physician's service, payment is made to the physician by the carrier in accordance with the rules for 'incident to" services. When Aranesp is administered in the renal facility, the service is not an "incident to" service and not under the "incident to" provision.

With the implementation of the ESRD PPS, ESRD-related Aranesp is included in the ESRD PPS payment amount and is not separately payable on Part B claims with dates of service on or after January 1,2011 for other providers, with the exception of a hospital billing for an emergency or unscheduled dialysis session.

100-4, Chapter-8, 60.4.6.5

Payment for Darbepoetin Alfa (Aranesp) in the Hospital Outpatient Department

When ESRD patients come to the hospital for an unscheduled or emergency dialysis treatment they may also require the administration of Aranesp. For patients with ESRD who are on a regular course of dialysis, Aranesp administered in a hospital outpatient department is paid the MMA Drug Pricing File rate. Effective January 1, 2005, Aranesp will be paid based on the ASP Pricing File.

Hospitals use bill type 13X (or 85X for Critical Access Hospitals) and report charges under revenue code 0636. The total number of units as a multiple of 1mcg is placed in the unit field. Value code 49 must be reported with the hematocrit value for the hospital outpatient visits prior to January 1, 2006, and for all claims with dates of service on or after January 1, 2008.

100-4, Chapter-8, 60.4.7

Payment for Peginesatide in the Hospital Outpatient Department

When ESRD patients come to the hospital for an unscheduled or emergency dialysis treatment they may also require the administration of an ESA, such as peginesatide. When hospitals bill for an unscheduled or emergency outpatient dialysis session (G0257) they may include the administration of an ESA.

100-4, Chapter-8, 60.6

Vaccines Furnished to ESRD Patients

The Medicare program covers hepatitis B, influenza virus and Pneumococcal pneumonia virus (PPV) vaccines and their administration when furnished to eligible beneficiaries in accordance with coverage rules. Payment may be made for both the vaccine and the administration. The costs associated with the syringe and supplies are included in the administration fee: HCPCS code A4657 should not be billed for these vaccines.

Vaccines and their administration are reported using separate codes. See Chapter 18 of this manual for the codes required for billing vaccines and the administration of the vaccine.

Payment for vaccine administration (PPV, Influenza Virus, and Hepatitis B Virus) to freestanding RDFs is based on the Medicare Physician Fee Schedule (MPFS) according to the rate in the MPFS associated with code 90782 for services provided prior to March 1, 2003 and code 90471 for services provided March 1, 2005 and later and on reasonable cost for provider-based RDFs.

Vaccines remain separately payable under the ESRD PPS.

100-4, Chapter-9, 150

Initial Preventive Physical Examination (IPPE)

Effective for services furnished on or after January 1, 2005, Section 611 of the Medicare Prescription Drug Improvement and Modernization Act of 2003 (MMA) provides for coverage under Part B of one initial preventive physical examination (IPPE) for new beneficiaries only, subject to certain eligibility and other limitations. For RHCs the Part B deductible for IPPE is waived for services provided on or after January 1, 2009. FQHC services are always exempt from the Part B deductible. Coinsurance is applicable. For RHCs and FQHCs coinsurance is waived for services provided on or after January 1, 2011.

Payment for the professional services will be made under the all-inclusive rate. Encounters with more than one health professional and multiple encounters with the same health professionals that take place on the same day and at a single location generally constitute a single visit. However, in rare circumstances an RHC/FQHC can receive a separate payment for an encounter in addition to the payment for the IPPE when they are performed on the same day.

RHCs and FQHCs must HCPCS code for IPPE for the following reasons:

- To avoid application of deductible (on RHC claims);
- To assure payment for this service in addition to another encounter on the same day if they are both separate, unrelated, and appropriate; and
- To update the CWF record to track this once in a lifetime benefit.

Beginning with dates of service on or after January 1, 2009 if an IPPE is provided in an RHC or FQHC, the professional portion of the service is billed to the FI or Part A MAC using TOBs 71X and 73X/77X, respectively, and the appropriate site of service revenue code in the 052X revenue code series, and must include HCPCS code G0402. Additional information on IPPE can be found in Chapter 18, section 80 of this manual.

NOTE: The technical component of an EKG performed at a clinic/center is not a Medicare-covered RHC/FQHC service and is not billed by the independent RHC/FQHC. Rather, it is billed to Medicare carriers or Part B MACs on professional claims (Form CMS-1500 or 837P) under the practitioner's ID following instructions for submitting practitioner claims. Likewise, the technical component of the EKG performed at a provider-based clinic/center is not a Medicare-covered RHC/FQHC service and is not billed by the provider-based RHC\FQHC. Instead, it is billed on the applicable TOB and submitted to the FI or Part A MAC using the base provider's ID following instructions for submitting claims to the FI/Part A MAC from the base provider. For the professional component of the EKG, there is no separate payment and no separate billing of it. The IPPE is the only HCPCS code for which the deductible is waived under this benefit. For more information on billing for a screening EKG see chapter 18 section 80 of this manual.

100-4, Chapter-9, 160

Ultrasound Screening for Abdominal Aortic Aneurysm (AAA)

Section 5112 of the Deficit Reduction Act of 2005 amended the Social Security Act to provide coverage under Part B of the Medicare program for a one-time ultrasound screening for abdominal aortic aneurysms (AAA). Payment for the professional services that meet all of the program requirements will be made under the all-inclusive rate. For RHCs the Part B deductible for screening AAA is waived for dates of service on or after January 1, 2007. FQHC services are always exempt from the Part B deductible. Coinsurance is applicable. For RHCs and FQHCs, coinsurance for screening AAA is waived for dates of service on or after January 1, 2011. Additional information on AAA can be found in Chapter 18, section 110 of this manual.

If the screening is provided in an RHC or FQHC, the professional portion of the service is billed to the FI or Part A MAC using TOBs 71X and 73X/77X, respectively, and the appropriate site of service revenue code in the 052X revenue code series and must include HCPCS code G0389.

If the AAA screening is provided in an independent RHC or freestanding FQHC, the technical component of the service can be billed by the practitioner to the carrier or Part B MAC under the practitioner's ID following instructions for submitting practitioner claims.

If the screening is provided in a provider-based RHC/FQHC, the technical component of the service can be billed by the base provider to the FI or Part A MAC under the base provider's ID, following instructions for submitting claims to the FI/Part A MAC from the base provider.

100-4, Chapter-9, 181

Diabetes Self-Management Training (DSMT) Services Provided by RHCs and FQHCs

A – FQHCs

Previously, DSMT type services rendered by qualified registered dietitians or nutrition professionals were considered incident to services under the FQHC benefit, if all relevant program requirements were met. Therefore, separate all-inclusive encounter rate payment could not be made for the provision of DSMT services. With passage of DRA, effective January 1, 2006, FQHCs are eligible for a separate payment under Part B for these services provided they meet all program requirements. See Pub. 100-04, chapter 18, section 120. Payment is made at the all-inclusive encounter rate to the FQHC. This payment can be in addition to payment for any other qualifying visit on the same date of service as the beneficiary received qualifying DSMT services.

For FQHCs to qualify for a separate visit payment for DSMT services, the services must be a one-on-one face-to-face encounter. Group sessions don't constitute a billable visit for any FQHC services. Rather, the cost of group sessions is included in the calculation of the all-inclusive FQHC visit rate. To receive separate payment for DSMT services, the DSMT services must be billed on TOB 73x/77x with HCPCS code G0108 and the appropriate site of service revenue code in the 052X revenue code series. This payment can be in addition to payment for any other qualifying visit on the same date of service that the beneficiary received qualifying DSMT services as long as the claim for DSMT services contains the appropriate coding specified above. Additional information on DSMT can be found in Chapter 18, section 120 of this manual.

NOTE: DSMT is not a qualifying visit on the same day that MNT is provided.

Group services (G0109) do not meet the criteria for a separate qualifying encounter. All line items billed on TOBs 73x/77x with HCPCS codes for DSMT services will be denied.

B – RHCs

Separate payment to RHCs for these practitioners/services continues to be precluded as these services are not within the scope of Medicare-covered RHC benefits. Note that the provision of the services by registered dietitians or nutritional professionals, might be considered incident to services in the RHC setting, provided all applicable conditions are met. However, they do not constitute an RHC visit, in and of themselves. All line items billed on TOB 71x with HCPCS code 0108 or G0109 will be denied.

100-4, Chapter-9, 182

Medical Nutrition Therapy (MNT) Services

A – FQHCs

Previously, MNT type services were considered incident to services under the FQHC benefit, if all relevant program requirements were met. Therefore, separate all-inclusive encounter rate payment could not be made for the provision of MNT services. With passage of DRA, effective January 1, 2006, FQHCs are eligible for a separate payment under Part B for these services provided they meet all program requirements. Payment is made at the all-inclusive encounter rate to the FQHC. This payment can be in addition to payment for any other qualifying visit on the same date of service as the beneficiary received qualifying MNT services.

For FQHCs to qualify for a separate visit payment for MNT services, the services must be a one-on-one face-to-face encounter. Group sessions don't constitute a billable visit for any FQHC services. Rather, the cost of group sessions is included in the calculation of the all-inclusive FQHC visit rate. To receive payment for MNT services, the MNT services must be billed on TOB 73/x77x with the appropriate individual MNT HCPCS code (97802, 97803, or G0270) and with the appropriate site of service revenue code in the 052X revenue code series. This payment can be in addition to payment for any other qualifying visit on the same date of service as the beneficiary received qualifying MNT services as long as the claim for MNT services contain the appropriate coding specified above.

NOTE: MNT is not a qualifying visit on the same day that DSMT is provided.

Additional information on MNT can be found in Chapter 4, section 300 of this manual. Group services (HCPCS code 97804 or G0271) do not meet the criteria for a separate qualifying encounter. All line items billed on TOB 73x/77x with HCPCS code 97804 or G0271 will be denied.

B – RHCs

Separate payment to RHCs for these practitioners/services continues to be precluded as these services are not within the scope of Medicare-covered RHC benefits. All line items billed on TOB 71x with HCPCS codes for MNT services will be denied.

100-4, Chapter 10, 40.2

HH PPS Claims

The following data elements are required to submit a claim under home health PPS. For billing of home health claims not under an HH plan of care (not under HH PPS), see §90. Home health services under a plan of care are paid based on a 60-day episode of care. Payment for this episode will usually be made in two parts. After an RAP has been paid and a 60-day episode has been completed, or the patient has been discharged, the HHA submits a claim to receive the balance of payment due for the episode.

HH PPS claims will be processed in Medicare claims processing systems as debit/credit against the record created by the RAP, except in the case of "NRAP" LUPA claims (see §40.3). As the claim is processed the payment on the RAP will be reversed in full and the full payment due for the episode will be made on the claim. Both the debit and credit actions will be reflected on the remittance advice (RA) so the net payment on the claim can be easily understood.

Billing Provider Name, Address, and Telephone Number

Required–The HHA's minimum entry is the agency's name, city, State, and ZIP Code. The post office box number or street name and number may be included. The State may be abbreviated using standard post office abbreviations. Five or nine-digit ZIP Codes are acceptable. Medicare contractors use this information in connection with the provider identifier to verify provider identity.

Patient Control Number and Medical/Health Record Number

Required-The patient's control number may be shown if the patient is assigned one and the number is needed for association and reference purposes.

The HHA may enter the number assigned to the patient's medical/health record. If this number is entered, the Medicare contractor must carry it through their system and return it on the remittance record.

Type of Bill

Required -This 4-digit alphanumeric code gives two pieces of information. The first three digits indicate the base type of bill. The fourth digit indicates the sequence of this bill in this particular episode of care. The types of bill accepted for HH PPS requests for anticipated payment are: 100-4, Chapter 11, 10.1

100-4, Chapter 10, 90.1

Osteoporosis Injections as HHA Benefit

A -Billing Requirements

The administration of the drug is included in the charge for the skilled nursing visit billed using type of bill 32X. The cost of the drug is billed using type of bill 34X, using revenue code 0636. Drugs that have the ingredient calcitonin are billed using HCPCS code J0630. Drugs that have the ingredient teriparatide may be billed using HCPCS code J3110, if all existing guidelines for coverage under the home health benefit are met. All other osteoporosis drugs that are FDA approved and are awaiting an HCPCS code must use the miscellaneous code of J3490 until a specific HCPCS code is approved for use.

HCPCS code J0630 is defined as up to 400 units. Therefore, the provider must calculate units for the bill as follows:

Units Furnished During Billing Period	Units of Service Entry on Bill
100-400	1
401-800	2
801-1200	3
1201-1600	4
1601-2000	5
2001-2400	6

HCPCS code J3110 is defined as 10 mcg. Providers should report 1 unit for each 10 mcg dose provided during the billing period. These codes are paid on a reasonable cost basis, using the provider's submitted charges to make initial payments, which are subject to annual cost settlement. Coverage requirements for osteoporosis drugs are found in Pub. 100-02, Medicare Benefit Policy Manual, chapter 7, section 50.4.3. Coverage requirements for the home health benefit in general are found in Pub. 100-02, Medicare Benefit Policy Manual, chapter 7, section 30.

B -Edits

Medicare system edits require that the date of service on a 34Xclaim for covered osteoporosis drugs falls within the start and end dates of an existing home health PPS episode. Once the system ensures the service dates on the 34X claim fall within an HH PPS episode that is open for the beneficiary on CWF, CWF edits to assure that the provider number on the 34X claim matches the provider number on the episode file. This is to reflect that although the osteoporosis drug is paid separately from the HH PPS episode rate it is included in consolidated billing requirements(see §10.1.25 regarding consolidated billing).

Claims are also edited to assure that the claim is an HH claim (type of bill 34X), the beneficiary is female and that the diagnosis code 733.01 (post-menopausal osteoporosis) is present.

100-4, Chapter 11, 10.1

Hospice Pre-Election Evaluation and Counseling Services

Effective January 1, 2005, Medicare allows payment to a hospice for specified hospice pre-election evaluation and counseling services when furnished by a physician who is either the medical director of or employee of the hospice.

Medicare covers a one-time only payment on behalf of a beneficiary who is terminally ill, (defined as having a prognosis of 6 months or less if the disease follows its normal course), has no previous hospice elections, and has not previously received hospice pre-election evaluation and counseling services.

HCPCS code G0337 "Hospice Pre-Election Evaluation and Counseling Services" is used to designate that these services have been provided by the medical director or a physician employed by the ho spice. Hospice agencies bill their Medicare contractor with home health and hospice jurisdiction directly using HCPCS G0337 with Revenue Code 0657. No other revenue codes may appear on the claim.

Claims for "Hospice Pre-Election and Counseling Services", HCPCS code G0337, are not subject to the editing usually required on hospice claims to match the claim to an established hospice period. Further, contractors do not apply payments for hospice pre-election evaluation and counseling consultation services to the overall hospice cap amount.

Medicare must ensure that this counseling service occurs only one time per beneficiary by imposing safeguards to detect and prevent duplicate billing for similar services. If "new patient" physician services (HCPCS codes 99201-99205) are submitted by a Medicare contractor to CWF for payment authorization but HCPCS code G0337 (Hospice Pre-Election Evaluation and Counseling Services) has already been approved for a hospice claim for the same beneficiary, for the same date of service, by the same physician, the physician service will be rejected by CWF and the service shall be denied as a duplicate. Medicare contractors use the following messages in this case:

HCPCS code G0337 is only payable when billed on a hospice claim. Contractors shall not make payment for HCPCS code G0337 on professional claims. Contractors shall deny line items on professional claims for HCPCS code G0337 and use the following messages:

100-4, Chapter 11, 30.3

Data Required on the Institutional Claim to Medicare Contractor

See Pub. 100-02, Medicare Benefit Policy Manual, Chapter 9, sections 10 and 20.2 for coverage requirements for Hospice benefits. This section addresses only the submittal of claims. Before submitting claims, the hospice must submit a Notice of Election (NOE) to the Medicare contractor. See section 20, of this chapter for information on NOE transaction types.

The Social Security Act at §1862 (a)(22) requires that all claims for Medicare payment must be submitted in an electronic form specified by the Secretary of Health and Human Services, unless an exception described at §1862 (h) applies. The electronic form required for billing hospice services is the ANSI X12N 837 Institutional claim transaction. Since the data structure of the 837 transaction is difficult to express in narrative form and to provide assistance to small providers excepted from the electronic claim requirement, the instructions below are given relative to the data element names on the UB-04 (Form CMS-1450) hardcopy form. Each data element name is shown in bold type. Information regarding the form locator numbers that correspond to these data element names and a table to crosswalk UB-04 form locators to the 837 transaction is found in Chapter 25.

Because claim formats serve the needs of many payers, some data elements may not be needed by a particular payer. Detailed information is given only for items required for Medicare hospice claims. Items not listed need not be completed although hospices may complete them when billing multiple payers.

Provider Name, Address, and Telephone Number

The hospice enters this information for their agency.

Type of Bill

This three-digit alphanumeric code gives three specific pieces of information. The first digit identifies the type of facility. The second classifies the type of care. The third indicates the sequence of this bill in this particular benefit period. It is referred to as a "frequency" code.

Code Structure

1st Digit -Type of Facility
8- Specialfacility (Hospice)

2nd Digit -Classification (Special Facility Only)
1- Hospice(Nonhospital based)
2- Hospice(Hospital based)

3rd Digit –Frequency	Definition
0- Nonpayment/Zero Claims	Used when no payment from Medicare is anticipated.

3rd Digit –Frequency	Definition
I- Admit Through Discharge Claim	This code is used for a bill encompassing an entire Course of hospice treatment For which the provider expects Payment from the payer, i.e. No further bills will be submitted For this patient.
2- Interim–First Claim	This code is used for the first of an expected series of payment bills for a hospice course of treatment.
3- Interim-Continuing Claim	This code is used when a payment bill for a hospice course of Treatment has already been Submitted and further bills are expected to be submitted.
4- Interim-Last Claim	This code is used for a payment bill that is the last of a series for a hospice course of treatment. The "Through" date of this bill is the discharge date, transfer date, or date of death.
5 - Late Charges	Use this code for late charges that need to be billed. Late charges can be submitted only for revenue codes not on the original bill. Effective April 1, 2012, hospice late charge claims are no longer accepted by Medicare. Providers should use type of bill frequency 7. See below
7- Replacement of Prior Claim	This code is used by the provider When it wants to correct a previously submitted bill. This is the code used on the corrected or "new " bill. For additional information on replacement bills see Chapter 3 of this manual
8- Void/Cancel of a Prior Claim	This code is used to cancel a previously processed claim. For additional information on void/cancel bills see Chapter 3 of this manual

Statement Covers Period (From-Through)

The hospice shows the beginning and ending dates of the period covered by this bill in numeric fields (MM-DD-YY).The hospice does not show days before the patient's Entitlement began. Since the 12-month hospice "cap period" (see §80.2) ends each year on October 31, hospices must submit separate bills for October and November.

Patient Name/Identifier

The hospice enters the beneficiary's name exactly as it appears on the Medicare card.

Patient Address
Patient Birth date
Patient Sex

The hospice enters the appropriate address, date of birth and gender information describing the beneficiary.

Admission/Start of Care Date

The hospice enters the admission date, which must be the same date as the effective date of the hospice election or change of election. The date of admission may not precede the physician's certification by more than 2 calendar days.

The admission date stays the same on all continuing claims for the same hospice election.

Patient Discharge Status

This code indicates the patient's status as of the "Through" date of the billing period. The hospice enters the most appropriate National Uniform Billing Committee (NUBC) approved code.

NOTE: patient discharge status code 20 is not used on hospice claims. If the patient has died during the billing period, use codes 40, 41 or 42 as appropriate.

Medicare regulations at 42 CFR 418.26 define three reasons for discharge from hospice care:

1. The beneficiary moves out of the hospice's service area or transfers to another hospice,

2. The hospice determines that the beneficiary is no longer terminally ill or

3. The hospice determines the beneficiary meets their internal policy regarding discharge for cause.

Each of these discharge situations requires different coding on Medicare claims.

Reason 1: A beneficiary may move out of the hospice's service area either with, or without, a transfer to another hospice. In the case of a discharge when the beneficiary moves out of the hospice's service area without a transfer, the hospice uses the NUBC approved discharge status code that best describes the beneficiary's situation and appends condition code 52. The hospice does not report occurrence code 42 on their claim. This discharge claim will terminate the beneficiary's current hospice benefit period as of the "Through" date on the claim. The beneficiary may re-elect the hospice benefit at any time as long they remain eligible for the benefit.

In the case of a discharge when the beneficiary moves out of the hospice's service area and transfers to another hospice, the hospice uses discharge status code 50 or 51, depending on whether the beneficiary is transferring to home hospice or hospice in a medical facility. The hospice does not report occurrence code 42 on their claim. This discharge claim does not terminate the beneficiary's current hospice benefit period. The admitting hospice submits a transfer Notice of Election (type of bill 8xC) after the transfer has occurred and the beneficiary's hospice benefit is not affected.

Reason 2: In the case of a discharge when the hospice determines the beneficiary is no longer terminally ill, the hospice uses the NUBC approved discharge status code that best describes the beneficiary's situation. The hospice does not report occurrence code 42 on their claim. This discharge claim will terminate the beneficiary's current hospice benefit period as of the Through" date on the claim.

Reason 3: In the case of a discharge for cause, the hospice uses the NUBC approved discharge status code that best describes the beneficiary's situation. The hospice does not report occurrence code 42 on their claim. Instead, the hospice reports condition code H2 to indicate a discharge for cause. The effect of this discharge claim on the beneficiary's current hospice benefit period depends on the discharge status.

If the beneficiary is transferred to another hospice (discharge status codes 50 or 51) the claim does not terminate the beneficiary's current hospice benefit period. The admitting hospice submits a transfer Notice of Election (type of bill 8xC) after the transfer has occurred and the beneficiary's hospice benefit is not affected. If any other appropriate discharge status code is used, this discharge claim will terminate the beneficiary's current hospice benefit period as of the "Through" date on the claim. The beneficiary may re-elect the hospice

benefit if they are certified as terminally ill and eligible for the benefit again in the future and are willing to be compliant with care.

If the beneficiary has chosen to revoke their hospice election, the provider uses the NUBC approved discharge patient status code and the occurrence code 42 indicating the date the beneficiary revoked the benefit. The beneficiary may re-elect the hospice benefit if they are certified as terminally ill and eligible for the benefit again in the future.

Discharge Reason	Coding Required in Addition to Patient Status Code
Beneficiary Revokes	Occurrence Code 42
Beneficiary Transfers Hospices	Patient Status Code 50 or 51; no other indicator
Beneficiary No Longer Terminally Ill	No other indicator
Beneficiary Discharged for Cause	Condition code H2
Beneficiary Moves Out of Service Area	Condition code 52

If a hospice beneficiary is discharged alive or if a hospice beneficiary revokes the election of hospice care, the hospice shall file a timely-filed Notice of Election Termination / Revocation (NOTR) using type of bill 8xB, unless it has already filed a final claim. A timely-filed NOTR is a NOTR that is submitted to the Medicare contractor and accepted by the Medicare contractor within 5 calendar days after the effective date of discharge or revocation. While a timely-filed NOTR is one that is submitted to and accepted by the Medicare contractor within 5 calendar days after the hospice election, posting to the CWF may not occur within that same time frame. The date of posting to the CWF is not a reflection of whether the NOTR is considered timely-filed. A NOTR (type of bill 8xB) is entered via Direct Data Entry in the same way as an NOE (type of bill 8xA). Hospices continue to have 12 months from the date of service in which to file their claims timely.

Untimely Face-to-Face Encounters and Discharge

When a required face-to-face encounter occurs prior to, but no more than 30 calendar days prior to, the third benefit period recertification and every benefit period recertification thereafter, it is considered timely. A timely face-to-face encounter would be evident when examining the face-to-face attestation, which is part of the recertification, as that attestation includes the date of the encounter. If the required face-to-face encounter is not timely, the hospice would be unable to recertify the patient as being terminally ill, and the patient would cease to be eligible for the Medicare hospice benefit. In such instances, the hospice must discharge the patient from the Medicare hospice benefit because he or she is not considered terminally ill for Medicare purposes.

When a discharge from the Medicare hospice benefit occurs due to failure to perform a required face-to-face encounter timely, the claim should include the most appropriate patient discharge status code. The hospice can re-admit the patient to the Medicare hospice benefit once the required encounter occurs, provided the patient continues to meet all of the eligibility requirements and the patient (or representative) files an election statement in accordance with CMS regulations. Where the only reason the patient ceases to be eligible for the Medicare hospice benefit is the hospice's failure to meet the face-to-face requirement, we would expect the hospice to continue to care for the patient at its own expense until the required encounter occurs, enabling the hospice to re-establish Medicare eligibility.

Occurrence span code 77 does not apply to the above described situations when the face-to-face encounter has not occurred timely.

While the face-to-face encounter itself must occur no more than 30 calendar days prior to the start of the third benefit period recertification and each subsequent recertification, its accompanying attestation must be completed before the claim is submitted.

Condition Codes

The hospice enters any appropriate NUBC approved code(s) identifying conditions related to this bill that may affect processing.

Codes listed below are only those most frequently applicable to hospice claims. For a complete list of codes, see the NUBC manual.

07	Treatment of Non-terminal Condition for Hospice	Code indicates the patient has elected hospice care but the provider is not treating the terminal condition, and is, therefore, requesting regular Medicare payment.
20	Beneficiary Requested Billing	Code indicates the provider realizes the services on this bill are at a noncovered level of care or otherwise excluded from coverage, but the beneficiary has requested a formal determination.
21	Billing for Denial Notice	Code indicates the provider realizes services are at a noncovered level of care or excluded, but requests a denial notice from Medicare in order to bill Medicaid or other insurers.
H2	Discharge by a Hospice Provider for Cause	Discharge by a Hospice Provider for Cause. NOTE: Used by the provider to indicate the patient meets the hospice's documented policy addressing discharges for cause.
52	Out of Hospice Service Area	Code indicates the patient is discharged for moving out of the hospice service area. This can include patients who relocate or who go on vacation outside of the hospice's service area, or patients who are admitted to a hospital or SNF that does not have contractual arrangements with the hospice.

Occurrence Codes and Dates

The hospice enters any appropriate NUBC approved code(s) and associated date(s) defining specific event(s) relating to this Billing period .Event codes are two numeric digits, and dates are Six numeric digits (MM-DD-YY).If there are more occurrences than there are spaces on the form, use the occurrence span code fields to record additional occurrences and dates.

Codes listed below are only those most frequently applicable to hospice claims. For a complete list of codes, see the NUBC manual.

Code	Title	Definition
23	Cancellation of Hospice Election Period (Medicare contractor USE ONLY)	Code indicates date on which a hospice period of election is cancelled by a Medicare contractor as opposed to revocation by the beneficiary.
24	Date Insurance Denied	Code indicates the date of receipt of a denial of coverage by a higher priority payer

Code	Title	Definition
27	Date of Hospice Certification or ReCertification	Code indicates the date of certification or recertification of the hospice benefit period, beginning with the first 2 initial benefit periods of 90 days each and the subsequent 60-day benefit periods. **NOTE:** regarding transfers from one hospice to another hospice: If a patient is in the first certification period when they transfer to another hospice, the receiving hospice would use the same certification date as the previous hospice until the next certification period. However, if they were in the next certification at the time of transfer, then they would enter that date in the Occurrence Code 27 and date
42	Date of Termination of Hospice Benefit	Enter code to indicate the date on which beneficiary terminated his/her election to receive hospice benefits. This code can be used only when the beneficiary has revoked the benefit. It is not used in transfer situations

Occurrence code 27 is reported on the claim for the billing period in which the certification or re-certification was obtained. When the re-certification is late and not obtained during the month it was due, the occurrence span code 77 should be reported with the through date of the span code equal to the through date of the claim.

Occurrence Span Code and Dates

The hospice enters any appropriate NUBC approved code(s) and associated beginning and ending date(s) defining a specific event Relating to this billing period are shown. Event codes are two Alphanumeric digits and dates are shown numerically as MM-DD-YY.

Codes listed below are only those most frequently applicable to hospice claims. For a complete list of codes, see the NUBC manual.

Code	Title	Definition
M2	Dates of Inpatient Respite Care	Code indicates From/Through dates of a period of inpatient respite care for hospice patients to differentiate separate respite periods of less than 5 days each. M2 is used when respite care is provided more than once during a benefit period.
77	Provider Liability – Utilization Charged	Code indicates From/Through dates for a period of non-covered hospice care for which the provider accepts payment liability (other than for medical necessity or custodial care).

Hospices must use occurrence span code 77 to identify days of care that are not covered by Medicare due to untimely physician recertification. This is particularly important when the non-covered days fall at the beginning of a billing period.

Value Codes and Amounts

The hospice enters any appropriate NUBC approved code(s) and the associated value amounts identifying numeric information related to this bill that may affect processing. The most commonly used value codes on hospice claims are value codes 61 and G8, which are used to report the location of the site of hospice services. Otherwise, value codes are commonly used only to indicate Medicare is secondary to another payer.

For detailed information on reporting Medicare secondary payer information, see the Medicare Secondary Payer Manual.

Code	Title	Definition
61	Place of Residence where Service is Furnished (Routine Home Care and Continuous Home Care)	MSA or Core-Based Statistical Area (CBSA) number (or rural State code) of the location where the hospice service is delivered. A residence can be an inpatient facility if an individual uses that facility as a place of residence. It is the level of care that is required and not the location where hospice services are provided that determines payment. In other words, if an individual resides in a freestanding hospice facility and requires routine home care, then claims are submitted for routine home care.
G8	Facility where Inpatient Hospice Service is Delivered (General Inpatient and Inpatient Respite Care).	MSA or Core Based Statistical Area (CBSA) number (or rural State code) of the facility where inpatient hospice services are delivered. Hospices must report value code 61 when billing revenue codes 0651 and 0652. Hospices must report value code G8 when billing revenue codes 0655 and 0656.

A residence can be an inpatient facility if an individual uses that facility as a place of residence. It is the level of care that is required and not the location where hospice services are provided that determines payment. In other words, if an individual resides in a freestanding hospice facility and requires routine home care, then claims are submitted for routine home care.

Hospices must report value code 61 when billing revenue codes 0651 and 0652.G8 Facility where Inpatient Hospice MSA or Core Based Statistical Area (CBSA) Service is Delivered (General Inpatient and Inpatient Respite Care).

Number (or rural State code) of the facility where inpatient hospice services are delivered.

Hospices must report value code G8 when billing revenue codes 0655 and 0656.

If hospice services are provided to the beneficiary in more than one CBSA area during the billing period, the hospice reports the CBSA that applies at the end of the billing period. For routine home care and continuous home care (e.g., the beneficiary's residence changes between locations in different CBSAs), report the CBSA of the beneficiary's residence at the end of the billing period. For general inpatient and inpatient respite care (e.g., the beneficiary is served in inpatient facilities in different CBSAs), report the CBSA of the latest facility that served the beneficiary. If the beneficiary receives both home and inpatient care during the billing period, the latest home CBSA is reported with value code 61 and the latest facility CBSA is reported with value code G8.

Revenue Codes

The hospice assigns a revenue code for each type of service provided and enters the appropriate four-digit numeric revenue code to explain each charge. For claims with dates of service before July 1, 2008, hospices only reported the revenue codes in the table below. Effective on claims with dates of service on or after January 1, 2008, additional revenue codes will be reported describing the visits provided under each level of care. However, Medicare payment will continue to be reflected only on claim lines with the revenue codes in this table.

Hospice claims are required to report separate line items for the level of care each time the level of care changes. This includes revenue codes 0651, 0655 and 0656. For example, if a patient begins the month receiving routine home care followed by a period of general inpatient care and then later returns to routine home care all in the same month, in addition to the one line reporting the general inpatient care days, there should be two separate line items for routine home care. Each routine home care line reports a line item date of service to indicate the first date that level of care began for that consecutive period. This will ensure visits and calls reported on the claim will be associated with the level of care being billed.

Code	Description	Standard Abbreviation
0651*	Routine Home Care	RTN Home
0652*	Continuous Home Care	CTNS Home A minimum of 8 hours of primarily nursing care within a 24-hour period. The 8-hours of care do not need to be continuous within the 24-hour period, but a need for an aggregate of 8 hours of primarily nursing care is required. Nursing care must be provided by a registered nurse or a licensed practical nurse. If skilled intervention is required for less than 8 aggregate hours (or less than 32 units) within a 24 hour period, then the care rendered would be covered as a routine home care day. Services provided by a nurse practitioner as the attending physician are not included in the CHC computation nor is care that is not directly related to the crisis included in the computation. CHC billing should reflect direct patient care during a period of crisis and should not reflect time related to staff working hours, time taken for meal breaks, time used for educating staff, time used to report etc.
0655***	Inpatient Respite Care	IP Respite
0656***	General Inpatient Care	GNL IP
0657**	Physician Services	PHY SER (must be accompanied by a physician procedure code)

A minimum of 8 hours of primarily nursing care within a 24-hour period. The 8-hours of care do not need to be continuous within the 24-hour period, but a need for an aggregate of 8 hours of primarily nursing care is required. Nursing care must be provided by a registered nurse or a licensed practical nurse. If skilled intervention is required for less than 8 aggregate hours (or less than 32 units) within a 24 hour period, then the care rendered would be covered as a routine home care day. Services provided by a nurse practitioner as the attending physician are not included in the CHC computation nor is care that is not directly related to the crisis included in the computation. CHC billing should reflect direct patient care during a period of crisis and should not reflect time related to staff working hours, time taken for meal breaks, time used for educating staff, time used to report etc.

* Reporting of value code 61 is required with these revenue codes.

**Reporting of modifier GV is required with this revenue code when billing physician services performed by a nurse practitioner.

***Reporting of value code G8 is required with these revenue codes.

NOTE: Hospices use revenue code 0657 to identify hospice Charges for services furnished to patients by physician or nurse practitioner employees, or physicians or nurse practitioners receiving compensation from the hospice. Physician services performed by a nurse practitioner require the addition of the modifier GV in conjunction with revenue code 0657. Procedure codes are required in order for the Medicare contractor to determine the reimbursement rate for the physician services. Appropriate procedure codes are available from the Medicare contractor.

Effective on claims with dates of service on or after July 1, 2008, hospices must report the number of visits that were provided to the beneficiary in the course of delivering the hospice levels of care billed with the codes above. Charges for these codes will be reported on the appropriate level of care line. Total number of patient care visits is to be reported by the discipline (registered nurse, nurse practitioner, licensed nurse, home health aide (also known as a hospice aide), social worker, physician or nurse practitioner serving as the beneficiary's attending physician) for each week at each location of service. If visits are provided in multiple sites, a separate line for each site and for each discipline will be required. The total number of visits does not imply the total number of activities or interventions provided. If patient care visits in a particular discipline are not provided under a given level of care or service location, do not report a line for the corresponding revenue code.

To constitute a visit, the discipline, (as defined above) must have provided care to the beneficiary. Services provided by a social worker to the beneficiary's family also constitute a visit. For example, phone calls, documentation in the medical/clinical record, interdisciplinary group meetings, obtaining physician orders, rounds in a facility or any other activity that is not related to the provision of items or services to a beneficiary, do not count towards a visit to be placed on the claim. In addition, the visit must be reasonable and necessary for the palliation and management of the terminal illness and related conditions as described in the patient's plan of care.

Example 1: Week 1: A visit by the RN was made to the beneficiary's home on Monday and Wednesday where the nurse assessed the patient, verified effect of pain medications, provided patient teaching, obtained vital signs and documented in the medical record. A home health aide assisted the patient with a bath on Tuesday and Thursday. There were no social work or physician visits. Thus for that week there were 2 visits provided by the nurse and 2 by the home health aide. Since there were no visits by the social worker or by the physician, there would not be any line items for each of those disciplines.

Example 2: If a hospice patient is receiving routine home care while residing in a nursing home, the hospice would record visits for all of its physicians, nurses, social workers, and home health aides who visit the patient to provide care for the palliation and management of the terminal illness and related conditions, as described in the patient's plan of care. In this example the nursing home is acting as the patient's home. Only the patient care provided by the hospice staff constitutes a visit.

Hospices must enter the following visit revenue codes, when applicable as of July 1, 2008:

Revenue Code	Required Detail
055x Skilled Nursing	Required detail: The earliest date of service this discipline was provided during the delivery of each level of care in each service location, service units which represent the number of visits provided in that location, and a charge amount.
056x Medical Social Services	Required detail: The earliest date of service this discipline was provided during the delivery of each level of care in each service location, service units which represent the number of visits provided in that location, and a charge amount.
057x Home Health Aide	Required detail: The earliest date of service this discipline was provided during the delivery of each level of care in each service location, service units which represent the number of visits provided in that location, and a charge amount.

For services provided on or after January 1, 2010, hospices report social worker phone calls and visits performed by hospice staff for other than General Inpatient (GIP) care in 15 minute increments using the following revenue codes and associated HCPCS.

Revenue Code	Required HCPCS	Required Detail
042x Physical Therapy	G0151	Required detail: Each visit is identified on a separate line item with the appropriate line item date of service and a charge amount. The units reported on the claim are the multiplier for the total time of the visit defined in the HCPCS description.
043x Occupational Therapy	G0152	Required detail: Each visit is identified on a separate line item with the appropriate line item date of service and a charge amount. The units reported on the claim are the multiplier for the total time of the visit defined in the HCPCS description.
044x Speech Therapy – Language Pathology	G0153	Required detail: Each visit is identified on a separate line item with the appropriate line item date of service and a charge amount. The units reported on the claim are the multiplier for the total time of the visit defined in the HCPCS description.
055x Skilled Nursing	G0154	Required detail: Each visit is identified on a separate line item with the appropriate line item date of service and a charge amount. The units reported on the claim are the multiplier for the total time of the visit defined in the HCPCS description.
056x Medical Social Services	G0155	Required detail: Each visit is identified on a separate line item with the appropriate line item date of service and a charge amount. The units reported on the claim are the multiplier for the total time of the visit defined in the HCPCS description.
0569 Other Medical Social Services	G0155	Required detail: Each social service phone call is identified on a separate line item with the appropriate line item date of service and a charge amount. The units reported on the claim are the multiplier for the total time of the call defined in the HCPCS description.
057x Aide	G0156	Required detail: Each visit is identified on a separate line item with the appropriate line item date of service and a charge amount. The units reported on the claim are the multiplier the total time of the visit defined in the HCPCS description.

Visits by registered nurses, licensed vocational nurses and nurse practitioners (unless the nurse practitioner is acting as the beneficiary's attending physician) are reported under revenue code 055x.

All visits to provide care related to the palliation and management of the terminal illness or related conditions, whether provided by hospice employees or provided under arrangement, must be reported. The two exceptions are related to General Inpatient Care and Respite care. CMS is not requiring hospices to report visit data at this time for visits made by non-hospice staff providing General Inpatient Care or respite care in contract facilities. However, General Inpatient Care or respite care visits related to the palliation and management of the terminal illness or related conditions provided by hospice staff in contract facilities must be reported, and all General Inpatient Care and respite care visits related to the palliation and management of the terminal illness or related conditions provided in hospice-owned facilities must be reported.

Charges associated with the reported visits are covered under the hospice bundled payment and reflected in the payment for the level of care billed on the claim. No additional payment is made on the visit revenue lines. The visit charges will be identified on the provider remittance advice notice with remittance code 97 "Payment adjusted because the benefit for this service is included in the payment / allowance for another service/procedure that has already been adjudicated."

Effective January 1, 2010, Medicare will require hospices to report additional detail for visits on their claims. For all Routine Home Care (RHC), Continuous Home Care (CHC) and Respite care billing, Medicare hospice claims should report each visit performed by nurses, aides, and social workers who are employed by the hospice, and their associated time per visit in the number of 15 minute increments, on a separate line. The visits should be reported using revenue codes 055x (nursing services), 057x (aide services), or 056x (medical social services), with the time reported using the associated HCPCS G-code in the range G0154 to G0156. Hospices should report in the unit field on the line level the units as a multiplier of the visit time defined in the HCPCS description.

Additionally, providers should begin reporting each RHC, CHC, and Respite visit performed by physical therapists, occupational therapists, and speech-language therapists and their associated time per visit in the number of 15 minute increments on a separate line. Providers should use existing revenue codes 042x for physical therapy, 043x for occupational therapy, and 044x for speech language therapy, in addition to the appropriate HCPCS G-code for recording of visit length in 15 minute increments. HCPCS G-codes G0151 to G0153 will be used to describe the therapy discipline and visit time reported on a particular line item. Hospices should report in the unit field on the line level the units as a multiplier of the visit time defined in the HCPCS description. If a hospice patient is receiving Respite care in a contract facility, visit and time data by non-hospice staff should not be reported.

Social worker phone calls made to the patient or the patient's family should be reported using revenue code 0569, and HCPCS G-code G0155 for the length of the call, with each call being a separate line item. Hospices should report in the unit field on the line level the units as a multiplier of the visit time defined in the HCPCS description. Only phone calls that are necessary for the palliation and management of the terminal illness and related conditions as described in the patient's plan of care (such as counseling, or speaking with a patient's family or arranging for a placement) should be reported. Report only social worker phone calls related to providing and or coordinating care to the patient and family and documented as such in the clinical records.

When recording any visit or social worker phone call time, providers should sum the time for each visit or call, rounding to the nearest 15 minute increment. Providers should not include travel time or documentation time in the time recorded for any visit or call. Additionally, hospices may not include interdisciplinary group time in time and visit reporting.

HCPCS/Accommodation Rates/HIPPS Rate Codes

For services provided on or before December 31, 2006, HCPCS codes are required only to report procedures on service lines for attending physician services (revenue 657). Level of care revenue codes (651, 652, 655 or 656) do not require HCPCS coding.

For services provided on or after January 1, 2007, hospices must also report a HCPCS code along with each level of care revenue code (651, 652, 655 and 656) to identify the type of service location where that level of care was provided.

The following HCPCS codes will be used to report the type of service location for hospice services:

HCPCS Code	Definition
Q5001	HOSPICE CARE PROVIDED IN PATIENT'S HOME/ RESIDENCE
Q5002	HOSPICE CARE PROVIDED IN ASSISTED LIVING FACILITY
Q5003	HOSPICE CARE PROVIDED IN NURSING LONG TERM CARE FACILITY (LTC) OR NON-SKILLED NURSING FACILITY (NF)
Q5004	HOSPICE CARE PROVIDED IN SKILLED NURSING FACILITY (SNF)
Q5005	HOSPICE CARE PROVIDED IN INPATIENT HOSPITAL
Q5006	HOSPICE CARE PROVIDED IN INPATIENT HOSPICE FACILITY
Q5007	HOSPICE CARE PROVIDED IN LONG TERM CARE HOSPITAL (LTCH)
Q5008	HOSPICE CARE PROVIDED IN INPATIENT PSYCHIATRIC FACILITY
Q5009	HOSPICE CARE PROVIDED IN PLACE NOT OTHERWISE SPECIFIED (NOS)
Q5010	Hospice home care provided in a hospice facility

If care is rendered at multiple locations, each location is to be identified on the claim with a corresponding HCPCS code. For example, routine home care may be provided for a portion of the billing period in the patient's residence and another portion in an assisted living facility. In this case, report one revenue code 651 line with HCPCS code Q5001 and the number of days of routine home care provided in the residence and another revenue code 651 line with HCPCS code Q5002 and the number of days of routine home care provided in the assisted living facility.

Q5003 is to be used for hospice patients in an unskilled nursing facility (NF) or hospice patients in the NF portion of a dually certified nursing facility, who are receiving unskilled care from the facility staff.

Q5004 is to be used for hospice patients in a skilled nursing facility (SNF), or hospice patients in the SNF portion of a dually certified nursing facility, who are receiving skilled care from the facility staff.

NOTE: Q5003 should be used for hospice patients located in a NF; many of these patients may also have Medicaid. Q5004 should be used when the hospice patient is in a SNF, and receiving skilled care from the facility staff, such as would occur in a GIP stay. For Q5004 to be used, the facility would have to be certified as a SNF. Some facilities are dually certified as a SNF and a NF; the hospice will have to determine what level of care the facility staff is providing (skilled or unskilled) in deciding which type of bed the patient is in, and therefore which code to use. When a patient is in the NF portion of a dually certified nursing facility, and receiving only unskilled care from the facility staff, Q5003 should be reported. Note that GIP care that is provided in a nursing facility can only be given in a SNF, because GIP requires a skilled level of care.

These service location HCPCS codes are not required on revenue code lines describing the visits provided under each level of care (e.g. 055X, 056X, 057X).

Service Date

The HIPAA standard 837 Institutional claim format requires line item dates of service for all outpatient claims. Medicare classifies hospice claims as outpatient claims (see Chapter 1, §60.4). For services provided on or before December 31, 2006, CMS allows hospices to satisfy the line item date of service requirement by placing any valid date within the Statement Covers Period dates on line items on hospice claims.

For services provided on or after January 1, 2007, service date reporting requirements will vary between continuous home care lines (revenue code 652) and other revenue code lines.

Revenue code 652 –report a separately dated line item for each day that continuous home care is provided, reporting the number of hours, or parts of hours rounded to 15-minute increments, of continuous home care that was provided on that date.

Other payment revenue codes –report a separate line for each level of care provided at each service location type, as described in the instructions for HCPCS coding reported above. Hospices report the earliest date that each level of care was provided at each service location. Attending physician services should be individually dated, reporting the date that each HCPCS code billed was delivered.

Non-payment service revenue codes –report dates as described in the table above under Revenue Codes.

For services provided on or after January 1, 2010, hospices report social worker phone calls and visits performed by hospice staff for other than GIP care as separate line items for each with the appropriate line item date of service. GIP visit reporting has not changed with the January 2010 update. GIP visits will continue to be reported as the number of visits per week.

For service visits that begin in one calendar day and span into the next calendar day, report one visit using the date the visit ended as the service date.

Service Units

The hospice enters the number of units for each type of service. Units are measured in days for revenue codes 651, 655, and 656, in hours for Revenue code 652, and in procedures for revenue code 657. For services provided on or after January 1, 2007, hours for revenue code 652 are reported in 15 -minute increments. For services provided on or after January 1, 2008, units for visit discipline revenue codes are measured by the number of visits.

For services provided on or after January 1, 2010, hospices report social worker phone calls and visits performed by hospice staff for other than GIP care as a separate line item with the appropriate line item date of service and the units as an increment of 15 minutes. GIP visit reporting has not changed with the January 2010 update. The units for visits under GIP level of care continue to reflect the number of visits per week.

Report in the unit field on the line level the units as a multiplier of the visit time defined in the HCPCS description.

Total Charges

The hospice enters the total charge for the service described on each revenue code line. This information is being collected for purposes of research and will not affect the amount of reimbursement.

Payer Name

The hospice identifies the appropriate payer(s) for the claim.

National Provider Identifier –Billing Provider.

The hospice enters its own National Provider Identifier (NPI).

Principal Diagnosis Code

The hospice enters diagnosis coding as required by ICD-9-CM / ICD-10-CM Coding Guidelines. The principal diagnosis listed is to be determined by the certifying hospice physician(s) as the diagnosis most contributory to the terminal conditions.

Other Diagnosis Codes

The hospice enters diagnosis coding as required by ICD-9-CM and ICD-10-CM Coding Guidelines.

Attending Provider Name and Identifiers

For claims with dates of service before January 1, 2010, the hospice enters the National Provider Identifier (NPI) and name of the physician currently responsible for certifying the terminal illness, and signing the individual's plan of care for medical care and treatment.

For claims with dates of service on or after January 1, 2010 the hospice shall enter the NPI and name of the attending physician designated by the patient as having the most significant role in the determination and delivery of the patient's medical care.

Other Provider Name and Identifiers

For claims with dates of service before January 1, 2010, if the attending physician is a nurse practitioner, the hospice enters the NPI and name of the nurse practitioner.

For claims with dates of service on or after January 1, 2010, the hospice enters the NPI and name of the hospice physician responsible for certifying that the patient is terminally ill, with a life expectancy of 6 months or less if the disease runs its normal course. **Note:** Both the attending physician and other physician fields should be completed unless the patient's designated attending physician is the same as the physician certifying the terminal illness. When the attending physician is also the physician certifying the terminal illness, only the attending physician is required to be reported.

NOTE: for electronic claims using version 5010 or later, this information is reported in Loop ID 2310F –Referring Provider Name.

100-4, Chapter 11, 40.1.3.1

Care Plan Oversight

Care plan oversight (CPO) exists where there is physician supervision of patients under care of hospices that require complex and multidisciplinary care modalities involving regular physician development and/or revision of care plans. Implicit in the concept of CPO is the expectation that the physician has coordinated an aspect of the patient's care with the hospice during the month for which CPO services were billed.

For a physician or NP employed by or under arrangement with a hospice agency, CPO functions are incorporated and are part of the hospice per diem payment and as such may not be separately billed.

For information on separately billable CPO services by the attending physician or nurse practitioner see Chapter 12, §180 of this manual.

100-4, Chapter 11, 100.1

Billing for Denial of Hospice Room and Board Charges

Hospice providers wishing to receive a line item denial for room and board charges may submit the charges as non-covered using revenue code 0659 with HCPCS A9270 and modifier GY on an otherwise covered hospice claim.

100-4, Chapter 12, 30.4

Cardiovascular System (Codes 92950-93799)

A. Echocardiography Contrast Agents

Effective October 1, 2000, physicians may separately bill for contrast agents used in echocardiography. Physicians should use HCPCS Code A9700 (Supply of Injectable Contrast Material for Use in Echocardiography, per study). The type of service code is 9. This code will be carrier-priced.

B. Electronic Analyses of Implantable Cardioverter-defibrillators and Pacemakers

The CPT® codes 93731, 93734, 93741 and 93743 are used to report electronic analyses of single or dual chamber pacemakers and single or dual chamber implantable cardioverter-defibrillators. In the office, a physician uses a device called a programmer to obtain information about the status and performance of the device and to evaluate the patient's cardiac rhythm and response to the implanted device.

Advances in information technology now enable physicians to evaluate patients with implanted cardiac devices without requiring the patient to be present in the physician's office. Using a manufacturer's specific monitor/transmitter, a patient can send complete device data and specific cardiac data to a distant receiving station or secure Internet server. The electronic analysis of cardiac device data that is remotely obtained provides immediate and long-term data on the device and clinical data on the patient's cardiac functioning equivalent to that obtained during an in-office evaluation. Physicians should report the electronic analysis of an implanted cardiac device using remotely obtained data as described above with CPT® code 93731, 93734, 93741 or 93743, depending on the type of cardiac device implanted in the patient.

100-4, Chapter 12, 30.6.15.4

Power Mobility Devices (PMDs) (Code G0372)

Section 302(a)(2)(E)(iv) of the Medicare Prescription Drug, Improvement, and Modernization Act of 2003 (MMA) sets forth revised conditions for Medicare payment of Power Mobility Devices (PMDs). This section of the MMA states that payment for motorized or power wheelchairs may not be made unless a physician (as defined in §1861(r)(1) of the Act), a physician assistant, nurse practitioner, or a clinical nurse specialist (as those terms are defined in §1861(aa)(5)) has conducted a face-to-face examination of the beneficiary and written a prescription for the PMD.

Payment for the history and physical examination will be made through the appropriate evaluation and management (E&M) code corresponding to the history and physical examination of the patient. Due to the MMA requirement that the physician or treating practitioner create a written prescription and a regulatory requirement that the physician or treating practitioner prepare pertinent parts of the medical record for submission to the durable medical equipment supplier, code G0372 (physician service required to establish and document the need for a power mobility device)has been established to recognize additional physician services and resources required to establish and document the need for the PMD.

The G code indicates that all of the information necessary to document the PMD prescription is included in the medical record, and the prescription and supporting documentation is delivered to the PMD supplier within 30 days after the face-to-face examination.

Effective October 25, 2005, G0372 will be used to recognize additional physician services and resources required to establish and document the need for the PMD and will be added to the Medicare physician fee schedule.

100-4, Chapter 12,80.1

Coverage of Physicians' Services Provided in Comprehensive Outpatient Rehabilitation Facility
B3-2220

Rehabilitation services furnished by comprehensive outpatient rehabilitation facilities (CORFs) are covered by Medicare Part B.

Under §1832(a)(2)(E), §1861(cc)(2), and related provisions of the Act, a CORF is recognized as a provider of services on the basis of its reasonable costs. Except for diagnostic and therapeutic services provided by physicians to individual patients, payment is made to the CORF by intermediaries (acting in the role of the Part B carrier.)

Physicians' diagnostic and therapeutic services furnished to a CORF patient are not considered CORF physician's services. Instead they are services that the physician must bill to the Part B carrier. If covered services, payment is made according to the Medicare Physician Fee Schedule. When physician's diagnostic and therapeutic services are furnished in a CORF, the claim must be annotated to show the CORF as the place of treatment.

Services considered administrative services provided by the physician associated with the CORF are considered CORF services reimbursable to the CORF by the FI. Administrative services include consultation with and medical supervision of nonphysician staff, establishing and reviewing the plan of treatment, and other medical and facility administration activities.

100-4, Chapter 12, 100.1.1

Evaluation and Management (E/M) Services

A .General Documentation Instructions and Common Scenarios

Evaluation and Management (E/M) Services --For a given encounter, the selection of the appropriate level of E/M service should be determined according to the code definitions in the American Medical Association's Current Procedural Terminology (CPT®) and any applicable documentation guidelines.

For purposes of payment, E/M services billed by teaching physicians require that they personally document at least the following;

- That they performed the service or were physically present during the key or critical portions of the service when performed by the resident; and
- The participation of the teaching physician in the management of the patient.

When assigning codes to services billed by teaching physicians, reviewers will combine the documentation of both the resident and the teaching physician.

Documentation by the resident of the presence and participation of the teaching physician is not sufficient to establish the presence and participation of the teaching physician.

On medical review, the combined entries into the medical record by the teaching physician and the resident constitute the documentation for the service and together must support the medical necessity of the service.

Following are four common scenarios for teaching physicians providing E/M services:

Scenario 1:

The teaching physician personally performs all the required elements of an E/M service without a resident. In this scenario the resident may or may not have performed the E/M service independently.

In the absence of a note by a resident, the teaching physician must document as he/she would document an E/M service in a nonteaching setting.

Where a resident has written notes, the teaching physician's note may reference the resident's note. The teaching physician must document that he/she performed the critical or key portion(s) of the service, and that he/she was directly involved in the management of the patient. For payment, the composite of the teaching physician's entry and the resident's entry together must support the medical necessity of the billed service and the level of the service billed by the teaching physician.

Scenario 2:

The resident performs the elements required for an E/M service in the presence of, or jointly with, the teaching physician and the resident documents the service. In this case, the teaching physician must document that he/she was present during the performance of the critical or key portion(s) of the service and that he/she was directly involved in the management of the patient. The teaching physician's note should reference the resident's note. For payment, the composite of the teaching physician's entry and the resident's entry together must support the medical necessity and the level of the service billed by the teaching physician.

Scenario 3:

The resident performs some or all of the required elements of the service in the absence of the teaching physician and documents his/her service. The teaching physician independently performs the critical or key portion(s) of the service with or without the resident present and, as appropriate, discusses the case with the resident. In this instance, the teaching physician must document that he/she personally saw the patient, personally performed critical or key portions of the service, and participated in the management of the patient. The teaching physician's note should reference the resident's note. For payment, the composite of the teaching physician's entry and the resident's entry together must support the medical necessity of the billed service and the level of the service billed by the teaching physician.

Scenario 4

When a medical resident admits a patient to a hospital late at night and the teaching physician does not see the patient until later, including the next calendar day.

- The teaching physician must document that he/she personally saw the patient and participated in the management of the patient. The teaching physician may reference the resident's note in lieu of re-documenting the history of present illness, exam, medical decision-making, review of systems and/or past family/social history provided that the patient's condition has not changed, and the teaching physician agrees with the resident's note.
- The teaching physician's note must reflect changes in the patient's condition and clinical course that require that the resident's note be amended with further information to address the patient's condition and course at the time the patient is seen personally by the teaching physician.
- The teaching physician's bill must reflect the date of service he/she saw the patient and his/her personal work of obtaining a history, performing a physical, and participating in medical decision-making regardless of whether the combination of the teaching physician's and resident's documentation satisfies criteria for a higher level of service. For payment, the composite of the teaching physician's entry and the resident's entry together must support the medical necessity of the billed service and the level of the service billed by the teaching Physician.

Following are examples of minimally acceptable documentation for each of these scenarios:

Scenario 1:

Admitting **Note:** "I performed a history and physical examination of the patient and discussed his management with the resident. I reviewed the resident's note and agree with the documented findings and plan of care".

Follow-up Visit: "Hospital Day #3. I saw and evaluated the patient. I agree with the findings and the plan of care as documented in the resident's note".

Follow-up Visit: "Hospital Day #5. I saw and examined the patient. I agree with the resident's note except the heart murmur is louder, so I will obtain an echo to evaluate".

> (**NOTE:** In this scenario if there are no resident notes, the teaching physician must document as he/she would document an E/M service in a non-teaching setting.)

Scenario 2:

Initial or Follow-up Visit: "I was present with the resident during the history and exam. I discussed the case with the resident and agree with the findings and plan as documented in the resident's note."

Follow-up Visit: "I saw the patient with the resident and agree with the resident's findings and plan."

Scenarios 3 and 4:

Initial Visit: "I saw and evaluated the patient. I reviewed the resident's note and agree, except that picture is more consistent with pericarditis than myocardial ischemia. Will begin NSAIDs."

Initial or Follow-up Visit: "I saw and evaluated the patient. Discussed with resident and agree with resident's findings and plan as documented in the resident's note."

Follow-up Visit: "See resident's note for details. I saw and evaluated the patient and agree with the resident's finding and plans as written."

Follow-up Visit: "I saw and evaluated the patient. Agree with resident's note but lower extremities are weaker, now 3/5; MRI of L/S Spine today."

Following are examples of unacceptable documentation:

"Agree with above.", followed by legible countersignature or identity;"Rounded, Reviewed, Agree.", followed by legible countersignature or identity;

"Discussed with resident. Agree.", followed by legible countersignature or identity;"Seen and agree.", followed by legible countersignature or identity;

"Patient seen and evaluated.", followed by legible countersignature or identity; and

A legible countersignature or identity alone.

Such documentation is not acceptable, because the documentation does not make it possible to determine whether the teaching physician was present, evaluated the patient, and/or had any involvement with the plan of care.

B. E/M Service Documentation Provided By Students

Any contribution and participation of a student to the performance of a billable service (other than the review of systems and/or past family/social history which are not separately billable, but are taken as part of an E/M service) must be performed in the physical presence of a teaching physician or physical presence of a resident in a service meeting the requirements set forth in this section for teaching physician billing.

Students may document services in the medical record. However, the documentation of an E/M service by a student that may be referred to by the teaching physician is limited to documentation related to the review of systems and/or past family/social history. The teaching physician may not refer to a student's documentation of physical exam findings or medical decision making in his or her personal note. If the medical student documents E/M services, the teaching physician must verify and redocument the history of present illness as well as perform and redocument the physical exam and medical decision making activities of the service.

C. Exception for E/M Services Furnished in Certain Primary Care Centers

Teaching physicians providing E/M services with a GME program granted a primary care exception may bill Medicare for lower and mid-level E/M services provided by residents. For the E/M codes listed below, teaching physicians may submit claims for services furnished by residents in the absence of a teaching physician:

New Patient	Established Patient
99201	99211
99202	99212
99203	99213

Effective January 1, 2005, the following code is included under the primary care exception: HCPCS code G0402 (Initial preventive physical examination; face-to-face visit services limited to new beneficiary during the first 12 months of Medicare enrollment).

Effective January 1, 2011, the following codes are included under the primary care exception: HCPCS codes G0438 (Annual wellness visit, including personal preventive plan service, first visit) and G0439 (Annual wellness visit, including personal preventive plan service, subsequent visit).

If a service other than those listed above needs to be furnished, then the general teaching physician policy set forth in §100.1 applies. For this exception to apply, a center must attest in writing that all the following conditions are met for a particular residency program. Prior approval is not necessary, but centers exercising the primary care exception must maintain records demonstrating that they qualify for the exception.

The services must be furnished in a center located in the outpatient department of a hospital or another ambulatory care entity in which the time spent by residents in patient care activities is included in determining direct GME payments to a teaching hospital by the hospital's FI. This requirement is not met when the resident is assigned to a physician's office away from the center or makes home visits. In the case of a nonhospital entity, verify with the FI that the entity meets the requirements of a written agreement between the hospital and the entity set forth at 42 CFR 413.78(e)(3)(ii).

Under this exception, residents providing the billable patient care service without the physical presence of a teaching physician must have completed at least 6 months of a GME approved residency program. Centers must maintain information under the provisions at 42 CFR 413.79(a)(6).

Teaching physicians submitting claims under this exception may not supervise more than four residents at any given time and must direct the care from such proximity as to constitute immediate availability. Teaching physicians may include residents with less than 6 months in a GME approved residency program in the mix of four residents under the teaching physician's supervision. However, the teaching physician must be physically present for the critical or key portions of services furnished by the residents with less than 6 months in a GME approved residency program. That is,the primary care exception does not apply in the case of residents with less than 6 months in a GME approved residency program.

Teaching physicians submitting claims under this exception must:

- Not have other responsibilities (including the supervision of other personnel) at the time the service was provided by the resident;
- Have the primary medical responsibility for patients cared for by the residents;

- Ensure that the care provided was reasonable and necessary;
- Review the care provided by the resident during or immediately after each visit. This must include a review of the patient's medical history, the resident's findings on physical examination, the patient's diagnosis, and treatment plan (i.e., record of tests and therapies); and
- Document the extent of his/her own participation in the review and direction of the services furnished to each patient.

Patients under this exception should consider the center to be their primary location for health care services. The residents must be expected to generally provide care to the same group of established patients during their residency training. The types of services furnished by residents under this exception include:

- Acute care for undifferentiated problems or chronic care for ongoing conditions including chronic mental illness;
- Coordination of care furnished by other physicians and providers; and,
- Comprehensive care not limited by organ system or diagnosis.

Residency programs most likely qualifying for this exception include family practice, general internal medicine, geriatric medicine, pediatrics, and obstetrics/gynecology.

Certain GME programs in psychiatry may qualify in special situations such as when the program furnishes comprehensive care for chronically mentally ill patients. These would be centers in which the range of services the residents are trained to furnish, and actually do furnish, include comprehensive medical care as well as psychiatric care. For example, antibiotics are being prescribed as well as psychotropic drugs.

100-4, Chapter 12, 180

Care Plan Oversight Services

The Medicare Benefit Policy Manual, Chapter 15, contains requirements for coverage for medical and other health services including those of physicians and non-physician practitioners.

Care plan oversight (CPO)is the physician supervision of a patient receiving complex and/or multidisciplinary care as part of Medicare-covered services provided by a participating home health agency or Medicare approved hospice. CPO services require complex or multidisciplinary care modalities involving:

- Regular physician development and/or revision of care plans;
- Review of subsequent reports of patient status;
- Review of related laboratory and other studies;
- Communication with other health professionals not employed in the same practice who are involved in the patient's care;
- Integration of new information into the medical treatment plan; and/or
- Adjustment of medical therapy.

The CPO services require recurrent physician supervision of a patient involving 30 or more minutes of the physician's time per month. Services not countable toward the 30 minutes threshold that must be provided in order to bill for CPO include, but are not limited to:

- Time associated with discussions with the patient, his or her family or friends to adjust medication or treatment;
- Time spent by staff getting or filing charts;
- Travel time; and/or
- Physician's time spent telephoning prescriptions into the pharmacist unless the telephone conversation involves discussions of pharmaceutical therapies .

Implicit in the concept of CPO is the expectation that the physician has coordinated an aspect of the patient's care with the home health agency or hospice during the month for which CPO services were billed. The physician who bills for CPO must be the same physician who signs the plan of care.

Nurse practitioners, physician assistants, and clinical nurse specialists, practicing within the scope of State law, may bill for care plan oversight. These non-physician practitioners must have been providing ongoing care for the beneficiary through evaluation and management services. These non-physician practitioners may not bill for CPO if they have been involved only with the delivery of the Medicare-covered home health or hospice service.

A. Home Health CPO

Non-physician practitioners can perform CPO only if the physician signing the plan of care provides regular ongoing care under the same plan of care as does the NPP billing for CPO and either:

- The physician and NPP are part of the same group practice; or
- If the NPP is a nurse practitioner or clinical nurse specialist, the physician signing the plan of care also has a collaborative agreement with the NPP; or
- If the NPP is a physician assistant, the physician signing the plan of care is also the physician who provides general supervision of physician assistant services for the practice. Billing may be made for care plan oversight services furnished by an NPP when:
- The NPP providing the care plan oversight has seen and examined the patient;
- The NPP providing care plan oversight is not functioning as a consultant whose participation is limited to a single medical condition rather than multidisciplinary coordination of care; and
- The NPP providing care plan oversight integrates his or her care with that of the physician who signed the plan of care. NPPs may not certify the beneficiary for home health care.

NPPs may not certify the beneficiary for home health care.

B. Hospice CPO

The attending physician or nurse practitioner (who has been designated as the attending physician) may bill for hospice CPO when they are acting as an "attending physician". An "attending physician" is one who has been identified by the individual, at the time he/she elects hospice coverage, as having the most significant role in the determination and delivery of their medical care. They are not employed nor paid by the hospice. The care plan oversight services are billed using Form CMS-1500 or electronic equivalent. For additional information on hospice CPO, see Chapter 11, §40.1.3.1 of this manual.

100-4, Chapter 12, 180.1

Care Plan Oversight Billing Requirements

A. Codes for Which Separate Payment May Be Made

Effective January 1, 1995, separate payment may be made for CPO oversight services for 30 minutes or more if the requirements specified in the Medicare Benefits Policy Manual, Chapter 15 are met.

Providers billing for CPO must submit the claim with no other services billed on that claim and may bill only after the end of the month in which the CPO services were rendered. CPO services may not be billed across calendar months and should be submitted (and paid) only for one unit of service.

Physicians may bill and be paid separately for CPO services only if all the criteria in the Medicare Benefit Policy Manual, Chapter 15 are met.

B. Physician Certification and Recertification of Home Health Plans of Care

Effective 2001, two new HCPCS codes for the certification and recertification and development of plans of care for Medicare-covered home health services were created.

See the Medicare General Information, Eligibility, and Entitlement Manual, Pub. 100-01, Chapter 4, "Physician Certification and Recertification of Services," §10-60, and the Medicare Benefit Policy Manual, Pub. 100-02, Chapter 7, "Home Health Services", §30.

The home health agency certification code can be billed only when the patient has not received Medicare-covered home health services for at least 60 days. The home health agency recertification code is used after a patient has received services for at least 60 days (or one certification period) when the physician signs the certification after the initial certification period. The home health agency recertification code will be reported only once every 60 days, except in the rare situation when the patient starts a new episode before 60 days elapses and requires a new plan of care to start a new episode.

C. Provider Number of Home Health Agency (HHA) or Hospice

For claims for CPO submitted on or after January 1, 1997, physicians must enter on the Medicare claim form the 6-character Medicare provider number of the HHA or hospice providing Medicare-covered services to the beneficiary for the period during which CPO services was furnished and for which the physician signed the plan of care. Physicians are responsible for obtaining the HHA or hospice Medicare provider numbers.

Additionally, physicians should provide their UPIN to the HHA or hospice furnishing services to their patient.

NOTE: There is currently no place on the HIPAA standard ASC X12N 837 professional format to specifically include the HHA or hospice provider number required for a care plan oversight claim. For this reason, the requirement to include the HHA or hospice provider number on a care plan oversight claim is temporarily waived until a new version of this electronic standard format is adopted under HIPAA and includes a place to provide the HHA and hospice provider numbers for care plan oversight claims.

100-4, Chapter 12, 190.3

List of Medicare Telehealth Services

The use of a telecommunications system may substitute for an in-person encounter for professional consultations, office visits, office psychiatry services, and a limited number of other physician fee schedule (PFS) services. The various services and corresponding current procedure terminology (CPT®) or Healthcare Common Procedure Coding System (HCPCS) codes are listed below.

- Consultations (CPT® codes 99241 -99275) -Effective October 1, 2001 –December 31, 2005;
- Consultations (CPT® codes 99241 -99255) -Effective January 1, 2006 –December 31, 2009;
- Telehealth consultations, emergency department or initial inpatient (HCPCS codes G0425 –G0427) -Effective January 1, 2010;
- Follow-up inpatient telehealth consultations (HCPCS codes G0406, G0407, and G0408) -Effective January 1, 2009;
- Office or other outpatient visits (CPT® codes 99201 -99215);
- Subsequent hospital care services, with the limitation of one telehealth visit every 3 days (CPT® codes 99231, 99232, and 99233) –Effective January 1, 2011;
- Subsequent nursing facility care services, with the limitation of one telehealth visit every 30 days (CPT® codes 99307, 99308,99309, and 99310) –Effective January 1, 2011;
- Pharmacologic management (CPT® code 90862) – Effective March 1, 2003 –December 31, 2012; (HCPCS code G0459) –Effective January 1, 2013;
- Individual psychotherapy (CPT® codes 90804 -90809); Psychiatric diagnostic interview examination (CPT® code 90801) –Effective March 1, 2003 –December 31, 2012;
- Individual psychotherapy (CPT® codes 90832 –90834, 90836 –90838); Psychiatric diagnostic interview examination (CPT® codes 90791 --90792) –Effective January 1, 2013.
- Neurobehavioral status exam (CPT® code 96116) -Effective January 1, 2008;
- End Stage Renal Disease (ESRD) related services (HCPCS codes G0308, G0309, G0311, G0312, G0314, G0315, G0317, and G0318) –Effective January 1, 2005 –December 31, 2008;
- End Stage Renal Disease (ESRD) related services (CPT® codes 90951, 90952, 90954, 90955, 90957, 90958, 90960, and 90961) –Effective January 1, 2009;
- Individual and group medical nutrition therapy (HCPCS codes G0270, 97802, 97803, and 97804) –Individual effective January 1, 2006; group effective January 1, 2011;
- Individual and group health and behavior assessment and intervention (CPT® codes 96150 –96154) –Individual effective January 1, 2010; group effective January 1, 2011.
- Individual and group kidney disease education (KDE) services (HCPCS codes G0420 and G0421) –Effective January 1, 2011; and
- Individual and group diabetes self-management training (DSMT) services, with a minimum of 1 hour of in-person instruction to be furnished in the initial year training period to ensure effective injection training (HCPCS codes G0108 and G0109) -Effective January 1, 2011.
- Smoking Cessation Services (CPT® codes 99406 and 99407 and HCPCS codes G0436 and G0437) –Effective January 1, 2012.
- Alcohol and/or substance (other than tobacco) abuse structured assessment and intervention services

(HCPCS codes G0396 and G0397) –Effective January 1, 2013.

- Annual alcohol misuse screening (HCPCS code G0442) –Effective January 1, 2013.
- Brief face-to-face behavioral counseling for alcohol misuse (HCPCS code G0443)–Effective January 1, 2013.
- Annual Depression Screening (HCPCS code G0444) – Effective January 1, 2013.
- High-intensity behavioral counseling to prevent sexually transmitted infections (HCPCS code G0445) –Effective January 1, 2013.
- Annual, face-to-face Intensive behavioral therapy for cardiovascular disease (HCPCS code G0446) –Effective January 1, 2013.
- Face-to-face behavioural counseling for obesity (HCPCS code G0447)–Effective January 1, 2013.
- Transitional Care Management Services (CPT® codes 99495 -99496) – Effective January 1, 2014.

NOTE: Beginning January 1, 2010, CMS eliminated the use of all consultation codes, except for inpatient telehealth consultation G-codes. CMS no longer recognizes office/outpatient or inpatient consultation CPT® codes for payment of office/outpatient or inpatient visits. Instead, physicians and practitioners are instructed to bill a new or established patient office/outpatient visit CPT® code or appropriate hospital or nursing facility care code, as appropriate to the particular patient, for all office/outpatient or inpatient visits.

100-4, Chapter 12, 190.3.1

Telehealth Consultation Services, Emergency Department or Initial Inpatient versus Inpatient Evaluation and Management (E/M) Visits

A consultation service is an evaluation and management (E/M) service furnished to evaluate and possibly treat a patient's problem(s). It can involve an opinion, advice, recommendation, suggestion, direction, or counsel from a physician or qualified nonphysician practitioner (NPP) at the request of another physician or appropriate source.

Section 1834(m) of the Social Security Act includes "professional consultations" in the definition of telehealth services. Inpatient or emergency department consultations furnished via telehealth can facilitate the provision of certain services and/or medical expertise that might not otherwise be available to a patient located at an originating site.

The use of a telecommunications system may substitute for an in-person encounter for emergency department or initial and follow-up inpatient consultations.

Medicare contractors pay for reasonable and medically necessary inpatient or emergency department telehealth consultation services furnished to beneficiaries in hospitals or SNFs when all of the following criteria for the use of a consultation code are met:

- An inpatient or emergency department consultation service is distinguished from other inpatient or emergency department evaluation and management (E/M) visits because it is provided by a physician or qualified nonphysician practitioner (NPP) whose opinion or advice regarding evaluation and/or management of a specific problem is requested by another physician or other appropriate source. The qualified NPP may perform consultation services within the scope of practice and

licensure requirements for NPPs in the State in which he/she practices;

- A request for an inpatient or emergency department telehealth consultation from an appropriate source and the need for an inpatient or emergency department telehealth consultation (i.e., the reason for a consultation service) shall be documented by the consultant in the patient's medical record and included in the requesting physician or qualified NPP's plan of care in the patient's medical record; and
- After the inpatient or emergency department telehealth consultation is provided, the consultant shall prepare a written report of his/her findings and recommendations, which shall be provided to the referring physician.

The intent of an inpatient or emergency department telehealth consultation service is that a physician or qualified NPP or other appropriate source is asking another physician or qualified NPP for advice, opinion, a recommendation, suggestion, direction, or counsel, etc. in evaluating or treating a patient because that individual has expertise in a specific medical area beyond the requesting professional's knowledge.

Unlike inpatient or emergency department telehealth consultations, the majority of subsequent inpatient hospital, emergency department and nursing facility care services require in-person visits to facilitate the comprehensive, coordinated, and personal care that medically volatile, acutely ill patients require on an ongoing basis.

Subsequent hospital care services are limited to one telehealth visit every 3 days. Subsequent nursing facility care services are limited to one telehealth visit every 30 days.

100-4, Chapter 12, 190.3.2

Telehealth Consultation Services, Emergency Departmentor Initial Inpatient Defined

Emergency department or initial inpatient telehealth consultations are furnished to beneficiaries in hospitals or SNFs via telehealth at the request of the physician of record, the attending physician, or another appropriate source. The physician or practitioner who furnishes the emergency department or initial inpatient consultation via telehealth cannot be the physician of record or the attending physician, and the emergency department or initial inpatient telehealth consultation would be distinct from the care provided by the physician of record or the attending physician. Counseling and coordination of care with other providers or agencies is included as well, consistent with the nature of the problem(s) and the patient's needs. Emergency department or initial inpatient telehealth consultations are subject to the criteria for emergency department or initial inpatient telehealth consultation services, as described in section 190.3.1 of this chapter.

Payment for emergency department or initial inpatient telehealth consultations includes all consultation related services furnished before, during, and after communicating with the patient via telehealth. Pre-service activities would include, but would not be limited to, reviewing patient data (for example, diagnostic and imaging studies, interim labwork) and communicating with other professionals or family members. Intra-service activities must include the three key elements described below for each procedure code. Post-service activities would include, but would not be limited to, completing medical records or other documentation and communicating results of the consultation and further care plans to other health care professionals. No additional E/M service could be billed for work related to an emergency department or initial inpatient telehealth consultation.

Emergency department or initial inpatient telehealth consultations could be provided at various levels of complexity:

- Practitioners taking a problem focused history, conducting a problem focused examination, and engaging in medical decision making that is straightforward, would bill HCPCS code G0425 (Telehealth consultation, emergency department or initial inpatient, typically 30 minutes communicating with the patient via telehealth).
- Practitioners taking a detailed history, conducting a detailed examination, and engaging in medical decision making that is of moderate complexity, would bill HCPCS code G0426 (Telehealth consultation, emergency department or initial inpatient, typically 50 minutes communicating with the patient via telehealth).
- Practitioners taking a comprehensive history, conducting a comprehensive examination, and engaging in medical decision making that is of high complexity, would bill HCPCS code G0427 (Telehealth consultation, emergency department or initial inpatient, typically 70 minutes or more communicating with the patient via telehealth).

Although emergency department or initial inpatient telehealth consultations are specific to telehealth, these services must be billed with either the -GT or -GQ modifier to identify the telehealth technology used to provide the service.

100-4, Chapter 12, 190.3.3

Follow-Up Inpatient Telehealth Consultations Defined

Follow-up inpatient telehealth consultations are furnished to beneficiaries in hospitals or SNFs via telehealth to follow up on an initial consultation, or subsequent consultative visits requested by the attending physician. The initial inpatient consultation may have been provided in-person or via telehealth.

Follow-up inpatient telehealth consultations include monitoring progress, recommending management modifications, or advising on a new plan of care in response to changes in the patient's status or no changes on the consulted health issue. Counseling and coordination of care with other providers or agencies is included as well, consistent with the nature of the problem(s) and the patient's needs.

The physician or practitioner who furnishes the inpatient follow-up consultation via telehealth cannot be the physician of record or the attending physician, and the follow-up inpatient consultation would be distinct from the follow-up care provided by the physician of record or the attending physician. If a physician consultant has initiated treatment at an initial consultation and participates thereafter in the patient's ongoing care management, such care would not be included in the definition of a follow-up inpatient consultation. Follow-up inpatient telehealth consultations are subject to the criteria for inpatient telehealth consultation services, as described in section 190.3.1 of this chapter.

Payment for follow-up inpatient telehealth consultations includes all consultation related services furnished before, during, and after communicating with the patient via telehealth. Pre-service activities would include, but would not be limited to, reviewing patient data (for example, diagnostic and imaging studies, interim labwork) and communicating with other professionals or family members. Intra-service activities must include at least two of the three key elements described below for each procedure code. Post-service activities would include, but would not be limited to, completing medical records or other documentation and communicating results of the consultation and further care plans to other health care professionals. No additional evaluation and management service could be billed for work related to a follow-up inpatient telehealth consultation.

Follow-up inpatient telehealth consultations could be provided at various levels of complexity:

- Practitioners taking a problem focused interval history, conducting a problem focused examination, and engaging in medical decision making that is straightforward or of low complexity, would bill a limited service, using HCPCS code G0406 (Follow-up inpatient telehealth consultation, limited, physicians typically spend 15 minutes communicating with the patient via telehealth).
- Practitioners taking an expanded focused interval history, conducting an expanded problem focused examination, and engaging in medical decision making that is of moderate complexity, would bill an intermediate service using HCPCS code G0407 (Follow-up inpatient telehealth consultation, intermediate, physicians typically spend 25 minutes communicating with the patient via telehealth).
- Practitioners taking a detailed interval history, conducting a detailed examination, and engaging in medical decision making that is of high complexity, would bill a complex service, using HCPCS code G0408 (Follow-up inpatient telehealth consultation, complex, physicians typically spend 35 minutes or more communicating with the patient via telehealth). Although follow-up inpatient telehealth consultations are specific to telehealth, these services must be billed with either the -GT or –GQ modifier to identify the telehealth technology used to provide the service.

100-4, Chapter 12, 190.6

Originating Site Facility Fee Payment Methodology

1. Originating site defined

The term originating site means the location of an eligible Medicare beneficiary at the time the service being furnished via a telecommunications system occurs. For asynchronous, store and forward telecommunications technologies, an originating site is only a Federal telemedicine demonstration program conducted in Alaska or Hawaii.

2. Facility fee for originating site

The originating site facility fee is a separately billable Part B payment. The contractor pays it outside of other payment methodologies. This fee is subject to post payment verification.

For telehealth services furnished from October 1, 2001, through December 31, 2002, the originating site facility fee is the lesser of $20 or the actual charge. For services furnished on or after January 1 of each subsequent year, the originating site facility fee is updated by the Medicare Economic Index. The updated fee is included in the Medicare Physician Fee Schedule (MPFS) Final Rule, which is published by November 1 prior to the start of the calendar year for which it is effective. The updated fee for each calendar year is also issued annually in a Recurring Update Notification instruction for January of each year.

3. Payment amount:

The originating site facility fee is a separately billable Part B payment. The payment amount to the originating site is the lesser of 80 percent of the actual charge or 80 percent of the originating site facility fee, except CAHs. The beneficiary is responsible for any unmet deductible amount and Medicare coinsurance.

The originating site facility fee payment methodology for each type of facility is clarified below.

Hospital outpatient department. When the originating site is a hospital outpatient department, payment for the originating site facility fee must be made as described above and not under the outpatient prospective payment system (OPPS). Payment is not based on the OPPS payment methodology.

Hospital inpatient. For hospital inpatients, payment for the originating site facility fee must be made outside the diagnostic related group (DRG) payment, since this is a Part B benefit, similar to other services paid separately from the DRG payment, (e.g., hemophilia blood clotting factor).

Critical access hospitals. When the originating site is a critical access hospital, make payment separately from the cost-based reimbursement methodology. For CAH's, the payment amount is 80 percent of the originating site facility fee.

Federally qualified health centers (FQHCs) and rural health clinics (RHCs). The originating site facility fee for telehealth services is not an FQHC or RHC service. When an FQHC or RHC serves as the originating site, the originating site facility fee must be paid separately from the center or clinic all-inclusive rate.

Physicians' and practitioners' offices. When the originating site is a physician's or practitioner's office, the payment amount, in accordance with the law, is the lesser of 80 percent of the actual charge or 80 percent of the originating site facility fee, regardless of geographic location. The carrier shall not apply the geographic practice cost index (GPCI) to the originating site facility fee. This fee is statutorily set and is not subject to the geographic payment adjustments authorized under the MPFS.

Hospital-based or critical access-hospital based renal dialysis center (or their satellites). When a hospital-based or critical access hospital-based renal dialysis center (or their satellites) serves as the originating site, the originating site facility fee is covered in addition to any composite rate or MCP amount.

Skilled nursing facility (SNF). The originating site facility fee is outside the SNF prospective payment system bundle and, as such, is not subject to SNF consolidated billing. The originating site facility fee is a separately billable Part B payment.

Community Mental Health Center (CMHC). The originating site facility fee is not a partial hospitalization service. The originating site facility fee does not count towards the number of services used to determine payment for partial hospitalization services. The originating site facility fee is not bundled in the per diem payment for partial hospitalization. The originating site facility fee is a separately billable Part B payment.

To receive the originating facility site fee, the provider submits claims with HCPCS code "Q3014, telehealth originating site facility fee"; short description "telehealth facility fee." The type of service for the telehealth originating site facility fee is "9, other items and services." For carrier-processed claims, the "office" place of service (code 11) is the only payable setting for code Q3014. There is no participation payment differential

for code Q3014. Deductible and coinsurance rules apply to Q3014. By submitting Q3014 HCPCS code, the originating site authenticates they are located in either a rural HPSA or non-MSA county.

This benefit may be billed on bill types 12X, 13X, 22X, 23X, 71X, 72X, 73X, 76X, and 85X. Unless otherwise applicable, report the originating site facility fee under revenue code 078X and include HCPCS code "Q3014, telehealth originating site facility fee."

Hospitals and critical access hospitals bill their intermediary for the originating site facility fee. Telehealth bills originating in inpatient hospitals must be submitted on a 12X TOB using the date of discharge as the line item date of service.

Independent and provider-based RHCs and FQHCs bill the appropriate intermediary using the RHC or FQHC bill type and billing number. HCPCS code Q3014 is the only non-RHC/FQHC service that is billed using the clinic/center bill type and provider number. All RHCs and FQHCs must use revenue code 078X when billing for the originating site facility fee. For all other non-RHC/FQHC services, provider based RHCs and FQHCs must bill using the base provider's bill type and billing number. Independent RHCs and FQHCs must bill the carrier for all other non-RHC/FQHC services. If an RHC/FQHC visit occurs on the same day as a telehealth service, the RHC/FQHC serving as an originating site must bill for HCPCS code Q3014 telehealth originating site facility fee on a separate revenue line from the RHC/FQHC visit using revenue code 078X.

Hospital-based or CAH-based renal dialysis centers (including satellites) bill their local FIs and/or Part A MACs for the originating site facility fee. Telehealth bills originating in renal dialysis centers must be submitted on a 72X TOB. All hospital-based or CAH-based renal dialysis centers (including satellites) must use revenue code 078X when billing for the originating site facility fee. The renal dialysis center serving as an originating site must bill for HCPCS code Q3014, telehealth originating site facility fee, on a separate revenue line from any other services provided to the beneficiary.

Skilled nursing facilities (SNFs) bill their local FIs and/or Part A MACs for the originating site facility fee. Telehealth bills originating in SNFs must be submitted on TOB 22X or 23X. For SNF inpatients in a covered Part A stay, the originating site facility fee must be submitted on a 22X TOB. All SNFs must use revenue code 078X when billing for the originating site facility fee. The SNF serving as an originating site must bill for HCPCS code Q3014, telehealth originating site facility fee, on a separate revenue line from any other services provided to the beneficiary.

Community mental health centers (CMHCs) bill their local FIs and/or Part A MACs for the originating site facility fee. Telehealth bills originating in CMHCs must be submitted on a 76X TOB. All CMHCs must use revenue code 078X when billing for the originating site facility fee. The CMHC serving as an originating site must bill for HCPCS code Q3014, telehealth originating site facility fee, on a separate revenue line from any other services provided to the beneficiary. Note that Q3014 does not count towards the number of services used to determine per diem payments for partial hospitalization services.

The beneficiary is responsible for any unmet deductible amount and Medicare coinsurance.

100-4, Chapter 12, 190.7

Contractor Editing of Telehealth Claims

Medicare telehealth services (as listed in section 190.3) are billed with either the "GT" or "GQ" modifier. The contractor shall approve covered telehealth services if the physician or practitioner is licensed under State law to provide the service. Contractors must familiarize themselves with licensure provisions of States for which they process claims and disallow telehealth services furnished by physicians or practitioners who are not authorized to furnish the applicable telehealth service under State law. For example, if a nurse practitioner is not licensed to provide individual psychotherapy under State law, he or she would not be permitted to receive payment for individual psychotherapy under Medicare. The contractor shall install edits to ensure that only properly licensed physicians and practitioners are paid for covered telehealth services.

If a contractor receives claims for professional telehealth services coded with the "GQ" modifier (representing "via asynchronous telecommunications system"), it shall approve/ pay for these services only if the physician or practitioner is affiliated with a Federal telemedicine demonstration conducted in Alaska or Hawaii. The contractor may require the physician or practitioner at the distant site to document his or her participation in a Federal telemedicine demonstration program conducted in Alaska or Hawaii prior to paying for telehealth services provided via asynchronous, store and forward technologies.

If a contractor denies telehealth services because the physician or practitioner may not bill for them, the contractor uses MSN message 21.18: "This item or service is not covered when performed or ordered by this practitioner." The contractor uses remittance advice message 52 when denying the claim based upon MSN message 21.18.

If a service is billed with one of the telehealth modifiers and the procedure code is not designated as a covered telehealth service, the contractor denies the service using MSN message 9.4: "This item or service was denied because information required to make payment was incorrect." The remittance advice message depends on what is incorrect, e.g., B18 if procedure code or modifier is incorrect, 125 for submission billing errors, 4-12 for difference inconsistencies. The contractor uses B18 as the explanation for the denial of the claim.

The only claims from institutional facilities that FIs shall pay for telehealth services at the distant site, except for MNT services, are for physician or practitioner services when the distant site is located in a CAH that has elected Method II, and the physician or practitioner has reassigned his/her benefits to the CAH. The CAH bills its regular FI for the professional services provided at the distant site via a telecommunications system, in any of the revenue codes 096x, 097x or 098x. All requirements for billing distant site telehealth services apply.

Claims from hospitals or CAHs for MNT services are submitted to the hospital's or CAH's regular FI. Payment is based on the non-facility amount on the Medicare Physician Fee Schedule for the particular HCPCS codes.

100-4, Chapter 12, 210

Outpatient Mental Health Treatment Limitation

Regardless of the actual expenses a beneficiary incurs in connection with the treatment of mental, psychoneurotic, and personality disorders while the beneficiary is not an inpatient of a hospital at the time such expenses are incurred, the amount of those expenses that may be recognized for Part B deductible and payment purposes is limited to 62.5 percent of the Medicare approved amount for those services. This limitation is called the outpatient mental health treatment limitation (the limitation). The 62.5 percent limitation has been in place since the inception of the Medicare Part B program and it will remain effective at this percentage amount until January 1, 2010. However, effective January 1, 2010, through January 1, 2014, the limitation will be phased out as follows:

- January 1, 2010 –December 31, 2011, the limitation percentage is 68.75%.
  (Medicare pays 55% and the patient pays 45%).
- January 1, 2012 –December 31, 2012, the limitation percentage is 75%.
  (Medicare pays 60% and the patient pays 40%).
- January 1, 2013 –December 31, 2013, the limitation percentage is 81.25%.
  (Medicare pays 65% and the patient pays 35%).
- January 1, 2014 –onward, the limitation percentage is 100%.
  (Medicare pays 80% and the patient pays 20%).

For additional details concerning computation of the limitation, please see the examples under section 210.1 E.

100-4, Chapter 12, 210.1

Application of the Limitation

A. Status of Patient

The limitation is applicable to expenses incurred in connection with the treatment of an individual who is not an inpatient of a hospital. Thus, the limitation applies to mental health services furnished to a person in a physician's office, in the patient's home, in a skilled nursing facility, as an outpatient, and so forth. The term "hospital" in this context means an institution, which is primarily engaged in providing to inpatients, by or under the supervision of a physician(s):

- Diagnostic and therapeutic services for medical diagnosis, treatment and care of injured, disabled, or sick persons;
- Rehabilitation services for injured, disabled, or sick persons; or
- Psychiatric services for the diagnosis and treatment of mentally ill patients.

B. Disorders Subject to the Limitation

The term "mental, psychoneurotic, and personality disorders" is defined as the specific psychiatric diagnoses described in the International Classification of Diseases, 9th Revision (ICD-9), under the code range 290-319. When the treatment services rendered are both for a psychiatric diagnosis as defined in the ICD-9 and one or more nonpsychiatric conditions, separate the expenses for the psychiatric aspects of treatment from the expenses for the nonpsychiatric aspects of treatment. However, in any case in which the psychiatric treatment component is not readily distinguishable from the nonpsychiatric treatment component, all of the expenses are allocated to whichever component constitutes the primary diagnosis.

1. Diagnosis Clearly Meets Definition –If the primary diagnosis reported for a particular service is the same as or equivalent to a condition described in the ICD-9 under the code range 290-319 that represents mental,

psychoneurotic and personality disorders, the expense for the service is subject to the limitation except as described in subsection

2. Diagnosis Does Not Clearly Meet Definition -When it is not clear whether the primary diagnosis reported meets the definition of mental, psychoneurotic, and personality disorders, it may be necessary to contact the practitioner to clarify the diagnosis. In deciding whether contact is necessary in a given case, give consideration to such factors as the type of services rendered, the diagnosis, and the individual's previous utilization history.

C. Services Subject to the Limitation

Medicare Contractors must apply the limitation to claims for professional services that represent mental health treatment furnished to individuals who are not hospital inpatients by physicians, clinical psychologists, clinical social workers, nurse practitioners, clinical nurse specialists and physician assistants. Items and supplies furnished by physicians or other mental health practitioners in connection with treatment are also subject to the limitation.

Generally, Medicare Contractors must apply the limitation only to treatment services. However, diagnostic psychological and neuropsychological testing services performed to evaluate a patient's progress during treatment are considered part of treatment and are subject to the limitation.

D. Services Not Subject to the Limitation

1. Diagnosis of Alzheimer's Disease or Related Disorder -When the primary diagnosis reported for a particular service is Alzheimer's Disease or an Alzheimer's related disorder, Medicare Contractors must look to the nature of the service that has been rendered in determining whether it is subject to the limitation. Alzheimer's disease is coded 331.0 in the "International Classification of Diseases, 9th Revision", which is outside the code range 290-319 that represents mental, psychoneurotic and personality disorders. Additionally, Alzheimer's related disorders are identified by contractors under ICD-9 codes that are within the 290-319 code range (290.XX or others as contractors determine appropriate) or outside the 290-319 code range as determined appropriate by contractors. When the primary treatment rendered to a patient with a diagnosis of Alzheimer's disease or a related disorder is psychotherapy, it is subject to the limitation. However, typically, treatment provided to a patient with a diagnosis of Alzheimer's Disease or a related disorder represents medical management of the patient's condition (such as described under CPT® code 90862 or any successor code) and is not subject to the limitation. CPT® code 90862 describes pharmacologic management, including prescription, use, and review of medication with no more than minimal medical psychotherapy.

2. Brief Office Visits for Monitoring or Changing Drug Prescriptions -Brief office visits for the sole purpose of monitoring or changing drug prescriptions used in the treatment of mental, psychoneurotic and personality disorders are not subject to the limitation. These visits are reported using HCPCS code M0064 or any successor code (brief office visit for the sole purpose of monitoring or changing drug prescriptions used in the treatment of mental, psychoneurotic, and personality disorders). Claims where the diagnosis reported is a mental, psychoneurotic, or personality disorder (other than a diagnosis specified in subsection A) are subject to the limitation except for

the procedure identified by HCPCS code M0064 or any successor code.

3. Diagnostic Services –Medicare Contractors do not apply the limitation to psychiatric diagnostic evaluations and diagnostic psychological and neuropsychological tests performed to establish or confirm the patient's diagnosis. Diagnostic services include psychiatric diagnostic evaluations billed under CPT® codes 90801 or 90802 (or any successor codes) and, psychological and neuropsychological tests billed under CPT® code range 96101-96118 (or any successor code range).

An initial visit to a practitioner for professional services often combines diagnostic evaluation and the start of therapy. Such a visit is neither solely diagnostic nor solely therapeutic. Therefore, contractors must deem the initial visit to be diagnostic so that the limitation does not apply. Separating diagnostic and therapeutic components of a visit is not administratively feasible, unless the practitioner already has separately identified them on the bill. Determining the entire visit to be therapeutic is not justifiable since some diagnostic work must be done before even a tentative diagnosis can be made and certainly before therapy can be instituted. Moreover, the patient should not be disadvantaged because therapeutic as well as diagnostic services were provided in the initial visit. In the rare cases where a practitioner's diagnostic services take more than one visit, Medicare contractors must not apply the limitation to the additional visits. However, it is expected such cases are few. Therefore, when a practitioner bills for more than one visit for professional diagnostic services, Medicare contractors may find it necessary to request documentation to justify the reason for more than one diagnostic visit.

4. Partial Hospitalization Services Not Directly Provided by a Physician or a Practitioner -The limitation does not apply to partial hospitalization services that are not directly provided by a physician, clinical psychologist, nurse practitioner, clinical nurse specialist or a physician assistant. Partial hospitalization services are billed by hospital outpatient departments and community mental health centers (CMHCs) to Medicare Contractors. However, services furnished by physicians, clinical psychologists, nurse practitioners, clinical nurse specialists, and physician assistants to partial hospitalization patients are billed separately from the partial hospitalization program of services. Accordingly, these professional's mental health services to partial hospitalization patients are paid under the physician fee schedule by Medicare Contractors and may be subject to the limitation. (See chapter 4, section 260.1C).

E. Computation of Limitation

Medicare Contractors determine the Medicare approved payment amount for services subject to the limitation. They:

- Multiply the approved amount by the limitation percentage amount;
- Subtract any unsatisfied deductible; and,
- Multiply the remainder by 0.8 to obtain the amount of Medicare payment.

The beneficiary is responsible for the difference between the amount paid by Medicare and the full Medicare approved amount.

The following examples illustrate the application of the limitation in various circumstances as it is gradually reduced under section 102 of the Medicare Improvements for Patients

171

and Providers Act (MIPPA). Please note that although the calendar year 2009 Part B deductible of $135 is used under these examples, the actual deductible amount for calendar year 2010 and future years is unknown and will be subject to change.

Example #1: In 2010, a clinical psychologist submits a claim for $200 for outpatient treatment of a patient's mental disorder. The Medicare-approved amount is $180. Since clinical psychologists must accept assignment, the patient is not liable for the $20 in excess charges. The patient previously satisfied the $135 annual Part B deductible. The limitation reduces the amount of incurred expenses to 68 ¾ percent of the approved amount. Medicare pays 80 percent of the remaining incurred expenses. The Medicare payment and patient liability are computed as follows:

1. Actual charges $200.00
2. Medicare-approved amount $180.00
3. Medicare incurred expenses (0.6875 x line 2 .... $123.75
4. Unmet deductible $0.00
5. Remainder after subtracting deductible
   (line 3 minus line 4) $123.75
6. Medicare payment (0.80 x line 5) $99.00
7. Patient liability (line 2 minus line 6) $81.00

Example #2: In 2012, a clinical social worker submits a claim for $135 for outpatient treatment of a patient's mental disorder. The Medicare-approved amount is $120. Since clinical social workers must accept assignment, the patient is not liable for the $15 in excess charges. The limitation reduces the amount of incurred expenses to 75 percent of the approved amount. The patient previously satisfied $70 of the $135 annual Part B deductible, leaving $65 unmet. The Medicare payment and patient liability are computed as follows:

1. Actual charges $135.00
2. Medicare-approved amount $120.00
3. Medicare incurred expenses (0.75 x line 2) $90.00
4. Unmet deductible $65.00
5. Remainder after subtracting deductible
   (line 3 minus line 4) $25.00
6. Medicare payment (0.80 x line 5) $20.00
7. Patient liability (line 2 minus line 6) $100.00

Example #3: In calendar year 2013, a physician who does not accept assignment submits a claim for $780 for services in connection with the treatment of a mental disorder that did not require inpatient hospitalization. The Medicare-approved amount is $750. Because the physician does not accept assignment, the patient is liable for the $30 in excess charges. The patient has not satisfied any of the $135 Part B annual deductible. The Medicare payment and patient liability are computed as follows:

1. Actual charges $780.00
2. Medicare-approved amount $750.00
3. Medicare incurred expenses (0.8125 x line 2) $609.38
4. Unmet deductible $135.00
5. Remainder after subtracting deductible
   (line 3 minus line 4) $474.38
6. Medicare payment (0.80 x line 5) $379.50
7. Patient liability (line 1 minus line 6) $400.50

Example #4: A patient's Part B expenses during calendar year 2014 are for a physician's services in connection with the treatment of a mental disorder that initially required inpatient hospitalization, with subsequent physician services furnished on an outpatient basis. The patient has not satisfied any of the $135 Part B deductible. The physician accepts assignment and submits a claim for $780. The Medicare-approved amount is

$750. Since the limitation will be completely phased out as of January 1, 2014, the entire $750 Medicare-approved amount is recognized as the total incurred expenses because such expenses are no longer reduced. Also, there is no longer any distinction between mental health services the patient receives as an inpatient or outpatient. The Medicare payment and patient liability are computed as follows:

1. Actual charges $780.00
2. Medicare-approved amount $750.00
3. Medicare incurred expenses (1.00 x line 2) $750.00
4. Unmet deductible $135.00
5. Remainder after subtracting deductible
   (line 3 minus line 4) $615.00
6. Medicare payment (0.80 x line 5) $492.00
   Beneficiary liability (line 2 minus line 6) $258.00

100-4, Chapter 13, 40

Magnetic Resonance Imaging (MRI) Procedures

Effective September 28, 2009

The Centers for Medicare & Medicaid Services (CMS) finds that the non-coverage of magnetic resonance imaging (MRI) for blood flow determination is no longer supported by the available evidence. CMS is removing the phrase "blood flow measurement" and local Medicare contractors will have the discretion to cover (or not cover).

Consult Publication (Pub.) 100-03, National Coverage Determinations (NCD) Manual, chapter 1, section 220.2, for specific coverage and non-coverage indications associated with MRI and MRA (Magnetic Resonance Angiography).

Prior to January 1, 2007

Carriers do not make additional payments for three or more MRI sequences. The relative value units (RVUs) reflect payment levels for two sequences.

The technical component (TC) RVUs for MRI procedures that specify "with contrast" include payment for paramagnetic contrast media. Carriers do not make separate payment under code A4647.

A diagnostic technique has been developed under which an MRI of the brain or spine is first performed without contrast material, then another MRI is performed with a standard (0.1mmol/kg) dose of contrast material and, based on the need to achieve a better image, a third MRI is performed with an additional double dosage (0.2mmol/kg) of contrast material. When the high-dose contrast technique is utilized, carriers:

- Do not pay separately for the contrast material used in the second MRI procedure;
- Pay for the contrast material given for the third MRI procedure through supply code Q9952, the replacement code for A4643, when billed with Current Procedural Terminology (CPT®) codes 70553, 72156, 72157, and 72158;
- Do not pay for the third MRI procedure. For example, in the case of an MRI of the brain, if CPT® code 70553 (without contrast material, followed by with contrast material(s) and further sequences) is billed, make no payment for CPT® code 70551 (without contrast material(s)), the additional procedure given for the purpose of administering the double dosage, furnished during the same session. Medicare does not pay for the third procedure (as distinguished from the contrast material) because the CPT® definition of code 70553 includes all further sequences; and

- Do not apply the payment criteria for low osmolar contrast media in §30.1.2 to billings for code Q9952, the replacement code for A4643.

Effective January 1, 2007

With the implementation for calendar year 2007 of a bottom-up methodology, which utilizes the direct inputs to determine the practice expense (PE) relative value units (RVUs), the cost of the contrast media is not included in the PE RVUs. Therefore, a separate payment for the contrast media used in various imaging procedures is paid. In addition to the CPT® code representing the imaging procedure, separately bill the appropriate HCPCS "Q" code (Q9945 –Q9954; Q9958-Q9964) for the contrast medium utilized in performing the service.

Effective February 24, 2011

Medicare will allow for coverage of MRI for beneficiaries with implanted PMs or cardioverter defibrillators (ICDs) for use in an MRI environment in a Medicare-approved clinical study as described in section 220.C.1 of the NCD manual.

Effective July 7, 2011

Medicare will allow for coverage of MRI for beneficiaries with implanted pacemakers (PMs) when the PMs are used according to the Food and Drug Administration (FDA)-approved labeling for use in an MRI environment as described in section 220.2.C.1 of the NCD Manual.

100-4, Chapter 13, 40.1.2

HCPCS Coding Requirements

Providers must report HCPCS codes when submitting claims for MRA of the chest, abdomen, head, neck or peripheral vessels of lower extremities. The following HCPCS codes should be used to report these services:

MRA of head	70544, 70544-26, 70544-TC
MRA of head	70545, 70545-26, 70545-TC
MRA of head	70546, 70546-26, 70546-TC
MRA of neck	70547, 70547-26, 70547-TC
MRA of neck	70548, 70548-26, 70548-TC
MRA of neck	70549, 70549-26, 70549-TC
MRA of chest	71555, 71555-26, 71555-TC
MRA of pelvis	72198, 72198-26, 72198-TC
MRA of abdomen (dates of service on or after July 1, 2003) –see below.	74185, 74185-26, 74185-TC
MRA of peripheral vessels of lower extremities	73725, 73725-26, 73725-TC

100-4, Chapter 13, 60

Positron Emission Tomography (PET) Scans – General Information

Positron emission tomography (PET) is a noninvasive imaging procedure that assesses perfusion and the level of metabolic activity in various organ systems of the human body. A positron camera (tomograph) is used to produce cross-sectional tomographic images which are obtained by detecting radioactivity from a radioactive tracer substance (radiopharmaceutical) that emits a radioactive tracer substance (radiopharmaceutical FDG) such as 2 –[F-18] flouro-D-glucose FDG, that is administered intravenously to the patient.

The Medicare National Coverage Determinations (NCD) Manual, chapter 1, §220.6, contains additional coverage instructions to indicate the conditions under which a PET scan is performed.

A. Definitions

For all uses of PET, excluding Rubidium 82 for perfusion of the heart, myocardial viability and refractory seizures, the following definitions apply:

Diagnosis: PET is covered only in clinical situations in which the PET results may assist in avoiding an invasive diagnostic procedure, or in which the PET results may assist in determining the optimal anatomical location to perform an invasive diagnostic procedure. In general, for most solid tumors, a tissue diagnosis is made prior to the performance of PET scanning. PET scans following a tissue diagnosis are generally performed for the purpose of staging, rather than diagnosis. Therefore, the use of PET in the diagnosis of lymphoma, esophageal and colorectal cancers, as well as in melanoma, should be rare. PET is not covered for other diagnostic uses, and is not covered for screening (testing of patients without specific signs and symptoms of disease).

Staging: PET is covered in clinical situations in which (1) (a) the stage of the cancer remains in doubt after completion of a standard diagnostic workup, including conventional imaging (computed tomography, magnetic resonance imaging, or ultrasound) or, (b) the use of PET would also be considered reasonable and necessary if it could potentially replace one or more conventional imaging studies when it is expected that conventional study information is insufficient for the clinical management of the patient and, (2) clinical management of the patient would differ depending on the stage of the cancer identified.

NOTE: Effective for services on or after April 3, 2009, the terms "diagnosis" and "staging" will be replaced with "Initial Treatment Strategy." For further information on this new term, refer to Pub. 100-03, NCD Manual, section 220.6.17.

Restaging: PET will be covered for restaging: (1) after the completion of treatment for the purpose of detecting residual disease, (2) for detecting suspected recurrence ,or metastasis, (3) to determine the extent of a known recurrence, or (4) if it could potentially replace one or more conventional imaging studies when it is expected that conventional study information is to determine the extent of a known recurrence, or if study information is insufficient for the clinical management of the patient. Restaging applies to testing after a course of treatment is completed and is covered subject to the conditions above.

Monitoring: Use of PET to monitor tumor response to treatment during the planned course of therapy (i.e., when a change in therapy is anticipated).

NOTE: Effective for services on or after April 3, 2009, the terms "restaging" and "monitoring" will be replaced with "Subsequent Treatment Strategy." For further information on this new term, refer to Pub. 100-03, NCD Manual, section 220.6.17.

B. Limitations

For staging and restaging: PET is covered in either/or both of the following circumstances:

- The stage of the cancer remains in doubt after completion of a standard diagnostic workup, including conventional imaging (computed tomography, magnetic resonance imaging, or ultrasound); and/or

- The clinical management of the patient would differ depending on the stage of the cancer identified. PET will be covered for restaging after the completion of treatment for the purpose of detecting residual disease, for detecting suspected recurrence, or to determine the extent of a known recurrence. Use of PET would also be considered reasonable and necessary if it could potentially replace one or more conventional imaging studies when it is expected that conventional study information is insufficient for the clinical management of the patient.

The PET is not covered for other diagnostic uses, and is not covered for screening (testing of patients without specific symptoms). Use of PET to monitor tumor response during the planned course of therapy (i.e., when no change in therapy is being contemplated) is not covered.

100-4, Chapter 13, 60.3

PET Scan Qualifying Conditions and HCPCS Code Chart

Below is a summary of all covered PET scan conditions, with effective dates.

NOTE: The G codes below except those a # can be used to bill for PET Scan services through January 27, 2005. Effective for dates of service on or after January 28, 2005, providers must bill for PET Scan services using the appropriate CPT® codes. See section 60.3.1. The G codes with a # can continue to be used for billing after January 28, 2005 and these remain non-covered by Medicare. (**NOTE:** PET Scanners must be FDA-approved.)

Conditions	Coverage Effective Date	****HCPCS/ CPT®
*Myocardial perfusion imaging (following previous PET G0030-G0047) single study, rest or stress (exercise and/or pharmacologic)	3/14/95	G0030
*Myocardial perfusion imaging (following previous PET G0030-G0047) multiple studies, rest or stress (exercise and/or pharmacologic)	3/14/95	G0031
*Myocardial perfusion imaging (following rest SPECT, 78464); single study, rest or stress (exercise and/or pharmacologic)	3/14/95	G0032
*Myocardial perfusion imaging (following rest SPECT 78464); multiple studies, rest or stress (exercise and/or pharmacologic)	3/14/95	G0033
*Myocardial perfusion (following stress SPECT 78465); single study, rest or stress (exercise and/or pharmacologic)	3/14/95	G0034
*Myocardial Perfusion Imaging (following stress SPECT 78465); multiple studies, rest or stress (exercise and/or pharmacologic)	3/14/95	G0035
*Myocardial Perfusion Imaging (following coronary angiography 93510-93529); single study, rest or stress (exercise and/or pharmacologic)	3/14/95	G0036

Conditions	Coverage Effective Date	****HCPCS/ CPT®
*Myocardial Perfusion Imaging, (following coronary angiography), 93510-93529); multiple studies, rest or stress (exercise and/or pharmacologic)	3/14/95	G0037
*Myocardial Perfusion Imaging (following stress planar myocardial perfusion, 78460); single study, rest or stress (exercise and/or pharmacologic)	3/14/95	G0038
*Myocardial Perfusion Imaging (following stress planar myocardial perfusion, 78460); multiple studies, rest or stress (exercise and/or pharmacologic)	3/14/95	G0039
*Myocardial Perfusion Imaging (following stress echocardiogram 93350); single study, rest or stress (exercise and/or pharmacologic)	3/14/95	G0040
*Myocardial Perfusion Imaging (following stress echocardiogram, 93350); multiple studies, rest or stress (exercise and/or pharmacologic)	3/14/95	G0041
*Myocardial Perfusion Imaging (following stress nuclear ventriculogram 78481 or 78483); single study, rest or stress (exercise and/or pharmacologic)	3/14/95	G0042
*Myocardial Perfusion Imaging (following stress nuclear ventriculogram 78481 or 78483); multiple studies, rest or stress (exercise and/or pharmacologic)	3/14/95	G0043
*Myocardial Perfusion Imaging (following stress ECG, 93000); single study, rest or stress (exercise and/or pharmacologic)	3/14/95	G0044
*Myocardial perfusion (following stress ECG, 93000), multiple studies; rest or stress (exercise and/or pharmacologic)	3/14/95	G0045
*Myocardial perfusion (following stress ECG, 93015), single study; rest or stress (exercise and/or pharmacologic)	3/14/95	G0046
*Myocardial perfusion (following stress ECG, 93015); multiple studies, rest or stress (exercise and/or pharmacologic)	3/14/95	G0047
PET imaging regional or whole body; single pulmonary nodule	1/1/98	G0125
Lung cancer, non-small cell (PET imaging whole body) Diagnosis, Initial Staging, Restaging	7/1/01	G0210 G0211 G0212
Colorectal cancer (PET imaging whole body) Diagnosis, Initial Staging, Restaging	7/1/01	G0213 G0214 G0215
Melanoma (PET imaging whole body) Diagnosis, Initial Staging, Restaging	7/1/01	G0216 G0217 G0218
Melanoma for non-covered indications	7/1/01	#G0219
Lymphoma (PET imaging whole body) Diagnosis, Initial Staging, Restaging	7/1/01	G0220 G0221 G0222

Conditions	Coverage Effective Date	****HCPCS/ CPT®
Head and neck cancer; excluding thyroid and CNS cancers (PET imaging whole body or regional) Diagnosis, Initial Staging, Restaging	7/1/01	G0223 G0224 G0225
Esophageal cancer (PET imaging whole body) Diagnosis, Initial Staging, Restaging	7/1/01	G0226 G0227 G0228
Metabolic brain imaging for pre-surgical evaluation of refractory seizures	7/1/01	G0229
Metabolic assessment for myocardial viability following inconclusive SPECT study	7/1/01	G0230
Recurrence of colorectal or colorectal metastatic cancer (PET whole body, gamma cameras only)	1/1/02	G0231
Staging and characterization of lymphoma (PET whole body, gamma cameras only)	1/1/02	G0232
Recurrence of melanoma or melanoma metastatic cancer (PET whole body, gamma cameras only)	1/1/02	G0233
Regional or whole body, for solitary pulmonary nodule following CT, or for initial staging of non-small cell lung cancer (gamma cameras only)	1/1/02	G0234
Non-Covered Service PET imaging, any site not otherwise specified	1/28/05	#G0235
Non-Covered Service Initial diagnosis of breast cancer and/or surgical planning for breast cancer (e.g., initial staging of axillary lymph nodes), not covered (full- and partial-ring PET scanners only)	10/1/02	#G0252
Breast cancer, staging/restaging of local regional recurrence or distant metastases, i.e., staging/restaging after or prior to course of treatment (full- and partial-ring PET scanners only)	10/1/02	G0253
Breast cancer, evaluation of responses to treatment, performed during course of treatment (full- and partial-ring PET scanners only)	10/1/02	G0254
Myocardial imaging, positron emission tomography (PET), metabolic evaluation)	10/1/02	78459
Restaging or previously treated thyroid cancer of follicular cell origin following negative I-131 whole body scan (full- and partial-ring PET scanner only)	10/1/03	G0296
Tracer Rubidium**82 (Supply of Radiopharmaceutical Diagnostic Imaging Agent) (This is only billed through Outpatient Perspective Payment System, OPPS.) (Carriers must use HCPCS Code A4641).	10/1/03	Q3000
Supply of Radiopharmaceutical Diagnostic Imaging Agent, Ammonia N-13	01/1/04	A9526

Conditions	Coverage Effective Date	****HCPCS/ CPT®
PET imaging, brain imaging for the differential diagnosis of Alzheimer's disease with aberrant features vs. fronto-temporal dementia	09/15/04	Appropriate CPT® Code from section 60.3.1
PET Cervical Cancer Staging as adjunct to conventional imaging, other staging, diagnosis, restaging, monitoring	1/28/05	Appropriate CPT® Code from section 60.3.1

*NOTE: Carriers must report A4641 for the tracer Rubidium 82 when used with PET scan codes G0030 through G0047 for services performed on or before January 27, 2005.

**NOTE: Not FDG PET

***NOTE: For dates of service October 1, 2003, through December 31, 2003, use temporary code Q4078 for billing this radiopharmaceutical.

100-4, Chapter 13, 60.3.1

Appropriate CPT® Codes Effective for PET Scans for Services Performed on or After January 28, 2005

NOTE: All PET scan services require the use of a radiopharmaceutical diagnostic imaging agent (tracer). The applicable tracer code should be billed when billing for a PET scan service. See section 60.3.2 below for applicable tracer codes.

CPT® Code	Description
78459	Myocardial imaging, positron emission tomography (PET), metabolic evaluation
78491	Myocardial imaging, positron emission tomography (PET), perfusion, single study at rest or stress
78492	Myocardial imaging, positron emission tomography (PET), perfusion, multiple studies at rest and/or stress
78608	Brain imaging, positron emission tomography (PET); metabolic evaluation
78811	Tumor imaging, positron emission tomography (PET); limited area (eg, chest, head/neck)
78812	Tumor imaging, positron emission tomography (PET); skull base to mid-thigh
78813	Tumor imaging, positron emission tomography (PET); whole body
78814	Tumor imaging, positron emission tomography (PET) with concurrently acquired computed tomography (CT) for attenuation correction and anatomical localization; limited area (e.g., chest, head/neck)
78815	Tumor imaging, positron emission tomography (PET) with concurrently acquired computed tomography (CT) for attenuation correction and anatomical localization; skull base to mid-thigh
78816	Tumor imaging, positron emission tomography (PET) with concurrently acquired computed tomography (CT) for attenuation correction and anatomical localization; whole body

100-4, Chapter 13, 60.3.2

Tracer Codes Required for PET Scans

The following tracer codes are applicable only to CPT® 78491 and 78492. They can not be reported with any other code.

Institutional providers billing the fiscal intermediary

HCPCS	Description
*A9555	Rubidium Rb-82, Diagnostic, Per study dose, Up To 60 Millicuries
* Q3000 (Deleted effective 12/31/05)	Supply of Radiopharmaceutical Diagnostic Imaging Agent, Rubidium Rb-82, per dose
A9526	Nitrogen N-13 Ammonia, Diagnostic, Per study dose, Up To 40 Millicuries

NOTE: For claims with dates of service prior to 1/01/06, providers report Q3000 for supply of radiopharmaceutical diagnostic imaging agent, Rubidium Rb-82. For claims with dates of service 1/01/06 and later, providers report A9555 for radiopharmaceutical diagnostic imaging agent, Rubidium Rb-82 in place of Q3000.

Physicians / practitioners billing the carrier:

*A4641	Supply of Radiopharmaceutical Diagnostic Imaging Agent, Not Otherwise Classified
A9526	Nitrogen N-13 Ammonia, Diagnostic, Per study dose, Up To 40 Millicuries
A9555	Rubidium Rb-82, Diagnostic, Per study dose, Up To 60 Millicuries

*NOTE: Effective January 1, 2008, tracer code A4641 is not applicable for PET Scans.

The following tracer codes are applicable only to CPT® 78459, 78608, 78811-78816. They can not be reported with any other code:

Institutional providers billing the fiscal intermediary:

* A9552	Fluorodeoxyglucose F18, FDG, Diagnostic, Per study dose, Up to 45 Millicuries
* C1775 (Deleted effective 12/31/05)	Supply of Radiopharmaceutical Diagnostic Imaging Agent, Fluorodeoxyglucose F18, (2-Deoxy-2-18F Fluoro-D-Glucose), Per dose (4-40 Mci/Ml)
**A4641	Supply of Radiopharmaceutical Diagnostic Imaging Agent, Not Otherwise Classified

The following tracer codes are applicable only to CPT® 78811-78816. They can not be reported with any other code:

A9580	Sodium Fluoride F-18, Diagnostic, per study dose, up to 30 Millicuries

NOTE: For claims with dates of service prior to 1/01/06, OPPS hospitals report C1775 for supply of radiopharmaceutical diagnostic imaging agent, Fluorodeoxyglucose F18. For claims with dates of service 1/01/06 and later, providers report A9552 for radiopharmaceutical diagnostic imaging agent, Fluorodeoxyglucose F18 in place of C1775.

**NOTE: Effective January 1, 2008, tracer code A4641 is not applicable for PET Scans.

***NOTE: Effective for claims with dates of service February 26, 2010 and later, tracer code A9580 is applicable for PET Scans.

Physicians / practitioners billing the carrier:

A9552	Fluorodeoxyglucose F18, FDG, Diagnostic, Per study dose, Up to 45 Millicuries
*A4641	Supply of Radiopharmaceutical Diagnostic Imaging Agent, Not Otherwise Classified

The following tracer code is applicable only to 78811-78816. They can not be reported with any other code:

A9580	Sodium Fluoride F-18, Diagnostic, per study dose, up to 30 Millicuries

*NOTE: Effective January 1, 2008, tracer code A4641 is not applicable for PET Scans.

***NOTE: Effective for claims with dates of service February 26, 2010 and later, tracer code A9580 is applicable for PET Scans.

CPT®	Short Descriptor	Tracer/ Code	or	Tracer/ Code	Comment
78459	Myocardial imaging, positron emission tomography (PET), metabolic imaging	FDG A9552	--	--	N/A
78491	Myocardial imaging, positron emission tomography (PET), perfusion; single study at rest or stress	N-13 A9526	or	Rb-82 A9555	N/A
78492	Myocardial imaging, positron emission tomography (PET), perfusion; multiple studies at rest and/or stress	N-13 A9526	or	Rb-82 A9555	N/A
78608	Brain imaging, positron emission tomography (PET); metabolic evaluation	FDG A9552	--	--	Covered indications: Alzheimer's disease/ dementias, intractable seizures Note: This code is also covered for dedicated PET brain tumor imaging.
78609	Brain imaging, positron emission tomography (PET); perfusion evaluation	--	--	--	Nationally noncovered
78811	Positron emission tomography (PET) imaging; limited area (e.g, chest, head/neck)	FDG A9552	or	NaF-18 A9580	NaF-18 PET is covered only to identify bone metastasis of cancer.
78812	Positron emission tomography (PET) imaging, skull base to mid-thigh	FDG A9552	or	NaF-18 A9580	NaF-18 PET is covered only to identify bone metastasis of cancer.
78813	Positron emission tomography (PET) imaging, whole body	FDG A9552	or	NaF-18 A9580	NaF-18 PET s covered only to identify bone metastasis of cancer.

CPT®	Short Descriptor	Tracer/ Code	or	Tracer/ Code	Comment
78814	PET/CT imaging, limited area (e.g., chest, head/neck)	FDG A9552	or	NaF-18 A9580	NaF-18 PET is covered only to identify bone metastasis of cancer.
78815	PET/CT imaging, skull base to mid-thigh	FDG A9552	or	NaF-18 A9580	NaF-18 PET is covered only to identify bone metastasis of cancer.
78816	PET/CT imaging, whole body	FDG A9552	or	NaF-18 A9580	NaF-18 PET is covered only to identify bone metastasis of cancer.

Format 100-4, Chapter 13, 60.13

Billing Requirements for PET Scans for Specific Indications of Cervical Cancer for Services Performed on or After January 28, 2005

Contractors shall accept claims for these services with the appropriate CPT® code listed in section 60.3.1. Refer to Pub. 100-03, section 220.6.17, for complete coverage guidelines for this new PET oncology indication. The implementation date for these CPT® codes will be April 18, 2005. Also see section 60.17, of this chapter for further claims processing instructions for cervical cancer indications.

100-4, Chapter 13, 60.14

Billing Requirements for PET Scans for Non-Covered Indications

For services performed on or after January 28, 2005, contractors shall accept claims with the following HCPCS code for non-covered PET indications:

-G0235: PET imaging, any site not otherwise specified Short Descriptor: PET not otherwise specified Type of Service:4

NOTE: This code is for a non-covered service.

100-4, Chapter 13, 60.15

Billing Requirements for CMS -Approved Clinical Trials and Coverage With Evidence Development Claims for PET Scans for Neurodegenerative Diseases, Previously Specified Cancer Indications, and All Other Cancer Indications Not Previously Specified

-Parts A and B Medicare Administrative Contractors (MACs)

Effective for services on or after January 28, 2005, contractors shall accept and pay for claims for Positron Emission Tomography (PET) scans for lung cancer, esophageal cancer, colorectal cancer, lymphoma, melanoma, head & neck cancer, breast cancer, thyroid cancer, soft tissue sarcoma, brain cancer, ovarian cancer, pancreatic cancer, small cell lung cancer, and testicular cancer, as well as for neurodegenerative diseases and all other cancer indications not previously mentioned in this chapter, if these scans were performed as part of a Centers for Medicare & Medicaid (CMS)-approved clinical trial. (See Pub. 100-03, National Coverage Determinations (NCD) Manual, sections 220.6.13 and 220.6.17.)

Contractors shall also be aware that PET scans for all cancers not previously specified at Pub. 100-03, NCD Manual, section 220.6.17, remain nationally non-covered unless performed in conjunction with a CMS-approved clinical trial.

Effective for dates of service on or after June 11, 2013, Medicare has ended the coverage with evidence development (CED) requirement for FDG (2-[F18] fluoro-2-deoxy-D-glucose) PET and PET/computed tomography (CT) and PET/magnetic resonance imaging (MRI) for all oncologic indications contained in section 220.6.17 of the NCD Manual. Modifier -Q0 (Investigational clinical service provided in a clinical research study that is in an approved clinical research study) or -Q1 (routine clinical service provided in a clinical research study that is in an approved clinical research study) is no longer mandatory for these services when performed on or after June 11, 2013.

-Part B MACs Only

Part B MACs shall pay claims for PET scans for beneficiaries participating in a CMS-approved clinical trial submitted with an appropriate current procedural terminology (CPT®) code from section 60.3.1 of this chapter and modifier -Q0/-Q1 for services performed on or after January 1, 2008, through June 10, 2013. (NOTE: Modifier -QR (Item or service provided in a Medicare specified study) and -QA (FDA investigational device exemption) were replaced by modifier -Q0 effective January 1, 2008.) Modifier -QV (item or service provided as routine care in a Medicare qualifying clinical trial) was replaced by modifier -Q1 effective January 1, 2008.) Beginning with services performed on or after June 11, 2013, modifier -Q0/-Q1 is no longer required for PET FDG services.

Part A MACs Only

In order to pay claims for PET scans on behalf of beneficiaries participating in a CMS-approved clinical trial, Part A MACs require providers to submit claims with ICD-9/ICD-10 code V70.7/Z00.6 in the primary/secondary diagnosis position on the CMS-1450 (UB-04), or the electronic equivalent, with the appropriate principal diagnosis code and an appropriate CPT® code from section 60.3.1. Effective for PET scan claims for dates of service on or after January 28, 2005, through December 31, 2007, FIs shall accept claims with the –QR, -QV, or -QA modifier on other than inpatient claims. Effective for services on or after January 1, 2008, through June 10, 2013, modifier -Q0 replaced the -QR and –QA modifier, modifier –Q1 replaced the –QV modifier. Modifier -Q0/-Q1 is no longer required for services performed on or after June 11, 2013.

100-4, Chapter 13, 60.16

Billing and Coverage Changes for PET Scans Effective for Services on or After April 3, 2009

A. Summary of Changes

Effective for services on or after April 3, 2009, Medicare will not cover the use of FDG PET imaging to determine initial treatment strategy in patients with adenocarcinoma of the prostate.

Medicare will also not cover FDG PET imaging for subsequent treatment strategy for tumor types other than breast, cervical, colorectal, esophagus, head and neck (non-CNS/thyroid), lymphoma ,melanoma, myeloma, non-small cell lung, and ovarian, unless the FDG PET is provided under the coverage with evidence development (CED) paradigm (billed with modifier -Q0/-Q1, see section 60.15 of this chapter).

Medicare will cover FDG PET imaging for initial treatment strategy for myeloma.

For further information regarding the changes in coverage, refer to Pub.100-03, NCD Manual, section 220.6.17.

B. Modifiers for PET Scans

Effective for claims with dates of service on or after April 3, 2009, the following modifiers have been created for use to inform for the initial treatment strategy of biopsy-proven or strongly suspected tumors or subsequent treatment strategy of cancerous tumors:

PI -Positron Emission Tomography (PET) or PET/Computed Tomography (CT) to inform the initial treatment strategy of tumors that are biopsy proven or strongly suspected of being cancerous based on other diagnostic testing.

Short descriptor: PET tumor init tx strat

PS -Positron Emission Tomography (PET) or PET/Computed Tomography (CT) to inform the subsequent treatment strategy of cancerous tumors when the beneficiary's treatment physician determines that the PET study is needed to inform subsequent anti-tumor strategy.

Short descriptor: PS -PET tumor subsq tx strategy

C. Billing for A/B MACs

Effective for claims with dates of service on or after April 3, 2009, contractors shall accept FDG PET claims billed to inform initial treatment strategy with the following CPT® codes AND modifier –PI: 78608, 78811, 78812, 78813, 78814, 78815, 78816.

Effective for claims with dates of service on or after April 3, 2009, contractors shall accept FDG PET claims with modifier –PS for the subsequent treatment strategy for solid tumors using a CPT® code above AND a cancer diagnosis code.

Contractors shall also accept FDG PET claims billed to inform initial treatment strategy or subsequent treatment strategy when performed under CED with one of the PET or PET/CT CPT® codes above AND modifier -PI OR modifier -PS AND a cancer diagnosis code AND modifier -Q0/Q1. Effective for services performed on or after June 11, 2013, the CED requirement has ended and modifier -Q0/-Q1, along with condition code 30 (institutional claims only), or V70.7 (both institutional and practitioner claims) are no longer required

D. Medicare Summary Notices, Remittance Advice Remark Codes, and Claim Adjustment Reason Codes

Effective for dates of service on or after April 3, 2009, contractors shall return as unprocessable/return to provider claims that do not include the -PI modifier with one of the PET/PET/CT CPT® codes listed in subsection C. above when billing for the initial treatment strategy for solid tumors in accordance with Pub.100-03, NCD Manual, section 220.6.17

In addition, contractors shall return as unprocessable/return to provider claims that do not include the -PS modifier with one of the CPT® codes listed in subsection C. above when billing for the subsequent treatment strategy for solid tumors in accordance with Pub.100-03, NCD Manual, section 220.6.17.

The following messages apply:

-Claim Adjustment Reason Code (CARC) 4 –the procedure code is inconsistent with the modifier used or a required modifier is missing.

-Remittance Advice Remark Code (RARC) MA-130 -Your claim contains incomplete and/or invalid information, and no appeal rights are afforded because the claim is unprocessable. Submit a new claim with the complete/correct information.

-RARC M16 -Alert: See our Web site, mailings, or bulletins for more details concerning this policy/procedure/decision.

Also, effective for claims with dates of service on or after April 3, 2009, through June 10, 2013, contractors shall return as unprocessable/return to provider FDG PET claims billed to inform initial treatment strategy or subsequent treatment strategy when performed under CED without one of the PET/PET/CT CPT® codes listed in subsection C. above AND modifier -PI OR modifier -PS AND a cancer diagnosis code AND modifier -Q0/-Q1.

The following messages apply to return as unprocessable claims:

100-4, Chapter 13, 60.17

Billing and Coverage Changes for PET Scans for Cervical Cancer Effective for Services on or After November 10, 2009

A. Billing Changes for A/B MACs, FIs, and Carriers

Effective for claims with dates of service on or after November 10, 2009, contractors shall accept FDG PET oncologic claims billed to inform initial treatment strategy; specifically for staging in beneficiaries who have biopsy-proven cervical cancer when the beneficiary's treating physician determines the FDG PET study is needed to determine the location and/or extent of the tumor as specified in Pub. 100-03, section 220.6.17.

EXCEPTION: CMS continues to non-cover FDG PET for initial diagnosis of cervical cancer related to initial treatment strategy.

NOTE: Effective for claims with dates of service on and after November 10, 2009, the –Q0 modifier is no longer necessary for FDG PET for cervical cancer.

B. Medicare Summary Notices, Remittance Advice Remark Codes, and Claim Adjustment Reason Codes

Additionally, contractors shall return as unprocessable /return to provider for FDG PET for cervical cancer for initial treatment strategy billed without the following: one of the PET/PET/ CT CPT® codes listed in 60.16 C above AND modifier –PI AND an ICD-9 cervical cancer diagnosis code.

Use the following messages:

-Claim Adjustment Reason Code 4 –the procedure code is inconsistent with the modifier used or a required modifier is missing.

-Remittance Advice Remark Code MA-130 -Your claim contains incomplete and/or invalid information, and no appeal rights are afforded because the claim is unprocessable. Submit a new claim with the complete/correct information.

-Remittance Advice Remark Code M16 -Alert: See our Web site, mailings, or bulletins for more details concerning this policy/procedure/decision.

100-4, Chapter 13, 60.18

Billing and Coverage Changes for PET (NaF-18) Scans to Identify Bone Metastasis of Cancer Effective for Claims With Dates of Services on or After February 26, 2010

A. Billing Changes for A/B MACs, FIs, and Carriers

Effective for claims with dates of service on and after February 26, 2010, contractors shall pay for NaF-18 PET oncologic claims to inform of initial treatment strategy (PI) or subsequent treatment strategy (PS) for suspected or biopsy proven bone metastasis ONLY in the context of a clinical study and as specified in Pub. 100-03, section 220.6. All other claims for NaF-18 PET oncology claims remain non-covered.

B. Medicare Summary Notices, Remittance Advice Remark Codes, and Claim Adjustment Reason Codes

Effective for claims with dates of service on or after February 26, 2010, contractors shall return as unprocessable NaF-18 PET oncologic claims billed with modifier TC or globally (for FIs modifier TC or globally does not apply) and HCPCS A9580 to inform the initial treatment strategy or subsequent treatment strategy for bone metastasis that do not include ALL of the following:

- PI or –PS modifier AND
- PET or PET/CT CPT® code (78811, 78812, 78813, 78814, 78815, 78816) AND
- ICD-9 cancer diagnosis code AND
- Q0 modifier –Investigational clinical service provided in a clinical research study, are present on the claim.

NOTE: For institutional claims, continue to include diagnosis code V70.7 and condition code 30 to denote a clinical study.

Use the following messages:

-Claim Adjustment Reason Code 4 –The procedure code is inconsistent with the modifier used or a required modifier is missing. **Note:** Refer to the 835 Healthcare Policy Identification Segment (loop 2110 Service Payment Information REF), if present.

-Remittance Advice Remark Code MA-130 -Your claim contains incomplete and/or invalid information, and no appeal rights are afforded because the claim is unprocessable. Submit a new claim with the complete/correct information.

-Remittance Advice Remark Code M16 -Alert: See our Web site, mailings, or bulletins for more details concerning this policy/procedure/decision.

-Claim Adjustment Reason Code 167 –This (these) diagnosis(es) is (are) not covered.

Effective for claims with dates of service on or after February 26, 2010, contract ors shall accept PET oncologic claims billed with modifier 26 and modifier KX to inform the initial treatment strategy or strategy or subsequent treatment strategy for bone metastasis that include the following:

- PI or –PS modifier AND
- PET or PET/CT CPT® code (78811, 78812, 78813, 78814, 78815, 78816) AND
- ICD-9 cancer diagnosis code AND
- Q0 modifier –Investigational clinical service provided in a clinical research study, are present on the claim.

NOTE: If modifier KX is present on the professional component service, Contractors shall process the service as PET NaF-18 rather than PET with FDG.

Contractors shall also return as unprocessable NaF-18 PET oncologic professional component claims (i.e., claims billed with modifiers 26and KX) to inform the initial treatment strategy or strategy or subsequent treatment strategy for bone metastasis billed with HCPCS A9580 and use the following message:

Claim Adjustment Reason Code 97 –The benefit for this service is included in the payment/allowance for another service/procedure that has already been adjudicated.

NOTE: Refer to the 835 Healthcare Policy identification Segment (loop 2110 Service Payment Information REF), if present.

100-4, Chapter 13, 140

Bone Mass Measurements (BMMs)

Sections 1861(s)(15)and (rr)(1)of the Social Security Act (the Act) (as added by §4106 of the Balanced Budget Act (BBA) of 1997) standardize Medicare coverage of medically necessary bone mass measurements by providing for uniform coverage under Medicare Part B. This coverage is effective for claims with dates of service furnished on or after July 1, l998.

Effective for dates of service on and after January 1, 2007, the CY 2007 Physician Fee Schedule final rule expanded the number of beneficiaries qualifying for BMM by reducing the dosage requirement for glucocorticoid (steroid) therapy from 7.5 mg of prednisone per day to 5.0 mg. It also changed the definition of BMM by removing coverage for a single-photon absorptiometry as it is not considered reasonable and necessary under section 1862 (a)(1)(A) of the Act. Finally, it required that in the case of monitoring and confirmatory baseline BMMs, they be performed with a dual-energy x-ray absorptiometry (axial) test.

Conditions of Coverage for BMMs are located in Pub.100-02, Medicare Benefit Policy Manual, chapter 15.

100-4, Chapter 14, 40.3

Payment for Intraocular Lens (IOL)

Prior to January 1, 2008, payment for facility services furnished by an ASC for IOL insertion during or subsequent to cataract surgery includes an allowance for the lens. The procedures that include insertion of an IOL are:

Payment Group 6: CPT®-4 Codes 66985 and 66986

Payment Group 8: CPT®-4 Codes 66982, 66983 and 66984

Physicians or suppliers are not paid for an IOL furnished to a beneficiary in an ASC after July 1, 1988. Separate claims for IOLs furnished to ASC patients beginning March 12, 1990 are denied. Also, effective March 12, 1990, procedures 66983 and 66984 are treated as single procedures for payment purposes.

Beginning January 1, 2008, the Medicare payment for the IOL is included in the Medicare ASC payment for the associated surgical procedure. Consequently, no separate payment for the IOL is made, except for a payment adjustment for NTIOLs established according to the process outlined in 42 CFR 416.185. ASCs should not report separate charges for conventional IOLs because their payment is included in the Medicare payment for the associated surgical procedure. The

ASC payment system logic that excluded $150 for IOLs for purposes of the multiple surgery reduction in cases of cataract surgery prior to January 1, 2008 no longer applies, effective for dates of service on or after January 1, 2008.

Effective for dates of service on and after February 27, 2006, through February 26, 2011, Medicare pays an additional $50 for specified Category 3 NTIOLs that are provided in association with a covered ASC surgical procedure. The list of Category 3 NTIOLS is available at:http://www.cms.hhs.gov/ASCPayment/08_NTIOLs.asp#TopOfPage.

ASCs should use HCPCS code Q1003 to bill for a Category 3 NTIOL. HCPCS code Q1003, along with one of the approved surgical procedure codes (CPT® codes 66982, 66983, 66984, 66985, 66986) are to be used on all NTIOL Category 3 claims associated with reduced spherical aberration from February 27, 2006, through February 26, 2011. The payment adjustment for the NTIOL is subject to beneficiary coinsurance but is not wage-adjusted.

Any subsequent IOL recognized by CMS as having the same characteristics as the first NTIOL recognized by CMS for a payment adjustment as a Category III NTIOL (those of reduced spherical aberration) will receive the same adjustment for the remainder of the 5-year period established by the first recognized IOL.

100-4, Chapter 14, 40.8

Payment When a Device is Furnished With No Cost or With Full or Partial Credit Beginning January 1, 2008

Contractors pay ASCs a reduced amount for certain specified procedures when a specified device is furnished without cost or for which either a partial or full credit is received (e.g., device recall). For specified procedure codes that include payment for a device, ASCs are required to include modifier –FB on the procedure code when a specified device is furnished without cost or for which full credit is received. If the ASC receives a partial credit of 50 percent or more of the cost of a specified device, the ASC is required to include modifier –FC on the procedure code if the procedure is on the list of specified procedures to which the -FC reduction applies. A single procedure code should not be submitted with both modifiers –FB and -FC. The pricing determination related to modifiers –FB and -FC is made prior to the application of multiple procedure payment reductions. Contractors adjust beneficiary coinsurance to reflect the reduced payment amount. Tables listing the procedures and devices to which the payment adjustments apply, and the full and partial adjustment amounts, are available on the CMS Web site.

In order to report that the receipt of a partial credit of 50 percent or more of the cost of a device, ASCs have the option of either: 1) Submitting the claim for the procedure to their Medicare contractor after the procedure's performance but prior to manufacturer acknowledgement of credit for a specified device, and subsequently contacting the contractor regarding a claims adjustment once the credit determination is made; or 2) holding the claim for the procedure until a determination is made by the manufacturer on the partial credit and submitting the claim with modifier –FC appended to the implantation procedure HCPCS code if the partial credit is 50 percent or more of the cost of the device. If choosing the first billing option, to request a claims adjustment once the credit determination is made, ASCs should keep in mind that the initial Medicare payment for the procedure involving the device is conditional and subject to adjustment.

100-4, Chapter 14, 40.9

Payment and Coding for Presbyopia Correcting IOLs (P-C IOLs) and Astigmatism Correcting IOLs (A-C IOLs)

CMS payment policies and recognition of P-C IOLs and A-C IOLs are contained in Transmittal 636 (CR3927) and Transmittal 1228 (CR5527) respectively.

Effective for dates of service on and after January 1, 2008, when inserting an approved A-C IOL in an ASC concurrent with cataract extraction, HCPCS code V2787 (Astigmatism-correcting function of intraocular lens) should be billed to report the non-covered charges for the A-C IOL functionality of the inserted intraocular lens. Additionally, note that HCPCS code V2788 (Presbyopia-correcting function of intraocular lens) is no longer valid to report non-covered charges associated with the A-C IOL. However, this code continues to be valid toreport non-covered charges for a P-C IOL. The payment for the conventional lens portion of the A-C IOL and P-C IOL continues to be bundled with the ASC procedure payment.

Effective for services on and after January 1, 2010, ASCs are to bill for insertion of a Category 3 new technology intraocular lens (NTIOL) that is also an approved A-C IOL or P-C IOL, concurrent with cataract extraction, using three separate codes. ASCs shall use HCPCS code V2787 or V2788, as appropriate, to report charges associated with the non-covered functionality of the A-C IOL or P-C IOL, the appropriate HCPCS code 66982 (Extracapsular cataract removal with insertion of intraocular lens prosthesis (one stage procedure), manual or mechanical technique (e.g., irrigation and aspiration or phacoemulsification), complex, requiring devices or techniques not generally used in routine cataract surgery (e.g., iris expansion device, suture support for intraocular lens, or primary posterior capsulorrhexis) or performed on patients in the amblyogenic developmental stage); 66983 (Intracapsular cataract extraction with insertion of intraocular lens prosthesis (1 stage procedure)); or 66984 (Extracapsular cataract removal with insertion of intraocular lens prosthesis (1 stage procedure), manual or mechanical technique (e.g., irrigation and aspiration or phacoemulsification)), to report the covered cataract extraction and insertion procedure; and Q1003 (New technology, intraocular lens, category 3 (reduced spherical aberration) as defined in Federal Register notice, Vol. 65, dated May 3, 2000) to report the covered NTIOL aspect of the lens on claims for insertion of an A-C IOL or P-C IOL that is also designated as an NTIOL. Listings of the CMS-approved Category 3 NTIOLs, A-C IOLs, and P-C IOLs are available on the CMS Web site.

100-4, Chapter 14, 60.1

Applicable Messages for NTIOLs

Contractors shall return as unprocessable any claims for NTIOLs containing Q1003 alone or with a code other than one of the procedure codes listed in 40.3. Use the following messages for these returned claims:

- Claim Adjustment Reason Code 16 -Claim/service lacks information which is needed for adjudication. Additional information is supplied using remittance advice remark codes whenever appropriate.
- RA Remark Code M67 -Missing/Incomplete/Invalid other procedure codes.
- RA Remark Code MA130 -Your claim contains incomplete and/or invalid information, and no appeal rights are afforded because the claim is unprocessable.

Please submit a new claim with the complete/correct information.

Contractors shall deny payment for Q1003 if services are furnished in a facility other than a Medicare-approved ASC. Use the following messages when denying these claims:

- MSN 16.2 -This service cannot be paid when provided in this location/facility.
- Claims Adjustment Reason Code 58 -Payment adjusted because treatment was deemed by the payer to have been rendered in an inappropriate or invalid place of service.

Contractors shall deny payment for Q1003 if billed by an entity other than a Medicare-approved ASC. Use the following messages when denying these claims:

- MSN 33.1 -The ambulatory surgical center must bill for this service.
- Claim Adjustment Reason Code 170 -Payment is denied when performed/billed by this type of provider.

Contractors shall deny payment for Q1003 if submitted for payment past the discontinued date (after the 5-year period, or after February 26, 2011). Use the following messages when denying these claims:

- MSN 21.11 -This service was not covered by Medicare at the time you received it.
- Claim Adjustment Reason Code 27 Expenses incurred after coverage terminated.

Contractors shall deny payment for Q1003 if submitted for payment past the discontinued date (after the 5-year period, or after February 26, 2011). Use the following messages when denying these claims:

- MSN 21.11 -This service was not covered by Medicare at the time you received it.
- Claim Adjustment Reason Code 27 -Expenses incurred after coverage terminated.

Carriers shall deny payment for Q1003 if services are furnished in a facility other than a Medicare-approved ASC. Use the following messages when denying these claims:

- MSN 16.2 -This service cannot be paid when provided in this location/facility.
- Claims Adjustment Reason Code 58 -Payment adjusted because treatment was deemed by the payer to have been rendered in an inappropriate or invalid place of service.

Carriers shall deny payment for Q1003 if billed by an entity other than a Medicare -approved ASC. Use the following messages when denying these claims:

- MSN 33.1 -The ambulatory surgical center must bill for this service.
- Claim Adjustment Reason Code 170 -Payment is denied when performed/billed by this type of provider.

Carriers shall deny payment for Q1003 if submitted for payment past the discontinued date (after the 5-year period, or after February 26, 2011). Use the following messages when denying these claims:

- MSN 21.11 -This service was not covered by Medicare at the time you received it.
- Claim Adjustment Reason Code 27 -Expenses incurred after coverage terminated.

100-4, Chapter 15, 20.1.4

Components of the Ambulance Fee Schedule

The mileage rates provided in this section are the base rates that are adjusted by the yearly ambulance inflation factor (AIF). The payment amount under the fee schedule is determined as follows:

- **For ground ambulance services,** the fee schedule amount includes:
  1. A money amount that serves as a nationally uniform base rate, called a "conversion factor" (CF), for all ground ambulance services;
  2. A relative value unit (RVU) assigned to each type of ground ambulance service;
  3. A geographic adjustment factor (GAF) for each ambulance fee schedule locality area (geographic practice cost index (GPCI));
  4. A nationally uniform loaded mileage rate;
  5. An additional amount for certain mileage for a rural point-of-pickup; and
  6. For specified temporary periods, certain additional payment amounts as described in section 20.1.4A, below.

- **For air ambulance services**, the fee schedule amount includes:
  1. A nationally uniform base rate for fixed wing and a nationally uniform base rate for rotary wing;
  2. A geographic adjustment factor (GAF) for each ambulance fee schedule locality area (GPCI);
  3. A nationally uniform loaded mileage rate for each type of air service; and
  4. A rural adjustment to the base rate and mileage for services furnished for a rural point-of-pickup

A. Ground Ambulance Services

1. Conversion Factor

The conversion factor (CF) is a money amount used to develop a base rate for each category of ground ambulance service. The CF is updated annually by the ambulance inflation factor and for other reasons as necessary.

2. Relative Value Units

Relative value units (RVUs) set a numeric value for ambulance services relative to the value of a base level ambulance service. Since there are marked differences in resources necessary to furnish the various levels of ground ambulance services, different levels of payment are appropriate for the various levels of service. The different payment amounts are based on level of service. An RVU expresses the constant multiplier for a particular type of service (including, where appropriate, an emergency response). An RVU of 1.00 is assigned to the BLS of ground service, e.g., BLS has an RVU of 1; higher RVU values are assigned to the other types of ground ambulance services, which require more service than BLS.

The RVUs are as follows:

Service Level	RVU
BLS	1.00
BLS - Emergency	1.60
ALS1	1.20
ALS1- Emergency	1.90
ALS2	2.75
SCT	3.25
PI	1.75

3. Geographic Adjustment Factor (GAF)

The GAF is one of two factors intended to address regional differences in the cost of furnishing ambulance services. The GAF for the ambulance FS uses the non-facility practice expense (PE) of the geographic practice cost index (GPCI) of the Medicare physician fee schedule to adjust payment to account for regional differences. Thus, the geographic areas applicable to the ambulance FS are the same as those used for the physician fee schedule.

The location where the beneficiary was put into the ambulance (POP) establishes which GPCI applies. For multiple vehicle transports, each leg of the transport is separately evaluated for the applicable GPCI. Thus, for the second (or any subsequent) leg of a transport, the POP establishes the applicable GPCI for that portion of the ambulance transport.

For ground ambulance services, the applicable GPCI is multiplied by 70 percent of the base rate. Again, the base rate for each category of ground ambulance services is the CF multiplied by the applicable RVU. The GPCI is not applied to the ground mileage rate.

4. Mileage

In the context of all payment instructions, the term "mileage" refers to loaded mileage. The ambulance FS provides a separate payment amount for mileage. The mileage rate per statute mile applies for all types of ground ambulance services, except Paramedic Intercept, and is provided to all Medicare contractors electronically by CMS as part of the ambulance FS. Providers and suppliers must report all medically necessary mileage, including the mileage subject to a rural adjustment, in a single line item.

5. Adjustment for Certain Ground Mileage for Rural Points of Pickup (POP)

The payment rate is greater for certain mileage where the POP is in a rural area to account for the higher costs per ambulance trip that are typical of rural operations where fewer trips are made in any given period.

If the POP is a rural ZIP Code, the following calculations should be used to determine the rural adjustment portion of the payment allowance. For loaded miles 1-17, the rural adjustment for ground mileage is 1.5 times the rural mileage allowance.

For services furnished during the period July 1, 2004 through December 31, 2008, a 25 percent increase is applied to the appropriate ambulance FS mileage rate to each mile of a transport (both urban and rural POP) that exceeds 50 miles (i.e., mile 51 and greater).

The following chart summarizes the above information:

Service	Dates of Service	Bonus	Calculation
Loaded miles 1-17, Rural POP	Beginning 4/1/02	50%	FS Rural mileage * 1.5
Loaded miles 18-50, Rural POP	4/1/02 – 12/31/03	25%	FS Rural mileage * 1.25
All loaded miles (Urban or Rural POP) 51+	7/1/04 – 12/31/08	25%	FS Urban or Rural mileage * 1.25

The POP, as identified by ZIP Code, establishes whether a rural adjustment applies to a particular service. Each leg of a multi-leg transport is separately evaluated for a rural adjustment application. Thus, for the second (or any subsequent) leg of a transport, the ZIP Code of the POP establishes whether a rural adjustment applies to such second (or subsequent) transport.

For the purpose of all categories of ground ambulance services except paramedic intercept, a rural area is defined as a U.S. Postal Service (USPS) ZIP Code that is located, in whole or in part, outside of either a Metropolitan Statistical Area (MSA) or in New England, a New England County Metropolitan Area (NECMA), or is an area wholly within an MSA or NECMA that has been identified as rural under the "Goldsmith modification." (The Goldsmith modification establishes an operational definition of rural areas within large counties that contain one or more metropolitan areas. The Goldsmith areas are so isolated by distance or physical features that they are more rural than urban in character and lack easy geographic access to health services.)

For Paramedic Intercept, an area is a rural area if:

- It is designated as a rural area by any law or regulation of a State;
- It is located outside of an MSA or NECMA; or
- It is located in a rural census tract of an MSA as determined under the most recent Goldsmith modification.

See IOM Pub. 100-02, Medicare Benefit Policy Manual, chapter 10 –Ambulance Services, section 30.1.1 –Ground Ambulance Services for coverage requirements for the Paramedic Intercept benefit. Presently, only the State of New York meets these requirements.

Although a transport with a POP located in a rural area is subject to a rural adjustment for mileage, Medicare still pays the lesser of the billed charge or the applicable FS amount for mileage. Thus, when rural mileage is involved, the contractor compares the calculated FS rural mileage payment rate to the provider's/supplier's actual charge for mileage and pays the lesser amount.

The CMS furnishes the ambulance FS files to claims processing contractors electronically. A version of the Ambulance Fee Schedule is also posted to the CMS website (http://www.cms.hhs.gov/AmbulanceFeeSchedule/02_afspuf. asp) for public consumption. To clarify whether a particular ZIP Code is rural or urban, please refer to the most recent version of the Medicare supplied ZIP Code file.

6. Regional Ambulance FS Payment Rate Floor for Ground Ambulance Transports

For services furnished during the period July 1, 2004 through December 31, 2009, the base rate portion of the payment under the ambulance FS for ground ambulance transports is subject to a minimum amount. This minimum amount depends upon the area of the country in which the service is furnished. The country is divided into 9 census divisions and each of the census divisions has a regional FS that is constructed using the same methodology as the national FS. Where the regional FS is greater than the national FS, the base rates for ground ambulance transports are determined by a blend of the national rate and the regional rate in accordance with the following schedule:

Year	National FS Percentage	Regional FS Percentage
7/1/04 - 12/31/04	20%	80%
CY 2005	40%	60%
CY 2006	60%	40%
CY 2007 – CY 2009	80%	20%
CY 2010 and thereafter	100%	0%

Where the regional FS is not greater than the national FS, there is no blending and only the national FS applies. Note that this provision affects only the FS portion of the blended transition payment rate. This floor amount is calculated by CMS centrally and is incorporated into the FS amount that appears in the FS file maintained by CMS and downloaded by CMS contractors. There is no calculation to be done by the Medicare B/MAC or A/MAC in order to implement this provision.

7. Adjustments for FS Payment Rate for Certain Rural Ground Ambulance Transports

For services furnished during the period July 1, 2004 through December 31, 2010, the base rate portion of the payment under the FS for ground ambulance transports furnished in certain rural areas is increased by a percentage amount determined by CMS . Section 3105 (c) and 10311 (c) of the Affordable Care Act amended section 1834 (1) (13) (A) of the Act to extend this rural bonus for an additional year through December 31, 2010. This increase applies if the POP is in a rural county (or Goldsmith area) that is comprised by the lowest quartile by population of all such rural areas arrayed by population density. CMS will determine this bonus amount and the designated POP rural ZIP Codes in which the bonus applies. Beginning on July 1, 2004, rural areas qualifying for the additional bonus amount will be identified with a "B" indicator on the national ZIP Code file. Contractors must apply the additional rural bonus amount as a multiplier to the base rate portion of the FS payment for all ground transports originating in the designated POP ZIP Codes.

Subsequently, section of 106 (c) of the MMEA again amended section 1843 (l) (13) (A) of the Act to extend the rural bonus an additional year, through December 31, 2011

8. Adjustments for FS Payment Rates for Ground Ambulance Transports

The payment rates under the FS for ground ambulance transports (both the fee schedule base rates and the mileage amounts) are increased for services furnished during the period July 1, 2004 through December 31, 2006 as well as July 1, 2008 through December 31, 2010. For ground ambulance transport services furnished where the POP is urban, the rates are increased by 1 percent for claims with dates of service July 1, 2004 through December 31, 2006 in accordance with Section 414 of the Medicare Modernization Act (MMA) of 2004 and by 2 percent for claims with dates of service July 1, 2008 through December 31, 2010 in accordance with Section 146(a) of the Medicare Improvements for Patients and Providers Act of 2008 and Sections 3105(a) and 10311(a) of the Patient Protection and Affordable Care Act (ACA) of 2010. For ground ambulance transport services furnished where the POP is rural, the rates are increased by 2 percent for claims with dates of service July 1, 2004 through December 31, 2006 in accordance with Section 414 of the Medicare Modernization Act (MMA) of 2004 and by 3 percent for claims with dates of service July 1, 2008 through December 31, 2010 in accordance with Section 146(a) of the Medicare Improvements for Patients and Providers Act of 2008 and Sections 3105(a) and 10311(a) of the Patient Protection and Affordable Care Act (ACA) of 2010. Subsequently, section 106 (a) of the Medicare and Medicaid Extenders Act of 2010 (MMEA) again amended section 1834 (1) (12) (A) of the Act to extend the payment increases for an additional year, through December 31, 2011. These amounts are incorporated into the fee schedule amounts that appear in the Ambulance FS file maintained by CMS and downloaded by CMS contractors. There is no calculation to be done by the Medicare carrier or intermediary in order to implement this provision.

The following chart summarizes the Medicare Prescription Drug, Improvement, and Modernization Act (MMA) of 2003 payment changes for ground ambulance services that became effective on July 1, 2004 as well as the Medicare Improvement for Patients and Providers Act (MIPPA) of 2008 changes that became effective July 1, 2008 and were extended by the Patient Protection and Affordable Care Act of 2010 and the Medicare and Medicaid Extenders Act of 2010 (MMEA).

Summary Chart of Additional Payments for Ground Ambulance Services Provided by MMA, MIPPA and MMEA

Service	Effective Dates	Payment Increase*
All rural miles	7/1/04 - 12/31/06	2%
All rural miles	7/1/08 – 12/31/11	3%
Rural miles 51+	7/1/04 - 12/31/08	25% **
All urban miles	7/1/04 - 12/31/06	1%
All urban miles	7/1/08 – 12/31/11	2%
Urban miles 51+	7/1/04 - 12/31/08	25% **
All rural base rates	7/1/04 - 12/31/06	2%
All rural base rates	7/1/08 – 12/31/11	3%
Rural base rates (lowest quartile)	7/1/04 - 12/31/11	22.6 %**
All urban base rates	7/1/04 - 12/31/06	1%
All urban base rates	7/1/08 – 12/31/11	2%
All base rates (regional fee schedule blend)	7/1/04 - 12/31/09	Floor

NOTES: *All payments are percentage increases and all are cumulative.

**Contractor systems perform this calculation. All other increases are incorporated into the CMS Medicare Ambulance FS file.

B. Air Ambulance Services

1. Base Rates

Each type of air ambulance service has a base rate. There is no conversion factor (CF) applicable to air ambulance services.

2. Geographic Adjustment Factor (GAF)

The GAF, as described above for ground ambulance services, is also used for air ambulance services. However, for air ambulance services, the applicable GPCI is applied to 50 percent of each of the base rates (fixed and rotary wing).

3. Mileage

The FS for air ambulance services provides a separate payment for mileage.

4. Adjustment for Services Furnished in Rural Areas

The payment rates for air ambulance services where the POP is in a rural area are greater than in an urban area. For air ambulance services (fixed or rotary wing), the rural adjustment is an increase of 50 percent to the unadjusted FS amount, e.g., the applicable air service base rate multiplied by the GAF plus the mileage amount or, in other words, 1.5 times both the applicable air service base rate and the total mileage amount.

The basis for a rural adjustment for air ambulance services is determined in the same manner as for ground services. That is, whether the POP is within a rural ZIP Code as described above for ground services.

100-4, Chapter 15, 20.2

Payment for Mileage Charges

Charges for mileage must be based on loaded mileage only, e.g., from the pickup of a patient to his/her arrival at destination. It is presumed that all unloaded mileage costs are taken into account when a supplier establishes his basic charge for ambulance services and his rate for loaded mileage. Suppliers should be notified that separate charges for unloaded mileage will be denied.

Instructions on billing mileage are found in §30.

100-4, Chapter 15, 20.3

Air Ambulance

Refer to IOM Pub. 100-02, Medicare Benefit Policy Manual, chapter 10 -Ambulance Services, section 10.4 –Air Ambulance Services, for additional information on the coverage of air ambulance services. Under certain circumstances, transportation by airplane or helicopter may qualify as covered ambulance services. If the conditions of coverage are met, payment may be made for the air ambulance services.

Air ambulance services are paid at different rates according to two air ambulance categories:

- AIR ambulance service, conventional air services, transport, one way, fixed wing (FW) (HCPCS code A0430)
- AIR ambulance service, conventional air services, transport, one way, rotary wing(RW) (HCPCS code A0431)

Covered air ambulance mileage services are paid when the appropriate HCPCS code is reported on the claim:

- HCPCS code A0435 identifies FIXED WING AIR MILEAGE
- HCPCS code A0436 identifies ROTARY WING AIR MILEAGE

Air mileage must be reported in whole numbers of loaded statute miles flown. Contractors must ensure that the appropriate air transport code is used with the appropriate mileage code.

Air ambulance services may be paid only for ambulance services to a hospital. Other destinations e.g., skilled nursing facility, a physician's office, or a patient's home may not be paid air ambulance. The destination is identified by the use of an appropriate modifier As defined in Section 30(A) of this chapter.

Claims for air transports may account for all mileage from the point of pickup, including where applicable: ramp to taxiway, taxiway to runway, takeoff run, air miles, roll out upon landing, and taxiing after landing. Additional air mileage may be allowed by the contractor in situations where additional mileage is incurred, due to circumstances beyond the pilot's control. These circumstances include, but are not limited to, the following:

- Military base and other restricted zones, air-defense zones, and similar FAA restrictions and prohibitions;
- Hazardous weather; or
- Variances in departure patterns and clearance routes required by an air traffic controller.

If the air transport meets the criteria for medical necessity, Medicare pays the actual miles flown for legitimate reasons as determined by the Medicare contractor, once the Medicare beneficiary is loaded onto the air ambulance.

IOM Pub. 100-08, Medicare Program Integrity Manual, chapter 6 –Intermediary MR Guidelines for Specific Services contains instructions for Medical Review of Air Ambulance Services.

100-4, Chapter 15, 20.6

Payment for Non-Emergency Trips to/from ESRD Facilities

Section 637 of the American Taxpayer Relief Act of 2012 requires that, effective for transports occurring on and after October 1, 2013, fee schedule payments for non-emergency basic life support (BLS) transports of individuals with end-stage renal disease (ESRD) to and from renal dialysis treatment be reduced by 10%. The payment reduction affects transports (base rate and mileage) to and from hospital-based and freestanding renal dialysis treatment facilities for dialysis services provided on a non-emergency basis. Non-emergency BLS ground transports are identified by Healthcare Common Procedure Code System (HCPCS) code A0428. Ambulance transports to and from renal dialysis treatment are identified by modifier codes "G" (hospital-based ESRD) and "J" (freestanding ESRD facility) in either the first position (origin code) or second position (destination code) within the two-digit ambulance modifier. (See Section 30 (A) for information regarding modifiers specific to ambulance.)

Effective for claims with dates of service on and after October 1, 2013, the 10% reduction will be calculated and applied to HCPCS code A0428 when billed with modifier code "G" or "J". The reduction will also be applied to any mileage billed in association with a non-emergency transport of a beneficiary with ESRD to and from renal dialysis treatment. BLS mileage is identified by HCPCS code A0425.

The 10% reduction will be taken after calculation of the normal fee schedule payment amount, including any add-on or bonus payments , and will apply to transports in rural and urban areas as well as areas designated as "super rural".

Payment for emergency transports is not affected by this reduction. Payment for non-emergency BLS transports to other destinations is also not affected. This reduction does not affect or change the Ambulance Fee Schedule.

Note: The 10% reduction applies to beneficiaries with ESRD that are receiving non-emergency BLS transport to and from renal dialysis treatment. While it is possible that a beneficiary who is not diagnosed with ESRD will require routine transport to and from renal dialysis treatment, it is highly unlikely. However, contractors have discretion to override or reverse the reduction on appeal if they deem it appropriate based on supporting documentation.

100-4, Chapter 15, 30.1.2

Coding Instructions for Paper and Electronic Claim Forms

Except as otherwise noted, beginning with dates of service on or after January 1, 2001, the following coding instructions must be used.

In item 23 of the CMS-1500 Form, billers shall code the 5-digit ZIP Code of the point of pickup.

Electronic billers using ANSI X12N 837 should refer to the Implementation Guide to determine how to report the origin information (e.g., the ZIP Code of the point of pickup).

Beginning with the early implementation of the version 5010 837P claim format on January 1, 2011, electronic billers will be required to submit, in addition to the loaded ambulance trip's origin information(e.g., the ZIP Code of the point of pickup), the loaded ambulance trip's destination information (e.g., the ZIP code of the point of drop-off). Again, please refer to the appropriate Implementation Guide to determine how to report the destination information. It is important to remember that only the ZIP Code of the point of pickup will be used to adjudicate and price the ambulance claim, not the point of drop-off, but that the point of drop-off will be an additional reporting requirement on the version 5010 837P claim format.

Since the ZIP Code is used for pricing, more than one ambulance service may be reported on the same paper claim for a beneficiary if all points of pickup have the same ZIP Code.

Suppliers must prepare a separate paper claim for each trip if the points of pickup are located in different ZIP Codes.

Claims without a ZIP Code in item 23 on the CMS-1500 Form item 23, or with multiple ZIP Codes in item 23, must be returned as unprocessable. Carriers use message N53 on the remittance advice in conjunction with reason code 16. ZIP Codes must be edited for validity.

The format for a ZIP Code is five numerics. If a nine-digit ZIP Code is submitted, the last four digits are ignored. If the data submitted in the required field does not match that format, the claim is rejected.

Generally, each ambulance trip will require two lines of coding, e.g., one line for the service and one line for the mileage. Suppliers who do not bill mileage would have one line of code for the service.

Beginning with dates of service on or after January 1, 2011, if mileage is billed it must be reported as fractional units in Item 24G of the Form CMS-1500 paper claim or the corresponding loop and segment of the ANSI X12N837P electronic claim for trips totaling up to100 covered miles. When reporting fractional mileage, suppliers must round the total miles up to the nearest tenth of a mile and report the resulting number with the appropriate HCPCS code for ambulance mileage. The decimal must be used in the appropriate place (e.g., 99.9).

For trips totaling 100 covered miles and greater, suppliers must report mileage rounded up to the next whole number mile without the use of a decimal (e.g., 998.5 miles should be reported as 999).

For trips totaling less than 1 mile, enter a "0" before the decimal (e.g., 0.9).

Fractional mileage reporting applies only to ambulance services billed on a Form CMS-1500 paper claim, ANSI X12N 837P, or 837I electronic claims. It does not apply to providers billing on the Form CMS-1450.

For mileage HCPCS billed on a Form CMS-1500 or ANSI X12N 837P only, contractors shall automatically default to "0.1" units when the total mileage units are missing in Item 24G.

100-4, Chapter 15, 30.2

Fiscal Intermediary Shared System (FISS) Guidelines

For SNF Part A, the cost of medically necessary ambulance transportation to receive most services included in the RUG rate is included in the cost for the service. Payment for the SNF claim is based on the RUGs, which takes into account the cost of such transportation to receive the ancillary services.

Refer to Pub. 100-04, Medicare Claims Processing Manual, chapter 6 –SNF Inpatient Part A Billing, Section 20.3.1 – Ambulance Services, for additional information on SNF consolidated billing and ambulance transportation.

Refer to Pub. 100-04, Medicare Claims Processing Manual, chapter 3 –Inpatient Hospital Billing, section 10.5 –Hospital Inpatient Bundling, for additional information on hospital inpatient bundling of ambulance services.

In general, the A/MAC processes claims for Part B ambulance services provided by an ambulance supplier under arrangements with hospitals or SNFs. These providers bill A/MACs using only Method2.

The provider must furnish the following data in accordance with A/MAC instructions. The A/MAC will make arrangements for the method and media for submitting the data:

- A detailed statement of the condition necessitateing the ambulance service;
- A statement indicating whether the patient was admitted as an inpatient. If yes the name and address of the facility must be shown;
- Name and address of certifying physician;
- Name and address of physician ordering service if other than certifying physician;
- Point of pickup (identify place and completed address);
- Destination (identify place and complete address);
- Number of loaded miles (the number of miles traveled when the beneficiary was in the ambulance);
- Cost per mile;
- Mileage charge;
- Minimum or base charge; and
- Charge for special items or services. Explain.

A. General

The reasonable cost per trip of ambulance services furnished by a provider of services may not exceed the prior year's reasonable cost per trip updated by the ambulance inflation factor. This determination is effective with services furnished during Federal Fiscal Year (FFY) 1998 (between October 1, 1997, and September 30, 1998). Providers are to bill for Part B ambulance services using the billing method of base rate including supplies, with mileage billed separately as described below.

The following instructions provide billing procedures implementing the above provisions.

B. Applicable Bill Types

The appropriate type of bill (13X, 22X, 23X, 83X, and 85X) must be reported. For SNFs, ambulance cannot be reported on a 21X type of bill.

C. Value Code Reporting

For claims with dates of service on or after January 1, 2001, providers must report on every Part B ambulance claim value code A0 (zero) and the related ZIP Code of the geographic location from which the beneficiary was placed on board the ambulance in Value Code field. The value code is defined as "ZIP Code of the location from which the beneficiary is initially placed on board the ambulance."Providers report the number in dollar portion of the form location right justified to the left to the dollar/cents delimiter.

More than one ambulance trip may be reported on the same claim if the ZIP Codes of all points of pickup are the same. However, since billing requirements do not allow for value codes (ZIP Codes) to be line item specific and only one ZIP Code may be reported per claim, providers must prepare a separate claim for a beneficiary for each trip if the points of pickup are located in different ZIP Codes.

For claims with dates of service on or after April 1, 2002, providers must report value code 32 (multiple patient ambulance transport) when an ambulance transports more than one patient at a time to the same destination. Providers must report value code 32 and the number of patients transported in the amount field as a whole number to the left of the delimiter.

NOTE: Information regarding the claim form locator that corresponds to the Value Code field and a table to crosswalk the CMS-1450 form locator to the 837 transaction is found in Pub.100-04, Medicare Claims Processing Manual, chapter 25 –Completing and Processing the Form CMS-1450 Data Set.

D. Revenue Code/HCPCS Code Reporting

Providers must report revenue code 054X and, for services provided before January 1, 2001, one of the following CMS HCPCS codes for each ambulance trip provided during the billing period:

A0030 (discontinued 12/31/2000); A0040 (discontinued 12/31/2000);A0050 (discontinued 12/31/2000); A0320 (discontinued 12/31/2000); A0322 (discontinued 12/31/2000); A0324 (discontinued 12/31/2000); A0326 (discontinued 12/31/2000); A0328, (discontinued 12/31/2000); or A0330 (discontinued 12/31/2000).

In addition, providers report one of A0380 or A0390 for mileage HCPCS codes. No other HCPCS codes are acceptable for reporting ambulance services and mileage. Providers report one of the following revenue codes:

Given below data is missing after this line, please add, you can also check the same from 5th number word file of pub-100.

0540;
0542;
0543;
0545;
0546; or
0548.

Do not report revenue codes 0541, 0544, or 0547.

For claims with dates of service on or after January 1, 2001, providers must report revenue code 540 and one of the following HCPCS codes for each ambulance trip provided during the billing period:

A0426; A0427;
A0428; A0429; A0430; A0431; A0432; A0433; or
A0434.

Providers using an ALS vehicle to furnish a BLS level of service report HCPCS code, A0426 (ALS1) or A0427 (ALS1 emergency), and are paid accordingly. In addition, all providers report one of the following mileage HCPCS codes: A0380; A0390; A0435; or A0436.

Since billing requirements do not allow for more than one HCPCS code to be reported for per revenue code line, providers must report revenue code 0540 (ambulance) on two separate and consecutive lines to accommodate both the Part B ambulance service and the mileage HCPCS codes for each ambulance trip provided during the billing period. Each loaded

(e.g., a patient is onboard) 1-way ambulance trip must be reported with a unique pair of revenue code lines on the claim. Unloaded trips and mileage are NOT reported.

However, in the case where the beneficiary was pronounced dead after the ambulance is called but before the ambulance arrives at the scene: Payment may be made for a BLS service if a ground vehicle is dispatched or at the fixed wing or rotary wing base rate, as applicable, if an air ambulance is dispatched. Neither mileage nor a rural adjustment would be paid. The blended rate amount will otherwise apply. Providers report the A0428 (BLS) HCPCS code. Providers report modifier QL (Patient pronounced dead after ambulance called) in Form Locator (FL) 44"HCPCS/Rates" instead of the origin and destination modifier. In addition to the QL modifier, providers report modifier QM or QN.

NOTE: Information regarding the claim form locator that corresponds to the HCPCS code and a table to crosswalk its CMS-1450 form locator to the 837 transaction is found in Pub. 100-04, Medicare Claims Processing Manual, chapter 25 – Completing and Processing the FormCMS-1450 Data Set.

E. Modifier Reporting

See the above Section 30 (A)(Modifiers Specific to Ambulance Service Claims)for instructions regarding the usage of modifiers.

F. Line-Item Dates of Service Reporting

Providers are required to report line-item dates of service per revenue code line. This means that they must report two separate revenue code lines for every ambulance trip provided during the billing period along with the date of each trip. This includes situations in which more than one ambulance service is provided to the same beneficiary on the same day. Line-item dates of service are reported in the Service Date field.

NOTE: Information regarding the claim form locator that corresponds to the Service Date and a table to crosswalk its CMS-1450 form locator to the 837 transaction is found in Pub. 100-04, Medicare Claims Processing Manual, chapter 25 – Completing and Processing the Form CMS-1450 Data Set.

G. Service Units Reporting

For line items reflecting HCPCS code A0030, A0040, A0050, A0320, A0322,A0324, A0326, A0328, or A0330 (services before January 1, 2001) or code A0426, A0427, A0428, A0429, A0430, A0431, A0432, A0433, or A0434 (services on and after January 1, 2001), providers are required to report in Service Units each ambulance trip provided during the billing period. Therefore, the service units for each occurrence of these HCPCS codes are always equal to one. In addition, for line items reflecting HCPCS code A0380 or A0390, the number of loaded miles must be reported. (See examples below.)

Therefore, the service units for each occurrence of these HCPCS codes are always equal to one. In addition, for line items reflecting HCPCS code A0380, A0390, A0435, or A0436, the number of loaded miles must be reported.

H. Total Charges Reporting

For line items reflecting HCPCS codes A0426, A0427, A0428, A0429, A0430, A0431, A0432, A0433, or A0434;

Providers are required to report in Total Charges the actual charge for the ambulance service including all supplies used for the ambulance trip but excluding the charge for mileage. For line items reflecting HCPCS code A0380, A0390, A0435, or A0436, report the actual charge for mileage.

NOTE: There are instances where the provider does not incur any cost for mileage, e.g., if the beneficiary is pronounced dead after the ambulance is called but before the ambulance arrives at the scene. In these situations, providers report the base rate ambulance trip and mileage as separate revenue code lines. Providers report the base rate ambulance trip in accordance with current billing requirements. For purposes of reporting mileage, they must report the appropriate HCPCS code, modifiers, and units as a separate line item. For the related charges, providers report $1.00 in FL48 for non-covered charges. Intermediaries should assign ANSI Group Code OA to the $1.00 non-covered mileage line, which in turn informs the beneficiaries and providers that they each have no liability.

Prior to submitting the claim to CWF, the intermediary will remove the entire revenue code line containing the mileage amount reported in Non-covered Charges to avoid non-acceptance of the claim.

NOTE: Information regarding the claim form locator that corresponds to the Charges fields and a table to crosswalk its CMS-1450 form locator to the 837 transaction is found in Pub. 100-04, Medicare Claims Processing Manual, chapter 25 – Completing and Processing the Form CMS-1450 Data Set.

EXAMPLES: The following provides examples of how bills for Part B ambulance services should be completed based on the reporting requirements above. These examples reflect ambulance services furnished directly by providers. Ambulance services provided under arrangement between the provider and an ambulance company are reported in the same manner except providers report a QM modifier instead of a QN modifier.

EXAMPLE 1: Claim containing only one ambulance trip:

For the hard copy CMS-1450 Form, providers report as follows:

Revenue Code	HCPCS/ Modifiers	Date of Service	Units	Total Charges
0540	A0428RHQN	082701	1 (trip)	100.00
0540	A0380RHQN	082701	4 (mileage)	8.00

EXAMPLE 2: Claim containing multiple ambulance trips:

For the hard copy Form CMS-1450, providers report as follows:

Revenue Code	HCPCS	Modifiers #1	Modifiers #2	Date of Service	Units	Total Charges
0540	A0429	RH	QN	082801	1 (trip)	100.00
0540	A0380	RH	QN	082801	2 (mileage)	4.00
0540	A0330	RH	QN	082901	1 (trip)	400.00
0540	A0390	RH	QN	082901	3 (mileage)	6.00

EXAMPLE 3: Claim containing more than one ambulance trip provided on the same day:

For the hard copy CMS-1450, providers report as follows:

Revenue Code	HCPCS	Modifiers		Date of Service	Units	Total Charges
0540	A0429	RH	QN	090201	1 (trip)	100.00
0540	A0380	RH	QN	090201	2 (mileage)	4.00
0540	A0429	HR	QN	090201	1 (trip)	100.00
0540	A0380	HR	QN	090201	2 (mileage)	4.00

I. Edits

A/MACs edit to assure proper reporting as follows:

- For claims with dates of service on or after January 1, 2001, each pair of revenue codes 0540 must have one of the following ambulance HCPCS codes -A0426, A0427, A0428, A0429, A0430, A0431, A0432, A0433, oA0434; and one of the following mileage HCPCS codes –A0435, A0436 or for claims with dates of service on or after April 1,2002, A0425;

- For claims with dates of service on or after January 1, 2001, the presence of an origin and destination modifier and a QM or QN modifier for every line item containing revenue code 0540;

- The units field is completed for every line item containing revenue code 0540;

- For claims with dates of service on or after January 1, 2001, the units field is completed for every line item containing revenue code 0540;

- Service units for line items containing HCPCS codes A0426, A0427, A0428, A0429, A0430, A0431, A0432, A0433, or A0434 always equal "1"

For claims with dates of service on or after July 1, 2001, each 1-way ambulance trip, line-item dates of service for the ambulance service, and corresponding mileage are equal.

100-4, Chapter 15, 30.2.1

A/MAC Bill Processing Guidelines Effective April 1, 2002, as a Result of Fee Schedule Implementation

For SNF Part A, the cost of medically necessary ambulance transportation to receive most services included in the RUG rate is included in the cost for the service. Payment for the SNF claim is based on the RUGs, which takes into account the cost of such transportation to receive the ancillary services.

Refer to IOM Pub. 100-04, Medicare Claims Processing Manual, chapter 6 –SNF Inpatient Part A Billing, Section 20.3.1 –Ambulance Services for additional information on SNF consolidated billing and ambulance transportation.

Refer to IOM Pub. 100-04, Medicare Claims Processing Manual, chapter 3 –Inpatient Hospital Billing, section 10.5 –Hospital Inpatient Bundling, for additional information on hospital inpatient bundling of ambulance services.

In general, the A/MAC processes claims for Part B ambulance services provided by an ambulance supplier under arrangements with hospitals or SNFs. These providers bill A/MACs using only Method 2.

The provider must furnish the following data in accordance with A/MAC instructions. The A/MAC will make arrangements for the method and media for submitting the data:

- A detailed statement of the condition necessitating the ambulance service;

- A statement indicating whether the patient was admitted as an inpatient. If yes the name and address of the facility must be shown;

- Name and address of certifying physician;

- Name and address of physician ordering service if other than certifying physician;

- Point of pickup (identify place and completed address);

- Destination (identify place and complete address);

- Number of loaded miles (the number of miles traveled when the beneficiary was in the ambulance);
- Cost per mile;
- Mileage charge;
- Minimum or base charge; and
- Charge for special items or services. Explain.

A. Revenue Code Reporting

Providers report ambulance services under revenue code 540 in FL 42 "Revenue Code."

B. HCPCS Codes Reporting

Providers report the HCPCS codes established for the ambulance fee schedule. No other HCPCS codes are acceptable for the reporting of ambulance services and mileage. The HCPCS code must be used to reflect the type of service the beneficiary received, not the type of vehicle used. Providers must report one of the following HCPCS codes in FL 44 "HCPCS/Rates" for each base rate ambulance trip provided during the billing period:

A0426;

A0427;

A0428;

A0429;

A0430;

A0431;

A0432;

A0433; or

A0434.

These are the same codes required effective for services January 1,2001.

In addition, providers must report one of HCPCS mileage codes:

A0425;

A0435; or

A0436

Since billing requirements do not allow for more than one HCPCS code to be reported per revenue code line, providers must report revenue code 540 (ambulance) on two separate and consecutive line items to accommodate both the ambulance service and the mileage HCPCS codes for each ambulance trip provided during the billing period. Each loaded (e.g., a patient is onboard) 1-way ambulance trip must be reported with a unique pair of revenue code lines on the claim. Unloaded trips and mileage are NOT reported.

For UB-04 hard copy claims submission prior to August 1, 2011, providers code one mile for trips less than a mile. Miles must be entered as whole numbers. If a trip has a fraction of a mile, round up to the nearest whole number.

Beginning with dates of service on or after January 1, 2011, for UB-04 hard copy claims submissions August 1, 2011 and after, mileage must be reported as fractional units. When reporting fractional mileage, providers must round the total miles up to the nearest tenth of a mile and the decimal must be used in the appropriate place (e.g., 99.9).

For trips totaling less than 1 mile, enter a "0" before the decimal (e.g., 0.9).

For electronic claims submissions prior to January 1, 2011, providers code one mile for trips less than a mile. Miles must be entered as whole numbers. If a trip has a fraction of a mile, round up to the nearest whole number.

Beginning with dates of service on or after January 1, 2011, for electronic claim submissions only, mileage must be reported as fractional units in the ANSI X12N 837I element SV205 for trips totaling up to 100 covered miles. When reporting fractional mileage, providers must round the total miles up to the nearest tenth of a mile and the decimal must be used in the appropriate place (e.g., 99.9).

For trips totaling 100 covered miles and greater, providers must report mileage rounded up to the nearest whole number mile (e.g., 999) and not use a decimal when reporting whole number miles over 100 miles.

For trips totaling less than 1 mile, enter a "0" before the decimal (e.g., 0.9).

C. Modifier Reporting

Providers must report an origin and destination modifier for each ambulance trip provided and either a QM (Ambulance service provided under arrangement by a provider of services) or QN (Ambulance service furnished directly by a provider of services) modifier in FL 44 "HCPCS/Rates".

D. Service Units Reporting

For line items reflecting HCPCS codes A0426, A0427, A0428, A0429, A0430, A0431, A0432, A0433, or A0434,providers are required to report in FL 46 "Service Units" for each ambulance trip provided. Therefore, the service units for each occurrence of these HCPCS codes are always equal to one. In addition, for line items reflecting HCPCS code A0425, A0435, orA0436, providers must also report the number of loaded miles.

E. Total Charges Reporting

For line items reflecting HCPCS codes A0426, A0427, A0428, A0429,A0430, A0431, A0432, A0433, or A0434, providers are required to report in FL 47, "Total Charges," the actual charge for the ambulance service including all supplies used for the ambulance trip but excluding the charge for mileage. For line items reflecting HCPCS codes A0425, A0435, or A0436, providers are to report the actual charge for mileage.

NOTE: There are instances where the provider does not incur any cost for mileage, e.g., if the beneficiary is pronounced dead after the ambulance is called but before the ambulance arrives at the scene. In these situations, providers report the base rate ambulance trip and mileage as separate revenue code lines. Providers report the base rate ambulance trip in accordance with current billing requirements. For purposes of reporting mileage, they must report the appropriate HCPCS code, modifiers, and units. For the related charges, providers report $1.00 in non-covered charges. A/MACs should assign ANSI Group Code OA to the $1.00 non-covered mileage line, which in turn informs the beneficiaries and providers that they each have no liability.

F. Edits (A/MAC Claims with Dates of Service On or After 4/1/02)

For claims with dates of service on or after April 1, 2002, A/MACs perform the following edits to assure proper reporting:

- Edit to assure each pair of revenue codes 540 have one of the following ambulance HCPCS codes -A0426, A0427, A0428, A0429, A0430, A0431, A0432, A0433, or A0434; and one of the following mileage HCPCS codes -A0425, A0435, or A0436.

- Edit to assure the presence of an origin, destination modifier, and a QM or QN modifier for every line item containing revenue code 540;

- Edit to assure that the unit's field is completed for every line item containing revenue code 540;

- Edit to assure that service units for line items containing HCPCS codes A0426, A0427, A0428, A0429, A0430, A0431, A0432, A0433, or A0434 always equal "1"; and

- Edit to assure on every claim that revenue code 540, a value code of A0 (zero), and a corresponding ZIP Code are reported. If the ZIP Code is not a valid ZIP Code in accordance with the USPS assigned ZIP Codes, intermediaries verify the ZIP Code to determine if the ZIP Code is a coding error on the claim or a new ZIP Code from the USPS not on the CMS supplied ZIP Code File.

- Beginning with dates of service on or after April 1, 2012, edit to assure that only non-emergency trips (i.e., HCPCS A0426, A0428 [when A0428 is billed without modifier QL]) require an NPI in the Attending Physician field. Emergency trips do not require an NPI in the Attending Physician field (i.e., A0427, A0429, A0430, A0431, A0432, A0433, A0434 and A0428 [when A0428 is billed with modifier QL])

G. CWF (A/MACs)

A/MACs report the procedure codes in the financial data section (field 65a-65j). They include revenue code, HCPCS code, units, and covered charges in the record. Where more than one HCPCS code procedure is applicable to a single revenue code, the provider reports each HCPCS code and related charge on a separate line, and the A/MAC reports this to CWF. Report the payment amount before adjustment for beneficiary liability in field 65g "Rate" and the actual charge in field 65h, "Covered Charges."

100-4, Chapter 15, 30.2.4

Non-covered Charges on Institutional Ambulance Claims

Medicare law contains a restriction that miles beyond the closest available facility cannot be billed to Medicare. Non-covered miles beyond the closest facility are billed with HCPCS procedure code A0888 ("non-covered ambulance mileage per mile, e.g., for miles traveled beyond the closest appropriate facility"). These non-covered line items can be billed on claims also containing covered charges. Ambulance claims may use the –GY modifier on line items for such non-covered mileage, and liability for the service will be assigned correctly to the beneficiary.

The method of billing all miles for the same trip, with covered and non-covered portions, on the same claim is preferable in this scenario. However, billing the non-covered mileage using condition code 21 claims is also permitted, if desired, as long as all line items on the claims are non-covered and the beneficiary is liable. Additionally, unless requested by the beneficiary or required by specific Medicare policy, services excluded by statute do not have to be billed to Medicare.

When the scenario is point of pick up outside the United States, including U.S. territories but excepting some points in Canada and Mexico in some cases, mileage is also statutorily excluded from Medicare coverage. Such billings are more likely to be submitted on entirely non-covered claims using condition code 21. This scenario requires the use of a different message on the Medicare Summary Notice (MSN) sent to beneficiaries.

Another scenario in which billing non-covered mileage to Medicare may occur is when the beneficiary dies after the ambulance has been called but before the ambulance arrives. The –QL modifier should be used on the base rate line in this scenario, in place of origin and destination modifiers, and the line is submitted with covered charges. The –QL modifier should also be used on the accompanying mileage line, if submitted, with non-covered charges. Submitting this non-covered mileage line is optional for providers.

Non-covered charges may also apply is if there is a subsidy of mileage charges that are never charged to Medicare. Because there are no charges for Medicare to share in, the only billing option is to submit non-covered charges, if the provider bills Medicare at all (it is not required in such cases). These non-covered charges are unallowable, and should not be considered in settlement of cost reports. However, there is a difference in billing if such charges are subsidized, but otherwise would normally be charged to Medicare as the primary payer. In this latter case, CMS examination of existing rules relating to grants policy since October 1983, supported by Federal regulations (42CFR 405.423), generally requires providers to reduce their costs by the amount of grants and gifts restricted to pay for such costs. Thereafter, section 405.423 was deleted from the regulations.

Thus, providers were no longer required to reduce their costs for restricted grants and gifts, and charges tied to such grants/gifts/subsidies should be submitted as covered charges. This is in keeping with Congress's intent to encourage hospital philanthropy, allowing the provider receiving the subsidy to use it, and also requiring Medicare to share in the unreduced cost. Treatment of subsidized charges as non-covered Medicare charges serves to reduce Medicare payment on the Medicare cost report contrary to the 1983 change in policy.

Medicare requires the use of the –TQ modifier so that CMS can track the instances of the subsidy scenario for non-covered charges. The –TQ should be used whether the subsidizing entity is governmental or voluntary. The -TQ modifier is not required in the case of covered charges submitted when a subsidy has been made, but charges are still normally made to Medicare as the primary payer.

If providers believe they have been significantly or materially penalized in the past by the failure of their cost reports to consider covered charges occurring in the subsidy case, since Medicare had previous billing instructions that stated all charges in the case of a subsidy, not just charges when the entity providing the subsidy never charges another entity/primary payer, should be submitted as non-covered charges, they may contact their FI about reopening the reports in question for which the time period in 42 CFR 405.1885 has not expired. FIs have the discretion to determine if the amount in question warrants reopening. The CMS does not expect many such cases to occur.

Billing requirements for all these situations, including the use of modifiers, are presented in the chart below:

Mileage Scenario	HCPCS	Modifiers*	Liability	Billing	Remit. Requirements	MSN Message
STATUTE: Miles beyond closest facility, OR **Pick up point outside of U.S.	A0888 on line item for the non-covered mileage	-QM or –QN, origin/destination modifier, and –GY unless condition code 21 claim used	Beneficiary	Bill mileage line item with A0888 –GY and other modifiers as needed to establish liability, line item will be denied; OR bill service on condition code 21 claim, no –GY required, claim will be denied	Group code PR, reason code 96	16.10 "Medicare does not pay for this item or service"; OR, "Medicare no paga por este artículo o servicio"
Beneficiary dies after ambulance is called	Most appropriate ambulance HCPCS mileage code (i.e., ground, air)	–QL unless condition code –21 claim	Provider	Bill mileage line item with –QL as non-covered, line item will be denied	Group Code CO, reason code 96	16.58 "The provider billed this charge as non-covered. You do not have to pay this amount."; OR, "El proveedor facuró este cargo como no cubierto. Usted no tiene que pagar ests cantidad."
Subsidy or government owned Ambulance, Medicare NEVER billed***	A0888 on line item for the non-covered mileage	-QM or –QN, origin/destination modifier, and -TQ must be used for policy purposes	Provider	Bill mileage line item with A0888, and modifiers as non-covered, line item will be denied	Group Code CO, reason code 96	16.58 "The provider billed this charge as non-covered. You do not have to pay this amount."; OR, "El proveedor facuró este cargo como no cubierto. Usted no tiene que pagar ests cantidad."

*Current ambulance billing requirements state that either the –QM or –QN modifier must be used on services. The –QM is used when the "ambulance service is provided under arrangement by a provider of services," and the –QN when the "ambulance service is provided directly by a provider of services." Line items using either the –QM or–QN modifiers are not subject to the FISS edit associated with FISS reason code 31322 so that these lines items will process to completion. Origin/destination modifiers, also required by current instruction, combine two alpha characters: one for origin, one for destination, and are not non-covered by definition.

** This is the one scenario where the base rate is not paid in addition to mileage, and there are certain exceptions in Canada and Mexico where mileage is covered as described in existing ambulance instructions.

***If Medicare would normally have been billed, submit mileage charges as covered charges despite subsidies.

Medicare systems may return claims to the provider if they do not comply with the requirements in the table.

100-4, Chapter 15, 40

Medical Conditions List and Instructions

The following list is intended as primarily an educational guideline. This list was most recently updated by CMS Transmittal 1185, Change Request 5542 issued February 23, 2007. It will help ambulance providers and suppliers to communicate the patient's condition to Medicare contractors, as reported by the dispatch center and as observed by the ambulance crew. Use of the medical conditions list does not guarantee payment of the claim or payment for a certain level of service. Ambulance providers and suppliers must retain adequate documentation of dispatch instructions, patient's condition, other on-scene information, and details of the transport (e.g., medications administered, changes in the patient's condition, and miles travelled), all of which may be subject to medical review by the Medicare contractor or other oversight authority. Medicare contractors will rely on medical record documentation to justify coverage, not simply the HCPCS code or the condition code by themselves. All current Medicare ambulance policies remain in place.

The Medical Conditions List is set up with an initial column of primary ICD-9-CM codes, followed by an alternative column of ICD-9-CM codes. The primary ICD-9-CM code column contains general ICD-9-CM codes that fit the transport conditions as described in the subsequent columns. Ambulance crew or billing staff with limited knowledge of ICD-9-CM coding would be expected to choose the one or one of the two ICD-9-CM codes listed in this column to describe the appropriate ambulance transport and then place the ICD-9-CM code in the space on the claim form designated for an ICD-9-CM code. The option to include other information in the narrative field always exists and can be used whenever an ambulance provider or supplier believes that the information may be useful for claims processing purposes. If an ambulance crew or billing staff member has more comprehensive clinical knowledge, then that person may select an ICD-9-CM code from the alternative ICD-9-CM code column. These ICD-9-CM codes are more specific and detailed. An ICD-9-CM code does not need to be selected from both the primary column and the alternative column. However, in several instances in the alternative ICD-9-CM code column, there is a selection of codes and the word "PLUS." In these instances, the ambulance provider or supplier would select an ICD-9-CM code from the first part of the alternative listing (before the word "PLUS") and at least one other ICD-9-CM code from the second part of the alternative listing (after the word "PLUS"). The ambulance claim form does provide space for the use of multiple ICD-9-CM codes. Please see the example below:

The ambulance arrives on the scene. A beneficiary is experiencing the specific abnormal vital sign of elevated blood pressure; however, the beneficiary does not normally suffer from hypertension (ICD-9-CM code 796.2 (from the alternative column on the Medical Conditions List)). In addition, the beneficiary is extremely dizzy (ICD-9-CM code 780.4 (fits the "PLUS any other code" requirement when using the alternative list for this condition (abnormal vital signs)). The ambulance crew can list these two ICD-9-CM codes on the claim form, or the general ICD-9-CM code for this condition (796.4 –Other Abnormal Clinical Findings) would work just as well. None of these ICD-9-CM codes will determine whether or not this claim will be paid; they will only assist the contractor in making a medical review determination provided all other Medicare ambulance coverage policies have been followed.

While the medical conditions/ICD-9-CM code list is intended to be comprehensive, there may be unusual circumstances that warrant the need for ambulance services using ICD-9-CM codes not on this list. During the medical review process contractors may accept other relevant information from the providers or suppliers that will build the appropriate case that justifies the need for ambulance transport for a patient condition not found on the list.

Because it is critical to accurately communicate the condition of the patient during the ambulance transport, most claims will contain only the ICD-9-CM code that most closely informs the Medicare contractor why the patient required the ambulance transport. This code is intended to correspond to the description of the patient's symptoms and condition once the ambulance personnel are at the patient's side. For example, if an Advanced Life Support (ALS) ambulance responds to a condition on the medical conditions list that warrants an ALS-level response and the patient's condition on-scene also corresponds to an ALS-level condition, the submitted claim need only include the code that most accurately reflects the on-scene condition of the patient as the reason for transport. (All claims are required to have HCPCS codes on them, and may have modifiers as well.) Similarly, if a Basic Life Support (BLS) ambulance responds to a condition on the medical conditions list that warrants a BLS-level response and the patient's condition on-scene also corresponds to a BLS-level condition, the submitted claim need only include the code that most accurately reflects the on-scene condition of the patient as the reason for transport.

When a request for service is received by ambulance dispatch personnel for a condition that necessitates the skilled assessment of an advanced life support paramedic based upon the medical conditions list, an ALS-level ambulance would be appropriately sent to the scene. If upon arrival of the ambulance the actual condition encountered by the crew corresponds to a BLS-level situation, this claim would require two separate condition codes from the medical condition list to be processed correctly. The first code would correspond to the "reason for transport" or the on-scene condition of the patient. Because in this example, this code corresponds to a BLS condition, a second code that corresponds to the dispatch information would be necessary for inclusion on the claim in order to support payment at the ALS level. In these cases, when MR is performed, the Medicare contractor will analyze all claim information (including both codes) and other supplemental medical documentation to support the level of service billed on the claim.

Contractors may have (or may develop) individual local policies that indicate that some codes are not appropriate for payment in some circumstances. These continue to remain in effect.

Information on appropriate use of transportation indicators:

When a claim is submitted for payment, an ICD-9-CM code from the medical conditions list that best describes the patient's condition and the medical necessity for the transport may be chosen. In addition to this code, one of the transportation indicators below may be included on the claim to indicate why it was necessary for the patient to be transported in a particular way or circumstance. The provider or supplier will place the transportation indicator in the "narrative" field on the claim.

- Air and Ground
- Transportation Indicator "C1": Transportation indicator "C1" indicates an inter facility transport (to a higher level of care) determined necessary by the originating facility based upon EMTALA regulations and guidelines. The patient's condition should also be reported on the claim with a code selected from either the emergency or non-emergency category on the list.
- Transportation Indicator "C2": Transportation indicator "C2" indicates a patient is being transported from one facility to another because a service or therapy required to treat the patient's condition is not available at the originating facility. The patient's condition should also be reported on the claim with a code selected from either the emergency or non-emergency category on the list. In addition, the information about what service the patient requires that was not available should be included in the narrative field of the claim.
- Transportation Indicator "C3": Transportation indicator "C3" may be included on claims as a secondary code where a response was made to a major incident or mechanism of injury. All such responses –regardless of the type of patient or patients found once on scene –are appropriately Advanced Level Service responses. A code that describes the patient's condition found on scene should also be included on the claim, but use of this modifier is intended to indicate that the highest level of service available response was medically justified. Some examples of these types of responses would include patient(s) trapped in machinery, explosions, a building fire with persons reported inside, major incidents involving aircraft, buses, subways, trains, watercraft and victims entrapped in vehicles.
- Transportation Indicator "C4": Transportation indicator "C4" indicates that an ambulance provided a medically necessary transport, but the number of miles on the claim form appear to be excessive. This should be used only if the facility is on divert status or a particular service is not available at the time of transport only. The provider or supplier must have documentation on file clearly showing why the beneficiary was not transported to the nearest facility and may include this information in the narrative field.
- Ground Only
- Transportation Indicator "C5": Transportation indicator "C5" has been added for situations where a patient

with an ALS-level condition is encountered, treated and transported by a BLS-level ambulance with no ALS level involvement whatsoever. This situation would occur when ALS resources are not available to respond to the patient encounter for any number of reasons, but the ambulance service is informing you that although the patient transported had an ALS-level condition, the actual service rendered was through a BLS-level ambulance in a situation where an ALS-level ambulance was not available.

- For example, a BLS ambulance is dispatched at the emergency level to pick up a 76-year old beneficiary who has undergone cataract surgery at the Eye Surgery Center. The patient is weak and dizzy with a history of high blood pressure, myocardial infarction, and insulin-dependent diabetes melitus. Therefore, the on-scene ICD-9-CM equivalent of the medical condition is 780.02 (unconscious, fainting, syncope, near syncope, weakness, or dizziness –ALS Emergency). In this case, the ICD-9-CM code 780.02 would be entered on the ambulance claim form as well as transportation indicator C5 to provide the further information that the BLS ambulance transported a patient with an ALS-level condition, but there was no intervention by an ALS service. This claim would be paid at the BLS level.

- Transportation Indicator "C6": Transportation indicator "C6" has been added for situations when an ALS-level ambulance would always be the appropriate resource chosen based upon medical dispatch protocols to respond to a request for service. If once on scene, the crew determines that the patient requiring transport has a BLS-level condition, this transportation indicator should be included on the claim to indicate why the ALS-level response was indicated based upon the information obtained in the operation's dispatch center. Claims

including this transportation indicator should contain two primary codes. The first condition will indicate the BLS-level condition corresponding to the patient's condition found on-scene and during the transport. The second condition will indicate the ALS-level condition corresponding to the information at the time of dispatch that indicated the need for an ALS-level response based upon medically appropriate dispatch protocols.

- Transportation Indicator C7-Transportation indicator "C7" is for those circumstances where IV medications were required en route. C7 is appropriately used for patients requiring ALS level transport in a non-emergent situation primarily because the patient requires monitoring of ongoing medications administered intravenously. Does not apply to self-administered medications. Does not include administration of crystalloid intravenous fluids (i.e., Normal Saline, Lactate Ringers, 5% Dextrose in Water, etc.). The patient's condition should also be reported on the claim with a code selected from the list.

- Air Only

- All "transportation indicators" imply a clinical benefit to the time saved with transporting a patient by an air ambulance versus a ground or water ambulance.

- D1 Long Distance -patient's condition requires rapid transportation over a long distance.

- D2 Under rare and exceptional circumstances, traffic patterns preclude ground transport at the time the response is required.

- D3 Time to get to the closest appropriate hospital due to the patient's condition precludes transport by ground ambulance. Unstable patient with need to minimize out-of-hospital time to maximize clinical benefits to the patient.

- D4 Pick up point not accessible by ground transportation.

Ambulance Fee Schedule - Medical Conditions List

Emergency Conditions - Non-Traumatic

ICD 9 Primary Code	ICD 9 Alternative Specific Code	Condition (General)	Condition (Specific)	Service Level	Comments and Examples (not all-inclusive)	HCPCS Crosswalk
535.50	458.9, 780.2, 787.01, 787.02, 787.03, 789.01, 789.02, 789.03, 789.04, 789.05, 789.06, 789.07, 789.09, 789.60 through 789.69, or 789.40 through 789.49 PLUS any other code from 780 through 799 except 793, 794, and 795.	Severe abdominal pain	With other signs or symptoms	ALS	Nausea, vomiting, fainting, pulsatile mass, distention, rigid, tenderness on exam, guarding.	A0427/A0433
789.00	726.2, 789.01, 789.02, 789.03, 789.04, 789.05, 789.06, 789.07, or 789.09	Abdominal pain	Without other signs or symptoms	BLS		A0429
427.9	426.0, 426.3, 426.4, 426.6, 426.11, 426.13, 426.50, 426.53, 427.0, 427.1, 427.2, 427.31, 427.32, 427.41, 427.42, 427.5, 427.60, 427.61, 427.69, 427.81, 427.89, 785.0, 785.50, 785.51, 785.52, or 785.59.	Abnormal cardiac rhythm/Cardiac dysrythmia.	Potentially life-threatening	ALS	Bradycardia, junctional and ventricular blocks, non-sinus tachycardias, PVC's >6, bi- and trigeminy, ventricular tachycardia, ventricular fibrillation, atrial flutter, PEA, asystole, AICD/AED fired	A0427/A0433
780.8	782.5 or 782.6	Abnormal skin signs		ALS	Diaphorhesis, cyanosis, delayed cap refill, poor turgor, mottled.	A0427/A0433
796.4	458.9, 780.6, 785.9, 796.2, or 796.3 PLUS any other code from 780 through 799	Abnormal vital signs (includes abnormal pulse oximetry)	With or without symptoms.	ALS		A0427/A0433

ICD 9 Primary Code	ICD 9 Alternative Specific Code	Condition (General)	Condition (Specific)	Service Level	Comments and Examples (not all-inclusive)	HCPCS Crosswalk
995.0	995.1, 995.2, 995.3, 995.4, 995.60, 995.61, 995.62, 995.63, 995.64, 995.65, 995.66, 995.67, 995.68, 995.69, or 995.7	Allergic reaction	Potentially life threatening	ALS	Other emergency conditions, rapid progression of symptoms, prior history of anaphylaxis, wheezing, difficulty swallowing.	A0427/A0433
692.9	692.0, 692.1, 692.2, 692.3, 692.4, 692.5, 692.6, 692.70, 692.71, 692.72, 692.73, 692.74, 692.75, 692.76, 692.77, 692.79, 692.81, 692.82, 692.83, 692.89, 692.9, 693.0, 693.1, 693.8, 693.9, 695.9, 698.9, 708.9, 782.1.	Allergic reaction	Other	BLS	Hives, itching, rash, slow onset, local swelling, redness, erythema.	A0429
790.21	790.22, 250.02, or 250.03.	Blood glucose	Abnormal <80 or >250, with symptoms.	ALS	Altered mental status, vomiting, signs of dehydration.	A0427/A0433
799.1	786.02, 786.03, 786.04, or 786.09.	Respiratory arrest		ALS	Apnea, hypoventilation requiring ventilatory assistance and airway management.	A0427/A0433
786.05		Difficulty breathing		ALS		A0427/A0433
427.5		Cardiac arrest – resuscitation in progress		ALS		A0427/A0433
786.50	786.51, 786.52, or 786.59.	Chest pain (non-traumatic)		ALS	Dull, severe, crushing, substernal, epigastric, left sided chest pain associated with pain of the jaw, left arm, neck, back, and nausea, vomiting, palpitations, pallor, diaphoresis, decreased LOC.	A0427/A0433
784.99	933.0 or 933.1.	Chocking episode	Airway obstructed or partially obstructed	ALS		A0427/A0433
991.6		Cold exposure	Potentially life or limb threatening	ALS	Temperature < 95F, deep frost bite, other emergency conditions.	A0427/A0433
991.9	991.0, 991.1, 991.2, 991.3, or 991.4.	Cold exposure	With symptoms	BLS	Shivering, superficial frost bite, and other emergency conditions	A0429
780.97	780.02, 780.03, or 780.09.	Altered level of consciousness (nontraumatic)		ALS	Acute condition with Glascow Coma Scale < 15.	A0427/A0433
780.39	345.00, 345.01, 345.2, 345.3, 345.10, 345.11, 345.40, 345.41, 345.50, 345.51, 345.60, 345.61, 345.70, 345.71, 345.80, 345.81, 345.90, 345.91, or 780.31.	Convulsions, seizures	Seizing, immediate post-seizure, postictal, or at risk of seizure and requires medical monitoring/ observation.	ALS		A0427/A0433
379.90	368.11, 368.12, or 379.91	Eye symptoms, non-traumatic	Acute vision loss and/or severe pain	BLS		A0429
437.9	784.0 PLUS 781.0, 781.1, 781.2, 781.3, 781.4, or 781.8.	Non-traumatic headache	With neurologic distress conditions or sudden severe onset	ALS		A0427/A0433
785.1		Cardiac symptoms other than chest pain.	Palpitations, skipped beats	ALS		A0472/A0433

ICD 9 Primary Code	ICD 9 Alternative Specific Code	Condition (General)	Condition (Specific)	Service Level	Comments and Examples (not all-inclusive)	HCPCS Crosswalk
536.2	787.01, 787.02, 787.03, 780.79, 786.8, or 786.52.	Cardiac symptoms other than chest pain.	Atypical pain or other symptoms	ALS	Persistent nausea and vomiting, weakness, hiccups, pleuritic pain, feeling of impending doom, and other emergency conditions.	A0427/A0433
992.5	992.0, 992.1, 992.3, 992.4, or 992.5	Heat exposure	Potentially life-threatening	ALS	Hot and dry skin, Temp>105, neurologic distress, signs of heat stroke or heat exhaustion, orthostatic vitals, other emergency conditions.	A0427/A0433
992.2	992.6, 992.7, 992.8, or 992.9.	Heat exposure	With symptoms	BLS	Muscle cramps, profuse sweating, fatigue.	A0429
459.0	569.3, 578.0, 578.1, 578.9, 596.7, 596.8, 623.8, 626.9, 637.1, 634.1, 666.00, 666.02, 666.04, 666.10, 666.12, 666.14, 666.20, 666.22, 666.24, 674.30, 674.32, 674.34, 786.3, 784.7, or 998.11	Hemorrhage	Severe (quantity) and potentially life-threatening	ALS	Uncontrolled or significant signs of shock or other emergency conditions. Severe, active vaginal, rectal bleeding, hematemesis, hemoptysis, epistaxis, active post- surgical bleeding.	A0472/A0433
038.9	136.9, any other condition in the 001 through 139 code range which would require isolation.	Infectious diseases requiring isolation procedures / public health risk.		BLS		A0429
987.9	981, 982.0, 982.1, 982.2, 982.3, 982.4, 982.8, 983.0, 983.1, 983.2, 983.9, 984.0, 984.1, 984.8, 984.9, 985.0, 985.1, 985.2, 985.3, 985.4, 985.5, 985.6, 985.8, 985.9, 986, 987.0, 987.1, 987.2, 987.3, 987.4, 987.5, 987.6, 987.7, 987.8, 989.1, 989.2, 989.3, 989.4, 989.6, 989.7, 989.9, or 990.	Hazmat exposure		ALS	Toxic fume or liquid exposure via inhalation, absorption, oral, radiation, smoke inhalation.	A0472/A0433
996.00	996.01, 996.02, 996.04, 996.09, 996.1, or 996.2.	Medical device failure	Life or limb threatening malfunction, failure, or complication.	ALS	Malfunction of ventilator, internal pacemaker, internal defibrillator, implanted drug delivery service.	A0427/A0433
996.30	996.31, 996.40, 996.41, 996.42, 996.43, 996.44, 996.45, 996.46, 996.47, 996.49, or 996.59.	Medical device failure	Health maintenance device failures that cannot be resolved on location.	BLS	Oxygen system supply malfunction, orthopedic device failure.	A0429
436	291.3, 293.82, 298.9, 344.9, 368.16, 369.9, 780.09, 780.4, 781.0, 781.2, 781.94, 781.99, 782.0, 784.3, 784.5, or 787.2.	Neurologic distress	Facial drooping; loss of vision; aphasia; difficulty swallowing; numbness, tingling extremity; stupor, delirium, confusion, hallucinations; paralysis, paresis (focal weakness); abnormal movements; vertigo; unsteady gait/balance; slurred speech, unable to speak	ALS		A0427/A0433
780.96		Pain, severe not otherwise specified in this list.	Acute onset, unable to ambulate or sit due to intensity of pain.	ALS	Pain is the reason for the transport. Use severity scale (7-10 for severe pain) or patient receiving pharmalogic intervention.	A0427/A0433
724.5	724.2 or 785.9	Back pain – non-traumatic (T and/or LS).	Suspect cardiac or vascular etiology	ALS	Other emergency conditions, absence of or decreased leg pulses, pulsatile abdominal mass, severe tearing abdominal pain.	A0427/A0433

ICD 9 Primary Code	ICD 9 Alternative Specific Code	Condition (General)	Condition (Specific)	Service Level	Comments and Examples (not all-inclusive)	HCPCS Crosswalk
724.9	724.2, 724.5, 847.1, or 847.2.	Back pain – non-traumatic (T and/or LS).	Sudden onset of new neurologic symptoms.	ALS	Neurologic distress list.	A0427/A0433
977.9	Any code from 960 through 979.	Poisons, ingested, injected, inhaled, absorbed.	Adverse drug reaction, poison exposure by inhalation, injection, or absorption.	ALS		A0427/A0433
305.0	303.00, 303.01, 303.02, 303.03, or any code from 960 through 979.	Alcohol intoxication or drug overdose (suspected).	Unable to care for self and unable to ambulate. No airway compromise.	BLS		A0429
977.3		Severe alcohol intoxication.	Airway may or may not be at risk. Pharmacological intervention or cardiac monitoring may be needed. Decreased level of consciousness resulting or potentially resulting in airway compromise.	ALS		A0427/A0433
998.9	674.10, 674.12, 674.14, 674.20, 674.22, 674.24, 997.69, 998.31, 998.32, or 998.83.	Post-operative procedure complications.	Major wound dehiscence, evisceration, or requires special handling for transport.	BLS	Non-life threatening	A0429
650	Any code from 630 through 679.	Pregnancy complication/childbirth/labor		ALS		A0427/A0433
292.9	291.0, 291.3, 291.81, 292.0, 292.81, 292.82, 292.83, 292.84, or 292.89.	Psychiatric/Behavioral	Abnormal mental status; drug withdrawal.	ALS	Disoriented, DTs, withdrawal symptoms.	A0427/A0433
298.9	300.9	Psychiatric/Behavioral	Threat to self or others, acute episode or exacerbation of paranoia, or disruptive behavior.	BLS	Suicidal, homicidal, or violent.	A0429
036.9	780.6 PLUS either 784.0 or 723.5.	Sick person – fever	Fever with associated symptoms (headache, stiff neck, etc.). Neurological changes.	BLS	Suspected spinal meningitis.	A0429
787.01	787.02, 787.03, or 787.91.	Severe dehydration	Nausea and vomiting, diarrhea, severe and incapacitating resulting in severe side effects of dehydration.	ALS		A0427/A0433
780.02	780.2 or 780.4	Unconscious, fainting, syncope, near syncope, weakness, or dizziness.	Transient unconscious episode or found unconscious. Acute episode or exacerbation.	ALS		A0427/A0433

Emergency Conditions - Trauma

ICD 9 Primary Code	ICD 9 Alternative Specific Code	Condition (General)	Condition (Specific)	Service Level	Comments and Examples (not all-inclusive)	HCPCS Crosswalk
959.8	800.00 through 804.99, 807.4, 807.6, 808.8, 808.9, 812.00 through 812.59, 813.00 through 813.93, 813.93, 820.00 through 821.39, 823.00 through 823.92, 851.00 through 866.13, 870.0 through 879.9, 880.00 through 887.7, or 890.0 through 897.7.	Major trauma	As defined by ACS Field Triage Decision Scheme. Trauma with one of the following: Glascow <14; systolic BP<90; RR<10 or >29; all penetrating injuries to head, neck, torso, extremities proximal to elbow or knee; flail chest; combination of trauma and burns; pelvic fracture; 2 or more long bone fractures; open or depressed skull fracture; paralysis; severe mechanism of injury including: ejection, death of another passenger in same patient compartment, falls >20", 20" deformity in vehicle or 12" deformity of patient compartment, auto pedestrian/bike, pedestrian thrown/run over, motorcycle accident at speeds >20 mph and rider separated from vehicle.	ALS	See "Condition (Specific)" column	A0427/ A0433
518.5		Other trauma	Need to monitor or maintain airway	ALS	Decreased LOC, bleeding into airway, trauma to head, face or neck.	A0427/ A0433
958.2	870.0 through 879.9, 880.00 through 887.7, 890.0 through 897.7, or 900.00 through 904.9.	Other trauma	Major bleeding	ALS	Uncontrolled or significant bleeding.	A0427/ A0433
829.0	805.00, 810.00 through 819.1, or 820.00 through 829.1.	Other trauma	Suspected fracture/dislocation requiring splinting/immobilization for transport.	BLS	Spinal, long bones, and joints including shoulder elbow, wrist, hip, knee and ankle, deformity of bone or joint.	A0429
880.00	880.00 through 887.7 or 890.0 through 897.7	Other trauma	Penetrating extremity injuries	BLS	Isolated bleeding stopped and good CSM.	A0429
886.0 or 895.0	886.1 or 895.1	Other trauma	Amputation – digits	BLS		A0429
887.4 or 897.4	887.0, 887.1, 887.2, 887.3, 887.6, 887.7, 897.0, 897.1, 897.2, 897.3, 897.5, 897.6, or 897.7.	Other trauma	Amputation – all other	ALS		A0427/ A0433
869.0 or 869.1	511.8, 512.8, 860.2, 860.3, 860.4, 860.5, 873.8, 873.9, or 959.01.	Other trauma	Suspected internal, head, chest, or abdominal injuries.	ALS	Signs of closed head injury, open head injury, pneumothorax, hemothorax, abdominal bruising, positive abdominal signs on exam, internal bleeding criteria, evisceration.	A0427/ A0433

ICD 9 Primary Code	ICD 9 Alternative Specific Code	Condition (General)	Condition (Specific)	Service Level	Comments and Examples (not all-inclusive)	HCPCS Crosswalk
949.3	941.30 through 941.39, 942.30 through 942.39, 943.30 through 943.39, 944.30 through 944.38, 945.30 through 945.39, or 949.3.	Burns	Major – per American Burn Association (ABA)	ALS	Partial thickness burns > 10% total body surface area (TBSA); involvement of face, hands, feet, genitalia, perineum, or major joints; third degree burns; electrical; chemical; inhalation; burns with preexisting medical disorders; burns and trauma	A0472/ A0433
949.2	941.20 through 941.29, 942.20 through 942.29, 943.20 through 943.29, 944.20 through 944.28, 945.20 through 945.29, or 949.2.	Burns	Minor – per ABA	BLS	Other burns than listed above.	A0429
989.5		Animal bites, stings, envenomation.	Potentially life or limb-threatening.	ALS	Symptoms of specific envenomation, significant face, neck, trunk, and extremity involvement; other emergency conditions.	A0427/ A0433
879.8	Any code from 870.0 through 897.7.	Animal bites/sting/ envonmation.	Other	BLS	Local pain and swelling or special handling considerations (not related to obesity) and patient monitoring required.	A0429
994.0		Lightning		ALS		A0427/ A0433
994.8		Electrocution		ALS		A0427/ A0433
994.1		Near drowning	Airway compromised during near drowning event	ALS		A0427/ A0433
921.9	870.0 through 870.9, 871.0, 871.1, 871.2, 871.3, 871.4, 871.5, 871.6, 871.7, 871.9, or 921.0 through 921.9.	Eye injuries	Acute vision loss or blurring, severe pain or chemical exposure, penetrating, severe lid lacerations.	BLS		A0429
995.83	995.53 or V71.5 PLUS any code from 925.1 through 929.9, 930.0 through 939.9, 958.0 through 958.8, or 959.01 through 959.9.	Sexual assault	With major injuries	ALS	Reference codes 959.8, 958.2, 869.0/869.1	A0427/ A0433
995.80	995.53 or V71.5 PLUS any code from 910.0 through 919.9, 920 through 924.9, or 959.01 through 959.9.	Sexual assault	With minor or no injuries	BLS		

Non-Emergency

ICD 9 Primary Code	ICD 9 Alternative Specific Code	Condition (General)	Condition (Specific)	Service Level	Comments and Examples (not all-inclusive)	HCPCS Crosswalk
428.9		Cardiac/hemodynamic monitoring required en route.		ALS	Expectation monitoring is needed before and after transport.	A0426
518.81 or 518.89	V46.11 or V46.12.	Advanced airway management		ALS	Ventilator dependent, apnea monitor, possible intubation needed, deep suctioning.	A0426, A0434

ICD 9 Primary Code	ICD 9 Alternative Specific Code	Condition (General)	Condition (Specific)	Service Level	Comments and Examples (not all-inclusive)	HCPCS Crosswalk
293.0		Chemical restraint.		ALS		A0426
496	491.20, 491.21, 492.0 through 492.8, 493.20, 493.21, 493.22, 494.0, or 494.1.	Suctioning required en route, need for titrated O2 therapy or IV fluid management.		BLS	Per transfer instructions.	A0428
786.09		Airway control/positioning required en route.		BLS	Per transfer instructions.	A0428
492.8	491.20, 491.21, 492.0 through 492.8, 493.20, 493.21, 493.22, 494.0, or 494.1.	Third party assistance/attendant required to apply, administer, or regulate or adjust oxygen en route.		BLS	Does not apply to patient capable of self-administration of portable or home O2. Patient must require oxygen therapy and be so frail as to require assistance.	A0428
298.9	Add 295.0 through 295.9 with 5th digits of 0, 1, 3, or 4, 296.00 or 299.90.	Patient safety: Danger to self or others – in restraints.		BLS	Refer to definition in 42 CFR Section 482.13(e).	A0428
293.1		Patient safety: Danger to self or others – monitoring.		BLS	Behavioral or cognitive risk such that patient requires monitoring for safety.	A0428
298.8	Add 295.0 through 295.9 with 5th digits of 0, 1, 3, or 4, 296.00 or 299.90	Patient safety: Danger to self or others – seclusion (flight risk).		BLS	Behavioral or cognitive risk such that patient requires attendant to assure patient does not try to exit the ambulance prematurely. Refer to 42 CFR Section 482.13(f) for definition.	A0428
781.3	Add 295.0 through 295.9 with 5th digits of 0, 1, 3, or 4, 296.00 or 299.90.	Patient safety: Risk of falling off wheelchair or stretcher while in motion (not related to obesity).		BLS	Patient's physical condition is such that patient risks injury during vehicle movement despite restraints. Indirect indicators include MDS criteria.	A0428
041.9		Special handling en route – isolation.		BLS	Includes patients with communicable diseases or hazardous material exposure who must be isolated from public or whose medical condition must be protected from public exposure; surgical drainage complications.	A0428
907.2		Special handling en route to reduce pain – orthopedic device.		BLS	Backboard, halotraction, use of pins and traction etc. Pain may be present.	A0428
719.45 or 719.49	718.40, 718.45, 718.49, or 907.2.	Special handling en route – positioning requires specialized handling.		BLS	Requires special handling to avoid further injury (such as with > grade 2 decubiti on buttocks). Generally does not apply to shorter transfers of < 1 hour. Positioning in wheelchair or standard car seat inappropriate due to contractures or recent extremity fractures – post-op hip as an example.	A0428

Transportation Indicators

Transportation Indicators Air and Ground	Transportation Category	Transportation Indicator Description		Service Level	Comments and Examples (not all-inclusive)	HCPCS Crosswalk
C1	Inter-facility Transport	EMTALA-certified inter-facility transfer to a higher level of care.	Beneficiary requires higher level of care.	BLS, ALS, SCT, FW, RW	Excludes patient-requested EMTALA transfer.	A0428, A0429, A0426, A0427, A0433, A043
C2	Inter-facility transport	Service not available at originating facility, and must meet one or more emergency or non-emergency conditions.		BLS, ALS, SCT, FW,RW		A0428, A0429, A0426, A0427, A0433, A043

Transportation Indicators Air and Ground	Transportation Category	Transportation Indicator Description		Service Level	Comments and Examples (not all-inclusive)	HCPCS Crosswalk
C3	Emergency Trauma Dispatch Condition Code	Major incident or mechanism of injury	Major Incident-This transportation indicator is to be used ONLY as a secondary code when the on-scene encounter is a BLS-level patient.	ALS	Trapped in machinery, close proximity to explosion, building fire with persons reported inside, major incident involving aircraft, bus, subway, metro, train and watercraft. Victim entrapped in vehicle.	A0427/ A0433
C4	Medically necessary transport but not to the nearest facility.	BLS or ALS response	Indicates to A/B MAC (A or B) that an ambulance provided a medically necessary transport, but that the number of miles on the Medicare claim form may be excessive.	BLS/ALS	This should occur if the facility is on divert status or the particular service is not available at the time of transport only. In these instances the ambulance units should clearly document why the beneficiary was not transported to the nearest facility.	Based on transport level.
C5	BLS transport of ALS-level patient	ALS-level condition treated and transport by a BLS-level ambulance.	This transportation indicator is used for ALL situations where a BLS-level ambulance treats and transports a patient that presents an ALS-level condition. No ALS-level assessment or intervention occurs at all during the patient encounter.	BLS		A0429
C6	ALS-level response to BLS-level patient	ALS response required based upon appropriate dispatch protocols – BLS-level patient transport	Indicates to A/B MAC (A or B) that an ALS-level ambulance responded appropriately based upon the information received at the time the call was received in dispatch and after a clinically appropriate ALS-assessment was performed on scene, it was determined that the condition of the patient was at a BLS level. These claims, properly documented, should be reimbursed at an ALS-1 level based upon coverage guidelines under the Medicare Ambulance Fee Schedule.	ALS		A0427
C7		IV meds required en route.	This transportation indicator is used for patients that require an ALS level transport in a non- emergent situation primarily because the patient requires monitoring of ongoing medications administered intravenously. Does not apply to self-administered medications. Does not include administration of crystalloid intravenous fluids (i.e., Normal Saline, Lactate Ringers, 5% Dextrose in Water, etc.). The patient's condition should also be reported on the claim with a code selected from the list	ALS	Does not apply to self-administered IV medications.	A0426

Air Ambulance Transportation Indicators

Air Ambulance Transportation Indicators	Transportation Indicator Description	Service Level	Comments and Examples (not all-inclusive)	HCPCS Crosswalk
D1	Long Distance-patient's condition requires rapid transportation over a long distance	FW, RW	If the patient's condition warrants only.	A0430, A0431
D2	Under rare and exceptional circumstances, traffic patterns preclude ground transport at the time the response is required.	FW, RW		A0430, A0431
D3		FW, RW		A0430, A0431
D4		FW, RW		A0430, A0431

Note: HCPCS Crosswalk to ALS1E (A0427) and ALS2 (A0433) would ultimately be determined by the number and type of ALS level services provided during transport. All medical condition codes can be cross walked to fixed wing and rotor wing HCPCS provided the air ambulance service has documented the medical necessity for air ambulance service versus ground or water ambulance. As a result, codes A0430 (Fixed Wing) and A0431 (Rotor Wing) can be included in Column 7 for each condition listed.

100-4, Chapter 16, 60.1.4

Coding Requirements for Specimen Collection

The following HCPCS codes and terminology must be used:

- 36415 –Collection of venous blood by venipuncture.
- P96I5 –Catheterization for collection of specimen(s).

The allowed amount for specimen collection in each of the above circumstances is included in the laboratory fee schedule distributed annually by CMS.

100-4, Chapter 16, 60.2

Travel Allowance

In addition to a specimen collection fee allowed under §60.1, Medicare, under Part B, covers a specimen collection fee and travel allowance for a laboratory technician to draw a specimen from either a nursing home patient or homebound patient under §1833(h)(3) of the Act and payment is made based on the clinical laboratory fee schedule. The travel allowance is intended to cover the estimated travel costs of collecting a specimen and to reflect the technician's salary and travel costs.

The additional allowance can be made only where a specimen collection fee is also payable, i.e., no travel allowance is made where the technician merely performs a messenger service to pick up a specimen drawn by a physician or nursing home personnel. The travel allowance may not be paid to a physician unless the trip to the home, or to the nursing home was solely for the purpose of drawing a specimen. Otherwise travel costs are considered to be associated with the other purposes of the trip. The travel allowance is not distributed by CMS. Instead, the carrier must calculate the travel allowance for each claim using the following rules for the particular Code. The following HCPCS codes are used for travel allowances:

Per Mile Travel Allowance (P9603)

- The minimum "per mile travel allowance" is $1.01. The per mile travel allowance is to be used in situations where the average trip to patients' homes is longer than 20 miles round trip, and is to be pro-rated in situations where specimens are drawn or picked up from non-Medicare patients in the same trip. -one way, in connection with medically necessary laboratory specimen collection drawn from homebound or nursing home bound patient; prorated miles actually traveled (carrier allowance on per mile basis); or

- The per mile allowance was computed using the Federal mileage rate plus an additional 45 cents a mile to cover the technician's time and travel costs. Contractors have the option of establishing a higher per mile rate in excess of the minimum ($1.01 a mile in CY 2014) if local conditions warrant it. The minimum mileage rate will be reviewed and updated in conjunction with the clinical lab fee schedule as needed. At no time will the laboratory be allowed to bill for more miles than are reasonable or for miles not actually traveled by the laboratory technician.

Example 1: In CY 2014, a laboratory technician travels 60 miles round trip from a lab in a city to a remote rural location, and back to the lab to draw a single Medicare patient's blood. The total reimbursement would be $60.60 (60 miles x $1.01 cents a mile), plus the specimen collection fee.

Example 2: In CY 2014, a laboratory technician travels 40 miles from the lab to a Medicare patient's home to draw blood, and then travels an additional 10 miles to a non-Medicare patient's home and then travels 30 miles to return to the lab. The total miles traveled would be 80 miles. The claim submitted would be for one half of the miles traveled or $40.40 (40 x $1.01), plus the specimen collection fee.

Flat Rate (P9604)

The CMS will pay a minimum of $10.10 one way flat rate travel allowance. The flat rate travel allowance is to be used in areas where average trips are less than 20 miles round trip. The flat rate travel fee is to be pro-rated for more than one blood drawn at the same address, and for stops at the homes of Medicare and non-Medicare patients. The laboratory does the pro-ration when the claim is submitted based on the number of patients seen on that trip. The specimen collection fee will be paid for each patient encounter.

This rate is based on an assumption that a trip is an average of 15 minutes and up to 10 miles one way. It uses the Federal mileage rate and a laboratory technician's time of $17.66 an hour, including overhead. Contractors have the option of establishing a flat rate in excess of the minimum of $10.10, if local conditions warrant it. The minimum national flat rate will be reviewed and updated in conjunction with the clinical laboratory fee schedule, as necessitated by adjustments in the Federal travel allowance and salaries.

The claimant identifies round trip travel by use of the LR modifier

Example 3: A laboratory technician travels from the laboratory to a single Medicare patient's home and returns to the laboratory without making any other stops. The flat rate would be calculated as follows: 2 x $10.10 for a total trip reimbursement of $20.20, plus the specimen collection fee.

Example 4: A laboratory technician travels from the laboratory to the homes of five patients to draw blood, four of the patients are Medicare patients and one is not. An additional flat rate would be charged to cover the 5 stops and the return trip to the lab (6 x $10.10 = $60.60). Each of the claims submitted would be for $12.12 ($60.60/5 = $12.12). Since one of the patients is non-Medicare, four claims would be submitted for $12.12 each, plus the specimen collection fee for each.

Example 5: A laboratory technician travels from a laboratory to a nursing home and draws blood from 5 patients and returns to the laboratory. Four of the patients are on Medicare and one is not. The $10.10 flat rate is multiplied by two to cover the return trip to the laboratory (2 x $10.10 = $20.20) and then divided by five (1/5 of $20.20 = $4.04). Since one of the patients is non-Medicare, four claims would be submitted for $4.04 each, plus the specimen collection fee.

If a carrier determines that it results in equitable payment, the carrier may extend the former payment allowances for additional travel (such as to a distant rural nursing home) to all circumstances where travel is required. This might be appropriate, for example, if the carrier's former payment allowance was on a per mile basis. Otherwise, it should establish an appropriate allowance and inform the suppliers in its service area. If a carrier decides to establish a new allowance, one method is to consider developing a travel allowance consisting of:

- The current Federal mileage allowance for operating personal automobiles, plus a personnel allowance per mile to cover personnel costs based upon an estimate of average hourly wages and average driving speed.

Carriers must prorate travel allowance amounts claimed by suppliers by the number of patients (including Medicare and non-Medicare patients) from whom specimens were drawn on a given trip.

The carrier may determine that payment in addition to the routine travel allowance determined under this section is appropriate if:

- The patient from whom the specimen must be collected is in a nursing home or is homebound; and
- The clinical laboratory tests are needed on an emergency basis outside the general business hours of the laboratory making the collection.
- Subsequent updated travel allowance amounts will be issued by CMS via Recurring Update Notification (RUN) on an annual basis.

100-4, Chapter 16, 70.8

Certificate of Waiver

Effective September 1, 1992, all laboratory testing sites (except as provided in 42CFR 493.3(b)) must have either a CLIA certificate of waiver, certificate for provider-performed microscopy procedures, certificate of registration, certificate of compliance, or certificate of accreditation to legally perform clinical laboratory testing on specimens from individuals in the United States.

The Food and Drug Administration approves CLIA waived tests on a flow basis. The CMS identifies CLIA waived tests by providing an updated list of waived tests to the Medicare contractors on a quarterly basis via a Recurring Update Notification. To be recognized as a waived test, some CLIA waived tests have unique HCPCS procedure codes and some must have a QW modifier included with the HCPCS code.

For a list of specific HCPCS codes subject to CLIA see

http://www.cms.hhs.gov/CLIA/downloads/waivetbl.pdf

100-4, Chapter 17, 80.4.1

Clotting Factor Furnishing Fee

The Medicare Modernization Act section 303(e)(1) added section 1842(o)(5)(C) of the Social Security Act which requires that, beginning January 1, 2005, a furnishing fee will be paid for items and services associated with clotting factor.

Beginning January 1, 2005, a clotting factor furnishing fee is separately payable to entities that furnish clotting factor unless the costs associated with furnishing the clotting factor is paid through another payment system.

The clotting factor furnishing fee is updated each calendar year based on the percentage increase in the consumer price index (CPI) for medical care for the 12-month period ending with June of the previous year. The clotting factor furnishing fees applicable for dates of service in each calendar year (CY) are listed below:

CY 2005 -$0.140 per unit

CY 2006 -$0.146 per unit

CY 2007 -$0.152 per unit

CY 2008 -$0.158 per unit

CY 2009 -$0.164 per unit

CY 2010 -$0.170 per unit

CY 2011 -$0.176 per unit

CY 2012 -$0.181 per unit

CY 2013 -$0.188 per unit

CY 2014 -$0.192 per unit

Annual updates to the clotting factor furnishing fee are subsequently communicated by a Recurring Update Notification.

CMS includes this clotting factor furnishing fee in the nationally published payment limit for clotting factor billing codes. When the clotting factor is not included on the Average Sales Price (ASP) Medicare Part B Drug Pricing File or Not Otherwise Classified (NOC) Pricing File, the contractor must make payment for the clotting factor as well as make payment for the furnishing fee.

100-4, Chapter 17, 90.3

Hospital Outpatient Payment Under OPPS for New, Unclassified Drugs and Biologicals After FDA Approval But Before Assignment of a Product-Specific Drug or Biological HCPCS Code

Section 621(a) of the MMA amends Section 1833(t) of the Social Security Act by adding paragraph (15), Payment for New Drugs and Biologicals Until HCPCS Code Assigned. Under this provision, payment for an outpatient drug or biological that is furnished as part of covered outpatient department services for which a product-specific HCPCS code has not been assigned shall be paid an amount equal to 95 percent of average wholesale price (AWP). This provision applies only to payments under the hospital outpatient prospective payment system (OPPS).

Beginning January 1, 2004, hospital outpatient departments may bill for new drugs and biologicals that are approved by the FDA on or after January 1, 2004, for which a product-specific HCPCS code has not been assigned. Beginning on or after the date of FDA approval, hospitals may bill for the drug or biological using HCPCS code C9399, Unclassified drug or biological.

Hospitals report in the ANSI ASC X12 837 I in specific locations, or in the "Remarks" section of the CMS 1450):

1. the National Drug Code (NDC),
2. the quantity of the drug that was administered, expressed in the unit of measure applicable to the drug or biological, and
3. the date the drug was furnished to the beneficiary.

Contractors shall manually price the drug or biological at 95 percent of AWP. They shall pay hospitals 80 percent of the calculated price and shall bill beneficiaries 20 percent of the calculated price, after the deductible is met. Drugs and biologicals that are manually priced at 95 percent of AWP are not eligible for outlier payment.

HCPCS code C9399 is only to be reported for new drugs and biologicals that are approved by FDA on or after January 1, 2004, for which there is no HCPCS code that describes the drug.

100-4, Chapter 18, 10.1.2

Influenza Virus Vaccine

Effective for services furnished on or after May 1, 1993, the influenza virus vaccine and its administration is covered when furnished in compliance with any applicable State law. Typically, this vaccine is administered once a flu season. Medicare does not require for coverage purposes that a doctor of medicine or osteopathy order the vaccine. Therefore, the beneficiary may receive the vaccine upon request without a physician's order and without physician supervision. Since there is no yearly limit, contractors determine whether such services are reasonable and allow payment if appropriate.

See Pub. 100-02, Medicare Benefit Policy Manual, Chapter 15, Section 50.4.4.2 for additional coverage requirements for influenza virus vaccine.

100-4, Chapter 18, 10.2.1

Healthcare Common Procedure Coding System (HCPCS) and Diagnosis Codes

Vaccines and their administration are reported using separate codes. The following codes are for reporting the vaccines only

HCPCS	Definition
90653	Influenza virus vaccine, inactivated, subunit, adjuvanted, for intramuscular use
90654	Influenza virus vaccine, split virus, preservative-free, for intradermal use, for adults ages 18 – 64;
90655	Influenza virus vaccine, split virus, preservative free, for children 6-35 months of age, for intramuscular use;
90656	Influenza virus vaccine, split virus, preservative free, for use in individuals 3 years and above, for intramuscular use;
90657	Influenza virus vaccine, split virus, for children 6-35 months of age, for intramuscular use;
90660	Influenza virus vaccine, live, for intranasal use;
90661	Influenza virus vaccine, derived from cell cultures, subunit, preservative and antibiotic free, for intramuscular use
90662	Influenza virus vaccine, split virus, preservative free, enhanced immunogenicity via increased antigen content, for intramuscular use
90669	Pneumococcal conjugate vaccine, polyvalent, for children under 5 years, for intramuscular use
90670	Pneumococcal conjugate vaccine, 13 valent, for intramuscular use
90672	Influenza virus vaccine, live, quadrivalent, for intranasal use
90673	Influenza virus vaccine, trivalent, derived from recombinant DNA (RIV3), hemagglutinin (HA) protein only, preservative and antibiotic free, for intramuscular use
90685	Influenza virus vaccine, quadrivalent, split virus, preservative free, when administered to children 6-35 months of age, for intramuscular use
90686	Influenza virus vaccine, quadrivalent, split virus, preservative free, when administered to individuals 3 years of age and older, for intramuscular use

HCPCS	Definition
90687	Influenza virus vaccine, quadrivalent, split virus, when administered to children 6-35 months of age, for intramuscular use
90688	Influenza virus vaccine, quadrivalent, split virus, when administered to individuals 3 years of age and older, for intramuscular use
90732	Pneumococcal polysaccharide vaccine, 23-valent, adult or immunosuppressed patient dosage, for use in individuals 2 years or older, for subcutaneous or intramuscular use;
90739	Hepatitis B vaccine, adult dosage (2 dose schedule), for intramuscular use
90740	Hepatitis B vaccine, dialysis or immunosuppressed patient dosage (3 dose schedule), for intramuscular use;
90743	Hepatitis B vaccine, adolescent (2 dose schedule), for intramuscular use;
90744	Hepatitis B vaccine, pediatric/adolescent dosage (3 dose schedule), for intramuscular use;
90746	Hepatitis B vaccine, adult dosage, for intramuscular use; and
90747	Hepatitis B vaccine, dialysis or immunosuppressed patient dosage (4 dose schedule), for intramuscular use.

The following codes are for reporting administration of the vaccines only. The administration of the vaccines is billed using:

HCPCS	Definition
G0008	Administration of influenza virus vaccine;
G0009	Administration of pneumococcal vaccine; and
*G0010	Administration of hepatitis B vaccine.
*90471	Immunization administration. (For OPPS hospitals billing for the hepatitis B vaccine administration)
*90472	Each additional vaccine. (For OPPS hospitals billing for the hepatitis B vaccine administration)

*** NOTE:** For claims with dates of service prior to January 1, 2006, OPPS and non-OPPS hospitals report G0010 for hepatitis B vaccine administration. For claims with dates of service January 1, 2006 until December 31, 2010, OPPS hospitals report 90471 or 90472 for hepatitis B vaccine administration as appropriate in place of G0010. Beginning January 1, 2011, providers should report G0010 for billing under the OPPS rather than 90471 or 90472 to ensure correct waiver of coinsurance and deductible for the administration of hepatitis B vaccine.

One of the following diagnosis codes must be reported as appropriate. If the sole purpose for the visit is to receive a vaccine or if a vaccine is the only service billed on a claim the applicable following diagnosis code may be used.

Diagnosis Code	Description
V03.82	Pneumococcus
V04.81**	Influenza
V06.6***	Pneumococcus and Influenza
V05.3	Hepatitis B

**Effective for influenza virus claims with dates of service October 1, 2003 and later.

***Effective October 1, 2006, providers may report diagnosis code V06.6 on claims for pneumococcus and/or influenza virus vaccines when the purpose of the visit was to receive both vaccines.

If a diagnosis code for pneumococcus, hepatitis B, or influenza virus vaccination is not reported on a claim, contractors may not enter the diagnosis on the claim. Contractors must follow current resolution processes for claims with missing diagnosis codes.

If the diagnosis code and the narrative description are correct, but the HCPCS code is incorrect, the carrier or intermediary may correct the HCPCS code and pay the claim. For example, if the reported diagnosis code is V04.81 and the narrative description (if annotated on the claim) says "flu shot" but the HCPCS code is incorrect, contractors may change the HCPCS code and pay for the flu vaccine. Effective October 1, 2006, carriers/AB MACs should follow the instructions in Pub. 100-04, Chapter 1, Section 80.3.2.1.1 (Carrier Data Element Requirements) for claims submitted without a HCPCS code.

Claims for hepatitis B vaccinations must report the I.D. Number of the referring physician. In addition, if a doctor of medicine or osteopathy does not order the influenza virus vaccine, the intermediary claims require:

- UPIN code SLF000 to be reported on claims submitted prior to May 23, 2008, when Medicare began accepting NPIs, only
- The provider's own NPI to be reported in the NPI field for the attending physician on claims submitted on or after May 23, 2008, when NPI requirements were implemented.

100-4, Chapter-18, 10.2.2.1

FI/AB MAC Payment for Pneumococcal Pneumonia Virus, Influenza Virus, and Hepatitis B Virus Vaccines and Their Administration

Payment for Vaccines

Payment for all of these vaccines is on a reasonable cost basis for hospitals, home health agencies (HHAs), skilled nursing facilities (SNFs), critical access hospitals (CAHs), and hospital-based renal dialysis facilities (RDFs). Payment for comprehensive outpatient rehabilitation facilities (CORFs), Indian Health Service hospitals (IHS), IHS CAHs and independent RDFs is based on 95 percent of the average wholesale price (AWP). Section 10.2.4 of this chapter contains information on payment of these vaccines when provided by RDFs or hospices. See §10.2.2.2 for payment to independent and provider-based Rural Health Centers and Federally Qualified Health Clinics.

Payment for these vaccines is as follows:

Facility	Type of Bill	Payment
Hospitals, other than Indian Health Service (IHS) Hospitals and Critical Access Hospitals (CAHs)	12x, 13x	Reasonable cost
IHS Hospitals	12x, 13x, 83x	95% of AWP
IHS CAHs	85x	95% of AWP
CAHs	85x	Reasonable cost
Method I and Method II		
Skilled Nursing Facilities	22x, 23x	Reasonable cost

Facility	Type of Bill	Payment
Home Health Agencies	34x	Reasonable cost
Comprehensive Outpatient Rehabilitation Facilities	75x	95% of AWP
Independent Renal Dialysis Facilities	72x	95% of AWP
Hospital-based Renal Dialysis Facilities	72x	Reasonable cost

Payment for Vaccine Administration

Payment for the administration of influenza virus and pneumococcal vaccines is as follows:

Facility	Type of Bill	Payment
Hospitals, other than IHS Hospitals and CAHs	12x, 13x	Outpatient Prospective Payment System (OPPS) for hospitals subject to OPPS Reasonable cost for hospitals not subject to OPPS
IHS Hospitals	12x, 13x, 83x	MPFS as indicated in guidelines below.
IHS CAHs	85x	MPFS as indicated in guidelines below.
CAHs	85x	Reasonable cost
Method I and II		
Skilled Nursing Facilities	22x, 23x	MPFS as indicated in guidelines below.
Home Health Agencies	35x	OPPS
Comprehensive Outpatient Rehabilitation Facilities	75x	MPFS as indicated in guidelines below.
Independent RDFs	72x	MPFS as indicated in guidelines below.
Hospital-based RDFs	72x	Reasonable cost

Guidelines for pricing pneumococcal and influenza virus vaccine administration under the MPFS.

Make reimbursement based on the rate in the MPFS associated with the CPT® code 90782 or 90471 as follows:

HCPCS code	Effective prior to March 1, 2003	Effective on and after March 1, 2003
G0008	90782	90471
G0009	90782	90471

See §10.2.2.2 for payment to independent and provider based Rural Health Centers and Federally Qualified Health Clinics.

Payment for the administration of hepatitis B vaccine is as follows:

Facility	Type of Bill	Payment
Hospitals other than IHS hospitals and CAHs	12x, 13x	Outpatient Prospective Payment System (OPPS) for hospitals subject to OPPS Reasonable cost for hospitals not subject to OPPS
IHS Hospitals	12x, 13x, 83x	MPFS as indicated in the guidelines below
CAHs	85x	Reasonable cost
Method I and II		
IHS CAHs	85x	MPFS as indicated in the guidelines below
Skilled Nursing Facilities	22x, 23x	MPFS as indicated in the chart below
Home Health Agencies	34x	OPPS
Comprehensive Outpatient Rehabilitation Facilities	75x	MPFS as indicated in the guidelines below
Independent RDFs	75x	MPFS as indicated in the chart below
Hospital-based RDFs	72x	Reasonable cost

Guidelines for pricing hepatitis B vaccine administration under the MPFS.

Make reimbursement based on the rate in the MPFS associated with the CPT® code 90782 or 90471 as follows:

HCPCS code	Effective prior to March 1, 2003	Effective on and after March 1, 2003
G0010	90782	90471

See §10.2.2.2 for payment to independent and provider based Rural Health Centers and Federally Qualified Health Clinics.

100-4, Chapter-18, 10.2.5.2

Carrier/AB MAC Payment Requirements

Payment for pneumococcal, influenza virus, and hepatitis B vaccines follows the same standard rules that are applicable to any injectable drug or biological. (See chapter 17 for procedures for determining the payment rates for pneumococcal and influenza virus vaccines.)

Effective for claims with dates of service on or after February 1, 2001, §114, of the Benefits Improvement and Protection Act of 2000 mandated that all drugs and biologicals be paid based on mandatory assignment. Therefore, all providers of influenza virus and pneumococcal vaccines must accept assignment for the vaccine.

Prior to March 1, 2003, the administration of pneumococcal, influenza virus, and hepatitis B vaccines, (HCPCS codes G0008, G0009, and G0010), though not reimbursed directly through the MPFS, were reimbursed at the same rate as HCPCS code 90782 on the MPFS for the year that corresponded to the date of service of the claim.

Prior to March 1, 2003, HCPCS codes G0008, G0009, and G0010 are reimbursed at the same rate as HCPCS code 90471. Assignment for the administration is not mandatory, but is applicable should the provider be enrolled as a provider type "Mass Immunization Roster Biller," submits roster bills, or participates in the centralized billing program.

Carriers/AB MACs may not apply the limiting charge provision for pneumococcal, influenza virus vaccine, or hepatitis B vaccine and their administration in accordance with §§1833(a)(1)and 1833(a)(10)(A)of the Social Security Act (the Act.) The administration of the influenza virus vaccine is covered in the influenza virus vaccine benefit under §1861(s)(10)(A)of the Act, rather than under the physicians' services benefit. Therefore, it is not eligible for the 10 percent Health Professional Shortage Area (HPSA) incentive payment or the 5 percent Physician Scarcity Area (PSA) incentive payment.

No Legal Obligation to Pay

Nongovernmental entities that provide immunizations free of charge to all patients, regardless of their ability to pay, must provide the immunizations free of charge to Medicare beneficiaries and may not bill Medicare. (See Pub. 100-02, Medicare Benefit Policy Manual, chapter 16.) Thus, for example, Medicare may not pay for influenza virus vaccinations administered to Medicare beneficiaries if a physician provides free vaccinations to all non-Medicare patients or where an employer offers free vaccinations to its employees. Physicians also may not charge Medicare beneficiaries more for a vaccine than theywould charge non-Medicare patients. (See §1128(b)(6)(A)of the Act.) When an employer offers free vaccinations to its employees, it must also offer the free vaccination to an employee who is also a Medicare beneficiary. It does not have to offer free vaccinations to its non-Medicare employees.

Nongovernmental entities that do not charge patients who are unable to pay or reduce their charges for patients of limited means, yet expect to be paid if the patient has health insurance coverage for the services provided, may bill Medicare and expect payment.

Governmental entities (such as PHCs) may bill Medicare for pneumococcal, hepatitis B, and influenza virus vaccines administered to Medicare beneficiaries when services are rendered free of charge to non-Medicare beneficiaries.

100-4, Chapter-18, 10.3.1.1

Centralized Billing for Influenza Virus and Pneumococcal Vaccines to Medicare Carriers/AB MACs

The CMS currently authorizes a limited number of providers to centrally bill for influenza virus and pneumococcal immunization claims. Centralized billing is an optional program available to providers who qualify to enroll with Medicare as the provider type "Mass Immunization Roster Biller," as well as to other individuals and entities that qualify to enroll as regular Medicare providers. Centralized billers must roster bill, must accept assignment, and must bill electronically.

To qualify for centralized billing, a mass immunizer must be operating in at least three payment localities for which there are three different contractors processing claims. Individuals and entities providing the vaccine and administration must be properly licensed in the State in which the immunizations are given and the contractor must verify this through the enrollment process.

Centralized billers must send all claims for influenza virus and pneumococcal immunizations to a single contractor for payment, regardless of the jurisdiction in which the vaccination was administered. (This does not include claims for the Railroad Retirement Board, United Mine Workers or Indian Health Services. These claims must continue to go to the appropriate processing entity.) Payment is made based on the payment locality where the service was provided. This process is only available for claims for the influenza virus and pneumococcal vaccines and their administration. The general coverage and coding rules still apply to these claims.

This section applies only to those individuals and entities that provide mass immunization services for influenza virus and pneumococcal vaccinations and that have been authorized by CMS to centrally bill. All other providers, including those individuals and entities that provide mass immunization services that are not authorized to centrally bill,must continue to bill for these claims to their regular carrier/AB MAC per the instructions in §10.3.1 of this chapter.

The claims processing instructions in this section apply only to the designated processing contractor. However, all carriers/AB MACs must follow the instructions in §10.3.1.1.J, below, "Provider Education Instructions for All Carriers/AB MACs."

A. Processing Contractor

Trailblazers Health Enterprises is designated as the sole contractor for the payment of influenza virus and pneumococcal claims for centralized billers from October 1, 2000, through the length of the contract. The CMS central office will notify centralized billers of the appropriate contractor to bill when they receive their notification of acceptance into the centralized billing program.

B. Request for Approval

Approval to participate in the CMS centralized billing program is a two part approval process. Individuals and corporations who wish to enroll as a CMS mass immunizer centralized biller must send their request in writing. CMS will complete Part 1 of the approval process by reviewing preliminary demographic information included in the request for participation letter. Completion of Part 1 is not approval to set up vaccination clinics, vaccinate beneficiaries, and bill Medicare for reimbursement. All new participants must complete Part 2 of the approval process (Form CMS-855 Application)before they may set up vaccination clinics, vaccinate Medicare beneficiaries, and bill Medicare for reimbursement. If an individual or entity's request is approved for centralized billing, the approval is limited to 12 months from September to August 31 of the next year. It is the responsibility of the centralized biller to reapply for approval each year. The designated contractor shall provide in writing to CMS and approved centralized billers notification of completion and approval of Part 2 of the approval process. The designated contractor may not process claims for any centralized biller who has not completed Parts 1 and 2 of the approval process. If claims are submitted by a provider who has not received approval of Parts 1 and 2 of the approval process to participate as a centralized biller, the contractor must return the claims to the provider to submit to the local carrier/AB MAC for payment.

C. Notification of Provider Participation to the Processing Contractor

Before September 1 of every year, CMS will provide the designated contractor with the names of the entities that are authorized to participate in centralized billing for the 12 month period beginning September 1 and ending August 31 of the next year.

D. Enrollment

Though centralized billers may already have a Medicare provider number, for purposes of centralized billing, they must also obtain a provider number from the processing contractor for centralized billing through completion of the Form CMS-855 (Provider Enrollment Application). Providers/suppliers

are encouraged to apply to enroll as a centralized biller early as possible. Applicants who have not completed the entire enrollment process and received approval from CMS and the designated contractor to participate as a Medicare mass immunizer centralized biller will not be allowed to submit claims to Medicare for reimbursement.

Whether an entity enrolls as a provider type "Mass Immunization Roster Biller" or some other type of provider, all normal enrollment processes and procedures must be followed. Authorization from CMS to participate in centralized billing is dependent upon the entity's ability to qualify as some type of Medicare provider. In addition, as under normal enrollment procedures, the contractor must verify that the entity is fully qualified and certified per State requirements in each State in which they plan to operate.

The contractor will activate the provider number for the 12-month period from September 1 through August 31 of the following year. If the provider is authorized to participate in the centralized billing program the next year, the contractor will extend the activation of the provider number for another year. The entity need not re-enroll with the contractor every year. However, should there be changes in the States in which the entity plans to operate, the contractor will need to verify that the entity meets all State certification and licensure requirements in those new States.

E. Electronic Submission of Claims on Roster Bills

Centralized billers must agree to submit their claims on roster bills in an Electronic Media Claims standard format using the appropriate version of American National Standards Institute (ANSI) format. Contractors should refer to the appropriate ANSI Implementation Guide to determine the correct location for this information on electronic claims. The processing contractor must provide instructions on acceptable roster billing formats to the approved centralized billers. Paper claims will not be accepted.

F. Required Information on Roster Bills for Centralized Billing

In addition to the roster billing instructions found in §10.3.1 of this chapter, centralized billers must complete on the electronic format the area that corresponds to Item 32 and 33 on Form CMS 1500 (08-05). The contractor must use the ZIP Code in Item 32 to determine the payment locality for the claim. Item 33 must be completed to report the provider of service/supplier's billing name, address, ZIP Code, and telephone number. In addition, the NPI of the billing provider or group must be appropriately reported.

For electronic claims, the name, address, and ZIP Code of the facility are reported in:

- The HIPAA compliant ANSI X12N 837: Claim level loop 2310D NM101=FA. When implemented, the facility (e.g., hospitals) NPI will be captured in the loop 2310D NM109 (NM108=XX) if one is available. Prior to NPI, enter the tax information in loop 2310D NM109 (NM108=24 or 34) and enter the Medicare legacy facility identifier in loop 2310D REF02 (REF01=1C). Report the address, city, state, and ZIP Code in loop 2310D N301 and N401, N402, and N403. Facility data is not required to be reported at the line level for centralized billing.

G. Payment Rates and Mandatory Assignment

The payment rates for the administration of the vaccinations are based on the Medicare Physician Fee Schedule (MPFS) for the appropriate year. Payment made through the MPFS is based on geographic locality. Therefore, payments vary based on the geographic locality where the service was performed.

The HCPCS codes G0008 and G0009 for the administration of the vaccines are not paid on the MPFS. However, prior to March 1, 2003, they must be paid at the same rate as HCPCS code 90782, which is on the MPFS. The designated contractor must pay per the correct MPFS file for each calendar year based on the date of service of the claim. Beginning March 1, 2003, HCPCS codes G0008, G0009, and G0010 are to be reimbursed at the same rate as HCPCS code 90471.

In order to pay claims correctly for centralized billers, the designated contractor must have the correct name and address, including ZIP Code, of the entity where the service was provided.

The following remittance advice and Medicare Summary Notice (MSN) messages apply:

Claim adjustment reason code 16 , "Claim/service lacks information which is needed for adjudication. At least one Remark Code must be provided (may be comprised of either the Remittance Advice Remark Code or NCPDP Reject Reason Code.)"

and

Remittance advice remark code MA114, "Missing/ incomplete/invalid information on where the services were furnished."

and

MSN 9.4-"This item or service was denied because information required to make payment was incorrect."

The payment rates for the vaccines must be determined by the standard method used by Medicare for reimbursement of drugs and biologicals. (See chapter 17 for procedures for determining the payment rates for vaccines.)

Effective for claims with dates of service on or after February 1, 2001, §114, of the Benefits Improvement and Protection Act of 2000 mandated that all drugs and biologicals be paid based on mandatory assignment. Therefore, all providers of influenza virus and pneumococcal vaccines must accept assignment for the vaccine. In addition, as a requirement for both centralized billing and roster billing, providers must agree to accept assignment for the administration of the vaccines as well. This means that they must agree to accept the amount that Medicare pays for the vaccine and the administration. Also, since there is no coinsurance or deductible for the influenza virus and pneumococcal benefit, accepting assignment means that Medicare beneficiaries cannot be charged for the vaccination.

H. Common Working File Information

To identify these claims and to enable central office data collection on the project, special processing number 39 has been assigned. The number should be entered on the HUBC claim record to CWF in the field titled Demonstration Number.

I. Provider Education Instructions for the Processing Contractor

The processing contractor must fully educate the centralized billers on the processes for centralized billing as well as for roster billing. General information on influenza virus and pneumococcal coverage and billing instructions is available on the CMS Web site for providers.

J. Provider Education Instructions for All Carriers/AB MACs

By April 1 of every year, all carriers/AB MACs must publish in their bulletins and put on their Web sites the following notification to providers. Questions from interested providers should be forwarded to the central office address below. Carriers/AB MACs must enter the name of the assigned processing contractor where noted before sending.

NOTIFICATION TO PROVIDERS

Centralized billing is a process in which a provider, who provides mass immunization services for influenza virus and pneumococcal pneumonia virus (PPV) immunizations, can send all claims to a single contractor for payment regardless of the geographic locality in which the vaccination was administered. (This does not include claims for the Railroad Retirement Board, United Mine Workers or Indian Health Services. These claims must continue to go to the appropriate processing entity.) This process is only available for claims for the influenza virus and pneumococcal vaccines and their administration. The administration of the vaccinations is reimbursed at the assigned rate based on the Medicare physician fee schedule for the appropriate locality. The vaccines are reimbursed at the assigned rate using the Medicare standard method for reimbursement of drugs and biologicals.

Individuals and entities interested in centralized billing must contact CMS central office, in writing, at the following address by June 1 of the year they wish to begin centrally billing.

> Center for Medicare & Medicaid Services
> Division of Practitioner Claims Processing
> Provider Billing and Education Group
> 7500 Security Boulevard
> Mail Stop C4-10-07
> Baltimore, Maryland 21244

By agreeing to participate in the centralized billing program, providers agree to abide by the following criteria.

CRITERIA FOR CENTRALIZED BILLING

- To qualify for centralized billing, an individual or entity providing mass immunization services for influenza virus and pneumococcal vaccinations must provide these services in at least three payment localities for which there are at least three different contractors processing claims.

- Individuals and entities providing the vaccine and administration must be properly licensed in the State in which the immunizations are given.

- Centralized billers must agree to accept assignment (i.e., they must agree to accept the amount that Medicare pays for the vaccine and the administration). Since there is no coinsurance or deductible for the influenza virus and pneumococcal benefit, accepting assignment means that Medicare beneficiaries cannot be charged for the vaccination, i.e., beneficiaries may not incur any out-of-pocket expense. For example, a drugstore may not charge a Medicare beneficiary $10 for an influenza virus vaccination and give the beneficiary a coupon for $10 to be used in the drugstore.

NOTE: The practice of requiring a beneficiary to pay for the vaccination upfront and to file their own claim for reimbursement is inappropriate. All Medicare providers are required to file claims on behalf of the beneficiary per §1848(g)(4)(A) of the Social Security Act and centralized billers may not collect any payment.

- The contractor assigned to process the claims for centralized billing is chosen at the discretion of CMS based on such considerations as workload, user-friendly software developed by the contractor for billing claims, and overall performance. The assigned contractor for this year is [Fill in name of contractor.]

- The payment rates for the administration of the vaccinations are based on the Medicare physician fee schedule (MPFS) for the appropriate year. Payment made through the MPFS is based on geographic locality. Therefore, payments received may vary based on the geographic locality where the service was performed. Payment is made at the assigned rate.

- The payment rates for the vaccines are determined by the standard method used by Medicare for reimbursement of drugs and biologicals. Payment is made at the assigned rate.

- Centralized billers must submit their claims on roster bills in an approved Electronic Media Claims standard format. Paper claims will not be accepted.

- Centralized billers must obtain certain information for each beneficiary including name, health insurance number, date of birth, sex, and signature. [Fill in name of contractor] must be contacted prior to the season for exact requirements. The responsibility lies with the centralized biller to submit correct beneficiary Medicare information (including the beneficiary's Medicare Health Insurance Claim Number) as the contractor will not be able to process incomplete or incorrect claims.

- Centralized billers must obtain an address for each beneficiary so that a Medicare Summary Notice (MSN) can be sent to the beneficiary by the contractor. Beneficiaries are sometimes confused when they receive an MSN from a contractor other than the contractor that normally processes their claims which results in unnecessary beneficiary inquiries to the Medicare contractor. Therefore, centralized billers must provide every beneficiary receiving an influenza virus or pneumococcal vaccination with the name of the processing contractor. This notification must be in writing, in the form of a brochure or handout, and must be provided to each beneficiary at the time he or she receives the vaccination.

- Centralized billers must retain roster bills with beneficiary signatures at their permanent location for a time period consistent with Medicare regulations. [Fill in name of contractor] can provide this information.

- Though centralized billers may already have a Medicare provider number, for purposes of centralized billing, they must also obtain a provider number from [Fill in name of contractor]. This can be done by completing the Form CMS-855 (Provider Enrollment Application), which can be obtained from [Fill in name of contractor].

- If an individual or entity's request for centralized billing is approved, the approval is limited to the 12 month period from September 1 through August 31 of the following year. It is the responsibility of the centralized biller to reapply to CMS CO for approval each year by June 1. Claims will not be processed for any centralized biller without permission from CMS.

- Each year the centralized biller must contact [Fill in name of contractor] to verify understanding of the coverage policy for the administration of the pneumococcal vaccine, and for a copy of the warning language that is required on the roster bill.

- The centralized biller is responsible for providing the beneficiary with a record of the pneumococcal vaccination.

The information in items 1 through 8 below must be included with the individual or entity's annual request to participate in centralized billing:

1. Estimates for the number of beneficiaries who will receive influenza virus vaccinations;

2. Estimates for the number of beneficiaries who will receive pneumococcal vaccinations;

3. The approximate dates for when the vaccinations will be given;

4. A list of the States in which influenza virus and pneumococcal clinics will be held;

5. The type of services generally provided by the corporation (e.g., ambulance, home health, or visiting nurse);

6. Whether the nurses who will administer the influenza virus and pneumococcal vaccinations are employees of the corporation or will be hired by the corporation specifically for the purpose of administering influenza virus and pneumococcal vaccinations;

7. Names and addresses of all entities operating under the corporation's application;

8. Contact information for designated contact person for centralized billing program.

100-4, Chapter-18, 10.4.1

CWF Edits on FI/AB MAC Claims

In order to prevent duplicate payment by the same FI/AB MAC, CWF edits by line item on the FI/AB MAC number, the beneficiary Health Insurance Claim (HIC) number, and the date of service, the influenza virus procedure codes 90653, 90654, 90655, 90656, 90657, 90660, 90661, 90662, 90672, 90673, 90685, 90686, 90687, or 90688 and the pneumococcal procedure codes 90669, 90670, or 90732, and the administration codes G0008 or G0009.

If CWF receives a claim with either HCPCS codes 90653, 90654, 90655, 90656, 90657, 90660, 90661, 90662, 90672, 90673, 90685, 90686, 90687, or 90688 and it already has on record a claim with the same HIC number, same FI/AB MAC number, same date of service, and any one of those HCPCS codes, the second claim submitted to CWF rejects.

If CWF receives a claim with HCPCS codes 90669, 90670, or 90732 and it already has on record a claim with the same HIC number, same FI/AB MAC number, same date of service, and the same HCPCS code, the second claim submitted to CWF rejects when all four items match.

If CWF receives a claim with HCPCS administration codes G0008 or G0009 and it already has on record a claim with the same HIC number, same FI/AB MAC number, same date of service, and same procedure code, CWF rejects the second claim submitted when all four items match.

CWF returns to the FI/AB MAC a reject code "7262" for this edit. FIs/AB MACs must deny the second claim and use the same messages they currently use for the denial of duplicate claims.

100-4, Chapter-18, 10.4.2

CWF Edits on Carrier/AB MAC Claims

In order to prevent duplicate payment by the same carrier/AB MAC, CWF will edit by line item on the carrier/AB MAC number, the HIC number, the date of service, the influenza virus procedure codes 90653, 90654, 90655, 90656, 90657, 90660, 90661, 90662, 90672, 90673, 90685, 90686, 90687, or 90688; the pneumococcal procedure codes 90669, 90670, or 90732; and the administration code G0008 or G0009.

If CWF receives a claim with either HCPCS codes 90653, 90654, 90655, 90656, 90657, 90660, 90661, 90662, 90672, 90673, 90685, 90686, 90687, or 90688 and it already has on record a claim with the same HIC number, same carrier/AB MAC number, same date of service, and any one of those HCPCS codes, the second claim submitted to CWF will reject.

If CWF receives a claim with HCPCS codes 90669, 90670, or 90732 and it already has on record a claim with the same HIC number, same carrier/AB MAC number, same date of service, and the same HCPCS code, the second claim submitted to CWF will reject when all four items match.

If CWF receives a claim with HCPCS administration codes G0008 or G0009 and it already has on record a claim with the same HIC number, same carrier/AB MAC number, same date of service, and same procedure code, CWF will reject the second claim submitted.

CWF will return to the carrier/AB MAC a specific reject code for this edit. Carriers/AB MACs must deny the second claim and use the same messages they currently use for the denial of duplicate claims.

In order to prevent duplicate payment by the centralized billing contractor and local carrier/AB MAC, CWF will edit by line item for carrier number, same HIC number, same date of service, the influenza virus procedure codes 90653, 90654, 90655, 90656, 90657, 90660, 90661, 90662, 90672, 90673, 90685, 90686, 90687, or 90688; the pneumococcal procedure codes 90669, 90670, or 90732; and the administration code G0008 or G0009.

If CWF receives a claim with either HCPCS codes 90653, 90654, 90655, 90656, 90657, 90660, 90661, 90662, 90672, 90673, 90685, 90686, 90687, or 90688 and it already has on record a claim with a different carrier/AB MAC number, but same HIC number, same date of service, and any one of those same HCPCS codes, the second claim submitted to CWF will reject.

If CWF receives a claim with HCPCS codes 90669, 90670, or 90732 and it already has on record a claim with the same HIC number, different carrier/AB MAC number, same date of service, and the same HCPCS code, the second claim submitted to CWF will reject.

If CWF receives a claim with HCPCS administration codes G0008 or G0009 and it already has on record a claim with a different carrier/AB MAC number, but the same HIC number, same date of service, and same procedure code, CWF will reject the second claim submitted.

CWF will return a specific reject code for this edit. Carriers/AB MACs must deny the second claim. For the second edit, the reject code should automatically trigger the following Medicare Summary Notice (MSN) and Remittance Advice (RA) messages.

MSN: 7.2 –"This is a duplicate of a claim processed by another contractor. You should receive a Medicare Summary Notice from them."

Claim adjustment reason code 18 –duplicate claim or service

100-4, Chapter-18, 10.4.3

CWF A/B Crossover Edits for FI/AB MAC and Carrier/AB MAC Claims

When CWF receives a claim from the carrier/AB MAC, it will review Part B outpatient claims history to verify that a duplicate claim has not already been posted.

CWF will edit on the beneficiary HIC number; the date of service; the influenza virus procedure codes 90653, 90654, 90655, 90656, 90657, 90660, 90661, 90662, 90672, 90673, 90685, 90686, 90687, or 90688; the pneumococcal procedure codes 90669, 90670, or 90732; and the administration code G0008 or G0009.

CWF will return a specific reject code for this edit. Contractors must deny the second claim and use the same messages they currently use for the denial of duplicate claims.

100-4, Chapter-18, 20

Mammography Services (Screening and Diagnostic)

A. Screening Mammography

Beginning January 1, 1991, Medicare provides Part B coverage of screening mammographies for women. Screening mammographies are radiologic procedures for early detection of breast cancer and include a physician's interpretation of the results. A doctor's prescription or referral is not necessary for the procedure to be covered. Whether payment can be made is determined by a woman's age and statutory frequency parameter. See Pub. 100-02, Medicare Benefit Policy Manual, chapter 15, section 280.3 for additional coverage information for a screening mammography.

Section 4101 of the Balanced Budget Act (BBA) of 1997 provides for annual screening mammographies for women over age 39 and waives the Part B deductible. Coverage applies as follows:

Age Groups	Screening Period
Under age 35	No payment allowed for screening mammography.
35-39	Baseline (pay for only one screening mammography performed on a woman between her 35th and 40th birthday)
Over age 39	Annual (11 full months have elapsed following the month of last screening

NOTE: Count months between screening mammographies beginning the month after the date of the examination. For example, if Mrs. Smith received a screening mammography examination in January 2005, begin counting the next month (February 2005) until 11 months have elapsed. Payment can be made for another screening mammography in January 2006.

B. Diagnostic Mammography

A diagnostic mammography is a radiological mammogram and is a covered diagnostic test under the following conditions:

- A patient has distinct signs and symptoms for which a mammogram is indicated;
- A patient has a history of breast cancer; or

- A patient is asymptomatic, but based on the patient's history and other factors the physician considers significant, the physician's judgment is that a mammogram is appropriate.
- Beginning January 1, 2005, Medicare Prescription Drug, Improvement, and Modernization Act (MMA) of 2003, §644, Public Law 108-173 has changed the way Medicare pays for diagnostic mammography. Medicare will pay based on the MPFS in lieu of OPPS or the lower of the actual change.

100-4, Chapter-18, 20.4

Billing Requirements –FI/A MAC Claims

Contractors use the weekly-updated MQSA file to verify that the billing facility is certified by the FDA to perform mammography services, and has the appropriate certification to perform the type of mammogram billed (film and/or digital). (See §20.1.) FIs/A/B MACs use the provider number submitted on the claim to identify the facility and use the MQSA data file to verify the facility's certification(s). FIs/A/B MACs complete the following activities in processing mammography claims:

- If the provider number on the claim does not correspond with a certified mammography facility on the MQSA file, then intermediaries/A/B MACs deny the claim.
- When a film mammography HCPCS code is on a claim, the claim is checked for a "1" film indicator.
- If a film mammography HCPCS code comes in on a claim and the facility is certified for film mammography, the claim is paid if all other relevant Medicare criteria are met.
- If a film mammography HCPCS code is on a claim and the facility is certified for digital mammography only, the claim is denied.
- When a digital mammography HCPCS code is on a claim, the claim is checked for "2" digital indicator.
- If a digital mammography HCPCS code is on a claim and the facility is certified for digital mammography, the claim is paid if all other relevant Medicare criteria are met.
- If a digital mammography HCPCS code is on a claim and the facility is certified for film mammography only, the claim is denied.

NOTE: The Common Working File (CWF) no longer receives the mammography file for editing purposes.

Except as provided in the following sections for RHCs and FQHCs, the following procedures apply to billing for screening mammographies:

The technical component portion of the screening mammography is billed on Form CMS-1450 under bill type 12X, 13X, 14X**, 22X, 23X or 85X using revenue code 0403 and HCPCS code 77057* (76092*).

The technical component portion of the diagnostic mammography is billed on Form CMS-1450 under bill type 12X, 13X, 14X**, 22X, 23X or 85X using revenue code 0401 and HCPCS code 77055* (76090*), 77056* (76091*), G0204 and G0206.

Separate bills are required for claims for screening mammographies with dates of service prior to January 1, 2002. Providers include on the bill only charges for the screening mammography. Separate bills are not required for claims for screening mammographies with dates of service on or after January 1, 2002.

See separate instructions below for rural health clinics (RHCs) and federally qualified health centers (FQHCs).

* For claims with dates of service prior to January 1, 2007, providers report CPT® codes 76090, 76091, and 76092. For claims with dates of service January 1, 2007 and later, providers report CPT® codes 77055, 77056, and 77057 respectively.

** For claims with dates of service April 1, 2005 and later, hospitals bill for all mammography services under the 13X type of bill or for dates of service April 1, 2007 and later, 12X or 13X as appropriate. The 14X type of bill is no longer applicable. Appropriate bill types for providers other than hospitals are 22X, 23X, and 85X.

In cases where screening mammography services are self-referred and as a result an attending physician NPI is not available, the provider shall duplicate their facility NPI in the attending physician identifier field on the claim.

100-4, Chapter-18, 60.1

Payment

Payment (contractor) is under the MPFS except as follows:

- Fecal occult blood tests (82270* (G0107*) and G0328) are paid under the clinical diagnostic lab fee schedule except reasonable cost is paid to all non-OPPS hospitals, including CAHs, but not IHS hospitals billing on TOB 83x. IHS hospitals billing on TOB 83x are paid the ASC payment amount. Other IHS hospitals (billing on TOB 13x) are paid the OMB approved AIR, or the acility specific per visit amount as applicable. Deductible and coinsurance do not apply for these tests. See section A below for payment to Maryland waiver on TOB 13X. Payment from all hospitals for non-patient laboratory specimens on TOB 14X will be based on the clinical diagnostic fee schedule, including CAHs and Maryland waiver hospitals.
- Flexible sigmoidoscopy (code G0104) is paid under OPPS for hospital outpatient departments and on a reasonable cost basis for CAHs; or current payment methodologies for hospitals not subject to OPPS.
- Colonoscopies (G0105 and G0121) and barium enemas (G0106 and G0120) are paid under OPPS for hospital outpatient departments and on a reasonable costs basis for CAHs or current payment methodologies for hospitals not subject to OPPS. Also colonoscopies may be done in an Ambulatory Surgical Center (ASC) and when done in an ASC the ASC rate applies. The ASC rate is the same for diagnostic and screening colonoscopies. The ASC rate is paid to IHS hospitals when the service is billed on TOB 83x.

Prior to January 1, 2007, deductible and coinsurance apply to HCPCS codes G0104, G0105, G0106, G0120, and G0121. Beginning with services provided on or after January 1, 2007, Section 5113 of the Deficit Reduction Act of 2005 waives the requirement of the annual Part B deductible for these screening services. Coinsurance still applies.

Coinsurance and deductible applies to the diagnostic colorectal service codes listed below.

The following screening codes must be paid at rates consistent with the diagnostic codes indicated.

Screening Code	Diagnostic Code
G0104	45330
G0105 and G0121	45378
G0106 and G0120	74280

A. Special Payment Instructions for TOB 13X Maryland Waiver Hospitals

For hospitals in Maryland under the jurisdiction of the Health Services Cost Review Commission, screening colorectal services HCPCS codes G0104, G0105, G0106, 82270* (G0107*), G0120, G0121 and G0328 are paid according to the terms of the waiver, that is 94% of submitted charges minus any unmet existing deductible, co-insurance and non-covered charges. Maryland Hospitals bill TOB 13X for outpatient colorectal cancer screenings.

B. Special Payment Instructions for Non-Patient Laboratory Specimen (TOB 14X) for all hospitals

Payment for colorectal cancer screenings (82270* (G0107*) and G0328) to a hospital for a non-patient laboratory specimen (TOB 14X), is the lesser of the actual charge, the fee schedule amount, or the National Limitation Amount (NLA), (including CAHs and Maryland Waiver hospitals). Part B deductible and coinsurance do not apply.

*NOTE: For claims with dates of service prior to January 1, 2007, physicians, suppliers, and providers report HCPCS code G0107. Effective January 1, 2007, code G0107 is discontinued and replaced with CPT® code 82270.

100-4, Chapter-18, 60.2

HCPCS Codes, Frequency Requirements, and Age Requirements (If Applicable)

Effective for services furnished on or after January 1, 1998, the following codes are used for colorectal cancer screening services:

- 82270* (G0107*) -Colorectal cancer screening; fecal-occult blood tests, 1-3 simultaneous determinations;
- G0104 - Colorectal cancer screening; flexible sigmoidoscopy;
- G0105 - Colorectal cancer screening; colonoscopy on individual at high risk;
- G0106 - Colorectal cancer screening; barium enema; as an alternative to G0104, screening sigmoidoscopy;
- G0120- Colorectal cancer screening; barium enema; as an alternative to G0105, screening colonoscopy.

Effective for services furnished on or after July 1, 2001, the following codes are used for colorectal cancer screening services:

- G0121 - Colorectal cancer screening; colonoscopy on individual not meeting criteria for high risk. Note that the description for this code has been revised to remove the term "noncovered".
- G0122 - Colorectal cancer screening; barium enema (noncovered).

Effective for services furnished on or after January 1, 2004, the following code is used for colorectal cancer screening services as an alternative to 82270* (G0107*):

- G0328 - Colorectal cancer screening; immunoassay, fecal-occult blood test, 1-3 simultaneous determinations

*NOTE: For claims with dates of service prior to January 1, 2007, physicians, suppliers, and providers report HCPCS code

G0107. Effective January 1, 2007, code G0107 is discontinued and replaced with CPT® code 82270.

G0104 - Colorectal Cancer Screening; Flexible Sigmoidoscopy

Screening flexible sigmoidoscopies (code G0104) may be paid for beneficiaries who have attained age 50, when performed by a doctor of medicine or osteopathy at the frequencies noted below.

For claims with dates of service on or after January 1, 2002, contractors pay for screening flexible sigmoidoscopies (code G0104) for beneficiaries who have attained age 50 when these services were performed by a doctor of medicine or osteopathy, or by a physician assistant, nurse practitioner, or clinical nurse specialist (as defined in §1861(aa)(5)of the Act and in the Code of Federal Regulations at 42 CFR 410.74, 410.75, and 410.76) at the frequencies noted above. For claims with dates of service prior to January 1, 2002, contractors pay for these services under the conditions noted only when a doctor of medicine or osteopathy performs them.

For services furnished from January 1, 1998, through June 30, 2001, inclusive:

- Once every 48 months (i.e., at least 47 months have passed following the month in which the last covered screening flexible sigmoidoscopy was done).

For services furnished on or after July 1, 2001:

- Once every 48 months as calculated above unless the beneficiary does not meet the criteria for high risk of developing colorectal cancer (refer to §60.3 of this chapter) and he/she has had a screening colonoscopy (code G0121) within the preceding 10 years. If such a beneficiary has had a screening colonoscopy within the preceding 10 years, then he or she can have covered a screening flexible sigmoidoscopy only after at least 119 months have passed following the month that he/she received the screening colonoscopy (code G0121).

NOTE: If during the course of a screening flexible sigmoidoscopy a lesion or growth is detected which results in a biopsy or removal of the growth; the appropriate diagnostic procedure classified as a flexible sigmoidoscopy with biopsy or removal should be billed and paid rather than code G0104.

G0105 -Colorectal Cancer Screening; Colonoscopy on Individual at High Risk

Screening colonoscopies (code G0105) may be paid when performed by a doctor of medicine or osteopathy at a frequency of once every 24 months for beneficiaries at high risk for developing colorectal cancer (i.e., at least 23 months have passed following the month in which the last covered G0105 screening colonoscopy was performed). Refer to §60.3 of this chapter for the criteria to use in determining whether or not an individual is at high risk for developing colorectal cancer.

NOTE: If during the course of the screening colonoscopy, a lesion or growth is detected which results in a biopsy or removal of the growth, the appropriate diagnostic procedure classified as a colonoscopy with biopsy or removal should be billed and paid rather than code G0105.

A. Colonoscopy Cannot be Completed Because of Extenuating Circumstances

1. FIs

When a covered colonoscopy is attempted but cannot be completed because of extenuating circumstances, Medicare will pay for the interrupted colonoscopy as long as the coverage conditions are met for the incomplete procedure. However, the frequency standards associated with screening colonoscopies will not be applied by CWF. When a covered colonoscopy is next attempted and completed, Medicare will pay for that colonoscopy according to its payment methodology for this procedure as long as coverage conditions are met, and the frequency standards will be applied by CWF. This policy is applied to both screening and diagnostic colonoscopies. When submitting a facility claim for the interrupted colonoscopy, providers are to suffix the colonoscopy HCPCS codes with a modifier of "–73" or "–74" as appropriate to indicate that the procedure was interrupted. Payment for covered incomplete screening colonoscopies shall be consistent with payment methodologies currently in place for complete screening colonoscopies, including those contained in 42 CFR 419.44(b). In situations where a critical access hospital (CAH) has elected payment Method II for CAH patients, payment shall be consistent with payment methodologies currently in place as outlined in Chapter 3. As such, instruct CAHs that elect Method II payment to use modifier "–53" to identify an incomplete screening colonoscopy (physician professional service(s) billed in revenue code 096X, 097X, and/or 098X). Such CAHs will also bill the technical or facility component of the interrupted colonoscopy in revenue code 075X (or other appropriate revenue code) using the "-73" or "-74" modifier as appropriate.

Note that Medicare would expect the provider to maintain adequate information in the patient's medical record in case it is needed by the contractor to document the incomplete procedure.

2. Carriers

When a covered colonoscopy is attempted but cannot be completed because of extenuating circumstances (see Chapter 12), Medicare will pay for the interrupted colonoscopy at a rate consistent with that of a flexible sigmoidoscopy as long as coverage conditions are met for the incomplete procedure. When a covered colonoscopy is next attempted and completed, Medicare will pay for that colonoscopy according to its payment methodology for this procedure as long as coverage conditions are met. This policy is applied to both screening and diagnostic colonoscopies. When submitting a claim for the interrupted colonoscopy, professional providers are to suffix the colonoscopy code with a modifier of "–53" to indicate that the procedure was interrupted. When submitting a claim for the facility fee associated with this procedure, Ambulatory Surgical Centers (ASCs) are to suffix the colonoscopy code with "–73" or "–74" as appropriate. Payment for covered screening colonoscopies, including that for the associated ASC facility fee when applicable, shall be consistent with payment for diagnostic colonoscopies, whether the procedure is complete or incomplete.

Note that Medicare would expect the provider to maintain adequate information in the patient's medical record in case it is needed by the contractor to document the incomplete procedure.

G0106 - Colorectal Cancer Screening; Barium Enema; as an Alternative to G0104, Screening Sigmoidoscopy

Screening barium enema examinations may be paid as an alternative to a screening sigmoidoscopy (code G0104). The same frequency parameters for screening sigmoidoscopies (see those codes above) apply.

In the case of an individual aged 50 or over, payment may be made for a screening barium enema examination (code G0106) performed after at least 47 months have passed following the month in which the last screening barium enema or screening flexible sigmoidoscopy was performed. For example, the beneficiary received a screening barium enema examination as an alternative to a screening flexible sigmoidoscopy in January 1999. Start counts beginning February 1999. The beneficiary is eligible for another screening barium enema in January 2003.

The screening barium enema must be ordered in writing after a determination that the test is the appropriate screening test. Generally, it is expected that this will be a screening double contrast enema unless the individual is unable to withstand such an exam. This means that in the case of a particular individual, the attending physician must determine that the estimated screening potential for the barium enema is equal to or greater than the screening potential that has been estimated for a screening flexible sigmoidoscopy for the same individual. The screening single contrast barium enema also requires a written order from the beneficiary's attending physician in the same manner as described above for the screening double contrast barium enema examination.

82270* (G0107*) - Colorectal Cancer Screening; Fecal-Occult Blood Test, 1-3 Simultaneous Determinations

Effective for services furnished on or after January 1, 1998, screening FOBT (code 82270* (G0107*) may be paid for beneficiaries who have attained age 50, and at a frequency of once every 12 months (i.e., at least 11 months have passed following the month in which the last covered screening FOBT was performed). This screening FOBT means a guaiac-based test for peroxidase activity, in which the beneficiary completes it by taking samples from two different sites of three consecutive stools. This screening requires a written order from the beneficiary's attending physician. (The term "attending physician" is defined to mean a doctor of medicine or osteopathy (as defined in §1861(r)(1)of the Act) who is fully knowledgeable about the beneficiary's medical condition, and who would be responsible for using the results of any examination performed in the overall management of the beneficiary's specific medical problem.)

Effective for services furnished on or after January 1, 2004, payment may be made for a Immunoassay-based FOBT (G0328, described below) as an alternative to the guaiac-based FOBT, 82270* (G0107*). Medicare will pay for only one covered FOBT per year, either 82270* (G0107*) or G0328, but not both.

NOTE: For claims with dates of service prior to January 1, 2007, physicians, suppliers, and providers report HCPCS code G0107. Effective January 1, 2007, code G0107 is discontinued and replaced with CPT® code 82270.

G0328-Colorectal Cancer Screening; Immunoassay, Fecal-Occult Blood Test, 1-3 Simultaneous Determinations

Effective for services furnished on or after January 1, 2004, screening FOBT, (code G0328) may be paid as an alternative to 82270* (G0107*) for beneficiaries who have attained age 50. Medicare will pay for a covered FOBT (either 82270* (G0107*) or G0328, but not both) at a frequency of once every 12 months (i.e., at least 11 months have passed following the month in which the last covered screening FOBT was performed). Screening FOBT,immunoassay, includes the use of a spatula to collect the appropriate number of samples or the use of a special brush for the collection of samples, as determined by the individual manufacturer's instructions. This screening requires a written order from the beneficiary's attending physician. (The term "attending physician" is defined to mean a doctor of medicine or osteopathy (as defined in §1861(r)(1)of the Act) who is fully knowledgeable about the beneficiary's medical condition, and who would be responsible for using the results of any examination performed in the overall management of the beneficiary's specific medical problem.)

G0120 -Colorectal Cancer Screening; Barium Enema; as an Alternative to or G0105, Screening Colonoscopy

Screening barium enema examinations may be paid as an alternative to a screening colonoscopy (code G0105) examination. The same frequency parameters for screening colonoscopies (see those codes above) apply.

In the case of an individual who is at high risk for colorectal cancer, payment may be made for a screening barium enema examination (code G0120) performed after at least 23 months have passed following the month in which the last screening barium enema or the last screening colonoscopy was performed. For example, a beneficiary at high risk for developing colorectal cancer received a screening barium enema examination (code G0120) as an alternative to a screening colonoscopy (code G0105) in January 2000. Start counts beginning February 2000. The beneficiary is eligible for another screening barium enema examination (code G0120) in January 2002.

The screening barium enema must be ordered in writing after a determination that the test is the appropriate screening test. Generally, it is expected that this will be a screening double contrast enema unless the individual is unable to withstand such an exam. This means that in the case of a particular individual, the attending physician must determine that the estimated screening potential for the barium enema is equal to or greater than the screening potential that has been estimated for a screening colonoscopy, for the same individual. The screening single contrast barium enema also requires a written order from the beneficiary's attending physician in the same manner as described above for the screening double contrast barium enema examination.

G0121 - Colorectal Screening; Colonoscopy on Individual Not Meeting Criteria for High Risk -Applicable On and After July 1, 2001

Effective for services furnished on or after July 1, 2001, screening colonoscopies (code G0121) performed on individuals not meeting the criteria for being at high risk for

developing colorectal cancer (refer to §60.3 of this chapter) may be paid under the following conditions:

- At a frequency of once every 10 years (i.e., at least 119 months have passed following the month in which the last covered G0121 screening colonoscopy was performed.)
- If the individual would otherwise qualify to have covered a G0121 screening colonoscopy based on the above but has had a covered screening flexible sigmoidoscopy (code G0104), then he or she may have covered a G0121 screening colonoscopy only after at least 47 months have passed following the month in which the last covered G0104 flexible sigmoidoscopy was performed.

NOTE: If during the course of the screening colonoscopy, a lesion or growth is detected which results in a biopsy or removal of the growth, the appropriate diagnostic procedure classified as a colonoscopy with biopsy or removal should be billed and paid rather than code G0121.

G0122 -Colorectal Cancer Screening; Barium Enema

The code is not covered by Medicare.

100-4, Chapter-18, 60.6

Billing Requirements for Claims Submitted to FIs

Follow the general bill review instructions in Chapter 25. Hospitals use the ANSI X12N 837I to bill the FI or on the hardcopy Form CMS-1450. Hospitals bill revenue codes and HCPCS codes as follows:

Screening Test/ Procedure	Revenue Code	HCPCS Code	TOB
Fecal Occult blood test	030X	82270*** (G0107***), G0328	12X, 13X, 14X**, 22X, 23X, 83X, 85X
Barium enema	032X	G0106, G0120, G0122	12X, 13X, 22X, 23X, 85X****
Flexible Sigmoidoscopy	*	G0104	12X, 13X, 22X, 23X, 83X, 85X****
Colonoscopy-high risk	*	G0105, G0121	12X, 13X, 22X, 23X, 83X, 85X****

* The appropriate revenue code when reporting any other surgical procedure.

** 14X is only applicable for non-patient laboratory specimens.

*** For claims with dates of service prior to January 1, 2007, physicians, suppliers, and providers report HCPCS code G0107. Effective January 1, 2007, code G0107, is discontinued and replaced with CPT® code 82270.

**** CAHs that elect Method II bill revenue code 096X, 097X, and/or 098X for professional services and 075X (or other appropriate revenue code) for the technical or facility component.

Special Billing Instructions for Hospital Inpatients

When these tests/procedures are provided to inpatients of a hospital or when Part A benefits have been exhausted, they are covered under this benefit. However, the provider bills on bill type 12X using the discharge date of the hospital stay to avoid editing in the Common Working File (CWF) as a result of the hospital bundling rules.

100-4, Chapter-18, 80

Initial Preventive Physical Examination (IPPE)

(**NOTE:** For billing and payment requirements for the Annual Wellness Visit, see chapter 18, section 140, of this manual.)

Background: Effective for services furnished on or after January 1, 2005, Section 611 of the Medicare Prescription Drug Improvement and Modernization Act of 2003 (MMA) provides for coverage under Part B of one initial preventive physical examination (IPPE) for new beneficiaries only, subject to certain eligibility and other limitations. CMS amended §§411.15 (a)(1) and 11.15 (k)(11) of the Code of Federal Regulations (CFR) to permit payment for an IPPE as described at 42 CFR §410.16, added by 69 FR 66236, 66420 (November 15, 2004) not later than 6 months after the date the individual's first coverage period begins under Medicare Part B.

Under the MMA of 2003, the IPPE may be performed by a doctor of medicine or osteopathy as defined in section 1861 (r)(1) of the Social Security Act (the Act) or by a qualified mid-level nonphysician practitioner (NPP) (nurse practitioner, physician assistant or clinical nurse specialist), not later than 6 months after the date the individual's first coverage begins under Medicare Part B. (See section 80.3 for a list of bill types of facilities that can bill fiscal intermediaries (FIs) for this service.) This examination will include: (1) review of the individual's medical and social history with attention to modifiable risk factors for disease detection, (2) review of the individual's potential (risk factors) for depression or other mood disorders, (3) review of the individual's functional ability and level of safety; (4) a physical examination to include measurement of the individual's height, weight, blood pressure, a visual acuity screen, and other factors as deemed appropriate by the examining physician or qualified non physician practitioner (NPP), (5) performance and interpretation of an electrocardiogram (EKG); (6) education, counseling, and referral, as deemed appropriate, based on the results of the review and evaluation services described in the previous 5 elements, and (7) education, counseling, and referral including a brief written plan (e.g., a checklist or alternative) provided to the individual for obtaining the appropriate screening and other preventive services, which are separately cove red under Medicare Part B benefits. The EKG performed as a component of the IPPE will be billed separately. Medicare will pay for only one IPPE per beneficiary per lifetime. The Common Working File (CWF) will edit for this benefit.

As required by statute under the MMA of 2003, the total IPPE service includes an EKG, but the EKG is billed with its own unique HCPCS code(s). The IPPE does not include other preventive services that are currently separately covered and paid under Section 1861 of the Act under Medicare Part B screening benefits. (That is, pneumococcal, influenza and hepatitis B vaccines and their administration, screening mammography, screening pap smear and screening pelvic examinations, prostate cancer screening tests, colorectal cancer screening tests, diabetes outpatient self-management training services, bone mass measurements, glaucoma screening, medical nutrition therapy for individuals with diabetes or renal disease, cardiovascular screening blood tests, and diabetes screening tests.)

Section 5112 of the Deficit Reduction Act of 2005 allows for one ultrasound screening for Abdominal Aortic Aneurysm

(AAA) as a result of a referral from an IPPE effective January 1, 2007. For AAA physician/practitioner billing, correct coding, and payment policy information, refer to section 110 of this chapter.

Effective January 1, 2009, Section 101(b) of the Medicare Improvement for Patients and Providers Act (MIPPA) of 2008 updates the IPPE benefit described under the MMA of 2003. The MIPPA allows the IPPE to be performed not later than 12 months after the date the individual's first coverage period begins under Medicare Part B, requires the addition of the measurement of an individual's body mass index to the IPPE, adds end-of-life planning (upon an individual's consent) to the IPPE, and removes the screening EKG as a mandatory service of the IPPE. The screening EKG is optional effective January 1, 2009, and is permitted as a once-in-a-lifetime screening service as a result of a referral from an IPPE.

The MIPPA of 2008 allows for possible future payment for additional preventive services not otherwise described in Title XVIII of the Act that identify medical conditions or risk factors for eligible individuals if the Secretary determines through the national coverage determination (NCD) process (as defined in section 1869(f)(1)(B) of the Act) that they are: (1) reasonable and necessary for the prevention or early detection of illness or disability, (2) recommended with a grade of A or B by the United States Preventive Services Task Force, and, (3) appropriate for individuals entitled to benefits under Part A or enrolled under Part B, or both. MIPPA requires that there be education, counseling, and referral for additional preventive services, as appropriate, under the IPPE, if the Secretary determines in the future that such services are covered.

For the physician/practitioner billing correct coding and payment policy, refer to chapter 12, section 30.6.1.1, of this manual.

100-4, Chapter-18, 80.1

Healthcare Common Procedure Coding System (HCPCS) Coding for the IPPE

The HCPCS codes listed below were developed for the IPPE benefit effective January 1, 2005, for individuals whose initial enrollment is on or after January 1, 2005.

G0344: Initial preventive physical examination; face-to-face visit, services limited to new beneficiary during the first 6 months of Medicare enrollment

Short Descriptor: Initial Preventive Exam

G0366: Electrocardiogram, routine ECG with 12 leads; performed as a component of the initial preventive examination with interpretation and report

Short Descriptor: EKG for initial prevent exam

G0367: tracing only, without interpretation and report, performed as a component of the initial preventive examination

Short Descriptor: EKG tracing for initial prev

G0368: interpretation and report only, performed as a component of the initial preventive examination

Short Descriptor: EKG interpret & report preve

The following new HCPCS codes were developed for the IPPE benefit effective January 1, 2009, and replaced codes G0344, G0366, G0367, and G0368 shown above beginning with dates of service on or after January 1, 2009:

G0402: Initial preventive physical examination; face-to-face visit, services limited to new beneficiary during the first 12 months of Medicare enrollment

>   **Short Descriptor:** Initial Preventive exam

G0403: Electrocardiogram, routine ECG with 12 leads; performed as a screening for the initial preventive physical examination with interpretation and report

>   **Short Descriptor:** EKG for initial prevent exam

G0404: Electrocardiogram, routine ECG with 12 leads; tracing only, without interpretation and report, performed as a screening for the initial preventive physical examination

>   **Short Descriptor:** EKG tracing for initial prev

G0405: Electrocardiogram, routine ECG with 12 leads; interpretation and report only, performed as a screening for the initial preventive physical examination

>   **Short Descriptor:** EKG interpret & report preve

100-4, Chapter-18, 80.2

A/B Medicare Administrative Contractor (MAC) and Contractor Billing Requirements

Effective for dates of service on and after January 1, 2005, through December 31, 2008, contractors shall recognize the HCPCS codes G0344, G0366, G0367, and G0368 shown above in §80.1 for an IPPE. The type of service (TOS) for each of these codes is as follows:

G0344: TOS = 1

G0366: TOS = 5

G0367: TOS = 5

G0368: TOS = 5

Contractors shall pay physicians or qualified nonphysician practitioners for only one IPPE performed not later than 6 months after the date the individual's first coverage begins under Medicare Part B, but only if that coverage period begins on or after January 1, 2005.

Effective for dates of service on and after January 1, 2009, contractors shall recognize the HCPCS codes G0402, G0403, G0404, and G0405 shown above in §80.1 for an IPPE. The TOS for each of these codes is as follows:

G0402: TOS = 1

G0403: TOS = 5

G0404: TOS = 5

G0405: TOS = 5

Under the MIPPA of 2008, contractors shall pay physicians or qualified nonphysician practitioners for only one IPPE performed not later than 12 months after the date the individual's first coverage begins under Medicare Part B only if that coverage period begins on or after January 1, 2009.

Contractors shall allow payment for a medically necessary Evaluation and Management (E/M) service at the same visit as the IPPE when it is clinically appropriate. Physicians and qualified nonphysician practitioners shall use CPT® codes 99201-99215 to report an E/M with CPT® modifier 25 to indicate that the E/M is a significant, separately identifiable service from the IPPE code reported (G0344 or G0402, whichever applies based on the date the IPPE is performed). Refer to chapter 12, §30.6.1.1, of this manual for the physician/practitioner billing correct coding and payment policy regarding E/M services.

If the EKG performed as a component of the IPPE is not performed by the primary physician or qualified NPP during the IPPE visit, another physician or entity may perform and/or interpret the EKG. The referring physician or qualified NPP needs to make sure that the performing physician or entity bills the appropriate G code for the screening EKG, and not a CPT® code in the 93000 series. Both the IPPE and the EKG should be billed in order for the beneficiary to receive the complete IPPE service. Effective for dates of service on and after January 1, 2009, the screening EKG is optional and is no longer a mandated service of an IPPE if performed as a result of a referral from an IPPE.

Should the same physician or NPP need to perform an additional medically necessary EKG in the 93000 series on the same day as the IPPE, report the appropriate EKG CPT® code(s) with modifier 59, indicating that the EKG is a distinct procedural service.

Physicians or qualified nonphysician practitioners shall bill the contractor the appropriate HCPCS codes for IPPE on the Form CMS-1500 claim or an approved electronic format. The HCPCS codes for an IPPE and screening EKG are paid under the Medicare Physician Fee Schedule (MPFS). The appropriate deductible and coinsurance applies to codes G0344, G0366, G0367, G0368, G0403, G0404, and G0405. The deductible is waived for code G0402 but the coinsurance still applies.

100-4, Chapter-18, 80.3.3

Outpatient Prospective Payment System (OPPS) Hospital Billing

Hospitals subject to OPPS (TOBs 12X and 13X) must use modifier -25 when billing the IPPE G0344 along with the technical component of the EKG, G0367, on the same claim. The same is true when billing IPPE code G0402 along with the technical component of the screening EKG, code G0404. This is due to an OPPS Outpatient Code Editor (OCE) which contains an edit that requires a modifier -25 on any evaluation and management (E/M) HCPCS code if there is also a status "S" or "T" HCPCS procedure code on the claim.

100-4, Chapter-18, 80.4

Coinsurance and Deductible

The Medicare deductible and coinsurance apply for the IPPE provided before January 1, 2009.

The Medicare deductible is waived effective for the IPPE provided on or after January 1, 2009. Coinsurance continues to apply for the IPPE provided on or after January 1, 2009.

As a result of the Affordable Care Act, effective for the IPPE provided on or after January 1, 2011, the Medicare deductible and coinsurance (for HCPCS code G0402 only) are waived.

100-4, Chapter-18, 120.1

Coding and Payment of DSMT Services

The following HCPCS codes are used to report DSMT:

- G0108-Diabetes outpatient self-management training services, individual, per 30 minutes.
- G0109 -Diabetes outpatient self-management training services, group session (2 or more), per 30 minutes.

The type of service for these codes is 1.

Payment to physicians and providers for outpatient DSMT is made as follows:

Type of Facility	Payment Method	Type of Bill
Physician (billed to the carrier)	MPFS	NA
Hospitals subject to OPPS	MPFS	12X, 13X
Method I and Method II Critical Access Hospitals (CAHs) (technical services)	101% of reasonable cost	12X and 85X
Indian Health Service (IHS) providers billing hospital outpatient Part B	OMB-approved outpatient per visit all inclusive rate (AIR)	13X
IHS providers billing inpatient Part B	All-inclusive inpatient ancillary per diem rate	12X
IHS CAHs billing outpatient Part B	101% of the all-inclusive facility specific per visit rate	85X
IHS CAHs billing inpatient Part B	101% of the all-inclusive facility specific per diem rate	12X
FQHCs*	All-inclusive encounter rate with other qualified services. Separate visit payment available with HCPCS.	73X
Skilled Nursing Facilities **	MPFS non-facility rate	22X, 23X
Maryland Hospitals under jurisdiction of the Health Services Cost Review Commission (HSCRC)	94% of provider submitted charges in accordance with the terms of the Maryland Waiver	12X, 13X
Home Health Agencies (can be billed only if the service is provided outside of the treatment plan)	MPFS non-facility rate	34X

* Effective January 1, 2006, payment for DSMT provided in an FQHC that meets all of the requirements as above, may be made in addition to one other visit the beneficiary had during the same day, if this qualifying visit is billed on TOB 73X, with HCPCS G0108 or G0109, and revenue codes 0520, 0521, 0522, 0524, 0525, 0527, 0528, or 0900.

** The SNF consolidated billing provision allows separate part B payment for training services for beneficiaries that are in skilled Part A SNF stays, however, the SNF must submit these services on a 22 bill type. Training services provided by other provider types must be reimbursed by X the SNF.

NOTE: An ESRD facility is a reasonable site for this service, however, because it is required to provide dietician and nutritional services as part of the care covered in the composite rate, ESRD facilities are not allowed to bill for it separately and do not receive separate reimbursement. Likewise, an RHC is a reasonable site for this service, however it must be provided in an RHC with other qualifying services and paid at the all-inclusive encounter rate.

Deductible and co-insurance apply.

100-4, Chapter-18, 130.1

Healthcare Common Procedure Coding System (HCPCS) for HIV Screening Tests

Effective for claims with dates of service on and after December 8, 2009, implemented with the April 5, 2010, IOCE, the following HCPCS codes are to be billed for HIV screening:

- G0432- Infectious agent antibody detection by enzyme immunoassay (EIA) technique, HIV-1 and/or HIV-2, screening,
- G0433 - Infectious agent antibody detection by enzyme-linked immunosorbent assay (ELISA) technique, HIV-1 and/or HIV-2, screening, and,
- G0435 -Infectious agent antibody detection by rapid antibody test, HIV-1 and/or HIV-2, screening.

100-4, Chapter-18, 130.2

Billing Requirements

Effective for dates of service December 8, 2009, and later, contractors shall recognize the above HCPCS codes for HIV screening.

Medicare contractors shall pay for voluntary HIV screening as follows in accordance with Pub. 100-03, Medicare National Coverage Determinations Manual, sections 190.14 and 210.7:

- A maximum of once annually for beneficiaries at increased risk for HIV infection (11 full months must elapse following the month the previous test was performed in order for the subsequent test to be covered), and,
- A maximum of three times per term of pregnancy for pregnant Medicare beneficiaries beginning with the date of the first test when ordered by the woman's clinician.

Claims that are submitted for HIV screening shall be submitted in the following manner:

For beneficiaries reporting increased risk factors, claims shall contain HCPCS code G0432, G0433, or G0435 with diagnosis code V73.89 (Special screening for other specified viral disease) as primary, and V69.8 (Other problems related to lifestyle), as secondary.

For beneficiaries not reporting increased risk factors, claims shall contain HCPCS code G0432, G0433, or G0435 with diagnosis code V73.89 only.

For pregnant Medicare beneficiaries, claims shall contain HCPCS code G0432, G0433, or G0435 with diagnosis code V73.89 as primary, and one of the following ICD-9 diagnosis codes: V22.0 (Supervision of normal first pregnancy), V22.1 (Supervision of other normal pregnancy), or V23.9 (Supervision of unspecified high-risk pregnancy), as secondary.

100-4, Chapter-18, 130.3

Payment Method

Payment for HIV screening is under the Medicare Clinical Laboratory Fee Schedule for TOBs 12X, 13X, 14X, 22X, and 23X beginning January 1, 2011. For TOB 85X payment is based on reasonable cost. Deductible and coinsurance do not apply. Between December 8, 2009, and April 4, 2010, these services can be billed with unlisted procedure code 87999. Between April 5, 2010, and January 1, 2011, the G codes will be contractor priced.

100-4, Chapter-18, 130.4

Types of Bill (TOBs) and Revenue Codes

The applicable bill types for HIV screening are: 12X, 13X, 14X, 22X, 23X, and 85X. (Effective April 1, 2006, TOB 14X is for non-patient laboratory specimens.)

Use revenue code 030X (laboratory, clinical diagnostic)

100-4, Chapter-18, 130, 130.5

Diagnosis Code Reporting

A claim that is submitted for HIV screening shall be submitted with one or more of the following diagnosis codes in the header and pointed to the line item:

a. For claims where increased risk factors are reported: V73.89 as primary and V69.8 as secondary.

b. For claims where increased risk factors are NOT reported: V73.89 as primary only.

c. For claims for pregnant Medicare beneficiaries, the following diagnosis codes shall be submitted in addition to V73.89 to allow for more frequent screening than once per 12-month period:

V22.0 – Supervision of normal first pregnancy, or,

V22.1 – Supervision of other normal pregnancy, or,

V23.9 - Supervision of unspecified high-risk pregnancy).

100-4, Chapter-18, 140

Annual Wellness Visit (AWV)

Pursuant to section 4103 of the Affordable Care Act of 2010, the Centers for Medicare & Medicaid Services (CMS) amended section 411.15(a)(1) and 411.15(k)(15) of 42 CFR (list of examples of routine physical examinations excluded from coverage) effective for services furnished on or after January 1, 2011. This expanded coverage is subject to certain eligibility and other limitations that allow payment for an annual wellness visit (AWV), including personalized prevention plan services (PPPS), for an individual who is no longer within 12 months after the effective date of his or her first Medicare Part B coverage period, and has not received either an initial preventive physical examination (IPPE) or an AWV within the past 12 months.

The AWV will include the establishment of, or update to, the individual's medical/family history, measurement of his/her height, weight, body-mass index (BMI) or waist circumference, and blood pressure (BP), with the goal of health promotion and disease detection and encouraging patients to obtain the screening and preventive services that may already be covered and paid for under Medicare Part B. CMS amended 42 CFR §§411.15(a)(1) and 411.15(k)(15) to allow payment on or after January 1, 2011, for an AWV (as established at 42 CFR 410.15) when performed by qualified health professionals.

Coverage is available for an AWV that meets the following requirements:

1. It is performed by a health professional;

2. It is furnished to an eligible beneficiary who is no longer within 12 months after the effective date of his/her first Medicare Part B coverage period, and he/she has not received either an IPPE or an AWV providing PPPS within the past 12 months.

See Pub. 100-02,Medicare Benefit Policy Manual, chapter 15, section 280.5, for detailed policy regarding the AWV, including definitions of: (1) detection of cognitive impairment, (2) eligible beneficiary, (3) establishment of, or an update to, an individual's medical/family history, (4&5) first and subsequent AWVs providing PPPS, (6) health professional, and, (7) review of an individual's functional ability/level of safety.

100-4, Chapter-18, 140.1

Healthcare Common Procedure Coding System (HCPCS) Coding for the AWV

The HCPCS codes listed below were developed for the AWV benefit effective January 1, 2011, for individuals whose initial enrollment is on or after January 1, 2011.

G0438 -Annual wellness visit; includes a personalized prevention plan of service (PPPS); first visit

G0439 –Annual wellness visit; includes a personalized prevention plan of service (PPPS); subsequent visit

100-4, Chapter-18, 140.5

Coinsurance and Deductible

Sections 4103 and 4104 of the Affordable Care Act provide for a waiver of Medicare coinsurance/copayment and Part B deductible requirements for the AWV effective for services furnished on or after January 1, 2011.

100-4, Chapter-18, 140.6

Common Working File (CWF) Edits

Effective for claims with dates of service on and after January 1,2011, CWF shall reject:

- AWV claims for G0438 when a previous (first) AWV, HCPCS code G0438, is paid in history regardless of when it occurred.

- AWV claims when a previous AWV, G0438 or G0439, is paid in history within the previous 12 months.

- Beginning January 1, 2011, AWV claims when a previous IPPE, HCPCS code G0402, is paid in history within the previous 12 months.

- AWV claims (G0438 and G0439) billed for a date of service within 12 months after the effective date of a beneficiary's first Medicare PartB coverage period.

The following change shall be effective for claims processed on or after April 1, 2013. Typically, when a preventive service is posted to a beneficiary's utilization history, separate entries are posted for a "professional" service (the professional claim for the delivery of the service itself) and a "technical" service (the institutional claims for a facility fee). However, in the case of AWV services, since there is no separate payment for a facility fee, the AWV claim will be posted as the "professional" service only, regardless of whether it is paid on a professional claim or an institutional claim.

100-4, Chapter-18, 150

Counseling to Prevent Tobacco Use

Effective for claims with dates of service on and after August 25, 2010, the Centers for Medicare & Medicaid Services (CMS) will cover counseling to prevent tobacco use services for outpatient and hospitalized Medicare beneficiaries:

1. Who use tobacco, regardless of whether they have signs or symptoms of tobacco-related disease;

2. Who are competent and alert at the time that counseling is provided; and,

3. Whose counseling is furnished by a qualified physician or other Medicare-recognized practitioner.

These individuals who do not have signs or symptoms of tobacco-related disease will be covered under Medicare Part

B when the above conditions of coverage are met, subject to certain frequency and other limitations.

Conditions of Medicare Part A and Medicare Part B coverage for counseling to prevent tobacco use are located in the Medicare National Coverage Determinations (NCD)Manual, Publication 100-3, chapter1, section 210.4.1.

100-4, Chapter-18, 150.1

Healthcare Common Procedure Coding System (HCPCS) and Diagnosis Coding

The CMS has created two new G codes for billing for tobacco cessation counseling services to prevent tobacco use for those individuals who use tobacco but do not have signs or symptoms of tobacco-related disease. These are in addition to the two CPT® codes 99406 and 99407 that currently are used for smoking and tobacco-use cessation counseling for symptomatic individuals.

The following HCPCS codes should be reported when billing for counseling to prevent tobacco use effective January 1, 2011:

G0436- Smoking and tobacco cessation counseling visit for the asymptomatic patient; intermediate, greater than 3 minutes, up to 10 minutes

Short descriptor: Tobacco-use counsel 3-10 min

G0437 - Smoking and tobacco cessation counseling visit for the asymptomatic patient; intensive, greater than 10 minutes

Short descriptor: Tobacco-use counsel >10min

NOTE: The above G codes will not be active in contractors' systems until January 1, 2011. Therefore, contractors shall advise non-outpatient perspective payment system (OPPS) providers to use unlisted code 99199 to bill for counseling to prevent tobacco use and tobacco-related disease services during the interim period of August 25, 2010, through December 31, 2010.

On January 3, 2011, contractor's systems will accept the new G codes for services performed on or after August 25, 2010.

Two new C codes have been created for facilities paid under OPPS when billing for counseling to prevent tobacco use and tobacco-related disease services during the interim period of August 25, 2010, through December 31, 2010:

C9801- Smoking and tobacco cessation counseling visit for the asymptomatic patient, intermediate, greater than 3 minutes, up to 10 minutes

Short descriptor: Tobacco-use counsel 3-10 min

C9802- Smoking and tobacco cessation counseling visit for the asymptomatic patient, intensive, greater than 10 minutes

Short descriptor: Tobacco-use counsel >10min

Claims for smoking and tobacco use cessation counseling services G0436 and G0437 shall be submitted with diagnosis code V15.82, history of tobacco use, or 305.1, non-dependent tobacco use disorder.

Contractors shall allow payment for a medically necessary E/M service on the same day as the smoking and tobacco-use cessation counseling service when it is clinically appropriate. Physicians and qualified non-physician practitioners shall use an appropriate HCPCS code to report an E/M service with modifier -25 to indicate that the E/M service is a separately identifiable service from G0436 or G0437.

100-4, Chapter-18, 150.2

Carrier Billing Requirements

Carriers shall pay for counseling to prevent tobacco use services billed with code G0436 or G0437 for dates of service on or after January 1, 2011. Carriers shall pay for counseling services billed with code 99199 for dates of service performed on or after August 25, 2010 through December 31, 2010. The type of service (TOS) for each of the new codes is 1.

Carriers pay for counseling services billed based on the Medicare Physician Fee Schedule (MPFS). Deductible and coinsurance apply for services performed on August 25, 2010, through December 31, 2010. For claims with dates of service on and after January 1, 2011, coinsurance and deductible do not apply on G0436 and G0437.

Physicians or qualified non-physician practitioners shall bill the carrier for counseling to prevent tobacco use services on Form CMS-1500 or an approved electronic format.

NOTE: The above G codes will not be active in contractors' systems until January 1, 2011. Therefore, contractors shall advise providers to use unlisted code 99199 to bill for counseling to prevent tobacco use services during the interim period of August 25, 2010, through December 31, 2010.

100-4, Chapter-18, 150.2.1

Fiscal Intermediary (FI) Billing Requirements

The FIs shall pay for counseling to prevent tobacco use services with codes G0436 and G0437 for dates of service on or after January 1, 2011. FIs shall pay for counseling services billed with code 99199 for dates of service performed on or after August 25, 2010, through December 31, 2010. For facilities paid under OPPS, FIs shall pay for counseling services billed with codes C9801 and C9802 for dates of service performed on or after August 25, 2010, through December 31, 2010.

Claims for counseling to prevent tobacco use services should be submitted on Form CMS-1450 or its electronic equivalent.

The applicable bill types are 12X, 13X, 22X, 23X, 34X, 71X, 77X, and 85X.

Payment for outpatient services is as follows:

Type of Facility	Method of Payment
Rural Health Centers (RHCs) TOB 71X/Federally Qualified Health Centers (FQHCs)TOB 77X	All-inclusive rate (AIR) for the encounter
Hospitals TOBs 12X and 13X	OPPS for hospitals subject to OPPS MPFS for hospitals not subject to OPPS
Indian Health Services (IHS) Hospitals TOB 13X	AIR for the encounter
Skilled Nursing Facilities (SNFs) TOBs 22X and 23X	Medicare Physician Fee Schedule (MPFS)
Home Health Agencies (HHAs) TOB 34X	MPFS
Critical Access Hospitals (CAHs) TOB 85X	Method I: Technical services are paid at 101% of reasonable cost. Method II: technical services are paid at 101% of reasonable cost, and Professional services are paid at 115% of the MPFS Data Base

217

Type of Facility	Method of Payment
IHS CAHs TOB 85X	Based on specific rate
Maryland Hospitals	Payment is based according to the Health Services Cost Review Commission (HSCRC). That is 94% of submitted charges subject to any unmet deductible, coinsurance, and non-covered charges policies.

Deductible and coinsurance apply for services performed on August 25, 2010, through December 31, 2010. For claims with dates of service on and after January 1, 2011, coinsurance and deductible do not apply for G0436 and G0437.

100-4, Chapter-18, 150.4

Common Working File (CWF)

The Common Working File (CWF) shall edit for the frequency of service limitations of counseling to prevent tobacco use sessions and smoking and tobacco-use cessation counseling services (G0436, G0437, 99398, 99407) rendered to a beneficiary for a combined total of 8 sessions within a 12-month period. The beneficiary may receive another 8 sessions during a second or subsequent year after 11 full months have passed since the first Medicare covered counseling session was performed. To start the count for the second or subsequent 12-month period, begin with the month after the month in which the first Medicare covered counseling session was performed and count until 11 full months have elapsed.

By entering the beneficiary's health insurance claim number (HICN), providers have the capability to view the number of sessions a beneficiary has received for this service via inquiry through CWF.

100-4, Chapter-18, 160

Intensive Behavioral Therapy (IBT) for Cardiovascular Disease (CVD)

For services furnished on or after November 8, 2011, the Centers for Medicare & Medicaid Services (CMS) covers intensive behavioral therapy (IBT) for cardiovascular disease (CVD). See National Coverage Determinations (NCD) Manual (Pub. 100-03) §210.11 for complete coverage guidelines.

100-4, Chapter-18, 160.1

Coding Requirements for IBT for CVD Furnished on or After November 8, 2011

The following is the applicable Healthcare Procedural Coding System (HCPCS) code for IBT for CVD:

G0446: Annual, face-to-face intensive behavioral therapy for cardiovascular disease, individual, 15 minutes

Contractors shall not apply deductibles or coinsurance to claim lines containing HCPCS code G0446.

100-4, Chapter-18, 160.2.1

Correct Place of Service (POS) Codes for IBT for CVD on Professional Claims

Contractors shall pay for IBT CVD, G0446 only when services are provided at the following POS:

11- Physician's Office

22- Outpatient Hospital

49- Independent Clinic

72- Rural Health Clinic

Claims not submitted with one of the POS codes above will be denied.

The following messages shall be used when Medicare contractors deny professional claims for incorrect POS:

Claim Adjustment Reason Code (CARC) 58: "Treatment was deemed by the payer to have been rendered in an inappropriate or invalid place of service." **NOTE:** Refer to the 835 Healthcare Policy Identification Segment (loop 2110 Service Payment Information REF), if present.

Remittance Advice Remark Code (RARC) N428: "Not covered when performed in this place of service."

Medicare Summary Notice (MSN) 21.25: "This service was denied because Medicare only covers this service in certain settings."

Spanish Version: El servicio fue denegado porque Medicare solamente lo cubre en ciertas situaciones."

Group Code PR (Patient Responsibility) assigning financial liability to the beneficiary, if a claim is received with a GA modifier indicating a signed ABN is on file.

Group Code CO (Contractual Obligation) assigning financial liability to the provider, if a claim is received with a GZ modifier indicating no signed ABN is on file.

100-4, Chapter-18, 160.2.2

Provider Specialty Edits for IBT for CVD on Professional Claims

Contractors shall pay claims for HCPCS code G0446 only when services are submitted by the following provider specialty types found on the provider's enrollment record:

01= General Practice

08 = Family Practice

11= Internal Medicine

16 = Obstetrics/Gynecology

37= Pediatric Medicine

38 = Geriatric Medicine

42= Certified Nurse Midwife

50 = Nurse Practitioner

89 = Certified Clinical Nurse Specialist

97= Physician Assistant

Contractors shall deny claim lines for HCPCS code G0446 performed by any other provider specialty type other than those listed above.

The following messages shall be used when Medicare contractors deny IBT for CVD claims billed with invalid provider specialty types:

CARC 185: "The rendering provider is not eligible to perform the service billed."

NOTE: Refer to the 835 Healthcare Policy Identification Segment (loop 2110 Service Payment Information REF), if present.

RARC N95: "This provider type/provider specialty may not bill this service."

MSN 21.18: "This item or service is not covered when performed or ordered by this provider."

Spanish version: "Este servicio no esta cubierto cuando es ordenado o rendido por este proveedor."

Group Code PR (Patient Responsibility) assigning financial liability to the beneficiary, if a claim is received with a GA modifier indicating a signed ABN is on file.

Group Code CO (Contractual Obligation) assigning financial liability to the provider, if a claim is received with a GZ modifier indicating no signed ABN is on file.

100-4, Chapter-18, 160.3

Correct Types of Bill (TOB) for IBT for CVD on Institutional Claims

Effective for claims with dates of service on and after November 8, 2011, the following types of bill (TOB) may be used for IBT for CVD: 13X, 71X, 77X, or 85X. All other TOB codes shall be denied.

The following messages shall be used when Medicare contractors deny claims for G0446 when submitted on a TOB other than those listed above:

CARC 170: Payment is denied when performed/billed by this type of provider. *Note:* Refer to the 835 Healthcare Policy Identification Segment (loop 2110 Service Payment Information REF), if present.

RARC N428: Not covered when performed in this place of service."

MSN 21.25: "This service was denied because Medicare only covers this service in certain settings."

Spanish Version: El servicio fue denegado porque Medicare solamente lo cubre en ciertas situaciones."

Group Code PR (Patient Responsibility) assigning financial liability to the beneficiary, if a claim is received with a GA modifier indicating a signed ABN is on file.

Group Code CO (Contractual Obligation) assigning financial liability to the provider, if a claim is received with a GZ modifier indicating no signed ABN is on file.

100-4, Chapter-18, 160.4

Frequency Edits for IBT for CVD Claims

Contractors shall allow claims for G0446 no more than once in a 12-month period.

NOTE: 11 full months must elapse following the month in which the last G0446 IBT for CVD took place.

Contractors shall deny claims IBT for CVD claims that exceed one (1) visit every 12 months.

Contractors shall allow one professional service and one facility fee claim for each visit.

The following messages shall be used when Medicare contractors deny IBT for CVD claims that exceed the frequency limit:

CARC 119: "Benefit maximum for this time period or occurrence has been reached."

RARC N362: "The number of days or units of service exceeds our acceptable maximum."

MSN 20.5: "These services cannot be paid because your benefits are exhausted at this time."

Spanish Version: "Estos servicios no pueden ser pagados porque sus beneficios se hanagotado."

Group Code PR (Patient Responsibility) assigning financial liability to the beneficiary, if a claim is received with a GA modifier indicating a signed ABN is on file.

Group Code CO (Contractual Obligation) assigning financial liability to the provider, if a claim is received with a GZ modifier indicating no signed ABN is on file.

100-4, Chapter-18, 160.5

Common Working File (CWF) Edits for IBT for CVD Claims

When applying frequency, CWF shall count 11 full months following the month of the last IBT for CVD, G0446 before allowing subsequent payment of another G0446 screening.

When applying frequency limitations to G0446, CWF shall allow both a claim for the professional service and a claim for the facility fee. CWF shall identify the following institutional claims as facility fee claims for screening services: TOB 13X, TOB85X when the revenue code is not 096X, 097X, or 098X. CWF shall identify all other claims as professional service claims for screening services. *NOTE:* This does not apply to RHCs and FQHCs.

100-4, Chapter-18, 170.1

Healthcare Common Procedure Coding System (HCPCS) Codes for Screening for STIs and HIBC to Prevent STIs

Effective for claims with dates of service on and after November 8, 2011, the claims processing instructions for payment of screening tests for STI will apply to the following HCPCS codes:

- Chlamydia: 86631, 86632, 87110, 87270, 87320, 87490, 87491, 87810, 87800 (used for combined chlamydia and gonorrhea testing)
- Gonorrhea: 87590, 87591, 87850, 87800 (used for combined chlamydia and gonorrhea testing)
- Syphilis: 86592, 86593, 86780
- Hepatitis B: (hepatitis B surface antigen): 87340, 87341

Effective for claims with dates of service on and after November 8, 2011, implemented with the January 2, 2012, IOCE, the following HCPCS code is to be billed for HIBC to prevent STIs

- G0445 –high-intensity behavioral counseling to prevent sexually transmitted infections, face-to-face, individual, includes: education, skills training, and guidance on how to change sexual behavior, performed semi-annually, 30minutes.

100-4, Chapter-18, 170.2

Diagnosis Code Reporting

A claim that is submitted for screening chlamydia, gonorrhea, syphilis, and/or hepatitis B shall be submitted with one or more of the following diagnosis codes in the header and pointed to the line item:

a. For claims for screening for chlamydia, gonorrhea, and syphilis in women at increased risk who are not pregnant use the following diagnosis codes:

- V74.5 – Screening, bacterial – sexually transmitted; and
- V69.8 - Other problems related to lifestyle as secondary (This diagnosis code is used to indicate high/increased risk for STIs).

b. For claims for screening for syphilis in men at increased risk use the following diagnosis codes:

- V74.5 – Screening, bacterial –sexually transmitted; and
- V69.8 - Other problems related to lifestyle as secondary.

c. For claims for screening for chlamydia and gonorrhea in pregnant women at increased risk for STIs use the following diagnosis codes:

- V74.5 – Screening, bacterial –sexually transmitted; and
- V69.8- Other problems related to lifestyle, and,
- V22.0 –Supervision of normal first pregnancy, or
- V22.1 –Supervision of other normal pregnancy, or,
- V23.9 –Supervision of unspecified high-risk pregnancy.

d. For claims for screening for syphilis in pregnant women use the following diagnosis codes:

- V74.5 – Screening, bacterial –sexually transmitted; and
- V22.0 –Supervision of normal first pregnancy, or,
- V22.1–Supervision of other normal pregnancy, or,
- V23.9–Supervision of unspecified high-risk pregnancy.

e. For claims for screening for syphilis in pregnant women at increased risk for STIs use the following diagnosis codes:

- V74.5–Screening, bacterial –sexually transmitted; and
- V69.8 -Other problems related to lifestyle, and,
- V22.0 –Supervision of normal first pregnancy, or
- V22.1 –Supervision of other normal pregnancy, or,
- V23.9 –Supervision of unspecified high-risk pregnancy.

f. For claims for screening for hepatitis B in pregnant women use the following diagnosis codes:

- V73.89–Screening, disease or disorder,viral, specified type NEC; and
- V22.0 –Supervision of normal first pregnancy, or,
- V22.1 –Supervision of other normal pregnancy, or,
- V23.9 –Supervision of unspecified high-risk pregnancy.

g. For claims for screening for hepatitis B in pregnant women at increased risk for STIs use the following diagnosis codes:

- V73.89–Screening, disease or disorder, viral, specified type NEC; and
- V69.8 -Other problems related to lifestyle, and,
- V22.0 –Supervision of normal first pregnancy, or,
- V22.1 –Supervision of other normal pregnancy, or,
- V23.9 –Supervision of unspecified high-risk pregnancy.

ICD-10 Diagnosis Coding:

Contractors shall note the appropriate ICD-10 code(s) that are listed below for future implementation. Contractors shall track the ICD-10 codes and ensure that the updated edit is turned on as part of the ICD-10 implementation effective October 1, 2013.

ICD-10	Description
Z113	Encounter for screening for infections with a predominantly sexual mode of transmission
Z1159	Encounter for screening for other viral diseases
Z7289	Other problems related to lifestyle
Z3400	Encounter for supervision of normal first pregnancy, unspecified trimester
Z3480	Encounter for supervision of other normal pregnancy, unspecified trimester
O0990	Supervision of high risk pregnancy, unspecified, unspecified trimester

100-4, Chapter-18, 170.3

Billing Requirements

Effective for dates of service November 8, 2011, and later, contractors shall recognize HCPCS code G0445 for HIBC. Medicare shall cover up to two occurrences of G0445 when billed for HIBC to prevent STIs. A claim that is submitted with HCPCS code G0445 for HIBC shall be submitted with ICD-9 diagnosis code V69.8.

Medicare contractors shall pay for screening for chlamydia, gonorrhea, and syphilis (As indicated by the presence of ICD-9 diagnosis code V74.5); and/or hepatitis B (as indicated by the presence of ICD-9 diagnosis code V73.89) as follows:

- One annual occurrence of screening for chlamydia, gonorrhea, and syphilis (i.e., 1 per 12-month period) in women at increased risk who are not pregnant,
- One annual occurrence of screening for syphilis (i.e., 1 per 12-month period) in men at increased risk,
- Up to two occurrences per pregnancy of screening for chlamydia and gonorrhea in pregnant women who are at increased risk for STIs and continued increased risk for the second screening,
- One occurrence per pregnancy of screening for syphilis in pregnant women,•Up to an additional two occurrences per pregnancy of screening for syphilis in pregnant women if the beneficiary is at continued increased risk for STIs,
- One occurrence per pregnancy of screening for hepatitis B in pregnant women, and,
- One additional occurrence per pregnancy of screening for hepatitis B in pregnant women who are at continued increased risk for STIs.

100-4, Chapter-18, 170.4

Types of Bill (TOBs) and Revenue Codes

The applicable types of bill (TOBs) for HIBC screening, HCPCS code G0445, are: 13X, 71X, 77X, and 85X.

On institutional claims, TOBs 71X and 77X, use revenue code 052X to ensure coinsurance and deductible are not applied.

Critical access hospitals (CAHs) electing the optional method of payment for outpatient services report this service under revenue codes 096X, 097X, or 098X.

100-4, Chapter-18, 170.4.1

Payment Method

Payment for HIBC is based on the all-inclusive payment rate for rural health clinics (TOBs 71X) and federally qualified health centers (TOB 77X). Hospital outpatient departments (TOB 13X) are paid based on the outpatient prospective payment system and CAHs (TOB 85X) are paid based on reasonable cost. CAHs electing the optional method of payment for outpatient services are paid based on 115% of the lesser of the Medicare Physician Fee Schedule (MPFS) amount or submitted charge.

Effective for dates of service on and after November 8, 2011, deductible and coinsurance do not apply to claim lines with G0445.

HCPCS code G0445 may be paid on the same date of service as an annual wellness visit, evaluation and management (E&M) code, or during the global billing period for obstetrical care, but only one G0445 may be paid on any one date of service. If billed on the same date of service with an E&M code, the E&M code should have a distinct diagnosis code other than the diagnosis code used to indicate high/increased risk for STIs for the G0445 service. An E&M code should not be billed when the sole reason for the visit is HIBC to prevent STIs.

For Medicare Part B physician and non-practitioner claims, payment for HIBC to prevent STIs is based on the MPFS amount for G0445.

100-4, Chapter-18, 170.5

Specialty Codes and Place of Service (POS)

Medicare provides coverage for screening for chlamydia, gonorrhea, syphilis, and/or hepatitis B and HIBC to prevent STIs only when ordered by a primary care practitioner (physician or non-physician) with any of the following specialty codes:

- 01 –General Practice
- 08 –Family Practice
- 11 –Internal Medicine
- 16 –Obstetrics/Gynecology
- 37 –Pediatric Medicine
- 38 –Geriatric Medicine
- 42 –Certified Nurse Midwife
- 50 –Nurse Practitioner
- 89 –Certified Clinical Nurse Specialist
- 97 –Physician Assistant

Medicare provides coverage for HIBC to prevent STIs only when provided by a primary care practitioner (physician or non-physician) with any of the specialty codes identified above.

Medicare provides coverage for HIBC to prevent STIs only when the POS billed is 11, 22, 49, or 71.

100-4, Chapter-18, 180

Alcohol Screening and Behavioral Counseling Interventions in Primary Care to Reduce Alcohol Misuse

The United States Preventive Services Task Force (USPSTF) defines alcohol misuse as risky, hazardous, or harmful drinking which places an individual at risk for future problems with alcohol consumption. In the general adult population, alcohol consumption becomes risky or hazardous when consuming:

- Greater than 7 drinks per week or greater than 3 drinks per occasion for women and persons greater than 65 years old.
- Greater than 14 drinks per week or greater than 4 drinks per occasion for men 65 years old and younger.

100-4, Chapter-18, 180.1

Policy

Claims with dates of service on and after October 14, 2011, the Centers for Medicare & Medicaid Services (CMS) will cover annual alcohol misuse screening (HCPCS code G0442) consisting of 1 screening session, and for those that screen positive, upto 4 brief, face-to-face behavioral counseling sessions (HCPCS code G0443) per 12-month period for Medicare beneficiaries, including pregnant women.

Medicare beneficiaries that may be identified as having a need for behavioral counseling sessions include those:

- Who misuse alcohol, but whose levels or patterns of alcohol consumption do not meet criteria for alcohol dependence (defined as at least three of the following: tolerance, withdrawal symptoms, impaired control, preoccupation with acquisition and/or use, persistent desire or unsuccessful efforts to quit, sustains social, occupational, or recreational disability, use continues despite adverse consequences); and,
- Who are competent and alert at the time that counseling is provided; and,
- Whose counseling is furnished by qualified primary care physicians or other primary care practitioners in a primary care setting.

Once a Medicare beneficiary has agreed to behavioral counseling sessions, the counseling sessions are to be completed based on the 5As approach adopted by the United States Preventive Services Task Force (USPSTF.) The steps to the 5As approach are listed below.

1. *Assess:* Ask about/assess behavioral health risk(s) and factors affecting choice of behavior change goals/methods.
2. *Advise:* Give clear, specific, and personalized behavior change advice, including information about personal health harms and benefits.
3. *Agree:* Collaboratively select appropriate treatment goals and methods based on the patient's interest in and willingness to change the behavior.
4. *Assist:* Using behavior change techniques (self-help and/or counseling), aid the patient in achieving agreed-upon goals by acquiring the skills, confidence, and social/environmental supports for behavior change, supplemented with adjunctive medical treatments when appropriate.
5. *Arrange:* Schedule follow-up contacts (in person or by telephone) to provide ongoing assistance/support and to adjust the treatment plan as needed, including referral to more intensive or specialized treatment.

Institutional Billing Requirements

For claims with dates of service on and after October 14, 2011, Medicare will allow coverage for annual alcohol misuse screening, 15 minutes, G0442, and brief, face-to-face behavioral counseling for alcohol misuse, 15 minutes, G0443 for:

- Rural Health Clinics (RHCs) -type of bill (TOB) 71X only –based on the all-inclusive payment rate
- Federally Qualified Health Centers (FQHCs) -TOB 77X only –based on the all-inclusive payment rate
- Outpatient hospitals –TOB 13X -based on Outpatient Prospective Payment System (OPPS)
- Critical Access Hospitals (CAHs) -TOB 85X–based on reasonable cost
- CAH Method II –TOB 85X -based on 115% of the lesser of the Medicare Physician Fee Schedule (MPFS) amount or actual charge as applicable with revenue codes 096X, 097X, or 098X.

For RHCs and FQHCs the alcohol screening/counseling is not separately payable with another face-to-face encounter on the same day. This does not apply to the Initial Preventive Physical Examination (IPPE), unrelated services denoted with modifier 59, and 77X claims containing Diabetes Self Management Training (DSMT) and Medical Nutrition Therapy (MNT) services. DSMT and MNT apply to FQHCs only. However, the screening/counseling sessions alone when rendered as a face-to-face visit with a core practitioner do constitute an encounter and is paid based on the all-inclusive payment rate.

Note: For outpatient hospital settings, as in any other setting, services covered under this NCD must be provided by a primary care provider.

Claims submitted with alcohol misuse screening and behavioral counseling HCPCS codes G0442 and G0443 on a TOB other than 13X, 71X, 77X, and 85X will be denied.

Effective October 14, 2011, deductible and co-insurance should not be applied for line items on claims billed for alcohol misuse screening G0442 and behavioral counseling for alcohol misuse G0443.

100-4, Chapter-18, 180.3

Professional Billing Requirements

For claims with dates of service on and after October 14, 2011, CMS will allow coverage for annual alcohol misuse screening, 15 minutes, G0442, and behavioral counseling for alcohol misuse, 15 minutes, G0443, only when services are submitted by the following provider specialties found on the provider's enrollment record:

01 -General Practice

08 -Family Practice

11 -Internal Medicine

16 -Obstetrics/Gynecology

37 -Pediatric Medicine

38 -Geriatric Medicine

42 –Certified Nurse-Midwife

50 -Nurse Practitioner

89 -Certified Clinical Nurse Specialist

97 -Physician Assistant

Any claims that are not submitted from one of the provider specialty types noted above will be denied.

For claims with dates of service on and after October 14, 2011, CMS will allow coverage for annual alcohol misuse screening, 15 minutes, G0442, and behavioral counseling for alcohol misuse, 15 minutes, G0443, only when submitted with one of the following place of service (POS) codes:

11 -Physician's Office

22 -Outpatient Hospital

49 -Independent Clinic

71 -State or local public health clinic or

Any claims that are not submitted with one of the POS codes noted above will be denied.

The alcohol screening/counseling services are payable with another encounter/visit on the same day. This does not apply for IPPE.

100-4, Chapter-18, 180.4

Claim Adjustment Reason Codes, Remittance Advice Remark Codes, Group Codes, and Medicare Summary Notice Messages

Contractors shall use the appropriate claim adjustment reason codes (CARCs), remittance advice remark codes (RARCs), group codes, or Medicare summary notice (MSN) messages when denying payment for alcohol misuse screening and alcohol misuse behavioral counseling sessions:

- For RHC and FQHC claims that contain screening for alcohol misuse HCPCS code G0442 and alcohol misuse counseling HCPCS code G0443 with another encounter/visit with the same line item date of service, use group code CO and reason code:
  - Claim Adjustment Reason Code (CARC) 97 –The benefit for this service is included in the payment/allowance for another service/procedure that has already been adjudicated. **Note:** Refer to the 835 Healthcare Policy Identification Segment (loop 2110 Service Payment Information REF) if present
- Denying claims containing HCPCS code G0442 and HCPCS code G0443 submitted on a TOB other than 13X, 71X, 77X, and 85X:
  - Claim Adjustment Reason Code (CARC) 5 -The procedure code/bill type is inconsistent with the place of service. **Note:** Refer to the 835 Healthcare Policy Identification Segment (loop 2110 Service Payment Information REF) if present
  - Remittance Advice Remark Code (RARC) M77 –Missing/incomplete/invalid place of service
  - Group Code PR (Patient Responsibility) assigning financial liability to the beneficiary, if a claim is received with a GA modifier indicating a signed ABN is on file.
  - Group Code CO (Contractual Obligation) assigning financial liability to the provider, if a claim is received with a GZ modifier indicating no signed ABN is on file.
- Denying claims that contains more than one alcohol misuse behavioral counseling session G0443 on the same date of service:
  - Medicare Summary Notice (MSN) 15.6 –The information provided does not support the need for this many services or items within this period of time.
  - Claim Adjustment Reason Code (CARC) 151 –Payment adjusted because the payer deems the information submitted does not support this many/frequency of services.
  - Remittance Advice Remark Code (RARC) M86 –Service denied because payment already made for same/similar procedure within set time frame.

- Group Code PR (Patient Responsibility) assigning financial liability to the beneficiary, if a claim is received with a GA modifier indicating a signed ABN is on file.
- Group Code CO (Contractual Obligation) assigning financial liability to the provider, if a claim is received with a GZ modifier indicating no signed ABN is on file.
- Denying claims that are not submitted from the appropriate provider specialties:
  - Medicare Summary Notice (MSN) 21.18 –This item or service is not covered when performed or ordered by this provider.
  - Claim Adjustment Reason Code (CARC) 185 -The rendering provider is not eligible to perform the service billed. **NOTE:** Refer to the 835 Healthcare Policy Identification Segment (loop 2110 Service Payment Information REF), if present.
  - Remittance Advice Remark Code (RARC) N95 -This provider type/provider specialty may not bill this service.
  - Group Code PR (Patient Responsibility) assigning financial liability to the beneficiary, if a claim is received with a GA modifier indicating a signed ABN is on file.
  - Group Code CO (Contractual Obligation) assigning financial liability to the provider, if a claim is received with a GZ modifier indicating no signed ABN is on file.
- Denying claims without the appropriate POS code:
  - Medicare Summary Notice (MSN) 21.25 –This service was denied because Medicare only covers this service in certain settings.
  - Claim Adjustment Reason Code (CARC) 58 – Treatment was deemed by the payer to have been rendered in an inappropriate or invalid place of service. *Note:* Refer to the 835 Healthcare Policy Identification Segment (loop 2110 Service Payment Information REF) if present.
  - Remittance Advice Remark Code (RARC) N428 –Not covered when performed in this place of service.
  - Group Code PR (Patient Responsibility) assigning financial liability to the beneficiary, if a claim is received with a GA modifier indicating a signed ABN is on file.
  - Group Code CO (Contractual Obligation) assigning financial liability to the provider, if a claim is received with a GZ modifier indicating no signed ABN is on file.
- Denying claims for alcohol misuse screening HCPCS code G0442 more than once in a 12-month period, and denying alcohol misuse counseling sessions HCPCS code G0443 more than four times in the same 12-month period:
  - Medicare Summary Notice (MSN) 20.5 –These services cannot be paid because your benefits are exhausted at this time.
  - Claim Adjustment Reason Code (CARC) 119 –Benefit maximum for this time period or occurrence has been reached.
  - Remittance Advice Remark Code (RARC) N362 – The number of Days or Units of service exceeds our acceptable maximum.
  - Group Code PR (Patient Responsibility) assigning financial liability to the beneficiary, if a claim is received with a GA modifier indicating a signed ABN is on file.

- Group Code CO (Contractual Obligation) assigning financial liability to the provider, if a claim is received with a GZ modifier indicating no signed ABN is on file.

100-4, Chapter-18, 180.5

CWF Requirements

When applying frequency, CWF shall count 11 full months following the month of the last alcohol misuse screening visit, G0442, before allowing subsequent payment of another G0442 screening. Additionally, CWF shall create an edit to allow alcohol misuse brief behavioral counseling, HCPCS G0443, no more than 4 times in a 12-month period and make this edit overridable. CWF shall also count four alcohol misuse counseling sessions HCPCS G0443 in the same 12-month period used for G0442 counting from the date the G0442 screening session was billed.

When applying frequency limitations to G0442 screening on the same date of service as G0443 counseling, CWF shall allow both a claim for the professional service and a claim for a facility fee. CWF shall identify the following institutional claims as facility fee claims for screening services: TOB 13X, TOB 85X when the revenue code is not 096X, 097X, or 098X. CWF shall identify all other claims as professional service claims for screening services. **NOTE:** This does not apply to RHCs and FQHCs.

100-4, Chapter-18, 190

Screening for Depression in Adults (Effective October 14, 2011)

A. Coverage Requirements

Effective October 14, 2011, the Centers for Medicare & Medicaid Services (CMS) will cover annual screening up to 15 minutes for Medicare beneficiaries in primary care settings that have staff-assisted depression care supports in place to assure accurate diagnosis, effective treatment, and follow-up. Various screening tools are available for screening for depression. CMS does not identify specific depression screening tools. Rather, the decision to use a specific tool is at the discretion of the clinician in the primary care setting. Screening for depression is non-covered when performed more than one time in a 12-month period. The Medicare coinsurance and Part B deductible are waived for this preventive service.

Additional information on this National Coverage Determination (NCD) for Screening for Depression in Adults can be found in Publication 100-03, NCD Manual, Section 210.9.

100-4, Chapter-18, 190.1

A/B MAC and Carrier Billing Requirements

Effective October 14, 2011, contractors shall recognize new HCPCS G0444, annual depression screening, 15 minutes.

100-4, Chapter-18, 190.2

Frequency

Medicare contractors shall pay for annual depression screening, G0444, no more than once in a 12-month period.

NOTE: 11 full months must elapse following the month in which the last annual depression screening took place.

100-4, Chapter-18, 190.3

Place of Service (POS)

Contractors shall pay for annual depression screening claims, G0444, only when services are provided at the following places of service (POS):

11 –Office

22 –Outpatient Hospital

49 –Independent Clinic

71 –State or Local Public Health Clinic

100-4, Chapter-18, 200

Intensive Behavioral Therapy for Obesity (Effective November 29, 2011)

The United States Preventive Services Task Force (USPSTF) found good evidence that body mass index (BMI) is a reliable and valid indicator for identifying adults at increased risk for mortality and morbidity due to overweight and obesity. It also good evidence that high intensity counseling combined with behavioral interventions in obese adults (as defined by a BMI $\geq$30 kg/m2) produces modest, sustained weight loss.

100-4, Chapter-18, 200.1

Policy

For services furnished on or after November 29, 2011, the Centers for Medicare & Medicaid Services (CMS) will cover Intensive Behavioral Therapy for Obesity. Medicare beneficiaries with obesity (BMI $\geq$30 kg/m2) who are competent and alert at the time that counseling is provided and whose counseling is furnished by a qualified primary care physician or other primary care practitioner in a primary care setting are eligible for:

- One face-to-face visit every week for the first month;
- One face-to-face visit every other week for months 2-6;
- One face-to-face visit every month for months 7-12, if the beneficiary meets the 3kg (6.6 lbs) weight loss requirement during the first six months as discussed below.

The counseling sessions are to be completed based on the 5As approach adopted by the United States Preventive Services Task Force (USPSTF.) The steps to the 5As approach are listed below:

1. **Assess:** Ask about/assess behavioral health risk(s) and factors affecting choice of behavior change goals/methods.

2. **Advise:** Give clear, specific, and personalized behavior change advice, including information about personal health harms and benefits.

3. **Agree:** Collaboratively select appropriate treatment goals and methods based on the patient's interest in and willingness to change the behavior.

4. **Assist:** Using behavior change techniques (self-help and/or counseling), aid the patient in achieving agreed-upon goals by acquiring the skills, confidence, and social/environmental supports for behavior change, supplemented with adjunctive medical treatments when appropriate.

5. **Arrange:** Schedule follow-up contacts (in person or by telephone) to provide ongoing assistance/support and to

adjust the treatment plan as needed, including referral to more intensive or specialized treatment.

Medicare will cover Face-to-Face Behavioral Counseling for Obesity, 15 minutes, G0447, along with 1 of the ICD-9 codes for BMI 30.0-BMI 70 (V85.30-V85.39 and V85.41-V85.45), up to 22 sessions in a 12-month period for Medicare beneficiaries. The Medicare coinsurance and Part B deductible are waived for this preventive service.

Contractors shall note the appropriate ICD-10 code(s) that are listed below for future implementation. Contractors shall track the ICD-10 codes and ensure that the updated edit is turned on as part of the ICD-10 implementation effective October 1, 2013.

ICD-10	Description
Z68.30	BMI 30.0-30.9, adult
Z68.31	BMI 31.0-31.9, adult
Z68.32	BMI 32.0-32.9, adult
Z68.33	BMI 33.0-33.9, adult
Z68.34	BMI 34.0-34.9, adult
Z68.35	BMI 35.0-35.9, adult
Z68.36	BMI 36.0-36.9, adult
Z68.37	BMI 37.0-37.9, adult
Z68.38	BMI 38.0-38.9, adult
Z68.39	BMI 39.0-39.9, adult
Z68.41	BMI 40.0-44.9, adult
Z68.42	BMI 45.0-49.9, adult
Z68.43	BMI 50.0-59.9, adult
Z68.44	BMI 60.0-69.9, adult
Z68.45	BMI 70 or greater, adult

See National Coverage Determinations (NCD) Manual (Pub. 100-03) §210.12 for complete coverage guidelines.

100-4, Chapter-18, 200.2

Institutional Billing Requirements

Effective for claims with dates of service on and after November 29, 2011, providers may use the following types of bill (TOB) when submitting HCPCS code G0447: 13x, 71X, 77X, or 85X. Service line items on other TOBs shall be denied.

The service shall be paid on the basis shown below:

- Rural Health Clinics (RHCs) -type of bill (TOB) 71X only –based on the all-inclusive payment rate
- Federally Qualified Health Centers (FQHCs) -TOB 77X only –based on the all-inclusive payment rate
- Outpatient hospitals –TOB 13X -based on Outpatient Prospective Payment System (OPPS)
- Critical Access Hospitals (CAHs) -TOB 85X –based on reasonable cost
- CAH Method II –TOB 85X - based on 115% of the lesser of the Medicare Physician Fee Schedule (MPFS) amount or actual charge as applicable with revenue codes 096X, 097X, or 098X.

For RHCs and FQHCs, obesity counseling is not separately payable with another face-to-face encounter on the same day. This does not apply to claims for the Initial Preventive Physical Examination (IPPE), claims with unrelated services denoted with modifier 59, and FQHC claims containing Diabetes Self

Management Training (DSMT) and Medical Nutrition Therapy (MNT) services. However, the counseling sessions alone when rendered as a face-to-face visit with a core practitioner do constitute an encounter and are paid based on the all-inclusive payment rate.

Note: For outpatient hospital settings, as in any other setting, services covered under this NCD must be provided by a primary care provider.

100-4, Chapter-18, 200.3

Professional Billing Requirements

For claims with dates of service on or after November 29, 2011, CMS will allow coverage for Face-to-Face Behavioral Counseling for Obesity, 15 minutes, G0447, along with 1 of the ICD-9 codes for BMI 30.0-BMI 70 (V85.30-V85.39 and V85.41-V85.45), only when services are submitted by the following provider specialties found on the provider's enrollment record:

01 -General Practice

08 -Family Practice

11 -Internal Medicine

16 -Obstetrics/Gynecology

37 -Pediatric Medicine

38 -Geriatric Medicine

50 -Nurse Practitioner

89 -Certified Clinical Nurse Specialist

97 -Physician Assistant

Any claims that are not submitted from one of the provider specialty types noted above will be denied.

For claims with dates of service on or after November 29, 2011, CMS will allow coverage for Face-to-Face Behavioral Counseling for Obesity, 15 minutes, G0447, along with 1of the ICD-9 codes for BMI 30.0-BMI 70 (V85.30-V85.39 and V85.41-V85.45), only when submitted with one of the following place of service (POS) codes:

11 –Physician's Office

22 –Outpatient Hospital

49 –Independent Clinic

71 –State or Local Public Health Clinic

Any claims that are not submitted with one of the POS codes noted above will be denied.

100-4, Chapter-18, 200.4

Claim Adjustment Reason Codes (CARCs), Remittance Advice Remark Codes (RARCs), Group Codes, and Medicare Summary Notice (MSN) Messages

Contractors shall use the appropriate claim adjustment reason codes (CARCs), remittance advice remark codes (RARCs), group codes, or Medicare summary notice (MSN) messages when denying payment for obesity counseling sessions:

- Denying services submitted on a TOB other than 13X, 71X, 77X, and 85X:

  CARC 5 -The procedure code/bill type is inconsistent with the place of service.

Note: Refer to the 835 Healthcare Policy Identification Segment (loop 2110 Service Payment Information REF), if present.

RARC M77 -Missing/incomplete/invalid place of service

MSN 21.25: "This service was denied because Medicare only covers this service in certain settings."

Group Code PR (Patient Responsibility) assigning financial responsibility to the beneficiary (if a claim is received with a GA modifier indicating a signed ABN is on file).

Group Code CO (Contractual Obligation) assigning financial liability to the provider (if a claim is received with a GZ modifier indicating no signed ABN is on file).

NOTE: For modifier GZ, use CARC 50 and MSN 8.81 per instructions in CR 7228/TR 2148.

- For RHC and FQHC services that contain HCPCS code G0447 with another encounter/visit with the same line item date of service:

  Claim Adjustment Reason Code (CARC) 97 –The benefit for this service is included in the payment/ allowance for another service/procedure that has already been adjudicated. *Note:* Refer to the 835 Healthcare Policy Identification Segment (loop 2110 Service Payment Information REF) if present

  Group Code CO (Contractual Obligation)

- Denying services for obesity counseling sessions HCPCS code G0447 with 1 of the ICD-9 codes (V85.30-V85.39 or V85.41-V85.45) for more than 22 times in the same 12-month period:

  CARC 119 – Benefit maximum for this time period or occurrence has been reached.

  RARC N362 – The number of days or units of service exceeds our acceptable maximum.

  MSN 20.5 –These services cannot be paid because your benefits are exhausted at this time.

  Group Code PR (Patient Responsibility) assigning financial responsibility to the beneficiary (if a claim is received with a GA modifier indicating a signed ABN is on file).

  Group Code CO (Contractual Obligation) assigning financial liability to the provider (if a claim is received with a GZ modifier indicating no signed ABN is on file).

  NOTE: For modifier GZ, use CARC 50 and MSN 8.81 per instructions in CR 7228/TR 2148.

- Denying claim lines for obesity counseling sessions HCPCS code G0447 without 1 of the appropriate ICD-9 codes (V85.30-V85.39 or V85.41-V85.45):

  CARC 167 –This (these) diagnosis(es) is (are) not covered. *Note:* Refer to the 835 Healthcare Policy Identification Segment (loop 2110 Service Payment Information REF), if present.

  RARC N386 – This decision was based on a National Coverage Determination (NCD). An NCD provides a coverage determination as to whether a particular item or service is covered. A copy of this policy is available at www.cms.gov/mcd/search.asp. If you do not have web access, you may contact the contractor to request a copy of the NCD.

MSN 14.9 -Medicare cannot pay for this service for the diagnosis shown on the claim.

Group Code PR (Patient Responsibility) assigning financial responsibility to the beneficiary (if a claim is received with a GA modifier indicating a signed ABN is on file).

Group Code CO (Contractual Obligation) assigning financial liability to the provider (if a claim is received with a GZ modifier indicating no signed ABN is on file).

NOTE: For modifier GZ, use CARC 50 and MSN 8.81 per instructions in CR 7228/TR 2148.

- Denying claim lines without the appropriate POS code:

  CARC 58 – Treatment was deemed by the payer to have been rendered in an inappropriate or invalid place of service. **Note:** Refer to the 835 Healthcare Policy Identification Segment (loop 2110 Service Payment Information REF), if present.

  RARC N428 -Not covered when performed in certain settings.

  MSN 21.25 - This service was denied because Medicare only covers this service in certain settings.

  Group Code PR (Patient Responsibility) assigning financial responsibility to the beneficiary (if a claim is received with a GA modifier indicating a signed ABN is on file).

  Group Code CO (Contractual Obligation) assigning financial liability to the provider (if a claim is received with a GZ modifier indicating no signed ABN is on file).

  NOTE: For modifier GZ, use CARC 50 and MSN 8.81 per instructions in CR 7228/TR 2148.

- Denying claim lines that are not submitted from the appropriate provider specialties:

  CARC 185 - The rendering provider is not eligible to perform the service billed.

  NOTE: Refer to the 835 Healthcare Policy Identification Segment (loop 2110 Service Payment Information REF), if present.

  RARCN95 -This provider type/provider specialty may not bill this service.

  MSN 21.18 -This item or service is not covered when performed or ordered by this provider.

  Group Code PR (Patient Responsibility) assigning financial responsibility to the beneficiary (if a claim is received with a GA modifier indicating a signed ABN is on file).

  Group Code CO (Contractual Obligation) assigning financial liability to the provider (if a claim is received with a GZ modifier indicating no signed ABN is on file).

  NOTE: For modifier GZ, use CARC 50 and MSN 8.81 per instructions in CR 7228/TR 2148.

100-4, Chapter-18, 200.5

Common Working File (CWF) Edits

When applying frequency, CWF shall count 22 counseling sessions of G0447, along with 1 ICD-9 code from V85.30-V85.39 or V85.41-V85.45 in a 12-month period. When applying frequency limitations to G0447 counseling CWF shall allow both a claim for the professional service and a claim for a facility fee. CWF shall identify the following institutional claims as facility fee claims for this service: TOB 13X, TOB 85X when the revenue code is not 096X, 097X, or 098X. CWF shall identify all other claims as professional service claims. **NOTE:** This does not apply to RHCs and FQHCs.

100-4, Chapter-20, 30.1.2

Transcutaneous Electrical Nerve Stimulator (TENS)

In order to permit an attending physician time to determine whether the purchase of a TENS is medically appropriate for a particular patient, contractors pay 10 percent of the purchase price of the item for each of 2 months. The purchase price and payment for maintenance and servicing are determined under the same rules as any other frequently purchased item, except that there is no reduction in the allowed amount for purchase due to the two months rental.

Effective June 8, 2012, CMS will allow coverage for TENS use in the treatment of chronic low back pain (CLBP) only under specific conditions which are described in the NCD Manual, Pub. 100-03, chapter 1 Section 160.27.

100-4, Chapter-20, 100.2.2

Evidence of Medical Necessity for Parenteral and Enteral Nutrition (PEN) Therapy

The PEN coverage is determined by information provided by the treating physician and the PEN supplier. A completed certification of medical necessity (CMN) must accompany and support initial claims for PEN to establish whether coverage criteria are met and to ensure that the PEN therapy provided is consistent with the attending or ordering physician's prescription. Contractors ensure that the CMN contains pertinent information from the treating physician. Uniform specific medical data facilitate the review and promote consistency in coverage determinations and timelier claims processing.

The medical and prescription information on a PEN CMN can be most appropriately completed by the treating physician or from information in the patient's records by an employee of the physician for the physician's review and signature. Although PEN suppliers sometimes may assist in providing the PEN services, they cannot complete the CMN since they do not have the same access to patient information needed to properly enter medical or prescription information. Contractors use appropriate professional relations issuances, training sessions, and meetings to ensure that all persons and PEN suppliers are aware of this limitation of their role.

When properly completed, the PEN CMN includes the elements of a prescription as well as other data needed to determine whether Medicare coverage is possible. This practice will facilitate prompt delivery of PEN services and timely submittal of the related claim.

100-4, Chapter-20, 160.1

Billing for Total Parenteral Nutrition and Enteral Nutrition Furnished to Part B Inpatients

Inpatient Part A hospital or SNF care includes total parenteral nutrition (TPN) systems and enteral nutrition (EN).

For inpatients for whom Part A benefits are not payable (e.g., benefits are exhausted or the beneficiary is entitled to Part B only), total parenteral nutrition (TPN) systems and enteral nutrition (EN) delivery systems are covered by Medicare as prosthetic devices when the coverage criteria are met. When these criteria are met, the medical equipment and medical supplies (together with nutrients) being used comprise covered prosthetic devices for coverage purposes rather than durable medical equipment. However, reimbursement rules relating to DME continue to apply to such items.

When a facility supplies TPN or EN systems that meet the criteria for coverage as a prosthetic device to an inpatient whose care is not covered under Part A, the facility must bill one of the DME MACs. Additionally, HHAs, SNFs, and hospitals that provide PEN supplies, equipment and nutrients as a prosthetic device under Part B must use the ASC X12 837 professional claim format or if permissible the Form CMS-1500 paper form to bill the appropriate DME MAC. The DME MACis determined according to the residence of the beneficiary. Refer to §10 for jurisdiction descriptions.

A/B MACs (Aand HHH) return claims containing PEN charges for Part B services where the bill type is 12x, 13x, 22x, 23x, 32x, 33x, or 34x with instructions to the provider to bill the DME MAC.

100-4, Chapter-23, 60.3

Gap-filling DMEPOS Fees

The DME MACs and Part B MACs must gap-fill the DMEPOS fee schedule for items for which charge data were unavailable during the fee schedule data base year using the fee schedule amounts for comparable equipment, using properly calculated fee schedule amounts from a neighboring carrier, or using supplier price lists with prices in effect during the fee schedule data base year. Data base "year" refers to the time period mandated by the statute and/or regulations from which Medicare allowed charge data is to be extracted in order to compute the fee schedule amounts for the various DMEPOS payment categories. For example, the fee schedule base year for inexpensive or routinely purchased durable medical equipment is the 12 month period ending June 30,1987. Mail order catalogs are particularly suitable sources of price information for items such as urological and ostomy supplies which require constant replacement. DME MACs will gap-fill based on current instructions released each year for implementing and updating the new year's payment amounts.

If the only available price information is from a period other than the base period, apply the deflation factors that are included in the current year implementation instructions against current pricing in order to approximate the base year price for gap-filling purposes.

The deflation factors for gap-filling purposes are:

Year*	OX	CR	PO	SD	PE	SC	IL
1987	0.965	0.971	0.974	n/a	n/a	n/a	n/a
1988	0.928	0.934	0.936	n/a	n/a	n/a	n/a
1989	0.882	0.888	0.890	n/a	n/a	n/a	n/a
1990	0.843	0.848	0.851	n/a	n/a	n/a	n/a
1991	0.805	0.810	0.813	n/a	n/a	n/a	n/a
1992	0.781	0.786	0.788	n/a	n/a	n/a	n/a
1993	0.758	0.763	0.765	0.971	n/a	n/a	n/a
1994	0.740	0.745	0.747	0.947	n/a	n/a	n/a

Year*	OX	CR	PO	SD	PE	SC	IL
1995	0.718	0.723	0.725	0.919	n/a	n/a	n/a
1996	0.699	0.703	0.705	0.895	0.973	n/a	n/a
1997	0.683	0.687	0.689	0.875	0.951	n/a	n/a
1998	0.672	0.676	0.678	0.860	0.936	n/a	n/a
1999	0.659	0.663	0.665	0.844	0.918	n/a	n/a
2000	0.635	0.639	0.641	0.813	0.885	n/a	n/a
2001	0.615	0.619	0.621	0.788	0.857	n/a	n/a
2002	0.609	0.613	0.614	0.779	0.848	n/a	n/a
2003	0.596	0.600	0.602	0.763	0.830	n/a	n/a
2004	0.577	0.581	0.582	0.739	0.804	n/a	n/a
2005	0.563	0.567	0.568	0.721	0.784	n/a	n/a
2006	0.540	0.543	0.545	0.691	0.752	n/a	n/a
2007	0.525	0.529	0.530	0.673	0.732	n/a	n/a
2008	0.500	0.504	0.505	0.641	0.697	n/a	n/a
2009	0.508	0.511	0.512	0.650	0.707	n/a	n/a
2010	0.502	0.506	0.507	0.643	0.700	n/a	n/a
2011	0.485	0.488	0.490	0.621	0.676	n/a	n/a
2012	0.477	0.480	0.482	0.611	0.665	n/a	n/a
2013	0.469	0.472	0.473	0.600	0.653	n/a	0.983

* Year price in effect

Payment Category Key:

OX	Oxygen & oxygen equipment (DME)
CR	Capped rental (DME)
IN	Inexpensive/routinely purchased (DME)
FS	Frequently serviced (DME)
SU	DME supplies
PO	Prosthetics & orthotics
SD	Surgical dressings
OS	Ostomy, tracheostomy, and urological supplies
PE	Parental and enteral nutrition
TS	Therapeutic Shoes
SC	Splints and Casts
IL	Intraocular Lenses inserted in a physician's office

IN, FS, OS and SU category deflation factors=PO deflation factors

After deflation, the result must be increased by 1.7 percent and by the cumulative covered item update to complete the gap-filling (e.g., an additional .6 percent for a 2002 DME fee).

NOTE: When gap-filling for capped rental items, it is necessary to first gap-fill the purchase price then compute the base period fee schedule at 10 percent of the base period purchase price.

For used equipment, establish fee schedule amounts at 75 percent of the fee schedule amount for new equipment.

When gap-filling, for those carrier areas where a sales tax was imposed in the base period, add the applicable sales tax, e.g., five percent, to the gap-filled amount where the gap-filled amount does not take into account the sales tax, e.g., where the gap-filled amount is computed from pre-tax price lists or from another carrier area without a sales tax. Likewise, if the gap-filled amount is calculated from another carrier's fees where a sales tax is imposed, adjust the gap-filled amount to reflect the applicable local sales tax circumstances.

Contractors send their gap-fill information to CMS. After receiving the gap-filled base fees each year, CMS develops national fee schedule floors and ceilings and new fee schedule amounts for these codes and releases them as part of the July update file each year and during the quarterly updates.

100-4, Chapter-32, 11.1

Electrical Stimulation

A. Coding Applicable to Carriers & Fiscal Intermediaries (FIs)

Effective April 1, 2003, a National Coverage Decision was made to allow for Medicare coverage of Electrical Stimulation for the treatment of certain types of wounds. The type of wounds overed are chronic Stage III or Stage IV pressure ulcers, arterial ulcers, diabetic ulcers and venous stasis ulcers. All other uses of electrical stimulation for the treatment of wounds are not covered by Medicare. Electrical stimulation will not be covered as an initial treatment modality.

The use of electrical stimulation will only be covered after appropriate standard wound care has been tried for at least 30 days and there are no measurable signs of healing. If electrical stimulation is being used, wounds must be evaluated periodically by the treating physician but no less than every 30 days by a physician. Continued treatment with electrical stimulation is not covered if measurable signs of healing have not been demonstrated within any 30-day period of treatment. Additionally, electrical stimulation must be discontinued when the wound demonstrates a 100% epithelialzed wound bed.

Coverage policy can be found in Pub. 100-03, Medicare National Coverage Determinations

Manual, Chapter 1, Section 270.1

(http://www.cms.hhs.gov/manuals/103_cov_determ/ncd103index.asp)

The applicable Healthcare Common Procedure Coding System (HCPCS) code for Electrical Stimulation and the covered effective date is as follows:

HCPSC	Definition	Effective Date
G0281	Electrical Stimulation, (unattended), to one or more areas for chronic Stage III and Stage IV pressure ulcers, arterial ulcers, diabetic ulcers and venous stasis ulcers not demonstrating measurable signs of healing after 30 days of conventional care as part of a therapy plan of care.	04/01/2003

B. FI Billing Instructions

The applicable types of bills acceptable when billing for electrical stimulation services are 12X, 13X, 22X, 23X, 71X, 73X, 74X, 75X, and 85X. Chapter 25 of this manual provides general billing instructions that must be followed for bills submitted to FIs. FIs pay for electrical stimulation services under the Medicare Physician Fee Schedule for a hospital, Comprehensive Outpatient Rehabilitation Facility (CORF), Outpatient Rehabilitation Facility (ORF), Outpatient Physical Therapy (OPT) and Skilled Nursing Facility (SNF). Payment methodology for independent Rural Health Clinic (RHC), provider-based RHCs, free-standing Federally Qualified Health Center (FQHC)and provider based FQHCs is made under the all-inclusive rate for the visit furnished to the RHC/FQHC

patient to obtain the therapy service. Only one payment will be made for the visit furnished to the RHC/FQHC patient to obtain the therapy service. As of April 1, 2005, RHCs/FQHCs are no longer required to report HCPCS codes when billing for these therapy services.

Payment Methodology for a Critical Access Hospital (CAH) is on a reasonable cost basis unless the CAH has elected the Optional Method and then the FI pays115% of the MPFS amount for the professional component of the HCPCS code in addition to the technical component.

In addition, the following revenues code must be used in conjunction with the HCPCS code identified:

Revenue Code	Description
420	Physical Therapy
430	Occupational Therapy
520	Federal Qualified Health Center *
521	Rural Health Center *
977,978	Critical Access Hospital-method II CAH professional services only

* *NOTE:* As of April 1, 2005, RHCs/FQHCs are no longer required to report HCPCS codes when billing for these therapy services.

C. Carrier Claims

Carriers pay for Electrical Stimulation services billed with HCPCS codes G0281 based on the MPFS. Claims for Electrical Stimulation services must be billed on Form CMS-1500 or the electronic equivalent following instructions in chapter 12 of this manual

(http://www.cms.hhs.gov/manuals/104_claims/clm104c12.pdf).

D. Coinsurance and Deductible

The Medicare contractor shall apply coinsurance and deductible to payments for these therapy services except for services billed to the FI by FQHCs. For FQHCs, only co-insurance applies.

100-4, Chapter-32, 11.2

Electromagnetic Therapy

A. HCPCS Coding Applicable to A/B MACs (A and B)

Effective July 1, 2004, a National Coverage Decision was made to allow for Medicare coverage of electromagnetic therapy for the treatment of certain types of wounds. The type of wounds covered are chronic Stage III or Stage IV pressure ulcers, arterial ulcers, diabetic ulcers and venous stasis ulcers. All other uses of electromagnetic therapy for the treatment of wounds are not covered by Medicare. Electromagnetic therapy will not be covered as an initial treatment modality.

The use of electromagnetic therapy will only be covered after appropriate standard wound care has been tried for at least 30 days and there are no measurable signs of healing. If electromagnetic therapy is being used, wounds must be evaluated periodically by the treating physician but no less than every 30 days. Continued treatment with electromagnetic therapy is not covered if measurable signs of healing have not been demonstrated within any 30-day period of treatment. Additionally, electromagnetic therapy must be discontinued when the wound demonstrates a 100% epithelialzed wound bed.

Coverage policy can be found in Pub. 100-03, Medicare National Coverage Determinations Manual, Chapter 1 section 270.1.

(http://www.cms.hhs.gov/manuals/103_cov_determ/ncd103index.asp)

The applicable Healthcare Common Procedure Coding System (HCPCS) code for Electrical Stimulation and the covered effective date is as follows:

HCPCS	Definition	Effective Date
G0329	Electromagnetic Therapy, to one or more areas for chronic Stage III and Stage IV pressure ulcers, arterial ulcers, diabetic ulcers and venous stasis ulcers not demonstrating measurable signs of healing after 30 days of conventional care as part of a therapy plan of care.	07/01/2004

Medicare will not cover the device used for the electromagnetic therapy for the treatment of wounds. However, Medicare will cover the service. Unsupervised home use of electromagnetic therapy will not be covered.

B. A/B MAC (A) Billing Instructions

The applicable types of bills acceptable when billing for electromagnetic therapy services are 2X, 13X, 22X, 23X, 71X, 73X, 74X, 75X, and 85X. Chapter 25 of this manual provides general billing instructions that must be followed for bills submitted to A/B MACs (A). A/B MACs (A) pay for electromagnetic therapy services under the Medicare Physician Fee Schedule for a hospital, CORF, ORF, and SNF.

Payment methodology for independent (RHC), provider-based RHCs, free-standing FQHC and provider based FQHCs is made under the all-inclusive rate for the visit furnished to the RHC/FQHC patient to obtain the therapy service. Only one payment will be made for the visit furnished to the RHC/FQHC patient to obtain the therapy service. As of April 1, 2005, RHCs/FQHCs are no longer required to report HCPCS codes when billing for the therapy service.

Payment Methodology for a CAH is payment on a reasonable cost basis unless the CAH has elected the Optional Method and then the A/B MAC (A) pays pay 115% of the MPFS amount for the professional component of the HCPCS code in addition to the technical component.

In addition, the following revenues code must be used in conjunction with the HCPCS code identified:

Revenue Code	Description
420	Physical Therapy
430	Occupational Therapy
520	Federal Qualified Health Center *
521	Rural Health Center *
977,978	Critical Access Hospital-method II CAH professional services only

* **NOTE:** As of April 1, 2005, RHCs/FQHCs are no longer required to report HCPCS codes when billing for the therapy service.

C. A/B MAC (B) Claims

A/B MACs (B) pay for Electromagnetic Therapy services billed with HCPCS codes G0329 based on the MPFS. Claims for electromagnetic therapy services must be billed using the ASC X12 837 professional claim format or Form CMS-1500

following instructions in chapter 12 of this manual (www.cms.hhs.gov/manuals/104_claims/clm104index.asp).

Payment information for HCPCS code G0329 will be added to the July 2004 update of the Medicare Physician Fee Schedule Database (MPFSD).

D. Coinsurance and Deductible

The Medicare contractor shall apply coinsurance and deductible to payments for electromagnetic therapy services except for services billed to the A/B MAC (A) by FQHCs.

For FQHCs only co-insurance applies.

100-4, Chapter-32, 11.3.1

Policy

Effective for claims with dates of service on or after August 2, 2012, contractors shall accept and pay for autologous platelet-rich plasma (PRP) only for the treatment of chronic non-healing diabetic, venous and/or pressure wounds only in the context of an approved clinical study in accordance with the coverage criteria outlined in Pub. 100-03, chapter 1, section 270.3, of the NCD Manual.

100-4, Chapter-32, 11.3.2

Healthcare Common Procedure Coding System (HCPCS) Codes and Diagnosis Coding

HCPCS Code

Effective for claims with dates of service on or after August 2, 2012 Medicare providers shall report HCPCS code G0460 for PRP services.

If ICD-9 Diagnosis coding is applicable

For claims with dates of service on or after August 2, 2012, PRP, for the treatment of chronic non-healing diabetic, venous and/or pressure wounds only in the context of an approved clinical study must be billed using the following ICD codes:

- V70.7
- ICD-9 code from the approved list of diagnosis codes maintained by the Medicare contractor.

If ICD-10 Diagnosis coding is applicable

For claims with dates of service on or after the implementation of ICD-10, ICD-10 CM diagnosis coding is applicable.

- Z00.6
- ICD-10 code from the approved list of diagnosis codes maintained by the Medicare contractor.

Additional billing requirement:

The following modifier and condition code shall be reported when billing for PRP services only in the context of an approved clinical study:

- Q0 modifier
- Condition code 30 (for institutional claims only)
- Value Code D4 with an 8-digit clinical trial number. **NOTE:** This is optional and only applies to Institutional claims.

100-4, Chapter-32, 11.3.3

Types of Bill (TOB)

The applicable TOBs for PRP services are: 12X, 13X, 22X, 23X, 71X, 75X, 77X, and 85X.

100-4, Chapter-32, 11.3.4

Payment Method

Payment for PRP services is as follows:

- Hospital outpatient departments TOBs 12X and 13X – based on OPPS
- SNFs TOBs 22X and 23X –based on MPFS
- TOB 71X –based on all-inclusive rate
- TOB 75X –based on MPFS
- TOB 77X –based on all-inclusive rate
- TOB 85X –based on reasonable cost
- CAHs TOB 85X and revenue codes 096X, 097X, or 098X –based on MPFS

Contractors shall pay for PRP services for hospitals in Maryland under the jurisdiction of the Health Services Cost Review Commission (HSCRC) on an outpatient basis, TOB 13X, in accordance with the terms of the Maryland waiver.

100-4, Chapter-32, 11.3.5

Place of Service (POS) for Professional Claims

Effective for claims with dates of service on or after August 2, 2012, place of service codes 11, 22, and 49 shall be used for PRP services.

100-4, Chapter-32, 11.3.6

Medicare Summary Notices (MSNs), Remittance Advice Remark Codes (RARCs), Claim Adjustment Reason Codes (CARCs) and Group Codes

Contractors shall use the following messages when returning to provider/returning as unprocessable claims when required information is not included on claims for autologous platelet-rich plasma (PRP) for the treatment of chronic non-healing diabetic, venous and/or pressure wounds only in the context of an approved clinical study:

CARC 16 -Claim/service lacks information or has submission/billing error(s) which is (are) needed for adjudication. At least one Remark Code must be provided (may be comprised of either the NCPDP Reject Reason Code, or Remittance Advice Remark Code that is not an ALERT.)

NOTE: Refer to the 835 Healthcare Policy Identification Segment (loop 2110 Service Payment Information REF), if present.

RARC MA130 – Your claim contains incomplete and/or invalid information, and no appeal rights are afforded because the claim is unprocessable. Please submit a new claim with the complete/correct information.

Contractors shall deny claims for RPR services, HCPCS code G0460, when services are provided on other than TOBs 12X, 13X, 22X, 23X, 71X, 75X, 77X, and 85X using:

MSN 21.25: "This service was denied because Medicare only covers this service in certain settings."

Spanish Version: "El servicio fue denegado porque Medicare solamente lo cubre en ciertas situaciones."

CARC 58: "Treatment was deemed by the payer to have been rendered in an inappropriate or invalid place of service. **NOTE:** Refer to the 832 Healthcare Policy Identification Segment (loop 2110 Service payment Information REF), if present.

RARC N428: "Service/procedure not covered when performed in this place of service."

Group Code –CO (Contractual Obligation)

Contractors shall deny claims for PRP services for POS other than 11, 22, or 49 using the following:

MSN 21.25: "This service was denied because Medicare only covers this service in certain settings."

Spanish Version: "El servicio fue denegado porque Medicare solamente lo cubre en ciertas situaciones."

CARC 58: "Treatment was deemed by the payer to have been rendered in an inappropriate or invalid place of service. NOTE; Refer to the 835 Healthcare Policy Identification Segment (loop 2110 Service payment Information REF), if present.

RARC N428: "Service/procedure not covered when performed in this place of service."

Group Code –CO (Contractual Obligation)

100-4, Chapter-32, 30.1

Billing Requirements for HBO Therapy for the Treatment of Diabetic Wounds of the Lower Extremities

Hyperbaric Oxygen Therapy is a modality in which the entire body is exposed to oxygen under increased atmospheric pressure. Effective April 1, 2003, a National Coverage Decision expanded the use of HBO therapy to include coverage for the treatment of diabetic wounds of the lower extremities. For specific coverage criteria for HBO Therapy, refer to the National Coverage Determinations Manual, Chapter 1, section 20.29.

NOTE: Topical application of oxygen does not meet the definition of HBO therapy as stated above. Also, its clinical efficacyhas not been established. Therefore, no Medicare reimbursement may be made for the topical application of oxygen.

I. Billing Requirements for A/B MACs (A)

Claims for HBO therapy should be submitted using the ASC X12 837 institutional claim format or, in rare cases,on Form CMS-1450.

a. Applicable Bill Types

The applicable hospital bill types are 11X, 13X and 85X.

b. Procedural Coding

- 99183 – Physician attendance and supervision of hyperbaric oxygen therapy, per session.
- C1300 – Hyperbaric oxygen under pressure, full body chamber, per 30-minute interval.

NOTE: Code C1300 is not available for use other than in a hospital outpatient department.

In skilled nursing facilities (SNFs), HBO therapy is part of the SNF PPS payment for beneficiaries in covered Part A stays.

For hospital inpatients and critical access hospitals (CAHs) not electing Method I, HBO therapy is reported under revenue code 940 without any HCPCS code. For inpatient services, if ICD-9-is applicable, show ICD-9-CM procedure code 93.59. If ICD-10 is applicable, show ICD-10-PCS code 5A05121.

For CAHs electing Method I, HBO therapy is reported under revenue code 940 along with HCPCS code 99183.

c. Payment Requirements for A/B MACs (A)

Payment is as follows:

A/B MAC (A) payment is allowed for HBO therapy for diabetic wounds of the lower extremities when performed as a physician service in a hospital outpatient setting and for inpatients. Payment is allowed for claims with valid diagnosis codes as shown above with dates of service on or after April 1, 2003. Those claims with invalid codes should be denied as not medically necessary.

For hospitals, payment will be based upon the Ambulatory Payment Classification (APC) or the inpatient Diagnosis Related Group (DRG). Deductible and coinsurance apply.

Payment to Critical Access Hospitals (electing Method I) is made under cost reimbursement. For Critical Access Hospitals electing Method II, the technical component is paid under cost reimbursement and the professional component is paid under the Physician Fee Schedule.

II. A/B MAC (B) Billing Requirements

Claims for this service should be submitted using the ASC X12 837 professional claim format or

Form CMS-1500.

The following HCPCS code applies:

- 99183 –Physician attendance and supervision of hyperbaric oxygen therapy, per session.

a. Payment Requirements for A/B MACs (B)

Payment and pricing information will occur through updates to the Medicare Physician Fee

Schedule Database (MPFSDB). Pay for this service on the basis of the MPFSDB.

Deductible and coinsurance apply. Claims from physicians or other practitioners where assignment was not taken, are subject to the Medicare limiting charge.

III. Medicare Summary Notices (MSNs)

Use the following MSN Messages where appropriate:

In situations where the claim is being denied on the basis that the condition does not meet our coverage requirements, use one of the following MSN Messages:

"Medicare does not pay for this item or service for this condition." (MSN Message 16.48)

The Spanish version of the MSN message should read:

"Medicare no paga por este articulo o servicio para esta afeccion."

In situations where, based on the above utilization policy, medical review of the claim results in a determination that the service is not medically necessary, use the following MSN message:

"The information provided does not support the need for this service or item." (MSN Message 15.4)

The Spanish version of the MSN message should read:

"La informacion proporcionada no confirma la necesidad para este servicio o articulo."

IV. Remittance Advice Notices

Use appropriate existing remittance advice remark codes and claim adjustment reason codes at the line level to express the specific reason if you deny payment for HBO therapy for the treatment of diabetic wounds of lower extremities.

100-4, Chapter-32, 40.1

Coverage Requirements

Effective January 1, 2002, sacral nerve stimulation is covered for the treatment of urinary urge incontinence, urgency-frequency syndrome and urinary retention. Sacral nerve stimulation involves both a temporary test stimulation to determine if an implantable stimulator would be effective and a permanent implantation in appropriate candidates. Both the test and the permanent implantation are covered.

The following limitations for coverage apply to all indications:

- Patient must be refractory to conventional therapy (documented behavioral, pharmacologic and/or surgical corrective therapy) and be an appropriate surgical candidate such that implantation with anesthesia can occur.

- Patients with stress incontinence, urinary obstruction, and specific neurologic diseases (e.g., diabetes with peripheral nerve involvement) that are associated with secondary manifestations of the above three indications are excluded.

- Patient must have had a successful test stimulation in order to support subsequent implantation. Before a patient is eligible for permanent implantation, he/she must demonstrate a 50% or greater improvement through test stimulation. Improvement is measured through voiding diaries.

- Patient must be able to demonstrate adequate ability to record voiding diary data such that clinical results of the implant procedure can be properly evaluated.

100-4, Chapter-32, 50

Deep Brain Stimulation for Essential Tremor and Parkinson's Disease

Deep brain stimulation (DBS) refers to high-frequency electrical stimulation of anatomic regions deep within the brain utilizing neurosurgically implanted electrodes. These DBS electrodes are stereotactically placed within targeted nuclei on one (unilateral) or both (bilateral) sides of the brain. There are currently three targets for DBS --the thalamic ventralis intermedius nucleus (VIM), subthalamic nucleus (STN) and globus pallidus interna (GPi).

Essential tremor (ET) is a progressive, disabling tremor most often affecting the hands. ET may also affect the head, voice and legs. The precise pathogenesis of ET is unknown. While it may start at any age, ET usually peaks within the second and sixth decades. Beta-adrenergic blockers and anticonvulsant medications are usually the first line treatments for reducing the severity of tremor. Many patients, however, do not adequately respond or cannot tolerate these medications. In these medically refractory ET patients, thalamic VIM DBS may be helpful for symptomatic relief of tremor.

Parkinson's disease (PD) is an age-related progressive neurodegenerative disorder involving the loss of dopaminergic cells in the substantia nigra of the midbrain. The disease is characterized by tremor, rigidity, bradykinesia and progressive postural instability. Dopaminergic medication is typically used as a first line treatment for reducing the primary symptoms of PD. However, after prolonged use, medication can become less effective and can produce significant adverse events such as dyskinesias and other motor function complications. For patients who become unresponsive to medical treatments and/or have intolerable side effects from medications, DBS for symptom relief may be considered.

100-4, Chapter-32, 60.4.1

Allowable Covered Diagnosis Codes

For services furnished on or after July 1, 2002, the applicable ICD-9-CM diagnosis code for this benefit is V43.3, organ or tissue replaced by other means; heart valve.

For services furnished on or after March 19, 2008, the applicable ICD-9-CM diagnosis codes for this benefit are:

- V43.3 (organ or tissue replaced by other means; heart valve),
- 289.81 (primary hypercoagulable state),
- 451.0-451.9 (includes 451.11, 451.19, 451.2, 451.80-451.84, 451.89) (phlebitis & thrombophlebitis),
- 453.0-453.3 (other venous embolism & thrombosis),
- 453.40-453.49 (includes 453.40-453.42, 453.6,453.8-453.9) (venous embolism and thrombosis of the deep vessels of the lower extremity, and other specified veins/unspecified sites),
- 415.11-415.12, 415.19 (pulmonary embolism & infarction),or,
- 427.31 (atrial fibrillation (established) (paroxysmal)).

For services furnished on or after the implementation of ICD-10 the applicable ICD-10-CM diagnosis codes for this benefit are:

Heart Valve Replacement

- Z95.2 - Presence of prosthetic heart valve

Primary Hypercoagulable State

ICD-10-CM Code	Code Description
D68.51	Activated protein C resistance
D68.52	Prothrombin gene mutation
D68.59	Other primary thrombophilia
D68.61	Antiphospholipid syndrome
D68.62	Lupus anticoagulant syndrome

Phlebitis & Thrombophlebitis

ICD-10-CM Code	Code Description
I80.00	Phlebitis and thrombophlebitis of superficial vessels of unspecified lower extremity
I80.01	Phlebitis and thrombophlebitis of superficial vessels of right lower extremity
I80.02	Phlebitis and thrombophlebitis of superficial vessels of left lower extremity
I80.03	Phlebitis and thrombophlebitis of superficial vessels of lower extremities, bilateral
I80.10	Phlebitis and thrombophlebitis of unspecified femoral vein
I80.11	Phlebitis and thrombophlebitis of right femoral vein
I80.12	Phlebitis and thrombophlebitis of left femoral vein
I80.13	Phlebitis and thrombophlebitis of femoral vein, bilateral
I80.201	Phlebitis and thrombophlebitis of unspecified deep vessels of right lower extremity
I80.202	Phlebitis and thrombophlebitis of unspecified deep vessels of left lower extremity
I80.203	Phlebitis and thrombophlebitis of unspecified deep vessels of lower extremities, bilateral
I80.209	Phlebitis and thrombophlebitis of unspecified deep vessels of unspecified lower extremity
I80.221	Phlebitis and thrombophlebitis of right popliteal vein

ICD-10-CM Code	Code Description
I80.222	Phlebitis and thrombophlebitis of left popliteal vein
I80.223	Phlebitis and thrombophlebitis of popliteal vein, bilateral
I80.229	Phlebitis and thrombophlebitis of unspecified popliteal vein
I80.231	Phlebitis and thrombophlebitis of right tibial vein
I80.232	Phlebitis and thrombophlebitis of left tibial vein
I80.233	Phlebitis and thrombophlebitis of tibial vein, bilateral
I80.239	Phlebitis and thrombophlebitis of unspecified tibial vein
I80.291	Phlebitis and thrombophlebitis of other deep vessels of right lower extremity
I80.292	Phlebitis and thrombophlebitis of other deep vessels of left lower extremity
I80.293	Phlebitis and thrombophlebitis of other deep vessels of lower extremity, bilateral
I80.299	Phlebitis and thrombophlebitis of other deep vessels of unspecified lower extremity
I80.3	Phlebitis and thrombophlebitis of lower extremities, unspecified
I80.211	Phlebitis and thrombophlebitis of right iliac vein
I80.212	Phlebitis and thrombophlebitis of left iliac vein
I80.213	Phlebitis and thrombophlebitis of iliac vein, bilateral
I80.219	Phlebitis and thrombophlebitis of unspecified iliac vein
I80.8	Phlebitis and thrombophlebitis of other sites
I80.9	Phlebitis and thrombophlebitis of unspecified site

Other Venous Embolism & Thrombosis

ICD-10-CM Code	Code Description
I82.0	Budd- Chiari syndrome
I82.1	Thrombophlebitis migrans
I82.211	Chronic embolism and thrombosis of superior vena cava
I82.220	Acute embolism and thrombosis of inferior vena cava
I82.221	Chronic embolism and thrombosis of inferior vena cava
I82.291	Chronic embolism and thrombosis of other thoracic veins
I82.3	Embolism and thrombosis of renal vein

Venous Embolism and thrombosis of the deep vessels of the lower extremity, and other specified veins/unspecified sites

ICD-10-CM Code	Code Description
I82.401	Acute embolism and thrombosis of unspecified deep veins of right lower extremity
I82.402	Acute embolism and thrombosis of unspecified deep veins of left lower extremity
I82.403	Acute embolism and thrombosis of unspecified deep veins of lower extremity, bilateral
I82.409	Acute embolism and thrombosis of unspecified deep veins of unspecified lower extremity
I82.411	Acute embolism and thrombosis of right femoral vein
I82.412	Acute embolism and thrombosis of left femoral vein
I82.413	Acute embolism and thrombosis of femoral vein, bilateral
I82.419	Acute embolism and thrombosis of unspecified femoral vein
I82.421	Acute embolism and thrombosis of right iliac vein

ICD-10-CM Code	Code Description
I82.422	Acute embolism and thrombosis of left iliac vein
I82.423	Acute embolism and thrombosis of iliac vein, bilateral
I82.429	Acute embolism and thrombosis of unspecified iliac vein
I82.431	Acute embolism and thrombosis of right popliteal vein
I82.432	Acute embolism and thrombosis of left popliteal vein
I82.433	Acute embolism and thrombosis of popliteal vein, bilateral
I82.439	Acute embolism and thrombosis of unspecified popliteal vein
I82.4Y1	Acute embolism and thrombosis of unspecified deep veins of right proximal lower extremity
I82.4Y2	Acute embolism and thrombosis of unspecified deep veins of left proximal lower extremity
I82.4Y3	Acute embolism and thrombosis of unspecified deep veins of proximal lower extremity, bilateral
I82.4Y9	Acute embolism and thrombosis of unspecified deep veins of unspecified proximal lower extremity
I82.441	Acute embolism and thrombosis of right tibial vein
I82.442	Acute embolism and thrombosis of left tibial vein
I82.443	Acute embolism and thrombosis of tibial vein, bilateral
I82.449	Acute embolism and thrombosis of unspecified tibial vein
I82.491	Acute embolism and thrombosis of other specified deep vein of right lower extremity
I82.492	Acute embolism and thrombosis of other specified deep vein of left lower extremity
I82.493	Acute embolism and thrombosis of other specified deep vein of lower extremity, bilateral
I82.499	Acute embolism and thrombosis of other specified deep vein of unspecified lower extremity
I82.4Z1	Acute embolism and thrombosis of unspecified deep veins of right distal lower extremity
I82.4Z2	Acute embolism and thrombosis of unspecified deep veins of left distal lower extremity
I82.4Z3	Acute embolism and thrombosis of unspecified deep veins of distal lower extremity, bilateral
I82.4Z9	Acute embolism and thrombosis of unspecified deep veins of unspecified distal lower extremity
I82.501	Chronic embolism and thrombosis of unspecified deep veins of right lower extremity
I82.502	Chronic embolism and thrombosis of unspecified deep veins of left lower extremity
I82.503	Chronic embolism and thrombosis of unspecified deep veins of lower extremity, bilateral
I82.509	Chronic embolism and thrombosis of unspecified deep veins of unspecified lower extremity
I82.591	Chronic embolism and thrombosis of other specified deep vein of right lower extremity
I82.592	Chronic embolism and thrombosis of other specified deep vein of left lower extremity
I82.593	Chronic embolism and thrombosis of other specified deep vein of lower extremity, bilateral
I82.599	Chronic embolism and thrombosis of other specified deep vein of unspecified lower extremity
I82.511	Chronic embolism and thrombosis of right femoral vein
I82.512	Chronic embolism and thrombosis of left femoral vein

ICD-10-CM Code	Code Description
I82.513	Chronic embolism and thrombosis of femoral vein, bilateral
I82.519	Chronic embolism and thrombosis of unspecified femoral vein
I82.521	Chronic embolism and thrombosis of right iliac vein
I82.522	Chronic embolism and thrombosis of left iliac vein
I82.523	Chronic embolism and thrombosis of iliac vein, bilateral
I82.529	Chronic embolism and thrombosis of unspecified iliac vein
I82.531	Chronic embolism and thrombosis of right popliteal vein
I82.532	Chronic embolism and thrombosis of left popliteal vein
I82.533	Chronic embolism and thrombosis of popliteal vein, bilateral
I82.539	Chronic embolism and thrombosis of unspecified popliteal vein
I82.5Y1	Chronic embolism and thrombosis of unspecified deep veins of right proximal lower extremity
I82.5Y2	Chronic embolism and thrombosis of unspecified deep veins of left proximal lower extremity
I82.5Y3	Chronic embolism and thrombosis of unspecified deep veins of proximal lower extremity, bilateral
I82.5Y9	Chronic embolism and thrombosis of unspecified deep veins of unspecified proximal lower extremity
I82.541	Chronic embolism and thrombosis of right tibial vein
I82.542	Chronic embolism and thrombosis of left tibial vein
I82.543	Chronic embolism and thrombosis of tibial vein, bilateral
I82.549	Chronic embolism and thrombosis of unspecified tibial vein
I82.5Z1	Chronic embolism and thrombosis of unspecified deep veins of right distal lower extremity
I82.5Z2	Chronic embolism and thrombosis of unspecified deep veins of left distal lower extremity
I82.5Z3	Chronic embolism and thrombosis of unspecified deep veins of distal lower extremity, bilateral
I82.5Z9	Chronic embolism and thrombosis of unspecified deep veins of unspecified distal lower extremity
I82.611	Acute embolism and thrombosis of superficial veins of right upper extremity
I82.612	Acute embolism and thrombosis of superficial veins of left upper extremity
I82.613	Acute embolism and thrombosis of superficial veins of upper extremity, bilateral
I82.619	Acute embolism and thrombosis of superficial veins of unspecified upper extremity
I82.621	Acute embolism and thrombosis of deep veins of right upper extremity
I82.622	Acute embolism and thrombosis of deep veins of left upper extremity
I82.623	Acute embolism and thrombosis of deep veins of upper extremity, bilateral
I82.629	Acute embolism and thrombosis of deep veins of unspecified upper extremity
I82.601	Acute embolism and thrombosis of unspecified veins of right upper extremity
I82.602	Acute embolism and thrombosis of unspecified veins of left upper extremity

ICD-10-CM Code	Code Description
I82.603	Acute embolism and thrombosis of unspecified veins of upper extremity, bilateral
I82.609	Acute embolism and thrombosis of unspecified veins of unspecified upper extremity
I82.A11	Acute embolism and thrombosis of right axillary vein
I82.A12	Acute embolism and thrombosis of left axillary vein
I82.A13	Acute embolism and thrombosis of axillary vein, bilateral
I82.A19	Acute embolism and thrombosis of unspecified axillary vein
I82.A21	Chronic embolism and thrombosis of right axillary vein
I82.A22	Chronic embolism and thrombosis of left axillary vein
I82.A23	Chronic embolism and thrombosis of axillary vein, bilateral
I82.A29	Chronic embolism and thrombosis of unspecified axillary vein
I82.B11	Acute embolism and thrombosis of right subclavian vein
I82.B12	Acute embolism and thrombosis of left subclavian vein
I82.B13	Acute embolism and thrombosis of subclavian vein, bilateral
I82.B19	Acute embolism and thrombosis of unspecified subclavian vein
I82.B21	Chronic embolism and thrombosis of right subclavian vein
I82.B22	Chronic embolism and thrombosis of left subclavian vein
I82.B23	Chronic embolism and thrombosis of subclavian vein, bilateral
I82.B29	Chronic embolism and thrombosis of unspecified subclavian vein
I82.C11	Acute embolism and thrombosis of right internal jugular vein
I82.C12	Acute embolism and thrombosis of left internal jugular vein
I82.C13	Acute embolism and thrombosis of internal jugular vein, bilateral
I82.C19	Acute embolism and thrombosis of unspecified internal jugular vein
I82.C21	Chronic embolism and thrombosis of right internal jugular vein
I82.C22	Chronic embolism and thrombosis of left internal jugular vein
I82.C23	Chronic embolism and thrombosis of internal jugular vein, bilateral
I82.C29	Chronic embolism and thrombosis of unspecified internal jugular vein
I82.210	Acute embolism and thrombosis of superior vena cava
I82.290	Acute embolism and thrombosis of other thoracic veins
I82.701	Chronic embolism and thrombosis of unspecified veins of right upper extremity
I82.702	Chronic embolism and thrombosis of unspecified veins of left upper extremity
I82.703	Chronic embolism and thrombosis of unspecified veins of upper extremity, bilateral
I82.709	Chronic embolism and thrombosis of unspecified veins of unspecified upper extremity
I82.711	Chronic embolism and thrombosis of superficial veins of right upper extremity

ICD-10-CM Code	Code Description
I82.712	Chronic embolism and thrombosis of superficial veins of left upper extremity
I82.713	Chronic embolism and thrombosis of superficial veins of upper extremity, bilateral
I82.719	Chronic embolism and thrombosis of superficial veins of unspecified upper extremity
I82.721	Chronic embolism and thrombosis of deep veins of right upper extremity
I82.722	Chronic embolism and thrombosis of deep veins of left upper extremity
I82.723	Chronic embolism and thrombosis of deep veins of upper extremity, bilateral
I82.729	Chronic embolism and thrombosis of deep veins of unspecified upper extremity
I82.811	Embolism and thrombosis of superficial veins of right lower extremities
I82.812	Embolism and thrombosis of superficial veins of left lower extremities
I82.813	Embolism and thrombosis of superficial veins of lower extremities, bilateral
I82.819	Embolism and thrombosis of superficial veins of unspecified lower extremities
I82.890	Acute embolism and thrombosis of other specified veins
I82.891	Chronic embolism and thrombosis of other specified veins
I82.90	Acute embolism and thrombosis of unspecified vein
I82.91	Chronic embolism and thrombosis of unspecified vein

Pulmonary Embolism & Infarction

ICD-10- CM Code	Code Description
I26.90	Septic pulmonary embolism without acute cor pulmonale
I26.99	Other pulmonary embolism without acute cor pulmonale
I26.01	Septic pulmonary embolism with acute cor pulmonale
I26.90	Septic pulmonary embolism without acute cor pulmonale
I26.09	Other pulmonary embolism with acute cor pulmonale
I26.99	Other pulmonary embolism without acute cor pulmonale

Atrial Fibrillation

ICD-10-CM Code	Code Description
I48.0	Paroxysmal atrial fibrillation
I48.2	Chronic atrial fibrillation
I48	-91 Unspecified atrial fibrillation Other
I23.6	Thrombosis of atrium, auricular appendage, and ventricle as current complications following acute myocardial infarction
I27.82	Chronic pulmonary embolism
I67.6	Nonpyogenic thrombosis of intracranial venous system
O22.50	Cerebral venous thrombosis in pregnancy, unspecified trimester
O22.51	Cerebral venous thrombosis in pregnancy, first trimester
O22.52	Cerebral venous thrombosis in pregnancy, second trimester
O22.53	Cerebral venous thrombosis in pregnancy, third trimester
O87.3	Cerebral venous thrombosis in the puerperium
Z79.01	Long term (current) use of anticoagulants

100-4, Chapter-32, 80

Billing of the Diagnosis and Treatment of Peripheral Neuropathy with Loss of Protective Sensation in People with Diabetes

Coverage Requirements -Peripheral neuropathy is the most common factor leading to amputation in people with diabetes. In diabetes, peripheral neuropathy is an anatomically diffuse process primarily affecting sensory and autonomic fibers; however, distal motor findings may be present in advanced cases. Long nerves are affected first, with symptoms typically beginning insidiously in the toes and then advancing proximally. This leads to loss of protective sensation (LOPS), whereby a person is unable to feel minor trauma from mechanical, thermal, or chemical sources. When foot lesions are present, the reduction in autonomic nerve functions may also inhibit wound healing.

Peripheral neuropathy with LOPS, secondary to diabetes, is a localized illness of the feet and falls within the regulation's exception to the general exclusionary rule (see 42 C.F.R. §411.15(l)(l)(i)). Foot exams for people with diabetic peripheral neuropathy with LOPS are reasonable and necessary to allow for early intervention in serious complications that typically afflict diabetics with the disease.

Effective for services furnished on or after July 1, 2002, Medicare covers, as a physician service, an evaluation (examination and treatment) of the feet no more often than every 6 months for individuals with a documented diagnosis of diabetic sensory neuropathy and LOPS, as long as the beneficiary has not seen a foot care specialist for some other reason in the interim. LOPS shall be diagnosed through sensory testing with the 5.07 monofilament using established guidelines, such as those developed by the National Institute of Diabetes and Digestive and Kidney Diseases guidelines. Five sites should be tested on the plantar surface of each foot, according to the National Institute of Diabetes and Digestive and Kidney Diseases guidelines. The areas must be tested randomly since the loss of protective sensation may be patchy in distribution, and the patient may get clues if the test is done rhythmically. Heavily callused areas should be avoided. As suggested by the American Podiatric Medicine Association, an absence of sensation at two or more sites out of 5 tested on either foot when tested with the 5.07 Semmes-Weinstein monofilament must be present and documented to diagnose peripheral neuropathy with loss of protective sensation.

100-4, Chapter-32, 80.2

Applicable HCPCS Codes

G0245 - Initial physician evaluation and management of a diabetic patient with diabetic sensory neuropathy resulting in a loss of protective sensation (LOPS) which must include:

1. The diagnosis of LOPS;
2. A patient history;
3. A physical examination that consists of at least the following elements:
   a. visual inspection of the forefoot, hindfoot, and toe web spaces,
   b. evaluation of a protective sensation,
   c. evaluation of foot structure and biomechanics,
   d. evaluation of vascular status and skin integrity,
   e. evaluation and recommendation of footwear, and
4. Patient education.

G0246 -Follow-up physician evaluation and management of a diabetic patient with diabetic sensory neuropathy resulting in a loss of protective sensation (LOPS) to include at least the following:

1. a patient history;
2. a physical examination that includes:
   a. (a) visual inspection of the forefoot, hindfoot, and toe web spaces,
   b. evaluation of protective sensation,
   c. evaluation of foot structure and biomechanics,
   d. evaluation of vascular status and skin integrity,
   e. evaluation and recommendation of footwear, and 3.patient education.

G0247 -Routine foot care by a physician of a diabetic patient with diabetic sensory neuropathy resulting in a LOPS to include if present, at least the following:

1. local care of superficial (i.e., superficial to muscle and fascia) wounds;
2. debridement of corns and calluses; and
3. trimming and debridement of nails.

NOTE: Code G0247 must be billed on the same date of service with either G0245 or G0246 in order to be considered for payment.

The short descriptors for the above HCPCS codes are as follows:

G0245 – INITIAL FOOT EXAM PTLOPS

G0246 – FOLLOWUP EVAL OF FOOT PT LOP

G0247 – ROUTINE FOOTCARE PT W LOPS

100-4, Chapter-32, 80.8

CWF Utilization Edits

Edit 1- Should CWF receive a claim from an FI for G0245 or G0246 and a second claim from a contractor for either G0245 or G0246 (or vice versa) and they are different dates of service and less than 6 months apart, the second claim will reject. CWF will edit to allow G0245 or G0246 to be paid no more than every 6 months for a particular beneficiary, regardless of who furnished the service. If G0245 has been paid, regardless of whether it was posted as a facility or professional claim, it must be 6 months before G0245 can be paid again or G0246 can be paid. If G0246 has been paid, regardless of whether it was posted as a facility or professional claim, it must be 6 months before G0246 can be paid again or G0245 can be paid. CWF will not impose limits on how many times each code can be paid for a beneficiary as long as there has been 6 months between each service.

The CWF will return a specific reject code for this edit to the contractors and FIs that will be identified in the CWF documentation. Based on the CWF reject code, the contractors and FIs must deny the claims and return the following messages:

MSN 18.4 -- This service is being denied because it has not been __ months since your last examination of this kind (**NOTE:** Insert 6 as the appropriate number of months.)

RA claim adjustment reason code 96 – Non-covered charges, along with remark code M86 – Service denied because payment already made for same/similar procedure within set time frame.

Edit 2

The CWF will edit to allow G0247 to pay only if either G0245 or G0246 has been submitted <u>and accepted as payable</u> on the same date of service. CWF will return a specific reject code for this edit to the contractors and FIs that will be identified in the CWF documentation. Based on this reject code, contractors and FIs will deny the claims and return the following messages:

MSN 21.21 - This service was denied because Medicare only covers this service under certain circumstances.

RA claim adjustment reason code 107 – The related or qualifying claim/service was not identified on this claim.

Edit 3

Once a beneficiary's condition has progressed to the point where routine foot care becomes a covered service, payment will no longer be made for LOPS evaluation and management services. Those services would be considered to be included in the regular exams and treatments afforded to the beneficiary on a routine basis. The physician or provider must then just bill the routine foot care codes, per Pub 100-02, Chapter 15, §290.

The CWF will edit to reject LOPS codes G0245, G0246, and/or G0247 when on the beneficiary's record it shows that one of the following routine foot care codes were billed and paid within the prior 6 months: 11055, 11056, 11057, 11719, 11720, and/or 11721.

The CWF will return a specific reject code for this edit to the contractors and FIs that will be identified in the CWF documentation. Based on the CWF reject code, the contractors and FIs must deny the claims and return the following messages:

MSN 21.21 - This service was denied because Medicare only covers this service under certain circumstances.

The RA claim adjustment reason code 96 –Non-covered charges, along with remark code M86 –Service denied because payment already made for same/similar procedure within set time frame.

100-4, Chapter-32, 100

Billing Requirements for Expanded Coverage of Cochlear Implantation

Effective for dates of services on and after April 4, 2005, the Centers for Medicare & Medicaid Services (CMS) has expanded the coverage for cochlear implantation to cover moderate-to-profound hearing loss in individuals with hearing test scores equal to or less than 40% correct in the best aided listening condition on tape-recorded tests of open-set sentence recognition and who demonstrate limited benefit from amplification. (See Publication 100-03, chapter 1, section 50.3, for specific coverage criteria).

In addition CMS is covering cochlear implantation for individuals with open-set sentence recognition test scores of greater than 40% to less than or equal to 60% correct but only when the provider is participating in, and patients are enrolled in, either:

- A Food and Drug Administration (FDA)-approved category B investigational device exemption (IDE) clinical trial; or
- A trial under the CMS clinical trial policy (see Pub. 100-03, section 310.1); or

A prospective, controlled comparative trial approved by CMS as consistent with the evidentiary requirements for national coverage analyses and meeting specific quality standards.

100-4, Chapter-32, 110.5

DMERC Billing Instructions

Effective for dates of service on or after April 27, 2005, DMERCs shall allow payment for ultrasonic osteogenic stimulators with the following HCPCS codes:

E0760 for low intensity ultrasound (include modifier "KF"), or;

E1399 for other ultrasound stimulation (include modifier "KF")

100-4, Chapter-32, 120.1

Payment for Services and Supplies

For an IOL inserted following removal of a cataract in a hospital, on either an outpatient or inpatient basis, that is paid under the hospital Outpatient Prospective Payment System (OPPS) or the Inpatient Prospective Payment System (IPPS), respectively; or in a Medicare-approved ambulatory surgical center (ASC) that is paid under the ASC fee schedule:

- Medicare does not make separate payment to the hospital or ASC for an IOL inserted subsequent to extraction of a cataract. Payment for the IOL is packaged into the payment for the surgical cataract extraction/lens replacement procedure.
- Any person or ASC, who presents or causes to be presented a bill or request for payment for an IOL inserted during or subsequent to cataract surgery for which payment is made under the ASC fee schedule, is subject to a civil money penalty.
- For a P-C IOL or A-C IOL inserted subsequent to removal of a cataract in a hospital, on either an outpatient or inpatient basis, that is paid under the OPPS or the IPPS, respectively; or in a Medicare-approved ASC that is paid under the ASC fee schedule:
- The facility shall bill for the removal of a cataract with insertion of a conventional IOL, regardless of whether a conventional, P-C IOL, or A-C IOL is inserted. When a beneficiary receives a P-C or A-C IOL following removal of a cataract, hospitals and ASCs shall report the same CPT® code that is used to report removal of a cataract with insertion of a conventional IOL. Physicians, hospitals and ASCs may also report an additional HCPCS code, V2788, to indicate any additional charges that accrue when a P-C IOL or A-C IOL is inserted in lieu of a conventional IOL until January 1, 2008. Effective for A-C IOL insertion services on or after January 1, 2008, physicians, hospitals and ASCs should use V2787 to report any additional charges that accrue. On or after January 1, 2008, physicians, hospitals, and ASCs should continue to report HCPCS code V2788 to indicate any additional charges that accrue for insertion of a P-C IOL. See Section 120.2 for coding guidelines.
- There is no Medicare benefit category that allows payment of facility charges for services and supplies required to insert and adjust a P-C or A-C IOL following removal of a cataract that exceed the facility charges for services and supplies required for the insertion and adjustment of a conventional IOL.
- There is no Medicare benefit category that allows payment of facility charges for subsequent treatments,

services and supplies required to examine and monitor the beneficiary who receives a P-C or A-C IOL following removal of a cataract that exceeds the facility charges for subsequent treatments, services and supplies required to examine and monitor a beneficiary after cataract surgery followed by insertion of a conventional IOL.

A -For a P-C IOL or A-C IOL inserted in a physician's office

-A physician shall bill for a conventional IOL, regardless of a whether a conventional, P-C IOL, or A-C IOL is inserted (see section 120.2, General Billing Requirements)

-There is no Medicare benefit category that allows payment of physician charges for services and supplies required to insert and adjust a P-C or A-C IOL following removal of a cataract that exceed the physician charges for services and supplies for the insertion and adjustment of a conventional IOL.

-There is no Medicare benefit category that allows payment of physician charges for subsequent treatments, service and supplies required to examine and monitor a beneficiary following removal of a cataract with insertion of a P-C or A-C IOL that exceed physician charges for services and supplies to examine and monitor a beneficiary following removal of a cataract with insertion of a conventional IOL.

B - For a P-C IOL or A-C IOL inserted in a hospital

-A physician may not bill Medicare for a P-C or A-C IOL inserted during a cataract procedure performed in a hospital setting because the payment for the lens is included in the payment made to the facility for the surgical procedure.

-There is no Medicare benefit category that allows payment of physician charges for services and supplies required to insert and adjust a P-C or A-C IOL following removal of a cataract that exceed the physician charges for services and supplies required for the insertion of a conventional IOL.

C - For a P-C IOL or A-C IOL inserted in an Ambulatory Surgical Center

-Refer to Chapter 14, Section 40.3 for complete guidance on payment for P-C IOL or A-C IOL in Ambulatory Surgical Centers.

100-4, Chapter-32, 120.2

Coding and General Billing Requirements

Physicians and hospitals must report one of the following Current Procedural Terminology (CPT®) codes on the claim:

- 66982 - Extracapsular cataract removal with insertion of intraocular lens prosthesis (one stage procedure), manual or mechanical technique (e.g., irrigation and aspiration or phacoemulsification), complex requiring devices or techniques not generally used in routine cataract surgery (e.g., iris expansion device, suture support for intraocular lens, or primary posterior capsulorrhexis) or performed on patients in the amblyogenic development stage.
- 66983- Intracapsular cataract with insertion of intraocular lens prosthesis (one stage procedure)
- 66984 - Extracapsular cataract removal with insertion of intraocular lens prosthesis (one stage procedure), manual or mechanical technique (e.g., irrigation and aspiration or phacoemulsification)
- 66985 - Insertion of intraocular lens prosthesis (secondary implant), not associated with concurrent cataract extraction

- 66986 - Exchange of intraocular lens

In addition, physicians inserting a P-C IOL or A-C IOL in an office setting may bill code V2632 (posterior chamber intraocular lens) for the IOL. Medicare will make payment for the lens based on reasonable cost for a conventional IOL. Place of Service (POS) = 11.

Effective for dates of service on and after January 1, 2006, physician, hospitals and ASCs may also bill the non-covered charges related to the P-C function of the IOL using HCPCS code V2788. Effective for dates of service on and after January 22, 2007 through January 1, 2008, non-covered charges related to A-C function of the IOL can be billed using HCPCS code V2788. The type of service indicator for the non-covered billed charges is Q. (The type of service is applied by the Medicare carrier and not the provider). Effective for A-C IOL insertion services on or after January 1, 2008, physicians, hospitals and ASCs should use V2787 rather than V2788 to report any additional charges that accrue.

When denying the non-payable charges submitted with V2787 or V2788, contractors shall use an appropriate Medical Summary Notice (MSN) such as 16.10 (Medicare does not pay for this item or service) and an appropriate claim adjustment reason code such as 96 (non-covered charges) for claims submitted with the non-payable charges.

Hospitals and physicians may use the proper CPT® code(s) to bill Medicare for evaluation and management services usually associated with services following cataract extraction surgery, if appropriate.

A - Applicable Bill Types

The hospital applicable bill types are 12X, 13X, 83X and 85X.

B - Other Special Requirements for Hospitals

Hospitals shall continue to pay CAHs method 2 claims under current payment methodologies for conditional IOLs.

100-4, Chapter-32, 130

External Counterpulsation (ECP) Therapy

Commonly referred to as enhanced external counterpulsation, is a non-invasive outpatient treatment for coronary artery disease refractory medical and/or surgical therapy. Effective for dates of service July 1, 1999, and after, Medicare will cover ECP when its use is in patients with stable angina (Class III or Class IV, Canadian Cardiovascular Society Classification or equivalent classification) who, in the opinion of a cardiologist or cardiothoracic surgeon, are not readily amenable to surgical intervention, such as PTCA or cardiac bypass, because:

- Their condition is inoperable, or at high risk of operative complications or post-operative failure;
- Their coronary anatomy is not readily amenable to such procedures; or
- They have co-morbid states that create excessive risk.

(Refer to Publication 100-03, section 20.20 for further coverage criteria.)

100-4, Chapter-32, 130.1

Billing and Payment Requirements

Effective for dates of service on or after January 1, 2000, use HCPCS code G0166 (External counterpulsation, per session) to report ECP services. The codes for external cardiac assist (92971), ECG rhythm strip and report (93040 or 93041), pulse oximetry (94760 or 94761) and plethysmography (93922 or

93923) or other monitoring tests for examining the effects of this treatment are not clinically necessary with this service and should not be paid on the same day, unless they occur in a clinical setting not connected with the delivery of the ECP. Daily evaluation and management service, e.g., 99201-99205, 99211-99215, 99217-99220, 99241-99245, cannot be billed with the ECP treatments. Any evaluation and management service must be justified with adequate documentation of the medical necessity of the visit. Deductible and coinsurance apply.

100-4, Chapter-32, 140.2.2.1

Correct Place of Service (POS) Code for CR and ICR Services on Professional Claims

Effective for claims with dates of service on and after January 1, 2010, place of service (POS) code 11 shall be used for CR and ICR services provided in a physician's office and POS 22 shall be used for services provided in a hospital outpatient setting. All other POS codes shall be denied. Contractors shall adjust their prepayment procedure edits as appropriate.

The following messages shall be used when contractors deny CR and ICR claims for POS:

Claim Adjustment Reason Code (CARC) 171 –Payment is denied when performed/billed by this type of provider in this type of facility.

NOTE: Refer to the 832 Healthcare Policy Identification Segment (loop 2110 Service payment Information REF), if present.

Remittance Advice Remark Code (RARC) N428 - Service/ procedure not covered when performed in this place of service.

Medicare Summary Notice (MSN) 21.25 -This service was denied because Medicare only covers this service in certain settings.

Group Code PR (Patient Responsibility) -Where a claim is received with the GA modifier indicating that a signed ABN is on file.

Group Code CO (Contractor Responsibility) –Where a claim is received with the GZ modifier indicating that no signed ABN is on file.

100-4, Chapter-32, 140.3

Intensive Cardiac Rehabilitation Program Services Furnished On or After January 1, 2010

As specified at 42 CFR 410.49, Medicare covers intensive cardiac rehabilitation items and services for patients who have experienced one or more of the following:

- An acute myocardial infarction within the preceding 12 months; or
- A coronary artery bypass surgery; or
- Current stable angina pectoris; or
- Heart valve repair or replacement; or
- Percutaneous transluminal coronary angioplasty (PTCA) or coronary stenting; or
- A heart or heart-lung transplant; or
- A stable, chronic heart failure defined as patients with left ventricular ejection fraction of 35% or less and New York Heart Association (NYHA) class II to IV symptoms despite being on optimal heart failure therapy for at least 6 weeks(effective February 18, 2014).

Intensive cardiac rehabilitation programs must include the following components:

- Physician-prescribed exercise each day cardiac rehabilitation items and services are furnished;
- Cardiac risk factor modification, including education, counseling, and behavioral intervention at least once during the program, tailored to patients' individual needs;
- Psychosocial assessment;
- Outcomes assessment; and
- An individualized treatment plan detailing how components are utilized for each patient.

Intensive cardiac rehabilitation programs must be approved by Medicare. In order to be approved, a program must demonstrate through peer-reviewed published research that it has accomplished one or more of the following for its patients:

- Positively affected the progression of coronary heart disease;
- Reduced the need for coronary bypass surgery; and
- Reduced the need for percutaneous coronary interventions.

An intensive cardiac rehabilitation program must also demonstrate through peer- reviewed published research that it accomplished a statistically significant reduction in five or more of the following measures for patients from their levels before cardiac rehabilitation services to after cardiac rehabilitation services:

- Low density lipoprotein;
- Triglycerides;
- Body mass index;
- Systolic blood pressure;
- Diastolic blood pressure; and
- The need for cholesterol, blood pressure, and diabetes medications.

Intensive cardiac rehabilitation items and services must be furnished in a physician's office or a hospital outpatient setting. All settings must have a physician immediately available and accessible for medical consultations and emergencies at all times items and services are being furnished under the program. This provision is satisfied if the physician meets the requirements for direct supervision of physician office services as specified at 42 CFR 410.26 and for hospital outpatient therapeutic services as specified at 42 CFR 410.27.

As specified at 42 CFR 410.49(f)(2), intensive cardiac rehabilitation program sessions are limited to 72 1-hour sessions, up to 6 sessions per day, over a period of up to 18 weeks.

100-4, Chapter-32, 140.3.1

Coding Requirements for Intensive Cardiac Rehabilitation Services Furnished On or After January 1, 2010

The following are the applicable HCPCS codes for intensive cardiac rehabilitation services:

G0422 (Intensive cardiac rehabilitation; with or without continuous ECG monitoring, with exercise, per hour, per session)

G0423 (Intensive cardiac rehabilitation; with or without continuous ECG monitoring, without exercise, per hour, per session)

Effective for dates of service on or after January 1, 2010, hospitals and practitioners may report a maximum of 6 1-hour sessions per day. In order to report one session of cardiac rehabilitation services in a day, the duration of treatment must be at least 31 minutes.

Additional sessions of intensive cardiac rehabilitation services beyond the first session may only be reported in the same day if the duration of treatment is 31 minutes or greater beyond the hour increment. In other words, in order to report 6 sessions of intensive cardiac rehabilitation services on a given date of service, the first five sessions would account for 60 minutes each and the sixth session would account for at least 31 minutes. If several shorter periods of intensive cardiac rehabilitation services are furnished on a given day, the minutes of service during those periods must be added together for reporting in 1-hour session increments.

Example: If the patient receives 20 minutes of intensive cardiac rehabilitation services in the day, no intensive cardiac rehabilitation session may be reported because less than 31 minutes of services were furnished.

Example: If a patient receives 20 minutes of intensive cardiac rehabilitation services in the morning and 35 minutes of intensive cardiac rehabilitation services in the afternoon of a single day, the hospital or practitioner would report 1 session of intensive cardiac rehabilitation services under 1 unit of the appropriate HCPCS G-code for the total duration of 55 minutes of intensive cardiac rehabilitation services on that day.

Example: If the patient receives 70 minutes of intensive cardiac rehabilitation services in the morning and 25 minutes of intensive cardiac rehabilitation services in the afternoon of a single day, the hospital or practitioner would report two sessions of intensive cardiac rehabilitation services under the appropriate HCPCS G-code(s) because the total duration of intensive cardiac rehabilitation services on that day of 95 minutes exceeds 90 minutes.

Example: If the patient receives 70 minutes of intensive cardiac rehabilitation services in the morning and 85 minutes of intensive cardiac rehabilitation services in the afternoon of a single day, the hospital or practitioner would report three sessions of intensive cardiac rehabilitation services under the appropriate HCPCS G-code(s) because the total duration of intensive cardiac rehabilitation services on that day is 155 minutes, which exceeds 150 minutes and is less than 211 minutes.

100-4, Chapter-32, 140.4

Pulmonary Rehabilitation Program Services Furnished On or After January 1, 2010

As specified in 42 CFR 410.47, Medicare covers pulmonary rehabilitation items and services for patients with moderate to very severe COPD (defined as GOLD classification II, III and IV), when referred by the physician treating the chronic respiratory disease.

Pulmonary rehabilitation programs must include the following components:

- Physician-prescribed exercise. Some aerobic exercise must be included in each pulmonary rehabilitation session;
- Education or training closely and clearly related to the individual's care and treatment which is tailored to the individual's needs, including information on respiratory problem management and, if appropriate, brief smoking cessation counseling;

- Psychosocial assessment;
- Outcomes assessment; and,
- An individualized treatment plan detailing how components are utilized for each patient.

Pulmonary rehabilitation items and services must be furnished in a physician's office or a hospital outpatient setting. All settings must have a physician immediately available and accessible for medical consultations and emergencies at all time items and services are being furnished under the program. This provision is satisfied if the physician meets the requirements for direct supervision of physician office services as specified at 42 CFR 410.26 and for hospital outpatient therapeutic services as specified at 42 CFR 410.27.

As specified at 42 CFR 410.47(f), pulmonary rehabilitation program sessions are limited to a maximum of 2 1-hour sessions per day for up to 36 sessions, with the option for an additional 36 sessions if medically necessary. Contractors shall accept the inclusion of the KX modifier on the claim lines as an attestation by the provider of the service that documentation is on file verifying that further treatment beyond the 36 sessions is medically necessary up to a total of 72 sessions for that beneficiary.

100-4, Chapter-32, 140.4.1

Coding Requirements for Pulmonary Rehabilitation Services Furnished On or After January 1, 2010

The following is the applicable HCPCS code for pulmonary rehabilitation services:

G0424 (Pulmonary rehabilitation, including exercise (includes monitoring), per hour, per session)

Effective for dates of service on or after January 1, 2010, hospitals and practitioners may report a maximum of 2 1-hour sessions per day. In order to report one session of pulmonary rehabilitation services in a day, the duration of treatment must be at least 31 minutes. Two sessions of pulmonary rehabilitation services may only be reported in the same day if the duration of treatment is at least 91 minutes. In other words, the first session would account for 60 minutes and the second session would account for at least 31 minutes, if two sessions are reported. If several shorter periods of pulmonary rehabilitation services are furnished on a given day, the minutes of service during those periods must be added together for reporting in 1-hour session increments.

Example: If the patient receives 20 minutes of pulmonary rehabilitation services in the day, no pulmonary rehabilitation session may be reported because less than 31 minutes of services were furnished.

Example: If a patient receives 20 minutes of pulmonary rehabilitation services in the morning and 35 minutes of pulmonary rehabilitation services in the afternoon of a single day, the hospital or practitioner would report 1 session of pulmonary rehabilitation services under 1 unit of the HCPCS G-code for the total duration of 55 minutes of pulmonary rehabilitation services on that day.

Example: If the patient receives 70 minutes of pulmonary rehabilitation services in the morning and 25 minutes of pulmonary rehabilitation services in the afternoon of a single day, the hospital or practitioner would report two sessions of pulmonary rehabilitation services under the HCPCS G-code because the total duration of pulmonary rehabilitation services on that day of 95 minutes exceeds 90 minutes.

Example: If the patient receives 70 minutes of pulmonary rehabilitation services in the morning and 85 minutes of pulmonary rehabilitation services in the afternoon of a single day, the hospital or practitioner would report two sessions of pulmonary rehabilitation services under the HCPCS G-code for the total duration of pulmonary rehabilitation services of 155 minutes. A maximum of two sessions per day may be reported, regardless of the total duration of pulmonary rehabilitation services.

100-4, Chapter-32, 250.1

Coverage Requirements

Effective August 3, 2009, pharmacogenomic testing to predict warfarin responsiveness is covered only when provided to Medicare beneficiaries who are candidates for anticoagulation therapy with warfarin; i.e., have not been previously tested for CYP2C9 or VKORC1 alleles; and have received fewer than five days of warfarin in the anticoagulation regimen for which the testing is ordered; and only then in the context of a prospective, randomized, controlled clinical study when that study meets certain criteria as outlined in Pub 100-03, section 90.1, of the NCD Manual.

NOTE: A new temporary HCPCS Level II code effective August 3, 2009, G9143, warfarin responsiveness testing by genetic technique using any method, any number of specimen(s), was developed to enable implementation of CED for this purpose.

100-4, Chapter-32, 250.2

Billing Requirements

Institutional clinical trial claims for pharmacogenomic testing for warfarin response are identified through the presence of all of the following elements:

- Value Code D4 and 8-digit clinical trial number (when present on the claim) -Refer to Transmittal 310, Change Request 5790, dated January 18, 2008;
- ICD-9 diagnosis code V70.7 -Refer to Transmittal 310, Change Request 5790, dated January 18, 2008;
- Condition Code 30 -Refer to Transmittal 310, Change Request 5790, dated January 18, 2008;
- HCPCS modifier Q0: outpatient claims only -Refer to Transmittal 1418, Change Request 5805, dated January18, 2008; and,
- HCPCS code G9143 (mandatory with the April 2010 Integrated Outpatient Code Editor (IOCE) and the January 2011 Clinical Laboratory Fee Schedule (CLFS) updates. Prior to these times, any trials should bill FIs for this test as they currently do absent these instructions, and the FIs should process and pay those claims accordingly.)

Practitioner clinical trial claims for pharmacogenomic testing for warfarin response are identified through the presence of all of the following elements:

- ICD-9 diagnosis code V70.7;
- 8-digit clinical trial number(when present on the claim);
- HCPCS modifier Q0; and
- HCPCS code G9143 (to be carrier priced for claims with dates of service on and after August 3, 2009, that are processed prior to the January 2011 CLFS update.)

100-4, Chapter-32, 260.1

Policy

The Centers for Medicare & Medicaid Services (CMS) received a request for national coverage of treatments for facial lipodystrophy syndrome (LDS) for human immunodeficiency virus (HIV)-infected Medicare beneficiaries. Facial LDS is often characterized by a loss of fat that results in a facial abnormality such as severely sunken cheeks. This fat loss can arise as a complication of HIV and/or highly active antiretroviral therapy. Due to their appearance and stigma of the condition, patients with facial LDS may become depressed, socially isolated, and in some cases may stop their HIV treatments in an attempt to halt or reverse this complication.

Effective for claims with dates of service on and after March 23, 2010, dermal injections for facial LDS are only reasonable and necessary using dermal fillers approved by the Food and Drug Administration for this purpose, and then only in HIV-infected beneficiaries who manifest depression secondary to the physical stigmata of HIV treatment.

See Pub. 100-03, National Coverage Decision manual, section 250.5, for detailed policy information concerning treatment of LDS.

100-4, Chapter-32, 260.2.1

Hospital Billing Instructions

A -Hospital Outpatient Claims

For hospital outpatient claims, hospitals must bill covered dermal injections for treatment of facial LDS by having all of the required elements on the claim:

- A line with HCPCS codes Q2026 or Q2027 with a Line Item Date of service (LIDOS) on or after March 23, 2010,
- A line with HCPCS code G0429 with a LIDOS on or after March 23, 2010,
- If ICD-9-CM is applicable,ICD-9-CM diagnosis codes 042 (HIV) and 272.6 (Lipodystrophy)or,
- If ICD-10-CM is applicable, ICD-10-CM diagnosis codes B20 Human Immunodeficiency Virus (HIV) disease and E88.1 Lipodystrophy, not elsewhere classified

The applicable NCD is 250.5 Facial Lipodystrophy.

B - Outpatient Prospective Payment System (OPPS) Hospitals or Ambulatory Surgical Centers (ASCs):

For line item dates of service on or after March 23, 2010, and until HCPCS codes Q2026 and Q2027 are billable, facial LDS claims shall contain a temporary HCPCS code C9800, instead of HCPCS G0429 and HCPCS Q2026/Q2027, as shown above.

C -Hospital Inpatient Claims

Hospitals must bill covered dermal injections for treatment of facial LDS by having all of the required elements on the claim:

- Discharge date on or after March 23, 2010,

If ICD-9-CM is applicable,

- ICD-9-CM procedure code 86.99 (other operations on skin and subcutaneous tissue, i.e., injection of filler material), or
- ICD-9-CM diagnosis codes 042 (HIV) and 272.6 (Lipodystrophy)
- If ICD-10-PCS is applicable,
- ICD-10-PCS procedure code 3E00XGC Introduction of Other Therapeutic Substance into Skin and Mucous Membranes, External Approach, or

- ICD-10-CM diagnosis codes B20 Human Immundodeficiency Virus [HIV] disease and E88.1 Lipodystrophy not elsewhere classified.

A diagnosis code for a comorbidity of depression may also be required for coverage on an outpatient and/or inpatient basis as determined by the individual Medicare contractor's policy.

100-4, Chapter-32, 260.2.2

Practitioner Billing Instructions

Practitioners must bill covered claims for dermal injections for treatment of facial LDS by having all of the required elements on the claim:

Performed in a non-facility setting:

- A line with HCPCS codes Q2026 or Q2027 with a LIDOS on or after March 23, 2010,
- A line with HCPCS code G0429 with a LIDOS on or after March 23, 2010,
- If ICD-9-CM applies,diagnosis codes 042 (HIV) and 272.6 (Lipodystrophy) or,
- If ICD-10-CM applies, diagnosis codes B20 Human Immunodeficiency Virus(HIV) disease and E88.1 (Lipodystrophy not elsewhere classified).

NOTE: A diagnosis code for a comorbidity of depression may also be required for coverage based on the individual Medicare contractor's policy.

Performed in a facility setting:

- A line with HCPCS code G0429 with a LIDOS on or after March 23, 2010,
- If ICD-9 applies,ICD-9-CM diagnosis codes 042 (HIV) and 272.6 (Lipodystrophy)or
- If ICD-10 applies, ICD-10-CM diagnosis codes B20 Human Immundodeficiency Virus (HIV) disease and E88.1 (Lipodystrophy not elsewhere classified).

NOTE: A diagnosis code for a comorbidity of depression may also be required for coverage based on the individual Medicare contractor's policy.

100-4, Chapter-32, 280.1

Policy

Effective for services furnished on or after June 30, 2011, a National Coverage Determination (NCD) provides coverage of sipuleucel-T (PROVENGE®) for patients with asymptomatic or minimally symptomatic metastatic, castrate-resistant (hormone refractory) prostate cancer. Conditions of Medicare Part A and Medicare Part B coverage for sipuleucel-T are located in the Medicare NCD Manual, Publication 100-03, section 110.22.

100-4, Chapter-32, 280.2

Healthcare Common Procedure Coding System (HCPCS) Codes and Diagnosis Coding
HCPCS Codes

Effective for claims with dates of service on June 30, 2011, Medicare providers shall report one of the following HCPCS codes for PROVENGE®:

- C9273 - Sipuleucel-T, minimum of 50 million autologous CD54+ cells activated with PAP-GM-CSF, including leukapheresis and all other preparatory procedures, per infusion, or

- J3490 –Unclassified Drugs, or
- J3590 –Unclassified Biologics.

NOTE: Contractors shall continue to process claims for HCPCS code C9273, J3490, and J3590, with dates of service June 30, 2011, as they do currently.

Effective for claims with dates of service on and after July 1, 2011, Medicare providers shall report the following HCPCS code:

Q2043 – Sipuleucel-T, minimum of 50 million autologous CD54+ cells activated with PAP-

GM-CSF, including leukapheresis and all other preparatory procedures, per infusion; short descriptor, Sipuleucel-T auto CD54+.

ICD-9 Diagnosis Coding

For claims with dates of service on and after July 1, 2011, for PROVENGE®, the on-label indication of asymptomatic or minimally symptomatic metastatic, castrate-resistant (hormone refractory) prostate cancer, must be billed using ICD-9 code 185 (malignant neoplasm of prostate) and at least one of the following ICD-9 codes:

ICD-9 Code	Description
196.1	Secondary and unspecified malignant neoplasm of intrathoracic lymph nodes
196.2	Secondary and unspecified malignant neoplasm of intra-abdominal lymph nodes
196.5	Secondary and unspecified malignant neoplasm of lymph nodes of inguinal region and lower limb
196.6	Secondary and unspecified malignant neoplasm of intrapelvic lymph nodes
196.8	Secondary and unspecified malignant neoplasm of lymph nodes of multiple sites
196.9	Secondary and unspecified malignant neoplasm of lymph node site unspecified -The spread of cancer to and establishment in the lymph nodes.
197.0	Secondary malignant neoplasm of lung –Cancer that has spread from the original (primary) tumor to the lung. The spread of cancer to the lung. This may be from a primary lung cancer, or from a cancer at a distant site.
197.7	Malignant neoplasm of liver secondary -Cancer that has spread from the original (primary) tumor to the liver. A malignant neoplasm that has spread to the liver from another (primary) anatomic site. Such malignant neoplasms may be carcinomas (e.g., breast, colon), lymphomas, melanomas, or sarcomas.
198.0	Secondary malignant neoplasm of kidney -The spread of the cancer to the kidney.This may be from a primary kidney cancer involving the opposite kidney, or from a cancer at a distant site.
198.1	Secondary malignant neoplasm of other urinary organs
198.5	Secondary malignant neoplasm of bone and bone marrow –Cancer that has spread from the original (primary) tumor to the bone. The spread of a malignant neoplasm from a primary site to the skeletal system. The majority of metastatic neoplasms to the bone are carcinomas.
198.7	Secondary malignant neoplasm of bone and bone marrow –Cancer that has spread from the original (primary) tumor to the bone. The spread of a malignant neoplasm from a primary site to the skeletal system. The majority of metastatic neoplasms to the bone are carcinomas.
198.82	Secondary malignant neoplasm of genital organs

Coding for Off-Label PROVENGE® Services

The use of PROVENGE® off-label for the treatment of prostate cancer is left to the discretion of the Medicare Administrative Contractors. Claims with dates of service on and after July 1, 2011, for PROVENGE® paid off-label for the treatment of prostate cancer must be billed using either ICD-9 code 233.4 (carcinoma in situ of prostate), or ICD-9 code 185 (malignant neoplasm of prostate) in addition to HCPCS Q2043. Effective with the implementation date for ICD-10 codes, off-label PROVENGE® services must be billed with either ICD-10 code D075(carcinoma in situ of prostate), or C61 (malignant neoplasm of prostate) in addition to HCPCS Q2043.

ICD-10 Diagnosis Coding

Contractors shall note the appropriate ICD-10 code(s) that are listed below for future implementation. Contractors shall track the ICD-10 codes and ensure that the updated edit is turned on as part of the ICD-10 implementation effective October 1, 2013.

ICD-10	Description
C61	Malignant neoplasm of prostate (for on-label or off-label indications)
D075	Carcinoma in situ of prostate (for off-label indications only)
C77.1	Secondary and unspecified malignant neoplasm of intrathoracic lymph nodes
C77.2	Secondary and unspecified malignant neoplasm of intra-abdominal lymph nodes
C77.4	Secondary and unspecified malignant neoplasm of inguinal and lower limb lymph nodes
C77.5	Secondary and unspecified malignant neoplasm of intrapelvic lymph nodes
C77.8	Secondary and unspecified malignant neoplasm of lymph nodes of multiple regions
C77.9	Secondary and unspecified malignant neoplasm of lymph node, unspecified
C78.00	Secondary malignant neoplasm of unspecified lung
C78.01	Secondary malignant neoplasm of right lung
C78.02	Secondary malignant neoplasm of left lung
C78.7	Secondary malignant neoplasm of liver
C79.00	Secondary malignant neoplasm of unspecified kidney and renal pelvis
C79.01	Secondary malignant neoplasm of right kidney and renal pelvis
C79.02	Secondary malignant neoplasm of left kidney and renal pelvis
C79.10	Secondary malignant neoplasm of unspecified urinary organs
C79.11	Secondary malignant neoplasm of bladder
C79.19	Secondary malignant neoplasm of other urinary organs
C79.51	Secondary malignant neoplasm of bone
C79.52	Secondary malignant neoplasm of bone marrow
C79.70	Secondary malignant neoplasm of unspecified adrenal gland
C79.71	Secondary malignant neoplasm of right adrenal gland
C79.72	Secondary malignant neoplasm of left adrenal gland
C79.82	Secondary malignant neoplasm of genital organs

100-4, Chapter-32, 280.4

Payment Method

Payment for PROVENGE® is as follows:

- TOBs 12X, 13X, 22X and 23X -based on the Average Sales Price (ASP) + 6%,
- TOB 85X –based on reasonable cost,
- TOBs 71X and 77X –based on all-inclusive rate.

For Medicare Part B practitioner claims, payment for PROVENGE® is based on ASP + 6%.

Contractors shall not pay separately for routine costs associated with PROVENGE®, HCPCS Q2043, except for the cost of administration. (Q2043 is all-inclusive and represents all routine costs except for its cost of administration).

100-4, Chapter-32, 280.5

Medicare Summary Notices (MSNs), Remittance Advice Remark Codes (RARCs), Claim Adjustment Reason Codes (CARCs), and Group Codes

Contractors shall use the following messages when denying claims for the on-label indication for PROVENGE®, HCPCS Q2043, submitted without ICD-9-CM diagnosis code 185 and at least one diagnosis code from the ICD-9 table in Section 280.2 above:

MSN 14.9 - Medicare cannot pay for this service for the diagnosis shown on the claim.

Spanish Version -Medicare no puede pagar por este servicio debido al diagnóstico indicado en la reclamación.

RARC 167 - This (these) diagnosis (es) are not covered. **Note:** Refer to the 835 Healthcare Policy Identification segment (loop 2110 Service Payment Information REF), if present.

Group Code – CO (Contractual Obligation)

Contractors shall use the following messages when denying claims for the off-label indication for PROVENGE®, HCPCS Q2043, submitted without ICD-9-CM diagnosis code 233.4:

MSN 14.9 - Medicare cannot pay for this service for the diagnosis shown on the claim.

Spanish Version - Medicare no puede pagar por este servicio debido al diagnóstico indicado en la reclamación.

RARC 167 - This (these) diagnosis (es) are not covered. **Note:** Refer to the 835 Healthcare Policy Identification segment (loop 2110 Service Payment Information REF), if present.

Group Code –CO (Contractual Obligation)

For claims with dates of service on or after July 1, 2012, processed on or after July 2, 2012, when denying claims for PROVENGE®, HCPCS Q2043® that exceed three (3) services in a patient's lifetime, contractors shall use the following messages:

MSN 20.5 - These services cannot be paid because your benefits are exhausted at this time.

Spanish Version - Estos servicios no pueden ser pagados porque sus beneficios se han agotado.

RARC N362 - The number of Days or Units of Service exceeds our acceptable maximum.

CARC 149 -Lifetime benefit maximum has been reached for this service/benefit category.

Group Code – CO (Contractual Obligation)

100-4, Chapter-32, 300

Billing Requirements for Ocular Photodynamic Therapy (OPT) with Verteporfin

Ocular Photodynamic Therapy (OPT) is used in the treatment of ophthalmologic diseases; specifically, for age-related macular degeneration (AMD), a common eye disease among the elderly. OPT involves the infusion of an intravenous photosensitizing drug called Verteporfin, followed by exposure to a laser. For complete Medical coverage guidelines, see National Coverage Determinations (NCD) Manual (Pub 100-03) § 80.2 through 80.3.1.

100-4, Chapter-32, 300.1

Coding Requirements for OPT with Verteporfin

The following are applicable Current Procedural Terminology (CPT®) codes for OPT with Verteporfin:

67221- Destruction of localized lesion of choroid (e.g. choroidal neovascularization); photodynamic therapy (includes intravenous infusion)

67225- Destruction of localized lesion of choroid (e.g. choroidal neovascularization); photodynamic therapy, second eye, at single session (List separately in addition to code for primary eye treatment)

The following are applicable Healthcare Common Procedure Coding System (HCPCS) code for OPT with Verteporfin:

J3396- Injection, Verteporfin, 0.1 mg

100-4, Chapter-32, 300.2

Claims Processing Requirements for OPT with Verteporfin Services on Professional Claims and Outpatient Facility Claims

OPT with Verteporfin is a covered service when billed with ICD-9-CM code 362.52 (Exudative Senile Macular Degeneration of Retina (Wet)) or ICD-10-CM code H35.32 (Exudative Age-related Macular Degeneration).

Coverage is denied when billed with either ICD-9-CM code 362.50 (Macular Degeneration (Senile), Unspecified) or 362.51 (Non-exudative Senile Macular Degeneration) or their equivalent ICD-10-CM code H35.30 (Unspecified Macular Degeneration) or H35.31 (Non-exudative Age-Related Macular Degeneration).

OPT with Verteporfin for other ocular indications are eligible for local coverage determinations through individual contractor discretion.

Payment for OPT service (CPT® code 67221/67225) must be billed on the same claim as the drug (J3396) for the same date of service.

Claims for OPT with Verteporfin for dates of service prior to April 3,2013 are covered at the initial visit as determined by a fluorescein angiogram (FA) CPT® code 92235. Subsequent follow-up visits also require a FA prior to treatment.

For claims with dates of service on or after April 3, 2013, contractors shall accept and process claims for subsequent follow-up visits with either a FA, CPT® code 92235, or optical coherence tomography (OCT), CPT® codes 92133 or 92134, prior to treatment.

Regardless of the date of service of the claim, the FA or OCT is not required to be submitted on the claim for OPT and can be maintained in the patient's file for audit purposes.

100-4, Chapter-32, 310

Transesophageal Doppler Used for Cardiac Monitoring

Effective May 17, 2007, Transesophageal Doppler used for cardiac monitoring is covered for ventilated patients in the ICU and operative patients with a need for intra-operative fluid optimization was deemed reasonable and necessary. See National Coverage Determinations Manual (Pub. 100-03)§220.5, for complete coverage guidelines.

A new Healthcare Common Procedure Coding System (HCPCS) code, G9157, Transesophageal Doppler used for cardiac monitoring, will be made effective for use for dates of service on or after January 1, 2013.

100-4, Chapter-32, 310.2

Coding Requirements for Transesophageal Doppler Cardiac Monitoring Furnished On or After January 1, 2013

After January 1, 2013, the applicable HCPCS code for Transesophageal Doppler cardiac monitoring is:

HCPCS G9157: Transesophageal Doppler used for cardiac monitoring

Contractors shall allow HCPCS G9157 to be billed when services are provided in POS 21 for ventilated patients in the ICU or for operative patients with a need for intra-operative fluid optimization.

Contractors shall deny HCPCS 76999 when billed for Esophageal Doppler for ventilated patients in the ICU or for operative patients with a need for intra-operative fluid optimization using the following messages:

CARC 189: "'Not otherwise classified' or 'unlisted' procedure code (CPT®/HCPCS) was billed when there is a specific procedure code for this procedure/service."

RARC M20: "Missing/incomplete/invalid HCPCS."

MSN 16.13: "The code(s) your provider used is/are not valid for the date of service billed." (English version) or "El/los código(s) que usó su proveedor no es/son válido(s) en la fecha de servicio facturada." (Spanish version).

Group Code: Contractual Obligation (CO)

100-4, Chapter-32, 310.3

Correct Place of Service (POS) Code for Transesophageal Doppler Cardiac Monitoring Services on Professional Claims

Contractors shall pay for Transesophageal Doppler cardiac monitoring, G9157, only when services are provided at POS 21.

Contractors shall deny HCPCS G9157 when billed globally in any POS other than 21 for ventilated patients in the ICU or for operative patients with a need for intra-operative fluid optimization using the following messages:

CARC 58:"Treatment was deemed by the payer to have been rendered in an inappropriate or invalid place of service. **Note:** Refer to the 835 Healthcare Policy Identification Segment (loop 2110 Service Payment Information REF), if present.

MSN 16.2: This service cannot be paid when provided in this location/facility.

Group Code: CO

100-4, Chapter-36, 50.14

Purchased Accessories & Supplies for Use With Grandfathered Equipment

Non-contract grandfathered suppliers must use the KY modifier on claims for CBA-residing beneficiaries with dates of service on or after January 1, 2011, for purchased, covered accessories or supplies furnished for use with rented grandfathered equipment. The following HCPCS codes are the codes for which use of the KY modifier is authorized:

- Continuous Positive Airway Pressure Devices, Respiratory Assistive Devices, and Related Supplies and Accessories – A4604, A7030, A7031, A7032, A7033, A7034, A7035, A7036, A7037, A7038, A7039, A7044, A7045, A7046, E0561, and E0562
- Hospital Beds and Related Accessories – E0271, E0272, E0280, and E0310
- Walkers and Related Accessories – E0154, E0156, E0157 and E0158

Grandfathered suppliers that submit claims for the payment of the aforementioned purchased accessories and supplies for use with grandfathered equipment should submit the applicable single payment amount for the accessory or supply as their submitted charge on the claim. Non-contract grandfathered suppliers should be aware that purchase claims submitted for these codes without the KY modifier will be denied. In addition, claims submitted with the KY modifier for HCPCS codes other than those listed above will be denied.

After the rental payment cap for the grandfathered equipment is reached, the beneficiary must obtain replacement supplies and accessories from a contract supplier. The supplier of the grandfathered equipment is no longer permitted to furnish the supplies and accessories once the rental payment cap is reached.

100-4, Chapter-36, 50.15

Hospitals Providing Walkers and Related Accessories to Their Patients on the Date of Discharge

Hospitals may furnish walkers and related accessories to their own patients for use in the home during an admission or on the date of discharge and receive payment at the applicable single payment amount, regardless of whether the hospital is a contract supplier or not. Separate payment is not made for walkers furnished by a hospital for use in the hospital, as payment for these items is included in the Part A payment for inpatient hospital services.

To be paid for walkers as a non-contract supplier, the hospital must use the modifier J4 in combination with the following HCPCS codes: A4636; A4637; E0130; E0135; E0140; E0141; E0143; E0144; E0147; E0148; E0149; E0154; E0155; E0156; E0157; E0158; and E0159. Under this exception, hospitals are advised to submit the claim for the hospital stay before or on the same day that they submit the claim for the walker to ensure timely and accurate claims processing.

Hospitals that are located outside a CBA that furnish walkers and/or related accessories to travelling beneficiaries who live in a CBA must affix the J4 modifier to claims submitted for these items.

The J4 modifier should not be used by contract suppliers.